Mathematics

Explorations & Applications

David M. Davison
Marsha Landau
Leah McCracken
Linda Thompson

PRENTICE HALL

Mathematics

Explorations & Applications

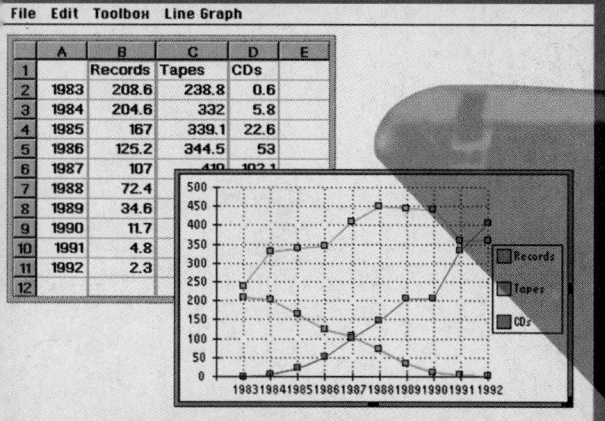

	A	B	C	D	E
1		Records	Tapes	CDs	
2	1983	208.6	238.8	0.6	
3	1984	204.6	332	5.8	
4	1985	167	339.1	22.6	
5	1986	125.2	344.5	53	
6	1987	107	410	102.1	
7	1988	72.4			
8	1989	34.6			
9	1990	11.7			
10	1991	4.8			
11	1992	2.3			
12					

Needham, Massachusetts
Englewood Cliffs, New Jersey

AUTHORS

David M. Davison, *Eastern Montana College, Billings, Montana*

Marsha S. Landau, *National-Louis University, Evanston, Illinois*

Leah McCracken, *Lockwood Junior High School, Billings, Montana*

Linda Thompson, *Warrenton, Oregon*

REVIEWERS

Bettye C. Hall, Director of Mathematics (retired), *Houston Independent School District, Houston, Texas*

Joanne Martin, Mathematics Teacher, *New Prague, Minnesota*

Jeffrey S. McIntire, Mathematics Teacher, *Maumee High School, Maumee, Ohio*

Elizabeth C. McNair, Mathematics Teacher, *Burns Junior High School, Brandon, Florida*

Connie Bain, Mathematics Teacher, *Bonneville Junior High School, Salt Lake City, Utah*

Staff Credits

Editorial
Barbara A. Bertell
Judith Buice
Edward de Leon
Christine Deliee
Mimi Jigarjian
Jo Ann Webber

Marketing
Bridget A. Hadley
Colleen J. Thomas
Christina Trinchero

Manufacturing
Holly Schuster

Production
David Graham
Dorothy M. Preston

Design
Russell Lappa
L. Christopher Valente
Stuart Wallace

ISBN 0-13-833484-6
Printed in the United States of America.

9 02 01 00

▼

PRENTICE HALL
dedicates
this mathematics program
to
all mathematics educators
and
their students

▲

Contents

What is a proof set?   **see p. 93**

2 Solving Equations

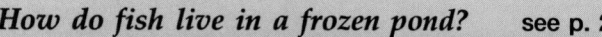

How do fish live in a frozen pond?   see p. 2

IN EVERY CHAPTER, LOOK FOR:

PROJECT ▼ WRITE ▼ DATA ▼ CALCULATOR ▼ COMPUTER ▼ ESTIMATION

What makes up population change? see p. 139

▼ DATA ▼ CALCULATOR ▼ COMPUTER ▼ ESTIMATION ▼ MENTAL MATH ▼

How long do most teens study per day? see p. 230

6   Ratios, Proportions, and Percent

7   Equations and Inequalities

8   Graphing in the Coordinate Plane

IN EVERY CHAPTER, LOOK FOR:

PROJECT ▼ WRITE ▼ DATA ▼ CALCULATOR ▼ COMPUTER ▼ ESTIMATION

What is the loft of a golf club? see p. 360

9 Algebra in Geometry and Measurement

10 Area and Volume Formulas

What is an animal's home range? see p. 405

▼ DATA ▼ CALCULATOR ▼ COMPUTER ▼ ESTIMATION ▼ MENTAL MATH ▼

Who designed the 1495 parachute?   see p. 450

IN EVERY CHAPTER, LOOK FOR:

PROJECT ▼ WRITE ▼ DATA ▼ CALCULATOR ▼ COMPUTER ▼ ESTIMATION

**Just how
cold
is
it?**

IF YOU DROP
a rubber ball into liquid
nitrogen (-320°F), and then
drop the ball from a height
of 2 ft, the ball will be so
brittle it will shatter.

PONDS IN WINTER

COOLING WATER becomes more dense until it
reaches 39°F when it becomes less dense.
Water at 39°F is always found at the
bottom of ponds, which is why
fish survive in the pond when
the surface is frozen.

Icy Surface 32°F

33°F

35°F

37°F

39°F

2

Integers and Expressions

▼ *Think about it...*

If you plunge a very cold glass into hot water, the glass will break. Why does this happen? How do engineers design products to withstand rapid changes in temperature?

FREEZING POINTS of common substances

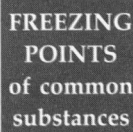

Water
32°F

Vinegar
2°F

Gasoline
GAS
-70°F

Sugar
300°F

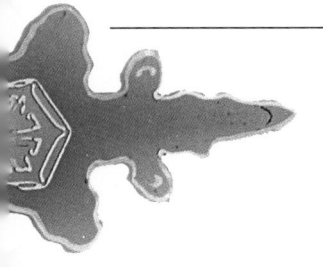

Salt
S
1,474°F

WIND CHILL

IN 1939, wind chill measurements were developed from experiments done in Antarctica. In 1943, Siple and Passell of the United States Army Climatic Research Unit used the concept of wind chill to help determine a soldier's clothing needs in very cold climates.

AIR TEMP (°F)	WIND SPEED IN MILES PER HOUR									
	0	5	10	15	20	25	30	35	40	
	Equivalent wind chill temperatures									
35	35	32	22	16	12	8	6	4	3	*Little danger of frostbite*
30	30	27	16	9	4	1	-2	-4	-5	
25	25	22	10	2	-3	-7	-10	-12	-13	
20	20	16	3	-5	-10	-15	-18	-20	-21	*Increased danger of frostbite*
15	15	11	-3	-11	-17	-22	-25	-27	-29	
10	10	6	-9	-18	-24	-29	-33	-35	-37	
5	5	0	-15	-25	-31	-36	-41	-43	-45	
0	0	-5	-22	-31	-39	-44	-49	-52	-53	
-5	-5	-10	-27	-38	-46	-51	-56	-58	-60	
-10	-10	-15	-34	-45	-53	-59	-64	-67	-69	
-15	-15	-21	-40	-51	-60	-66	-71	-74	-76	*High danger of frostbite*
-20	-20	-26	-46	-58	-67	-74	-79	-82	-84	
-25	-25	-31	-52	-65	-75	-81	-86	-89	-92	

1-1 Integers

▼ Suppose you earn $25 babysitting. The next week you spend $25 on sports equipment. You know that earning $25 is the *opposite* of spending $25. How can we represent this with numbers?

To represent earning $25, use a *positive integer:* +25, or 25.
To represent spending $25, use a *negative integer:* -25.

READ -25 as *negative 25* or *the opposite of 25.*

THINK What integer is neither negative nor positive?

Integers	The whole numbers and their opposites form the set of integers.

..., -4, -3, -2, -1, 0, 1, 2, 3, 4, ...

negative   zero   positive

Example 1   Write an integer to represent each situation.

    a. earning $50   **b.** a debt of $30

Solution   **a.** +50 or 50   **b.** -30

▼ You can represent integers on a number line.

Example 2   Write the integer represented by each point on the number line.

               D   A   C   B
                          0

    a. *A*   **b.** *B*   **c.** *C*   **d.** *D*

Solution   **a.** -2   **b.** 3   **c.** 0   **d.** -4

Opposites	Opposites are two integers the same distance from zero on a number line, but in opposite directions.

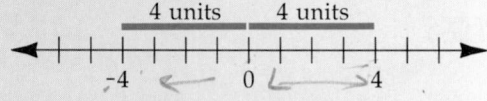

4 units   4 units

-4   0   4

How can you use integers to describe water levels at high tide and low tide?

Example 3 Graph ⁻6 and its opposite on a number line.

Solution Draw a number line. Make sure the tic marks are evenly spaced. Mark points on the number line at ⁻6 and 6.

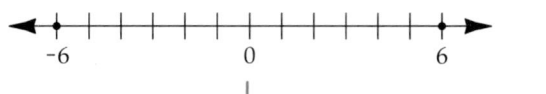

└─ Mark zero on the number line first.

▼ Opposite integers are the same distance from zero on a number line. This means they have the same *absolute value*.

Absolute Value	The absolute value of an integer is its distance from zero on a number line.

▼ **THINK** Why can't the absolute value of a number be negative?

Example 4 a. $|{-5}| = 5$ b. $|5| = 5$

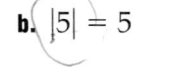

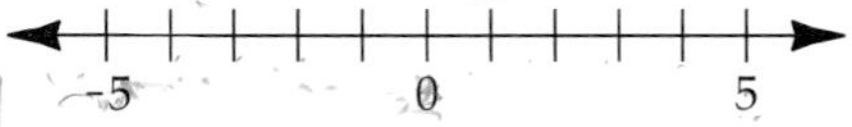

⁻5 is 5 units from 0.
5 is 5 units from 0.

▼ You can also use situations and number lines to compare integers.

Example 5 On Monday the temperature was ⁻10°. On Tuesday it was ⁻15°. It was colder on Tuesday since 15° below zero is colder than 10° below zero. Write: ⁻15 < ⁻10.

Example 6 To compare ⁻3 and ⁻6, think of a number line. On a horizontal number line, the integer farther to the right is the greater integer.

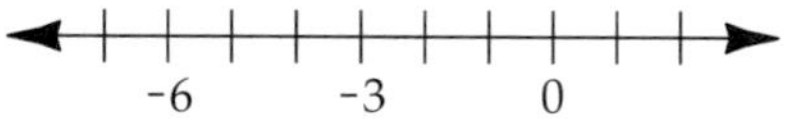

⁻3 > ⁻6 and ⁻6 < ⁻3

⁻3 is to the right of ⁻6, so ⁻3 is greater than ⁻6 and ⁻6 is less than ⁻3.

FLASHBACK

= *is equal to*
< *is less than*
> *is greater than*

THINK AND DISCUSS

1. Think of a number that is not an integer.

2. Explain how a thermometer is like a vertical number line.

3. Compare the set of positive integers with the set of nonnegative integers. Are they the same set? Explain.

CLASS EXERCISES

Give an integer to represent each situation.

1. a profit of $250   **2.** 18° below 0   **3.** 45 s before launch

Give the integer represented by each point on the number line.

4. *A*

5. *B*

6. *C*

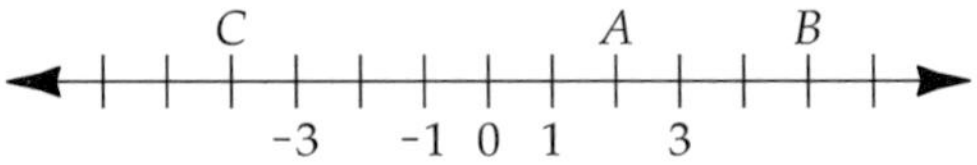

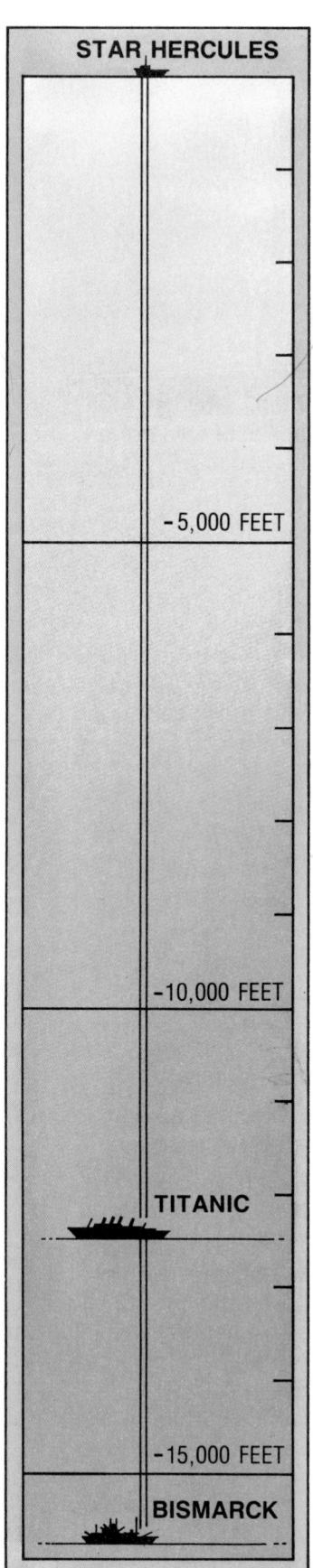

STAR HERCULES

-5,000 FEET

-10,000 FEET

TITANIC

-15,000 FEET

BISMARCK

Give each number.

7. the opposite of 4   **8.** the opposite of ⁻9   **9.** |18| **10.** |⁻3|

Name the greater integer.

11. ⁻2, ⁻4   **12.** 8, ⁻9   **13.** ⁻12, ⁻9   **14.** 0, ⁻6

WRITTEN EXERCISES

Write an integer to represent each situation.

1. a deposit of $110 *+110*   **2.** a debt of 50 *-50*   **3.** 300 ft below sea level *-300*
4. win by 7 points *+7*   **5.** a loss of 8 yd *-8*   **6.** an elevation of 3,400 ft *+3,400*

Describe a situation that each integer could represent.

▼▼ *SAMPLE* ⁻8: 8 min before liftoff

7. ⁻5   **8.** ⁻1,000   **9.** 28   **10.** 7   **11.** 0   **12.** ⁻126

lose by 5   deposit 1,000   28 ft above sea   Win by 7   one sea level   dept of 126

Write each integer.

13. the opposite of 6 *-6*   **14.** the opposite of ⁻2 *2*   **15.** |⁻3| *3*   **16.** |13| *13*

17. the absolute value of negative four *4*

18. the absolute value of the opposite of sixteen *16*

19. the opposite of the absolute value of negative nine *9*

20. the opposite of the opposite of eight *8*

Use the article below and the graph at the left.

21. a. Write integers that represent the positions of the *Titanic*, the *Bismarck*, and the *Star Hercules*.

b. *PROJECT* Research the *Titanic* or the *Bismarck*. Find out more about how and when each ship sank and was found.

Search Ends, Ships Found

In 1990 two historic ships were found deep in the North Atlantic Ocean. Both state-of-the-art ships survived less than one week.

The luxury passenger liner *Titanic* struck an iceberg. It came to rest 12,500 ft below sea level. The *Titanic* was 882 ft long, 92 ft wide, and displaced 66,000 t of water. The mighty warship *Bismarck* sank in battle. The *Bismarck* was 823 ft long, 118 ft wide, and displaced 50,000 t of water.

The *Star Hercules*, only 269 ft long, towed the underwater camera sled *Argo* that found the *Bismarck* under 15,617 ft of water.

Write the integer for each point on the number line,

22. A   **23.** B

24. C   **25.** D

Number line: D at -6, B at 2, C at 4, A at 6 (labels shown: -6, -2, 0, 2, 6)

26. 8 units to the left of -6 *-14*   **27.** 10 units to the right of -2 *0*

Graph each integer and its opposite on a number line.

28. 1, -3   **29.** -2, -8   **30.** 5, 0   **31.** 4, -1

Compare. Use >, <, or =.

32. -8 < 0   **33.** 4 > -25   **34.** |3| < |8| **35.** |-1| < |50|

36. -9 < -2   **37.** |-6| < |-12| **38.** -1 > -5   **39.** |10| = |-10|

Complete with a word that makes each statement true.

40. All ▢ integers are less than zero.

41. An integer is negative, positive, or ▢.

42. The opposite of a ▢ number is negative.

43. The absolute value of an integer is never ▢.

44. CALCULATOR

  a. Enter any positive integer on your calculator. Then enter (+/-). What appears in the display? What do you enter to display -25?

  b. What integer will appear in the display after you enter these keys? 6 (+/-)(+/-)(+/-)(+/-). Check by entering the keys on your calculator.

Complete with an integer that makes each statement true.

45. -5 > ▢   **46.** ▢ < 6   **47.** |-1| > ▢   **48.** |5| < 8

Write an integer between the given integers.

49. -6, 2   **50.** 0, -4   **51.** 5, 1   **52.** -8, -12

53. DATA FILE 1 (pp. 2–3)

  a. Find the wind chill temperature when the temperature is -5°F and the wind speed is 10 mi/h. *-27°*

  b. Starting at what wind chill temperature is there an increased danger of frostbite? a high danger of frostbite? *-20°*

  c. PROJECT Find the freezing points of two substances that are not listed.

54. WRITE Start a math journal. Use your journal to explain how to do an exercise you understand, to define new words in your own language, or to describe something you don't understand completely.

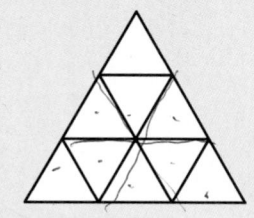

In 1970 Dr. Sylvia Earle Mead (b. 1935), marine biologist, lead the first United States team of female aquanauts. They lived underwater for two weeks near St. John, Virgin Islands, as part of the Tektite Underwater Research Project.

MIXED REVIEW

Find each answer.

1. 812 + 95

2. 1,061 − 247

3. 136 × 8

4. 378 ÷ 9

5. 7,920 − 48

6. How many triangles are in the figure shown?

OBJECTIVE:
*Use models to
discover rules about
integers.*

MATERIALS

• Algebra tiles, checkers,
  or squares of paper in
  two different colors

• Math journal to record
  work

Exploring Integers

▼ You can use models, such as colored tiles, to represent integers.

Let yellow tiles represent positive integers.    3

Let red tiles represent negative integers.   -2

1. Write the integer represented by each model.

a. 2   **b.** -5

c. -1 **d.** 8

2. Use models to represent each integer and its opposite.

a. -3   **b.** 5   **c.** -8   **d.** 7

▼ You can use models to represent number sentences.

    ▢▢▢ + ▢ = ▢▢▢▢   and   ■■ + ■■■ = ■■■■■
     3   + 1 =   4   -2 + (-3) =   -5

3. Model the sum 2 + 4 = 6. Model the sum -2 + (-4) = -6. How are
the sums the same? How are they different?

4. Write a number sentence for each model.

$5 + 2 = 8$ **a.** ▢▢▢ + ▢ = ▢▢▢▢   **b.** ▢▢ + ▢ = ▢▢▢ $3 + 2 = 5$

$-2 + -4 = -6$ **c.** ■ + ■■ = ■■■   **d.** ■■■ + ■■ = ■■■■■

5. Use your answers from Exercise 4. **Discuss** the following. $-6 + -3 = -9$

  a. the sum of two *positive* integers

  b. the sum of two *negative* integers

▼ Suppose you earn $5 and then spend $5. The result is a zero
change in money. You can use models to represent zero. An equal
number of yellow tiles and red tiles combine to make zero.

    ■▢ represents zero *or* ■ + ▢ = 0

6. a. Use models to represent a different sum of zero. How many of
   each color tile did you use? **Compare** with another group.

  b. If you use 12 yellow tiles, you will need ▢ red tiles to make zero.

  c. If you use 31 red tiles, you will need ▢ yellow tiles to make zero.

  d. What is the fewest number of red and yellow tiles you can
   combine to make zero?

  e. Summarize The sum of an integer and its opposite is ▢.

---

7. Combine tiles to make zeros. Write the integer for the remaining tiles.

a.

b.

c.

d.

8. *Explore* Use a different model to represent each integer from Exercise 7. Use both positive and negative tiles for each model. Compare your models with those of another group. In how many different ways can you represent a given integer?

9. Complete the model. Write a number sentence to show the sum.

a. ▦ + ▦

   ▦ + ▦ = ▦

b. ▦ + ▦

   ▦ + ▦ = ▦

c. ▦ + ▦

   ▦ + ▦ = ▦

d. ▦ + ▦

   ▦ + ▦ = ▦

10. Use models to find each sum.

a. $-7 + 3$ b. $10 + (-4)$ c. $-5 + (-4)$ d. $8 + (-11)$

11. *Analyze* your answers from Exercises 9 and 10.

a. When is the sum *positive?* When is the sum *negative?*

b. ***Summarize*** Write a rule for the sign of the sum when you add two integers with different signs. *Hint:* Use absolute value.

12. Complete the model. Then write a number sentence for each sum.

a. ▦ + ▦ = ▦

b. ▦ + ▦ = ▦

1-2 Adding Integers

▼ Adding integers can be easier if you think of a familiar situation. Suppose you borrow $5 from your friend. The next day you borrow $2 more from your friend. You owe your friend $7, so you are $7 in debt. Here is your situation written as a sum of integers.

$$-5 \quad + \quad -2 \quad = \quad -7$$
borrow $5 \quad borrow $2 more \quad $7 in debt

▼ You can use models to add integers.

Example 1   6 + (-4)

Solution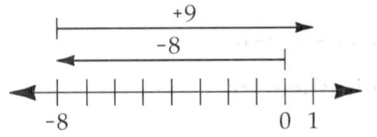

    6 + (-4) = 2

Four positive tiles and four negative tiles make a zero pair.

Two positive tiles are left.

▼ Another useful model for adding integers is the number line.

Example 2   -8 + 9

Solution

```
        +9
    ┌─────────────>
   <──────
    -8
<──┼┼┼┼┼┼┼┼┼┼┼┼──>
   -8          0 1
```

Notice that the sum falls on the same side of zero as the addend with the greater absolute value.

1. Begin at 0. Move 8 units to the *left* to *negative* eight.

2. Begin at -8. Move 9 units to the *right* to *positive* one.

    -8 + 9 = 1

NOTES & QUOTES

The early Egyptians drew pairs of legs walking in different directions to stand for addition and subtraction.

• *How is this model like the tiles and the number line?*

▼ It's not always convenient to use number lines or models. So, you can use these rules to add integers.

Adding Two Integers with the Same Sign	To add two integers with the same sign, add the absolute values of the integers. The sum has the same sign as the addends.

Adding Two Integers with Different Signs	To add two integers with different signs, find the *difference* of the absolute values of the addends. The sum has the sign of the integer with the greater absolute value.

Example 3 $-20 + 7$

Solution   **1.** Find absolute values. $|-20| = 20, |7| = 7$

          2. Subtract. $20 - 7 = 13$

          3. The sum is negative. $-20 + 7 = -13$

▼   You can use mental math or a calculator to find a sum.

Example 4   **a.** $-4 + (-1) + 4$ Use mental math.

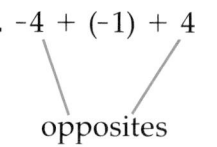

                                             Look for numbers

             opposites   to add in your head.

            $-4 + (-1) + 4 = -1$

          b. $-865 + 77 + 240$ Use a calculator.

             $865\boxed{+/-}\boxed{+}77\boxed{+}240\boxed{=}-548$

▼   Sometimes you will need to add integers to solve problems.

Example 5   To win a computer game, a player must have a positive number of points after ten rounds. The points for ten rounds are shown. Did the player win the game?

Solution   Make a table to organize the data into positive and negative points. Use a calculator to add.

          The player did not win the game since the final score was negative.

Positive	Negative
6	-10
24	-55
19	-33
21	-18
12	
30	
112	+ (-116) = -4

CLASS EXERCISES

Give a numerical expression for each situation. Find the sum.

1. Susan deposited $120, then wrote a check for $25.

2. A submarine at 35 ft below sea level moved up 10 ft.

Give a situation that describes each sum. Find the sum.

3. $235 + (-420)$ **4.** $100 + (-100)$ **5.** $-9 + (-1) + (-4)$

Give a numerical expression for the model. Find the sum.

6. ■■■■ + ⬚⬚⬚⬚⬚⬚⬚ $= -3$

7. ⬚⬚⬚⬚⬚ + ⬚■ $= -5$

Represent each sum on a number line. Find the sum.

8. $5 + (-7)$ **9.** $-7 + (-6)$ **10.** $4 + (-3) + 2$

Give the number sentence for the number line. In your own words, describe how each problem fits the rules.

11.

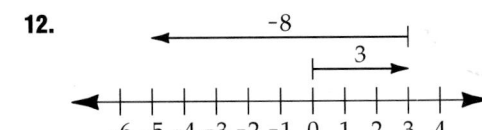

-2   -4

-6 -5 -4 -3 -2 -1 0

12.

-8

3

-6 -5 -4 -3 -2 -1 0 1 2 3 4

WRITTEN EXERCISES

Write a sum for each situation. Explain the result.

1. borrow $20, then pay back $18 *2*   **2.** save $200, then spend $75

125

3. temperature: -10°F drops 2°, rises 8°, drops 5°, drops 13°, rises 1°   *-2*

Use models to represent each sum. Find the sum.

4. -5 + 1   **5.** -3 + (-6)   **6.** -4 + 4 + (-5) + 0 + 8

Represent each sum on a number line. Find the sum.

7. -10 + 14   **8.** 5 + (-8)   **9.** -1 + (-6) + 12 + (-7) + 8 + 3

MENTAL MATH Find each sum mentally.

10. -5 + 5 + 16   *16*   **11.** -4 + (-2) + (-2) *-8*

12. -1 + (-1) + (-1) + 1 + (-1) + 1 *-2*   **13.** -120 + 100 + (-20)

-40

CALCULATOR Find each sum.

14. 145 + (-88) *57*   **15.** -355 + (-492)   **16.** -192 + 825 + (-862) + 69

-4047   *-160*

Find each sum. Choose a method to use.

17. -2 + (-3) *-5*   **18.** -1 + 10 *-11*   **19.** -9 + 9 *0*   **20.** 8 + (-12) *-4*

21. 14 + (-11) *-25* **22.** 0 + (-9) *-9*   **23.** -6 + (-7) *-13*   **24.** -18 + 4 *-14*

25. -5 + 20 *15*   **26.** 6 + (-6) *0*   **27.** -10 + (-3) *-13*   **28.** -94 + 68 *-26*

29. -8 + 7 + 5 *4*   **30.** 3 + (-2) + (-4) *-3*   **31.** -1 + (-9) + 4 *-6*

32. -3 + 2 + (-7) + 7 + 13 *12*   **33.** -20 + (-89) + 112 + 9 + (-3) *9*

Use the DATA at the left.

34. Write the low temperatures in order from lowest to highest.

35. Compare the lowest high temperature with the highest low temperature for the week. Use > or <.

36. **PROJECT** Find the lowest and highest recorded temperatures in your city and state.

Nebraska

Temperatures in Sioux
Week of January 22

Day	High (F°)	Low (F°)
Mon	8	-15
Tues	0	-24
Wed	4	-11
Thurs	-6	-21
Fri	1	-15
Sat	4	0
Sun	26	2

Write a numerical expression for each phrase. Find the sum.

37. negative two plus negative seven

38. twelve plus the absolute value of nine

39. positive three plus the opposite of eight

40. one hundred added to negative nineteen

Compare. Write >, <, or =.

41. ⁻6 + 1 < 5 + 1   **42.** 0 + 3 > ⁻2 + 0

43. ⁻20 + (⁻7) > ⁻11 + (⁻11) < 16 + 6

Solve.

44. Maria had $123. She spent $35, loaned $20 to a friend, and received her $90 paycheck. How much does she have now? 158

45. A football team gained 14 yd, lost 22 yd, gained 15 yd, lost 8 yd, and then lost 9 yd. Find the net gain or loss in yards. ⁻10 yds

46. **WRITE** and solve a word problem that uses the integers ⁻10, 3, 5, ⁻6, and ⁻7.

> **PROBLEM SOLVING HINT**
> Using a number line or model may be helpful.

Complete with integers.

47. ☐ + ☐ = 7   **48.** ☐ + ☐ = ⁻8   **49.** ☐ + ☐ = ⁻12

Critical Thinking
EXPLORING CLASSIFICATION

You can organize or *classify* numbers into categories by choosing a common *attribute* or characteristic.

⁻7	⁻198	0
	⁻19	⁻47
525	⁻50	⁻78

Look at the numbers in the box.

1. Classify three integers as odd.

2. Classify three integers as less than ⁻10.

3. Classify three integers as having a 7 as a digit.

4. Classify ⁻7, ⁻19, and ⁻50 by one common attribute.

5. Classify three integers as between ⁻49 and 0. Write three more integers that fit in this classification.

6. Now choose some classifications of your own. Design at least three more ways to classify the numbers. List your numbers, exchange with a partner, and analyze each other's lists to figure out the classification.

> **MIXED REVIEW**
> **Find each number.**
> **1.** the opposite of 8
> **2.** the opposite of ⁻12
> **3.** |⁻10| **4.** |16|
> **Complete with > or <.**
> **5.** ⁻9 ☐ ⁻6   **6.** ⁻2 ☐ ⁻7
> **7.** In how many ways can you make change for a quarter?
> **8.** Name the integer five units to the left of negative eight.

OBJECTIVE:
To subtract integers
using models,
patterns, and rules.

1-3 Subtracting Integers

▼ In one day in January 1916 the temperature change in Browning, Montana set a record. The temperature fell 100° from 44°F to -56°F. You can write the situation as subtraction of integers.

$$44 \quad - \quad 100 \quad = \quad -56$$
44° above zero   drop of 100°   new temperature

▼ You can think of a thermometer as a number line. The thermometer at the left shows the subtraction as a move along a number line.

▼ You can also use models to show subtraction situations.

Example 1   **a.** You have $5. You give away $1. You now have $4.

         b. You owe $3. You pay back $2. You now owe $1.

Solution   **a.** $5 - 1 = 4$ 

         b. $-3 - (-2) = -1$ Let 3 negative tiles stand for the money you owe. Take away 2 tiles.

Example 2   **a.** $4 - 5$ **b.** $5 - (-6)$

Solution   **a.** You don't have 5 positive tiles. So, add a zero pair.

         Now take away 5 positives.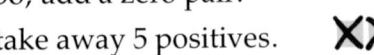

         $4 - 5 = -1$

         b. You don't have 6 negative tiles. Add some zero pairs.

         Now take away 6 negatives.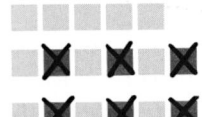

         $5 - (-6) = 11$

▼ You know how to subtract positive integers and how to add any integers. Look at the pattern for the sums and differences you know.

$5 - 4 = 1$	$7 - 3 = 4$	$12 - 5 = 7$	$14 - 6 = 8$
$5 + (-4) = 1$	$7 + (-3) = 4$	$12 + (-5) = 7$	$14 + (-6) = 8$

You can see the same pattern when adding or subtracting any integers.

$-10 - (-6) = -4$	$7 - 8 = -1$	$2 - (-9) = 11$
$-10 + 6 = -4$	$7 + (-8) = -1$	$2 + 9 = 11$

▼ The models and patterns suggest the following rule for subtracting integers.

| **Subtracting Integers** | To subtract an integer, add its opposite. |

Example 3   **a.** $-8 - 2$ **b.** $-12 - (-4)$ **c.** $|-3| - |-7|$

Solution   **a.** $-8 - 2 = -8 + (-2)$ Add the opposite of 2.
$$= -10$$

b. $-12 - (-4) = -12 + 4$ Add the opposite of -4.
$$= -8$$

c. $|-3| - |-7| = 3 - 7$ Find absolute values.
$$= 3 + (-7)$$ Add the opposite of 7.
$$= -4$$

CLASS EXERCISES

Write each subtraction as an equivalent addition.

1. $2 - 3$ -5   **2.** $-5 - (-6)$ -1   **3.** $-9 - (-7)$ -2   **4.** $1 - 8$ -9

5. $33 - (-18)$ 51   **6.** $0 - 75$ -75   **7.** $-12 - (-12)$ 0   **8.** $|-10| - |7|$ 3

Model each situation and give the result.

9. You are $3 in debt. You get a $10 gift. 7

10. You pay a bill for $15. You earn $7. -1

11. **WRITE** In your own words, summarize the rules for adding and subtracting integers. Use examples if necessary.

THINK AND DISCUSS

1. When is the absolute value of a difference the *same* as the difference of the absolute values?

2. When is the absolute value of a difference *greater* than the difference of the absolute values?

3. When is the absolute value of a difference *less* than the difference of the absolute values?

WRITTEN EXERCISES

Write a number sentence for each model or number line.

1.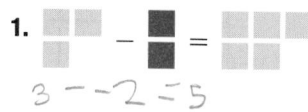

$3 - -2 = 5$

2.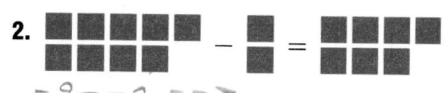

$-9 - -2 = -7$

3.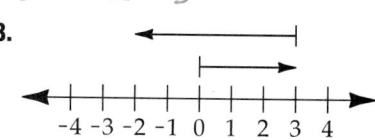

4.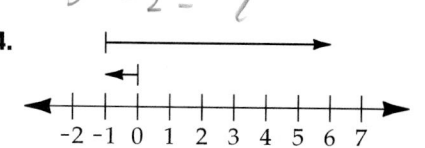

Write a numerical expression for each phrase.

5. A plane climbs 3,000 ft and then descends 600 ft.

6. The temperature increases to 15° and then drops 25°.

MENTAL MATH **Find each difference.**

7. -2 − 3   8. -7 − (-9)   9. -14 − 2

10. -6 − (-8)   11. -45 − 15   12. -7 − (-7) + (-7)

13. 100 − (-50)   14. 20 − (-10) − 20   15. -11 + 22 − (-55)

CALCULATOR **Find each difference.**

16. 88 − 97   17. -235 − (-39)   18. -49 − 75

19. 121 − (-57)   20. -81 − (-13)   21. 989 − 76

22. -59 − (-17)   23. -91 − (-79) − 19   24. 815 + 35 − (-79)

Find each sum or difference. Use any method you wish.

25. 16 − (-9)   26. 11 − 5   27. 802 + (-977)   28. 75 + (-25)

29. -144 − 278   30. 87 − (-9)   31. 22 + (-7)   32. 35 + (-15)

33. 100 − (-91)   34. -45 − 15   35. -92 + (-9)   36. 167 + (-3)

37. $|68| - |{-12}|$ 38. $|{-80}| + |{-28}|$

39. $|{-555}| - |199|$ 40. $|217| + |{-317}| + |0|$

41. $|{-12}| + |36| - |{-10}|$ 42. $|{-3}| - |{-2}| - |{-1}|$

43. Copy and complete. The first one is done for you.

    8 − (-4) = 12
   12 − (-4) = ▧
   16 − (-4) = ▧
   20 − (-4) = ▧
   24 − (-4) = ▧

If you begin at 8 and subtract -4 five times, the result is ▧.

In a magic square, each row, column, and diagonal has the same sum. Copy and complete each magic square.

44.

Sum = ▧

45.

Sum = ▧

46.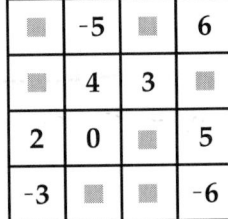

Sum = ▧

NOTES & QUOTES

The magic square below uses the integers from 1–16 once. This magic square appeared in an engraving by Albrecht Dürer (1471–1528) in 1514, a number that appears in the square.

16	3	2	13
5	10	11	8
9	6	7	12
4	15	14	1

• Find the magic sum.
• Find the sum of the four corner numbers.
• Find the sum of the numbers in the shaded squares.
• Find two other sets of four numbers that have the magic sum.

Balloon Trip, Dress Warmly

In 1862, a meteorologist named James Glaisher set off in a hot air balloon wearing nothing warmer than a jacket.

When the balloon landed, Mr. Glaisher was unconscious and the thermometer in the balloon read -84°C.

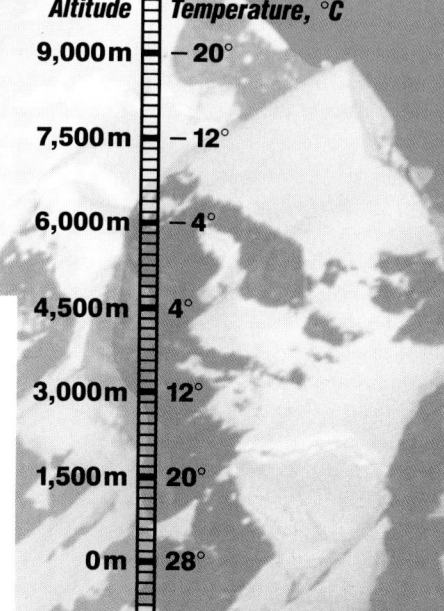

Altitude	Temperature, °C
9,000 m	-20°
7,500 m	-12°
6,000 m	-4°
4,500 m	4°
3,000 m	12°
1,500 m	20°
0 m	28°

47. DATA Use the article above and the graph at the right.

 a. As the altitude increases, what happens to the temperature?

 b. By how much does the temperature change from 1,500 m to 6,000 m?

 c. For every 1,500 m increase in altitude there is an 8° (increase, decrease) in temperature.

 d. Use the given thermometer reading to estimate the height Mr. Glaisher's balloon reached.

48. How much warmer is it when the temperature is 20° than when the temperature is -7°?

49. Suppose you had a score of 35 in a game. You then get a 50 point penalty. What is your new score?

Use positive and negative integers to write two different subtraction number sentences for each difference.

▼▼ *SAMPLE* ▧ − ▧ = -5 → -20 − (-15) = -5   17 − 22 = -5

50. ▧ − ▧ = 0   **51.** ▧ − ▧ = 10   **52.** ▧ − ▧ = -6

53. ▧ − ▧ = -15   **54.** ▧ − ▧ = |-3| **55.** ▧ − ▧ = |11|

ESTIMATION Round each number to a convenient place. Estimate each sum or difference.

▼▼ *SAMPLE* Estimate -2,216 + 488.
          -2,200 + 500 = -1,700

56. -45 + (-86)   **57.** 227 − 49   **58.** 398 − 67

59. -186 + 122   **60.** 88 + 521   **61.** 3,321 − 924

62. 5,436 − (-4,725)   **63.** -864 + (-2,735)   **64.** 4,599 − 3,099

MIXED REVIEW

Add or subtract.

1. -17 − 12

2. |60 − (-5)|

3. -8 + 15

4. -9 + (-4) + 7

5. Name an integer between -5 and -10.

6. 6 + ▧ = 0

Write a number sentence and solve.

7. A submarine at the surface dives 800 ft and then another 125 ft. Find the final depth.

Exploring Number Patterns

OBJECTIVE:
To explore and describe number patterns.

■ Some number patterns are familiar.

2, 4, 6, 8, 10, 12, 14
30, 25, 20, 15, 10, 5, 0
2, -2, 2, -2, 2, -2, 2, -2
1, 3, 4, 12, 13, 39, 40, 120, 360, 1080

1. **a.** *Write* the next three numbers in each pattern.

   b. *Write* a rule to describe each pattern.

   c. *Discuss*—How are the patterns alike? How are they different?

2. *Analyze* the integer triangle.

   a. *Describe* a pattern for each row and column.

   b. Copy the triangle and add four more rows.

   c. What is the middle number in each row?

   d. How many numbers appear in each row?

   e. What is the sum of the numbers in each row?

   f. *Describe* each pattern you found.

```
        1
      1 2 1
    1 2 3 2 1
  1 2 3 4 3 2 1
1 2 3 4 5 4 3 2 1
```

3. *Analyze* the triangle of even numbers.

   a. Copy the pattern and add six more rows.

   b. *Describe* what happens when you alternate subtracting and adding the numbers in each row.

   Copy and complete the table. Use the table to search for patterns. *Compare* with another group.

```
         0
       2   4
     6   8   10
  12  14  16  18
20  ■   ■   ■   ■
```

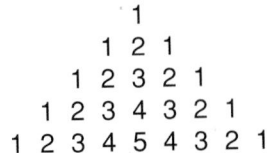

Row	1	2	3	4	5	6	7	8	9	10
Result	0	-2	8	-4	■	■	■	■	■	■

4. Make up a pattern of your own. Exchange with a partner. Figure out each other's pattern.

■ You can think about some sets of numbers in more than one way. Look at the following pattern in two different ways.

2, $\underset{+4}{\diagdown}$ 6, $\underset{+6}{\diagdown}$ 12, $\underset{+8}{\diagdown}$ 20, ...

$$2, \quad 6, \quad 12, \quad 20, \ldots$$
$$1 \cdot 2 \quad 2 \cdot 3 \quad 3 \cdot 4 \quad 4 \cdot 5$$

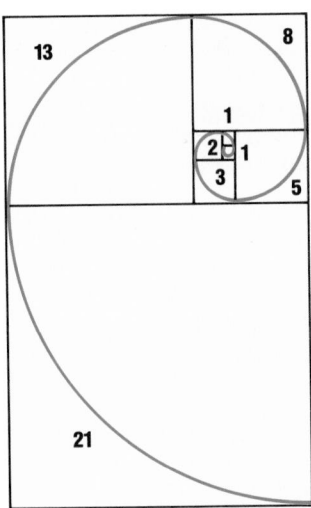

The spiral of a nautilus shell is an example of the Fibonacci numbers 1, 1, 2, 3, 5, 8, 13, . . .

• **Explain and extend the pattern.**

• **RESEARCH Find out how Fibonacci numbers occur in nature, music, and art.**

5. **a.** Extend the above patterns. Do they result in the same set of numbers? Is this what you expected?

   b. Which method of extending the pattern would you use to find the 10th number in the pattern? the 100th number?

6. Make up a number pattern that you can extend in two different ways. Exchange with a partner and solve.

1-4 Look for a Pattern

OBJECTIVE:
To solve problems by looking for a pattern.

READ
PLAN
LOOK BACK
SOLVE

■ You can solve many types of problems using patterns.

PROBLEM

News spreads quickly at River Dell High School. Each student who hears a story repeats that story to two other students in 15 min, and then tells no one else. A student hears some news at 8:00 A.M. How many students will know the news at 10:00 A.M.?

SOLUTION

READ ▸ Answer these questions to understand the given information.
How many students does each student tell? 2
How long does it take the news to reach two students? 15 min

PLAN ▸ Make a table to organize the given information. Then look for a pattern.

SOLVE ▸ Answer these questions to complete the table.
How many *new* students hear the news every 15 min? twice as many
How many students know the news after 15 min? $1 + 2 = 3$
after 30 min? $3 + 4 = 7$
after 45 min? $7 + 8 = 15$
Continue the pattern until you reach 10:00 A.M.

Time	8:00	8:15	8:30	8:45	9:00	9:15	9:30	9:45	10:00
Number of new students told	1	2	4	8	16	32	64	128	256
Number of students who know	1	3	7	15	31	63	127	255	511

By 10:00 A.M., 511 students know the story.

LOOK BACK ▸ One way to check a problem is to solve it another way. A tree diagram is a visual means to solving the problem.

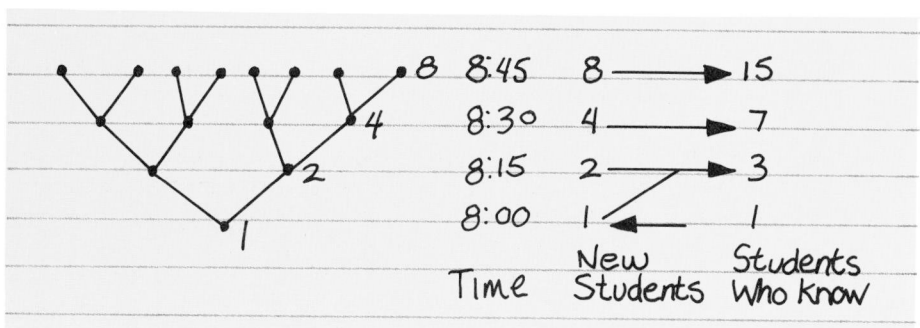

CLASS EXERCISES

Refer to the problem on page 19.

1. Describe two ways to use the pattern to tell the number of students who know at 10:15 A.M.

2. Suppose the news continues to spread through the school. There are 1,735 students at River Dell High. By what time will every student know the story?

Refer to the problem on page 19.

WRITTEN EXERCISES

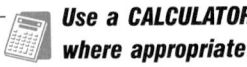

Use a CALCULATOR where appropriate.

Solve by looking for a pattern.

1. The students in the town of Brighton are going to march in a parade. There will be one first-grader, two second-graders, three third-graders, and so on through the twelfth grade. How many students will march in the parade?

2. Caroline is training for a swim meet. The first week she swims 1 lap per day. The second week she swims 3 laps per day. The third week she swims 6 laps per day. The fourth week she swims 10 laps per day. If she keeps to this training pattern, how many laps per day will Caroline swim in the eighth week?

3. Find each product and look for a pattern.

$2 \times 2 = $ ▦ $3 \times 3 = $ ▦
$1 \times 3 = $ ▦ $2 \times 4 = $ ▦
Difference = ▦   Difference = ▦
$4 \times 4 = $ ▦ $5 \times 5 = $ ▦
$3 \times 5 = $ ▦ $4 \times 6 = $ ▦
Difference = ▦   Difference = ▦

a. Which is greater, 10×12 or 11×11? how much greater?

b. Suppose you know that $47 \times 47 = 2,209$. How can you find 46×48?

c. Suppose you know that $64 \times 66 = 4,224$. How can you find 65×65?

4. Every day Maria saves twice as many pennies as she saved the day before. She starts by saving one penny on January 1. How much money will she have by January 10?

5. **DATA FILE 8 (pp. 312–313)** Did the population grow more between 1800 and 1810 or 1810 and 1820? How much more?

DATA FILE 8 (pp. 312–313)

NOTES & QUOTES

When the German mathematician Karl Friedrich Gauss (1777–1855) was about ten years old, his teacher became annoyed with the class. As punishment, the teacher asked the class to compute the sum of the first 100 counting numbers. Gauss thought for a moment and then wrote the correct answer on his slate.

RESEARCH Find out how Gauss used patterns to solve this problem.

Solve. Use any strategy you wish.

6. You can cut a pizza into two pieces with one straight cut. With two cuts you get four pieces. Three cuts will result in a maximum of seven pieces. What is the maximum number of pieces you can get with four cuts? with five cuts?

7. A restaurant offers special prices for groups dining together. For a buffet dinner, the restaurant charges $10 for one person, $20 for two people, $29 for three, $37 for four, and so on.

   a. How much does a buffet dinner for 8 cost? How much does the group save by eating together rather than alone?

   b. The buffet costs the restaurant $6 per person. What size group can the restaurant serve without losing money?

Critical Thinking

EXPLORING VENN DIAGRAMS

The principal wants to send invitations to a Science Fair to the homes of all students enrolled in biology and chemistry. Use the enrollment figures at the right to tell how many invitations are needed. A *Venn diagram* will help.

Course	Enrollment
Biology	127
Chemistry	124
Biology and Chemistry	17

- Draw intersecting circles. Label the circles with the given information.

- The *intersection* (overlap) tells the number of students enrolled in both courses. Write the number in the intersection.

- The total in the biology circle is 110 plus the 17 in the intersection. What number goes in the chemistry circle?

- Add the numbers in the three sections. How many invitations does the principal need?

Use a Venn diagram to solve.

A coach needs to notify soccer players and swimmers of a revised schedule. Use the data at the right and a Venn diagram to tell how many notices the coach must send.

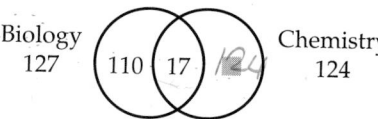

Sport	Players
Soccer	24
Swimming	19
Soccer and swimming	6

1-5 Multiplying Integers

▼ Suppose a football team loses 2 yd on each of 4 plays. At the end of the 4 plays the team loses 8 yd.

$$4 \quad \times \quad -2 \quad = \quad -8$$

4 plays   lose 2 yd/play   lose 8 yd

▼ You also can think of multiplication as repeated addition.

Example 1 $3 \times (-7)$

Solution $3 \times (-7) = (-7) + (-7) + (-7)$
                  $= -21$

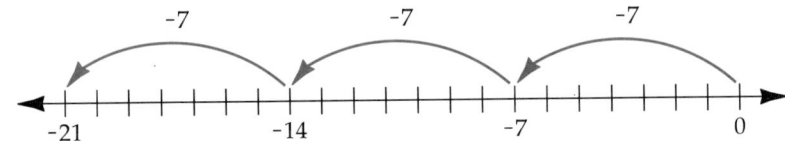

▼ Notice that the product of a negative number and a positive number is negative. You can use patterns to help find the product of two negative numbers.

Example 2   **Use patterns to find $-3(-6)$ and $-4(-5)$.**

Solution

$2(-6) = -12$	$3(-5) = -15$	**Start with products you know.**
$1(-6) = -6$	$2(-5) = -10$	
$0(-6) = 0$	$1(-5) = -5$	
	$0(-5) = 0$	
$-1(-6) = 6$	$-1(-5) = 5$	**Continue the pattern for the product of two negative integers.**
$-2(-6) = 12$	$-2(-5) = 10$	
$-3(-6) = 18$	$-3(-5) = 15$	
	$-4(-5) = 20$	

▼ From what you know about multiplying whole numbers and from the examples, you can write these rules for multiplying integers.

Multiplying Integers	To multiply two integers, find the product of the absolute values of the integers. Then use these rules.
	1. The product of two integers with the same sign is positive.
	$(+)(+) = +$ $(-)(-) = +$
	2. The product of two integers with different signs is negative.
	$(+)(-) = -$ $(-)(+) = -$

THINK Is the product increasing or decreasing? by how much?

▼ The rules are useful for finding the product of more than two integers.

Example 3   Use the rules and mental math to find the product of $-2 \cdot 8(-5)$.

Solution $-2 \cdot 8(-5)$

$\quad\quad\quad\quad 10 \cdot 8 = 80$

$\quad\quad -2 \cdot 8(-5) = 80$

You can multiply integers in any order. Choose factors that are easy to multiply in your head.

▼ You can use integers to solve problems.

Example 4   Your average time for a 10-km race is 54 min. You would like to take 2 min off your average time each month for 3 mo. What will be your new average time?

Solution   **1.** By how much do you want to reduce your average time? $2 \cdot 3$

2. Compute your new average time. $54 - (2 \cdot 3) = 48$

Your new average time will be 48 min.

CLASS EXERCISES

Without computing, tell whether the product is positive, negative, or zero.

1. $-3(8)(-24)$ **2.** $8(-83)$ **3.** $2(-4) \cdot 29$ **4.** $3(-21)(-12)$

Write each sum as a product. Find the product.

5. $-8 + (-8) + (-8) + (-8)$ **6.** $-2 + (-2) + (-2) + (-2) + (-2)$

Complete the pattern. Is the product increasing or decreasing? by how much?

7. $3(-3) = \blacksquare$
$\quad 2(-3) = \blacksquare$
$\quad 1(-3) = \blacksquare$
$\quad 0(-3) = \blacksquare$
$\quad -1(-3) = \blacksquare$
$\quad -2(-3) = \blacksquare$
$\quad -3(-3) = \blacksquare$

8. $2(-9) = \blacksquare$
$\quad 1(-9) = \blacksquare$
$\quad 0(-9) = \blacksquare$
$\quad -1(-9) = \blacksquare$
$\quad -2(-9) = \blacksquare$
$\quad -3(-9) = \blacksquare$
$\quad -4(-9) = \blacksquare$

9. Write a number sentence for the product shown on the number line.

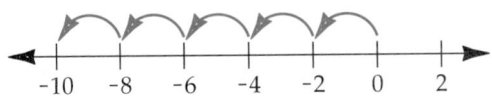

THINK AND DISCUSS

1. What is the product of -6 and -1? How are the product and -6 related? Complete: The product of any integer and -1 is the ■ of the integer.

2. Will the product of three negative integers be positive or negative? what about four negative integers? five negative integers?

3. Write a rule to use in deciding the sign for the product of more than two integers.

WRITTEN EXERCISES

Use repeated addition to find each product.

1. 10(-6) **2.** -12 · 4 **3.** 5(-6) **4.** 4(-11)

Use patterns to find each product.

5. -7(-3) **6.** -3(-6) **7.** -5(-4) **8.** -9(-12)

MENTAL MATH Find the point on the number line that shows each product.

9. -2 · 0 **10.** 4(-2) **11.** |-2| · |-2| **12.** 2(-2)

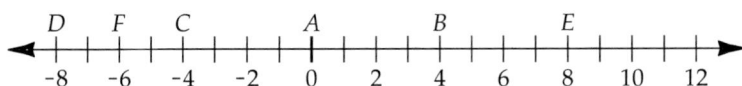

CALCULATOR Find each product.

13. -59(-79) **14.** 243(-88) **15.** -1,078(-43) **16.** 23(-54) · 42(-39)

Find each answer. Choose a method to use.

17. -5(-3)	**18.** -6 · 10	**19.** 8 · 3(-4)
20. -18(-12)	**21.** -11 · 20	**22.** -8 · 0
23. 24(-16)(-32)	**24.** -9(-8)(-5)	**25.** -8 · 25
26. |-9| + |-8|	**27.** |-2| · (-7) · 4	**28.** |-2| · (-7)
29. -9 - (-2)	**30.** -8 + 6 + (-6)	**31.** 0(-12) · 4
32. 14 · 9	**33.** -20 + (-6)	**34.** 17 - (-3)
35. 9(-9)	**36.** 38(-2)	**37.** -15 + (-4)

Write a product for each word phrase. Then find the product.

38. negative eleven times negative five

39. eight times the opposite of five

40. the product of fourteen and negative seven

41. the product of six and negative nine

42. the absolute value of the product of negative twelve and ten

Compare. Use >, <, or = to make a true statement.

43. (-9)(-6) ▨ 8(-10) **44.** 5(-2) ▨ (-6)(-1) **45.** |-6||-2| ▨ |-6(-2)|

Solve.

46. The temperature dropped 5° each hour for 7 h. Use an integer to represent the total change in temperature.

---

47. The price of a stock fell $3 each day over a 12-day period.

   a. What was the total change in price?

   b. The original stock price was $76 per share. What was the price after the drop?

48. A car loan requires equal payments of $378 per month for four years.

   a. What is the total amount paid for the four years?

   b. Suppose a down payment of $2,500 was made. What was the total cost of the car?

PROBLEM SOLVING HINT
How many months are in four years?

Find two integers that fit the given description.

49. sum: -7
   product: 12

50. sum: 0
   product: -9

51. sum: 4
   product: -5

52. DATA FILE 9 (pp. 360–361) Suppose your score for the first nine holes at the St. Andrew's golf course is 4 under par. What would be your score?

53. DATA Use the chart below.

   a. Can a balloon carry more weight at 5,000 ft at 40° or at 4,000 ft at 50°?

   b. Suppose people who weigh 150 lb, 112 lb, 129 lb, 183 lb, 108 lb, 75 lb, and 56 lb are planning a balloon trip. The balloon weighs 620 lb. Can the group rise to 4,000 ft if the temperature is 70°?

   c. WRITE Describe two patterns in the chart. Compare with a classmate. Did you find different patterns?

MAXIMUM WEIGHT A HOT AIR BALLOON CAN CARRY* (in pounds)							
	Temperature (°F)						
Altitude	30°	40°	50°	60°	70°	80°	90°
2,000 ft	1,415	1,315	1,215	1,100	1,000	885	800
3,000 ft	1,370	1,270	1,170	1,070	970	850	770
4,000 ft	1,330	1,230	1,130	1,030	930	820	750
5,000 ft	1,285	1,185	1,085	985	900	800	715
10,000 ft	1,060	985	900	815	750	660	600
15,000 ft	885	815	750	670	615	550	485

*Limits include weight of the balloon

Hot air balloon trips are usually planned for early morning. Why do you think this is true?

1-6 Dividing Integers

▼ A storm system moved through Minneapolis one day and the temperature dropped 28° in 4 h. To find the average change per hour, you can divide.

$$-28 \div 4 = -7$$

You can use a related multiplication sentence to see why the quotient is negative.

$$\text{Since } -7 \cdot 4 = -28, -28 \div 4 = -7$$

▼ Multiplication and division are inverse operations. One *undoes* the other. Because $3 \cdot 2 = 6$, we can write $6 \div 3 = 2$ and $6 \div 2 = 3$. You can use this relationship to find quotients of integers. The table shows related multiplication and division sentences.

Multiplication Number Sentence	Division Number Sentence
$8(6) = 48$	$48 \div 6 = 8$
$(-8)(6) = -48$	$-48 \div 6 = -8$
$8(-6) = -48$	$-48 \div (-6) = 8$
$(-8)(-6) = 48$	$48 \div (-6) = -8$

▼ The examples demonstrate the following rules for dividing integers.

Dividing Integers	To divide two integers, find the quotient of the absolute values of the integers. Then use the following rules.
	1. The quotient of two integers with the same sign is positive.
	$(+) \div (+) = +$ $\qquad (-) \div (-) = +$
	2. The quotient of two integers with different signs is negative.
	$(+) \div (-) = -$ $\qquad (-) \div (+) = -$

Example 1   **a.** $27 \div 9$ **b.** $-18 \div (-3)$

c. $100 \div (-10)$ **d.** $-56 \div 7$

Solution   **a.** $27 \div 9 = 3$ $\qquad (+) \div (+) = +$

b. $-18 \div (-3) = 6$ $\qquad (-) \div (-) = +$

c. $100 \div (-10) = -10$ $\qquad (+) \div (-) = -$

d. $-56 \div 7 = -8$ $\qquad (-) \div (+) = -$

Many of the numbers you see every day are averages. The *mean* is the average you see most often. Many of the problems you encounter will ask you to compute the mean.

Finding the Mean	To find the mean of a group of numbers: 1. Find the sum of the numbers. 2. Divide the sum by the number of items.

Example 2 A student's scores on five math tests were 98, 90, 87, 95, and 90. Find the mean score.

Solution
1. Find the sum.
   $98 \boxed{+} 90 \boxed{+} 87 \boxed{+} 95 \boxed{+} 90 = 460$
2. Divide by 5, the number of items.
   $460 \boxed{\div} 5 \boxed{=} 92$

The mean score is 92.

CLASS EXERCISES

Without computing, state whether the quotient is positive, negative or zero. Explain your reasoning.

1. $-25 \div 5$ **2.** $39 \div (-3)$ **3.** $35 \div (-7)$ **4.** $8 \div 3$

For each product, write a related division sentence and solve.

5. $-9 \cdot 4$ **6.** $9(-3)$ **7.** $-11 \cdot 11$ **8.** $8 \cdot 3$

Find the quotient.

9. $144 \div 12$ **10.** $55 \div 11$ **11.** $34 \div (-17)$ **12.** $-210 \div (-30)$

Find the mean.

13. temperatures: $-9°, -12°, 9°, 4°, -2°$
14. feet above and below sea level: 135, -56, 92, -29, -88, -60
15. test scores: 80, 75, 90, 88, 87
16. golf scores: 3, 5, 8, 6, 4, 5, 3, 6, 5
17. bank balance: $200, -$85, $120, $200, $280

THINK AND DISCUSS

1. Use a related multiplication sentence to explain why you can't divide by zero.

2. Compare the signs of quotients of integers with the signs of products of integers. What do you discover?

3. Must the mean of a group of a numbers be one of the numbers in the group?

WRITTEN EXERCISES

For each quotient, write a related multiplication sentence and solve.

1. $-90 \div (-9)$ **2.** $35 \div (-7)$ **3.** $56 \div 8$ **4.** $88 \div 11$

MENTAL MATH Find each quotient.

5. -63 ÷ 9   **6.** 66 ÷ 6   **7.** 250 ÷ (-50)   **8.** 1,200 ÷ (-40)

CALCULATOR Find each quotient.

9. -432 ÷ 48   **10.** 693 ÷ 21   **11.** -10,584 ÷ (-84)

12. 50,840 ÷ (-328)   **13.** 13,272 ÷ 237   **14.** -62,937 ÷ (-111)

Find each answer. Choose a method to use.

15. 48 ÷ 12   **16.** 1,000 ÷ (-50)   **17.** -38 ÷ (-2)

18. -3,132 ÷ 36   **19.** 24 ÷ (-24)   **20.** 0 ÷ (-56)

21. 225 ÷ (-15)   **22.** 18 ÷ (-1)   **23.** -64 · 6

24. -33 + 11   **25.** 5,959 ÷ (-101)   **26.** -58 ÷ (-1)

27. -200 - 25   **28.** 736 ÷ (-23)   **29.** -72 + (-8)

30. 204 ÷ (-12)   **31.** -1,225 ÷ 35   **32.** 0 ÷ (-8)

33. 128 + (-64)   **34.** 150 - (-15)   **35.** 225 · 15

36. $|-56 \cdot 12| \div (-24)$ **37.** $(-|-24(9)| \div |3(-8)|)$

Write a numerical expression for each word phrase. Then evaluate the expression.

38. negative twenty-four divided by negative eight

39. negative forty-two multiplied by three

40. zero divided by negative seven

41. two hundred subtracted from negative twenty-five

Find the mean.

42. temperature: -12°, -8°, -24°, 32°, 0°, -6°

43. weekly allowance: $3, $2, $5, $2, $3, $2, $2, $5

44. salary: $24,000; $18,000; $52,000; $27,000; $15,000

45. score: -203, 813, -446, -231, 466, -155, -329, -228, 312, 1

Write >, <, or = to make a true statement.

46. -10 ÷ (-2) ▨ 25 ÷ (-5)   **47.** -(-15 ÷ 5) ▨ -100 ÷ (-20)

48. $|-25| \div |-5|$ ▨ $|-25 \div (-5)|$ **49.** $-|-28| \div 7$ ▨ $-28 \div (-7)$

Write an integer between the given integers.

50. -2 · (-2) and 2 · 3   **51.** 10 + (-7) and 10 ÷ (-5)

52. 121 ÷ (-11) and $|-7| - |7|$ **53.** 50 + (-48) and 80 ÷ (-20)

Solve.

54. An integer multiplied by -8 equals -96. What is the integer?

MIXED REVIEW

Find each answer.

1. 5(-9)

2. -8(-3)

3. $|-3| \cdot 8 \cdot (-2)$

4. $|-5 \cdot (-2) \cdot 3|$

Write the next three numbers in each pattern.

5. -7, -2, 3, 8, ▨, ▨, ▨

6. 1, 4, 9, 16, ▨, ▨, ▨

7. Make up your own pattern. Write a rule to describe it.

55. An integer multiplied by 9 equals -135. What is the integer?

56. Find two integers with a sum of -10 and a product of -75.

57. A scuba diver descended to a depth of 50 ft in 25 s. How many feet per second did she dive?

58. *DATA FILE 9 (pp. 360–361)* Find the average length in yards for the first 9 holes at St. Andrew's golf course.

59. *PROJECT* Find the shoe sizes of ten classmates who are the same gender as you. Use the information to predict the average shoe size of students of your gender and age.

> **PROBLEM SOLVING HINT**
> Try guess and test.

60. The grade book shows students' math scores.

Name	Test 1	Test 2	Test 3	Test 4	Test 5
Abrams, Joel	88	87	74	69	92
Adams, Sam	66	72	88	81	88
Barcos, Elena	99	91	90	95	90
Cuomo, Terri	67	70	72	71	80

LETTER GRADES

A	90 - 100
B	80 - 89
C	70 - 79
D	60 - 69
F	0 - 59

a. Find each student's average grade. Use the chart at the right to assign a letter grade.

b. What would Sam Adams have needed to score on his first test to raise his grade to a B?

TEST YOURSELF

Compare. Use >, <, or =.

1. 3 ▨ -8

2. -10 ▨ -6

3. -4 + 3 ▨ 3 + (-4)

Find each number.

4. $|-8|$

5. $-|-85|$

6. the opposite of 12

Evaluate.

7. 3 + (-11)

8. 12 − (-8)

9. -9 · 5

10. -64 ÷ (-8)

Find the mean.

11. -4, 7, 0, -3, -2, 20

12. 20, 40, 25, 35, 100

Practice

Find each sum.

1. 27 + 28   55
2. 12 + (-4)   8
3. -15 + (-8)   -23
4. -25 + 38   13
5. 0 + (-19)   -19
6. 59 + (-62)   -3
7. -125 + 258   133
8. 278 + 179   457
9. -187 + (-147)   -334
10. -26 + 38 + (-28)   -16
11. 99 + (-127) + 268 + (-99)   141
12. -712 + 0 + (-88)   -800
13. 999 + (-90) + (-9) + (-1,000)   -100

Find each difference.

14. 36 - 17   19
15. 42 - (-21)   63
16. -44 - (-35)   -9
17. -57 - 32   -80
18. -48 - (-44)   -4
19. 0 - 62   -62
20. 125 - 63   62
21. -167 - 71   -238
22. -214 - (-158)   -56
23. -89 - (-12) - 147   -224
24. 268 - 188 - (-12)   92
25. -439 - 0 - 255 - 11   -705
26. 856 - (-327) - (-144)   1327

Find each product.

27. 9 · 7   63
28. 10 · (-2)   -20
29. -6 · 14   -84
30. -15(-4)   60
31. -18(9)   -162
32. 21(14)   294
33. -25 · (-15)   375
34. -27 · 0   0
35. -32 · 28   896
36. -1 · (-1) · (-1) · (-1)   1
37. -12 · 4 · 2(-3)   288
38. 33 · 17 · 0 · (-199)   0
39. -248 · 4 · (-2) · (-250)   -496000

Find each quotient.

40. 28 ÷ 4   7
41. 27 ÷ (-3)   -9
42. -35 ÷ (-7)   5
43. -42 ÷ 7   -6
44. -51 ÷ (-17)   3
45. 65 ÷ (-13)   -5
46. -1 ÷ (-1) ÷ 1 ÷ (-1)   -1
47. -333 ÷ 3 ÷ (-3)   18.5
48. 0 ÷ 23 ÷ (-34) ÷ (-13)   0
49. 444 ÷ 2 ÷ 2 ÷ (-3) $-37 0.\overline{33}$

Find each answer.

50. -75 + 24   -51
51. 132 - (-21)   153
52. -12 · 13   -156
53. -96 ÷ (-12)   8
54. -162 - 83   -245
55. 316 + (-174)   142
56. 19(-24)   -456
57. 340 ÷ (-17)   -20
58. 418 - (-319)   737
59. 483 ÷ (-161)   -3
60. -163 · (-83)   13529
61. -512 + 512   0
62. -48 + (-13) - 12 + (-3)   -76
63. 127 + (-23) - (-14) - 63   55
64. -12 · 3 · (-8) ÷ 6   48
65. 24 · (-5) · (-4) ÷ 48   10
66. [12 + (-3)] · (14 - 2)   108
67. (-14 + 29) ÷ (-12 - 3)   -1

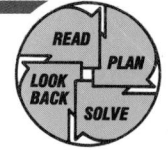

1-7 Fitness and Health

Calories (C) measure the energy provided by the food or drink you consume. You burn calories during any activity.

> When you eat a banana, you *take in* 100 C: +100.
> When you walk for 20 min, you *burn* 100 C: -100.

Example 1 Use the graph below and the chart at the left. Find the net calories if you swim for 40 min and then drink 2 c lemonade.

Solution

$40 \cdot (-10) = -400$	Swimming burns 10 C/min.
$2 \cdot 110 = 220$	Lemonade has 110 C/c.
$-400 + 220 = -180$	There is a net loss of 180 C.

For a weight loss or gain program, doctors recommend a change of diet combined with an exercise program.

> To *lose* a pound, *burn* 3,500 extra calories.
> To *gain* a pound, *take in* 3,500 extra calories.

Example 2 Jo wants to gain about 1 lb per week for 10 weeks. About how many extra calories should she take in each day?

Solution $3,500 \div 7 = 500$

Jo should take in about 500 extra calories per day.

Example 3 Find the net calories if you swim for 30 min and then drink 1 c grape juice.

Solution

$30 \cdot (-10) = -300$	Swim for 30 min at 10 C/min.
$+165$ C	Drink 1 c grape juice.
$-300 + 165 = -135$	net calories

Food	Calories
apple	70
banana	100
wheat bread, 1 slice	55
corn cereal, 1 c	210
muffin	70
cooked oatmeal, 1 c	130
scrambled egg	110
cheese, 1 slice	45
salad dressing, 1 c	80
mayonnaise, 1T	100
carrot	20
potato chips, 10	115
grape juice, 1 c	165
skim milk, 1 c	90
lemonade, 1 c	110
hamburger, 3 oz	245
canned tuna, 3 oz	170
chicken, 3 oz	115
frankfurter	170

Calories used during activities

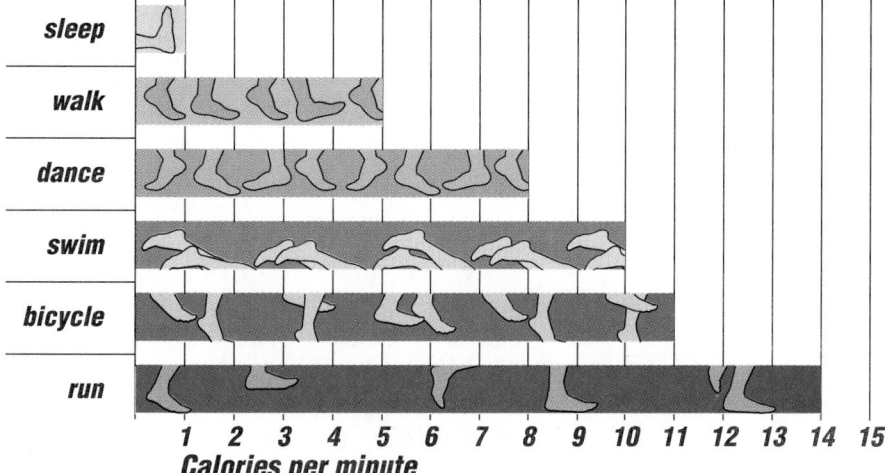

Calories per minute

CLASS EXERCISES

Use the line graph below.

1. On which days did George

    a. take in more calories than he used?

    b. use more calories than he took in?

    c. burn and take in the same number of calories?

2. Find George's net calories for the week.

    a. Did he have a net gain or a net loss of calories?

    b. If this pattern continues, how will George's weight change in a month? in a year?

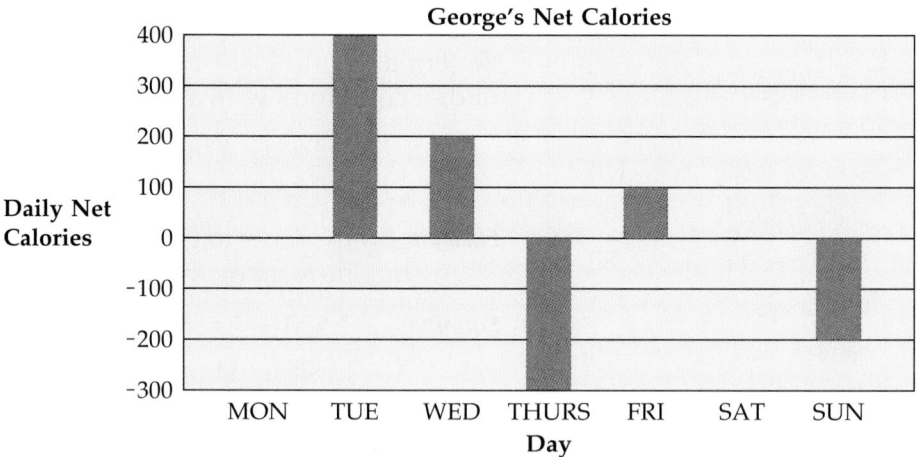

George's Net Calories

■■■■■■■ Decision Making ■ **DECISION MAKING** ■ Decision Making ■ Decision Making ■ Decision Making ■

FITNESS AND HEALTH

■ To be healthy, you must make good decisions about food and exercise. A nutritionally balanced diet and regular exercise will help you to look and feel your best.

■ **COLLECT DATA**

1. Find your normal daily intake of calories by one of the methods below.

    a. Record your daily calorie intake for a week, then find the average.

    b. Use an estimate of 16 C/lb of your weight.

    ■■ *SAMPLE* 135 lb: 135 · 16 = 2,160 C per day

2. Measure your height and weight. Look in a science book or an encyclopedia to find the ideal weight for a person your height and age.

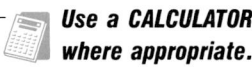
Use a CALCULATOR where appropriate.

Use the graph and table on page 31.

How many calories does each food provide?

1. 2 slices of cheese

2. 2 c skim milk

3. 20 potato chips

How many calories does each activity burn?

4. bicycle 40 min

5. dance 15 min

6. sleep 8 h

Find the net calories.

7. dance 2 h, eat a tuna sandwich

8. run 20 min, eat a muffin

Solve.

9. Suppose you bicycle for an hour. About how many calories would you burn? About how many hours would it take to burn 3,500 C?

10. Juan began running 30 min each day. In order to maintain his weight, he also increased his calorie intake. How many calories should he add to his daily diet?

11. Elizabeth joined the swim team. She swims 90 min every week day. How many calories will she burn swimming each day? How many in four weeks (20 days of swimming)?

I am one of those women who has had the creative joys of a medical career. I have also had the joys of a family. I cannot think of a better way of life.

–Dr. Jane C. Wright, Associate Dean, New York Medical College

■ *Decision Making* ■ *Decision Making* ■ *Decision Making* ■ *Decision Making* ■ *Decision Making* ■ *Decision Making* ■

■ **ANALYZE DATA**

3. Analyze your eating habits.

a. List the foods you eat often and the number of calories each food provides.

b. List other healthy foods that would help balance your diet.

4. Analyze your activities.

a. List the activities you do and the calories each activity burns.

b. List other activities you might like to do.

■ **MAKE DECISIONS**

5. Decide on a plan to maintain or improve your health.

a. Set a reasonable goal to gain, maintain, or lose weight.

b. Decide how to change your eating habits and activities.

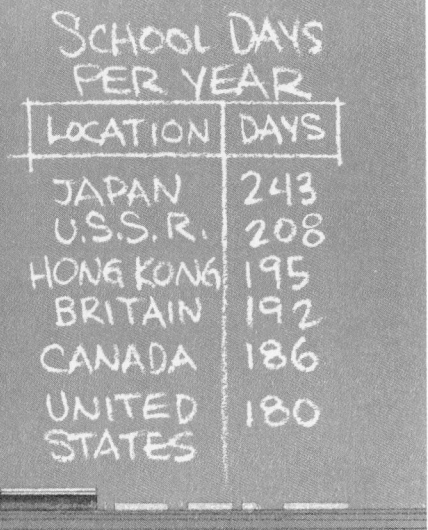

OBJECTIVE:
To assign variables and write variable expressions.

1-8 Expressions and Variables

▼ You can write a *numerical expression* to show the number of weeks in each school year if you assume a 5-day school week.

	Days Per Year		Days Per Week
Japan	243	÷	5
U.S.S.R.	208	÷	5
Hong Kong	195	÷	5
Britain	192	÷	5
Canada	186	÷	5
United States	180	÷	5

If you don't know the number of days in the school year, you can use a letter or other symbol, called a *variable*, to stand for the number. You can write a *variable expression* to show the number of weeks in the school year.

Days Per Year		Days Per Week
d	÷	5

Variable	A variable is a symbol (usually a letter) that stands for a number.

Variable Expression	A variable expression is an expression that contains at least one variable.

FLASHBACK
We usually write products involving variables without multiplication symbols. Write $60h$ not $60 \cdot h$ or $h60$.

Example 1 Write an expression for the number of minutes in:

      a. 1 hour   **b.** 5 hours   **c.** h hours

Solution   **a.** $60 \cdot 1$ **b.** $60 \cdot 5$ **c.** $60h$

                    numerical   variable
                  expressions   expression

FLASHBACK
Use yellow tiles for positive integers and red tiles for negative integers.

▼ Just as we use models to stand for integers, we can use models for variable expressions. Use green rectangles for variables.

Example 2

Expression	Model
$2x$	
$3y + 3$	

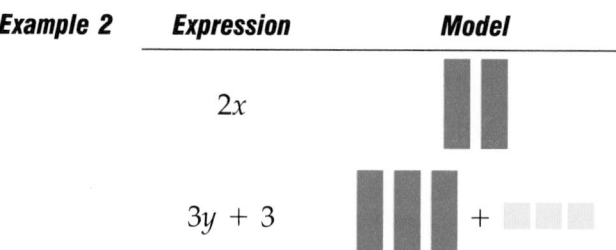

▼ You can use any letter or symbol as a variable. Mathematicians often use the first letter of a word, such as *t* for time, *w* for week, or *a* for age. The most commonly used variables are *x*, *y*, *z*, *n*, *a*, and *b*.

Example 3

Word Phrase	Variable Expression
a number plus nine	$y + 9$
three times a quantity decreased by four	$3z - 4$
negative one divided by a number	$-1 \div a$
the calories in two slices of toast with *c* calories per slice	$2c$
the cost of *b* books at \$5 per book	$5b$

▼ You can write variable expressions to describe situations.

Example 4 A student has several pencils in his desk. He takes out 5 pencils. Write an expression for the number of pencils left in the desk.

Solution 1. Choose a variable, say *p*, for the original number of pencils.

2. Then $p - 5$ is an expression for the number of pencils left in the desk.

Example 5 Suppose you study history for a different length of time each day for 3 days. Write an expression for the average amount of time you studied history each day.

Solution 1. Choose a variable, say *t*, for the total time spent studying for the three days.

2. Then $t \div 3$ is the average time spent each day.

THINK AND DISCUSS

1. How does the word *vary* relate to *variable*?

2. Why do you think letters of the alphabet are used as variables?

3. Describe how the expressions for each phrase differ.

• some number added to 12

• 12 equals some number

• the sum of some numbers is 12

CLASS EXERCISES

Tell whether each is a numerical expression or a variable expression. If it is a variable expression, name the variable.

1. $b + 6$ **2.** $9x$ **3.** $80 \div 8$ **4.** $14 - n$

Choose a variable and write a variable expression for each model.

5. 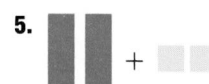 **6.**  **7.**

Write a variable expression for each word phrase.

8. 16 more than *m* **9.** *y* decreased by -4

10. the quotient of 6 and *z* **11.** the product of *c* and 3

Write a word phrase for each variable expression.

12. $m + 3$ **13.** $8 - t$ **14.** $-6k$ **15.** $t \div 12$

Write an expression for the situation.

16. The number of eggs in:

    a. 1 dozen   **b.** 5 dozen   **c.** d dozen

WRITTEN EXERCISES

Choose a variable and write a variable expression for each model.

1.    **2.**   **3.**

Use a model to represent each variable expression.

4. $6x$ **5.** $y + 5$ **6.** $-2 + 2a$ **7.** $m - (-4)$

Write a numerical expression for each word phrase.

8. the quotient of fourteen and negative seven

9. the product of twenty-three and negative nine

10. four more than one thousand

11. eight less than the opposite of six

Write a variable expression for each word phrase.

12. six subtracted from k **13.** m more than nineteen

14. eight less than z **15.** twelve times x

16. the sum of a and b **17.** n divided by negative one

18. one more than a number $3p$

19. the product of g and four times r

20. the difference of a number and three

21. the product of ten and a number

22. sixty-four decreased by a number

23. a number increased by two hundred

24. twice a number plus the absolute value of negative seven

Write two different word phrases for each variable expression.

25. $x + 2$ **26.** $12 - y$ **27.** $15 \div s$ **28.** $-20 + q$

29. $-5y$ **30.** $w - (-4)$ **31.** $100 + (-y)$ **32.** $|n| + 1$

Write an expression for each situation.

33. The number of days in:

    a. 1 week   **b.** 4 weeks   **c.** w weeks

34. The value, in cents, of:

    a. 10 pennies   **b.** 7 nickels   **c.** q quarters

35. Pam is 15 years old. Write an expression for Pam's age:

    a. 3 years ago   **b.** p years ago

    c. 10 years from now   **d.** f years from now

36. Peter has c cousins. Paul has 4 more cousins than Peter. How many cousins does Paul have?

37. Susan has $20 less than Charlotte. Charlotte has d dollars. How many dollars does Susan have?

38. There are twice as many sophomores as freshmen.

    a. If there are f freshmen, how many sophomores are there?

    b. If there are s sophomores, how many freshmen are there?

39. Richard ran b miles. Write a related situation for each expression.

    a. $b + 3$ **b.** $2b$ **c.** $10 - b$

40. A hot air balloon is at an altitude of m meters. Write a related situation for each expression.

    a. $m + 34$ **b.** $m - 2,000$ **c.** $3m$

41. Jeans sell for $25 and T-shirts sell for $12.

    a. Write a numerical expression for the selling price of 2 pairs of jeans and 4 T-shirts.

    b. Write a variable expression for the selling price of j pairs of jeans and t T-shirts.

42. **DATA** Use the calorie chart on page 31.

    a. Write a numerical expression for the number of calories in 3 eggs and a slice of wheat bread.

    b. Write a variable expression for the number of calories in e eggs and s slices of wheat bread.

Match each variable expression with a model.

43. $4x$

44. $4 + x$

45. $x \div 4$

46. $x - 4$

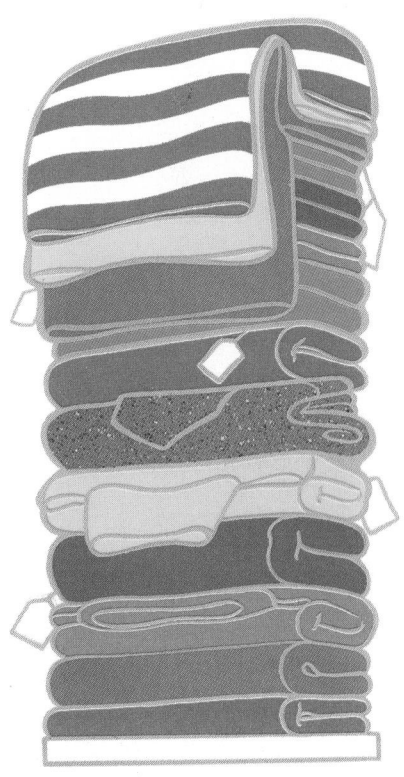

Exploring Spreadsheets

MATERIALS

- paper and pencil
- computer (optional)
- Math journal to record work

DATAPOINT

Cells can store numbers, letters, or a combination of letters and numbers.

■ A spreadsheet is a tool for organizing and analyzing data. The data are arranged in rows and columns. The spreadsheet below shows data for a school walkathon.

	A	B	C	D
1	Class	No. Students	Mi/Student	Tot. Distance
2	9th Grade	250	10	
3	10th Grade	234	15	
4	11th Grade	199	20	
5	12th Grade	176	20	
6			TOTAL	
7				

■ We call each section of a spreadsheet a *cell*. Cell B2 stores the value for the number of ninth-grade students who participated in the walkathon.

1. What amounts are stored in cells D2 through D5? in cell D6?

2. How are the amounts in column D found?

3. Copy the spreadsheet shown above. Use a calculator or paper and pencil to complete column D.

■ You enter data in a spreadsheet one cell at a time. The *cursor* shows you where the next character will be entered.

4. Look at the spreadsheet above. In which cell is the cursor?

■ For a spreadsheet to perform a calculation, you need to type a formula in a cell. Look at the spreadsheet below.

	A	B	C	D
1	Type of Seat	Tickets Sold	Ticket Price	Total
2	Balcony	25	$7.50	
3	Mezzanine	34	$8.50	
4	Front row	38	$15.00	
5	Standing room	42	$4.00	
6			TOTAL	
7				

Cell D2 stores the formula B2*C2. The computer multiplies the values in cells B2 and C2 and displays the product in cell D2.

5. Write formulas for cells D3 to D5.

6. What happens if you change the value in cell B4? Which other cells will change?

■ The spreadsheet below shows test results for five students.

	A	B	C	D	E	F	G
1	Student	Test 1	Test 2	Test 3	Test 4	Test 5	Average
2	Jane C.	76	87	88	85	92	
3	Art G.	87	84	75	83	94	
4	Jose F.	95	84	78	93	92	
5	Kim C.	76	77	83	84	100	
6	Dan H.	85	91	79	78	93	
7							

One formula for G2 is (B2 + C2 + D2 + E2 + F2)/5. A shorter formula using a range of cells is Sum(B2:F2)/5.

7. Write formulas for cells G3 to G6.

8. A student wrote the formula Sum(B6:G6)/5 for G6. What is wrong with this formula? What do you think would happen if you used this formula in cell G6?

9. Suppose you drop the lowest score for each student.

  a. How will the formulas in column G change? Write the new formulas.

  b. What value should you enter in the cell that has the lowest score for each student?

  c. Use a spreadsheet to find the average when the lowest score is dropped. If you do not have a computer, use a calculator or paper and pencil.

10. *Discuss* ideas for different types of spreadsheets with the class. Make a list of your ideas.

11. *PROJECT* Create a spreadsheet using one of the ideas from Exercise 10. Use these guidelines to plan your spreadsheet.

  • Include at least five rows and four columns of data.

  • At least one row or column should involve computation using the data in the other cells.

  • The formulas in the spreadsheet should use at least two of the four basic operations.

  a. Write a list of all the formulas used in your spreadsheet. Use these operation symbols: +, −, *, /.

  b. Draw your spreadsheet on a sheet of lined paper. Show it to your class and explain how the spreadsheet is organized.

  c. Use a spreadsheet program to create your spreadsheet. Change the data for various cells to check that your formulas are correct.

DATAPOINT

Check your spreadsheet program manual to learn how to show the formula for adding across a range of cells.

OBJECTIVE:
To study order of
operations using
paper and pencil and
a calculator.

1-9 Order of Operations

▼ Suppose you spend $4 and then earn $5/h mowing lawns for 3 h. The numerical expression $-4 + 5 \cdot 3$ shows how much money you have. How do you *evaluate* this numerical expression?

$$(-4 + 5) \cdot 3 = 3 \qquad \text{or} \qquad -4 + (5 \cdot 3) = 11$$

Since you earned $15 and spent $4, you would have $11 left. The order in which you compute changes your answer.

▼ To avoid confusion and have a standard way to compute expressions with several operations, mathematicians agree on an *order of operations*.

FLASHBACK	Order of Operations
Grouping symbols: ( ) parentheses [ ] brackets	1. Do all operations within grouping symbols first. 2. Multiply or divide in order from left to right. 3. Add or subtract in order from left to right.

▼ You can use order of operations to evaluate a numerical expression.

Example 1 Evaluate $-3 \cdot 5 - 8 \div 4 + 3$.

Solution
1. There are no grouping symbols. So, multiply and divide from left to right.

$$-3 \cdot 5 - 8 \div 4 + 3$$

2. Add and subtract from left to right.

$$-15 - 2 + 3$$
$$-17 + 3 = -14$$

Example 2 Evaluate $3(-8 + 5) - 12$.

Solution
1. Work in parentheses. $3(-8 + 5) - 12$
2. Multiply. $3 \ (-3) - 12$
3. Subtract. $-9 - 12 = -21$

▼ When there are two or more sets of grouping symbols, start at the inside and work out.

Example 3 Evaluate $-2[(-6 + 4) \div (3 - 5)] + 6$.

Solution
1. Parentheses first. $-2[(-6 + 4) \div (3 - 5)] + 6$
2. Work inside brackets. $-2 \ [-2 \div (-2)] + 6$
3. Multiply. $-2 \ (1) + 6$
4. Add. $-2 + 6 = 4$

▼ Absolute value symbols are a kind of grouping symbol.

Example 4 **Evaluate $-5 - |8 - (-2)|$.**

Solution
1. Work inside the absolute value symbols. $-5 - |8 - (-2)|$
2. Find the absolute value. $-5 - \quad |10| \quad = -5 - 10$
3. Subtract. $= -15$

▼ A scientific calculator follows order of operations. A standard calculator does not.

Example 5 **Use a calculator to evaluate $3 \cdot 5 - 4 \div 2 + (5 + 4)$.**

Solution **Scientific calculator**

$3\,\boxed{\times}\,5\,\boxed{-}\,4\,\boxed{\div}\,2\,\boxed{+}\,\boxed{(}\,5\,\boxed{+}\,4\,\boxed{)}\,\boxed{=}\,22$

Standard calculator

$5\,\boxed{+}\,4\,\boxed{=}\,\boxed{M+}$ grouping symbols
$3\,\boxed{\times}\,5\,\boxed{=}\,\boxed{M+}$ multiplication
$4\,\boxed{\div}\,2\,\boxed{=}\,\boxed{M-}$ division
$\boxed{MRC}\,22$

> ▼
> **THINK** Why must you use the memory key with the standard calculator?

CLASS EXERCISES

Which operation would you perform first? Explain.

1. $35 \cdot 98 - 50$
2. $-29 - (87 + 115)$
3. $4(67 \div 6)$

Evaluate.

4. $2 - 6 \div 3$
5. $14(-6) - 12$
6. $|13 - 21| + 5$
7. $2(1 - 9) \cdot 9$
8. $7 + 3(8 \div 4)$
9. $[2 + (6 \cdot 8)] - 1$

> ▼
> **THINK AND DISCUSS**
> **Is the answer positive or negative? Explain.**
> 1. $586 - 25 \cdot 30$
> 2. $(387 - 521) \cdot (-86)$
> 3. $-3|-5 \cdot 4|$
> 4. Why do we need to agree on an order of operations?

WRITTEN EXERCISES

Which operation would you perform first? Explain.

1. $14 + 15 - 10$
2. $-11 \div 4 + 99$
3. $75 \cdot 398 + |15 - 16|$

Evaluate.

4. $15 \cdot 3 - 2$
5. $-12 \div 4 - (-2)$
6. $2 + (-3) \cdot 24$
7. $|56 - 5| \div 17$
8. $(-21 + 15) \div (-3)$
9. $2 \cdot 2 + 0 \cdot (-4)$

MENTAL MATH **Evaluate.**

10. $12 - 8 \div 2$

11. $3(-8) + 4$

12. $6 \div (2)(-9)$

13. $3(-4) - 18$

14. $-21 \div 7 - (-15)$

15. $3(-6) + 15 \div 3$

CALCULATOR **Evaluate.**

16. $538 + 18 \cdot 24 - 677$

17. $450 \div 2 + 18$

18. $-8 - 3 \cdot 2 - (-8)$

19. $4 \div (-4) \cdot (-4) - (-4) + (-4)$

20. $2[8 + (3 - 5)] - 8$

21. $25(6 + 2)(-8) \div 4 + 6$

22. $6 \div 3 - 9 \cdot 4$

23. $-11 - 27 \div 9 \div (-1)$

Write an expression to match these keys on a standard calculator.

24. 5 [×] 4 [÷] 10 [+] 25 [÷] 9 [+/−] [=] -3

25. 7 [+] 8 [÷] 5 [+] 5 [×] 2 [+/−] [=] -16

26. How will the expressions for Exercises 24 and 25 change if you use a scientific calculator?

Compare. Use >, <, or =.

27. $8 + 12 \div (-4)$ ■ $(8 + 12) \div (-4)$

28. $(18 - (-15)) \div (5 + 6)$ ■ $18 - (-15) \div 5 + 6$

Insert grouping symbols to make each number sentence true.

29. $7 + 4 \cdot 6 = 66$

30. $7 \cdot 8 - 6 + 3 = 17$

31. $3 \cdot 8 - 2 + 5 - 12 = -3$

32. $2 \cdot 3 - 5 - 8 \cdot 2 + 1 = -28$

Which of the following equal 18?

33. $3 \cdot 2 + 4$

34. $(10 - 18) \div (-4) + (15 - (-17)) \div 2$

35. $27 - 13 \cdot 2 - 17(5 - 6)$

36. $16 \cdot 3 + 5 \div 5 - 18(-13)$

Solve.

37. Carmen worked 4 h on Monday and 7 h/day for the next 3 days. How many hours did she work in all?

38. Sam bought 8 CDs at $12 each and 4 tapes at $6 each. How much did he spend?

39. Alice's bowling score is 15 less than Ray's. Together, they scored 221. What did each score?

40. A cup of tomato juice has half the calories of a cup of skim milk. Together, they have 135 C. How many calories are in each?

41. Use the numbers -6, -8, 2, 4, and 6 exactly once to write a numerical expression with a value less than -100.

42. Use the digits 1–9 in order. Insert addition and subtraction signs, brackets, and parentheses to get an answer of 100.

43. Use the digits in the number of the year you were born, in order, plus operation symbols and parentheses. Write the greatest possible number and the least possible number that uses each digit exactly once.

▼▼ *SAMPLE* born 1966

greatest $(1 + 9) \cdot 6 \cdot 6 = (10)(36) = 360$

least $(1 + 9)(-6 \cdot 6) = -360$

44. WRITE a word problem to fit the numerical expression $3(4 + 3) + 2 \cdot 6$ and then solve.

Write and evaluate the numerical expression for each phrase.

45. five added to the product of four and nine

46. twenty-one minus the sum of fifteen and negative five

47. seventeen minus the quotient of twenty-five and five

48. one hundred divided by twenty plus the product of negative six and three

49. one hundred thirty added to the difference of one hundred sixteen and eight

50. DATA FILE 3 (pp. 96–97) Write a numerical expression for the value of the quarters minted each day.

Write a description of each numerical expression.

▼▼ *SAMPLE* The word *quantity* is a description for a grouping symbol.

The product of two and the quantity three plus four describes the numerical expression $2(3 + 4)$.

51. $2(3 + 5)$

52. $16 \div [3 - (-1)]$

53. $|4 + (-2)| \cdot (-3)$

54. $3(6 - 3) \div 9$

COMPUTER Write using computer symbols, then evaluate.

▼▼ *SAMPLE* The symbols for addition and subtraction are + and −. The multiplication symbol is an asterisk (*). The division symbol is a slash (/).

55. $74 + 5 \cdot 9 + (-7)$

56. $123 + (-5) \div (-1) + 18$

57. $70 + (8)(-9)$

58. $255 \div 5 + 117$

59. $2,087 \cdot 37 - 1,951$

60. $876 \div 12 + 13 \cdot 89$

61. COMPUTER Do computers follow order of operations? Use a computer to evaluate the expressions in Exercises 55–60. *Hint:* In BASIC, you use a PRINT statement such as PRINT 3*4/6 to evaluate the expression $(3 \cdot 4) \div 6$.

MIXED REVIEW

Write a variable expression.

1. the product of a number and 6

2. six less than a number

3. the sum of a number and the absolute value of -7

Complete with <, >, or =.

4. -16 ▨ -12

5. 8(-6) ▨ 48

6. 11 + (-15) ▨ -11 + 15

7. How many whole numbers between 10 and 200 have exactly two identical digits?

1-10 *Evaluating Expressions*

▼ Major league baseball teams use an average of 42 baseballs per game. The expression 42*g* represents the number of baseballs used in *g* games. You can *evaluate* 42*g* by replacing *g* with a number.

Suppose a team plays 50 games. Replace *g* with 50 to evaluate the expression.

$$42g = 42 \cdot 50$$
$$= 2{,}100$$

| **Evaluate an Expression** | To evaluate an expression, replace each variable with a number. Then compute, following order of operations. |

Example 1 **Evaluate each expression for the given value of the variable.**

  a. 12*b* for *b* = 3

  b. 4*y* − 15 for *y* = -30

Solution **a.** 12*b* = 12 · 3   Use mental math.
         = 36

  b. 4*y* − 15 = 4(-30) − 15   Multiply first,
         = -120 − 15   then subtract.
         = -135

▼ A variable expression can have more than one variable.

Example 2 **Evaluate 3*ab* − 2*c* for *a* = -2, *b* = -8, and *c* = -10.**

Solution 3*ab* − 2*c* = 3(-2)(-8) − 2(-10)   Replace each variable with
         = 48 − (-20)   a number.
         = 68   Follow order of operations.

▼ You can write and evaluate expressions to solve problems.

Example 3 Bob sells magazine subscriptions. He earns $20 per week plus $2 for each subscription he sells.

  a. Write an expression for his weekly earnings.

  b. Find Bob's weekly earnings if he sells 14 subscriptions.

Solution **a.** Let *s* stand for the number of subscriptions. Then 20 + 2*s* is an expression for Bob's weekly earnings.

  b. 20 + 2(14) = 20 + 28   Replace *s* with 14.
         = 48

  Bob earns $48 by selling 14 subscriptions in a week.

CLASS EXERCISES

Evaluate each expression for $x = 2$, $y = -3$, and $z = 10$.

1. $x + 5$ **2.** $16 - z$ **3.** $4y$ **4.** $-8 \div x$

5. $2z - 4$ **6.** $x - z$ **7.** $y + 5y$ **8.** $x \div 2 + (-9)$

9. xyz **10.** $8y \div x$ **11.** $3z - |x|$ **12.** $(z + x) \div y$

Solve.

13. A stenographer types 55 words/min. How many words does the stenographer type in m min? in 20 min?

14. An appliance repair center charges a $25 flat fee plus a fee of $10/h for labor. Find the cost of an oven repair that takes 3 h.

WRITTEN EXERCISES

Evaluate each expression for the given values of the variables.

1. $-12a$ for $a = 2$ **2.** $x - 6$ for $x = -16$

3. $2a + 5$ for $a = -5$ **4.** $-z$ for $z = 7$

5. $|a| + (-17)$ for $a = 5$ **6.** $|n - 10|$ for $n = -4$

7. $-6 \div a + 8$ for $a = -2$ **8.** $19 - (a - 4)$ for $a = 8$

9. $-3ab$ for $a = 1$, $b = -7$ **10.** $16 - 4mn$ for $m = 0$, $n = -3$

11. $4a - b$ for $a = 3$, $b = 5$ **12.** $3(a + b)$ for $a = 7$, $b = 9$

13. $2|a - b|$ for $a = 9$, $b = 19$ **14.** $(x - y) \div (-4)$ for $x = 52$, $y = 12$

MENTAL MATH Evaluate each expression for the given values of the variables.

15. $-7b$ for $b = 5$ **16.** $5 - b$ for $b = 4$

17. $-3b$ for $b = -7$ **18.** $x - 8$ for $x = 10$

19. $41 - 4b$ for $b = 10$ **20.** $5a + 7$ for $a = 20$

CALCULATOR Evaluate each expression for the given values of the variables.

21. $5m$ for $m = 85$ **22.** $-48 + n$ for $n = 933$

23. $-288 \div c$ for $c = -16$ **24.** $6ab$ for $a = 17$, $b = -21$

25. $7a - 13b$ for $a = 0$, $b = -9$ **26.** $5y - 5$ for $y = -178$

Find a value for each variable that makes the statement true.

27. $n > 1$ **28.** $n < -7$ **29.** $|n| = 8$ **30.** $3n = 12$

31. $n + 6 = 0$ **32.** $-4n = -4$ **33.** $3 + n = 3$ **34.** $n + 5 < 9$

35. Find a value of x for which $4x$ and $x + 9$ are equal.

36. Find values of a and b such that $a + b$ is 12 and $a - b$ is 16.

Solve.

37. Every minute about 265 babies are born in the world.

    a. Write an expression for the number of babies born in m min.

    b. *CALCULATOR* About how many babies are born in 6 min?

    c. *CALCULATOR* About how many babies are born in one day?

38. *CALCULATOR* The fastest speed of a sailfish is 68 mi/h.

    a. Write an expression for the number of miles a sailfish travels in h hours swimming at 68 mi/h.

    b. How many miles would a sailfish travel swimming for 3 h at 68 mi/h?

39. *DATA* Use the chart on page 31 to find how many calories are used per minute in running.

    a. Write an expression for the number of calories used in running m min.

    b. How many calories are used in running 25 min?

40. A carnival charges a $3 admission fee plus $1 per ride.

    a. Write an expression for the cost of riding r rides.

    b. Find the cost of riding 6 rides.

    c. How many rides can you afford if you have $10 to spend?

41. A club requires a $100 initiation fee and $25 each month. Find the cost of a one-year membership in the club.

MIXED REVIEW

Evaluate.

1. $3(-9) - 27$

2. $3 \cdot 4 \div (-2) \cdot 8$

3. $3 \cdot (-7) + 2 \cdot 8$

4. $4[2 \cdot (3 - 6)]$

Write a word phrase for each expression.

5. $6 + x$

6. $2(n - 2)$

7. $-12y$

8. Valerie has test grades of 97, 82, 78, and 75. What is her test average?

Copy and complete.

42.

x	$x + 5$
0	5
1	▨
2	▨
5	▨
▨	20

43.

n	$6n$
1	▨
2	▨
-2	▨
6	▨
▨	24

44.

a	$10 - a$
0	▨
5	▨
10	▨
15	▨
▨	-10

45. Evaluate $1 + 2 + 3 + 4 + \ldots + n$ for $n = 10$.

46. Evaluate each number in the pattern $1n, 2n, 3n, 4n, \ldots 10n$ for $n = 2$. *WRITE* a description of the pattern.

47. Find the length of each red segment for $x = 8$.

    a.   **b.**

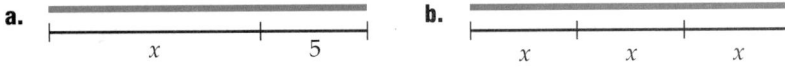

Problem Solving Practice

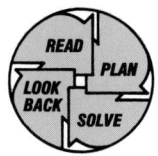

PROBLEM SOLVING STRATEGIES

Look for a Pattern
Guess and Test
Simplify the Problem
Account for all Possibilities
Make an Organized List
Work Backwards
Make a Table
Write an Equation
Solve by Graphing
Draw a Diagram
Make a Model
Simulate the Problem

Solve. The list at the left shows some possible strategies you can use.

1. Marjorie opened a savings account with $100 at the beginning of January. The table shows the interest earned each month for four months.

Month	Interest	Balance
January	$1.00	$101.00
February	$1.01	$102.01
March	$1.02	$103.03
April	$1.03	$104.06

   a. Describe the pattern for the values under the interest column.

   b. Use the pattern to extend the table for the next four months.

2. Particles have a positive charge, a negative charge, or no charge at all.

   a. How much charge do these particles have?

   b. How would you show a charge of -7?

   c. Opposite charges cancel each other out. What is the total amount of charge when 12 negative charges combine with 24 positive charges?

3. The stratosphere is higher in altitude than the troposphere, but not as high as the thermosphere. The mesosphere is just below the thermosphere. Arrange these regions in order from the highest altitude to the lowest.

4. **DATA FILE 9 (pp. 360–361)** The chart below shows a golfer's score at St. Andrew's golf course. Complete the third row.

Hole	1	2	3	4	5	6	7	8	9
Score	5	5	3	3	2	3	5	5	6
Par									

   Is the total score above or below par? by how much?

5. **DATA FILE 1 (pp. 2–3)** Suppose the temperature was -15°F. The wind speed changed from 5 mi/h to 20 mi/h. Find the change in wind chill temperature.

6. Jeff earns $1,200 more than his brother. Together they earn $65,200. How much does each earn?

The aurora borealis, or northern lights, occurs above the thermosphere.

Chapter 1 Review

Complete each statement. Use the vocabulary words given.

VOCABULARY

1. Parentheses, brackets, and the absolute value symbol are ▨ that help you determine ▨.

2. The ▨ of an integer is the same distance from zero on a number line as the integer, but in the opposite direction.

3. The whole numbers, their opposites, and zero form the ▨.

4. The ▨ of an integer is its distance from zero on a number line.

5. A ▨ is an expression that contains at least one ▨.

6. The ▨ is an average.

VOCABULARY

integers
variable
opposite
variable expression
absolute value
order of operations
mean
grouping symbols

Comparing Integers   1-1

To compare integers, think of the number line. The integer farther to the right is the greater integer.

Compare. Use <, >, or =.

7. -7 ▨ -9 **8.** 0 ▨ -3 **9.** $|-5|$ ▨ $|5|$ **10.** -6 ▨ 2 **11.** -4 ▨ $-(-5)$ **12.** $|-3|$ ▨ 1

Adding Integers and Subtracting Integers   1-2, 1-3

To add integers with the *same* sign, *add* the absolute values of the integers. The sum has the same sign as the addends. To add integers with *different* signs, *subtract* the absolute values of the integers. The sum has the sign of the integer with the greater absolute value. To subtract an integer, add its opposite.

Add or subtract.

13. $8 + (-15)$ **14.** $-9 + 21$ **15.** $-15 - (-6)$ **16.** $9 - (-5)$ **17.** $-8 - 4$

18. $32 - 48$ **19.** $-62 - (-59) - 24$ **20.** $14 + (-9) + (-20)$ **21.** $-4 + 12 + (-3) + (-6)$

Multiplying and Dividing Integers   1-5, 1-6

To multiply or divide integers, multiply or divide the absolute values of the integers. If the integers have the *same* sign, the product or quotient is *positive*. If the integers have *different* signs, the product or quotient is *negative*.

Multiply or divide.

22. $7(-6)$ **23.** $250 \div (-50)$ **24.** $(-9)(-8)$ **25.** $-56 \div (-8)$ **26.** $-120 \div 40$ **27.** $-15(11)$

Translating Word Phrases

1-8

To translate word phrases to algebraic expressions, look for key words that indicate operations.

addition (more than, sum)   subtraction (difference, less than)
multiplication (times, product)   division (quotient, ratio)

Write an algebraic expression for each phrase.

28. twenty-five less than x **29.** the product of n and $3r$ **30.** two more than y

Using Order of Operations

1-9

To evaluate numerical expressions:

1. Do all operations within grouping symbols first.

2. Multiply and divide from left to right.

3. Add and subtract from left to right.

Evaluate.

31. $7 + 2 \cdot 28 - 3 \cdot 9$ **32.** $9 \cdot 5 - 4(18 \div 6)$ **33.** $3 \cdot 8 - 6 + 49 \div 7$

34. $3 \cdot 7 + 6 \div 2$ **35.** $|-5 + 6| \cdot |3|$ **36.** $4 + 8 \div 2 \cdot 0$

Evaluating Algebraic Expressions

1-10

To evaluate an algebraic expression, substitute a number for the variable(s), and simplify. Follow order of operations.

Evaluate.

37. $3x + 4$ for $x = 5$ **38.** $10 - n$ for $n = 4$ **39.** $|y - 6| + 8$ for $y = -2$

40. $|m - 7|$ for $m = -7$ **41.** $15t \cdot 10$ for $t = -3$ **42.** $z + 3z$ for $z = 4$

Problem Solving

1-4, 1-7

To solve a problem, use a pattern.

Use a pattern to solve.

43. To run a classified ad for 7 days costs $28 for 4 lines. Each additional line costs $10.50. What is the cost of a 12-line ad?

44. The graph at the right gives Sue's net calories for this week. If Sue continues to eat as she did this week, will she gain or lose weight in a month?

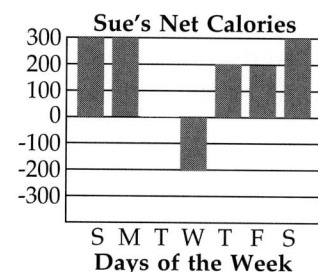

Daily Net Calories

Sue's Net Calories

Days of the Week

Chapter 1   Test

Write an integer.

1. opposite of 7

2. opposite of -9

3. |-5|

4. |12|

Compare. Use <, >, or =.

5. -6 ☐ -5

6. 8 ☐ -10

7. -3 ☐ 3

8. 0 ☐ -7

Find each answer.

9. $15 + (-7)$

10. $-8 - (-12)$

11. $-9(-7)$

12. $54 \div (-6)$

13. $-6 \cdot 48$

14. $-56 \div (-7)$

15. $119 - (-24)$

16. $-47 + (-21)$

17. $-83 + (-17) + 13$

18. $5 \cdot (-12) \cdot (-3) \cdot (-1)$

19. $420 \div (-6) \div 7 \div (-2)$

20. $8 \cdot 6 \div (2 + 1)$

21. $4 + 7 \cdot 2 + 8$

22. $4(11 + 7) - 9 \cdot 8$

23. $29 - 2 \cdot 3(9 - 4) \div 6$

24. $16 - 2 \cdot 5 + 3 - 6$

25. $|14 - (-9)|2$

Write an expression for each word phrase.

26. ten less than the absolute value of negative three

27. the product of x and negative five

28. a number increased by nineteen

29. the opposite of the quantity five more than y

Evaluate each expression for the given values of the variables.

30. $3a + 5$ for $a = -5$

31. $5m + 9 + 7n$ for $m = 8$, $n = 1$

32. $3|x - y| + x$ for $x = 1$, $y = 8$

33. $20 - 2(a - b)$ for $a = 3$, $b = 2$

Solve.

34. A submarine was at a depth of 250 m below sea level. It rose 75 m. Use an integer to describe the new depth of the submarine.

35. **DATA** Use the chart on page 31 to solve. John went swimming for $\frac{1}{2}$ h and cycling for an hour. He then ate two 3-oz hamburgers on wheat bread, and an apple, and drank 1 c of grape juice. Find his net calories.

36. You are in an elevator on the seventh floor. Go down 4 floors. Go up 8 floors. Go down 3 floors. Go up 9 floors. Following this pattern, what floor will you be on if the elevator goes down again and you get off?

37. A shirt costs $15 and jeans cost $25.

a. Write an expression for the cost of j jeans and s shirts.

b. Find the cost of 3 pairs of jeans and 5 shirts.

c. How many pairs of jeans can you buy for $60?

Chapter 1   Cumulative Review

$$3\overline{)210}$$

Choose the correct answer. Write A, B, C, or D.

1. What makes $-1 >$ ▨ true?
- **A.** -2
- **B.** 1
- **C.** 0
- **D.** not given

2. $7 + (-12)$
- **A.** 5
- **B.** -19
- **C.** -5
- **D.** not given

3. $|-10|$
- **A.** -10
- **B.** $\frac{1}{10}$
- **C.** 10
- **D.** not given

4. What is the variable expression for five less than $3n$?
- **A.** $5 - 3n$
- **B.** $3(n - 5)$
- **C.** $3n - 5$
- **D.** not given

5. 1, 2, 3, 5, 8, 13, . . .
- **A.** 13
- **B.** 20
- **C.** 16
- **D.** not given

6. $-9(-7)$
- **A.** 63
- **B.** -16
- **C.** -63
- **D.** not given

7. **DATA** Use the chart on page 31. How many calories are burned walking 2 h?
- **A.** 10 calories
- **B.** 600 calories
- **C.** 300 calories
- **D.** not given

8. Name the integer represented by the point on the number line.

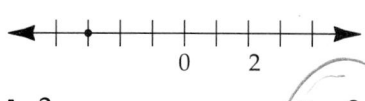

- **A.** 3
- **B.** -3
- **C.** -4
- **D.** not given

9. $210 \div (-3)$
- **A.** -7
- **B.** -70
- **C.** -63
- **D.** not given

10. $-8 - (-6)$
- **A.** -14
- **B.** -2
- **C.** 2
- **D.** not given

11. Evaluate $6x - 9$ for $x = 2$.
- **A.** -21
- **B.** 3
- **C.** 12
- **D.** not given

12. Which operation would you perform first?
$12 \div 4(3 - 5)$
- **A.** division
- **B.** subtraction
- **C.** multiplication
- **D.** not given

13. What is the opposite of 8?
- **A.** -8
- **B.** $\frac{1}{8}$
- **C.** 8
- **D.** not given

14. Evaluate $-10 \div |-2 + 3|$.
- **A.** 8
- **B.** 10
- **C.** -2
- **D.** not given

15. $-15 + (-3)$
- **A.** -5
- **B.** -20
- **C.** 5
- **D.** not given

16. Give the number sentence for the number line.

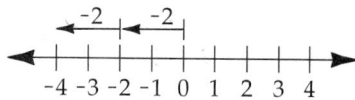

- **A.** $-2 + 2 = 0$
- **B.** $2 - (-2) = 4$
- **C.** $-2 + (-2) = -4$
- **D.** not given

The *bel*, named after Alexander Graham Bell, is a unit for measuring sound intensity. Ten bels equal one *decibel* (db).

RING THOSE BELS

	db	
db above 192 cause shock waves	190	
	180	
	170	some motorized toys
	160	
prolonged noise causes permanent deafness	150	rocket launch
	140	threshold of pain
sound levels above 90 are banned in factories	130	
	120	race cars, amplified rock band
	110	jet planes
	100	
	90	
	80	loud music, subway train
	70	snoring, telephone ring
	60	
safe range of sound intensity	50	loud conversation
	40	typewriter
	30	human speech
	20	whisper
	10	
	0	
below the threshold of human hearing	– 10	

SONAR (sound navigation and ranging) is a method that uses sound to locate underwater objects. A sonar device emits a sharp pulse of sound, which is reflected back when it hits an object. You can find the distance to the object by measuring the time it takes the sound to return. You can use a formula to find the distance.

Let s = the speed of sound
t = the time for the sound to strike the object and return

Then $\frac{ts}{2} = d$ is a formula to find the distance to an object.

Commercial fishing boats use sonar to detect schools of fish.

Solving Equations

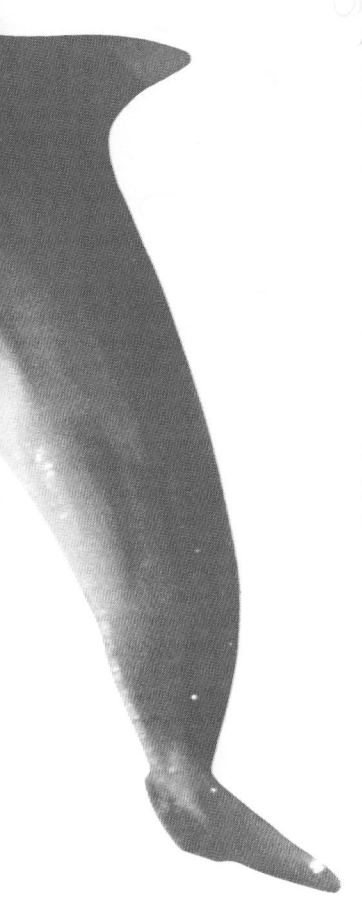

THUNDER is a shock wave produced by a lightning flash. Because light (299,460 km/s) travels faster than sound (346 m/s), you see lightning before you hear thunder. To determine how far away lightning is, you can count the seconds between the lightning flash and the thunder, then multiply by 346.

Think about it...

Look at the data about the speed of sound. What factors do you think determine the speed of sound in a given substance?

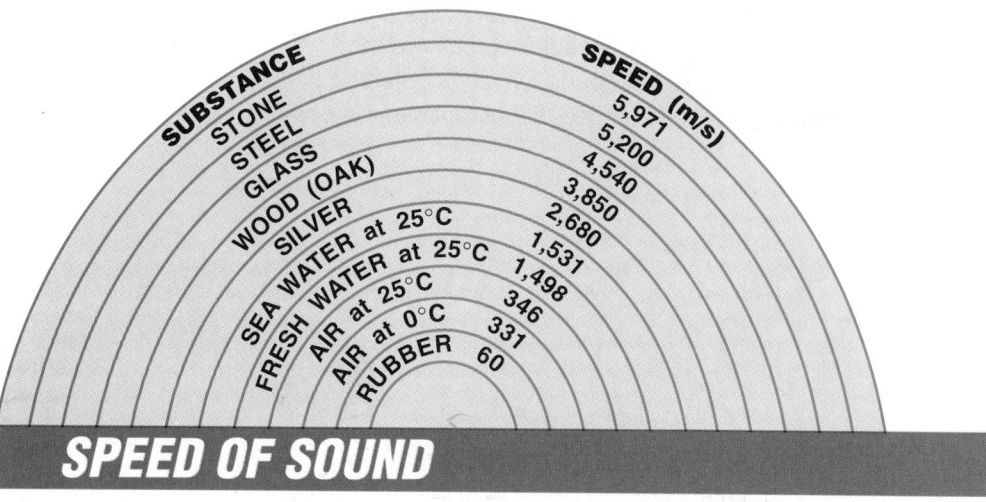

SUBSTANCE	SPEED (m/s)
STONE	5,971
STEEL	5,200
GLASS	4,540
WOOD (OAK)	3,850
SILVER	2,680
SEA WATER at 25°C	1,531
FRESH WATER at 25°C	1,498
AIR at 25°C	346
AIR at 0°C	331
RUBBER	60

SPEED OF SOUND

Variables and Equations

▼ A deep sea diver weighs 135 lb. When she puts on her diving equipment she weighs 165 lb. Let the variable w represent the weight of the equipment. You can write an *equation* to show this relationship.

$$135 + w = 165$$

Equation	An equation is a mathematical sentence with an equal sign.

THINK What is the difference between an expression and an equation?

▼ There are many types of equations.

Example 1 **a.** $9 + 2 = 11$ a numerical expression equal to a numerical expression

b. $x + 7 = 37$ a variable expression equal to a numerical expression

c. $a + (-3) = 2a + 5$ a variable expression equal to a variable expression

▼ An equation can be true or false.

Example 2 This is a true equation.   This is a false equation.

$6 + 12 = 18$ $6 = 4 + 3$

▼ Some equations are neither true nor false. They are called *open equations*.

Open Equation	An open equation is an equation that contains one or more variables.

Example 3 These are open equations.

        a. $c + 9 = 24$ **b.** $6x = -3 + 5x$

▼ You can replace a variable with a number to determine whether the number is a *solution* of the open equation.

Solution	A solution is a number that replaces a variable to make an open equation true.

Example 4   Is 30 a solution of the open equation $170 + x = 200$?

Solution $170 + x = 200$
$170 + 30 = 200$ **Replace x with 30.**
$200 = 200$ **True, so 30 is a solution.**

Example 5   Is 17 a solution of the open equation $9 = y - 10$?

Solution $9 = y - 10$
$9 = 17 - 10$ **Replace y with 17.**
$9 = 7$ **False, so 17 is not a solution.**

THINK Find a solution to the equation $9 = y - 10$ using mental math.

▼ You can write a sentence as an equation.

Example 6   **Write an equation for the sentence. Identify the equation as true, false, or open.**

Nine times the opposite of five is forty-five.

Solution $9 \cdot (-5) = 45$ This is a false equation.

FLASHBACK

The phrases *is equal to*, *equals*, and *is* denote the equal sign.

CLASS EXERCISES

Write true or false.

1. An equation can be false.
2. An open equation is true.
3. $3w - 7$ is an open equation.
4. An open equation must contain a variable.
5. $4 + 2x = 12$ is an equation.
6. An expression contains an equal sign.

THINK AND DISCUSS

1. Name one similarity between a sentence and an equation.

2. Can an expression be true or false? Why or why not?

3. Can zero be a solution to the equation $1 \div x = 2$? Why or why not?

State whether each equation is true, false, or open.

7. $15 = 3 \cdot 5$ 8. $4x - 8 = 25$ 9. $3(-9) = -36 + 6$

Replace c with -2. State whether the equation is true or false.

10. $c + 5 = 3$ 11. $24 = 2c + 29$ 12. $c \div 2 - 8 = 3(-3)$

Is 7 a solution of each equation?

13. $d + 4 = 12$ 14. $-12 = -2d + 2$ 15. $y - 2 = y - 2$

NOTES & QUOTES

Robert Recorde (ca. 1510–1558) first used the equal sign as we know it in *The Whetstone of Witte*, which was published in 1557. He chose two parallel line segments of equal length because he believed that no two things could be more equal.

FLASHBACK

Order of operations:

1. Do all operations within grouping symbols.

2. Multiply and divide from left to right.

3. Add and subtract from left to right.

WRITTEN EXERCISES

State whether each is an equation.

1. $10 = 5 + x$ Y

2. $2c + 6$ N

3. $3(-4) = 12$ Y

4. $-3 + 6b$ N

State whether each equation is true, false, or open.

5. $4c - 12 = 20$ open

6. $18 = -3(-6)$ T

7. $36 \div 6 + 1 = 5 + 3$ F

8. $6[-3 - (-5)] = 2(-4 + 10)$ T

9. $-24(-3 + 3) = 18(4 - 2)$ F

10. $-9 + x = 50 \div 10 + 3$ F

Replace y with 5. State whether the equation is true or false.

11. $-5 + y = 0$ T

12. $-2y - 3 = 7$ F

13. $-11 = 4 - 3y$ T

14. $2(y - 5) = 5 - y$ F

Replace each variable with the given number. State whether the equation is true or false.

15. $20 - c = 12; c = 8$ T

16. $8 = 2a + 3; a = 0$ F

17. $-x - 5 = -(-6); x = 1$ F

18. $3 - w = 2w + 12; w = -3$ T

19. $3b \div 18 = 2; b = 12$ T

20. $2(-4g) = 10 \cdot 5 - 2; g = -6$ T

Is 2 a solution of each equation?

21. $4 + d = 6$ Y

22. $12 = 26 \div x$ N

23. $4b - 9 = 8b - 17$ Y

24. $4(-8 + t) = 5t - 32$ N

Is the given number a solution of the equation?

25. $3a = 12 + a; a = 6$ Y

26. $-6w = -2w + 32; w = -11$ Y

27. $2m = m + 6; m = 4$ N

28. $2x \div 5 = 2(10 - 5); x = 25$ N

29. $-4c = 6 - c; c = -2$ Y

30. $9 - 3y = 2y + 24; y = -3$ N

CALCULATOR **Which of the numbers -2, 0, 2, 4, 6 is a solution?**

31. $253a = 0$ 0

32. $259 = 261 - a$ 2

33. $20 - 114z = 248$ -2

34. $53m + 106 = 53(m + 2)$ 0

35. $10(-2 + x) = 10x \div 2$ 4

36. $-21x + 129 = 3(-100 + 101)$ 6

MENTAL MATH **Is the solution greater than or less than zero?**

37. $-3x = -15$ >

38. $-5 + y = -35$ >

39. $-27 \div a = 9$ <

40. $-3 = y + 17$ <

41. $x + 25 = 50$ >

42. $-2 \cdot (-6) = -3a$ <

State which of the numbers listed are sensible replacements for the variable.

43. Let p represent the number of passengers on a fifty-passenger school bus. Can p be 30? $27\frac{1}{2}$? -5? 48? *30, 48*

44. Let c represent the amount of change equal to one dollar. Can c be 5 quarters? 10 dimes? 100 pennies? 17 nickels? *10, 100*

45. Let d represent the day of the month. Can d be 15? 56? 28? 0? *15, 28*

Write an equation for the sentence. Identify the equation as true, false, or open.

46. Four times the opposite of five equals negative twenty. $4(-5)=-20$

47. Zero times negative seven is negative seven. $0 \times 7 = -7$ F

48. Negative twelve divided by negative four is equal to three. $-12 \div -4$

49. The sum of fifteen and a number n is fifty. $15+n=50$ O

50. The product of negative twenty and nine is negative eleven. -20×9

51. The sum of negative seven and twelve equals negative five. $-7+12$ F

52. The difference of twenty-five and negative fifteen equals the sum of negative fifteen and twenty-five. $25-(-15)=-15+25$ f

53. *DATA FILE 3 (pp. 96–97)* Three sheets of paper times the number of bills per sheet is equal to ninety-six. $3 \cdot 32 = 96$ T

54. *DATA FILE 3 (pp. 96–97)* The value of 1940 proof set in 1965 equals the value of a 1955 proof set in 1990, minus twenty. T

55. *WRITE* Sentences are similar to equations.

a. The sentence *Abraham Lincoln was an American president* is a true sentence. Write two true sentences.

b. The sentence *Eleanor Roosevelt was an American president* is a false sentence. Write two false sentences.

c. The sentence *He is a professional baseball player* is an open sentence. It is not clear to whom the word *he* refers. Write two open sentences.

56. Write an equation relating the number of tickets (t) to the number of dollars (d). $5t=d$

tickets	1	2	3	t
dollars	5	10	15	d

57. Write an equation relating the number of flowers (f) to the number of bouquets (b). $13b=f$

flowers	13	26	39	f
bouquets	1	2	3	b

MIXED REVIEW

Evaluate when $a = 3$ and $b = -2$.

1. $a + 2b$ -1

2. $b - a + 15$ 10

3. $(3b - 2a) \div 4$

4. $|5b - 9 \div 3|$ 13

Write the next three numbers in each pattern.

5. 2, 3, 5, 8 13, 21, 34

6. 63, 48, 35, 24 15, 8, 3

Solve.

7. Kim worked 4 h a day for 3 days to build a suspension bridge model. How many hours were spent on the project? 12 h

2-2 Properties of Operations

▼ Stephanie won 6 tennis games in the first set and 4 games in the second set. Marcia won 4 games in the first set and 6 in the second set. Each won 10 games.

You can add 6 and 4 in any order and still get the same sum. This suggests the following property.

Commutative Property of Addition	You can add in any order without changing the sum.
	Arithmetic **Algebra**
	$6 + 4 = 4 + 6$ $a + b = b + a$

▼ You can also change the grouping of numbers before you add them. You may want to regroup numbers to add mentally.

Example 1 Carlos rented golf clubs for $7 and a golf cart for $8. He paid a greens fee of $12. Here are two ways he can calculate how much money he spent.

a. $(7 + 8) + 12 = 15 + 12$
$= 27$

b. $7 + (8 + 12) = 7 + 20$
$= 27$

No matter how you group the numbers, the sum is 27.

FLASHBACK

We use parentheses to show which numbers to add first.

▼ The mathematical name for the grouping property is the associative property.

Associative Property of Addition	You can change the grouping and then add without changing the sum.
	Arithmetic **Algebra**
	$(3 + 7) + 2 = 3 + (7 + 2)$ $(a + b) + c = a + (b + c)$

▼ You can also use the commutative and associative properties to multiply.

Commutative Property of Multiplication	You can multiply in any order without changing the product.
	Arithmetic **Algebra**
	$8 \cdot 4 = 4 \cdot 8$ $a \cdot b = b \cdot a$

Associative Property of Multiplication	You can change the grouping and then multiply without changing the product.
	Arithmetic **Algebra**
	$(7 \cdot 3)2 = 7(3 \cdot 2)$ $(ab)c = a(bc)$

▼ You can use the commutative and associative properties to write equivalent expressions.

Example 2
  a. $5 \cdot 7 = 7 \cdot 5$ commutative property

  b. $(5 + 4) + 9 = 5 + (4 + 9)$ associative property

  c. $7 + a = a + 7$ commutative property

  d. $5(xy) = (5x)y$ associative property

▼ Properties are helpful when adding or multiplying mentally.

Example 3 **Use mental math to evaluate $81 + 6 + 9$.**

THINK How do reordering and regrouping help you to add mentally?

Solution
$$81 + 6 + 9 = 81 + 9 + 6$$
$$= (81 + 9) + 6 \quad \text{associative property}$$
$$= (90) + 6 \quad \text{Add.}$$
$$= 96$$

▼ There are *identity* elements for addition and multiplication. You can compute with an identity element without changing the value of a number.

THINK How could you model the additive identity using algebra tiles?

Additive Identity	The additive identity is zero.
	Arithmetic **Algebra**
	$12 + 0 = 12$ $a + 0 = a$

Multiplicative Identity	The multiplicative identity is one.
	Arithmetic **Algebra**
	$10 \cdot 1 = 10$ $a \cdot 1 = a$

Example 4 **Use mental math to find the missing value.**

     a. $5 + \blacksquare = 5$ **b.** $9 \cdot \blacksquare = 9$

Solution
     a. $5 + 0 = 5$ When you add zero, the value does not change.

     b. $9 \cdot 1 = 9$ When you multiply by one, the value does not change.

THINK AND DISCUSS

1. Does the commutative property apply to subtraction? to division? Use examples to support your answers.

2. Does the associative property apply to subtraction? to division? Use examples to support your answer.

CLASS EXERCISES

State which property is shown.

1. $\square + 6 = 6 + \square$

2. $0 + 8 = 8$

3. $\triangle + s = s + \triangle$

4. $(5x)y = 5(xy)$

5. $999 \cdot 1 = 999$

6. $\blacksquare \cdot \triangle = \triangle \cdot \blacksquare$

What numbers would you combine first to evaluate mentally?

7. $5 + 36 + 95$

8. $5 \cdot 17 \cdot 2$

9. $50 \cdot 2 \cdot 43$

MENTAL MATH Evaluate.

10. $10 \cdot 13 \cdot 10$

11. $23 + 15 + 85$

12. $25 + 157 + 75$

13. $5 \cdot 20 \cdot 66$

14. $140 + 17 + 60$

15. $30 \cdot 30 \cdot 6$

WRITTEN EXERCISES

Match each equation with the property illustrated.

1. $a \cdot 1 = 1 \cdot a$

2. $\triangle + \blacktriangle = \blacktriangle + \triangle$

3. $(6x)y = 6(xy)$

4. $(6 + 5) + x = 6 + (5 + x)$

5. $6 \cdot 1 = 6$

6. $5 + 8 = 8 + 5$

7. $(3 \cdot 4)\blacksquare = 3(4 \cdot \blacksquare)$

8. $(3 + 2)(4 + 5) = (4 + 5)(3 + 2)$

9. $ab = ba$

10. $999 + 0 = 999$

a. commutative property of addition

b. associative property of addition

c. commutative property of multiplication

d. associative property of multiplication

e. additive identity

f. multiplicative identity

Use the commutative property to write an equivalent expression.

11. $25z$

12. $n + 2$

13. $(a + b)5$

14. $(a + b)(c + d)$

Use the associative property to write an equivalent expression.

15. $(3 \cdot 25) \cdot 4$

16. $34 + (16 + 35)$

17. $(4a)b$

Use the commutative and associative properties to evaluate.

18. $725 + 563 + 275$

19. $250 \cdot 47 \cdot 4$

20. $200 + 423 + 800$

21. $5 \cdot 20 \cdot 28$

22. $5 \cdot 11 \cdot 20 \cdot 3$

23. $79 + 17 + 1 + 3$

MIXED REVIEW

Is each equation true, false, or open?

1. $5 = 2 - (-3)$

2. $7 = a + 4$

For $w = -5$, is each equation true?

3. $9w = 45$

4. $|w - 8| = 13$

5. $2(w + 7) = -4$

6. $w + 0 = w$

Use ( ), +, −, · to write a true equation.

7. 3 4 7 6 = -3

Solve.

8. Mrs. Laurel has two sons. The product of their ages is 36 and the sum is 13. How old is each son?

What numbers would you combine first to evaluate mentally?

24. $5 \cdot 79 \cdot 20$ **25.** $3 + 7 + 67$ **26.** $10 \cdot 37 \cdot 10$

27. $730 + 693 + 270$ **28.** $5 \cdot 50 \cdot 20 \cdot 2$

1693

MENTAL MATH **Evaluate.**

29. $35 + 15 + 8$ *58*   **30.** $25 \cdot 4 \cdot 8$ **31.** $42 + 17 - 2 + 3$ *54*

32. $125 + 18 + 75 + 162$ **33.** $4 \cdot 6 \cdot 25 \cdot 50 \cdot 2$ *60,000*

WRITE **Explain your answer to each question below.**

34. a. Can you use the commutative property of addition with
   $4 + 2$ to evaluate the expression $3 \cdot 4 + 2 \div (-2)$?

   b. Can you use the commutative property of multiplication?

35. a. Can you use the associative property of addition with
   $-4 + 20 + 30$ to evaluate $6 \cdot 5 \cdot (-4) + 20 + 30 \div 5$?

   b. Can you use the associative property of multiplication?

Use the article below to answer each question.

A Fair Fare in Alaska

Railroads are a popular means of transportation in Alaska. The *Anchorage-Fairbanks Express* is a major line that travels 356 mi from Anchorage to Fairbanks.

A one-way coach fare for the $11\frac{1}{2}$-h trip is $98. A first-class fare is $140. Because of long hours of daylight in summer, passengers are sure to get their money's worth and not miss out on any of Alaska's beautiful wilderness and wildlife.

36. a. How much would it cost a family of four to travel first class
   when traveling round trip from Anchorage to Fairbanks?
   How much money could they save if they went coach?

   b. The *Anchorage-Fairbanks Express* departed Fairbanks at
   11:26 A.M. At what time will it arrive in Anchorage?

2-3 **The Distributive Property**

▼ Two rectangles, each having the same width but different lengths, are placed end to end. Find the total area.

Method 1 Placing the rectangles end to end forms one large rectangle. The length is (6 + 8) and the width is 4.

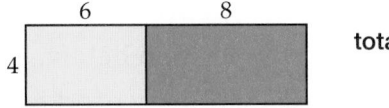

total area = 4(6 + 8)
= 4(14)
= 56

Method 2 You can find the area of each individual rectangle and then add the areas together.

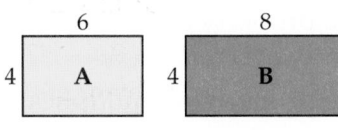

Area **A** = 4·6   Area **B** = 4·8

total area = area A + area B
= 24 + 32
= 56

The total area is the same no matter how you do the calculation. Therefore, the expression 4(6 + 8) has the same value as the expression 24 + 32. This illustrates the *distributive property*.

THINK Why does
$a(b + c) = (b + c)a$?

Distributive Property of Multiplication over Addition	You can distribute a factor to each term inside a set of parentheses.
	Arithmetic 3(2 + 6) = 3 · 2 + 3 · 6 (2 + 6)3 = 2 · 3 + 6 · 3
	Algebra $a(b + c) = ab + ac$ $(b + c)a = ba + ca$

Example 1 Evaluate 9(5 + 2) using the distributive property.

Solution   9(5 + 2) = 9 · 5 + 9 · 2   Distribute 9.
= 45 + 18   Multiply and add.
= 63

▼ You can also use the distributive property with subtraction.

THINK Why does
$a(b - c) = (b - c)a$?

Distributive Property of Multiplication over Subtraction	You can distribute a factor to each term inside a set of parentheses.
	Arithmetic 6(7 − 4) = 6 · 7 − 6 · 4 (7 − 4)6 = 7 · 6 − 4 · 6
	Algebra $a(b - c) = ab - ac$ $(b - c)a = ba - ca$

Example 2   Evaluate $(3 - 1)6$ using the distributive property.

Solution $(3 - 1)6 = 3 \cdot 6 - 1 \cdot 6$ Distribute 6.
$\qquad\qquad\quad = 18 - 6$ Multiply and subtract.
$\qquad\qquad\quad = 12$

▼ You can use the distributive property in reverse.

Example 3   Write $5 \cdot 3 + 5 \cdot 7$ using the distributive property.

Solution $5 \cdot 3 + 5 \cdot 7$ 5 multiplies 3 and 5 multiplies 7.
$\qquad\quad 5(3 + 7)$ 5 multiplies (3 + 7).

▼ You can use the distributive property to multiply mentally and solve word problems.

Example 4   Use the distributive property to evaluate 20(102) mentally.

Solution $20(102) = 20(100 + 2)$ Think of 102 as (100 + 2)
$\qquad\qquad\quad = 20 \cdot 100 + 20 \cdot 2$ Distribute 20.
$\qquad\qquad\quad = 2{,}000 + 40$ Multiply and add.
$\qquad\qquad\quad = 2{,}040$

Example 5   The PTA sold 397 tickets for their annual pancake breakfast. Each patron will receive four pancakes. How many pancakes will the PTA members make?

Solution $4(397) = 4(400 - 3)$ Think of 397 as (400 − 3).
$\qquad\qquad = 4 \cdot 400 - 4 \cdot 3$ Distribute 4.
$\qquad\qquad = 1{,}600 - 12$ Multiply and subtract.
$\qquad\qquad = 1{,}588$

CLASS EXERCISES

Write an expression to describe the total area.

1.

$2(1+3)$

2.
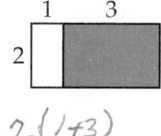
$8(3+6)$

3.
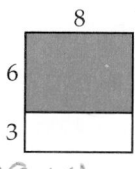
$7(a+b)$

State the number or variable that can be distributed.

4. $9(5 - 3)$
$9 \cdot 5 - 9 \cdot 3$

5. $(5 + 7 + a)2$
$2 \cdot 5 + 2 \cdot 7 + 2 \cdot a$

6. $z(x - y)$
$zx - zy$

THINK AND DISCUSS

1. What does the word *distribute* mean? How can you relate it to the way the distributive property is used?

2. How does the distributive property affect the rules for the order of operations?

3. How would you evaluate $6(3 + 11 + 4)$ using the distributive property?

State the number or variable that has been distributed. Rewrite using the distributive property in reverse.

7. $y \cdot 4 + y \cdot 6$ *y*

8. $a \cdot (-3) - b \cdot (-3)$ *−3*

Complete with the appropriate number or variable.

9. $9(5 + 4) = 9 \cdot \boxed{5} + 9 \cdot 4$

10. $(y - 6)z = y \cdot z - 6 \cdot \boxed{y}$

11. $12(3 + 5) = 12 \cdot 3 + \boxed{12} \cdot \boxed{5}$

12. $a(3 - b) = 3\boxed{a} - \boxed{a}b$

Use the distributive property to evaluate.

13. $6(4 + 8)$ *6·4+6·8*

14. $(14 - 9)2$ *2·14−2·9*

15. $-4(7 + 3 + 2)$ *−4·7+−4·3+−4·2*

16. $7(3 + 5)$ *7·3+7·5*

17. $12(10 - 2)$ *12·10−12·2*

18. $3(2 + 2)$ *3·2+3·2*

WRITTEN EXERCISES

Write an expression to describe the total area.

1.
w 7
4

$4(w + 7)$

2.
3
a
b

$3(a + b)$

3.
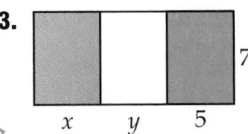
7
x *y* 5

$7(x + y + 5)$

State the number or variable which can be distributed.

4. $(10 - 2)7$ *7*

5. $-4(6 + 7 + 9)$ *−4*

6. $[3 + (-1)]x$ *x*

7. $(x - 4)c$ *C*

8. $r(s - t)$ *r*

9. $-w[9 + (-x)]$ *−w*

State the number or variable that has been distributed. Rewrite using the distributive property in reverse.

10. $9 \cdot 3 + 9 \cdot 4$ *9*

11. $-9 \cdot x + (-9) \cdot y$ *−9*

12. $a \cdot b + 3 \cdot b$ *b*

13. $(b \cdot e) - (c \cdot e) - (d \cdot e)$

14. $-6 \cdot 4 + 9 \cdot 4$ *4*

15. $-1 \cdot a + (-1) \cdot b$ *−1*

Complete with the appropriate number or variable.

16. $6(3 + 7) = 6 \cdot 3 + \boxed{6} \cdot 7$

17. $(w - x - z)y = (\boxed{w} \cdot y) - (x \cdot \boxed{y}) - (z \cdot y)$

18. $6 \cdot b + 12 \cdot b = (\boxed{6} + 12)\boxed{b}$

19. $[-2 + (-4)](-6) = \boxed{-2} \cdot (-6) + \boxed{-4} \cdot (-6)$

20. $-7 \cdot 12 - (-7) \cdot 17 = \boxed{} (\boxed{} - 17)$

21. $[10 - (-2)]5 = 10 \cdot \boxed{} - \boxed{} \cdot 5$

MENTAL MATH Use the distributive property to evaluate.

22. $2(122)$ **23.** $(280)4$ **24.** $2(670)$ **25.** $5(1,015)$

$2(100 + 22) = 2,100 + 2.22$ $4(200 + 80) = 4,200 + 4.80$ $2(600 + 70) = 2,600 + 2.70$ $5(1000 + 15) = 5,1000 + 5.15$

Use the distributive property to evaluate.

26. 4(5 + 11)   **27.** (3 − 6)4   **28.** -5(6 − 7)

29. [9 − (-1)](-3)   **30.** -3[2 + (-9)]   **31.** -7[2 + (-3)]

32. 6(8 + 2 + 12)   **33.** [26 + (-4) + 35]5

34. 2(5 + 3) − 3(4 − 2)   **35.** (20 − 12)6 − 4[5 − (-3)]

Solve using the distributive property.

36. A theater was filled to capacity, 294, three nights in a row. How many people were at the show in these three nights?

37. It is 1,549 mi from Boston to Dallas. How many miles would you travel if you drove round trip?

38. *DATA FILE 3 (pp. 96–97)* Find the total number of pennies produced in 5 days by the United States Mint.

Critical Thinking

EXPLORING LOGICAL THINKING

The table shows a mathematical operation, symbolized by ◆. In the table you can see that 2 ◆ 3 = 1.

◆	0	1	2	3
0	0	1	2	3
1	1	2	3	0
2	2	3	0	1
3	3	0	1	2

1. Use the table to find the following.

a. 1 ◆ 2   **b.** 1 ◆ 3   **c.** 3 ◆ 2

2. To investigate the properties, let us determine if ◆ is associative.

▼▼   *SAMPLE*   1 ◆ (3 ◆ 2) ▉ (1 ◆ 3) ◆ 2
   1 ◆ (1)   ▉   (0) ◆ 2
   2   =   2

a. Compare 3 ◆ (2 ◆ 2) ▉ (3 ◆ 2) ◆ 2. Think of other combinations. Check them.

b. Is the operation associative?

3. Is ◆ commutative? Does 2 ◆ 3 = 3 ◆ 2? Check other combinations.

4. Is there an identity? If so, what is it?

5. *WRITE* a description of the operation ◆.

Simplifying Variable Expressions

▼ The Texas state flag is made up of several rectangles and a star. You can represent the rectangles with the variable *r* and the star with the variable *s*. You can describe the parts of the flag by the following expression.

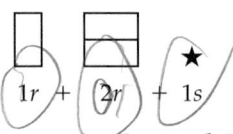

$$1r + 2r + 1s$$

This expression has three *terms*: 1*r*, 2*r*, and 1*s*. The terms are separated by addition symbols.

Term	A term is a part of an expression. Terms are separated by addition and subtraction symbols.

▼ **THINK** Are the terms *r* and 1*r* equivalent? Why or why not?

▼ The term 2*r* consists of two parts. The variable is *r* and the *numerical coefficient* is 2.

Numerical Coefficient	A numerical coefficient is a number that is multiplied by a variable.

▼ 1*r* and 2*r* have the same variable. They are *like terms*.

Like Terms	Like terms have the same variable(s).

Example 1 **State the number of terms in each expression. Name the numerical coefficients and the like terms.**

    a. $a + 5b - 3b$ **b.** $10xy + 5y + xy - 20$

Solution   **a.** three terms: *a*, 5*b*, and 3*b*
        numerical coefficients: 1, 5, and 3
        like terms: 5*b* and 3*b*

    b. four terms: 10*xy*, 5*y*, *xy*, and 20
        numerical coefficients: 10, 5, and 1
        like terms: 10*xy* and *xy*

▼ **THINK** Why is 10*xy* considered to be one term?

▼ Sometimes a term consists of a number without a variable. We call a term with no variable a *constant*.

Example 2 In the expression $5x + 2$, the constant is 2. No matter what value is substituted for *x*, the constant 2 remains the same.

▼ You can use models to represent an expression before you combine like terms to simplify the expression.

Example 3 Use algebra tiles or colored paper to simplify the expression $x + 1 + 2x$.

Solution

$$x + 1 + 2x \rightarrow 3x + 1$$

▽
THINK What is the value of the expression $3x + 1$ if $x = 3$? if $x = -2$?

▼ You can combine the numerical coefficients of like terms by using the distributive property.

Example 4 Simplify the expression $7x - 2x$ using the distributive property.

Solution

$$\begin{aligned} 7x - 2x &= 7 \cdot x - 2 \cdot x & \text{\textsf{x is distributed to 7 − 2.}} \\ &= (7 - 2)x & \text{\textsf{Subtract coefficients.}} \\ &= 5 \cdot x & \text{\textsf{Multiply.}} \\ &= 5x \end{aligned}$$

▼ Combining like terms and using algebraic properties are helpful in simplifying variable expressions.

Simplify an Expression	To simplify an expression, replace it with an equivalent expression that contains no like terms or parentheses.

Example 5 Simplify $4(5b)$.

Solution

$$\begin{aligned} 4(5b) &= (4 \cdot 5)b & \text{\textsf{associative property}} \\ &= 20 \cdot b & \text{\textsf{Multiply.}} \\ &= 20b \end{aligned}$$

▼ Sometimes you will need to use more than one property to simplify a variable expression.

Example 6 Simplify $4x + 3(3 + x)$.

Solution

$$\begin{aligned} 4x + 3(3 + x) &= 4x + 9 + 3x & \text{\textsf{distributive property}} \\ &= 4x + 3x + 9 & \text{\textsf{commutative property}} \\ &= (4x + 3x) + 9 & \text{\textsf{associative property}} \\ &= (4 \cdot x + 3 \cdot x) + 9 & \text{\textsf{x is distributed.}} \\ &= (4 + 3)x + 9 & \text{\textsf{Add coefficients.}} \\ &= 7 \cdot x + 9 & \text{\textsf{Multiply.}} \\ &= 7x + 9 \end{aligned}$$

NOTES & QUOTES

Francois Viète (1540–1603) introduced the use of vowels to represent unknown quantities.

1. What are some advantages of simplifying expressions?

2. □ and △ each stand for a different number. Which expression is equivalent to □ + 4△ + 7 + 3△ − 2□?

a. 15□△

b. □ + 7△ + 7

c. □ + 14△

d. □ + 7△ + 4 + 3

e. 7△ − □ + 7

CLASS EXERCISES

Give the number of terms in each expression. Name the numerical coefficients, the like terms, and the constants, if any.

1. $3x + 5y − 6x − 3$ **2.** $2x − 7$

3. $1a + 3b − 6c + 5a + 1$ **4.** $2r − 1s + 6r$

Combine the like terms using a model.

5. $12a + 7a$ **6.** $5 + 2b$

7. $4x − 7x + 3x$ **8.** $a + 2a + 3a − 4a$

Give the property that you can use to simplify each expression.

9. $−3(5x)$ **10.** $(n + 7) + 3$ **11.** $9x + 5x$ **12.** $(−5y)(−9)$

Simplify each expression.

13. $6(5b)$ **14.** $−6x + (9x − 3)$

15. $−4(a + 3) + 7a$ **16.** $4 + 3(a + b) − 6b$

WRITTEN EXERCISES

Give the number of terms in each expression. Name the numerical coefficients, the like terms, and the constants, if any.

1. $5a + 8a$ **2.** $6a + (−2b) + b$ **3.** $2x − (−7)$

4. $6xy − 5xy$ **5.** $−7c + 3$ **6.** $x + x + x$

7. $6ab − 4ba + 8 + ab$ **8.** $12 − 4x + 7w − 9x − w$

Combine the like terms using a model.

9. $4a + 5a$ **10.** $w − 3w + 2w$ **11.** $7b + b − 3b$

State the property that you can use to simplify each expression.

12. $6x + (−2x)$ **13.** $3(8k)$ **14.** $(4n + 3) + 8$

15. $8z + (−15z)$ **16.** $−2 + (7 + 8y)$ **17.** $−6(−5s)$

Combine the like terms using the distributive property.

18. $16z + 24z$ **19.** $52a − 47a$ **20.** $r + 6r − 3r$

Complete with the appropriate number or variable.

21. $6a + 4a + 7 = (6a + 4a) + 7$
$$= (6 + 4)a + 7$$
$$= \underline{}a + 7$$

Simplify each expression.

22. $5 + 2x + 8$ *13 + 2x* **23.** $5m + (-4m)$ *m* **24.** $4(-3y) + 7 - 3$ *-12y + 4*

25. $3a + 2a + a$ *6a* **26.** $9(4t) + 8$ *36t + 8* **27.** $18 + 6(9k) - 13$ *5 + 54k*

28. $8z + 8y + 3z$ *11z + 8y* **29.** $3(g + 5) + 2g$ *5g + 15* **30.** $6(3k + 2k)$ *30k*

31. $4(w + 2x) + 9(-4w)$ *-32w + 8x* **32.** $-7(2f + 5e) + 8(6 + 4e)$

33. $-12(5x) + 3(-7x) - 2x$ *-83x* **34.** $(2t + 4)3 + 6(-5t) - (-8)$ *-24t + 20*

35. $5(4a + b - c) + 8(3a - 8b + 3c)$

Simplify. Evaluate when $x = 3$, $y = -5$, and $z = 7$.

36. $2x + x + y$ *4* **37.** $-3(4y)$ *60* **38.** $z(2x + 3x)$ *2.5x 105*

39. $2y + 2z + y - 16$ *-10 -17* *3y + 2z - 16* **40.** $6(2x + y) + 2(x + 2y)$ *112* *12x + 6y + 2x + 4y*

Write an expression for each situation. Simplify. *14x + 10y*

41. Six bus loads containing x students each came to band day from one school, and 7 bus loads containing x students came from another school. Fourteen students came by car. *13x + 14c*

42. Arleen unloaded 4 boxes each containing v videotapes and 3 boxes each containing $y + 2$ videotapes. *4v + 3y + 6*

43. Janet bought three folders costing x cents each and two report covers costing x cents each. She also purchased a binder for $1.89. *5x + 1.89*

44. Mr. Unruh purchased five movie tickets for x dollars each. He also purchased a soda for $1.25 and popcorn for $2.25.

3x + 2x + 1.89 6x + 7x + 14c   *4v + 3(3y + 2)*

TEST YOURSELF

5x + 1.25 + 2.25

Is -4 a solution of each equation?

1. $2x - 6 = -14$ *N* **2.** $16 \div 2y = 2$ *x* **3.** $-21 = -2(3 - x)$ *Y*

State which property is shown.

4. $3 \cdot (-6) = -6 \cdot 3$ *comm* **5.** $(3a)b = 3(ab)$ *assoc*

6. $17 \cdot 1 = 17$ *ident* **7.** $6 + 0 = 0 + 6$ *commut*

8. $(3 + 2)(4 - 7) = (4 - 7)(3 + 2)$ *commx* **9.** $4(3 - 12) = 4 \cdot 3 - 4 \cdot 12$ *dist*

Simplify.

10. $5(10b)$ *50b* **11.** $96 + 73 + 4$ *173* **12.** $9y - 3y + 12y$ *18y*

13. $3(a + 2a)$ *9a* **14.** $-14 + 2(9 - 3)$ *-2* **15.** $7(2w) + 2(w - 3)$ *14w + 2w - 6*

MIXED REVIEW

Complete.

1. $7(2 - 5) = 7 \cdot 2 - \blacksquare \cdot 5$

2. $3 \cdot 5 + \blacksquare \cdot 8 = 3(5 + 8)$

3. $(2 + 5) + 7 = 2 + (\blacksquare + 7)$

4. $(5 \cdot 3) = (\blacksquare \cdot 5)$

Find the mean.

5. -7, -8, 2, -3

6. 88, 93, 76, 82, 91

Use a Venn diagram to solve.

7. There are 25 students in the French class and 29 in the Spanish class. Eight students are taking both classes. What is the total number of students enrolled?

2-4 Simplifying Variable Expressions   **69**

OBJECTIVE:
Use models to solve addition and subtraction equations.

MATERIALS

- Algebra tiles or two different color squares of paper and rectangles of a third color

- Math journal to record work

Exploring Equations

▼ You can model an addition equation using algebra tiles. Use rectangles for variables and squares for positive and negative integers.

Equation 1:   Equation 2:

1. **Discuss** What does the vertical bar represent?

2. **Write** an equation for each model.

3. **Model** each equation.

    a. $x + 3 = 5$ **b.** $z + 2 = -6$

    c. $y + 1 = 4$ **d.** $-3 = a - 4$

    e. $2b + 2 = 8$ **f.** $3 + 3x = -6$

▼ One way to find the solution of an equation is to *isolate* the variable. To isolate the variable, you use operations and properties to get the variable alone on one side of the equal sign.

4.

Model Equation

Isolate Variable

Solution

    a. Write What is the equation modeled in Step 1?

    b. Analyze What was done to isolate the variable?

    c. What property of integers was used to isolate the variable?

    d. What is the solution to the equation?

    e. Show mathematically what is represented in Steps 1–3.

5. **Model** and solve each equation.

    a. $x + 3 = 6$ **b.** $4 + y = -7$ **c.** $-3 = w + 2$

6. **Describe** another way you could isolate a variable in an addition equation.

▼ You can also model subtraction equations with algebra tiles.

$$y - 3 = 4 \qquad\qquad -3 = y - 2$$

WRITE $y + (-3) = 4$ **WRITE** $-3 = y + (-2)$

7. Why were the subtraction equations written as addition equations? Explain why you can write $y - 3 = 4$ as $y + (-3) = 4$.

8. *Analyze* How would you model each equation?

　a. $x - (-5) = 2$ 　　**b.** $x - (-3) = 5$

▼ You can also solve subtraction equations using algebra tiles.

$$x - 3 = 5$$

9. How would you model this equation?

　a. What do you need to add to both sides of the equation to isolate the variable?

　b. What is the solution to the equation? Compare your solution with those of other students in the class.

10. Model and solve each equation.

　a. $x - 4 = 2$ 　　**b.** $-5 = y - 3$

　c. $-6 = z - 3$

11. Is the equality of an equation affected when you add or subtract the same value on both sides?

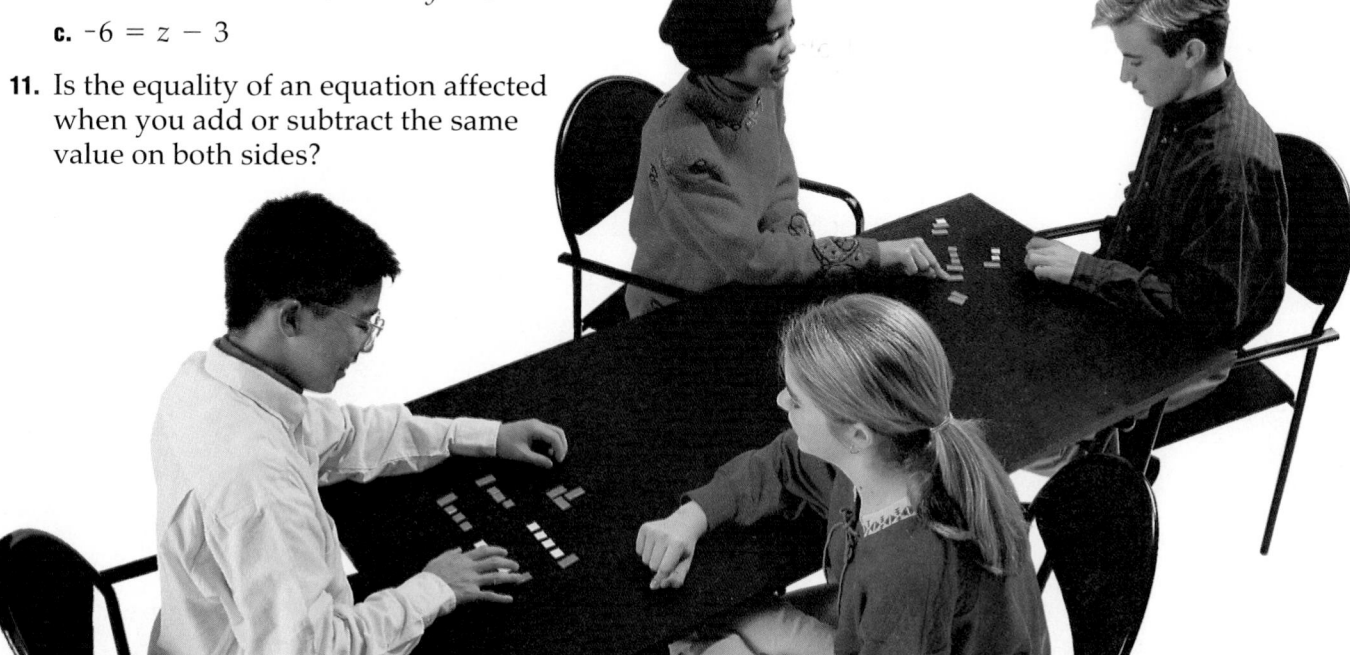

2-5 Addition and Subtraction Equations

▼ In the sixteenth century, only six planets were known to exist. By the twentieth century, all nine planets had been discovered. How many planets were discovered between the sixteenth and twentieth centuries?

If we let p represent the number of planets, we can describe the situation by an equation.

$$p + 6 = 9$$

THINK Is there another way to isolate the variable?

You can solve the equation $p + 6 = 9$ using a model.

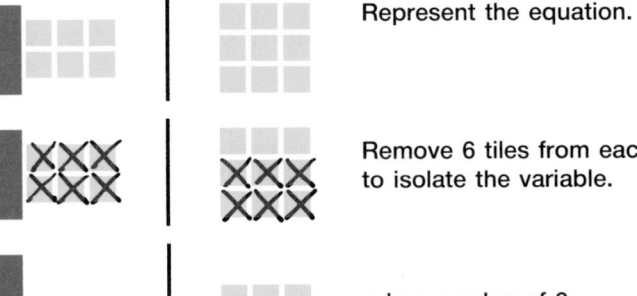

Represent the equation.

Remove 6 tiles from each side to isolate the variable.

p has a value of 3.

Three planets were discovered.

▼ Addition and subtraction are *inverse operations*. You can use subtraction to undo addition. When you subtract the same quantity from both sides of an equation, the result is an *equivalent equation*.

Subtraction Property of Equality	You can subtract the same value from both sides of an equation.
	Arithmetic **Algebra**
	$9 = 9$ If $a = b$,
	$9 - 4 = 9 - 4$ then $a - c = b - c$.

Example 1   Solve.

$$a + 22 = 28$$

Solution

$$a + 22 = 28$$
$$a + 22 - 22 = 28 - 22 \qquad \text{Subtract 22 from each side.}$$
$$a + 0 = 6$$
$$a = 6$$

Check $a + 22 = 28$
$6 + 22 = 28 \qquad$ Replace a with 6.
$28 = 28 \checkmark \qquad$ True, so 6 is the solution.

FLASHBACK

A solution makes an open equation true.

▼   To solve an equation involving subtraction, add the same value to both sides.

Addition Property of Equality	You can add the same value to both sides of an equation.
	Arithmetic **Algebra**
	$5 = 5$ If, $a = b$,
	$5 + 3 = 5 + 3$ then $a + c = b + c$.

Example 2   Solve.

$$b - 12 = 59$$

Solution

$$b - 12 = 59$$
$$b - 12 + 12 = 59 + 12 \qquad \text{Add 12 to each side.}$$
$$b + 0 = 71$$
$$b = 71$$

Check $b - 12 = 59$
$71 - 12 = 59 \qquad$ Replace b with 71.
$59 = 59 \checkmark \qquad$ True, so 71 is the solution.

THINK How would you graph a solution of 71 on the number line?

▼   If you remember that the sum of a number and its opposite is zero, you can solve equations in a different way.

Example 3   Solve $x - 3 = -2$ using a model.

Solution

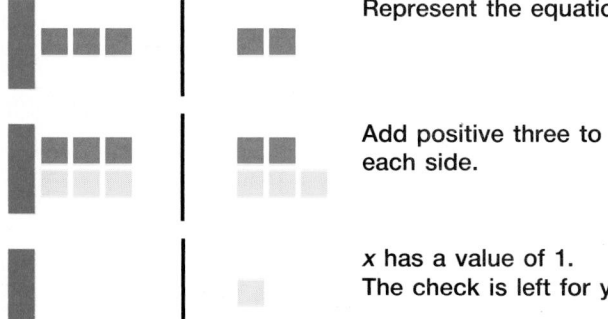

Represent the equation.

Add positive three to each side.

x has a value of 1.
The check is left for you.

FLASHBACK

$a + (-a) = 0$ and
$-a + a = 0$.

FLASHBACK

☐■ represents zero.

Example 4 Solve $x + 4 = -5$ using opposites.

Solution

$$x + 4 = -5$$
$$x + 4 + (-4) = -5 + (-4) \quad \text{Add -4 to each side.}$$
$$x + 0 = -9$$
$$x = -9 \quad \text{The check is left for you.}$$

THINK AND DISCUSS

1. Why is subtracting 8 from both sides of the equation $x + 8 = 17$ equivalent to adding -8 to both sides?

2. Which method do you prefer to use in solving an equation of the form $x + a = b$? Explain.

3. What properties do you need to use to show that $117 + n - 117$ is equal to n?

CLASS EXERCISES

Use a model to solve each equation. Graph each solution.

1. $6 + b = 9$ **2.** $-3 = n - 4$

State the first step in solving each equation.

3. $a + 8 = 12$ **4.** $54 + x = 98$ **5.** $34 = x - 19$ **6.** $-900 = 365 + x$

Solve each addition equation.

7. $x + 35 = 15$ **8.** $450 = x + 325$

Solve each subtraction equation.

9. $x - 34 = 20$ **10.** $-25 = b - 10$

WRITTEN EXERCISES

Use a model to solve each equation.

1. $x + 5 = 7$ **2.** $b - 4 = 3$ **3.** $-6 = w - 4$

Write and solve the equation represented by each model.

4.    **5.**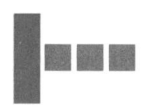

Solve each equation using the subtraction property.

6. $c + 9 = 37$ **7.** $b + 24 = 19$ **8.** $65 = n + 34$

9. $-47 = 7 + y$ **10.** $-45 = x + (-3)$ **11.** $298 + n = 924$

Solve each equation using the addition property.

12. $b - 15 = -9$ **13.** $43 = g - 39$ **14.** $x - 366 = -415$

15. $-27 = w - 14$ **16.** $-34 = c - 12$ **17.** $8,923 = r - 1,298$

Solve each equation using opposites.

18. $x - 19 = 34$ **19.** $13 + c = 54$ **20.** $432 = m - 391$

21. $48 = x + 9$ **22.** $c - 42 = 12$ **23.** $w + 3 = -8$

MENTAL MATH Solve each equation.

24. $130 = 30 + s$ **25.** $x + 800 = 500$ **26.** $95 = x - 15$

27. $-45 = b - 45$ **28.** $25 = x + 425$ **29.** $r - 316 = -8$

CALCULATOR Solve each equation.

30. $x + 49,023 = 15,911$ **31.** $265,970 = b - 1,098,645$

32. $398,452 = x + 799,376$ **33.** $c - 36,000 = 41,098$

Solve each equation.

34. $v - 493 = 513$ **35.** $400 + x = 900$ **36.** $c + (-90) = -58$

37. $56 = c - 9$ **38.** $-5 = -5 + n$ **39.** $-25 = -5 + n$

40. $32 + a = -32$ **41.** $2,314 = k + 716$ **42.** $e + (-43) = -45$

43. $34 + n + 12 = 78 - 7$ **44.** $n - 29 + (-16) = -24$

Complete.

45. If $x + a = b$, then $x = $ ▨.   **46.** If $x - a = b$, then $x = $ ▨.

Write an equation for each sentence. Solve for the variable.

47. A number d plus five is equal to seventeen.

48. Negative five is the same as x minus eight.

49. **DATA FILE 2 (pp. 52–53)** The number of decibels in a whisper is d decibels less than the number of decibels in a rocket launch.

50. Three hundred twenty-three is negative one hundred fifty-five plus y.

51. **DATA FILE 2 (pp. 52–53)** The speed of sound travels through steel h m/s faster than it travels through silver.

52. Thirty-three more than m is the same as negative seventeen.

53. **DATA FILE 4 (pp. 138–139)** The number of people who speak Chinese is p people more than the number who speak German.

54. Fifty-four less than a number k is equal to negative twenty-nine.

55. **PROJECT** Visit your town hall. Research the population of your town or city. Has the population increased or decreased? by how many people?

MIXED REVIEW

Find the number of terms.

1. $5w - 3z + 2w$

2. $8 + 9a + 3(2a)$

Simplify.

3. $9x - 5x + 4$

4. $5q + 8 - 3q + (-2)$

5. $27 \div (-3) + 4(3)$

6. $|3(-8) + 6 \cdot 2|$

Solve.

7. George studied math for 1 min the first week of school, 2 min the second, and 4 min the third. He continued to double his study time each week. How many minutes did he study the tenth week?

OBJECTIVE:
To solve one-step equations involving multiplication and division.

2-6 *Multiplication and Division Equations*

▼ Mark and Sara each have the same amount of money to spend at the basketball game. If they have a total of $6, how much does each have? Let m represent this amount. You can describe the situation by the following equation.

$$2m = 6$$

▼ You can solve a multiplication equation using a model.

Example 1 Solve the equation $2m = 6$ using a model.

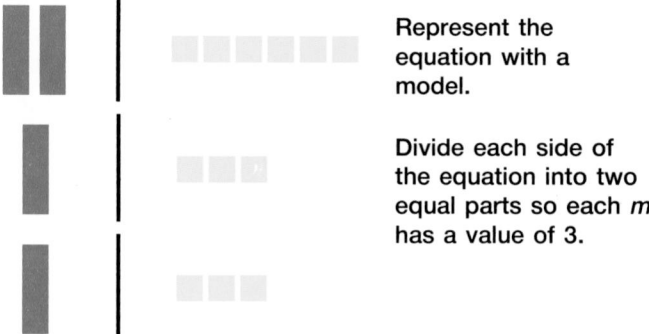

Represent the equation with a model.

Divide each side of the equation into two equal parts so each m has a value of 3.

Each person has $3 to spend.

THINK Why must you divide by a nonzero value?

▼ Division undoes multiplication. When you divide both sides of an equation by the same nonzero number, the result is an equivalent equation.

Division Property of Equality	You can divide both sides of an equation by the same nonzero value.
	Arithmetic **Algebra**
	$9 = 9$ If $a = b$,
	$9 \div 3 = 9 \div 3$ then $a \div c = b \div c$.
	$\frac{9}{3} = \frac{9}{3}$ $\frac{a}{c} = \frac{b}{c}, c \neq 0$

THINK How do you know that $\frac{5r}{5}$ is the same as $5r \div 5$?

Example 2 Solve $5r = -20$ using the division property of equality.

Solution
$$5r = -20$$
$$\frac{5r}{5} = \frac{-20}{5} \qquad \text{Divide both sides by 5.}$$
$$r = -4$$

Check
$$5r = -20 \qquad \text{Replace } r \text{ with } -4.$$
$$5 \cdot (-4) = -20 \checkmark$$

▼ To solve an equation involving division, multiply both sides by the same value.

Multiplication Property of Equality	You can multiply both sides of an equation by the same value.
	Arithmetic **Algebra**
	$12 = 12$ If $a = b$,
	$12 \cdot 2 = 12 \cdot 2$ then $ac = bc$.

Example 3   Solve $\frac{x}{-9} = -3$ using the multiplication property of equality.

Solution $\frac{x}{-9} = -3$

$$-9\left(\frac{x}{-9}\right) = -3 \cdot (-9) \quad \text{Multiply both sides by -9.}$$

$$x = 27$$

Check $\frac{x}{-9} = -3$ Replace x with 27.

$$\frac{27}{-9} = -3$$

$$-3 = -3 ✓$$

CLASS EXERCISES

State the first step in solving each equation.

1. $6x = 96$ **2.** $32 = c \div 3$ **3.** $\frac{r}{-5} = -4$

Solve each multiplication equation.

4. $8x = -48$ **5.** $-2x = 12$ **6.** $108 = 9x$

Solve each division equation.

7. $\frac{v}{3} = 14$ **8.** $-6 = n \div 4$ **9.** $\frac{m}{-2} = -20$

▼
THINK AND DISCUSS
1. Why is $1y = y$?
2. How would you solve the equation $\frac{25}{x} = 1$?
3. How are the procedures used to solve $3x = 9$ and $x + 3 = 12$ alike? How are they different?

WRITTEN EXERCISES

Use a model to solve each equation. Graph each solution.

1. $2g = 8$ **2.** $10 = 2m$ **3.** $4h = -12$

MENTAL MATH   Is -3 a solution of each equation?

4. $-6 = 2m$ **5.** $\frac{b}{-3} = 1$ **6.** $45p = 145$ **7.** $\frac{-18}{k} = -6$

Write and solve each equation represented by the model.

8.   **9.**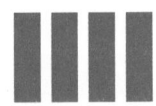

Solve each equation using the division property.

10. $4a = 28$ **11.** $-2b = 30$ **12.** $-45 = 9a$

13. $15c = 90$ **14.** $5w = 95$ **15.** $-28 = 7m$

16. $-10d = 100$ **17.** $125 = 25d$ **18.** $-35 = 5n$

Solve each equation using the multiplication property.

19. $\frac{m}{4} = 13$ **20.** $\frac{b}{-6} = 20$ **21.** $-2 = d \div 8$

22. $f \div 3 = -4$ **23.** $-50 = \frac{n}{-6}$ **24.** $9 = \frac{n}{8}$

25. $\frac{w}{12} = -2$ **26.** $13 = n \div -4$ **27.** $7 = \frac{y}{6}$

MENTAL MATH Solve each equation.

28. $20b = 2,000$ **29.** $\frac{v}{-50} = 300$

30. $75m = -7,500$ **31.** $3,823 = \frac{s}{100}$

CALCULATOR Solve each equation.

32. $358c = 80,550$ **33.** $x \div (-392) = 108$

34. $4,523 = \frac{n}{-921}$ **35.** $-48z = 76,128$

Solve each equation using any method.

36. $4c = -36$ **37.** $\frac{s}{-32} = 24$ **38.** $-84t = 0$

39. $-88 = 11w$ **40.** $6c = -96$ **41.** $56 = f \div 9$

42. $-34c = 34$ **43.** $15n = 225$ **44.** $-364 = \frac{c}{-3}$

45. $16s = 496$ **46.** $f \div 31 = 27$ **47.** $352 = 32v$

48. $25y = 500$ **49.** $0 = \frac{u}{254}$ **50.** $43x = 4,257$

51. A honeybee hive contains 35,000 cells. How many cells are there in 25 honeybee hives?

52. **DATA FILE 10 (pp. 404–405)** How many acres does one gray wolf require to survive?

53. Write an expression for the number of eggs in d dozen.

MIXED REVIEW

Solve.

1. $-4 = a + 7$

2. $n - 5 = 12$

3. $t - (-4) = -15$

Write the expression.

4. Subtract 3 from a, then add b.

5. Multiply 7 times the difference of 9 and w.

6. The absolute value of the sum of -8 and q.

Solve.

7. The number of seconds it takes the sound of thunder to reach you is about five times the number of miles between you and lightning. How long does it take the sound to reach you if lightning is 12 mi away?

For what values of x is each equation true?

54. $|x| = 7$

55. $\dfrac{|x|}{3} = 2$

56. $2|x| = 8$

Solve each equation for x.

57. $ax = b$

58. $\dfrac{x}{a} = b$

59. $x - a = b$

60. $x + a = b$

Critical Thinking

EXPLORING VISUAL THINKING

Find the missing piece.

To solve this problem, you must develop a plan. What characteristics does the missing piece have?

1. What happens to the lines of the pattern as they swirl inward?

2. At some point the lines will form a dot. Where will the dot be?

3. Is all of the dot on the missing piece or is part of it on the design?

4. Based on the characteristics, which piece is the best choice?

5. Here is another puzzle. Which figure will connect with part A to form a circle? Describe how you know.

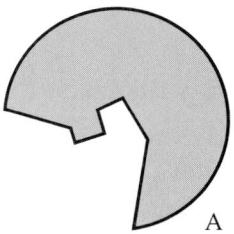
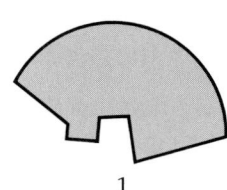

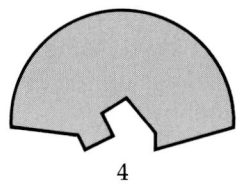

Writing Equations

OBJECTIVE:
To write an equation
for a word problem
or model.

▼ A group of artists is painting a large outdoor mural. The length of the mural is 410 ft. The mural has an area of 28,700 ft². How could you find the width of the painting?

To find the width, you can write an equation.

w	$A = 28,700 \text{ ft}^2$

$l = 410 \text{ ft}$

Sketch a diagram when appropriate.

$$\text{Area} = length \cdot width$$
$$\updownarrow \qquad \updownarrow$$
$$410 \cdot w = 28{,}700$$

Let *w* equal the width.

▼ To solve a word problem, you need to translate a sentence into an equation.

Example 1 **Write an equation.**

One more than three times the number of students in the class is equal to sixty-four.

Solution In this situation, we need to find the number of students.

Let s = *number of students.*   Identify the variable.

$3s$ = *three times* the number of students.   Include the coefficient.

$3s + 1$ = *one more than three times the number of students.*   Write the variable expression.

$3s + 1 = 64$ Write the equation.

▼ Before you write an equation decide on a variable to represent one unknown. Then write the other unknowns in terms of that variable.

THINK What if you let m = Joan's money? How would you write the expression for Eve's money?

Example 2 **Write an equation.**

Joan collected twice as much money as Eve for the walkathon. Together they collected $120.

Solution In this situation, we need to find the money that each collected.

Let m = Eve's money   Identify the variable.
$2m$ = Joan's money   Write any like terms.
$m + 2m = 120$ Write the equation.

▼ Equations can represent real situations.

Example 3   Write a word problem for the equation $12x = 496$.

Solution   One possible word problem is the following:

Janet makes 12 monthly payments for her automobile insurance. The yearly premium is $496. How much will she pay per month?

CLASS EXERCISES

Choose the best equation for each problem. Do not solve.

1. Kendra uses 14 C/min while running. If she burned 154 C, how many minutes (m) did she run?

   a. $m - 14 = 154$ **b.** $14m = 154$

   c. $m \div 154 = 14$ **d.** $m + 14 = 154$

2. Three less than the quantity $y - 7$ is equal to $^-6$.

   a. $y - 7 + 3 = {}^-6$ **b.** $3 - (y - 7) = {}^-6$

   c. $^-6 = (y - 7) - 3$ **d.** $^-6 = 3(y - 7)$

Write an equation for each problem. Do not solve.

3. The product of a number and 40 is equal to 360.

4. The sum of 45 and some number is $^-30$.

5. A number decreased by $^-5$ is 18.

6. Three more than six times the number of books on the shelf is 63.

7. The length of a rectangle is twice the width. The perimeter is 120.

Write a word problem for each equation.

8. $500 = 10t$ 9. $120 = 150 - x$

WRITTEN EXERCISES

Choose the best equation for each problem. Do not solve.

1. Suppose you travel 55 mi/h. How many hours (h) would it take you to go 275 mi?

   a. $55 + h = 275$ **b.** $h \div 55 = 275$

   c. $55h = 275$ **d.** $275 = h - 55$

2. The quantity $x - 9$ times -3 is equal to 21.

    a. $x - 9 \cdot (-3) = 21$ **b.** $(x - 9)(-3) = 21$

    c. $21 = 3 + (x - 9)$ **d.** $(x - 9) - 3 = 21$

Write an equation for each problem. Do not solve.

3. A number decreased by 24 is equal to -9.

4. Ten less than seven times the number of guests is sixty.

5. Sean bought 15 notebooks. Each cost the same amount. He spent a total of $30. How much was each notebook?

6. On Tuesday, 80 students were absent. The remaining 478 students were in school. How many students attend the school?

7. **PROJECT** Write an equation using one variable to represent the number of hours you study and the number of hours you watch television every week.

Write an equation for each problem. Then solve.

8. Kirsten sent out invitations for a surprise party. She then decided to invite eight more people. She sent out 52 invitations in all. How many invitations did she originally send?

9. Two sides of a triangle have lengths 46 mm and 54 mm. The perimeter is 150 mm. What is the length of the third side?

10. **DATA FILE 3 (pp. 96–97)**

    a. Jean has twice as many proof sets as Jim. They have the same type of proof sets. The 1990 value of their sets totals $10,500. What year were the proof sets made?

    b. **WRITE** a word problem using any of the data in the file. Exchange problems with a student and solve.

MIXED REVIEW

Evaluate using mental math.

1. 5(103)   **2.** (180)3

State the first step in solving.

3. $5x = 35$

4. $5 + x = 35$

5. $35 = x - 5$

6. $\frac{x}{5} = 35$

Solve.

7. Badwater, California, (-282 ft alt.) is the lowest point in the Western Hemisphere. The Dead Sea (-1,310 ft alt.) is the lowest surface point on Earth. How much lower is the Dead Sea than Badwater?

TEST YOURSELF

Solve.

1. $a + 92 = 112$ **2.** $-17 = y \div 4$ **3.** $-46 = -12 + x$

4. $96 = 3r$ **5.** $b - 16 = -39$ **6.** $-12w = 156$

Write an equation for each problem. Solve.

7. Twelve more than some number is twenty.

8. Three less than the quantity $c - 6$ is equal to negative ten.

Exploring Graphing

MATERIALS

- Graph paper

- Computer and graphing
software (optional)

- Math journal to record
work

■ Sometimes looking at a graph is an easier way to analyze data. You can use the data from a spreadsheet to create a graph.

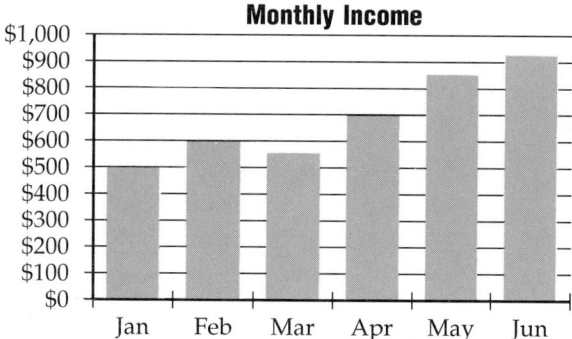

	A	B
1	Month	Income
2	Jan	$500.00
3	Feb	$600.00
4	Mar	$550.00
5	Apr	$700.00
6	May	$850.00
7	Jun	$925.00

Monthly Income

DATAPOINT

Many spreadsheet
programs allow you to
graph the spreadsheet
data.

1. What part of the spreadsheet does the horizontal axis stand for in the bar graph? What does the vertical axis represent?

2. Does the spreadsheet or bar graph let you see exact values?

3. On a sheet of graph paper, draw a bar graph using twice the value of the spreadsheet data. How is your graph similar to the one shown above? How is it different?

■ You can also use a computer to draw a line graph.

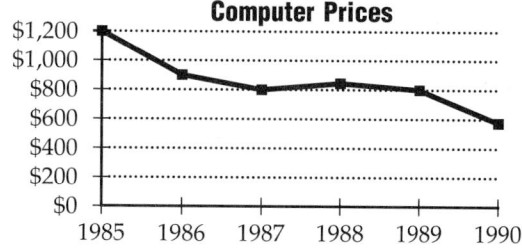

Computer Prices

4. **a.** Could you use the data in the line graph to construct a bar graph? Why or why not?

   b. *Analyze* Why would a line graph be inappropriate for the data from the spreadsheet shown earlier? Explain.

DATAPOINT

Here are some other types of graphs that you can draw with a graphing program:

- Stem and leaf plots
- Box and whisker plots
- Scattergrams
- Three-dimensional graphs

■ You can also use a computer to construct double bar graphs. The spreadsheet data below were used to construct the graph.

	A	B	C
1	Month	Income	Expenses
2	Jan	$500.00	$150.00
3	Feb	$600.00	$175.00
4	Mar	$550.00	$275.00
5	Apr	$700.00	$800.00

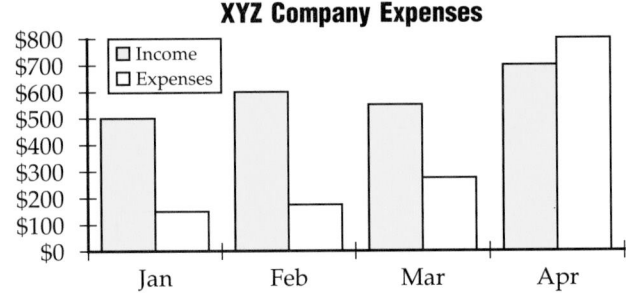

XYZ Company Expenses

5. **a. *Analyze*** Based on the graph, is this business doing well financially? Why or why not?

   b. *Explore* How does a graph help in analyzing data?

Fund-raising Results

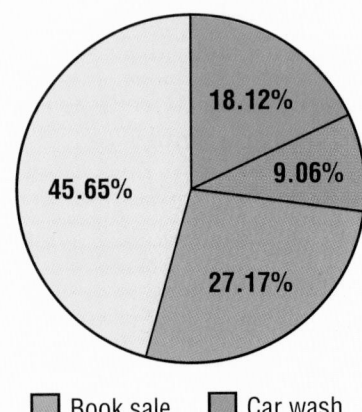

18.12%

9.06%

45.65%

27.17%

■ Book sale ■ Car wash
□ Food stand ■ Paper drive

■ You can also draw a circle graph with your data. The spreadsheet below shows the results of a class fund-raising drive.

	A	B
1	Car wash	$150.00
2	Paper drive	$75.00
3	Book sale	$225.00
4	Food stand	$378.00

6. The data are shown on the circle graph at the left.

   a. Which activity raised the most money? the least money? How are these two amounts shown on the graph?

   b. *Discuss* Would a bar graph of the data be more useful? Which type of graph would you use for the data? Explain.

   c. How could the circle graph be used in planning next year's fund-raiser? Which activities should the class emphasize?

7. ***PROJECT*** Draw a graph using data that you collect. Choose the two most appropriate types of graphs to display your data. If you have a computer graphing program, draw the graphs.

Chapter 2 Solving Equations

2-8 Guess and Test

OBJECTIVE:
To use guess and test to solve mathematical problems.

■ It is sometimes useful when solving a mathematics problem to guess what the answer will be. You can use the guessing strategy to solve the following problem.

NOTES & QUOTES

Certainly, let us learn proving, but also let us learn guessing.

George Polya

PROBLEM

Ronald Reagan is the oldest man to be elected president of the United States. John F. Kennedy was the youngest. The sum of their ages at the time of their election is 112. The difference is 26. How old was each man when elected president?

SOLUTION

READER What do you want to find?   Reagan's and Kennedy's ages when they were elected president

What is the sum of their ages
when each was elected?   112
What is the difference?   26

PLAN Find two numbers with a sum of 112.
Test whether their difference is 26.
Use each incorrect guess to make a better estimate.
Keep a record of your work in a table.

SOLVE

Guess	Test	Outcome
50 and 62	$50 + 62 = 112$ $62 - 50 = 12$	The difference is too small, so the numbers have to be farther apart.
40 and 72	$40 + 72 = 112$ $72 - 40 = 32$	The difference is too great, so the numbers have to be closer together.
43 and 69	$43 + 69 = 112$ $69 - 43 = 26$	Correct.

LOOK BACK Ronald Reagan was 69 years old when elected president.
John F. Kennedy was 43 years old when elected president.

CLASS EXERCISES

Make a reasonable guess for each question. Test your answer.

1. What is the length of your classroom? the width? the area?

2. How many times does your heart beat in a minute?

---

3. What are two whole numbers whose sum is 20 and whose difference is 2?

4. What are two whole numbers whose product is 50 and whose quotient is 2?

Which of the numbers 1, 2, 3, 4, or 5 is a solution?

5. a. $4y - 2 + 3y = 19$ **b.** $3 + \dfrac{b}{2} = 5$

WRITTEN EXERCISES

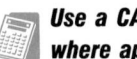
Use a CALCULATOR where appropriate.

Use guess and test to solve each problem.

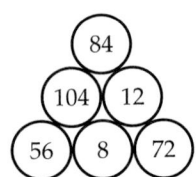

1. Find two pairs of numbers in the diagram whose quotient is 7.

2. The teller's drawer has some $5 bills, $10 bills, and some $20 bills. There are 15 bills worth a total of $185. How many $5 bills, $10 bills, and $20 bills are there?

3. The Smiths have two children. The sum of their ages is 23 and the product is 132. How old are the children?

4. The average of three consecutive integers is 10. Their sum is 30. What is the middle number?

Use any strategy to solve each problem.

5. Three consecutive integers have a sum of ⁻9 and a product of ⁻24. What are the three integers?

6. A vegetable garden has a length of 5 ft and a width of 8 ft. Two feet are added to the length. By how much will this increase the area?

7. Trains leave New York for Boston every 40 min. The first train leaves at 5:20 A.M. What is the departure time closest to 12:55 P.M.?

8. Jean's age of 16 is the same as Rafi's age divided by three. How old is Rafi?

9. A number that when multiplied by itself and then by itself again gives ⁻1,000. What is the number?

10. In a collection of quarters and nickels, there are four more nickels than quarters. How many nickels and quarters are there if the collection is worth $2.30?

11. A triangle has sides of lengths $3x$, $4x$, and $5x$. The perimeter is 120 ft. What is the length of each side?

FLASHBACK

Consecutive integers have a difference of 1. . . . ⁻2, ⁻1, 0, 1, 2 . . .

2-9 *Ecology*

OBJECTIVE:
To apply solving equations to ecology problems.

Americans throw away an average of four to five pounds of waste per person each day. As landfills across the United States fill up and the number of landfills decreases, disposing of solid waste is becoming a serious problem. One way to reduce the problem is to reduce the amount of solid waste.

FLASHBACK

1 ton (t) = 2,000 lb

Example 1 One aluminum can weighs about $\frac{1}{28}$ lb. Suppose your school starts a recycling drive. How many cans will your school need to recycle to reduce the trash by 1 t?

Solution Write an equation.

$$c \div 28 = 2,000 \qquad \text{Let } c = \text{number of cans.}$$
$$c \div 28 \cdot 28 = 2,000 \cdot 28 \qquad \text{Multiply both sides by 28.}$$
$$c = 56,000$$

Your school will need to recycle 56,000 cans.

Some companies pay for materials to recycle. The prices paid vary due to market conditions.

Example 2 Suppose recyclers pay $5/t for newspapers. How many tons of newspaper would your school have to recycle to earn $65?

Solution Write an equation.

$$5n = 65 \qquad \text{Let } n = \text{number of tons of newspaper.}$$
$$\frac{5n}{5} = \frac{65}{5} \qquad \text{Divide both sides by 5.}$$
$$n = 13$$

Your school will have to recycle 13 t of newspaper.

CLASS EXERCISES

United States Solid Waste
(lb/person/day)

Year	Generated	Recycled
1965	2.77	0.17
1970	3.16	0.21
1975	3.11	0.23
1980	3.35	0.32

Use the **DATA** at the left to solve.

1. In 1975, how many pounds of solid waste did the average person generate in seven days?

2. In 1980, what was the net amount of solid waste that one person generated? The net amount of waste is the difference between the waste generated and the waste recycled.

3. In 1970, the United States population was approximately 203,000,000 people. About how much solid waste did the entire population generate each day?

WRITTEN EXERCISES

TYPES AND AMOUNTS OF GARBAGE DISCARDED PER YEAR

60 billion cans
28 billion bottles
100 million tires
3 million cars
4 million tons of plastic
40 million tons of paper

Use the *DATA* at the left to solve each problem.

1. It costs $65/t to pick up garbage. How much will it cost per year to pick up just the paper and plastic discarded?

2. Tires weigh an average of 9 lb. It costs $72/t to dispose of tires. How much does it cost to dispose of one year's discarded tires?

3. ***ESTIMATION*** The weight of twenty-eight aluminum cans is approximately 1 lb.
   a. Estimate the weight of the cans discarded per year.
   b. Recycling one pound of cans saves 8 kW · h of electricity. About how many kilowatt hours of electricity would be saved if all the discarded cans were recycled?

4. A town with a population of 38,000 people discards an average of 4 lb of waste per person each day. About how many tons of waste do they discard in a week?

■■■■■■ Decision Making ■ **DECISION MAKING** ■ Decision Making ■ Decision Making ■ Decision Making ■

ECOLOGY

■ COLLECT DATA

1. How much waste does your school produce each week? Keep track of what you throw away. Make a chart like the one below to tally your results.

Type of Trash	Amount of Trash (in pounds)							
	Mon	**Tues**	**Wed**	**Thur**	**Fri**	**Sat**	**Sun**	**Total**
Newspaper								
Other paper								
Metal								
Plastic								
Glass								
Other								

2. Find out what kinds of recycling services are available in your community.

5. Suppose a state with a population of 5 million reduces the average waste per person from 5 lb to 3 lb. How much could they save on disposal costs if the waste pickup costs $65/t?

6. A town of 63,000 collects 1,800 lb of waste per person in a year. The area of landfill (in square yards) needed for this waste is found using the formula $A = \frac{\text{weight of waste}}{1{,}000 \cdot \text{depth in yards}}$.

   a. Find the area in square yards of the town's landfill if the landfill's depth will be 3 yd.

   b. *ESTIMATION* There are 4,840 yd^2 in an acre. Estimate the number of acres needed per year for the town's landfill.

7. *PROJECT*

   a. Technically, solid waste, trash, and garbage are not synonyms. Find out which materials are in each category.

   b. Determine ways, other than reducing the landfill problem, in which recycling benefits the environment.

   c. Research the environmental damage that can result from an improperly managed landfill. Find out what we can do to minimize these dangers.

■ *Decision Making* ■ *Decision Making* ■ *Decision Making* ■ *Decision Making* ■ *Decision Making* ■ *Decision Making* ■

■ **ANALYZE DATA**

3. Analyze the garbage your school discards.

   a. What materials can be recycled?

   b. Could you use the garbage in other ways?

4. Other than recycling or reusing items, what ways can you think of to reduce the amount of your school's garbage?

■ **MAKE DECISIONS**

5. Plan to reduce the amount of waste your school discards.

   a. Set a reasonable goal for reducing your amount of trash.

   b. Decide on methods you can use to meet your goal.

6. Many fast-food companies use plastic wrappers or foam containers instead of coated paper to wrap their foods.

   a. Compare the ease of recycling these materials.

   b. Which wrapping do you think is better? Explain.

   c. How do you think the companies could reduce their trash?

Practice

State whether each equation is true, false, or open.

1. $-17 = x + 5$ **2.** $\frac{-325}{-5} = 65$ **3.** $29 + (-3) = 26$

4. $25 \cdot 6 = 150$ **5.** $2x + 5 = 3x - 7$ **6.** $6 = -3[4 + (-2)]$

State whether the given number is a solution of the equation.

7. $12 = 2x + (-4); x = 4$

8. $-3[2y - (-5)] = 9; y = -4$

9. $2r - 4 + r = 89; r = 31$

10. $-2 = s - (-4) + 2s; s = 6$

11. $\frac{x}{5} - (-2) = -12; x = -50$

12. $2m + 6 = 2(m + 3); m = -2$

State which property is shown.

13. $(3r)s = 3(rs)$

14. $(a - b)(r + s) = (r + s)(a - b)$

15. $653 + 0 = 0 + 653$

16. $6(t - 5) = 6 \cdot t - 6 \cdot 5$

17. $17 \cdot 1 = 17$

18. $(3 + 9) + 0 = 3 + (9 + 0)$

Evaluate.

19. $-135 + (-341)$ **20.** $(8 - 5)6 + 37$ **21.** $120 + 16 + 80$

22. $-15 - (-56)$ **23.** $-550 \div 50 \cdot 2$ **24.** $-6[4 + (-12)] + 9$

25. $4\left(\frac{-12}{-6}\right) + (-3) \cdot 5 - 3(-11)$ **26.** $-17 + [5 - (-7) + 2]3$

27. $-3 + (-6) - [5 - (-2)]$ **28.** $7 \cdot (-4) + [8 - (-5)]3$

Simplify each expression.

29. $-5(3k)$ **30.** $2x + 5 - x$ **31.** $(g + 5)3 + 2g - 7$

32. $8 + (3c + 3)4$ **33.** $4(x + y - z)$ **34.** $8(a - b) + 2b - 2a$

35. $\frac{-9}{3} + 12w - (-7) - 3(5w)$ **36.** $23 + 2[b + (-15) + 3b]$

Solve each equation.

37. $c + 7 = 34$ **38.** $-550 = 10w$ **39.** $\frac{k}{-4} = -3$

40. $78 = t - (-47)$ **41.** $6d = 54$ **42.** $17 = z - 3$

43. $27 + v = -12$ **44.** $h + (-3) = 53$ **45.** $-192 = \frac{w}{-16}$

46. Find the sum of the magic square.
Write and solve equations to find a, b, and c.

a	3	8
5	7	b
c	11	4

Write an equation for each problem. Solve.

47. The sum of a number and 5 is equal to -123.

48. Six less than a is equal to 47.

Problem Solving Practice

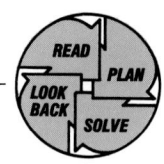

Solve each problem. The list at the left shows some possible strategies you can use.

PROBLEM SOLVING STRATEGIES

Look for a Pattern
Guess and Test
Simplify the Problem
Make an Organized List
Work Backwards
Account for All Possibilities
Make a Table
Write an Equation
Solve by Graphing
Draw a Diagram
Make a Model
Solve Another Way
Simulate the Problem

1. **DATA FILE 5 (pp. 180–181)** Look at the following two equations that are expressed with musical notes.

   a. How many quarter notes are equal to a whole note?

   b. How many eighth notes are equal to a whole note?

   c. Is there a pattern? Can you use the pattern to find the number of sixteenth and half notes in a whole note?

2. The average age of five students is 15. Two of the students are 12 years old. Three students are not 12, but are the same age. How old are the other three students?

3. **COMPUTER** Look at the spreadsheet below.

	A	B	C	D
1	Employee	Hours	Wage	
2	Jones, C.	4	4.50	= B2×C2
3	Smith, G.	5	4.25	= B3×C3
4	Garcia, H.	12	5.15	= B4×C4
5				
6				
7				

   a. What values do the formulas in cells D2–D4 represent?

   b. Suppose you wanted to find the total number of hours and the total amount of wages. What formulas would you use? In which cells would you enter the formulas?

4. You are given these directions to get to a friend's house:

   Drive east on State Street. Take a right on Main. Continue on Main and take a right on Broadway. Continue on Broadway and take a left on Center Street. The house is on the corner of Center and High streets.

   Assume the streets are arranged in a grid and there are no one-way streets. Is there a shorter route? If so, describe it.

5. **DATA FILE 3 (pp. 96–97)**

   a. Tom bought a 1937 proof set in 1965 and sold it in 1968. How much did he have to add to his profit in order to purchase three 1940 proof sets the next day?

   b. How long would it take to produce $1,920,000 in $5 bills?

Chapter 2 Review

Match each word with the example that illustrates its meaning.

1. Commutative property
2. Associative property
3. Solution
4. Identity
5. Distributive property
6. Term
7. Numerical coefficient
8. Constant
9. Simplify an expression
10. Property of equality
11. False equation

a. $a \cdot (b \cdot c) = (a \cdot b) \cdot c$

b. 4 in $4x + 5 = 9$

c. 5 in $4x + 5 = 9$

d. $3x + 4 + 5 = 3x + 9$

e. $x = 2$ for $3 + x = 5$

f. $a + b = b + a$

g. $4x + 5 - 5 = 9 - 5$

h. $-4 - 7 = 3$

i. $a + 0 = a$ and $a \cdot 1 = a$

j. $4x$ in $4x + 5 = 9$

k. $a(b + c) = (a \cdot b) + (a \cdot c)$

Using the Properties of Operations   2-1, 2-2

To evaluate an expression, use the commutative property to change
the order. Use the associative property to change the grouping.

Use the commutative and the associative properties to evaluate.

12. $125 + 347 + 75$

13. $58 + 16 + 2 + 4$

14. $4 \cdot 7 \cdot 25 \cdot 1$

15. $(20 \cdot 65) \cdot 5$

Using the Distributive Property   2-3

To evaluate an expression with parentheses, use the distributive
property to distribute a factor to each term inside the parentheses.

Use the distributive property to evaluate.

16. $5(20 + 3)$

17. $4(50 - 2)$

18. $2(25 + 8) + 2(15 - 8)$

19. $6(40 - 21) - 6(20 - 1)$

Simplifying Variable Expressions   2-4

To simplify a variable expression, combine like terms and eliminate
parentheses using the distributive property.

Simplify each expression.

20. $5x + 3y + 3x + 2y$

21. $4 + 6(a + 2) + 3a$

Addition and Subtraction Equations   2-5

To solve an addition or subtraction equation, add or subtract the same value from both sides of the equation.

Solve each equation.

22.

23.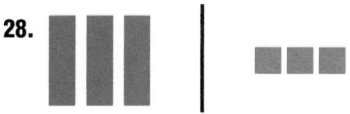

24. $a - 7 = 28$

25. $x + 19 = 30$

26. $38 + y - 18 = 500$

27. $n + (-13) = 7$

Multiplication and Division Equations   2-6

To solve a multiplication or division equation, multiply or divide both sides of the equation by the same nonzero value.

Solve each equation.

28.

29.

30. $\frac{m}{8} = -9$

31. $8b = 96$

32. $\frac{c}{12} = 24$

33. $-3k = -54$

Writing Equations   2-7

To write an equation for a word problem, you need to recognize words that imply the variable(s), the operation(s), and the equality.

Write an equation for each problem.

34. Twice a number increased by 28 is 54.

35. Seventeen less than a number is 12.

Write a word problem to describe the equation.

36. $x + 7 = 95$

37. $4x = 17$

Problem Solving   2-8, 2-9

To solve some problems, guess at the solution. Then use each incorrect guess to make a better estimate of the correct answer.

Use guess and test to solve.

38. Paper plates come in packages of 15 or 20. Helene bought 9 packages and had 155 plates. How many packages of 15 and how many packages of 20 did she buy?

Use the data on page 88.

39. How many pounds of paper are discarded per year?

State whether each equation is true, false, or open.

1. $24 = 3(-8)$

2. $5x + 28 = 153$

3. $18(-7 \div 7) = (-2)(9)$

4. $-6 + 15 = (120 \div 20) - (5 - 8)$

Use the commutative and the associative properties to evaluate.

5. $250 \cdot 38 \cdot 2$

6. $675 + (-8) - (75 - 8)$

Complete with the appropriate number or variable.

7. $9(8 + 5) = 9 \cdot 8 + \blacksquare \cdot 5$

8. $(x + y)\blacksquare = xz + yz$

9. $-3 \cdot 4 + \blacksquare \cdot 11 = \blacksquare(4 + 11)$

10. $4x + 6\blacksquare = \blacksquare(4 + 6)$

Simplify each expression.

11. $6y + 4(y + 1)$

12. $5a + 2b + 3a - 7b$

13. $3(m + 2n) - 2n$

14. $3(2r - 5) + 8(r + 2)$

15. $2(x + y) - 2y$

16. $(-2c + 3d)(-5) + 3(-2c) - (-8d)$

Solve each equation.

17.

18.

19.

20. $k - 23 = 17$

21. $\dfrac{t}{-5} = 15$

22. $-3f = -42$

23. $120 = 38 + p$

24. $7w = -217$

25. $\dfrac{h}{12} = 12$

Write an equation for each problem. Do not solve.

26. Five less than 8 times the number of students is 163.

27. Three times the quantity $t + 9$ is equal to -18.

Solve.

28. The length of a room is 4 m longer than the width. The perimeter of the room is 28 m. Find the width of the room.

29. Brian bought a used bike for $25 less than its original price. He paid a total of $88 for the bike. What was the original price of the bike?

30. Write a word problem to describe the equation $4x = 2$.

Chapters 1–2   Cumulative Review

Choose the correct answer. Write A, B, C, or D.

1. 0, 1, 4, 9, 16, 25, . . .

   A. 26   B. 36

   C. 35   D. not given

2. Which property is used?

   $(ab)c = c(ab)$

   A. associative   B. identity

   C. commutative   D. not given

3. $12 - (-15)$

   A. -3   B. 3

   C. 27   D. not given

4. Simplify $(3x + 4)2 + 3(-2x)$.

   A. $-3x + 8$ B. $-3x + 4$

   C. $12x + 8$ D. not given

5. Solve $x - (-3) = 12$.

   A. 9   B. 4

   C. 15   D. not given

6. What is the variable expression for *six less than the absolute value of a number*?

   A. $|n| - 6$ B. $6 - |n|$

   C. $|n - 6|$ D. not given

7. Evaluate $3xy - 2x$ for $x = -1$, $y = 2$.

   A. -4   B. 8

   C. 4   D. not given

8. Solve $x + (-9) = 36$.

   A. 27   B. -4

   C. 45   D. not given

9. What is the opposite of $|-3|$?

   A. 3   B. 0

   C. -3   D. not given

10. Which equation has the solution -2?

    A. $x + 7 = 9$ B. $\frac{x}{-2} = 1$

    C. $(-3)x = -6$ D. not given

11. Complete $4(9 + 7) = (4 \cdot \blacksquare) + (4 \cdot 7)$.

    A. 7   B. 9

    C. 4   D. not given

12. Find two numbers whose sum is 10 and whose product is -24.

    A. -6 and 4   B. -12 and 2

    C. -8 and -3   D. not given

13. Solve $\frac{y}{4} = -12$.

    A. 3   B. -3

    C. -48   D. not given

14. Evaluate $98 + 2 \cdot 7 + 3$.

    A. 110   B. 118

    C. 115   D. not given

15. Solve $-8y = 72$.

    A. -7   B. -9

    C. 9   D. not given

16. Write an equation for the model.

    A. $x + 2 = 1$ B. $2x = 1$

    C. $x - 2 = 1$ D. $2x = -1$

A PRINTING PRESS can produce 8,000 sheets of 32 bills every hour.

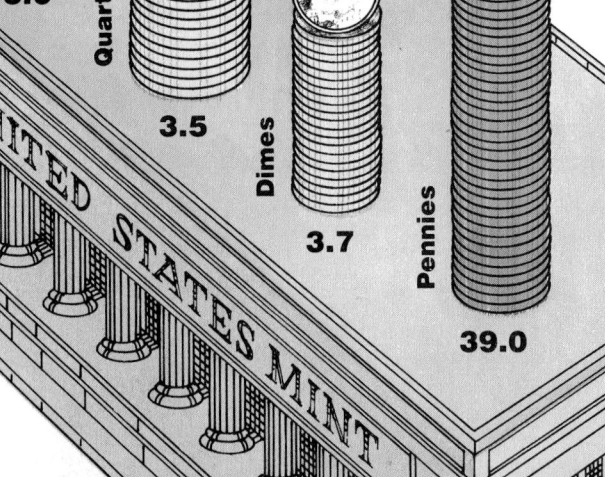

Nickels **3.0**

Quarters **3.5**

Dimes **3.7**

Pennies **39.0**

Daily Coin Production (in millions of coins)

UNITED STATES MINT

Decimals and Equations

Proof sets are special editions of a particular year's currency issued for collectors. A proof set comprises a penny, a nickel, a dime, a quarter, a half dollar, and, from 1973 to 1981, a silver dollar.

			Value		
Year	Number Produced	At time of Issue	in 1965	in 1968	in 1990
1936	3,837	$1.81	$400.00	$5,100.00	$5,050.00
1937	5,542	$1.81	$160.00	$3,500.00	$3,500.00
1940	11,246	$1.81	$50.00	$1,200.00	$1,450.00
1955	378,200	$2.10	$11.00	$60.00	$77.00
1961	3,028,244	$2.10	$3.00	$20.00	$16.00

PROOF SETS

Think about it...

Look at the information about proof sets. What factors do you think would increase or decrease the value of a coin?

Amount of payment for a partially destroyed bill

FULL VALUE if $\frac{3}{5}$ or more is left

HALF VALUE if between $\frac{2}{5}$ and $\frac{3}{5}$ is left

NOTHING if less than $\frac{2}{5}$ is left

A dollar bill has a 16-mo. life expectancy

Exploring Decimals

OBJECTIVE:
To explore decimals using decimal square models.

MATERIALS

- Decimal squares or graph paper

- Math journal to record work

▼ You can use decimal squares to model numbers less than 1.

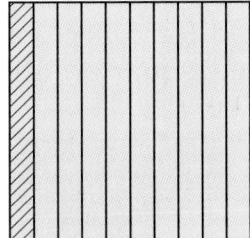

The figure above is divided into ten regions. Each region is called a *tenth*.

1. How many tenths are shaded? How many are not shaded?

2. *Model* each number using tenths' squares or graph paper.

   a. two tenths   **b.** four tenths

   c. all but three tenths   **d.** all but seven tenths

▼ In the figure below, each tenth has been divided into ten squares. Each small square is called a *hundredth*.

3. How many hundredths' are shaded? How many are not shaded?

4. *Model* each number using hundredths' squares or graph paper.

   a. five hundredths

   b. twenty-six hundredths

   c. all but twenty hundredths

   d. all but ninety hundredths

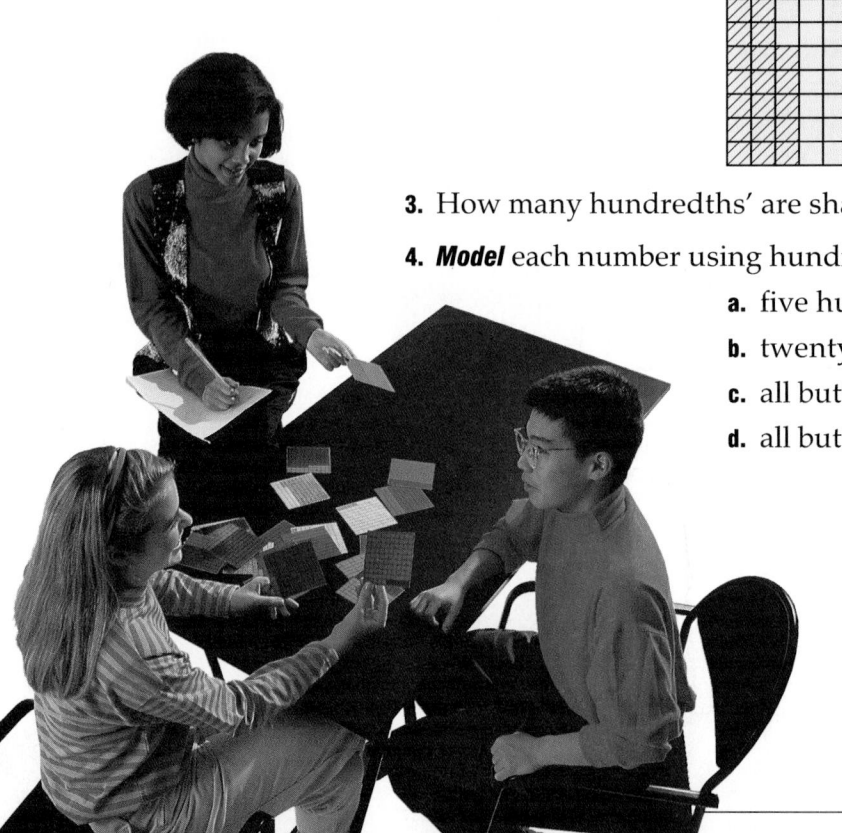

▼   You can use decimal squares to find equivalent decimals.

5. a. *Model* three tenths using tenths' squares.

b. *Model* thirty hundredths using hundredths' squares.

c. *Describe* and discuss how your models are different. How are they alike?

d. Is three tenths equivalent to thirty hundredths? Explain.

▼   You can write each phrase as a decimal.

three tenths = 0.3   thirty hundredths = 0.30

Because three tenths and thirty hundredths are less than one, we write a zero as a place holder to the left of the *decimal point*.

6. *Write* each phrase as a decimal.

a. four tenths   **b.** nine tenths   **c.** six tenths

d. eighty-nine hundredths   **e.** fifteen hundredths

7. *Determine* which of the following pairs of decimals are equivalent. *Model* the decimals to justify your answer.

a. three hundredths, three tenths

b. seventy hundredths, seven tenths

c. 0.5, 0.57   **d.** 0.4, 0.40

▼   You can compare decimals using models.

   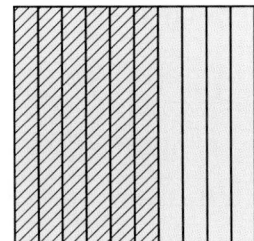

8. *Write* the decimals represented by the two models above.

a. Which decimal is greater? How do you know?

b. Write an inequality using the decimals.

9. *Determine* which decimal is greater. *Model* the decimals to justify your answer.

a. 0.60 or 0.65   **b.** 0.5 or 0.47

10. How can you compare the two decimals without using a model?

OBJECTIVE:
To compare, round,
and order decimals.

3-1 Decimals

▼ The smallest flowering plant is a water plant called duckweed. Its length is 0.02 in. and its width is 0.008 in. The length is read as *two hundredths* and the width is read as *eight thousandths*. The place value chart below shows how to read and write decimals.

hundred thousands	ten thousands	thousands	hundreds	tens	ones	and	tenths	hundredths	thousandths	ten-thousandths	hundred-thousandths
				7	2	.	9				
					0	.	0	0	2		

You read and write these decimals as *seventy-two and nine tenths* and *two thousandths.*

FLASHBACK

Zeros added to the right of a decimal do not change its value.
0.4 = 0.40 = 0.400

▼ You can graph decimals on a number line.

Example 1 **Give the decimal name for each point.**

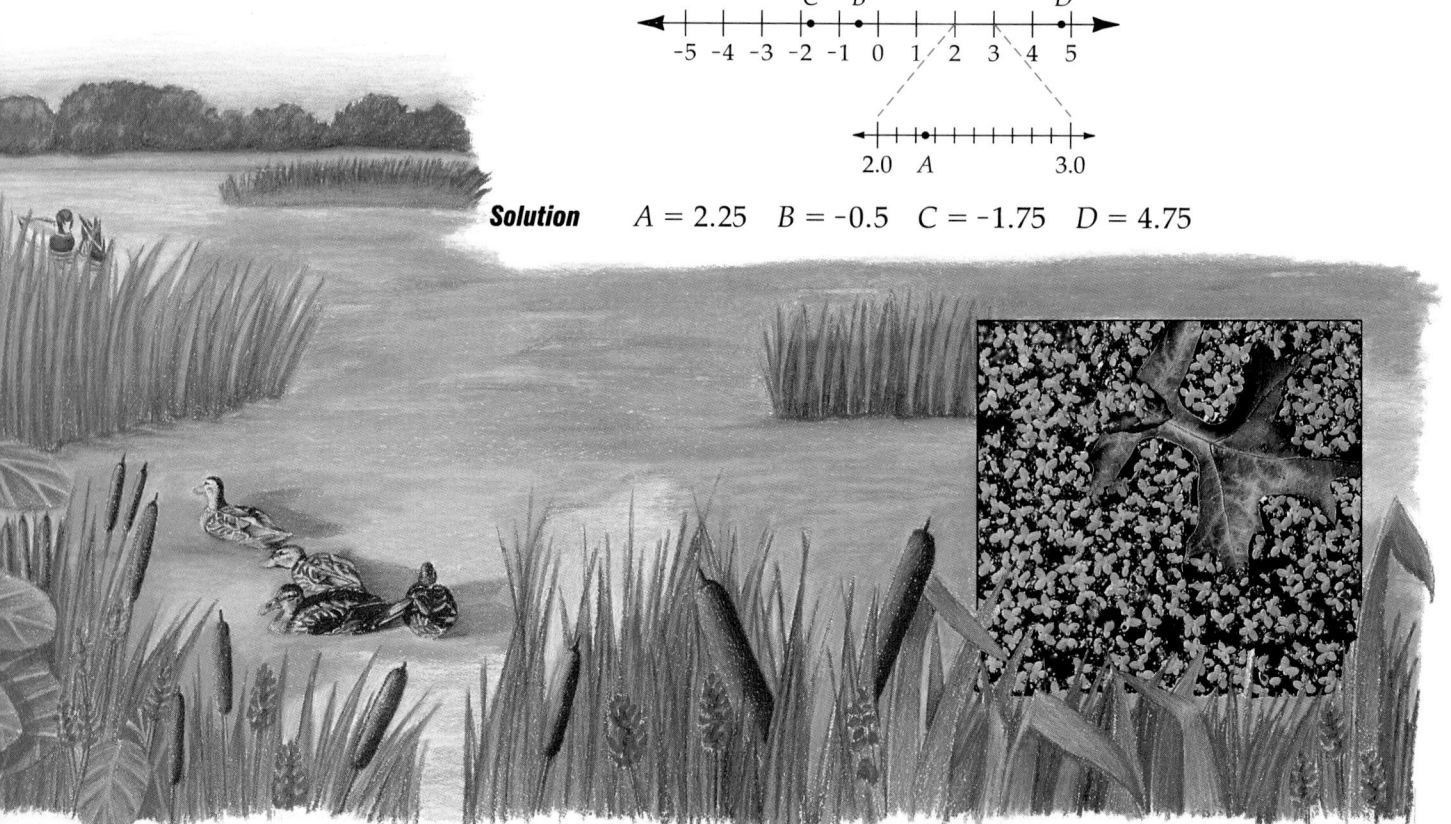

Solution $A = 2.25$ $B = -0.5$ $C = -1.75$ $D = 4.75$

▼ You can compare decimal numbers using a model.

Example 2   **Compare the decimals 0.57 and 0.69 using a model.**

Solution

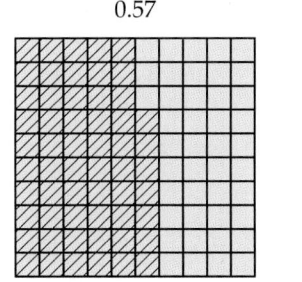

0.57   0.69

The area covered by 0.69 is greater than the area covered by 0.57. Therefore, 0.57 < 0.69.

▼ You can compare decimals using a number line.

Example 3   **Compare the decimals ⁻0.5 and ⁻1.25.**

Solution   On a horizontal number line, numbers are greater as you move to the right.

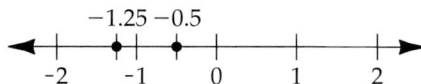

−1.25 −0.5

-2   -1   0   1   2

The decimal ⁻0.5 is to the right of ⁻1.25. So, ⁻1.25 < ⁻0.5.

THINK How could you compare the decimals 0.53 and 0.64 using the > symbol?

▼ You can compare decimals by comparing corresponding digits.

Example 4   Does Wilmington or Philadelphia receive more rain? Use the data at the right.

Solution   Compare the decimals 41.38 and 41.42.

The digits in the tens' and ones' places are the same. Compare the tenths' digits: 4 > 3. So, 41.42 > 41.38. Therefore, Philadelphia receives more rain.

▼ You can arrange decimals in order.

Example 5   **Order the cities according to their level of rainfall. Use the data at the right.**

Solution   Compare the decimals 41.84, 41.42, 41.76, and 41.38.

The digits in the tens' and ones' places are the same. Compare the tenths' digits: 8 > 7 > 4 > 3. Therefore, 41.84 > 41.76 > 41.42 > 41.38. So, the cities ranked from greatest rainfall to least rainfall are: Baltimore, Raleigh, Philadelphia, and Wilmington.

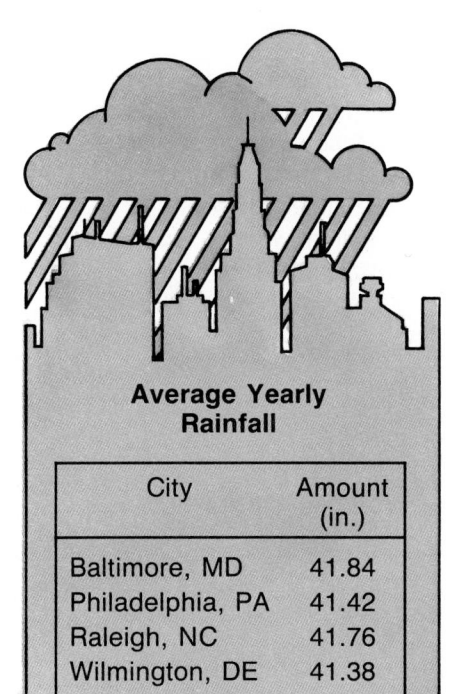

Average Yearly Rainfall

City	Amount (in.)
Baltimore, MD	41.84
Philadelphia, PA	41.42
Raleigh, NC	41.76
Wilmington, DE	41.38

THINK AND DISCUSS

1. The digit in the tenths' place of one decimal is less than the digit in the tenths' place of another decimal. Is the first decimal always less than the second? Explain.

2. Is 0.2 equivalent to 0.02? Why or why not?

3. For all nonzero decimals, is $a > -a$, where $-a$ is the opposite of a? Why or why not?

NOTES & QUOTES

Simon Stevin (1548–1620), a Flemish mathematician, extended decimal places to the right in 1585. Up until the sixteenth century, fractions were used instead of decimals.

CLASS EXERCISES

Write the decimal represented by the shaded region.

1. 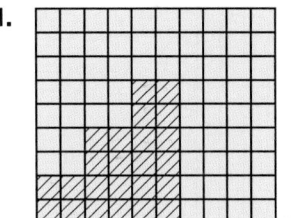 *0.3*

2. 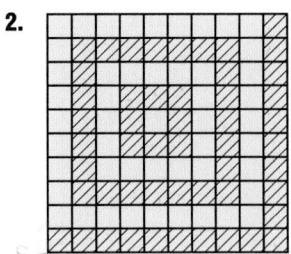 *0.52*

Read each decimal.

3. 0.42 *42 hundredths*

4. 0.006

5. 4.801 *4 and 801 thousandths*

6. 28.036

Write each decimal.

7. One kilometer is equivalent to *six hundred twenty-one thousandths* miles. *0.621*

8. One fathom is *one and eight thousand two hundred eighty-eight ten-thousandths* meters. *1.8288*

Give the decimal name for each point.

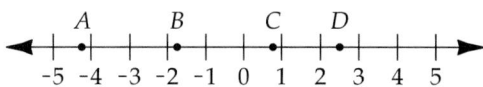

A   B   C   D

-5 -4 -3 -2 -1   0   1   2   3   4   5

9. A *-4.1*

10. B

11. C *0.9*

12. D

Compare using >, <, or =.

13. 0.6 *>* 0.06

14. 0.84 ▨ 0.840

15. -3.862 *<* -3.859

WRITTEN EXERCISES

Write each decimal in words.

1. 0.83 *eighty-three hundredths*

2. 2.006

3. 392.9075 *three hundred ninety 2 and 9 thousand 75/10000*

4. 0.00003

Write each decimal.

5. The world speed record for a motorcycle is *five hundred twelve and seventy-three hundredths* kilometers per hour. *512.73*

6. The smallest book published has a length and width of *one and four tenths* millimeters.

Graph each decimal on a number line.

7. 3.6   **8.** -2.9   **9.** |-9.65| **10.** -|-2.75|

Compare. Use >, <, or =.

11. 3.8 ▨ 3.08   **12.** -5.6 ▨ -5.60   **13.** -3.9 ▨ -3.9000

14. -0.05 ▨ 0.005   **15.** -1.01 ▨ -1.101   **16.** 4.721 ▨ 4.712

17. |-0.6| ▨ |-0.09| **18.** 24.3333 ▨ 24.33333

Order from greatest to least.

19. 4.05, 4.5, 4.049   **20.** -4.98, -4.908, -4.098

21. 0.03, 0.030008, 3.003, 0.30, 0.3002

22. 27.618, 27.681, -54.091, 27.6801, 54.0900

Write a decimal between the given decimals.

23. 1.5 and 2.5   **24.** 0.6 and 0.9   **25.** 23.5 and 23.6

26. -0.5 and 0   **27.** -0.678 and -0.679   **28.** 3.57 and 3.58

Round each decimal to the indicated place.

▼▼ *SAMPLE* Round 45.68 to the nearest tenth.

The number to the right of the tenths' place is eight. Since eight is greater than five, we increase the number in the tenths' place by one. So, 45.68 rounded to the nearest tenth is 45.7.

29. 0.76, nearest tenth   **30.** -9.095, nearest hundredth

31. 0.3632, nearest hundredth   **32.** 4.9677, nearest thousandth

33. 365,987.092, nearest integer   **34.** 5.9999, nearest thousandth

35. *DATA FILE 10 (pp. 404–405)* Order from least to greatest the home range in acres required by the species listed.

36. Order the data in the chart at the right from fastest winning speed to slowest winning speed of the Indianapolis 500.

37. Use the decimal 47.8364 to answer the following questions.

     a. Will interchanging the tenths' and hundredths' digits produce a greater or lesser decimal?

     b. Will interchanging the hundredths' and thousandths' digits produce a greater or lesser decimal?

     c. When will interchanging digits produce a greater decimal?

38. Which decimals make each equation true?

     a. $|x| = 0.03$ **b.** $|a| = 80.123$ **c.** $|x| = |-3.86|$

39. *WRITE* Use absolute value to describe a method for deciding when one negative number is greater than another.

MIXED REVIEW

Solve each equation.

1. -3 + x = -8

2. y - 12 = -9

3. -9y = 81

4. $\frac{a}{-3} = 15$

5. What are two whole numbers that when added give you 10 and when multiplied give you 21?

6. Mario had *d* dollars in his bank account and wrote a check for $40. He then had $182 in his account. Write an equation for this problem and solve for *d*.

Winning Speeds for Indianapolis 500

Year	Speed (mi/h)
1979	158.899
1980	142.862
1981	139.029
1982	162.029
1983	162.117
1984	162.962
1985	152.982
1986	170.722
1987	162.175
1988	144.809
1989	167.581
1990	185.984
1991	176.457
1992	134.477

OBJECTIVE:
To estimate sums,
differences, products,
and quotients of
decimals.

3-2 *Estimating with Decimals*

▼ You can estimate using decimals.

Example 1 **Estimate how much of each square is shaded. Write each estimate using decimal numbers.**

a. 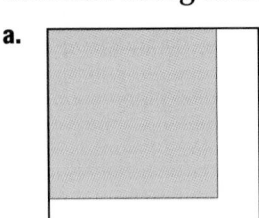   b.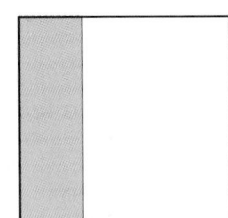

Solution **a.** 0.7   **b.** 0.3

▼ You can use *rounding* to estimate the sum, difference, product, or quotient of decimals.

Example 2 **Estimate the sum of 4.75, 2.2, and 9.86.**

Solution

$4.75 + 2.2 + 9.86$	Round to the nearest integer.
$\approx 5 + 2 + 10$	Add.
≈ 17	

The sum is approximately 17.

Example 3 **One orange contains 1.4 g of protein. Estimate how many grams of protein 2.5 oranges contain.**

Solution

$1.4 \cdot 2.5$	Round to the nearest integer.
$\approx 1 \cdot 3$	Multiply.
≈ 3	

There are approximately 3 g of protein in 2.5 oranges.

▼ You can use *front-end estimation* when adding decimals. This method is especially helpful when estimating dollar amounts.

Front-end Estimation	To use front-end estimation:
	1. Add the front-end digits.
	2. Adjust by estimating the sum of the remaining digits.
	3. Add the two values.

Example 4   The junior class held three events to raise money for their prom. Estimate their profit.

Solution   **1.** Add front-end digits. $100 + 500 + 300$ is 900.

   2. Adjust. $56.35 + 42.75 \approx 100.$
               $100 + 72.70 \approx 170.$

   3. Add the two values. $900 + 170 = 1{,}070$

The class earned a profit of about $1,070.

Junior Class Fund Raisers

Event	Profit
Bake Sale	$156.35
Car Wash	$542.75
Raffle	$372.70

▼ You can estimate quotients using *compatible numbers*.

Compatible Numbers	Compatible numbers are two numbers that are easy to divide mentally.

Example 5   Taylor earns $13.75 per hour. Last week he earned $385. About how many hours did he work?

Solution $385 \div 13.75$
   $\approx 390 \div 13$ **Use compatible numbers 390 and 13.**
   ≈ 30

Taylor worked approximately 30 h.

CLASS EXERCISES

Estimate using rounding.

1. $-86.5 + 45.99 + (-91.21)$ ~130   **2.** $858.32 - 281.319$

3. $-92.81 \cdot (-48.33)$ 4500   **4.** $318.09 \div 48.33$

Estimate using front-end estimation.

5. $\$3.75 + \$14.10 + \$23.30$ **6.** $\$88.50 - \$29.60$
   34

Estimate using compatible numbers.

7. $0.8622 \div (-4)$ **8.** $-43.08 \div 5.21$

3-2 Estimating with Decimals   **105**

THINK AND DISCUSS

1. In what situations would an estimate be preferred over an exact amount?

2. What is the quotient of $4{,}702 \div 81$ using rounding?

3. How could you get an estimate of the range within which an answer will fall?

Estimate the shaded region using decimal numbers.

1.

2.

.25

330

.23

Estimate using rounding.

3. 34.99 + 27.302 *60*

4. 416.98 − 28.301

5. 0.08 · 400

6. 16.092 · 9.21

7. 329.08 · (-56) *330 ÷ 60*

8. $378.90 ÷ 42

9. 45.87 + 35.912 + 126.08 + 83.234 *300*

10. 0.043 + 0.0591 + 0.088 + 0.0241 + 0.0473

Estimate using front-end estimation.

11. 3.57 + 2.95 + 1.681 *9*

12. $7.25 + $9.08 + $6.88 + $3.69

13. 9.033 + 2.82 + 6.18 + 8.953 *27*

14. $9.01 + $8.94 + $5.63 + $6.48 + $8.23

Estimate using compatible numbers.

15. 9.392 ÷ 2.9 *3.23*

16. -483.09 ÷ 72.3

17. -7.75 ÷ -1.98 *4*

18. $32.43 ÷ $4.68

19. 0.5863 ÷ 26.2 *0*

20. $78.92 ÷ $8.55

Estimate using the technique which seems best.

21. $43.92 · 54 *2,000*

22. -0.98 + (-0.34) + 0.66

23. 0.083 + 0.149 *0*

24. 416.98 − 28.301

25. -18.9 · (-12.02) *2,400*

26. 293.7 ÷ 42.03

27. -2.843 + (-5.022) + (-8.45) + (-3.991) *24.001*

28. 21.88 + (-9.88) + 35.901 + 28.03 + (-13.99) + 26.92

Use estimation to place the decimal point in each answer.

29. 7.008 · 3.2 = 224256

30. 98.003 (-1.8) = -1764054

31. 106.88 ÷ 0.5 = 21376

32. 14.39 + 6.132 + 0.684 = 21206

33. 94.02 + 9.011 + 18.34 + (-11.8) = 109571

34. 115.67 + 88.09 + (-113.6) = 9016

35. 46.872 · 0.05 + 65 = 673436

36. 0.5 · 200.8 ÷ 2 = 502

MIXED REVIEW

Round to the nearest hundredth.

1. -0.883

2. 4.1253

Find each product or quotient.

3. -3 · (-8)

4. 12 ÷ (-6)

5. -9 · 12

6. -88 ÷ (-8)

Solve.

7. Jon baked three pans of muffins. Each pan holds 12 muffins. How many muffins did Jon bake?

ESTIMATION Use the table at the right to solve.

37. Can biscuits, puppy food, and a collar be purchased for $10?

38. Amy has $20 to buy a collar and a leash. With the remaining money, what is the greatest number of toys she can buy?

39. Todd is in the check-out line with all six items and only $17. What is the least expensive item he can put back and still pay for the other five items?

Items to Buy for the New Puppy

Item	Cost
Leash	$6.37
Biscuits	$1.79
Food	$3.29
Collar	$4.37
Toy	$2.19
Shampoo	$1.97

Use the article below to answer each question.

English, Anyone?

In 1989, the *Oxford English Dictionary* was revised for the second time. It was dedicated to Queen Elizabeth II. The dictionary consists of 20 volumes. It contains 21,728 pages and defines 616,500 words. The longest word defined is *pneumonoultramicro-scopicsilicovolcanoconiosis*, a disease of the lungs. The 20 volumes weigh almost 138 lb and take up 45 in. of shelf space. Printing the first 10,000 sets of the dictionary required 6,243 lb of ink. The *Oxford English Dictionary* can be purchased for $2,500.

40. a. About how many pages are contained in each volume?

   b. Estimate the weight of each volume.

   c. About how many inches of shelf would 6 volumes require?

   d. What is the approximate value of each volume?

Solve.

41. Extra-large eggs cost $1.19 per dozen. Medium eggs cost $.98 per dozen. Estimate the savings on 10 dozen eggs if you buy medium instead of extra-large.

42. Grapes cost $1.14/lb. Estimate the cost of three bunches weighing 1.3 lb, 2.6 lb, and 1.9 lb. Explain your method.

43. The cost of sending a package is $23.80. Estimate the cost of sending 156 such packages.

44. *DATA FILE 4 (pp. 138–139)* About how many children are born in a minute? an hour? a day? a week? a month? a year?

45. *DATA FILE 9 (pp. 360–361)* Estimate the total number of yards at St. Andrew's golf club for holes one through nine.

46. *WRITE* Explain how you might estimate the total cost of your purchases at the grocery store.

3-3 Expressions with Decimals

▼ The number of hours a growing child should sleep each night depends on the child's age. You can find the recommended number of hours by evaluating the expression $17 - 0.5a$, where a is the child's age.

To find the number of hours a 7-year-old child should sleep in a night, evaluate the expression $17 - 0.5a$ for $a = 7$.

$$17 - 0.5a = 17 - 0.5(7)$$
$$= 17 \boxed{-} 0.5 \boxed{\times} 7 \boxed{=} 13.5$$

Replace a with 7.

A 7-year-old child should sleep 13.5 h.

▼ Expressions may contain more than one variable.

Example 1 Use a calculator to evaluate $3.7a - 4b$ for $a = -3.2$ and $b = 6.1$.

Solution
$$3.7a - 4b = 3.7(-3.2) - 4(6.1)$$
$$3.7 \boxed{\times} 3.2 \boxed{+/-} \boxed{-} 4 \boxed{\times} 6.1 \boxed{=} -36.24$$

Replace a with -3.2 and b with 6.1.

▼ You can simplify expressions involving decimals by using properties of addition and multiplication.

Example 2 Simplify $3.1x + 2.3y + 8.4x$.

Solution

$3.1x + 2.3y + 8.4x$	
$3.1x + 8.4x + 2.3y$	commutative property
$(3.1x + 8.4x) + 2.3y$	associative property
$(3.1 + 8.4)x + 2.3y$	distributive property
$11.5x + 2.3y$	Add coefficients.

Evaluate each expression for $x = -1.9$ and $y = 2.4$.

1. $2.5x$ _-4.75_   **2.** $3 - y$ **3.** $x - y$ _-4.3_

4. $x + y$ **5.** $-x + 2y$ _6.7_   **6.** $3x - 8 + 2y$

Simplify each expression.

7. $2.1x + 3.4x$ _5.5x_   **8.** $-1.2(7.9b)$ **9.** $-2(4.3a - 2.2a)$

10. $-9.4 + 3a + 16.25$ **11.** $2.03b + 0.08a - 4.211b$ _2.036_

1. Would the expression given at the beginning of this lesson work for a 36-year-old person? Explain.

2. For what numbers will the expression $-3.6w$ be positive? negative?

3. What does it mean to evaluate an expression?

WRITTEN EXERCISES

Use the expression $17 - 0.5a$ to find the number of hours a child of each age should sleep each day.

1. $a = 11$ _7_   **2.** $a = 1.5$ **3.** $a = 5.25$ _6_   **4.** $a = 0.5$

Evaluate each expression for $x = 3.9$.

5. $-2x$ _-7.8_   **6.** $28.07 - x$ **7.** $58.89 \div x$ _15.1_   **8.** $x + (-4.03)$

Evaluate each expression for $m = -7.06$ and $n = 13.2$.

9. $m + n$ _6.14_   **10.** $m - n$ **11.** $2m - 6.5$ _8_

12. $-4m + 18.234$ **13.** $-2m - 3n$ **14.** $1.5(m + n)$

15. $\frac{m - 4n}{4}$ _6_   **16.** $\frac{3m - 2n}{-118.95}$ **17.** $\frac{-n - m}{4 \div (3 - 1)}$

MENTAL MATH Evaluate each expression.

18. $-100x$ for $x = -3.882$ **19.** $50x$ for $x = -0.5$

20. $x + y$ for $x = -8.22$ and $y = 8.22$

21. $2x - y$ for $x = -4.22$ and $y = 12$

CALCULATOR Evaluate each expression.

22. $3.98x$ for $x = -42.91$ **23.** $\frac{x}{9.8}$ for $x = 29.4098$

24. $22.8x - 15.4y$ for $x = -0.092$ and $y = 21.3$.

25. $(x - a) - (y - b)$ for $a = -4.96$, $b = 12.03$, $x = -2.3$, and $y = 7$.

26. $x(2.703y - 5.6701)$ for $x = 0.051$ and $y = -3.682$.

Simplify.

27. $2.4(-16.84w)$ **28.** $-5.23x \cdot 14.1$ **29.** $8.24m \div (-10.3)$

30. $3.78(4.01m) \div 0.02$ **31.** $-5.6x + 13.2x$

MIXED REVIEW

Estimate each answer.

1. $\$35.98 + \$155.23$

2. $56,000.3 - 38,412.9$

3. $-5.33 \cdot 0.992$

4. $0.9341 \div 8.1$

Solve each equation.

5. $x + (-23) = -19$

6. $20 = a - 15$

Solve.

7. Ricky bought 9 pencils at $.23 per pencil and 5 pens at $.37 per pen. How much more did he spend on pencils than pens?

32. $0.007m - 0.04m$

33. $9.0578a - 4(6.057 - 2.0473a)$

34. $\dfrac{-4.79x + 1.79x}{0.003}$

35. $\dfrac{(0.2x)(4.98) - 37.2x}{20}$

ESTIMATION **Estimate the value if $x = 38.953$ and $y = 127.06$.**

36. $x + y$ **37.** $x - y$ **38.** $3x - 10$ **39.** $\dfrac{y}{x}$

40. ***WRITE*** a paragraph explaining how to find the value of $3.8 + (-7.1)x$ if x is -4.25. Tell how to find the sign as well as the numerical value of the answer.

Solve.

5.2a − 1.48

3a − 0.2

4.1a + 0.6

41. a. Express the perimeter of the triangle in simplest form.

    b. What is the perimeter if $a = 8.401$?

42. The interest earned on a bank account is $0.087x$, where x is the amount in the account. Find the interest earned on $10,000.

43. The selling price of a videotape is $c + 3.24$, where c is the cost of the tape. Find the selling price of a tape costing $18.43.

Critical Thinking

EXPLORING PATTERNS IN DIVISION

1. Follow the steps in the division problem below. Continue the pattern and describe what happens.

0.2 and 1.6		Begin with two numbers.
1.6 ÷ 0.2 = 8		Divide the second by the first.
8 ÷ 1.6 = 5		Divide the quotient by the number above it.
5 ÷ 8 = 0.625		Continue dividing each quotient by the number above it for four
0.625 ÷ 5 = 0.125		more divisions.

2. Follow the same pattern with the numbers 2.5 and 2. Describe your results. Did it matter that you began with a decimal number and a whole number?

3. Follow the pattern with the numbers 2 and -0.2. Describe your results. Did it matter that you began with a positive and a negative number?

4. ***Write*** a paragraph describing this pattern.

OBJECTIVE:
To solve addition and subtraction equations involving decimals.

3-4 Addition and Subtraction Equations

▼ Earth is 93 million miles from the sun. Mars is 141.71 million miles from the sun. What is the minimum number of miles from Earth to Mars? Let m represent the minimum number of millions of miles from Earth to Mars. You can describe the situation by the following equation.

$$93 + m = 141.71$$

You can solve this equation by using the subtraction property of equality.

$$93 + m = 141.71$$
$$93 + m - 93 = 141.71 - 93 \qquad \text{Subtract 93 from each}$$
$$m = 48.71 \qquad \text{side.}$$

Check $93 + m = 141.71$
$93 \boxed{+} 48.71 \boxed{=} 141.71 \checkmark$ Replace m with 48.71.

The minimum distance from Earth to Mars is 48.71 million miles.

▼ You can solve an equation involving subtraction by using the addition property of equality.

Example 1 Solve $n - 29.1 = {-30.85}$ and graph the solution.

Solution
$$n - 29.1 = {-30.85}$$
$$n - 29.1 + 29.1 = {-30.85} + 29.1 \qquad \text{Add 29.1 to each side.}$$
$$n = {-1.75}$$

Check $n - 29.1 = {-30.85}$
$-1.75 \boxed{-} 29.1 \boxed{=} {-30.85} \checkmark$ Replace n with -1.75.

Graph -1.75 on the number line.

$$\xleftarrow{\qquad} \overset{\textstyle\bullet}{\underset{-2\ \ -1\ \ \ 0\ \ \ 1}{|\quad|\quad|\quad|}} \xrightarrow{\qquad}$$

THINK How could you use estimation to decide if the solution is reasonable?

We know more about Mars than any other planet except Earth. Most of our information is from Mariner 9.

RESEARCH Find out when the Mariner 9 orbited Mars and what some of its findings were.

▼ You can also use opposites to solve addition and subtraction equations.

Example 2 Solve $5 = a + 2.02$ by using opposites.

Solution
$$5 = a + 2.02$$
$$5 + (-2.02) = a + 2.02 + (-2.02) \quad \text{Add } -2.02 \text{ to each side.}$$
$$2.98 = a + 0$$
$$2.98 = a \quad \text{The check is left for you.}$$

CLASS EXERCISES

THINK AND DISCUSS

1. Will the solution to $38.1 + x = 14.07$ be greater than or less than zero? Explain.

2. What properties would you need to use to show $a - 15.23 + 15.23$ is equivalent to a?

State the first step in solving each equation.

1. $x + 4.9 = 18.8$

2. $a - 19.2 = 24$

3. $12.703 = n - 16.51$

4. $3.78 + m = 0$

Solve each addition equation.

5. $a + 0.98 = 0.24$

6. $-4.26 + c = 22.991$

Solve each subtraction equation.

7. $m - 43.23 = 80.9$

8. $-0.09 = a - 0.224$

WRITTEN EXERCISES

Solve each equation using the subtraction property.

1. $x + 4.38 = -9.011$

2. $0 = y + 39.4$

3. $1.77 + c = 3.4$

4. $-8.32 = y + 3.211$

Solve each equation using opposites.

5. $0.402 + c = 0.0322$

6. $s + 12.85 = 4.9$

7. $-0.021 = x + 0.0023$

8. $309.462 + y = 500$

Solve each equation using the addition property.

9. $11.03 = w - 1.55$

10. $8.9 = b - 8.88$

11. $-3.98 = m - 5.012$

12. $u - 400.32 = -912.268$

Solve each equation using opposites.

13. $w + (-5.07) = 8.24$

14. $0 = n - 29.335$

15. $-45.02 = m - 21.9$

16. $t + (-0.66) = 0.66$

MENTAL MATH Solve each equation.

17. $a - 2.33 = 2.33$

18. $t + 45.023 = 45.023$

19. $9.45 = w + 7.45$

20. $m - 0.003 = 18.29$

CALCULATOR Solve each equation.

21. $60{,}000 = w - 392.0034$

22. $-0.34264 + x = 5.920154$

23. $m + 912.87 = 920.001$

24. $t - 982.0012 = -893.20876$

Solve each equation using any method. Graph each solution.

25. $y + 0.05 = 3.95$

26. $t - 79.4 = -46.7$

27. $m - (-0.88) = 0.88$

28. $-23.9 = x + 14.1$

29. $p - 18.8 = -24.2$

30. $k + (-35.9) = 24.8$

31. $48.003 + r = 50.903$

32. $b + 6.7 = 9.90$

33. $w - (-0.34) = 0.74$

34. $t - 43.8 = 0$

35. $b + 16 = -43.9$

36. $-1.78 = v - 0.98$

Use the article below and the table at the right to answer each question.

pHase Out Acid Rain

The pH scale measures the acidity of a substance. The scale ranges from most acidic, 0, to least acidic, 14. Many plants and animals can only survive in a narrow range of acidity. Acid rain changes the acidity level of the water and soil where organisms live. As a result, many plants and animals can be severely damaged or even die. Studies have shown that industry and motor vehicle emissions are among the major sources of acid rain.

Average PH Levels

Item	PH
Unpolluted rain	5.6
Acid rain	4.6
Grapes	4.1
Grapefruit	3.2
Orange	3.5
Apple	3.1
Sea water	7.36–8.21
Milk	6.5

37. a. Order the fruits from most acidic to least acidic.

b. Hydrangeas have blue flowers when grown in soil with a pH level less than 7. The flowers are pink when grown in soil with a pH level greater than 7. What color would the flowers be if grown in soil having the same pH level as grapes?

c. PROJECT Research smog, another form of air pollution. Write a short paragraph. Be sure to include the pH level.

Solve each equation for a.

38. $a - b = c$

39. $b = a + c$

40. $-c + a = b$

41. Find values for x and y that solve both equations:
$x + y = 0.03$ and $x - y = 0.13$.

42. a. Are the equations $1.7x + 2.4 = 1.5$ and $17x + 24 = 15$ equivalent? How do you know?

   b. **WRITE** a procedure for changing a decimal equation into one with integers. Show how your method would work for any of the equations in this lesson.

Write an equation for each sentence. Solve.

43. Fifty-eight thousandths less than some number is equal to fifty-eight hundredths. Find the number.

44. Seven and three hundred thirty-nine thousandths equals five and one hundred seventy-eight thousandths more than some number. Find the number.

45. One and ninety-nine ten-thousandths equals two more than some number. Find the number.

46. Eight hundred ninety-two and thirty-two hundredths less a number is equal to one thousand, four hundred eleven and twelve thousandths. Find the number.

47. Three plus some number equals eight and sixteen hundredths. Find the number.

TEST YOURSELF

Compare. Write $>$, $<$, or $=$.

1. 3.088 ▧ 3.808   **2.** 2.3 ▧ 2.300   **3.** -4.23 ▧ -4.991

Round to the nearest tenth.

4. -9.65   **5.** 4.3088   **6.** 17.952

Estimate the value of each expression.

7. $0.8823 \div 3$ **8.** $5.9 \cdot 3.88$ **9.** $437.02 - 188.54$

Evaluate if $x = 5.8$ and $y = -2.3$.

10. xy **11.** $x - 2$ **12.** $-2y - x$

Simplify.

13. $2.99 + x + (-3.08)$ **14.** $-3.55y - 9.01y$

Solve each equation.

15. $x - 9.09 = -15.8$ **16.** $24.011 = y + 23.9$

3-5 *Multiplication and Division Equations*

▼ On average, an oil well produces 16.8 barrels each day. In how many days will it produce 184.8 barrels? If we represent the number of days by the variable d, we can write an equation.

$$16.8d = 184.8$$

You can solve this equation using the division property of equality.

$$16.8d = 184.8$$
$$\frac{16.8d}{16.8} = \frac{184.8}{16.8}$$
$$d = 11$$

Divide both sides by 16.8, the coefficient of *d*.

Check $16.8d = 184.8$
$16.8(11) = 184.8$ **Replace *d* with 11.**
$184.8 = 184.8$ ✓

It will take 11 days to produce 184.8 barrels of oil.

▼ You can solve equations involving division by using the multiplication property of equality.

Example 1 Solve $\frac{x}{2.1} = -0.9$ and graph the solution.

Solution

$$\frac{x}{2.1} = -0.9$$
$$2.1\left(\frac{x}{2.1}\right) = -0.9(2.1)$$ **Multiply both sides by 2.1.**
$$x = -1.89$$

Check Use estimation to see if the solution is reasonable.

$$\frac{x}{2.1} = -0.9$$ **Round each decimal to the nearest integer.**

$$\approx \frac{-2}{2} = -1$$ **Since -1 is close to -0.9, the solution is reasonable.**

Graph -1.89 on the number line.

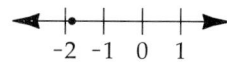

▼ You may need to round an answer when solving a problem.

Example 2 **Use a calculator to solve $3.98x = 470$. Round to the nearest tenth.**

Solution $470 \div 3.98 = 118.09045$
≈ 118.1 Round to the nearest tenth.

CLASS EXERCISES

State the first step in solving each equation.

1. $0.7x = -0.63$ **2.** $\frac{y}{0.6} = 1.2$

3. $1.5 = d \div 15$ **4.** $-1.2 = -0.4m$

Solve each multiplication equation.

5. $-0.5y = -0.73$ **6.** $0.8x = 0.448$

7. $-540 = -1.8t$ **8.** $13.133 = -2.3w$

Solve each division equation.

9. $\frac{y}{2.3} = -4.8$ **10.** $0.97 = \frac{c}{-2}$

11. $2{,}390 = z \div 0.033$ **12.** $\frac{m}{0.19} = -492.05$

WRITTEN EXERCISES

Solve using the division property of equality.

1. $2x = -4.88$ **2.** $-0.3y = 7.53$

3. $6.4x = 0.2816$ **4.** $-0.00051z = -2.026791$

5. $1.92 = 1.6s$ **6.** $0.004m = 0.12$

7. $3.17n = 135.042$ **8.** $2.21 = 1.7w$

Solve using the multiplication property of equality.

9. $\frac{n}{1.7} = 0.22$ **10.** $\frac{k}{2.01} = 0.04$ **11.** $4.5 = m \div (-3.3)$

12. $-33.04 = \frac{z}{-0.03}$ **13.** $-0.45 = x \div 12$ **14.** $\frac{m}{0.89} = 3{,}488$

15. $\frac{w}{-3.4} = -25.5$ **16.** $12{,}088.25 = \frac{v}{3.8}$ **17.** $\frac{c}{12.56} = 0.245$

MENTAL MATH Solve each equation.

18. $0.7x = 2.8$ **19.** $\frac{m}{7.08} = -100$ **20.** $6 = a \div 1.5$

21. $10,000r = 483.08$ **22.** $0.55t = 0.0055$

CALCULATOR Solve each equation. Round each answer to the nearest tenth.

23. $0.46x = 89.23$ **24.** $45.08t = -2,917.335$

25. $-0.93 = 0.0221z$ **26.** $-9.03m = 499,812.4$

CALCULATOR Solve each equation. Round each answer to the nearest hundredth.

27. $4.55x = 43.225$ **28.** $\frac{m}{7.08} = -35.992$

29. $y \div 84.6 = 2.79$ **30.** $90.43n = -298.0113$

Solve each equation using any method. Graph each solution.

31. $0.9 = \frac{m}{41}$ **32.** $100t = -45$

33. $\frac{z}{-0.4} = 0.5$ **34.** $3.94z = -21.67$

35. $t \div 0.4 = -15$ **36.** $-99.252 = -8.271r$

Solve each equation for x.

37. $x \div y = z$ **38.** $xz = y$ **39.** $y = \frac{x}{z}$

Write an equation for each sentence. Solve.

40. The quotient of some number t divided by -4.5 equals 200.6. Find the number.

41. Four thousandths times some number is equal to eighty-eight hundredths. Find the number.

42. The cost of an adult ticket is c. The cost of eight adult tickets is \$71.60. What is the price of one ticket?

43. A number divided by -2.35 is equal to 400.9. Find the number.

44. Nineteen and five thousand five hundred twenty-five ten thousandths is the same as five and five tenths times some number. Find the number.

45. **WRITE** Write a paragraph explaining how to use estimation to place the decimal point in a multiplication or division computation.

46. Find values for x and y that satisfy both equations: $xy = 0.42$ and $x + y = 1.3$.

47. ***COMPUTER*** A school needs to buy a minimum of 2,000 pencils, 1,000 pens, 500 notebooks, and 150 reams of paper. The budget cannot exceed $3,000.

	A	B	C	D
1	Item	Quantity	Unit Price	Total
2	Pencils		0.10	=B2*C2
3	Pens		0.50	=B3*C3
4	Notebooks		2.25	=B4*C4
5	Paper (ream)		4.75	=B5*C5
6			TOTAL	=SUM(D2:D5)
7				

a. What is the least amount the school can spend?

b. Suppose the remaining money is spent on notebooks. How many more notebooks can be bought?

c. Suppose the price of pencils increases to $.15 and the price of a ream of paper drops to $4.55. Can the school afford its minimum amount of supplies?

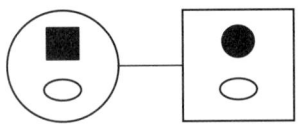

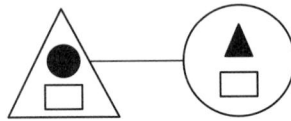

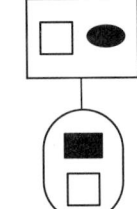

Critical Thinking

EXPLORING LOGICAL FAMILIES

The figures at the left are called Quipps.

1. What are the distinguishing characteristics of a Quipp?

2. Which of the following are Quipps?

a.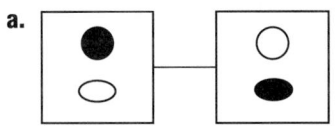

b.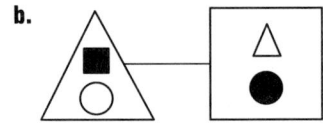

c.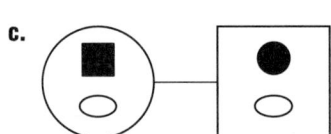

d.

3. Create two of your own Quipps.

4. Create a logical family consisting of three members. Trade with a classmate to see if they can determine the distinguishing characteristic.

Practice

Write each decimal in words.

1. 0.67   **2.** 2.90   **3.** 637.0004   **4.** 0.00007

Write each decimal.

5. two hundred fifteen and seventy-four hundredths

6. six and eight tenths

7. forty-two and seven hundredths

8. five hundred four thousandths

Compare using >, <, or =.

9. 9.9 ▨ 9.09   **10.** -4.2 ▨ -4.20   **11.** -8.600 ▨ 8.6

12. -0.06 ▨ 0.006   **13.** -3.47 ▨ -3.547   **14.** 85.706 ▨ 85.7

15. |-0.2| ▨ |0.2| **16.** |8.9| ▨ |-10.7| **17.** 0.36 ▨ 0.3600

Estimate using rounding, front-end estimation, or compatible numbers.

18. $57.96 · 45   **19.** 95.27 ÷ 5.2

20. 0.029 + 0.999   **21.** 0.98 ÷ 1.03

22. -490.6 − 25.302   **23.** $10.25 + $36.32 + $9.05

Evaluate each expression for $x = -2.3$ and $y = 8.92$.

24. $-x - y$ **25.** $y - (-x)$ **26.** $4x + 7.39$

27. $-10y - 4.8$ **28.** $x - 4y$ **29.** $-6.3(x + y)$

30. $\dfrac{x - y + y}{-x}$ **31.** $\dfrac{-x - y}{x + y}$ **32.** $-x + y$

Solve each equation.

33. $x + 0.25 = 8$ **34.** $\dfrac{w}{18} = -2.7$ **35.** $a - (-42.4) = 42.4$

36. $n \div 8 = 3.02$ **37.** $0.008z = 0.24$ **38.** $m - (-9.4) = 0$

39. $-0.96 = 0.8t$ **40.** $0.59 + s = -1.0$ **41.** $y - 42.76 = -0.05$

42. $-132 = 66i$ **43.** $25j = -100.9$ **44.** $d - (-0.04) = 0.74$

45. $8x = -15.52$ **46.** $-100.05 = c + 5$ **47.** $-18.07 - r = 0.5$

Solve each equation for m.

48. $m + n = p$ **49.** $n = \dfrac{m}{p}$ **50.** $p + m = n$

51. $p = \dfrac{n}{m}$ **52.** $n - m = p$ **53.** $mn = p$

Exploring Data in Tables

■ A sports camp holds track and field trials on the first day of camp. The table below shows the performance of the campers on several different measures.

MATERIALS

• Math journal to record work

Name	Running 50 m	Running 1,500 m	Jumping (cm) high jump	Jumping (cm) long jump	Shooting basketball throw (out of 20 shots)
Aimee	8.6 s	12 min 25 s	127.0	325.1	10
Barbara	10.3 s	15 min 49 s	106.7	299.7	8
Dwayne	8.5 s	12 min 4 s	139.7	365.8	15
Floyd	8.7 s	10 min 54 s	124.5	327.7	14
Hannah	7.9 s	11 min 0 s	129.6	294.6	17
Isaiah	8.1 s	10 min 37 s	116.8	342.9	15
Jane	8.4 s	10 min 37 s	132.1	332.7	15
Manuel	8.7 s	13 min 9 s	121.9	309.9	13
Nancy	7.4 s	9 min 4 s	139.2	364.8	18
Sydney	8.6 s	12 min 2 s	127.1	327.7	11
Tran	8.4 s	12 min 46 s	137.1	340.4	16
Warren	7.7 s	8 min 18 s	134.6	368.4	18

1. a. Which event best demonstrates the campers' endurance?

 b. Which best demonstrates the campers' speed? Which best demonstrates accuracy?

 c. Does the camper who runs the 50 m fastest also run the 1,500 m fastest? Is this true for the second-fastest runner? the third fastest? Is there a relationship between the time run in the 50 m and the time run in the 1,500 m? Explain.

 d. Who would you consider a better runner, the camper who runs the 50 m faster or the 1,500 m faster? Why?

2. a. Who is the highest jumper? Who is the longest jumper?

 b. Is the highest jumper the same person as the longest jumper? Is this always true? Explain.

 c. Is there a relationship between the best runners and the best jumpers? Explain.

3. Who is the best shooter? Is there a relationship between the campers' running, jumping, and shooting skills?

4. Who is the fastest runner in the 50-m run?

 a. List the campers in order from fastest to slowest.

 b. Could you list the campers in order from slowest to fastest? Explain.

c. Tran and Jane both ran the 50 m in 8.4 s. In what order will you list them? Explain.

d. In what order will you list Aimee, Sydney, Floyd, and Manuel?

5. Continue to list the campers in order in the 1,500-m run, the high jump, the long jump, and the basketball throw.

6. In the jumping events, could you order the campers from shortest distance jumped to longest distance jumped? Explain.

■ The camp uses the results to assign campers to teams. The first event is a 2,000-m relay race between three evenly matched teams.

7. How far must each camper run in the relay race?

8. Who do you think would run best in the relay race: the campers who ran the fastest in the 50 m or the 1,500 m? Why?

a. Would you take the campers' jumping and basketball throw scores into consideration? Explain.

b. What other factors will help you decide who should be on the three evenly matched teams?

9. Make a list of the three teams. **Compare** with another group.

■ The second sporting event is a basketball game. There will be two evenly matched teams, with five on a team. The two extra campers will rotate positions in the game.

10. The two guards need to be the fastest runners, and they also must have good endurance and shooting skills. Who would you pick? Why?

11. The center doesn't need to be as fast as the guards. It's important for the center to be a good shooter and jumper, and have good endurance. Who would you pick? Why?

12. The two forwards need to have excellent endurance and strength. They need to be good jumpers and they must be fast. Who would you pick? Why?

13. Make a list of the two teams. **Compare** with another group.

14. Did you choose the same teams the other groups chose? **Describe** and discuss why you made your choices. Is there one right answer?

15. **Summarize** For which event was it easiest to pick the teams? Why?

OBJECTIVE:
To explore the uses
of a computer data
base.

Exploring Data Bases

■ A *data base* is a collection of information. The data is usually arranged in rows and columns and can be rearranged in any order. Below is a data base of names and addresses.

Name	Street	City	State	Zip Code
Smith, Greg	123 Main St.	Tucson	Arizona	85726
Cruz, Maria	97 South St.	Burbank	California	91505
Chien, Janice	876 Water St.	Honolulu	Hawaii	96820
Jones, Carl	8 Division St.	Albany	New York	12266

MATERIALS

• Paper

• Computer and data base software (optional)

• Math journal to record work

1. In what order are the data arranged? How else can they be arranged?

2. Suppose you wanted to arrange the data in alphabetical order. Show the results on a sheet of paper (by last name).

3. Suppose you need to update the data base with this information.

Name	Street	City	State	Zip Code
Ales, George	24 Broadway	Dallas	Texas	74356
Costa, Anna	568 Beach St.	Miami	Florida	48576

Write the new data base in alphabetical order by name.

■ In a data base, each column is known as a *field*. Each row is known as a *record*.

DATAPOINT

Notice that the first field contains words and the other two contain numbers.

4. Look at the data base shown below.

Student	Grade	Grade Point Average
Adams, Karen	8	3.2
Eng, Charles	9	3.5
Garcia, Fran	8	3.4
Mitchell, Dennis	9	3.2

a. How many fields are there? What are they?

b. How many records are there?

5. The first field showing the student names could have been made up of two separate fields. What are they?

6. Arrange the data base by grade point average. Show the results of the new data base on a sheet of paper.

DATAPOINT

When you sort a data base, you rearrange the data in a particular order.

7. How did you sort the two records with the same grade point average in Question 6? In what other way could you have sorted them?

■ You enter data in a data base one record at a time. For example, the record below is from a data base that is used to keep track of inventory at a shoe store.

```
ITEM : Boots
QUANTITY (PAIRS) : 150
NEXT SHIPMENT DUE : Dec 10
```

8. How many field names are there? What are they?

■ After entering several records, you can view the data in rows and columns. This is part of the shoe store data base in column form.

Item	Quantity (on hand)	Next Shipment Due
Boots	150	Dec 10
Running shoes	34	Dec 5
Sandals	25	Dec 17
Loafers	16	Dec 28

9. Suppose it is the morning of December 1. On average, the store sells nine pairs of running shoes per day. Will there be enough before the next shipment arrives, which is scheduled for an evening delivery?

10. *Explore* What other fields could you add to this data base to keep an accurate count of the inventory? Share your results with your classmates.

■ A data base can help you keep track of information.

11. *PROJECT* Make up your own data base. Choose any data that you like. Use the following questions as a guide.

a. What kind of information will your data base contain?

b. How many fields will the data base have? Have you included every field needed to make a useful data base?

c. How will you gather the data? Is the data simple to obtain?

d. How many records will your data base have? Is there a limit to the number of records it can have?

e. How often do you need to update the data? How will you know when you need to change the data for a particular field?

f. How will you arrange the data?

g. If you have a computer and data base software, create a data base.

DATAPOINT

When you receive a form letter with your name on it, you know your name is part of a data base.

DATAPOINT

Here are some suggestions for data bases:

• Books that you own

• Any of the data found in the chapter Data Files

• CDs and records

• Address book

Problem Solving Practice

PROBLEM SOLVING STRATEGIES

Look for a Pattern
Guess and Test
Simplify the Problem
Make an Organized List
Work Backwards
Account for All Possibilities
Make a Table
Write an Equation
Solve by Graphing
Draw a Diagram
Make a Model
Solve Another Way
Simulate the Problem

Solve each problem. The list at the left shows some possible strategies you can use.

1. Lisa is slower than Christine, but faster than Nicole. Nicole is slower than Lisa, but faster than Jo Ann. Order the girls from fastest to slowest.

2. The convenience store sells pens for $0.05, $0.10, and $0.15. List all the ways that Joseph can spend exactly $0.45 on pens.

3. Miguel lives 2.75 mi from school. His friend lives 1.35 mi from school in the opposite direction. If Miguel rode his bicycle to school, visited his friend, and then returned home, how many miles would he ride in all?

4. Janet purchased three spools of thread at $.89 each, five yards of material at $2.29 per yard, one sewing pattern at $1.89, and five yards of ribbon at $.45 per yard. She gave the cashier a $20 bill. How much change should she receive? How many more spools of thread can she buy with her change?

5. **DATA FILE 2 (pp. 52–53)** Maria hears thunder 1.4 s after she sees a flash of lightning. Paul hears thunder 2.2 s after he sees a flash of lightning. How many meters farther from the lightning is Paul than Maria?

6. An art teacher is purchasing sketch paper for her students. She can buy a 12-package box with 300 sheets per package for $72.00, or a 6-package box with 200 sheets of paper per package for $30.00. Which is the better purchase?

7. The alarm on a clock rang at 6:00 A.M. It continued ringing at regular intervals. At 6:08 the buzzer was on, at 6:10 the buzzer was off, at 6:16 it was on, and at 6:48 it was on. Will the buzzer be on or off at 7:52? at 9:18?

8. Five women ran the 100-m dash. Their times were 11.6 s, 10.2 s, 9.9 s, 10.6 s, and 11.9 s. What was the average time? Is 10.787 s above or below this average?

9. It is 398 mi from Buffalo to Boston. Nan leaves in her car and drives at an average of 47 mi/h. Barb leaves in her car and drives at an average rate of 55 mi/h. If they both drive straight through, how many hours to the nearest tenth will Barb have to wait for Nan to arrive?

10. June earns d dollars per hour for the first 40 h of work each week and $1.5d$ for each hour over 40. June worked 46 hours and 15 minutes last week. How much did she earn if d equals 5?

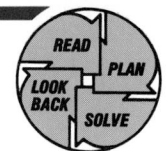

3-6 *Using the Metric System*

OBJECTIVE:
To solve density problems using metric units.

■ The units of length, mass, and capacity in the metric system are related by water. A cube measuring 1 cm on each side has a volume of 1 cm³. This is equivalent to 1 mL. A centimeter cube filled with water has a mass of 1 g.

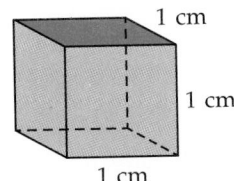

The *density* of a substance is its mass per cubic centimeter. The density of water is 1 g/cm³. Substances with densities greater than 1 g/cm³ sink in water. Substances with densities less than 1 g/cm³ float in water.

■ You can use the following formula to find density.

$$\text{density } (d) = \frac{\text{mass}}{\text{volume}}$$

FLASHBACK

Prefix	Meaning
milli-	0.001
centi-	0.01
deci-	0.10
kilo-	1,000

Symbol	
cm	centimeter
cm³	cubic centimeter
g	gram
L	liter
mL	milliliter

Example 1   A block of wood has a volume of 20.52 cm³. Its mass is 17 g. Find the density of the block in grams per cubic centimeter. Tell whether the block will float or sink in water.

Solution $\text{density} = \frac{\text{mass}}{\text{volume}}$ **Use the formula for density.**

$d = 17 \div 20.52$ **Substitute values.**

$\approx 0.83 \text{ g/cm}^3$

Since the density of the block is less than that of water, the block will float in water.

■ You can use the formula to find mass when density and volume are known or volume when density and mass are known.

Example 2   A diamond has a density of 3.5 g/cm³ and a volume of 0.5 cm³. Find the mass of the diamond.

Solution $\text{density} = \frac{\text{mass}}{\text{volume}}$ **Use the formula for density.**

$3.5 = \frac{m}{0.5}$ **Substitute values.**

$0.5 \cdot 3.5 = \frac{m}{0.5} \cdot 0.5$ **Multiply each side by 0.5.**

$m = 1.75 \text{ g}$

CLASS EXERCISES

Masses of Metal Blocks (V = 8 cm³)	
aluminum	22 g
gold	154.4 g
silver	84 g

Use the *DATA* at the left. Round to the nearest tenth.

1. Find the density of aluminum, gold, and silver.

2. How much greater is the mass of a cubic centimeter of gold than a cubic centimeter of silver?

3. How many milliliters of water equal the mass of a block of gold having a volume of 125 cm³?

Use a CALCULATOR where appropriate.

WRITTEN EXERCISES

Densities of Selected Substances (g/cm³)	
gasoline	0.68
ethyl alcohol	0.79
rubber	1.34
iron	7.9
copper	8.9
mercury	13.5

Use the *DATA* at the left to solve each problem. Express answers to the nearest tenth.

1. What is the mass in grams of a lump of copper that has a volume of 7.5 cm³?

2. What is the volume in cubic centimeters of a block of iron that has a mass of 100 g?

3. Which of the substances listed will float in water? in mercury?

■■■■■■ ■■ Decision Making ■ **DECISION MAKING** ■ Decision Making ■ Decision Making ■ Decision Making ■

USING THE METRIC SYSTEM

■ COLLECT DATA

1. Test various objects in the classroom to find out which ones sink and which float in water. First guess, then check your guess by putting the object in water to see whether it sinks or floats. Keep a record of your results.

Object	Substance	Sink	Float

2. Why would it not be good to have objects such as pencils or sponges on your list to use for Exercise 1?

■ ANALYZE DATA

Suppose you have a ruler, a clear drinking glass with vertical sides and flat bottom, a scale that measures in grams, and several marbles of the same size.

4. Will copper float in mercury? in ethyl alcohol?

5. How much greater is the mass of 1,000 mL of ethyl alcohol than 1,000 mL of gasoline?

6. What is the mass in kilograms of 20.75 L of gasoline?

Solve.

7. Water expands when it freezes. If you freeze 11 cm³ of water, you will get about 12 cm³ of ice. Use this fact to find the density of ice.

8. **ESTIMATION** A gasoline truck is going to take on 1,289 L more gasoline. The density of gasoline is 0.68 g/cm³. About how many kilograms more is the truck going to take on?

9. A silver necklace has a volume of 100 cm³. Use the chart on page 126 to find the density. Then find the mass of the necklace.

10. **PROJECT** Find out what the relationship is between density and buoyancy. Explain why a steel ocean liner floats in water.

Ice floats since it is less dense than water. How does this relate to the fact that 0.9 of an iceberg is below the surface of the water?

■ *Decision Making* ■ *Decision Making* ■ *Decision Making* ■ *Decision Making* ■ *Decision Making* ■ *Decision Making* ■

3. If you pour some water in the glass, how can you use the materials to find out how many cubic centimeters of space the water occupies?

4. If you take several marbles, how can you use the materials to find how many cubic centimeters of space they occupy?

■ **MAKE DECISIONS**

5. Decide how you could use the materials listed in the *Analyze Data* section to find the density of the glass from which the marbles are made. Describe your plan in a paragraph. Use diagrams as needed to explain your plan.

6. Decide how you could use the materials to find the density of something that will not sink in water. Describe your plan in a paragraph.

3-7 Using Formulas

▼ You can use the number of chirps a cricket makes in a minute to estimate the temperature in degrees Fahrenheit.

Chirps per min (n)	Temperature (°F)
12	40°
16	41°
20	42°
24	43°
28	44°

▼ A science class conducted an experiment. For five weekdays the class counted the number of chirps their pet cricket made in a minute. They recorded this information in a table, along with the actual temperature. The class observed that if they divided the number of chirps per minute (n) by 4, and added 37, the result was the temperature in degrees Fahrenheit (F). A student wrote the following *formula* on the board.

$$F = \frac{n}{4} + 37$$

Formula	A formula is an equation that shows the relationship between two or more variables.

THINK Will the formula $F = \frac{n}{4} + 37$ ever produce negative temperatures? Why or why not?

Example 1 If the class counted 32 cricket chirps in 1 min, what is the Fahrenheit temperature?

Solution 1. Write the formula. $F = \frac{n}{4} + 37$

2. Substitute values. $F = \frac{32}{4} + 37$

$= 45$

The Fahrenheit temperature is 45°.

▼ The *distance formula* is an important and useful formula. The distance formula is $d = rt$, where d is the distance, r is the rate at which you travel, and t is the time you spend traveling.

Example 2 **Find the distance Sara traveled if she drove 8.5 h at an average speed (rate) of 49.7 mi/h.**

Solution 1. Write the formula. $d = rt$

2. Substitute values. $d = (49.7)(8.5)$
$d = 422.45$

Sara traveled 422.45 mi.

▼ You can write a formula in more than one way.

Example 3 State whether each formula is equivalent to $d = rt$. If so, state what was done to each side of the equation.

a. $\frac{d}{r} = t$ b. $d + r = t$

Solution a. yes; both sides divided by r b. no

▼ Batting average is determined by the formula $a = \frac{h}{n}$, where a is the batting average, h is the number of hits made, and n is the number of times up at bat.

Example 4 Use a calculator to solve. How many hits did Babe Ruth make if he was up at bat 8,399 times and had a batting average of 0.342?

Solution **1.** Write the formula. $a = \frac{h}{n}$

2. Substitute values. $0.342 = \frac{h}{8,399}$

3. Multiply. $0.342 \boxed{\times} 8,399 \boxed{=} 2,872.458$

4. Round to nearest integer. $2,872$

Babe Ruth made 2,872 hits.

CLASS EXERCISES

Solve. Use the appropriate formula.

1. Find the temperature if a cricket chirps 44 times per minute.

2. A snail travels about 0.14 cm/s. To find how far the snail travels, in what unit should time be given? How far will the snail travel in one hour?

3. The spine-tailed swift is the fastest creature alive. It has been clocked traveling at 106.25 mi/h. At that speed, how far could the swift travel in 2.5 h?

4. Florence Griffith-Joyner holds the American record in the 100-m run. She ran in 10.49 s. If she could continue at this rate, how long would it take her to run 1,000 m?

THINK AND DISCUSS

1. What would you expect to happen to the number of times a cricket would chirp in 1 min if the temperature increased?

2. How many variables are there in the distance formula? To use the formula, how many variables must equal a number?

3. How are formulas and equations alike? How are they different?

WRITTEN EXERCISES

Use the formula $F = \frac{n}{4} + 37$, where n is the number of cricket chirps per minute, to find the temperature in degrees Fahrenheit.

1. $n = 200$ **2.** $n = 288$ **3.** $n = 60$ **4.** $n = 104$

Use the formula $d = rt$ to find the distance traveled.

5. $r = 38.5$ mi/h, $t = 12.1$ h   **6.** $r = 280$ mi/h, $t = 9.75$ h

7. $r = 213$ cm/s, $t = 8$ s   **8.** $r = 0.08$ ft/s, $t = 2.5$ h

9. ***ESTIMATE*** The first plane to fly faster than the speed of sound was piloted by Chuck Yeager. He flew at 670 mi/h. About how far could he fly in 9.8 h? Is this estimate high or low?

10. The solar probe *Helios B* reached a speed of 149,125 mi/h. Suppose the probe traveled at this speed for its entire journey. About how long would it take to reach the sun, which is 93,000,000 mi away? Round to the nearest hundredth.

Major League Lifetime Leading Batters

Player	At bats *(n)*	Hits *(h)*
Browning	4,795	1,664
Hornsby	8,173	2,930
Cobb	11,436	4,190
Delahanty	7,493	2,593
Keeler	8,570	2,955
Jackson	4,981	1,774

Use the formula $a = \frac{h}{n}$ and the table at the left to determine each batting average. Round answers to the nearest thousandth.

11. Browning   12. Hornsby   13. Cobb

14. Delahanty   15. Keeler   16. Jackson

17. Order each player from highest batting average to lowest.

Use the formula $w = rt + 1.5r \cdot o$ to find a person's wage. Let w be the wage, r the hourly rate of pay, t the number of hours worked at the hourly rate, and o the number of hours worked overtime. Round to the nearest cent where necessary.

	Worker	*r*	*t*	*o*
18.	Jeremy	6.20	40	8
19.	Elaine	9.75	40	10
20.	Eric	4.35	38	3
21.	Serena	12.55	41	9

CALCULATOR Use the formula $F = 1.8C + 32$ to find the temperature in degrees Fahrenheit, where C is the temperature in degrees Celsius.

22. Find the Fahrenheit temperature corresponding to 58°C, the highest recorded temperature in the world.

23. Find the Fahrenheit temperature corresponding to -89°C, the lowest recorded temperature in the world.

Bread and Milk

Years	Loaf of bread	Half gal of milk
1890s	$.03	$.14
1930s	$.09	$.28
1950s	$.18	$.48
1970s	$.24	$.66
1980s	$1.39	$1.09

Use the formula $I = N - O$ to find the price increase. Let I be the price increase, N the new price, and O the old price. Use the chart at the left to answer the following questions.

24. What was the price increase of a half gallon of milk from the 1930s to the 1970s?

25. What was the price increase of a half gallon of milk from the 1970s to the 1980s?

26. How much more was spent in the 1970s than in the 1890s for 5 loaves of bread and 6 half gallons of milk?

Use the formula $k = \frac{t \cdot w}{1,000}$ to find the number of kilowatt hours used. Let k = kilowatt hours, t = hours, and w = watts. Refer to the data at the right.

27. a. How many kilowatt hours are used by cooking in the microwave for 0.75 h per evening for one week? How many are used by cooking in a conventional oven?

   b. How much would each cost if the electric company charges $.04 per kilowatt hour?

   c. What is the savings over a year by using a microwave instead of a conventional oven?

28. Are more kilowatt hours used by working on the computer for 2.25 h or by drying your hair for 0.25 h?

29. PROJECT Find the local rate for electricity. Develop a plan for cutting back on your use of electricity. Determine how much money you would save in a year.

30. Gross earnings g is equal to net pay p, plus deductions d. Write a formula to find gross earnings. Solve the formula for d.

31. The voltage, V, across any part of a circuit is the product of the current I and the resistance R. Write a formula to find the voltage. Solve the formula for R.

Appliance	Watts of electricity used by appliance
Television	145
Computer	155
Hair dryer	1,000
Microwave	1,500
Conventional oven	12,200
Stereo	109
VCR	45

TEST YOURSELF

CALCULATOR Solve each equation.

1. $16.9376 = 6.32s$ **2.** $-8.125 = \frac{b}{0.023}$ **3.** $n \div (-7.34) = -2.758$

4. $\frac{w}{105.1} = 0.7352$ **5.** $0.0812g = 3.248$ **6.** $10.20807 = 3.369c$

Solve for variable a.

7. $c = ab$ **8.** $a + c = b$ **9.** $c = \frac{a}{b}$

Use the formula $d = rt$.

10. a. Find d when $r = 48$ and $t = 3.5$.

   b. Find t when $d = 693$ and $r = 63$.

   c. Hal drove a distance of 562 mi at an average rate of 58 mi/h. How many hours, to the nearest tenth, did Hal drive?

MIXED REVIEW
Solve each equation.
1. $-3n = 92.01$

2. $\frac{x}{0.43} = -5.2$

3. $10,000 \cdot 0.0034 = k$

Evaluate when $x = -3.1$ and $y = 10.7$.

4. $4x - 2y$

5. $x(-12 + y)$

Solve.

6. A stockholder owns 1,000 shares of stock. She receives a dividend of $.65 per share four times per year. How much is the yearly dividend?

3-8 *Simplify the Problem*

OBJECTIVE:
To solve problems by using a simpler problem.

■   Sometimes when you solve a problem, it helps to first solve one or more simpler problems that have similar conditions.

PROBLEM

A typesetter needs one piece of type for each digit in the page numbers of the book. How many pieces of type will the printer need to number pages 1–476?

SOLUTION

READD ▶ What do you want to find?

number of pieces of type required to number pages 1–476

PLAN ▶ Simplify the problem.

How many one-digit page numbers are there?	pages 1–9 9 pieces of type
How many two-digit page numbers are there?	pages 10–99 90 two-digit page numbers $90 \cdot 2 = 180$ pieces of type
How many three-digit page numbers are there?	pages 100–476 377 three-digit pages $377 \cdot 3 = 1{,}131$ pieces of type

SOLVE ▶ Add the numbers for the pieces of type required for the one-, two-, and three-digit numbers.

$$9 + 180 + 1{,}131 = 1{,}320$$

LOOK BACK ▶ Interpret your answer.
The printer will need 1,320 pieces of type to number pages 1–476.

CLASS EXERCISES

1. Janetta numbered the pages in her diary from 1 to 58. How many digits did she write?

2. A printer used 330 pieces of type to number the pages of a book. The first page is numbered one. How many numbered pages are in the book?

3. A book is opened. The product of the two page numbers that appear is 272. What are the two page numbers?

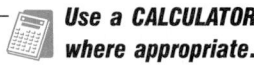
WRITTEN EXERCISES

Solve by using simpler problems.

1. A printer is typesetting a book. He needs one piece of type for each digit in the page numbers of the book. How many twos will he need to number pages 1–232?

2. One pastry chef can decorate 12 cupcakes in 14 min. The bakery receives an order for 672 cupcakes. To the nearest hour, how long will it take four pastry chefs to decorate the cupcakes?

Solve using any strategy.

3. A city has a population of 586,785. The area is 25 mi^2. Find the population per square mile.

4. To accommodate a wheelchair, Tom installed counter tops that were 0.72 ft lower than the original ones in his house. The new counter tops are 2.5 ft high. How high were the original counter tops?

5. The houses on Wheeler Avenue are numbered 1 to 138. How many house numbers contain at least one digit 6?

6. On their way to a concert, Betsy, Meg, and Mary each took turns driving. Mary drove seven miles more than Meg. Meg drove three times as far as Betsy. Betsy drove nine miles. How many total miles did they drive?

7. The carnival has two types of rides for children. Each airplane seats 4 children and each spaceship seats 6 children. Altogether there are 24 airplanes and spaceships that seat a total of 128 children. How many of each are there?

8. Jim has $8 in his savings account. Jo has $12 in her savings account. Jim will add $1 to his account each week and Jo will add $3 to her account each week. After how many weeks will Jo's account have twice as much money as Jim's?

9. Julie had to number 275 dance tickets by hand. How many digits did she have to write?

10. Aaron can work 21.5 h per week at the gas station for $5.75/h. He could also work 27.75 h per week at the convenience store for $4.80/h. At which job will he earn more per week?

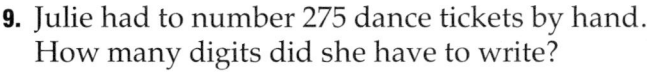

Chapter 3 Review

True or false? If false, change the underlined word(s) to make the statement true.

1. You read and write the decimal 0.05 as five <u>tenths</u>.
2. The steps for front-end estimation are:
   - Add the front-end digits.
   - Adjust by <u>finding</u> the sum of the remaining digits.
   - Add these two values.
3. <u>Compatible numbers</u> are used to make estimation easier.
4. To rank a set of data, write the data <u>in order</u>.
5. A formula is an equation that shows the relationship between two or more <u>numbers</u>.

Comparing Decimals   3-1

To compare decimals, think of a number line. The decimal farther to the right is the greater decimal.

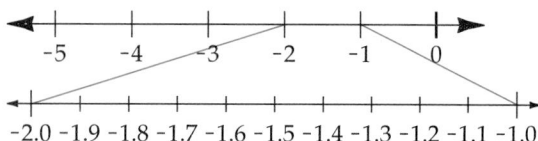

Compare using <, >, or =.

6. −1.9 ▨ −1.3   7. −1.0 ▨ −1   8. −2.0 ▨ −2.3   9. −1.25 ▨ −1.2   10. −1.4 ▨ 1.4

Estimating Decimals   3-2

To estimate decimals, use rounding, front-end estimation, or compatible numbers.

ESTIMATION Estimate each shaded region using decimals.

11. 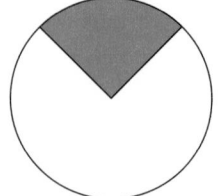   12. 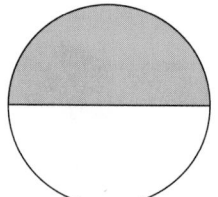   13.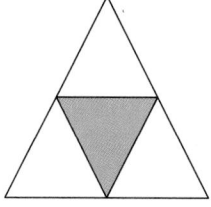

ESTIMATION Write the technique that seems best. Then estimate.

14. 9.21 + 28.301 + 16.092   15. 2.531 ÷ 3.915   16. $6.15 + $9.28 + $3.69 + $5.90

17. 0.7845 ÷ 4.3   18. 12,909.3 − 3.899   19. $48.75 + $22.95 + $7.50

Evaluating Expressions with Decimals

3-3

To evaluate an algebraic expression, substitute a number for the variable(s), and simplify. Follow order of operations.

Evaluate each expression for $x = -0.5$ and $y = 0.3$.

20. $2x + 3y - 1$ **21.** $4(x + 2y)$ **22.** $|2x| - 3y + 4$ **23.** $5x - 5y + |-15|$

Simplifying Expressions with Decimals

3-3

To simplify a variable expression, combine like terms and eliminate parentheses using the distributive property.

Simplify each expression.

24. $7.5a - 3(a - 0.2) + 2.5$ **25.** $\frac{(0.8x)(2.5) + 3x}{10}$ **26.** $5a + a(3 + b) + 12ab$

Solving Equations

3-4, 3-5

To solve an equation, use the properties of equality.

Solve.

27. $-3.8x = 19$ **28.** $m + 2.45 = 3$ **29.** $\frac{k}{3.5} = 2.1$ **30.** $y - 2.9 = 8.1$

31. $5.3t = 53$ **32.** $a - (-5.6) = 12.9$ **33.** $14w = 42$ **34.** $r + 7 = 10.8$

Using Formulas

3-7

To use a formula, substitute the known value(s) of the variable(s), and solve for the unknown value.

Use the formula $d = rt$. Solve.

35. $r = 55$ mi/h, $t = 3.5$ h   **36.** $r = 30$ ft/s, $t = 1.2$ s   **37.** $d = 365$ km, $r = 40$ km/h

Problem Solving

3-6, 3-8

To solve a problem that has difficult numbers, use simpler numbers to see *how* to solve the problem. Then use the real data.

Solve.

38. An auditorium was filled to capacity with 3,500 people. An usher estimated there were 3 adults for every 2 children. How many children were in the auditorium?

39. Use the table on page 126. Find the density of silver. Use the formula density $= \frac{\text{mass}}{\text{volume}}$.

Chapter 3 Test

Write each decimal.

1. four hundred fifty-three and fifty-nine hundredths
2. three and seven thousand eight hundred fifty-three ten thousandths

Compare using >, <, or =.

3. 0.125 ■ 0.333
4. -7.656 ■ -0.777
5. 0.1001 ■ 0.10010
6. 0.05 ■ -0.05

Round each decimal to the indicated place.

7. 2.547 nearest tenth
8. 8.029 nearest hundredth
9. 159.809 nearest unit
10. -0.352 nearest tenth
11. 0.295 nearest tenth
12. 14.953 nearest tenth

ESTIMATION **Estimate the shaded region using decimal numbers.**

13.

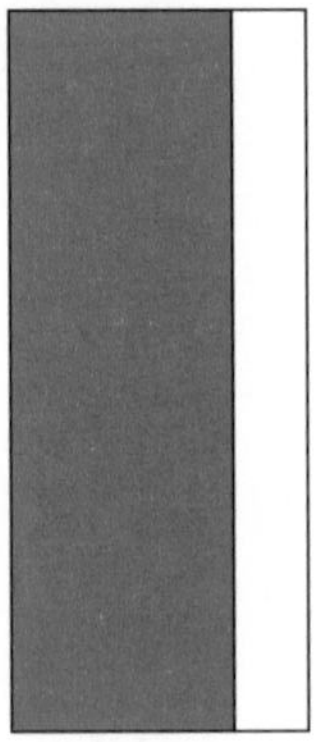

14.

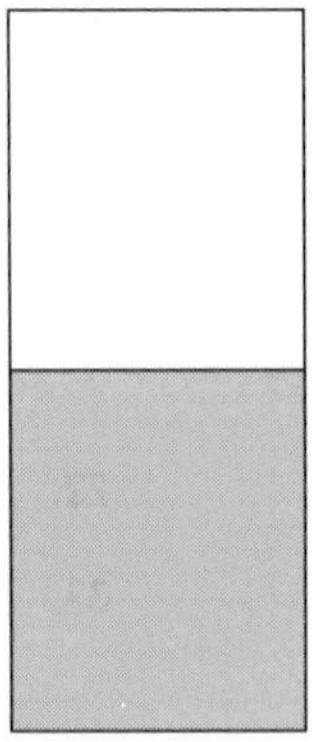

15.

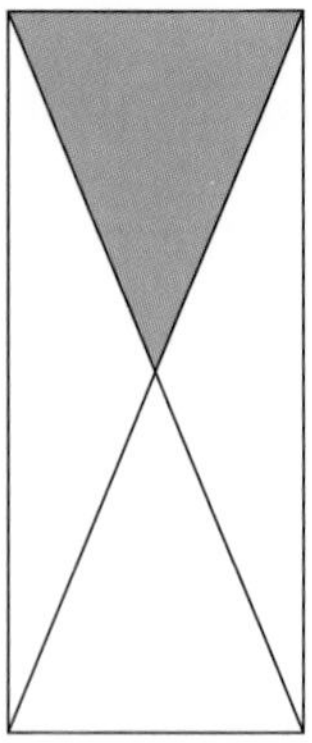

ESTIMATION **Use the technique that seems best.**

16. \$24.79 ÷ 62
17. -45.167 ÷ 13.92
18. 9.057 − 4.01
19. 31.597 ÷ 19
20. 300.5 + 98.2
21. 17.63 − 3.58
22. 1.78 + 2.12 + 18.49 + 7.23 + (-5.54)

Solve each equation.

23. $m + 7.8 = 5.2$
24. $z - (-8.9) = -2.1$
25. $-4r = -2.8$
26. $\frac{h}{11} = -0.3$
27. $a + (-3.24) = 5.8$
28. $\frac{x}{-0.2} = 0.6$
29. $0.9k = 2.7$
30. $b - 9.4 = 0.6$

Use the formula $C = \frac{(F - 32)}{1.8}$ to find the Celsius temperature where F is the temperature in degrees Fahrenheit. Round to the nearest tenth.

31. 86°F
32. 50°F
33. 4°F
34. 65°F
35. -10°F

Solve.

36. A city has a population of 8,276,386 people. The area is 359 mi². What is the population per square mile?
37. ***DATA*** Use the table on page 120. Dwayne is the top high jumper. How does Dwayne rank in the long jump? Who ranks second in the high jump?

Chapters 1–3   Cumulative Review

Choose the correct answer. Write A, B, C, or D.

1. Name the decimal represented by the point on the number line.

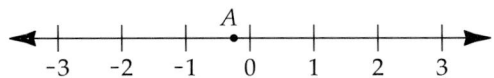

- **A.** 0.25
- **B.** -0.25
- **C.** -1.75
- **D.** not given

2. two hundred five and six hundredths
- **A.** 205.600
- **B.** 200.56
- **C.** 205.06
- **D.** not given

3. What integer represents 15 s before launch?
- **A.** -15
- **B.** +15
- **C.** |15|
- **D.** not given

4. $|-3| \cdot (-6) \cdot 2$
- **A.** 36
- **B.** -36
- **C.** -18
- **D.** not given

5. Find the mean temperature: 6°, -5°, 2°, 0°, -8°.
- **A.** -5°
- **B.** 1°
- **C.** -1°
- **D.** not given

6. What replacement for a will make the equation $4a - 7 = 25$ true?
- **A.** 5
- **B.** 7
- **C.** -8
- **D.** not given

7. $3 \cdot [2 \cdot (-4)] = (3 \cdot 2) \cdot (\blacksquare)$.
- **A.** -4
- **B.** 2
- **C.** 3
- **D.** not given

8. Write an expression for the total area of the figure.

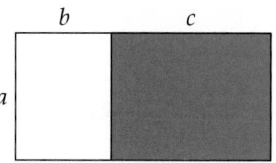

- **A.** $a \cdot (b \cdot c)$
- **B.** $a + (b + c)$
- **C.** $a(b + c)$
- **D.** not given

9. Round 6.54901 to the nearest tenth.
- **A.** 6.5
- **B.** 6.55
- **C.** 7
- **D.** not given

10. Solve $x - 2.5 = -5$.
- **A.** -2.5
- **B.** 7.5
- **C.** -7.5
- **D.** not given

11. Simplify $3x + (5 - 2x)0.5$.
- **A.** $2x + 2.5$
- **B.** $x + 2.5$
- **C.** $x - 2.5$
- **D.** not given

12. Solve $\frac{y}{1.2} = -3.6$.
- **A.** -0.3
- **B.** -4.32
- **C.** 0.3
- **D.** not given

13. Find the distance for $r = 50.5$ mi/h, and $t = 3$ h. Use $d = rt$.
- **A.** 16.5 mi
- **B.** 350 mi
- **C.** 151.5 mi
- **D.** not given

14. Solve $5.6 = x + 3.5$.
- **A.** 9.1
- **B.** 2.1
- **C.** 8.5
- **D.** not given

TOP 10 MOST SPOKEN LANGUAGES

(millions of speakers)

CHINESE	700
ENGLISH	400
RUSSIAN	265
SPANISH	240
HINDI	230
ARABIC	146
PORTUGUESE	145
BENGALI	144
GERMAN	119
JAPANESE	116

Population Facts

Most crowded:

Monaco with 15,000 people/km^2

Least crowded:

Western Sahara with 0.5 people/km^2

Fraction of population under 15 years of age:

Africa: about $\frac{1}{2}$ Europe: about $\frac{1}{5}$

DEMOGRAPHERS look for patterns in the size, movement, density, and other characteristics of human populations. Demographers use graphs, like the population pyramid, to look for trends and determine future growth patterns.

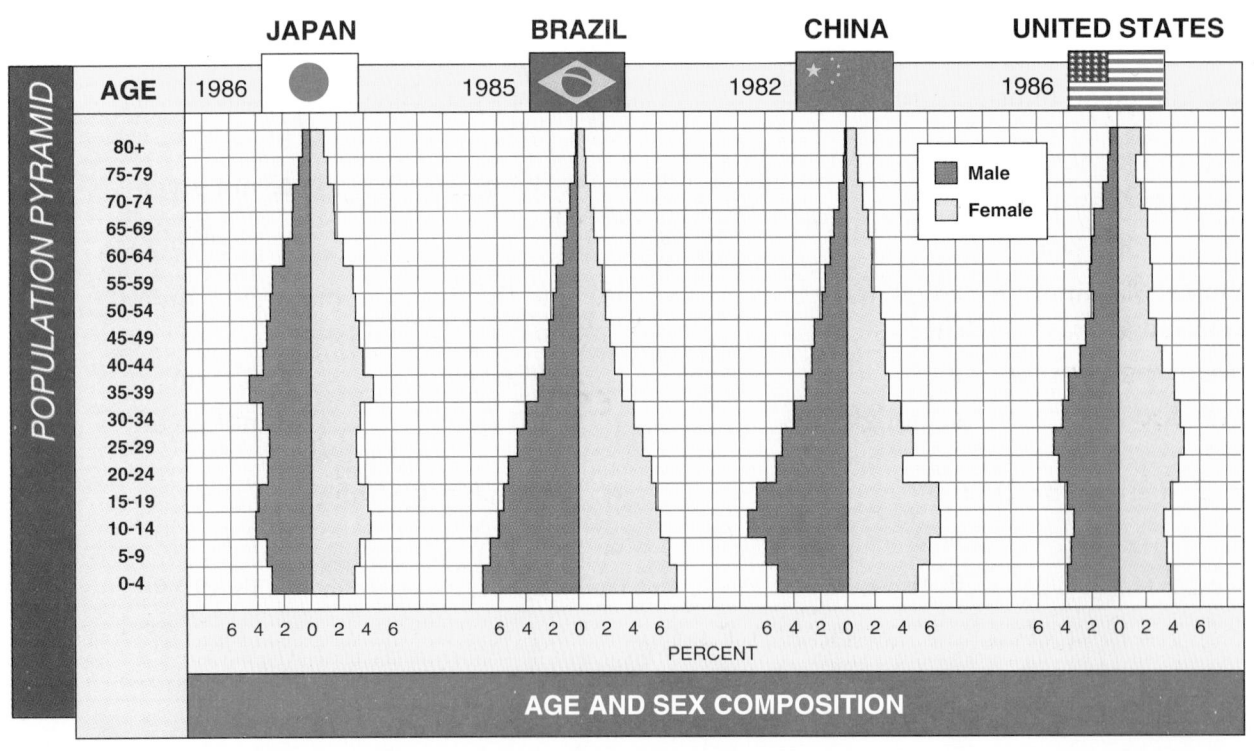

POPULATION PYRAMID

| AGE | JAPAN 1986 | BRAZIL 1985 | CHINA 1982 | UNITED STATES 1986 |

Male / Female

PERCENT

AGE AND SEX COMPOSITION

CHAPTER 4

Number Theory

WORLD POPULATION GROWTH ■ From 1450 to 1750 the world population doubled. It doubled again from 1750 to 1855, from 1855 to 1950, and from 1950 to 1989.

Each square stands for 100 million people

Each square stands for five years

1450 1500 1550 1600 1650 1700 1750 1800 1850 1900 1950 1990

▽
Think about it...

Look at the population growth graph. In 1989 the world population was about 5 billion. When do you think the population will double again?

A baby is born every 0.22 s.

A person dies every 0.67 s.

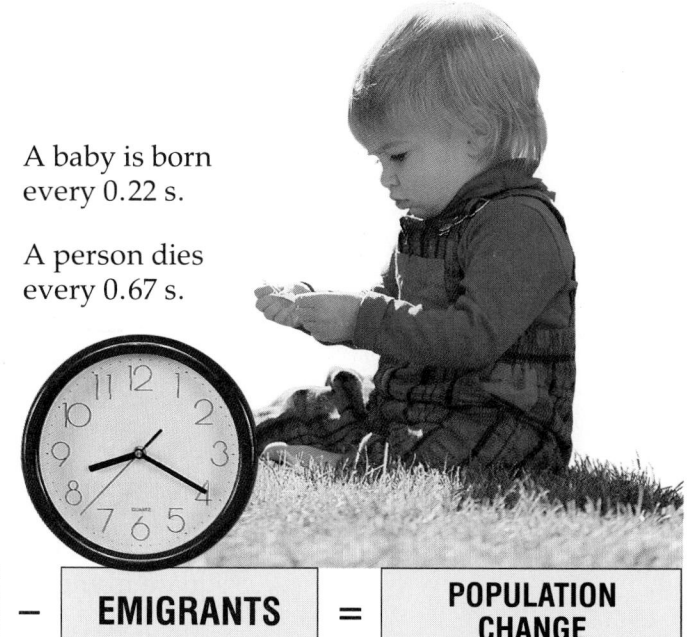

| BIRTHS | − | DEATHS | + | IMMIGRANTS | − | EMIGRANTS | = | POPULATION CHANGE |

OBJECTIVE:
To explore square numbers using patterns.

MATERIALS

- Graph paper or algebra tiles
- Math journal to record work

Exploring Square Numbers

▼ Each year the aviation club sponsors an air show. As part of the routine, the planes fly in formation. First one plane flies up, then three planes, then five, then seven.

1. Look at the table below. What was the total number of planes in the air after the third takeoff? after the fourth?

Group	Number of New Planes	Total Number in Air
1	1	1
2	3	4
3	5	9
4	7	16

2. If the flight pattern continued, how many planes would be in the fifth group? in the sixth group? Extend the table to organize your data.

3. What is the total number of planes in the air after the fifth group? after the sixth group?

4. **Describe** and discuss the relationship between the group number and the total number of planes in the air.

5. How do the models at the left show the relationship between the group number and the total number of planes in the air?

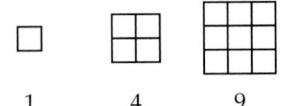

```
 1      4      9
```

▼ The numbers in the last column of the table are called *square numbers* or *squares*.

6. **Write** two characteristics that describe square numbers.

7. Without using the table, figure out how many planes would be in the air if there could be a group 20.

▼ The models below show the relationship between the number of new planes and square numbers.

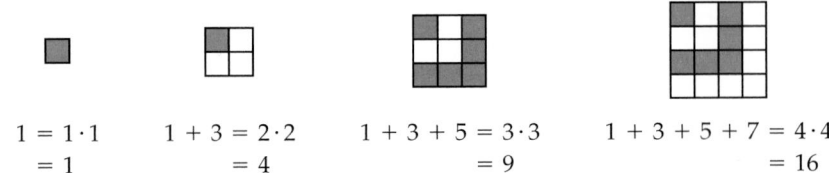

$$1 = 1 \cdot 1 \qquad 1 + 3 = 2 \cdot 2 \qquad 1 + 3 + 5 = 3 \cdot 3 \qquad 1 + 3 + 5 + 7 = 4 \cdot 4$$
$$= 1 \qquad\qquad = 4 \qquad\qquad = 9 \qquad\qquad = 16$$

8. Use tiles or graph paper to model this relationship for the next three square numbers. **Compare** with another group.

9. **Summarize**—How can you use an odd number of tiles to form a square number?

4-1 Exponents

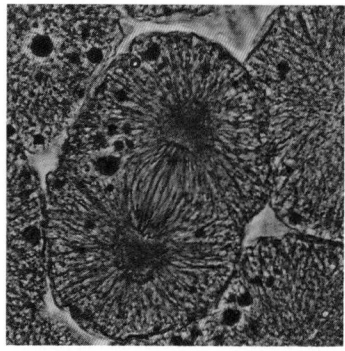

▼ Suppose a cell splits into two cells every hour. How many cells will there be after 12 hours?

The number of cells doubles every hour. You find the total by multiplying 2 twelve times.

$$2 \cdot 2 \cdot 2 \cdot 2 \cdot 2 \cdot 2 \cdot 2 \cdot 2 \cdot 2 \cdot 2 \cdot 2 \cdot 2 = 4{,}096$$

You can also express the product using an *exponent*.

$$\text{base} \rightarrow 2^{12} \leftarrow \text{exponent}$$

READ 2^{12} as *2 to the twelfth power.*

Base	The base is the number used as a factor.

Exponent	The exponent shows the number of times the base is used as a factor.

THINK Why does a^1 equal a?

▼ You can refer to expressions with exponents as *powers.*

Write	Read	Evaluate
2^0	*two to the zero power*	1
12^1	*twelve to the first power*	12
5^2	*five to the second power, or five squared*	$5 \cdot 5 = 25$
6^3	*six to the third power, or six cubed*	$6 \cdot 6 \cdot 6 = 216$
-3^4	*the opposite of the fourth power of three*	$-(3 \cdot 3 \cdot 3 \cdot 3) = -81$

THINK What is the base in -3^4? in $(-3)^4$?

Example 1 Write using exponents.

a. $5 \cdot 5 \cdot 5$ b. $-2 \cdot a \cdot 7 \cdot b \cdot b$

Solution   a. 5^3

b. $-2 \cdot 7 \cdot a \cdot b \cdot b = -14ab^2$ Use the commutative and associative properties of multiplication.

▼ You can extend the order of operations to include powers.

1. Do all operations within grouping symbols first.
2. Evaluate powers.
3. Multiply and divide from left to right.
4. Add and subtract from left to right.

Edward Kasner (1878–1955), an American mathematician, asked his nine-year-old nephew what he would call the number 1 followed by 100 zeros or 10^{100}. The child responded with the word *googol*.

Example 2 Evaluate.

    a. $5(3 + 2)^2$ **b.** $-2x^3 + 4y$ for $x = 2$, $y = -3$

Solution   **a.** $5(5)^2 = 5 \cdot 25$ **b.** $-2(2)^3 + 4(-3) = -2 \cdot 8 + (-12)$

             $= 125$ $= -16 + (-12)$

                                                    $= -28$

▼ A calculator is useful for evaluating expressions with exponents.

Example 3 Evaluate 8^5 using a calculator.

Solution Use the $\boxed{x^y}$ key.

        $8 \boxed{x^y} 5 \boxed{=} 32{,}768$

CLASS EXERCISES

Name the base and the exponent.

1. 7^4 **2.** $(-10)^2$ **3.** x^y **4.** -2^5

Read aloud and evaluate.

5. 4^4 **6.** $(-9)^0$ **7.** -4^3 **8.** -2^1

Write using exponents.

9. $6 \cdot 6 \cdot 6 \cdot 6 \cdot 6$ **10.** $4 \cdot y \cdot y \cdot y \cdot 3 \cdot x$

Evaluate.

11. $10(5 + 4)^2$ **12.** $[15 + (-18)]^2 + (-2)^3$

13. $x^2 + y^3$; $x = 3$ and $y = -1$ **14.** $-x^2 - 3 \cdot 2x$; $x = 3$

THINK AND DISCUSS

1. How and when are exponents useful?

2. Compare the values of -6^2 and $(-6)^2$. Why are they different?

3. Let n be any positive integer. Find the value of 1^n, -1^n.

4. In the expression a^0, how many times is a used as a factor? What is the value of a^0?

WRITTEN EXERCISES

Write using exponents.

1. $8 \cdot 8 \cdot 8$ **2.** $p \cdot p \cdot p \cdot p$ **3.** $2 \cdot r \cdot r \cdot r \cdot r \cdot s \cdot s$

4. $5 \cdot 5 \cdot y \cdot y$ **5.** $x \cdot x \cdot y \cdot y \cdot z$ **6.** $-9 \cdot m \cdot m \cdot (-4) \cdot n$

7. $\underbrace{n \cdot n \cdot n \cdot \ldots \cdot n}_{30 \text{ factors}}$ **8.** $\underbrace{m \cdot m \cdot m \cdot \ldots \cdot m}_{y \text{ factors}}$ **9.** $\underbrace{a \cdot a \cdot a \cdot \ldots \cdot a}_{a \text{ factors}}$

10. $(-4n)(-4n)(-4n)(-4n)(-4n)$ **11.** $(a + 1)(a + 1)(a + 1)$

Evaluate.

12. a. 5^3 **13. a.** 10^0 **14. a.** -1^8 **15. a.** -2^4
   b. 3^5 **b.** 10^6 **b.** $(-1)^9$ **b.** $(-2)^0$

16. x^5 for $x = 2$ **17.** $(3a)^2$ for $a = -2$ **18.** $-(4y)^2$ for $y = 3$

19. $-(x)^2$ for $x = -2$ **20.** $-2x^5$ for $x = -1$ **21.** $(-x)^5$ for $x = -1$

CALCULATOR You can use a calculator to find the positive *square root* of a number.

▼▼ *SAMPLE* $25 \boxed{\checkmark} \boxed{=} 5$. So, $\sqrt{25} = 5$ since $5^2 = 25$

Find the square root.

22. $\sqrt{36}$ **23.** $\sqrt{49}$ **24.** $\sqrt{64}$ **25.** $\sqrt{81}$ **26.** $\sqrt{100}$

Compare. Use $<$, $>$, or $=$.

27. $3^3 \; 5^2$ **28.** $4^3 \; 8^2$ **29.** $64 \div 8 \; 2^3$ **30.** $4 \cdot 10 \; 10^4$

31. $-5^3 \; -3^0$ **32.** $10^2 \; 2^{10}$ **33.** $3^4 \; 4^3$ **34.** $-10^3 \; (-10)^3$

Solve.

35. Which of the following is equal to 1?
   a. -1^2 **b.** $(-1)^3$ **c.** $-(-1)^2$ **d.** $|-1|^3$

36. MENTAL MATH Given that $2^{10} = 1,024$, find 2^{11} mentally.

37. MENTAL MATH Explain how to find $(-1)^{100}$ mentally.

38. WRITE a sentence that explains the roles of the base and the exponent of 8^4.

39. Make a table of the powers of 10: 10^0, 10^1, 10^2, 10^3, 10^4. Describe the pattern you see. Use the pattern to find 10^6 and 10^{10}.

40. The formula for the area of a square is $A = s^2$, where A is area and s is the length of a side.

   a. Find the area of a square with a side of length 3.5 cm.

   b. Find the length of a side of a square with area 144 m².

41. CALCULATOR

   a. Copy and complete the table.

n	$4n$	4^n	n^4
0			
1			
2			
3			
4			

   b. For what value(s) of n is each true?

   $4^n = n^4$
   $4^n < n^4$
   $4^n > n^4$

PROBLEM SOLVING HINT
Draw a diagram.

Find the value of n.

42. $5^n = 125$ 5

43. $3^n = 1$ 0

44. $n^3 = 8$ 2

For what positive value(s) of x is each true?

45. $1x = x^1$

46. $2x = x^2$

47. $9x = x^3$

48. Evaluate $(-1)^m$ for $m = 2, 4,$ and 6. Now let $m = 1, 3,$ and 5.
WRITE a rule for raising a negative number to an even power or an odd power.

49. COMPUTER You can use a spreadsheet to construct a bar graph for the powers of 2. Note that the caret (^) is used to indicate exponentiation. Use the spreadsheet data to construct a graph.

	A	B
1	Number	Power
2	2	=A2^2
3	2	=A3^3
4	2	=A4^4
5	2	=A5^5
6	2	=A6^6
7		

a. What do you notice about the bar for cell B2 compared to the bar for cell B3? Is the same true for cells B3 and B4?

b. **WRITE** a description for the bar graph of the powers of 2.

50. PROJECT Use a spreadsheet format similar to Exercise 49 to construct a bar graph for the powers of 3. Answer Exercise 49 (a) and (b) for this bar graph.

Critical Thinking
EXPLORING NUMBER PATTERNS

You know that the sum of consecutive odd integers is a square number. Now consider the odd numbers shown at the left.

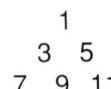

```
    1
   3  5
  7  9  11
```

1. Copy the odd number formation and add two more rows.

2. The sum of the first row is 1. What is the sum of the second row? the third row? the fourth row?

3. What is 1^3? 2^3? 3^3? 4^3?

4. Predict the sum of the tenth row.

4-2 Rules About Exponents

▼ Without evaluating the expressions, compare $7^2 \cdot 7^3$ and $7^4 \cdot 7^1$.
Use what you've learned about exponents.

$$7^2 \cdot 7^3 = (7 \cdot 7) \cdot (7 \cdot 7 \cdot 7) = 7^5$$
$$7^4 \cdot 7^1 = (7 \cdot 7 \cdot 7 \cdot 7) \cdot (7) = 7^5$$
$$7^2 \cdot 7^3 = 7^4 \cdot 7^1 \text{ since } 7^5 = 7^5$$

Notice that $7^2 \cdot 7^3 = 7^{2+3} = 7^5$. This suggests the following rule.

Rule of Exponents for Multiplication	To multiply numbers or variables with the *same* base, add exponents.
	Arithmetic **Algebra**
	$2^3 \cdot 2^4 = 2^{3+4} = 2^7$ $a^m \cdot a^n = a^{m+n}$

Example 1 Simplify using exponents.

      a. $a \cdot a^3 \cdot a^4$ **b.** $xy^2 \cdot x^3$

Solution   **a.** $a \cdot a^3 \cdot a^4 = a^{1+3+4}$ **b.** $xy^2 \cdot x^3 = x \cdot x^3 \cdot y^2$
                         $= a^8$ $= x^{1+3} \cdot y^2$
                                                $= x^4 y^2$

How do the blocks show 7^1, 7^2, and 7^3?

THINK How would you
simplify $(5^0)^3$? What is the
result?

▼ You can raise a power to a power.

Example 2 Simplify $(5^2)^3$.

Solution   **a.** Use the meaning   **b.** Use the rule for
             of exponents.   multiplication.
             $(5^2)^3 = 5^2 \cdot 5^2 \cdot 5^2$ $(5^2)^3 = 5^2 \cdot 5^2 \cdot 5^2$
                   $= (5 \cdot 5)(5 \cdot 5)(5 \cdot 5)$ $= 5^{2+2+2}$
                   $= 5^6$ $= 5^6$

▼ Notice that $(5^2)^3 = 5^6$. This suggests the following rule.

Rule of a Power Raised to a Power	To raise a power to a power, multiply the exponents.
	Arithmetic **Algebra**
	$(2^3)^4 = 2^{3 \cdot 4} = 2^{12}$ $(a^m)^n = a^{m \cdot n}$

Example 3 Simplify.

      a. $(3^2)^3$ **b.** $(a^6)^2$

Solution   **a.** $(3^2)^3 = 3^{2 \cdot 3}$ **b.** $(a^6)^2 = a^{6 \cdot 2}$
                   $= 3^6$ $= a^{12}$
                   $= 729$

▼ You can also raise a product to a power.

Example 4 Simplify $(xy^2)^3$.

Solution Use the meaning of exponents.

$$(xy^2)^3 = xy \cdot y \cdot xy \cdot y \cdot xy \cdot y$$
$$= (x \cdot x \cdot x) \cdot (y \cdot y \cdot y \cdot y \cdot y \cdot y)$$
$$= x^3y^6$$

▼ Notice that $(xy^2)^3 = x^3y^6$. This suggests the following rule.

Rule of a Product Raised to a Power	To raise a product to a power, raise each factor to the power and then use the rule of exponents for multiplication.
	Arithmetic **Algebra**
	$(10^3 \cdot 10^2)^4 = 10^{12} \cdot 10^8$ $(ab)^m = a^m b^m$
	$= 10^{20}$

Example 5 Simplify $(6x^4)^3$.

Solution $(6x^4)^3 = 6^3 \cdot (x^4)^3$
$$= 216x^{12}$$

THINK AND DISCUSS

1. Can you simplify $x^6 \cdot y^7$? Explain.

2. Evaluate $-(2^3)^2$ and $(-2^3)^2$. Compare your answers.

3. How many times is the expression xy^2 used as a factor in $(xy^2)^0$? What is the value of $(xy^2)^0$?

CLASS EXERCISES

Evaluate or simplify. No variable has a value of zero.

1. $(-4)^3$ **2.** -4^2 **3.** $(-2 + 3)^2$ **4.** $2^3 \cdot 2^0$ **5.** $4 \cdot 4^3$

6. $x \cdot x^2 \cdot x^5$ **7.** $4^7 \cdot 4^{10}$ **8.** $w^2(w^6)$ **9.** $(y^3)^5$ **10.** $(4x^5)^0$

Evaluate for $a = -1$, $b = -3$, $c = 2$.

11. a^3b **12.** abc^0 **13.** $(abc)^0$ **14.** $2a^5c$

15. $(a^3)^6$ **16.** $(a^2b^3)^5$ **17.** $(c^2 \cdot c)^8$ **18.** $(4c^2 \cdot 4c^3)^2$

WRITTEN EXERCISES

Evaluate. No variable has a value of zero.

1. $(-2)^3$ **2.** $(2)^3$ **3.** $-(2)^3$ **4.** $10^2 \cdot 10^5$

5. $(x^6)(x^3)$ **6.** $(x^2)(y^5)(x)$ **7.** $5x^3 \cdot 2x^6$ **8.** $a^{10} \div a^2$

9. $(2^3)(3^2)$ **10.** $(4^5)(4^3)$ **11.** $(-x^4)(-x)$ **12.** $(z^6)(-z^3)(z^2)$

13. $(-2a)^3 \cdot (-2a^3)$ **14.** $(a^4b^4)^4$ **15.** $(6y^3)^4$

16. $-(3xy)^2$ **17.** $(-3y^4)^3$ **18.** $(x^5)^7$

Evaluate each expression for $a = -3$, $b = 2$, $c = -1$.

19. $(2c)^3$ ~ *8* **20.** $5abc^0$ *1* **21.** $(a^2)^3 \cdot (a^3)^2$ *53144*

22. bc ~ *2* **23.** $(ac)^0$ *9* **24.** ab^3c^{100} *10024*

25. $a^2 + b^3$ *17* **26.** $(a + b)^3$ *-1* **27.** $(ab)^3$ *-216*

True or False? Explain your answer. No variable has a value of zero.

28. $x^8 \cdot x^2 = x^5 \cdot x^5$ *T* **29.** $x^5 \cdot x^3 = x^{15}$ *F*

30. $x^3 \cdot y^4 = (xy)^7$ *F* **31.** $5^0 = 7^0$ *F*

32. $(-r^3)^2 > 0$ *T* **33.** $-(r^2)^3 < 0$ *F* **34.** $1^8 = 1^{23}$ *F*

Which of the following is equal to 2^{13}?

35. $(2^3)^{10}$ *N* **36.** $2^5 \cdot 2^8$ *Y* **37.** $2^1 \cdot 2^0 \cdot 2^{13}$ *N* **38.** 8,190 *N*

Which of the following is twice the value of 2^{15}?

39. 2^{30} *N* **40.** 2^{16} *N* **41.** $2 \cdot 2^{15}$ *Y* **42.** 65,536 *Y*

Compare. Use >, <, or =.

43. $5^2 \; \square \; (5^3)^2$ **44.** $7^2 \cdot 7^5 \; \square \; (7^6)^2$ **45.** $(-2^2)^3 \; \square \; 2^5$

46. $25^2 \; \square \; (5^2)^2$ **47.** $(2^7)^7 \; \square \; (2^{25})^2$ **48.** $(4^5 \cdot 4^2)^3 \; \square \; (4^4)^0$

49. Without computing, determine which is greater: 2^{75} or 3^{50}. *Hint:* write each as an expression with the same exponent. *3^{50}*

Solve.

50. Is $(a^3)^4 = (a^4)^3$ a true equation? Explain your answer. *no, you cant use comm with exp.*

51. If $(3^2 + 3^2 + 3^2) \cdot 3^x = 243$ is a true equation, find x. *x = 2*

52. CALCULATOR Find a pattern in the last digits of the powers of 7.

  a. What is the last digit of 7^{10}? What is the last digit of 7^{11}? *3*

  b. Predict the last digit of 7^{21}. What method did you use to find the answer? *1*   *divide by 3*

53. COMPUTER In computer science, information is measured and stored in *bits*. Eight bits are equal to one *byte*.

  a. One *kilobyte* is defined as 2^{10} bytes. How many bytes are in a kilobyte? *200*

  b. ESTIMATION What is an approximate value for a kilobyte using a power of ten? *400*

  c. Write the number of bits in one byte as a power of 2. *48*

  d. A *megabyte* is 2^{20} bytes. Write the number of bytes in a megabyte as the product of exponents.

  e. Write the number of bits there are in one megabyte as the product of exponents. *2*

MIXED REVIEW

Estimate.

1. $3.8 + 4.62 - 5.3$

2. $42.7 \cdot 8.5$

Write using exponents.

3. $-5 \cdot a \cdot a \cdot a \cdot b \cdot b$

4. $2 \cdot c \cdot c \cdot (-7) \cdot d \cdot d \cdot d$

Evaluate for $x = 3$, $y = -2$.

5. $4(x + 3y)$

6. $\sqrt{x^3 + 3x}$

7. $(1 + y)^x$

8. DATA FILE 3 (pp. 96–97) Approximately how many times did the value of a 1961 proof set increase by 1990?

$3 \cdot 3^2 \cdot 3^x$
$= 3^3 \cdot 3^x$
$= 3^{3+x} = 243$
$3^3 \cdot 3^x = 243$
$3^x =$

54. Aunt Helen will open a savings account for you. You have a choice of two savings plans.

Plan A. Aunt Helen will deposit $20 each month for the next 15 months.

Plan B. Aunt Helen will deposit one cent the first month, two cents the second month, four cents the third month, and so on, doubling each month, for the next fifteen months.

a. For how many months is Plan A the better choice?

b. At what amount of money is Plan B the better choice?

EXPLORING PASCAL'S TRIANGLE

The number triangle below was published in China about 1300 A.D. It is usually called *Pascal's triangle,* after the French mathematician Blaise Pascal, who wrote about many of its patterns in a 1653 paper.

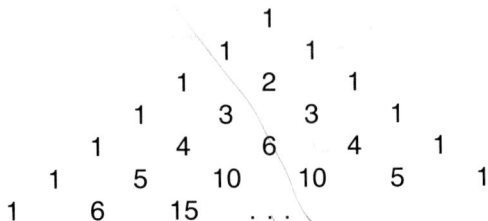

```
              1
           1     1
        1     2     1
     1     3     3     1
  1     4     6     4     1
1     5    10    10     5     1
1   6    15   . . .
```

1. Analyze the pattern.
Complete: Each entry in a row is the sum of ▓ .

If we call the row in which the number 2 first appears Row 2, the top row is Row 0.

2. What numbers appear in Row 6?

3. What is the sum of the numbers in Row 3?

4. Find the sum of the numbers in the twentieth row of Pascal's triangle. You may wish to use a calculator. *Hint:* Starting with Row 0, make a table that shows each row number and the sum of the numbers in that row. Look for a pattern.

4-3 Scientific Notation

▼ You can write a number in different ways without changing its value. Here are some ways to write 75.

$$60 + 15 \qquad 2(37.5) \qquad 150 \div 2 \qquad 100 - 25$$

▼ You can also write numbers using powers of 10. Here are some ways you can write 4,000 using powers of 10.

$$4 \cdot 1,000 = 4 \cdot 10^3$$
$$40 \cdot 100 = 40 \cdot 10^2$$
$$400 \cdot 10 = 400 \cdot 10^1$$

▼ *Scientific notation* is a way to write numbers using powers of 10.

Example 1 The numbers below on the left are written in scientific notation. The numbers below on the right are not.

3.45×10^3	34.5×10^2
9.5×10^2	0.95×10^1
2.0×10^4	200×10^2

Scientific Notation	A number is in scientific notation when it is written as the product of a number greater than or equal to 1 and less than 10, and a power of 10.

THINK How can you use mental math to find the exponent when writing a number in scientific notation?

▼ You can write large numbers in scientific notation.

Example 2 Write 5,460,000 in scientific notation.

Solution
1. Express as a number between 1 and 10. $\qquad$ 5.460000

2. To keep the value the same, multiply by a power of 10. $\qquad$ $5.46 \cdot 1,000,000$

3. Write the power of 10 with exponents. $\qquad$ 5.46×10^6

THINK How can you use mental math to multiply by a power of 10?

▼ By multiplying, you can write any number that is in scientific notation in *standard notation*.

Example 3 Write each number in standard notation.

    a. 9.3×10^7 $\qquad\qquad\qquad$ **b.** 4.235×10^2

Solution   **a.** $9.3 \cdot 10,000,000 = 93,000,000$ $\qquad$ **b.** $4.235 \cdot 100 = 423.5$

▼ You can multiply numbers in scientific notation.

Example 4 **Write the product in scientific notation.**

$(3.46 \times 10^5)(9.2 \times 10^3)$

Solution

1.	Multiply the decimals.	$3.46 \times 9.2 = 31.832$
2.	Multiply the powers of 10.	$10^5 \cdot 10^3 = 10^8$
3.	Write the product.	31.832×10^8
4.	Write the first factor in scientific notation.	$(3.1832 \times 10) \times 10^8$
5.	Simplify.	3.1832×10^9

THINK AND DISCUSS

1. How does scientific notation prevent careless error when working with very large numbers?

2. How would you add 1×10^5 and 1×10^4?

CLASS EXERCISES

Write each number in standard notation.

1. 10^6 1000000   **2.** 10^7 **3.** 0.93×10^4 9,300

Is each number written in scientific notation? Explain.

4. 10^4 **5.** 0.12×10^1 **6.** 5.24×10^1 **7.** 7.2×3^4

Write each number in scientific notation.

8. Some computers can process 3.5 million instructions per second.

9. Light travels 299,790,000 m/s.

Write each number in standard notation.

10. The radius of the earth is 5×10^6 m.

11. The estimated age of Earth is 4.7×10^9 years.

4,700,000,000

Write the result in scientific notation.

12. $(3.45 \times 10^6)(1.84 \times 10^2)$ **13.** $(4.32 \times 10^3) \cdot (2.4 \times 10^1)$

$103.68 \cdot 10^2$

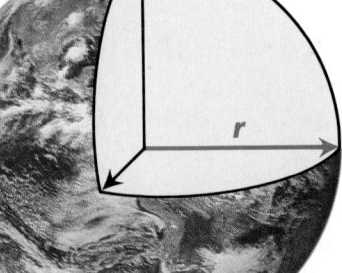

WRITTEN EXERCISES

$625 \cdot 10^6, \ 6.25 \cdot 10^8, \ 62.5 \cdot 10^8$

1. Write 625,000,000 three different ways using powers of 10.

2. Write 4.97×10^7 three different ways using powers of 10.

Write each number in scientific notation.

3. The average adult human male, weighing about 160 lb, consists of about 60,000,000,000,000 cells. $6 \cdot 10^{13}$

4. The temperature inside the sun is greater than 16,000,000°C.

5. *DATA FILE 10 (pp. 404–405)* Write the area of the Pacific Ocean in scientific notation.

Write each number in standard notation.

6. 10^8

7. 10^5 100,000

8. 59×10

9. 7.654×10^3 7654

10. 1.45×10^{10}

11. 6.0032×10^2 600.32

12. 9.84×10^5

13. 4.06×10^3 4060

14. 1.7×10^2

Simplify. Write each answer in scientific and standard notation. Round to the nearest tenth.

15. $(3 \times 10^2)(5 \times 10^2)$ $1.5 \times 10^5 = 150,000$

16. $(4.2 \times 10^3)(3.84 \times 10^1)$ 4200   38.4

17. $389,000 \cdot 25,475,000$ $9.9 \times 10^{12} = 9,900,000,000$

18. $0.00125 \times 50,000$

19. $(9.087 \times 10^6)0.52$ $4.7 \times 10^6 = 4,700,000$

20. $4(2.3 \times 10^5)$

Complete.

21. $8,450 = 8.45 \times 10^{3}$

22. $\blacksquare \times 10^2 = 8.45 \times 10^3$

23. $84.5 = 8.45 \times 10^1$

24. $8.45 = 8.45 \times 10^{\blacksquare}$

25. $0.845 = \blacksquare \times 10^3$ 0.000845

26. $\blacksquare \times 10^4 = 8.45 \times 10^3$

CALCULATOR **Solve using a scientific calculator. Round each answer to the nearest hundredth.**

▼▼   *SAMPLE* $(6.28 \times 10^{24}) \times (5.3 \times 10^7)$

       Enter: 6.28 (EXP) 24 (×) 5.3 (EXP) 7 (=)

       Display: 3.3284 E 32

27. $(7.892 \times 10^{17})(3.16 \times 10^3)$ 24.9×10^{21}

28. $(7.892 \times 10^{17})^2$

29. $(7.892 \times 10^{17}) \cdot 10^3$ 7.89×10^{20}

30. $(4.32 \times 10^5) \cdot 673$

31. $905,200,000,000,000,000 \cdot 3,560,090,000,000$ 322×10^{20}

32. How many seconds are there in 1,000 years?

DATA FILE 4 (pp. 138–139) **Solve.**

33. Write the number of speakers of Chinese in scientific notation.

34. Find the increase in population from 1900 to 1980. Express the number in scientific notation.

35. *PROJECT* Use an encyclopedia, almanac, or other reference book. Find the answers to the following questions and write in scientific notation.

   a. What is the diameter of a water molecule?

   b. How far from Earth is Mars?

   c. What is the shutter speed of the fastest still camera?

The Average Distance to the Sun (km)	
Planet	**Distance**
♆ Neptune	4.497×10^9
☿ Mercury	5.79×10^7
♃ Jupiter	7.783×10^8
♀ Venus	1.082×10^8
♄ Saturn	1.427×10^9
⊕ Earth	1.496×10^8
♅ Uranus	2.869×10^9
♂ Mars	2.279×10^8
♇ Pluto	5.9×10^9

Use the table at the left to solve.

36. Which is closer to the sun, Saturn or Jupiter? Earth or Venus?

37. Order the distances from the least to greatest.

38. **WRITE** a procedure for ordering numbers in scientific notation.

39. Alpha Centauri, the star closest to the sun, is about 40,600,000,000,000 km away. Write this in scientific notation.

40. Why do you think astronomers prefer scientific notation?

41. **PROJECT** Astronomers measure very great distances in *light years*. Find out what a light year is and the distance in light years from one side of our galaxy to the other.

Use the article at the left to solve.

42. How would you express the distance from Earth to the moon in meters? Express this distance using scientific notation.

43. How many 0.5-meter footsteps are there from here to the moon? Express using scientific notation.

44. **PROJECT** Find out why the footprints on the moon will be visible for 10 million years.

Our Nearest Neighbor

The moon is Earth's only satellite. Although it is not a planet, the moon is the closest object to Earth in our solar system. The moon is about 380,000 km from Earth.

On July 20, 1969, American astronauts from the *Apollo* mission were the first men to set foot on the moon. They returned to Earth with 382 kg of moon rocks and dust. The footsteps the astronauts left on the moon will probably be visible for at least 10 million years.

TEST YOURSELF

Write using exponents.

1. $a \cdot b \cdot a \cdot b \cdot b$

2. $-2 \cdot x \cdot (-2) \cdot y \cdot x \cdot x$

Evaluate.

3. 4^3

4. 12^2

5. $(-3)^5$

6. $(3^2)^0$

7. -5^4

8. $2^2 \cdot 2^3 \cdot 2^4$

Write each number in scientific notation.

9. 10,000

10. 100,000

11. 10,000,000

12. 75,000

13. 854,000

14. 1,645,123

OBJECTIVE:
To apply scientific notation to solve problems concerning water resources and usage.

4-4 Water Resources

■ Water is critical for life. Our bodies are 0.65 water. About 0.95 of the total weight of a tomato plant is water. We need water to grow the food we eat and to manufacture the goods we use. Without water, we could not exist.

Example 1 The total amount of water on Earth is about 3.26×10^8 mi³. A cubic mile of water contains about 1.1×10^{12} gal of water. In gallons, what is the total amount of water on Earth?

Solution Multiply the number of cubic miles of water by the number of gallons in each cubic mile.

$$(3.26 \times 10^8) \times (1.1 \times 10^{12}) = (3.26 \times 1.1) \times (10^8 \times 10^{12})$$
$$= 3.586 \times 10^{20}$$

There are about 3.586×10^{20} gal of water on Earth.

Example 2 Find the total number of gallons of ocean water.

Solution Multiply 0.97 by the result from Example 1.

$$(0.97)(3.586 \times 10^{20}) = (0.97 \times 3.586) \times (10^{20})$$
$$= 3.47842 \times 10^{20}$$

There are 3.47842×10^{20} gal of ocean water.

■ You can find the portion of water given an amount.

Example 3 For every 50,000 gal of Earth's water supply, how much is found in icecaps and glaciers?

Solution Multiply the amount by 0.023 and express the product in scientific notation.

$$(0.023)(50,000) = 1,150$$
$$= 1.15 \times 10^3$$

The amount of water is 1.15×10^3 gal.

Earth's Water Supply
(for every gallon)

Source	Amount
ocean	0.97
icecaps and glaciers	0.023
lakes and rivers	0.0001
underground	0.0059
atmosphere	0.001

CLASS EXERCISES

Use the DATA at the left to solve each problem. Give your answers in scientific notation.

1. There are 358,600,000,000,000,000,000 gal of water on Earth. What is the total amount from underground sources?

2. For every 75,000 gal of water, how much comes from lakes and rivers?

WRITTEN EXERCISES

Average Water Usage in United States Cities (per person/day)

home	70 gal
factories and businesses	70 gal
city services	10 gal

Use the *DATA* at the left to solve each problem. Express answers in scientific notation.

1. There are about 187,500,000 people that live in cities in the United States. About how many gallons of water will these people use each day in their homes?

2. In all, about how many gallons of water do the 187,500,000 people in cities use in a day for all purposes?

3. The population of the city of Chicago is about 4,000,000 people.

   a. About how many gallons of water do the people in Chicago use each day in their homes?

   b. Chicago gets its drinking water from Lake Michigan, the largest body of fresh water in the United States. If you took the top inch of water from Lake Michigan, you would get about 3.9×10^{11} gal of water. Suppose this water is used exclusively by Chicago's homes. About how many days of water would it supply?

■■■■■■ Decision Making ■ **DECISION MAKING** ■ Decision Making ■ Decision Making ■ Decision Making ■

WATER RESOURCES

■ **COLLECT DATA**

1. Survey how much water your family uses in one week. You can estimate the amounts. For example, to measure the amount of water it takes to fill a bathtub, estimate how many quart or one-gallon milk cartons of water it would take to cover the bottom of the bathtub. Record your estimates in a chart like the one below.

Amount of Water Used Each Day (gal)							
Type of Use	Mon	Tues	Wed	Thur	Fri	Sat	Sun
bath/shower							
dish washing							
drinking							
brushing teeth							
washing hands/ laundry							

4. Chicago's main water purification plant can produce nearly 1.75 billion gal of water each day. The plant serves about 4.5 million people in the city and suburbs. About how many times greater is the plant capacity than the daily water needed for homes, factories, businesses, and city services?

Solve.

5. Many places in the world do not have access to fresh water from lakes and rivers. They must purify ocean water. A desalting plant in Key West, Florida, can produce about 2 million gal of fresh water per day. Assume the plant operates every day. About how many gallons of pure water can the plant produce in a year?

6. The Great Salt Lake in Utah holds about 5.7 mi^3 of water and about 4.0×10^9 t of salt. About how many tons of salt is this per cubic mile?

7. The total amount of water on the planet is about 326,000,000 mi^3. About how many cubic miles are in glaciers and icecaps?

8. *PROJECT* Water is naturally recycled by the processes of *evaporation* and *condensation*. Research how ocean water and fresh water are recycled through these processes.

■ *Decision Making* ■ *Decision Making* ■ *Decision Making* ■ *Decision Making* ■ *Decision Making* ■ *Decision Making* ■

■ **ANALYZE DATA**

2. What is the total amount of water your family uses in one week? Which activities use more water?

3. Estimate the amount of water used for brushing your teeth if the water is left running. How much water would be used in a year?

4. What ways can you think of to reduce the amount of water you and your family use?

■ **MAKE DECISIONS**

5. Discuss ways your classmates and families can conserve water. Make a list of ideas that you can use at home.

6. Try several water-saving ideas. Keep track of your family's water consumption for another week. Record your data.

7. How much water did you save in one week? Compare your results with those of your classmates.

8. Make a poster with at least three suggestions and the amount of water they would save in a year.

OBJECTIVE:
To explore factors and multiples.

MATERIALS

- Graph paper or lined paper
- Math journal to record work

Exploring Factors and Multiples

▼ A high school has 1,000 lockers, numbered 1 to 1,000, and 1,000 students. The students enter the building one at a time.

- The first student opens all the lockers.
- The second student starts with locker 2 and closes every second locker.
- The third student starts with locker 3 and moves to every third locker. The student opens the closed lockers and closes the open ones.
- The fourth student changes every fourth locker starting with locker 4, and so on for the remaining students.

Answer the questions below to find out which lockers are open and which lockers are closed after all the students enter.

1. Which of the first nine lockers will be open after the first student passes through? the second student?

2. Using a table like the one below, find out which lockers will be open after the third student passes through.

Student Number	Locker Number								
	1	2	3	4	5	6	7	8	9
1	O	O	O	O	O	O	O	O	O
2	O	C	O	C	O	C	O	C	O
3	O	C	C	C	O	O	O	C	C
4	O	C	C	O	O	O	O	C	C

KEY
O   Open
C   Closed

3. Which students change the condition of locker 1? 2? 3?

4. *Extend* and complete the table for 12 students and 12 lockers.

5. Which students changed the condition of locker 12? Will any of the other 1,000 students change locker 12? Explain.

6. *Describe* and discuss the relationship between the numbers of the students who changed locker 12 and the number 12.

▼ The numbers that correspond to the students who changed locker 12 are *factors* of the number 12.

7. Use the relationship between the student number and the locker number to predict which students will change locker 20.

8. *Test* your prediction by extending and completing the table for 20 students and 20 lockers.

9. List all the factors of each number.

a. 1   **b.** 4   **c.** 6   **d.** 9

▼ Student 3 changed six of the first 20 lockers. List them.

10. Will student 3 change any other of the 1,000 lockers? Explain.

11. *Describe* and discuss the relationship between the student number and the number of lockers the student changes.

▼ The numbers of the lockers that student 3 changed are *multiples* of the number 3.

12. Use the relationship between the student and the locker number to predict which lockers student 25 will change.

13. List the multiples found in your table for each number.

a. 1   **b.** 4   **c.** 5   **d.** 6

14. Refer to your table.

a. Which of the 20 lockers will be open after 20 students pass through?

b. *Predict* the next two lockers that will be open.

c. What do you call these numbers? Do they have an odd or even number of factors? Is this true for all numbers of this type?

▼ After the 1,000 students pass through, each locker with an open door corresponds to a number with an odd number of factors.

15. Why do you think an odd number of factors would correspond to a locker with an open door?

16. Does an even number of factors correspond to a locker with a closed door? Explain.

17. *Write* a rule that explains which lockers are open and which are closed after the 1,000 students pass through.

18. *Calculator* Make a list of the numbers that correspond to an open locker once all the students have passed through.

Exploring Factors and Multiples

Practice

Write using exponents.

1. $5 \cdot 3 \cdot 3 \cdot 5 \cdot 5$ $5^3 \times 3^2$

2. $-3 \cdot t \cdot s \cdot s \cdot 4 \cdot s$ $\quad -12 \cdot t \cdot s^3$

3. $(-3a)(-3a)(-3a)(-3a)(-3a)$ $(-3a)^5$

4. $(2n - 1)(2n - 1)(2n - 1)$ $(2n-1)^3$

Evaluate.

5. 8^3 512

6. $(-1)^{17}$ -1

7. $(-3)^5$ -243

8. -4^3 64

9. 4^3 64

10. -2^5 -32

11. $(-4)^2$ -16

12. $\sqrt{36}$ 6

13. $7^3 \cdot 7^6$ 403536

14. $6^5 \cdot 6^3$ 167916

15. $16 \cdot 4^2$

16. $(4^5 \cdot 4^9)^0$ 7

17. $-3[5 - (-2)]^2$ -147

18. $[7 + (-2)]^4$ 625

19. $(3^2)(3^6)$ 656

20. $(2^4)(4^2) \div 4$ 64

21. $4^4 \cdot 4^6 \cdot 2^3$ 838668

22. $5^3 - 2^3 \cdot 2^1$ 109

Simplify.

23. $b \cdot b^2$ b^3

24. $g^{12} \cdot g^{10}$ g^{22}

25. $k^5 \cdot k^8$ k^{13}

26. $6x^4y^3$

27. $c \cdot c^6 \cdot c^4$ c^{11}

28. $a^3b^2c^6 \cdot a^0b^4c^5$ $a^3b^6c^{11}$

29. $(-y^3)(-y)^3$ (y^6)

30. $ab^6c^3 \cdot a^5bc^8$ $a^6b^7c^{11}$

31. $(3r^3)^5$ $(243r^{15})$

32. $(-3s)^4 \cdot 9^1$ $729s^4$

33. $(3m^2)^4 \cdot 5m^2$ $405m^{10}$

34. $(-4m^3y^7)^2$ $16m^6y^{14}$

Evaluate for $a = 4$, $b = -1$, and $c = -5$.

35. $-4b^3 + ac^2$ 104

36. $a^3 + 6cb^0$

37. $abc \cdot \sqrt{100}$

38. $(c^2 - a^2) \cdot (-3b^8c^0)$

39. $a^2c + b$ -81

40. $-(c)^2 - (b)^2 \cdot (a^2 + 3b)$

41. $(ab^2)^4 \cdot (4a^2b)$ $-16,384$

Write each number in standard notation.

42. 5×10^5

43. 24×10^7 $240,000,000$

44. 35.6×10^6

45. 10^7 $10,000,000$

46. 63.57×10^5

47. 9.83675×10^4 $98,367.5$

Write each number in scientific notation.

48. The height of Mt. Everest is 10,000 m.

49. The sun's diameter is 3,392,000 km. $3.392 \times 10^6 \text{ km}$

50. In an average lifetime a heart beats about 2,500,000,000,000 times.

51. The approximate weight of Earth is 5,880,000,000,000,000,000,000 t. $\quad 5.88 \times 10^{21}$

52. The radius of our solar system is 100,000,000,000 m.

53. The radius of the Milky Way galaxy is 10,000,000,000,000,000,000 m. $\quad 1 \times 10^{19}$

54. In the 1864 presidential election, 2,218,388 votes were cast for Abraham Lincoln.

Factors, Multiples, and Divisibility

OBJECTIVE:
To identify whole
number factors and
multiples of a number
and to determine
divisibility by 2, 3, 4,
5, 6, 9, or 10.

▼ The diagram at the right shows all the
different rectangles that you can make with
12 squares. The dimensions are 1 by 12,
2 by 6, and 3 by 4. The numbers 1, 2, 3, 4,
6, and 12 are the *factors* of 12. The number
12 is *divisible* by its factors.

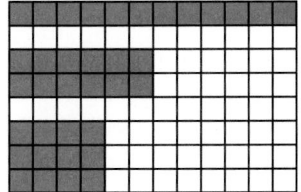

Divisible	A number is divisible by a second number if the second number divides the first with no remainder.

Factor	One number is a factor of another if it divides that number with no remainder.

Example 1 Find the factors of 15.

Solution   1 · 15   3 · 5

The factors of 15 are 1, 3, 5, and 15.

THINK Why is 8 not a factor
of 45?

Example 2 Are 5 and 8 factors of 45?

Solution 45 ÷ 5 = 9 ✓   Yes, 5 is a factor of 45.

45 ÷ 8 = 5.625 ✗   No, 8 is not a factor of 45.

▼ You can find the *multiples* of any number. The multiples of 12 are
12, 24, 36, 48, . . .

Multiple	A multiple of a number is the product of that number and any other non-zero whole number.

Example 3 Find the first three multiples of each number.

    a. 2   **b.** 10

Solution   **a.** 2 · 1 = 2   **b.** 10 · 1 = 10
                    2 · 2 = 4   10 · 2 = 20
                    2 · 3 = 6   10 · 3 = 30

Example 4 Is 45 a multiple of 15?

Solution The multiples of 15 are 15, 30, 45, 60, . . .

Yes, 45 is a multiple of 15 because 3 · 15 = 45.

▼ You can use divisibility tests to find out if one number is divisible by another.

Divisibility Tests	A number is divisible by 2 if the ones' digit is 0, 2, 4, 6, or 8.
	A number is divisible by 5 if the ones' digit is 0 or 5.
	A number is divisible by 10 if the ones' digit is 0.

▼ To discover a divisibility test for 3, analyze the following table.

Number	Sum of digits	Is the sum divisible by 3?	Is the number divisible by 3?
136	$1 + 3 + 6 = 10$	no	no
462	$4 + 6 + 2 = 12$	yes	yes
216	$2 + 1 + 6 = 9$	yes	yes
1,017	$1 + 0 + 1 + 7 = 9$	yes	yes

| Divisible by 3 | A number is divisible by 3 if the sum of its digits is divisible by 3. |

▼ To discover a divisibility test for 9, analyze the following table.

Number	Sum of digits	Is the sum divisible by 9?	Is the number divisible by 9?
136	$1 + 3 + 6 = 10$	no	no
462	$4 + 6 + 2 = 12$	no	no
216	$2 + 1 + 6 = 9$	yes	yes
1,017	$1 + 0 + 1 + 7 = 9$	yes	yes

| Divisible by 9 | A number is divisible by 9 if the sum of its digits is divisible by 9. |

THINK If a number is divisible by 3, is it also divisible by 9? Is the reverse true? Explain.

Example 5 Is the first number divisible by the second?

    a. 567; 2   **b.** 567; 3   **c.** 567; 5   **d.** 567; 9

Solution **a.** No, the ones' digit is not 0, 2, 4, 6, or 8.

    b. Yes, the sum of the digits is 18, which is divisible by 3. Write: 3|567 (3 divides 567 with no remainder).

    c. No, the ones' digit is not 0 or 5.

    d. Yes, the sum of the digits is divisible by 9. Write: 9|567.

True or *false*? Explain your answer.

1. 3|555 T

2. 981 is divisible by 9. T

3. 9 is a multiple of 18. F

4. 5 is a factor of 435. T

5. 6 divides 56. F

6. 2 divides every even number. T

7. If a number is divisible by both 2 and 5, it is divisible by 10. T

8. If a number is divisible by 6, then it is divisible by 2. T

9. If a number is divisible by 2, then it is divisible by 6. F

10. List the first ten multiples of 11.   11, 22, 3 3, 44, 5 5, 66, 77, 88, 99, 110

11. Write a missing digit so that the resulting number is divisible by 3.   4,826,▮51

12. Write a missing digit so that the resulting number is divisible by 9.   4,826,▮51

13. State a rule for divisibility by 100.   has to end with 2 0's

---

THINK AND DISCUSS

1. What number is a factor of all numbers?

2. How many multiples does any number have?

3. What number can never be a factor of a number?

2√126

Decide whether the first number is a factor of the second.

1. 8; 72 Y

2. 12; 54 n

3. 7; 91 Y

4. 6; 68 n

5. 9; 621 Y

6. 3; 101 n

7. 5; 46,582 n

8. 4; 128 Y

9. 10; 75,020 Y

10. 9; 74,520 Y

11. 3; 876 Y

12. 15; 120 Y

List all the factors of each number.

13. 30 1, 2, 3, 5, 6, 10, 15, 30

14. 1 1

15. 55 1, 5, 11, 55

16. 126 1, 2, 3, 6, 21, 42, 63, 126

17. 29 1, 29

List the first five multiples of each number.

18. 1 1, 2, 3, 4, 5

19. 12 12, 24, 36, 48, 60

20. 16 16, 32, 47, 53, 59

21. 25 25, 50, 75, 100, 125

State whether each number is divisible by 2, 3, 5, or 9.

22. 213 3, 9

23. 630 2, 3, 5, 9

24. 138 2, 3

25. 204 2, 3

26. 131 none

27. 4,805 5

28. 288 2

29. 4,719 3

30. Which numbers are divisible by both 2 and 3?

  a. 10   **b.** 66   **c.** 898   **d.** 47,820   **e.** 975

  f. *WRITE* a divisibility rule for 6.   if the # is divisible by 2 and 3

NOTES & QUOTES

A perfect number is a number that is the sum of all its possible factors, excluding itself. Six is the first perfect number (1 + 2 + 3 = 6). At present, only 30 perfect numbers have been calculated.

RESEARCH Can you find the second perfect number?

---

31. a. Copy and complete the table.

Number	Last two digits	Last 2 digits divisible by 4?	Is the number divisible by 4?
136	36	yes	yes
1,268	68	yes	yes
314	14	no	no
1,078	78	n	n
696	96	y	y

b. *WRITE* a divisibility rule for 4.

if last 2 digits are divisible by 4

Write the missing digit to make each number divisible by 9.

32. 29 3 ,634   **33.** 4 7 ,817   **34.** 8,03 3 ,373

Solve.

35. If a is divisible by 2, is $a + 1$ even or odd? *odd*

36. If a is divisible by 9, is $2a$ divisible by 9? *yes*

37. If a^2 is divisible by both 2 and 5, can $a = 10$? *y*

38. Find a number less than 100 that is divisible by the first six positive integers. *?*

MIXED REVIEW

Write an equation for each. Do not solve.

1. A number decreased by 5 equals -24.

2. Ten less than 3 times a number is 57.

Evaluate for $p = -3$, $r = 4$.

3. $5p - 2r$

4. $4p^2$

5. $-r^2 + p$

Write in scientific notation.

6. 3,480,000

7. 250

8. On a hot summer day in Germany, the temperature is 35°C. Using the formula $F = 1.8C + 32$, find the temperature in °F.

TEST YOURSELF

Write in standard notation.

1. 9.604×10^3 **2.** 1.23×10^4 **3.** $(42 \times 10^9)(0.68 \times 10^6)$

Write in scientific notation.

4. 9,650,000   **5.** 548   **6.** 30×10^5

List all the factors of each number.

7. 27   **8.** 45   **9.** 60

State whether each number is divisible by 2, 3, 5, or 9.

10. 45   **11.** 300   **12.** 369

Write using exponents.

13. $4 \cdot 4 \cdot 4 \cdot 4$ **14.** $17 \cdot 17 \cdot 17$ **15.** $z \cdot z \cdot z \cdot z$

Evaluate for $x = 2$ and $y = 5$.

16. x^2y **17.** y^2x **18.** $x^2 + y^2$ **19.** $x^4 - y^2$

OBJECTIVE:
To determine whether
a number is prime or
composite and to find
its prime
factorization.

4-6 Prime Factorization

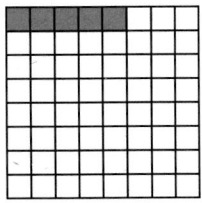

▼ The graph paper diagram shows all the possible factors of 5. Notice there is only one rectangle. The factors of 5 are 1 and 5. We call the number 5 a *prime number*.

Prime Number	A prime number is a whole number greater than one with exactly two factors, 1 and the number itself.

▼ Numbers greater than 1 that are not prime are *composite numbers*.

Example 1   **Prime numbers**   **Composite numbers**

2, 3, 5, 7, 11, 13 . . .   4, 6, 8, 9, 10, 12, 14, 15 . . .

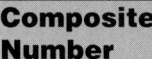

THINK Why is 2 the only even prime number?

Composite Number	A composite number is a whole number greater than one with more than two factors.

▼ A composite number is divisible by prime factors.

Example 2   **Tell whether each number is prime or composite.**

a. 129   b. 23

Solution   To test for divisibility, start with the smallest prime. Stop when you reach a prime whose square is greater than the number you are testing.

a. Is 129 divisible by 2? No, it is odd.

Is 129 divisible by 3? Yes, the sum of the digits is 12, a multiple of 3.

129 is composite.

b. Is 23 divisible by 2? No, it is odd.

Is 23 divisible by 3? No, the sum of the digits is 5.

Is 23 divisible by 5? No, the ones' digit is not 0 or 5.

Since $5^2 > 23$, 23 is prime.

What prime numbers are shown? How do you know they are prime?

▼ You can write a composite number as a product of its prime factors, called the *prime factorization*.

Example 3   Write the prime factorization of 60 using division.

Solution   Divide by prime numbers until the quotient is 1.

1. Is 60 divisible by 2? Yes. $60 \div 2 = 30$
2. Is 30 divisible by 2? Yes. $30 \div 2 = 15$
3. Is 15 divisible by 2? No.
4. Is 15 divisible by 3? Yes. $15 \div 3 = 5$
5. Is 5 divisible by 3? No.
6. Since $5 \div 5 = 1$, you are done. $5 \div 5 = 1$

$60 = 2 \cdot 2 \cdot 3 \cdot 5$, or $2^2 \cdot 3 \cdot 5$

THINK What other ways can you write the prime factorization of 825 using a factor tree?

Example 4   Write the prime factorization of 825 using a factor tree.

Solution
1. Write the composite number as the product of two factors.
2. Continue Step 1 with any remaining composite factors.
3. Stop when all factors are prime.
4. Write the prime factorization.

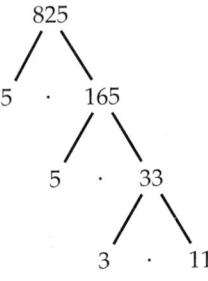

$5 \cdot 5 \cdot 3 \cdot 11 = 5^2 \cdot 3 \cdot 11$

CLASS EXERCISES

THINK AND DISCUSS

1. Why is the number 1 neither prime nor composite?

2. Why is zero neither prime nor composite?

3. Do you think there is a largest prime number? Explain.

Tell whether each number is prime or composite.

1. 102 C
2. 197 P
3. 253 p
4. 367 C
5. 221 p
6. 209 p

Write the prime factorization using division.

7. 150
8. 280
9. 225

Write the prime factorization using a factor tree.

10. 236
11. 294
12. 275

Find the number with the given prime factorization.

13. $2 \cdot 3^2 \cdot 5^2$
14. $3 \cdot 5 \cdot 7^2$

WRITTEN EXERCISES

Tell whether each number is prime or composite.

1. 45 *C*   **2.** 87   **3.** 97 *p*

4. 109   **5.** 301 *C*   **6.** 1,001

Write the prime factorization using division.

7. 425 $5^2 \times 17$ **8.** 240   **9.** 186 $2 \times 3 \times 31$

Write the prime factorization using a factor tree.

10. 650   **11.** 1,575 $3^2 \cdot 5^2 \times 7$ **12.** 1,617

CALCULATOR Find the number with the given prime factorization.

13. $2^5 \cdot 3 \cdot 11$ 1056   **14.** $2 \cdot 5 \cdot 17^2$ **15.** $2^5 \cdot 5 \cdot 7^3 \cdot 13^2$ 9,274,720

Use 5, 11, and 23 to find the prime factors of each number.

16. 115   **17.** 621 $3^3 \times 23$ **18.** 3,105   **19.** 253 11×23

Will each integer expression be even or odd?

20. $2ab^2$ **21.** $2(a + b)^2$ *even*   **22.** $2a^2b + 1$

Solve.

23. The numbers 2, 3, and 7 are factors of x. Find four other factors of x.   6, 14, 21, 42

24. Find a number between 50 and 100 whose prime factorization has two factors.

25. Ms. Schwartz wrote a number on the chalkboard and said, "I know that to be sure this number is prime, I must check each prime divisor from 2 to 29." What is the least number Ms. Schwartz could have written? What is the greatest number she could have written?   841, 960

26. Kim and her grandmother have the same birthday and they have a family party together every year. Kim's age was a divisor of her grandmother's age for six birthdays in a row. What were their ages at each of those birthdays?

27. *DATA FILE 4 (pp. 138–139)*

   a. Which country has the greatest percent of its population between the ages of 10 and 14?   China

   b. Which country has the greatest percent of its population between the ages of 0 and 4?   Brazil

NOTES & QUOTES

The largest prime number yet calculated (on a CRAY supercomputer in Houston, Texas, in 1985) has 65,050 digits. It is mathematically written as $2^{216091} - 1$. The computer worked at a rate of 400 million calculations per second for 3 h to insure that this number was in fact prime.

MIXED REVIEW

1. List the factors of 8.

2. List the first four multiples of 8.

3. List the factors of 36.

Evaluate.

4. $54 \div (9 - 15)$

5. $5(-4 + 7)^2$

6. $36 \div [2 - (-1)]^2$

7. *DATA FILE 1 (pp. 2–3)* Predict the equivalent wind chill temperature for air temperature -30°F and wind speed 10 mi/h.

PROBLEM SOLVING HINT
Use guess and test.

Eratosthenes of Cyrene (c. 276–195 B.C.) was a Greek mathematician. He established a procedure for determining all prime numbers less than a given value. This procedure is called the *Sieve of Eratosthenes.*

RESEARCH Find out how Eratosthenes used his sieve to determine prime numbers. Use his method to determine all prime numbers less than 150.

28. Find two prime numbers whose product is 221.

29. Twin primes are prime numbers whose difference is 2. For example, 11 and 13 are twin primes.

    a. List the first seven pairs of twin primes.

    b. What do these numbers have in common?

    c. Predict whether this will be true for all twin primes.

    d. Use a computer or sieve (see below) to generate primes less than 100.

    e. Test your prediction.

30. Find a pattern in the chart. Write an equation relating c and t.

chairs	5	10	15	c
tables	1	2	3	t

Critical Thinking

EXPLORING CLASSIFICATION

▼ You can use a *sieve* to find prime numbers. The first step is to list the numbers from 1 to 100 in rows of six on paper.

Mark out 1, since it's not prime. Circle 2, since it is prime. Mark out every multiple of 2.

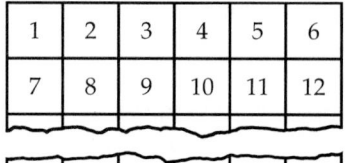

1. What pattern do you notice for the multiples of 2?

2. Circle the first number after 2 that is unmarked. This is the next prime number. Mark out all of its multiples. What pattern do you notice for these multiples?

3. The next prime is 5. Circle it and mark out all of its multiples. Describe the pattern formed by the multiples of 5.

4. What is the next prime number? Mark out its multiples.

5. Eleven is prime. Circle it. Why have you already marked out all of the multiples of 11?

6. What do you notice about the rest of the unmarked numbers? Why is this true?

7. Find all the primes less than 200. When is it no longer necessary to mark out multiples?

4-7 GCF and LCM

OBJECTIVE:
To find the GCF or LCM by listing or using prime factorization.

▼ At a school fund raiser, the math class raised $150 and the science class raised $120. Each class will divide the money it raised equally, in whole dollar amounts, and give to the same number of charities. What method could you use to find the possible number of charities? the greatest possible number of charities?

List the factors of 150 and 120. Find the factors that are the same.

150: **1, 2, 3, 5, 6, 10, 15,** 25, **30,** 50, 75, 150

120: **1, 2, 3,** 4, **5, 6,** 8, **10,** 12, **15,** 20, 24, **30,** 40, 60, 120

The *common factors* are 1, 2, 3, 5, 6, 10, 15, and 30. The *greatest common factor (GCF)* is 30. The classes can distribute whole dollar amounts of money to 1, 2, 3, 5, 6, 10, 15, or, at most, 30 charities.

Common Factor	The factors that are the same for a given set of numbers are their common factors.

Greatest Common Factor (GCF)	The greatest common factor of a set of numbers is the greatest number that is a factor of the given numbers.

▼ Another way to find the GCF is to use prime factorization.

Example 1 **Find the GCF of 40 and 140.**

Solution 1. Write the prime factorization for each number.

2. Circle each pair of common factors.

$$40 = 2 \cdot 2 \cdot 2 \cdot 5$$
$$140 = 2 \cdot 2 \cdot 5 \cdot 7$$

3. Multiply common factors. $2 \cdot 2 \cdot 5$

The GCF is 20.

▼ When the GCF of two numbers is 1, the numbers are *relatively prime*.

Example 2 **Find the GCF of 28 and 33.**

Solution 1. Write the prime factorization. $28 = 2 \cdot 2 \cdot 7$

2. Circle common factors. $33 = 3 \cdot 11$

There are no common prime factors. The GCF is 1.

THINK Do relatively prime numbers have any common factors besides 1?

▼ You can find the GCF of variable expressions by writing each expression as the product of its factors. This is called *algebraic factorization*.

Example 3 Find the GCF of $12a^3b$ and $15a^2b^2$.

Solution

1. Write the algebraic factorizations.

2. Circle the common factors.

$$12a^3b = 2 \cdot 2 \cdot 3 \cdot a \cdot a \cdot a \cdot b$$
$$15a^2b^2 = 3 \cdot 5 \cdot a \cdot a \cdot b \cdot b$$

3. Multiply.

$$3 \cdot a \cdot a \cdot b$$

The GCF is $3a^2b$.

▼ Some problems require that you work with *common multiples* and the *least common multiple (LCM)*.

THINK How many common multiples do any two numbers have?

Common Multiples	The multiples that are the same for a given set of whole numbers are the common multiples.

Least Common Multiple	The least common multiple is the least number that is a common multiple of two or more given numbers.

Example 4 Aisha and Tom visited their aunt today. Aisha visits every 4 days; Tom visits every 3 days. When will Aisha and Tom visit their aunt again on the same day?

Solution

1. List the multiples of each number.

2. Circle common multiples.

4: 4, 8, 12, 16, 20, 24 . . .
3: 3, 6, 9, 12, 15, 18, 21, 24 . . .

3. Write the least common multiple.   LCM = 12

Aisha and Tom will visit their aunt together in 12 days.

▼ You can find the LCM using prime factorization.

Example 5 Find the LCM of 72 and 60.

Solution

1. Write the prime factorizations.

2. Circle each factor the greatest number of times it appears.

$$72 = 2 \cdot 2 \cdot 2 \cdot 3 \cdot 3$$
$$60 = 2 \cdot 2 \cdot 3 \cdot 5$$

3. Multiply.

$$2 \cdot 2 \cdot 2 \cdot 3 \cdot 3 \cdot 5$$

The LCM is 360.

▼ You can find the LCM of variable expressions using algebraic factorization.

Example 6 Find the LCM of $4a^2$ and $6ab$.

Solution 1. Write the algebraic factorizations.

$4a^2 = 2 \cdot 2 \cdot a \cdot a$
$6ab = 2 \cdot 3 \cdot a \cdot b$

2. Circle each factor the greatest number of times it appears.

3. Multiply.

$2 \cdot 2 \cdot 3 \cdot a \cdot a \cdot b$

The LCM is $12a^2b$.

CLASS EXERCISES

Find the GCF of each set of numbers or expressions.

1. 10, 45   2. 6, 8, 12   3. $12r^3$, $8r$

Find the LCM of each set of numbers or expressions.

4. 10, 45   5. 6, 8, 12   6. $12r^3$, $8r$

Is the pair of numbers relatively prime? Write *yes* or *no*.

7. 51, 17   8. 9, 10   9. 13, 23

10. Find the GCF and the LCM for each pair of numbers. Find the product of the GCF and the LCM. Find the product of the two original numbers. What do you notice? Will this always be true? Is it true that the LCM of two numbers is a multiple of their GCF?

    a. 6, 8   b. 15, 18   c. 20, 30
    d. 20, 25   e. 12, 30   f. 84, 120

11. Name four numbers that have both 6 and 10 as factors. What is the least number that has 6 and 10 as factors?

12. *True* or *false*? Explain.

    a. If a and b are positive integers and $a|b$, then the LCM of a and b is b.

    b. The set of all common factors of two given positive integers is finite.

WRITTEN EXERCISES

Find the GCF of each set of numbers or expressions.

1. 14, 21   2. 54, 144   3. 52, 65

4. 18, 30 _6_   **5.** $27x^2y^4$, $46x^2yz$ _?_   **6.** 8, 15, 20 _1_

7. $180a^2$, $210ab$ _?_   **8.** $6a^3b$, $8ab^2$ _?_   **9.** 12, 15, 18
                                                                                                        _3_

Find the LCM of each set of numbers or expressions.

10. 10, 55 _110_   **11.** 12, 20 _60_   **12.** 54, 36 _60_

13. 180, 210 _1,260_   **14.** $8x$, $25y$ _?_   **15.** $6a^3b$, $8ab^2$ _?_

16. $6cd^3$, $8c$, $12d^2$ _?_   **17.** 12, 15, 18   **18.** 14, 18, 21
                                              _180_   _201_

CALCULATOR Find the GCF and LCM for each set of numbers.

19. 32, 12   **20.** 119, 391   **21.** 135; 280; 300
        _4 96_   _6, 491_   _5, 37,800_

22. The GCF of 30 and x is 6. Could x be each of the following?

   a. 15   **b.** 24   **c.** 60   **d.** 84

23. The LCM of 8 and x is a. Explain why a is divisible by 2^3.
         _?_

Solve.

24. When Jim sorts his stamps into piles of 2, 3, 4, or 5, there is always one stamp left over. What is the smallest number of stamps Jim can have? _2_

25. Two neon signs turn on at the same time. One blinks on every 10 s, the other blinks on every 6 s. How many times per minute do the signs blink on together? _2 per min_

26. The numbers of students attending a conference from three schools are 42, 48, and 60. The students will form discussion groups with an equal number of students from each school in each group. What is the greatest number of discussion groups that can be formed? _42_

27. There are two sizes of tables in a banquet hall. One size seats exactly 5 people and the other size seats exactly 8 people. Last night, 66 people were seated at fewer than 10 tables with no empty seats. How many tables of each size were there? _2, 5_
_7, 8_

28. A band of pirates shared 187 pieces of silver and 136 gold coins. Each pirate received a fair share. How many pirates were in the band? _200_

29. A farmer has three pieces of timber with lengths of 63 ft, 84 ft, and 105 ft. What is the length of the longest logs of equal length the farmer can cut from the timber? _21 ft_

DATA FILE 10 (pp. 404–405) Solve.

30. About how many acres should 22 grizzly bears have for a home range?

31. About how many striped skunks can live within 15,000 acres?

170   Chapter 4 Number Theory

MIXED REVIEW

Write the prime factorization using a factor tree.

1. 12

2. 123

3. What are all the factors of 12?

4. State the first four multiples of 12.

Solve.

5. $3.5n = 14$

6. $-7.3 = p + 4.1$

7. $\frac{n}{3.2} = -5$

Use guess and test.

8. Find two numbers that have a sum of 11 and product of 24.

OBJECTIVE:
To explore a problem using a systematic approach.

MATERIALS

- Graph paper

- Math journal to record work

Exploring Counting Problems

■ Counting figures can be confusing.

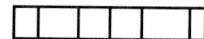

1. Count the rectangles. Are there more than six? Did you count the large rectangle bordering the figure?

2. Can a rectangle be made up of smaller rectangles? Can the rectangles overlap? How would this affect your total count?

3. How can you count the rectangles *systematically,* so you are sure you counted them all? **Discuss** with a partner.

■ One way to count the rectangles is to trace around the different rectangles, starting at the left and working across.

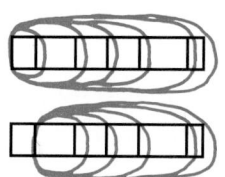

4. Start at the left vertical segment and count all the rectangles that use that segment as a left side. How many are there?

5. Continue with the next vertical segment.

6. Continue counting. When do you know you are done?

Number of Small Rectangles	Labeled Rectangles
1	A, B, C, D, E, F, G, H
2	AB, BC, CD, DE, EF, FG, GH

A B C D E F G H

■ Another systematic way to count the rectangles is to account for the different combinations of smaller rectangles. To keep track, label the smaller rectangles. Refer to the figure at the left.

7. How many rectangles include only one small rectangle? two small rectangles? Continue until you have counted all the combinations of small rectangles. Make a table to organize your data.

8. What is the total number of rectangles? How can you be sure you counted them all?

9. **Describe** the pattern in the table. Did you see this pattern when you used the tracing method?

10. Use the pattern to find the number of different rectangles in a figure with 5 regions; 15 regions.

11. **Compare** the two methods for counting. How are they the same? How are they different?

■ Now look at the squares in the figure at the left.

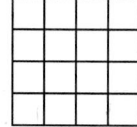

12. **Explore** a method of your own or use one of the counting methods above. Which method would you use? Why?

13. What is the total number of squares?

Exploring Counting Problems   **171**

OBJECTIVE:
To solve problems by accounting for all possibilities.

4-8 *Account for All Possibilities*

■ To account systematically for all possibilities, you can make an organized list, a table, or a diagram.

PROBLEM

Mandy invited Rachel, Sue, Jenny, Pam, Erica, and Latosha for lunch. They decided to take pictures of all seven girls with two in each picture. How many pictures did they take?

SOLUTION

READ ▶ Answer these questions to understand the given information.

What do you want to find?	the total number of pictures
How many girls are at the party?	seven
How many girls are in each picture?	two

PLAN ▶ One way to account for all the possibilities is to make an organized list of all the pairs of girls.

SOLVE ▶ Begin by pairing Mandy with her six friends. Next, pair Latosha with each of the five friends. Since Latosha and Mandy have already been paired, you don't need to count them again.

Mandy—Latosha

Mandy—Pam   Latosha—Pam

Mandy—Rachel   Latosha—Rachel   Pam—

Mandy—Sue   Latosha—Sue

Mandy—Jenny   Latosha—Jenny

Mandy—Erica   Latosha—Erica

Continue the list to find the total number of pairings. Altogether, there are 21 pairs of girls, so there will be 21 pictures.

LOOK BACK ▶ Another way to account systematically for all the possibilities is to use a diagram. Draw line segments to connect all the pairs of girls. If you count the segments as you draw them, you will count 21.

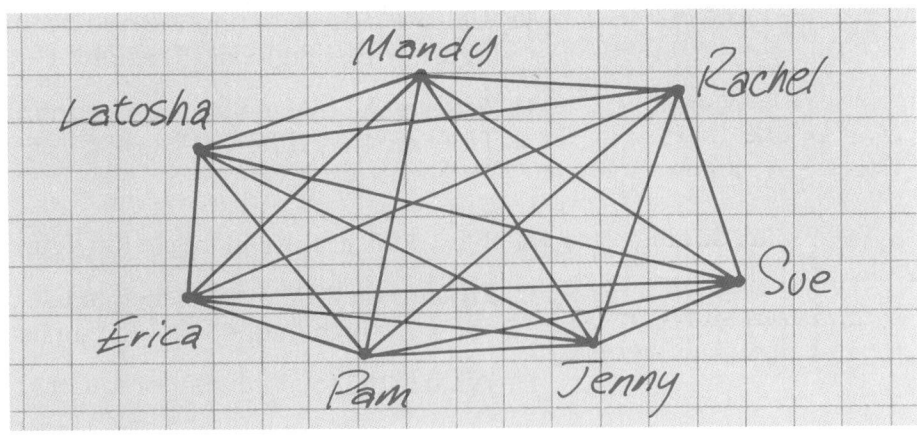

CLASS EXERCISES

Refer to the problem on page 172.

1. Complete the list of paired girls. Count how many pairs are in each group. What pattern do you see?

2. Suppose there were a total of ten girls at Mandy's party. Using the pattern you found, determine how many pictures there would be if there were two girls in each picture.

3. How many pictures would there be if there were a total of 20 girls at Mandy's party, with two girls in each picture? Use the pattern.

Solve.

4. André has a job making yogurt sundaes. The yogurt flavors are chocolate and vanilla. The toppings are granola, raisin, cherry, and coconut. How many *different* sundaes consisting of one scoop of yogurt and one topping can André make?

5. This year there are seven softball teams in the play-offs. Each team competes against each of the other teams twice. What is the total number of games played?

WRITTEN EXERCISES

 **Use a CALCULATOR where appropriate.**

Solve by accounting systematically for all possibilities.

1. Three darts are thrown at the target shown at the right. If each dart lands on the dart board, how many different point totals are possible?

2. You have four 25-cent stamps and three 30-cent stamps. How many different amounts of postage can you have?

3. Each of the small boxes in the figure at the right is a square. What is the total number of different squares shown in the figure?

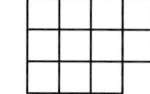

4. You have a collection of coins consisting of one penny, one nickel, one dime, and one quarter. How many different amounts of money can be made using one or more of these coins?

Solve. Use any strategy you wish.

5. Fred has a coordinated wardrobe consisting of three pairs of pants, four shirts, and two sweaters. How many different three-piece outfits can he make?

6. You have mushrooms, onions, green peppers, and olives. How many different pizzas can you make by adding any combinations of the ingredients to a plain pizza?

7. Without evaluating, what is the final digit of 8^{66}? How did you find the answer?

8. A collector sorted stamps into 2 piles and had 1 stamp left over. When she sorted them into piles of 3, there were 2 left over. For piles of 4, there were 3 left over. What is the least number of stamps the collector could have?

9. The Valley High chorus has 28 members. The band has 52 members. A total of 17 students are in both the band and the chorus. The music teacher wants to distribute the fewest possible tickets to the spring concert. How many tickets must the teacher distribute for each student in band or chorus to get at least one ticket?

10. This is a list of consecutive odd integers from 1 to n: $\{1, 3, 5, \ldots n\}$. The square root of the sum of the numbers is 10. What is the value of n? How did you find the answer?

11. Make a list of the two-digit square numbers. Find the difference between the digits of each number. What do you discover?

12. A runner averages 10 km/h. The runner takes a 10 min rest every 5 km. How long will it take to complete a course of 25 km?

13. Pete and Jack earned $12.50 babysitting. Edward earned half as much as Jack. Pete earned $2.50 less than Jack. How much money does Pete have?

14. A chime clock strikes once at one o'clock, twice at two o'clock, and so on. What is the total number of chimes the clock strikes in a twelve-hour period?

Problem Solving Practice

Solve. The list at the left shows some strategies you can use.

PROBLEM SOLVING STRATEGIES

Look for a Pattern
Guess and Test
Simplify the Problem
Make an Organized List
Work Backwards
Account for All Possibilities
Make a Table
Write an Equation
Solve by Graphing
Draw a Diagram
Make a Model
Solve Another Way
Simulate the Problem

1. A car dealer recommends an oil change every 3,000 mi and a tire rotation every 7,000 mi. When will the oil be changed and the tires rotated at the same time?

2. Thomas was training for a race for six weeks. Every week he ran one more mile than he ran the week before. Thomas ran a total of 51 miles while in training. How many miles did he run each week?

3. Bonnie had 16 coins in her pocket totaling $1.50. What are two combinations of coins she could have had in her pocket?

4. At 5 P.M., the temperature was 65°F. At 5:30 P.M., the temperature was 62°F. At 6 P.M., it was 59°F, at 6:30 P.M., it was 56°F. If the pattern continued, at what time would the temperature go below freezing?

5. How many different pizzas can be made if meatballs, anchovies, green peppers, or olives can be added to a plain pizza?

6. The florist orders carnations, roses, and tulips. Carnations can be bought only in bunches of sixteen. Roses come in bunches of four, and tulips in bunches of eight. The florist wants the same number of each flower. What is the least number of flowers the florist can order?

7. Copy the diagrams at the left.

   a. Using the paths shown, Jillian can walk directly to Trisha's house six different ways. Each route is four blocks long. Draw each route.

   b. There are 20 different routes Courtney can use to walk directly to Justin's house. Each route is six blocks long. How many can you find?

8. In a swim meet, Helen places 7.5 m behind Laney. Laney is 16.5 m ahead of Kay. Kay places 3.75 m behind Julia. How far is Julia behind Laney?

9. *DATA FILE 4 (pp. 138–139)*

   a. In what year was the world population five times the population in 1600?

   b. In what span of years was the world population one sixth of the population in 1975?

10. Five pears weigh the same as 3 apples and 2 strawberries. An apple weighs the same as 21 strawberries. How many strawberries equal the weight of a pear?

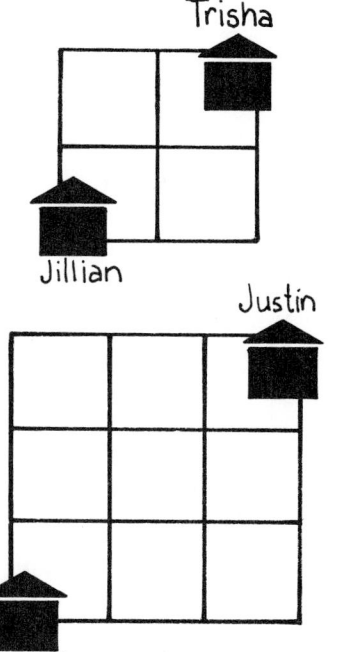

Chapter 4 Review

Match each word with the example that illustrates its meaning.

1. rules of exponents for multiplication
2. base
3. greatest common factor
4. rule of a power raised to a power
5. exponent
6. prime number
7. least common multiple
8. rule of a product raised to a power

a. 3 in 2^3
b. $3^2 \cdot 3^5 = 3^7$
c. 5
d. 2 in 2^3
e. 35 for 5 and 7
f. $(2^3)^2 = 2^6$
g. $(3 \cdot 5)^3 = 3^3 \cdot 5^3$
h. 3 for 12 and 15

Using Exponents   4-1

To evaluate a number that has exponents, remember the base is the number used as a factor and the exponent shows the number of times the base is used as a factor.

$$\text{base} \longrightarrow 3^5 \overset{\text{exponent}}{=} 3 \cdot 3 \cdot 3 \cdot 3 \cdot 3 = 243$$

Evaluate

9. 2^3
10. 5^0
11. 3^3
12. 25^1
13. $(3 + 1)^2$

Multiplication and Exponents   4-2

To simplify or evaluate multiplication expressions with exponents, use the following rules.

$3^2 \cdot 3^5 = 3^{2+5} = 3^7$ $(3^2)^5 = 3^{2 \cdot 5} = 3^{10}$ $(2 \cdot 3)^3 = 2^3 \cdot 3^3$

14. $a^2 \cdot a^3$
15. $(2a^2)^3$
16. $a(b^3 + b^2)$
17. $(a^2b)^2$
18. $ab^3a^2b^4$

Scientific Notation   4-3

To write a number in scientific notation, express it as a number between 1 and 10 times a power of 10 with exponents.

Write each number in scientific notation.

19. 465,000,000
20. 13,600,000
21. 1,280
22. 5,090,000

Write each number in standard form.

23. 2.1×10^5
24. 6.13×10^7
25. 1.05×10^3
26. 8.35×10^2

Factors, Multiples, and Divisibility

To help you to remember the meanings of these words, take a look at the number 15.

3 and 5 are factors of 15.

15 is a multiple of 3: 3, 6, 9, 12, 15.   15 is divisible by 3.
15 is a multiple of 5: 5, 10, 15.   15 is divisible by 5.

True or false. Explain your answer.

27. −378 is divisible by 9.   **28.** 800 is a multiple of 5.   **29.** 12 is a factor of 144.

30. 9 is a factor of 93.   **31.** 93 is divisible by 12.   **32.** 95 is a multiple of 19.

Prime Factorization
4-6

To write a composite number as the product of its prime factors, divide by prime numbers until the quotient is 1, or use a factor tree.

Write the prime factorization using division or a factor tree.

33. 75   **34.** 420   **35.** 108   **36.** 765   **37.** 228   **38.** 595

Finding the Greatest Common Factor, the Least Common Multiple
4-7

To find the GCF or LCM, use the prime factorization.

the GCF of 35 and 42   the LCM of 35 and 42
$35 = 5 \cdot 7$ $35 = 5 \cdot 7$
$42 = 2 \cdot 3 \cdot 7$ $42 = 2 \cdot 3 \cdot 7$
$GCF = 7$ $LCM = 2 \cdot 3 \cdot 5 \cdot 7 = 210$

Find the GCF of each set of numbers.

39. 16, 60   **40.** 24, 56   **41.** 36, 81, 27   **42.** $3x^2y, 6x^2$

Find the LCM of each set of numbers.

43. 12, 18   **44.** 8, 14   **45.** 3, 5, 7   **46.** $12x^2y, 15x^2y^3$ **47.** $18abc^2, 22ab^3$

Problem Solving
4-8

To account for all possibilities in a word problem, make an organized list, a table, or a diagram.

Solve.

48. There are 10 students competing for the tennis trophy. Each student plays another student once. How many games must be played?

Chapter 4 Review   **177**

Chapter 4   Test

Evaluate.

1. 5^3
2. $2^0 \cdot 2^3$
3. $3^2 + 3^3$
4. $4^2 \cdot 1^3$
5. $1{,}250^1$

Evaluate for $a = -2$, $b = 3$.

6. a^2b
7. $(a \cdot b)^2$
8. $b^3 \cdot b^0$
9. $(a + b)^5$
10. $2(a^2 + b^3)$

Write each number in scientific notation.

11. Every hour 2,500,000 plastic bottles are thrown away in the United States.

12. The estimated population of the U.S.S.R. is 287,000,000.

Write each number in standard notation.

13. 3.51×10^5
14. 1.9×10^7
15. 2.659×10^8
16. 4.2×10^3

List all the factors of each number.

17. 24
18. 56
19. 63
20. 105
21. 19

Tell whether each number is prime or composite.

22. 61
23. 57
24. 83
25. 4,563
26. 954
27. 771

Write the prime factorization.

28. 245
29. 378
30. 242
31. 525
32. 333
33. 848

Find the GCF of each set of numbers.

34. 15, 24
35. 36, 60
36. 56, 96
37. $14a^2b^3$, $21ab^2$

Find the LCM of each set of numbers.

38. 6, 8
39. 18, 36
40. 12, 15
41. $10x$, $15y$

Solve.

42. Vince has a job making pizzas. There is regular pizza and pan pizza. The choice of toppings is extra cheese, meatballs, or pepperoni. How many different pizzas can he make?

43. What is the total number of squares in the figure?

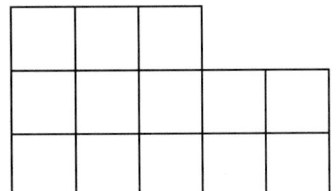

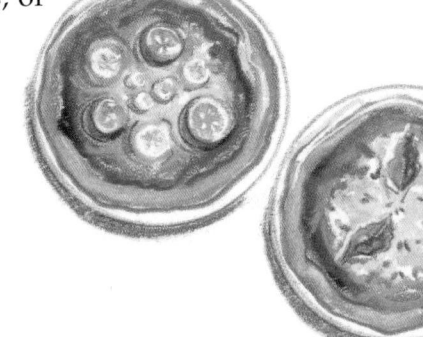

Chapters 1–4   Cumulative Review

Choose the correct answer. Write A, B, C, or D.

1. What relationship does this diagram represent?
   - **A.** $5 - 1 = 7 - 3 = 2^2$
   - **B.** $9 + 16 = 5^2$
   - **C.** $1 + 3 + 5 + 7 = 4^2$
   - **D.** not given

   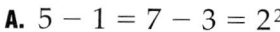

2. Simplify $x^2y \cdot xy^3$.
   - **A.** $2x^2y^3$
   - **B.** x^3y^4
   - **C.** x^2y^3
   - **D.** not given

3. Find a decimal between -1.5 and -1.3.
   - **A.** 1.4
   - **B.** -1.4
   - **C.** -1.2
   - **D.** not given

4. Solve $y + 0.5 = 3$.
   - **A.** 2.5
   - **B.** 1.5
   - **C.** 3.5
   - **D.** not given

5. -4 is a solution of which of the following?
   - **A.** $9x = 36$
   - **B.** $x - 9 = -5$
   - **C.** $x + 9 = 5$
   - **D.** not given

6. $56,600,000,000$
   - **A.** 5.65×10^8
   - **B.** 56.5×10^9
   - **C.** 5.6×10^{10}
   - **D.** not given

7. Compare $|-1|^3$ 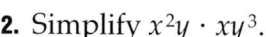 $-(-1)^3$.
   - **A.** $<$
   - **B.** $>$
   - **C.** $=$
   - **D.** not given

8. Which number is prime?
   - **A.** 57
   - **B.** 23
   - **C.** 49
   - **D.** not given

9. Solve.

   - **A.** -7
   - **B.** 4
   - **C.** 1
   - **D.** not given

10. Which of the following is equal to x^{12}?
    - **A.** $x^6 \cdot x^6$
    - **B.** $(x^4)^8$
    - **C.** $x^6 + x^6$
    - **D.** not given

11. What is the expression for *the square of the quantity 3 times the absolute value of negative 3?*
    - **A.** $3|(-3)^2|$
    - **B.** $3|-3|^2$
    - **C.** $(3|-3|)^2$
    - **D.** not given

12. Simplify $3(a + 2b) - 3a$.
    - **A.** $-6a + 6b$
    - **B.** $3a + 6b$
    - **C.** $2b$
    - **D.** not given

13. Evaluate $(-1)^7 \cdot (-2)^0$.
    - **A.** 2
    - **B.** -1
    - **C.** 1
    - **D.** not given

14. Which number is divisible by 9?
    - **A.** 1,578
    - **B.** 5,381
    - **C.** 8,622
    - **D.** not given

15. What is the prime factorization of 90?
    - **A.** $2 \cdot 45$
    - **B.** $2 \cdot 5 \cdot 9$
    - **C.** $2 \cdot 3^2 \cdot 5$
    - **D.** not given

16. Find the GCF of $4a^3b^2$ and $12ab^3$.
    - **A.** $4ab^2$
    - **B.** $12a^3b^3$
    - **C.** $3a^2b$
    - **D.** not given

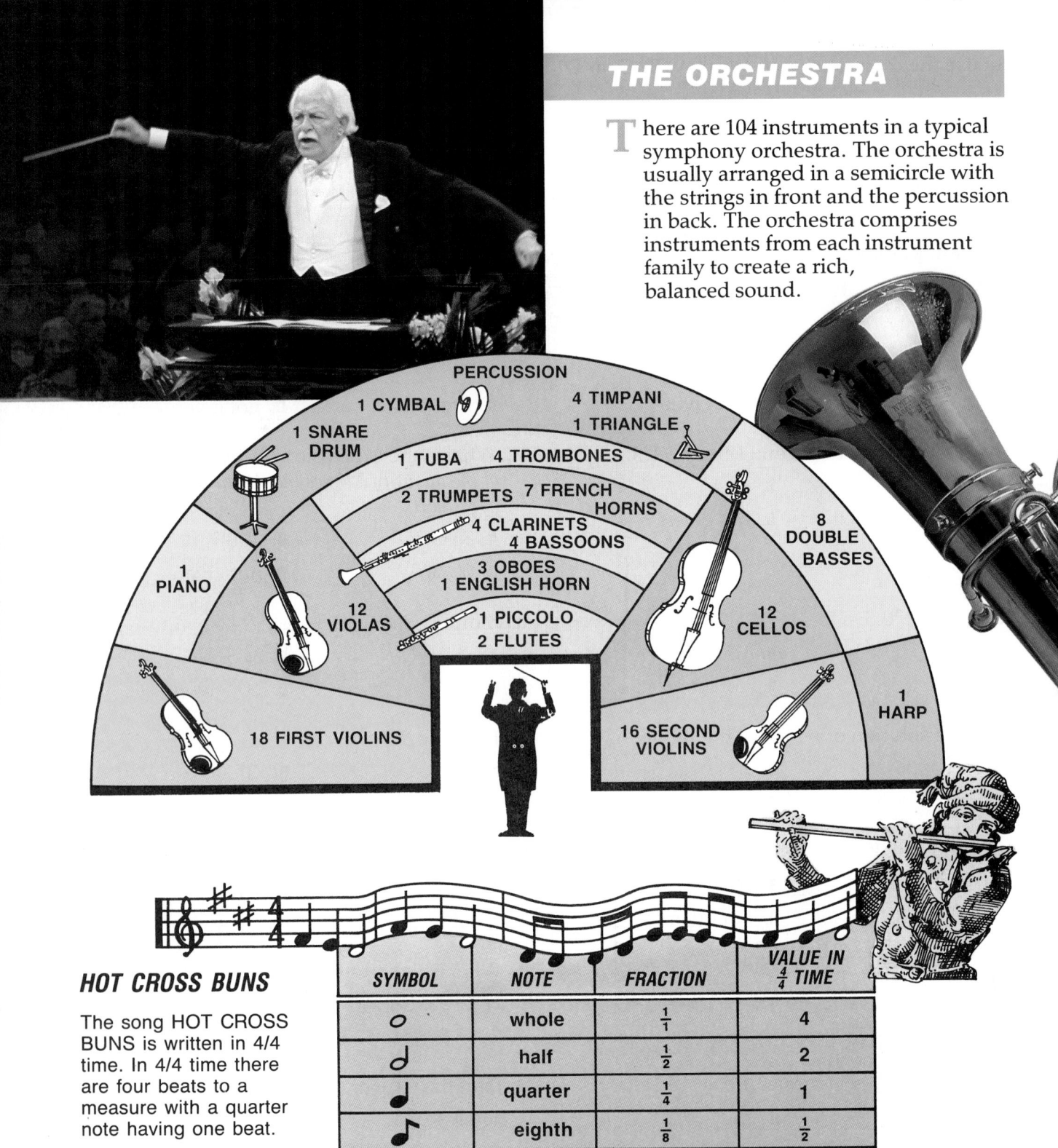

THE ORCHESTRA

There are 104 instruments in a typical symphony orchestra. The orchestra is usually arranged in a semicircle with the strings in front and the percussion in back. The orchestra comprises instruments from each instrument family to create a rich, balanced sound.

PERCUSSION
1 CYMBAL   4 TIMPANI
1 SNARE DRUM   1 TRIANGLE
1 TUBA   4 TROMBONES
2 TRUMPETS   7 FRENCH HORNS
4 CLARINETS
4 BASSOONS
3 OBOES
1 ENGLISH HORN
1 PICCOLO
2 FLUTES
1 PIANO
12 VIOLAS
8 DOUBLE BASSES
12 CELLOS
1 HARP
18 FIRST VIOLINS
16 SECOND VIOLINS

HOT CROSS BUNS

The song HOT CROSS BUNS is written in 4/4 time. In 4/4 time there are four beats to a measure with a quarter note having one beat.

SYMBOL	NOTE	FRACTION	VALUE IN $\frac{4}{4}$ TIME
𝅝	whole	$\frac{1}{1}$	4
𝅗𝅥	half	$\frac{1}{2}$	2
𝅘𝅥	quarter	$\frac{1}{4}$	1
𝅘𝅥𝅮	eighth	$\frac{1}{8}$	$\frac{1}{2}$
𝅘𝅥𝅯	sixteenth	$\frac{1}{16}$	$\frac{1}{4}$

Rational Numbers and Expressions

Think about it...

Look at the triple line graph. Do you think CDs will ever completely replace records and tapes?

A portion of the price you pay for a CD is paid to the artist who made the recording. Artists usually receive $\frac{1}{4}$ of the list price of the CD in the form of a royalty.

Bessie Smith (1894–1937) was a famous blues singer known for her beautiful singing voice. She recorded almost 200 songs.

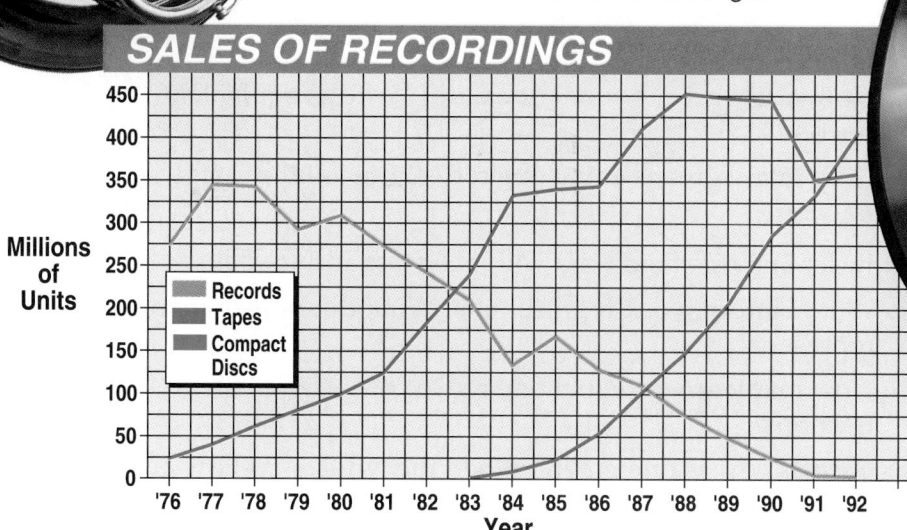

SALES OF RECORDINGS

Millions of Units

Records
Tapes
Compact Discs

450
400
350
300
250
200
150
100
50
0

'76 '77 '78 '79 '80 '81 '82 '83 '84 '85 '86 '87 '88 '89 '90 '91 '92

Year

Exploring Fractions

▼ You can use a variety of models to represent fractions. *Fraction bars* represent fractions as a shaded part of a region.

1. **Explain** how the numerator (3) and denominator (6) describe the model.

$\frac{3}{6}$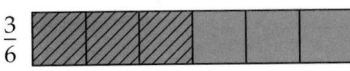

▼ Each fraction bar represents the same amount. The fraction bars show *equivalent fractions*.

$\frac{2}{4}$

2. **a.** Find or draw two other fraction bars that show the same fraction.

$\frac{1}{2}$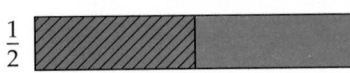

b. **Discuss** Can you find a thirds' bar that shows a fraction equivalent to $\frac{1}{2}$? Why or why not?

3. **Model** each pair of equivalent fractions.

a. $\frac{2}{3} = \frac{4}{6}$ **b.** $\frac{4}{12} = \frac{2}{6}$ **c.** $\frac{6}{6} = \frac{12}{12}$ **d.** $\frac{8}{6} = \frac{4}{3}$

MATERIALS

- Fraction bars
- Pattern blocks
- Graph paper
- Math journal to record work

▼ You can use *pattern blocks* to represent fractions as a part of a whole or part of a set.

4. Suppose one yellow stands for a whole.

a. Write the fraction for each piece.

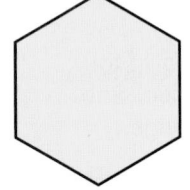   

b. How many greens equal one blue? Write as equivalent fractions.

c. How many greens equal one red? Write as equivalent fractions.

5. Now let one *red* stand for a whole. **Discuss** and model.

a. What pattern block represents $\frac{1}{3}$? What does one blue block represent?

b. How many greens equal one red? Write as equivalent fractions.

c. **Discuss** Why is one green $\frac{1}{6}$ when the whole is yellow and $\frac{1}{3}$ when the whole is red?

6. a. Suppose one green represents $\frac{1}{2}$. What piece represents a whole?

   b. Suppose one yellow represents $\frac{1}{2}$. What represents a whole?

▼ Estimation can help you understand fraction situations.

7. a. Take a sheet of paper and tear off a piece that you think is about $\frac{1}{3}$. Now fold another piece of paper in thirds and compare. How close were you? Compare with another member of your group.

   b. Repeat the tearing and comparing for the following fractions.

$$\frac{1}{2} \qquad \frac{3}{4} \qquad \frac{2}{3}$$

▼ You can estimate fractions by comparing the numerator to the denominator.

8. a. These fractions are close to zero. ***Write*** a rule to tell when a fraction is close to zero.

$$\frac{1}{14} \qquad \frac{3}{17} \qquad \frac{2}{25} \qquad \frac{7}{125}$$

   b. These fractions are close to $\frac{1}{2}$. ***Write*** a rule to tell when a fraction is close to $\frac{1}{2}$.

$$\frac{3}{8} \qquad \frac{6}{14} \qquad \frac{11}{23} \qquad \frac{51}{100}$$

   c. These fractions are close to 1. ***Write*** a rule to tell when a fraction is close to 1.

$$\frac{99}{100} \qquad \frac{3}{4} \qquad \frac{45}{50} \qquad \frac{79}{91}$$

▼ You can also compare the numerator and the denominator to decide if fractions are greater than, less than, or equal to one.

$\frac{5}{6}$	$\frac{25}{25}$	$\frac{17}{3}$	$\frac{100}{100}$
$\frac{7}{6}$	$\frac{2}{3}$	$\frac{9}{11}$	$\frac{7}{10}$
$\frac{81}{79}$	$\frac{4}{4}$	$\frac{7}{7}$	$\frac{10}{8}$

9. Use the fractions in the box at the right to complete.

   a. fractions less than one ▢, ▢, ▢, ▢

   b. fractions greater than one ▢, ▢, ▢, ▢

   c. fractions equal to one ▢, ▢, ▢, ▢

10. a. Complete to show fractions close to 0. $\frac{▢}{7}, \frac{▢}{3}, \frac{5}{▢}, \frac{17}{▢}$

   b. Complete to show fractions close to $\frac{1}{2}$. $\frac{▢}{7}, \frac{▢}{9}, \frac{13}{▢}, \frac{5}{▢}$

   c. Complete to show fractions close to 1. $\frac{▢}{22}, \frac{▢}{11}, \frac{4}{▢}, \frac{20}{▢}$

   d. Complete to show fractions greater than 1. $\frac{▢}{2}, \frac{▢}{7}, \frac{9}{▢}, \frac{15}{▢}$

Exploring Fractions   **183**

OBJECTIVE:
To write equivalent
fractions and
fractions in lowest
terms.

5-1 Equivalent Fractions and Lowest Terms

▼ Suppose you divide a pizza into eight equal size pieces and eat four of the pieces. You can draw a model and write a fraction to represent the amount eaten.

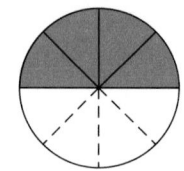

$$\frac{\text{numerator} \rightarrow 4}{\text{denominator} \rightarrow 8} \leftarrow \text{pieces eaten} \atop \leftarrow \text{pieces in all}$$

The model shows that the fractions $\frac{4}{8}$ and $\frac{1}{2}$ describe the same part of the pizza. They are *equivalent fractions*.

Equivalent Fractions	You can form equivalent fractions by multiplying or dividing the numerator and denominator by the same nonzero factor.

▼ You can write equivalent fractions using numbers, numbers and variables, or just variables.

Arithmetic   **Algebra**

$\frac{1}{2} = \frac{1 \cdot 2}{2 \cdot 2} = \frac{2}{4}$ $\frac{a}{b} = \frac{ac}{bc}$ $(b \neq 0, c \neq 0)$

$\frac{3}{6} = \frac{3 \div 3}{6 \div 3} = \frac{1}{2}$ $\frac{a}{b} = \frac{a \div c}{b \div c}$ $(b \neq 0, c \neq 0)$

THINK Why can you multiply the numerator and denominator by $\frac{2}{2}$, $\frac{3}{3}$, or $\frac{n}{n}$?

Example 1   Write a fraction equivalent to each fraction.

   a. $\frac{4}{6}$ **b.** $\frac{3x}{5y}$

Solution   **a.** We can divide by $1 = \frac{2}{2}$.   **b.** We can multiply by $1 = \frac{2}{2}$.

$$\frac{4}{6} = \frac{4 \div 2}{6 \div 2}$$

$$= \frac{2}{3}$$

$$\frac{3x}{5y} = \frac{3x \cdot 2}{5y \cdot 2}$$

$$= \frac{6x}{10y}$$

THINK Are there other possible solutions?

Example 2   Replace the variable to form equivalent fractions.

$$\frac{5}{8} = \frac{n}{24}$$

Solution $\frac{5 \cdot 3}{8 \cdot 3} = \frac{n}{24}$ Since $8 \cdot 3 = 24$, multiply both numerator and denominator by 3.

$$\frac{5}{8} = \frac{15}{24}$$

So, $n = 15$.

▼ When two fractions are equivalent, their *cross products* are equal. You can use this idea to test for equivalence.

Example 3   **a.** Is $\frac{6}{18} = \frac{7}{21}$?   **b.** Is $\frac{3}{15} = \frac{12}{45}$?

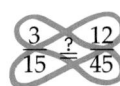

$$\frac{6}{18} \stackrel{?}{=} \frac{7}{21} \qquad\qquad \frac{3}{15} \stackrel{?}{=} \frac{12}{45}$$

Solution   **a.** $6 \cdot 21 \stackrel{?}{=} 18 \cdot 7$ **b.** $3 \cdot 45 \stackrel{?}{=} 15 \cdot 12$

$6 \,\boxed{\times}\, 21 \,\boxed{=}\, 126$ $3 \,\boxed{\times}\, 45 \,\boxed{=}\, 135$

$18 \,\boxed{\times}\, 7 \,\boxed{=}\, 126$ $15 \,\boxed{\times}\, 12 \,\boxed{=}\, 180$

The cross products are equal, so the fractions are equivalent.   The cross products are not equal, so the fractions are not equivalent.

▼ You can divide both terms of a fraction by the *greatest common factor (GCF)* to write the fraction in *lowest terms*.

Lowest Terms	When a fraction is in lowest terms, the only common factor of the numerator and denominator is 1.

Example 4   Write $\frac{18}{24}$ in lowest terms.

Solution $\dfrac{18}{24} = \dfrac{18 \div 6}{24 \div 6} = \dfrac{3}{4}$ Divide by 6, the GCF of 18 and 24.

▼ You also can write the numerator and denominator as a product of prime factors. Then divide by common factors to write in lowest terms.

Example 5 $\dfrac{18}{24} = \dfrac{\overset{1}{\cancel{2}} \cdot \overset{1}{\cancel{3}} \cdot 3}{\underset{1}{\cancel{2}} \cdot 2 \cdot 2 \cdot \underset{1}{\cancel{3}}} = \dfrac{3}{4}$ Divide common factors. Multiply the remaining factors.

▼ When a fraction includes variables you can divide common variable factors to write the fraction in lowest terms.

Example 6   Write $\frac{2a^2b}{6ac}$ in lowest terms.

Solution $\dfrac{2a^2b}{6ac} = \dfrac{2 \cdot a \cdot a \cdot b}{2 \cdot 3 \cdot a \cdot c}$ Write as a product of prime factors.

$= \dfrac{\overset{1}{\cancel{2}} \cdot \overset{1}{\cancel{a}} \cdot a \cdot b}{\underset{1}{\cancel{2}} \cdot 3 \cdot \underset{1}{\cancel{a}} \cdot c} = \dfrac{ab}{3c}$ Divide common factors. Multiply the remaining factors.

CLASS EXERCISES

1. During a 30-min radio broadcast there were 7 min of commercials.

   a. Write a fraction for the commercial time.

   b. Write a fraction for the noncommercial time.

Use or draw a model to represent each pair of equivalent fractions.

2. $\frac{2}{4} = \frac{3}{6}$ **3.** $\frac{6}{8} = \frac{9}{12}$ **4.** $\frac{3}{5} = \frac{6}{10}$

Write a fraction equivalent to each fraction.

5. $\frac{2}{3}$ **6.** $\frac{5w}{7x}$ **7.** $\frac{9}{10x}$ **8.** $\frac{13c}{26}$ **9.** $\frac{5a}{7a}$

Write in lowest terms.

10. $\frac{3}{9}$ **11.** $\frac{4}{10}$ **12.** $\frac{2}{8}$ **13.** $\frac{2a}{3a}$ **14.** $\frac{4ab^2}{12b}$

WRITTEN EXERCISES

Write a fraction for each sentence.

1. Three out of thirteen students are in the band. $\frac{3}{13}$

2. A student grew five-eighths inches. $\frac{5}{8}$

3. Copy and complete the chart.

Model	Word Name	Fraction
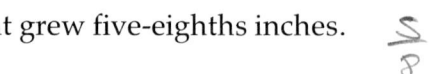	one-half	▦ $\frac{1}{2}$
⬤⬤◯◯◯◯	▦ one-fourth	$\frac{1}{4}$
▦	seven-eighths	$\frac{7}{8}$
★ ★ ★ ★ ★ ☆ ☆	▦ five-seventh	▦ $\frac{5}{7}$

Write a fraction for each shaded region.

4. 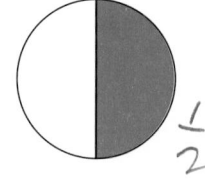 $\frac{1}{2}$

5. 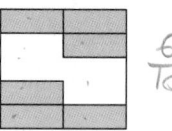 $\frac{6}{10}$

6. 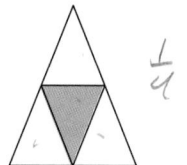 $\frac{1}{4}$

Write three fractions equivalent to each fraction.

7. $\frac{5}{6}$ $\frac{10}{12}$ $\frac{20}{24}$ $\frac{40}{48}$ 8. $\frac{12}{20}$ $\frac{6}{10}$ $\frac{3}{5}$ $\frac{24}{40}$ 9. $\frac{12}{36}$ $\frac{6}{18}$ $\frac{3}{9}$ $\frac{1}{3}$ 10. $\frac{1}{3}$ $\frac{2}{6}$ $\frac{4}{12}$ 11. $\frac{2}{5}$ $\frac{4}{10}$ $\frac{8}{20}$ $\frac{16}{40}$

12. $\frac{7b}{14c}$ 13. $\frac{8k}{9j}$ 14. $\frac{4t}{100w}$ 15. $\frac{25x}{75x}$ 16. $\frac{8p}{24p^2}$

MENTAL MATH Find the value of the variable to form equivalent fractions.

17. $\frac{1}{3} = \frac{n}{6}$ 2   18. $\frac{2}{5} = \frac{10}{y}$ 25   19. $\frac{3}{8} = \frac{a}{16}$ 6   20. $\frac{5}{10} = \frac{1}{b}$ 2

21. $\frac{12}{36} = \frac{x}{3}$ 1   22. $\frac{3a}{12} = \frac{1}{4}$ 23. $\frac{2}{7} = \frac{w}{14}$ 4   24. $\frac{3}{t} = \frac{1}{3}$

Write in lowest terms.

25. $\frac{5}{25}$ $\frac{1}{5}$ 26. $\frac{7}{14}$ $\frac{1}{2}$ 27. $\frac{6}{9}$ $\frac{2}{3}$ 28. $\frac{11}{22}$ $\frac{1}{2}$ 29. $\frac{25}{75}$ $\frac{1}{3}$

30. $\frac{3a}{6a}$ $\frac{a}{3a}$ 31. $\frac{4bc}{12b}$ $\frac{6c}{3b}$ 32. $\frac{xy}{3y}$?   33. $\frac{5x}{10t}$?   34. $\frac{abc}{5abc}$?

35. Use the numbers 3, 5, 6, and 10 to write three pairs of equivalent fractions. $\frac{3}{6}$ $\frac{5}{10}$ $\frac{6}{10}$ $\frac{3}{5}$

Use prime factors to write each fraction in lowest terms.

36. $\frac{15}{25}$ $\frac{3}{5}$ 37. $\frac{12}{16}$ $\frac{3}{4}$ 38. $\frac{6}{15}$ $\frac{2}{5}$ 39. $\frac{3a^2b}{5b}$?   40. $\frac{6mn}{9m}$?   41. $\frac{8p^3q}{12p^2}$?

CALCULATOR Use cross products. Compare using = or ≠.

42. $\frac{18}{30}$ ⬚ $\frac{15}{25}$ 43. $\frac{16}{21}$ ⬚ $\frac{12}{15}$ 44. $\frac{13}{24}$ ⬚ $\frac{11}{18}$ 45. $\frac{18}{32}$ ⬚ $\frac{27}{48}$

Solve.

46. The world production of gold in 1988 was about 58 million troy ounces. The United States produced about 6 million troy ounces. What fraction of the world's production came from the United States? Write your answer in lowest terms. $\frac{6}{58}$ $\frac{3}{29}$

47. For a money-raising project, the senior class baked a huge pizza. The class divided the pizza into 60 pieces. The swim team bought 24 pieces. What fraction of the pizza did the swim team buy? Write your answer in lowest terms. $\frac{24}{60}$ $\frac{2}{5}$

48. A survey of students revealed that the favorite music of half the group was rock. One-third preferred jazz and the rest liked country music. Draw a diagram to represent this data. *in book*

49. **PROJECT** Take a survey of the students in one of your classes. Determine the number of left-handed people. Compare this with the total number of students in the class. Write this information as a fraction.

MIXED REVIEW

Find the factors.

1. 32   2. 27

Find the prime factors. Then write using exponents.

3. 36   4. 54

Estimate.

5. $21.5 \cdot 12.8$

6. $42.8 + 13.6 + 18.23$

7. What are the GCF and the LCM of 18 and 12?

8. The lowest recorded temperature for Hawaii is 12°F. The lowest recorded temperature for Wisconsin is 66° lower. What is the record for Wisconsin?

5-2 Fractions and Decimals

▼ If you work more than 40 h/week, your rate of pay may be $1\frac{1}{2}$ times your regular rate. The number $1\frac{1}{2}$ is a *mixed number*.

▼ You can use models to write mixed numbers as *improper fractions*.

Example 1 Write $3\frac{1}{4}$ as an improper fraction using a model.

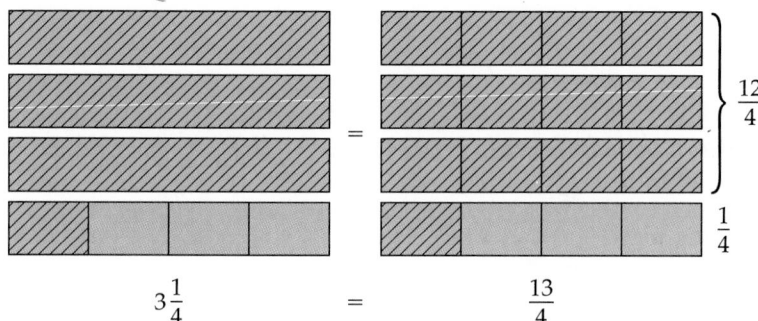

$$3\frac{1}{4} \qquad = \qquad \frac{13}{4}$$

▼ You can also write mixed numbers as improper fractions using equivalent fractions.

Example 2 Write $3\frac{1}{4}$ as an improper fraction.

Solution $\quad 3\frac{1}{4} = \frac{3}{1} + \frac{1}{4}$

$\qquad\qquad = \frac{12}{4} + \frac{1}{4} \qquad \frac{12}{4}$ and $\frac{3}{1}$ are equivalent fractions:

$\qquad\qquad = \frac{13}{4} \qquad\qquad \frac{3}{1} = \frac{3 \cdot 4}{1 \cdot 4} = \frac{12}{4}$

▼ You can divide to write improper fractions as mixed numbers or decimals.

Example 3 Write $\frac{7}{2}$ as a mixed number and as a decimal.

Solution $\quad \frac{7}{2} = 7 \div 2 = 3\frac{1}{2} = 3.5$

▼ You can write decimals as fractions in lowest terms.

Example 4 Write each decimal as a fraction or mixed number in lowest terms.

      a. 0.12   **b.** 1.625

Solution   **a.** $0.12 = \frac{12}{100}$ **b.** $1.625 = 1 + \frac{625}{1,000}$

$\qquad\qquad\qquad = \frac{12 \div 4}{100 \div 4} \qquad\qquad\qquad = 1 + \frac{625 \div 125}{1,000 \div 125}$

$\qquad\qquad\qquad = \frac{3}{25} \qquad\qquad\qquad\qquad = 1\frac{5}{8}$

▼ Sometimes it's necessary to write fractions as decimals before you solve word problems.

Example 5 You are at a delicatessen and ask for $\frac{3}{4}$ lb of potato salad. The scale reads 0.75. Are you getting the amount you requested?

Solution $\frac{3}{4} = 3 \div 4 = 0.75$ Use a calculator. Divide the numerator by the denominator.

Since $\frac{3}{4}$ equals 0.75, you received the right amount.

▼ Some fractions result in decimal patterns that repeat. Three dots at the right of a decimal indicate that digits repeat. You can also write a bar over the digits that repeat.

Example 6 Use a calculator to write each fraction as a decimal.

    a. $\frac{2}{3}$ **b.** $\frac{15}{11}$

Solution **a.** $\frac{2}{3} = 2 \div 3 = 0.6666\ldots$

    $\frac{2}{3} = 0.\overline{6}$ Write a bar over the 6.

    b. $\frac{15}{11} = 15 \div 11 = 1.3636\ldots$

    $\frac{15}{11} = 1.\overline{36}$ Write a bar over the repeating digits 3 and 6.

THINK What is the decimal equivalent for $5\frac{3}{4}$? for $12\frac{3}{4}$?

CLASS EXERCISES

Use a model to write as an improper fraction or mixed number.

1. $2\frac{3}{5}$ **2.** $1\frac{5}{8}$ **3.** $\frac{21}{4}$ **4.** $\frac{17}{6}$

Write as an improper fraction or mixed number.

5. $7\frac{1}{2}$ **6.** $\frac{11}{4}$ **7.** $\frac{19}{8}$ **8.** $\frac{21}{5}$

Write each decimal as a fraction in lowest terms.

9. 0.10   **10.** 0.5   **11.** 2.75   **12.** 3.25

CALCULATOR Write each fraction or mixed number as a decimal.

13. $\frac{7}{16}$ **14.** $4\frac{7}{16}$ **15.** $\frac{5}{12}$ **16.** $8\frac{5}{12}$

THINK AND DISCUSS

1. Where would you place the bar in the repeating decimal 12.032032 . . . ?

2. Use models to show the relationship between an improper fraction and a mixed number.

WRITTEN EXERCISES

Use each model to answer the questions.

1.

a. Let each piece represent $\frac{1}{4}$. What improper fraction is shown?

b. What mixed number is shown?

2.

a. Let each piece represent $\frac{1}{3}$. What improper fraction is shown?

b. What mixed number is shown?

3. Draw a model to show that $\frac{14}{5} = 2\frac{4}{5}$.

4. Write the length of the segment as an improper fraction and as a mixed number.

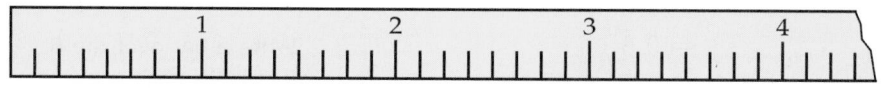

Write each mixed number as an improper fraction.

5. $1\frac{5}{8}$ **6.** $4\frac{3}{5}$ **7.** $5\frac{7}{8}$ **8.** $2\frac{9}{16}$

9. $6\frac{2}{3}$ **10.** $3\frac{7}{12}$ **11.** $2\frac{9}{11}$ **12.** $6\frac{1}{4}$

Write each improper fraction as a mixed number.

13. $\frac{17}{3}$ **14.** $\frac{16}{7}$ **15.** $\frac{23}{5}$ **16.** $\frac{31}{8}$

17. $\frac{19}{11}$ **18.** $\frac{37}{12}$ **19.** $\frac{10}{3}$ **20.** $\frac{53}{25}$

Write each decimal as a fraction or mixed number in lowest terms.

21. 0.8   **22.** 0.17   **23.** 5.15   **24.** 10.01

25. 2.5   **26.** 0.002   **27.** 6.05   **28.** 25.025

CALCULATOR Write as a decimal.

29. $\frac{7}{25}$ **30.** $\frac{3}{5}$ **31.** $\frac{5}{8}$ **32.** $\frac{9}{20}$

33. $\frac{5}{9}$ **34.** $\frac{7}{11}$ **35.** $5\frac{3}{8}$ **36.** $24\frac{7}{15}$

37. Copy and complete the chart. The first row is done for you.

Decimal	Read As	Fraction
0.23	twenty-three hundredths	$\frac{23}{100}$
▨	eighteen hundredths	▨
▨	▨	$5\frac{73}{100}$
▨	nine tenths	▨

38. Write an improper fraction with the greatest possible value using the digits 3, 5, and 6. Write this as a mixed number and as a decimal.

39. *DATA FILE 5 (pp. 180–181)* Write fractions to represent the number of instruments of each type in a typical symphony orchestra.

    a. woodwinds   **b.** brasses   **c.** percussion   **d.** bowed strings

40. *WRITE* Describe three situations when you would use fractions. Describe three situations when you would use decimals.

DATA **Use the circle graph at the right.**

41. Did about half the people respond that they see a movie less than once per month?

42. Did at least $\frac{1}{4}$ of the people asked say they see a movie two to three times a week?

43. Do one out of ten people see a movie once a week?

44. *CALCULATOR*

    a. Write each fraction as a decimal.

    b. Do at least 0.5 of the respondents see a movie more than once a week?

45. *PROJECT* Choose five movies or sports teams or a topic of your own. Collect data about the favorites in your class. Write fractions and decimals to describe the choices.

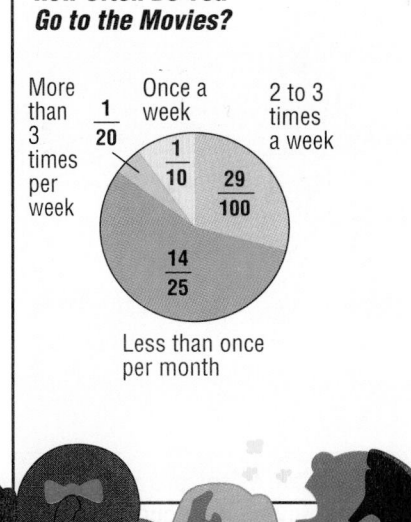

How Often Do You Go to the Movies?

More than 3 times per week $\frac{1}{20}$ Once a week $\frac{1}{10}$ 2 to 3 times a week $\frac{29}{100}$ $\frac{14}{25}$ Less than once per month

OBJECTIVE:
*To study the meaning
of rational numbers.*

5-3 *Rational Numbers*

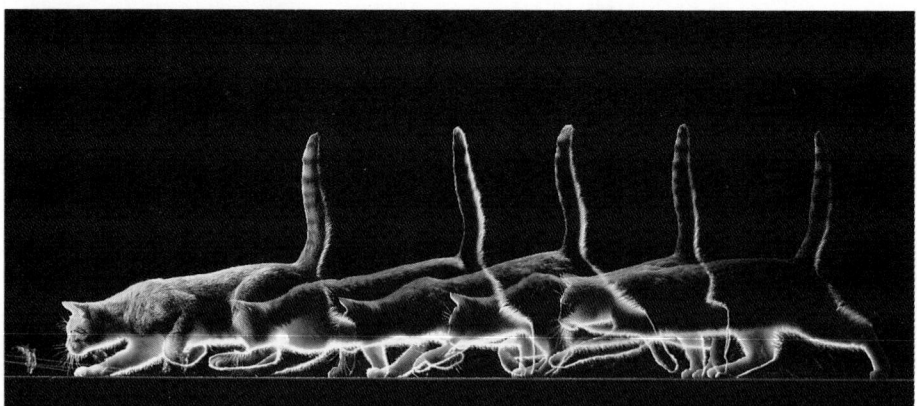

▼ The photograph above was taken with a strobe light that flashed at $\frac{1}{1,000}$ of a second intervals. We call the fraction $\frac{1}{1,000}$ a *rational number*.

THINK In $\frac{a}{b}$, why can't b equal zero?

Rational Number	A rational number is a number you write in the form $\frac{a}{b}$, where a is any integer, and b is a nonzero integer.

▼ Fractions are rational numbers. Other numbers are rational if you can express them as fractions.

Proper fractions	$\frac{2}{3}, -\frac{1}{2}$
Improper fractions	$\frac{4}{3}, \frac{10}{8}$
Mixed numbers	$1\frac{5}{6}, 2\frac{3}{11}$
Integers	$-6 = -\frac{6}{1}, 0 = \frac{0}{1}$
Variables	$\frac{a}{4}, \frac{3a}{4}, \frac{5a}{b}, \frac{2a}{3b}$
Some decimals	$0.5 = \frac{1}{2}, -9.8 = -\frac{98}{10}, 0.\overline{8} = \frac{8}{9}$

THINK What are some equivalent fractions for $\frac{a}{b}$?

▼ You can express a rational number as a set of equivalent fractions.

Example 1 $\quad \frac{1}{2} = \frac{2}{4} = \frac{3}{6} = \cdots \qquad$ Both numerator and denominator are positive.

$\qquad\qquad \frac{1}{2} = \frac{-1}{-2} = \frac{-2}{-4} = \frac{-3}{-6} = \cdots \qquad$ Both numerator and denominator are negative.

▼ You can write negative rational numbers in three ways.

Example 2 $\quad -\frac{7}{9} = \frac{-7}{9} = \frac{7}{-9}$

▼ You can show rational numbers on a number line.

Example 3 **Graph each point on a number line.**

      a. 0.5 **b.** $-1\frac{1}{2}$ **c.** $\frac{3}{4}$

Solution

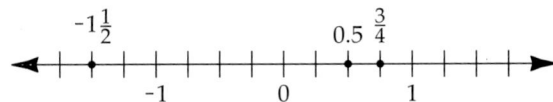

▼ You can find the absolute value of a rational number.

Example 4 The absolute value of $-\frac{5}{6}$ is $\frac{5}{6}$.

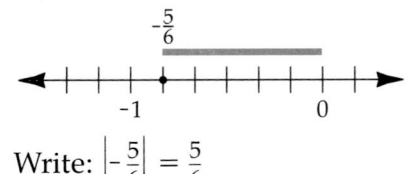

The distance from $-\frac{5}{6}$ to 0 is $\frac{5}{6}$.

Write: $\left|-\frac{5}{6}\right| = \frac{5}{6}$

THINK What is the opposite of $-\frac{a}{b}$?

▼ The fraction bar is a grouping symbol similar to parentheses.

Example 5 **Evaluate the expression** $\frac{x+5}{y}$ **for** $x = 7$ **and** $y = -8$.

Solution $\frac{x+5}{y} = \frac{7+5}{-8}$ Substitute values.

            $= \frac{12}{-8}$ Compute following order of operations.

            $= -1\frac{1}{2}$ Write as a mixed number.

CLASS EXERCISES

Give a rational number to represent each situation.

1. a loss of one-and-one-half pounds

2. moving the time ahead a quarter of an hour on a clock

Write a rational number for each point on the number line.

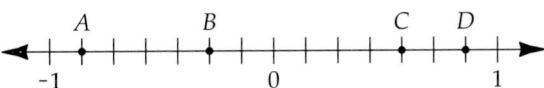

3. A **4.** B **5.** C **6.** D

Give the opposite and the absolute value.

7. $1\frac{1}{3}$ **8.** $-\frac{3}{5}$ **9.** $\frac{5}{-9}$ **10.** $-2\frac{2}{3}$

11. $\frac{1}{4}$ **12.** $\frac{4}{-5}$ **13.** $\frac{5}{8}$ **14.** $1\frac{1}{2}$

THINK AND DISCUSS

1. Is zero a rational number? Why or why not?

2. Is a set of equivalent fractions equal to the same decimal?

3. How many rational numbers are there between 1 and 2?

Evaluate for $a = 6$, and $b = -5$. Write in lowest terms.

15. $\dfrac{a + b}{3}$ **16.** $\dfrac{a - b}{4}$ **17.** $\dfrac{a + 9}{b}$

WRITTEN EXERCISES

Write a rational number to represent each situation.

1. the number of dollars in nine quarters.

2. a loss of two dollars and seventy-five cents

Write a rational number for each point on the number line.

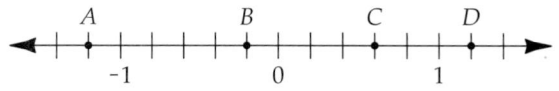

3. A **4.** B **5.** C **6.** D

Graph each point on a number line.

7. $1\frac{1}{2}$ **8.** -0.5 **9.** -3.5 **10.** $\frac{3}{4}$

Write the opposite and the absolute value.

11. $\dfrac{-4}{9}$ **12.** -1.73 **13.** $1\frac{2}{3}$ **14.** $-2\frac{1}{5}$

15. Which rational numbers are equal to $-\frac{4}{5}$?

a. $\dfrac{4}{-5}$ **b.** 0.8 **c.** $-\dfrac{16}{20}$ **d.** $\dfrac{-4}{-5}$

16. Which rational numbers are equal to $\frac{9}{5}$?

a. $\dfrac{-9}{-5}$ **b.** $-9 \cdot \dfrac{1}{-5}$ **c.** -1.8 **d.** $\dfrac{18}{10}$

Evaluate. Write in lowest terms.

17. $\dfrac{a}{b}$ for $a = 20$, $b = 25$ **18.** $\dfrac{a^2}{b^2}$ for $a = 4$, $b = -5$

19. $\dfrac{a + 3}{b}$ for $a = 5$, $b = -2$ **20.** $\dfrac{(a + 3)(a - 3)}{a^2 - 9}$ for $a = 5$

Write each rational number in lowest terms.

21. $\dfrac{4a}{8b}$ **22.** $\dfrac{2 \cdot 5 \cdot a}{4 \cdot 25 \cdot b}$ **23.** $\dfrac{4 \cdot a^2}{16 \cdot a \cdot b}$ **24.** $\dfrac{5 \cdot a^2 \cdot b}{25 \cdot a \cdot b^2}$

Write *sometimes*, *always*, or *never* to tell when each is true.

25. $\dfrac{3a}{3b} = \dfrac{a}{b}$ **26.** $\dfrac{a^2}{b} > \dfrac{a}{b}$ **27.** $\dfrac{a}{b} = \left|\dfrac{a}{b}\right|$ **28.** $\dfrac{a}{b}(-1) > 0$

Complete.

29. All ▨ rational numbers are less than zero.

30. The set of rational numbers is made up of the positive rational numbers, the negative rational numbers, and ▨.

31. The opposite of a ▨ rational number is positive.

32. The absolute value of a negative rational number is ▨.

33. A number is less than zero. Its opposite is a mixed number greater than zero. Is the number a rational number?

34. *DATA FILE 5 (pp. 180–181)* Write fractions that represent these musical notes: whole note, half note, quarter note, eighth note, and sixteenth note.

35. Copy and complete the chart. Write *yes* or *no*.

Number	Rational Number	Integer	Whole Number	Natural Number
2	▨	▨	▨	▨
$-\dfrac{1}{2}$	▨	▨	▨	▨
0.5	▨	▨	▨	▨
$\dfrac{-12}{-3}$	▨	▨	▨	▨
$0 \cdot \dfrac{a}{b}$	▨	▨	▨	▨

36. *WRITE* a sentence about rational numbers. How are rational numbers different from integers? How are they similar?

TEST YOURSELF

Write in lowest terms.

1. $\dfrac{12}{15}$ **2.** $\dfrac{18}{24}$ **3.** $\dfrac{6}{20}$ **4.** $\dfrac{5a^3b^2}{15ab^2}$ **5.** $\dfrac{35mn^3}{4m}$

Write three fractions equivalent to the given fraction.

6. $\dfrac{5}{8}$ **7.** $-1\dfrac{2}{5}$ **8.** $\dfrac{9}{12}$ **9.** $\dfrac{2b}{3c}$ **10.** $\dfrac{16r}{20s}$

Write the opposite and the absolute value.

11. $\dfrac{2}{3}$ **12.** $-2\dfrac{5}{6}$ **13.** $1\dfrac{7}{16}$ **14.** $-2\dfrac{3}{4}$

OBJECTIVE:
To compare and
order fractions and
decimals.

5-4 Comparing and Ordering Rational Numbers

▼ The Houston Rockets won 10 out of 12 home games. The Denver Stars won 8 out of 10 games. Which team won a greater fraction of games?

$$\text{Houston's games} \rightarrow \frac{10}{12}$$

$$\text{Denver's games} \rightarrow \frac{8}{10}$$

Compare $\frac{10}{12}$ and $\frac{8}{10}$ using fraction strips.

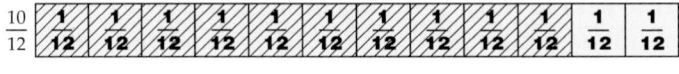

$$\frac{10}{12} > \frac{8}{10}$$

▼ You can also compare fractions by finding their *least common denominator (LCD)*.

Least Common Denominator	The least common denominator of two or more fractions is the LCM of the denominators.

Example 1 Compare $\frac{5}{12}$ and $\frac{4}{9}$.

Solution   1. Find the LCD.   The LCD of $\frac{5}{12}$ and $\frac{4}{9}$ is 36.

2. Find equivalent fractions.
$$\frac{5}{12} = \frac{15}{36}$$
$$\frac{4}{9} = \frac{16}{36}$$

3. Compare.
$$\frac{16}{36} > \frac{15}{36}, \text{ so } \frac{4}{9} > \frac{5}{12}.$$

▼ To compare fractions and decimals, you can first write each in the same form.

Example 2 Compare 0.8 and $\frac{3}{5}$.

Solution   1. Use a calculator to write $\frac{3}{5}$ as a decimal.
3 ÷ 5 = 0.6

2. Compare.
Since 0.8 > 0.6, 0.8 > $\frac{3}{5}$.

▼ Writing fractions as decimals often makes it easier to order the fractions from least to greatest.

Example 3 Order $\frac{13}{40}$, $\frac{9}{32}$, $\frac{5}{16}$, $\frac{8}{25}$ from least to greatest.

Solution Use a calculator to write each fraction as a decimal.

$$\frac{13}{40} = 0.325 \quad \frac{9}{32} = 0.28125 \quad \frac{5}{16} = 0.3125 \quad \frac{8}{25} = 0.32$$

$$0.28125 < 0.3125 < 0.32 < 0.325 \quad \text{Order the decimals.}$$

$$\updownarrow \qquad \updownarrow \qquad \updownarrow \qquad \updownarrow$$

$$\frac{9}{32} \quad < \quad \frac{5}{16} \quad < \quad \frac{8}{25} \quad < \quad \frac{13}{40} \quad \text{Order the fractions.}$$

▼ You can also order fractions on a number line.

Example 4 Order $\frac{1}{4}$, -0.2, 1.1, and $-\frac{3}{5}$ from least to greatest.

Solution Use a calculator to write fractions as decimals.

$$\frac{1}{4} = 0.25, \ -\frac{3}{5} = -0.6$$

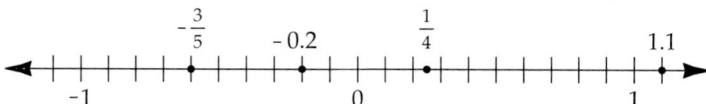

THINK How does writing fractions as decimals help when ordering on the number line?

CLASS EXERCISES

Write the two fractions modeled and compare them.

1.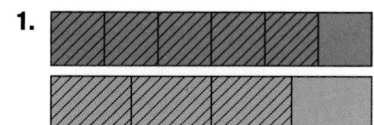

2.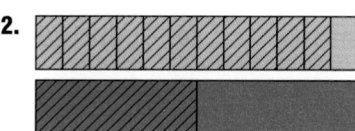

Compare. Use >, <, or =.

3. $\frac{5}{8}$ ◁ $\frac{3}{4}$

4. $\frac{7}{15}$ ◁ $\frac{2}{3}$

5. $\frac{5}{18}$ ◁ $\frac{1}{3}$

6. $\frac{33}{40}$ ▷ $\frac{5}{8}$

7. 0.3 ▩ $\frac{-1}{-3}$

8. 0.22 ◁ $\frac{2}{9}$

9. 0.63 ▩ $\frac{7}{-11}$

10. $3\frac{1}{4}$ ▷ 3.2

11. 4.985 ▭ $4\frac{985}{1,000}$

THINK AND DISCUSS

1. Suppose you are comparing a fraction and a decimal. Why is it easier to write the fraction as a decimal than to write the decimal as a fraction?

2. Some fractions result in decimals with several places. When comparing, are all of the digits important? Consider $\frac{1}{7}$ ▩ 0.142.

Order from least to greatest.

12. $\frac{2}{5}$, $\frac{7}{20}$, $\frac{3}{10}$

13. $\frac{11}{16}$, $\frac{5}{8}$, $-\frac{13}{24}$

14. $\frac{3}{4}$, $\frac{7}{10}$, $\frac{-29}{40}$

15. $\frac{6}{11}$, $\frac{11}{20}$, $\frac{5}{9}$, $\frac{14}{-25}$

16. $\frac{7}{33}$, $\frac{-2}{-9}$, $\frac{11}{50}$, $\frac{4}{17}$

17. $\frac{20}{37}$, $\frac{6}{11}$, $\frac{27}{50}$, $-\frac{51}{90}$

Solve.

1. $0.3x = 2.1$

2. $18.08 = a + 7.5$

Find each answer.

3. the opposite of $-7\frac{1}{3}$

4. $-1\frac{2}{5} + \blacksquare = 0$

5. $\left|-2\frac{7}{9}\right|$

6. $-4\frac{2}{3} = \frac{\blacksquare}{3}$

7. Write $-2\frac{3}{8}$ as a decimal.

8. How many miles will you travel in 3.5 h at a speed of 55 mi/h?

WRITTEN EXERCISES

Use a model to compare.

1. $\frac{3}{5} \blacksquare \frac{5}{8}$

2. $\frac{5}{6} \blacksquare \frac{7}{10}$

Compare. Use >, <, or =.

3. $\frac{13}{18} \blacksquare \frac{7}{9}$

4. $\frac{11}{12} \blacksquare \frac{5}{6}$

5. $-\frac{7}{9} \blacksquare -\frac{2}{3}$

6. $-\frac{5}{6} \blacksquare -\frac{19}{24}$

7. $\frac{3}{8} \blacksquare \frac{5}{12}$

8. $\frac{3}{4} \blacksquare \frac{5}{6}$

9. $-\frac{5}{12} \blacksquare \frac{7}{9}$

10. $\frac{3}{4} \blacksquare \frac{7}{10}$

MENTAL MATH Compare. Use >, <, or =.

11. $-\frac{3}{19} \blacksquare \frac{1}{200}$

12. $\frac{-4}{-17} \blacksquare -\frac{5}{2}$

13. $\frac{(-1) \cdot (-1)}{3} \blacksquare \frac{1}{3}$

CALCULATOR Compare. Use >, <, or =.

14. $\frac{17}{24} \blacksquare \frac{24}{35}$

15. $-\frac{11}{16} \blacksquare -\frac{19}{28}$

16. $\frac{15}{22} \blacksquare \frac{23}{34}$

17. $\frac{11}{25} \blacksquare \frac{17}{30}$

18. $\frac{3}{8} \blacksquare 0.39$

19. $\frac{3}{4} \blacksquare 0.752$

20. $-\frac{5}{12} \blacksquare -0.34$

21. $2\frac{3}{14} \blacksquare 2.22$

CALCULATOR Order from least to greatest.

22. $\frac{5}{6}, \frac{7}{8}, \frac{19}{24}$

23. $-\frac{5}{12}, -\frac{3}{8}, -\frac{1}{4}$

24. $-\frac{5}{11}, \frac{6}{13}, -\frac{8}{17}$

25. $-\frac{7}{10}, -\frac{11}{15}, -\frac{7}{12}, -\frac{13}{20}$

26. $\frac{17}{20}, \frac{23}{30}, \frac{23}{40}, \frac{13}{24}$

27. $2\frac{3}{50}, -2\frac{7}{8}, -2\frac{9}{16}, 2\frac{19}{25}$

Find a rational number between the given rational numbers.

28. $\frac{1}{2}$ and 1

29. -1 and -2

30. $2\frac{5}{12}$ and $2\frac{3}{4}$

31. $-1\frac{3}{4}$ and -2

Compare the rational numbers $\frac{5}{8}$ and $\frac{x}{4}$. Find the values of x that make each statement true.

32. $\frac{5}{8} = \frac{x}{4}$

33. $\frac{5}{8} > \frac{x}{4}$

34. $\frac{5}{8} < \frac{x}{4}$

35. **DATA FILE 5 (pp. 180–181)** Write as a fraction in lowest terms the number of tapes sold in 1976 compared with the number of tapes sold in 1986.

36. In the high school band there are 15 clarinets. The band has 80 members. Compare the number of clarinets to the number of band members. Write the number as a fraction in lowest terms and as a decimal.

OBJECTIVE:
To add and subtract
fractions and mixed
numbers.

5-5 Adding and Subtracting Rational Numbers

▼ Two thirds of the earth's surface is covered by oceans. Another tenth of the earth's surface is covered by glaciers. What fraction of the earth is covered by oceans and glaciers?

The total amount is the sum of the two fractions.

$\frac{2}{3} + \frac{1}{10} = \frac{20}{30} + \frac{3}{30}$ Find a common denominator.

$= \frac{23}{30}$

▼ You can add rational numbers using a model.

Example 1 $\frac{1}{4} + \frac{1}{6} = $ ▇

THINK Why must the last fraction bar have 12 sections?

Solution

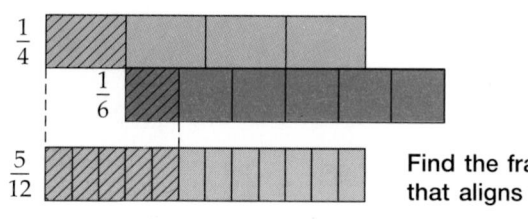

Find the fraction bar that aligns with the sum.

So, $\frac{1}{4} + \frac{1}{6} = \frac{5}{12}$.

▼ You can also subtract rational numbers expressed as fractions.

Example 2 $\frac{1}{12} - \frac{1}{3} = $ ▇

THINK Why do you subtract only the numerators?

Solution $\frac{1}{12} - \frac{1 \cdot 4}{3 \cdot 4} = \frac{1}{12} - \frac{4}{12}$ Write equivalent fractions and subtract numerators.

$= -\frac{3}{12}$ Write in lowest terms.

$= -\frac{1}{4}$

▼ You can add fractions that contain variables.

Example 3 $\frac{x}{5} + \frac{3}{4} = $ ▇

Solution $\frac{x \cdot 4}{5 \cdot 4} + \frac{3 \cdot 5}{4 \cdot 5} = $ ▇   Write equivalent fractions.

$\frac{4x}{20} + \frac{15}{20} = \frac{4x + 15}{20}$ Add numerators.

▼ To add mixed numbers, combine the integers and fractions separately.

Example 4 $2\frac{3}{4} + 4\frac{5}{12} = \blacksquare$

Solution

$$2\frac{3}{4} = \quad 2\frac{9}{12} \qquad \text{Write equivalent fractions.}$$

$$+4\frac{5}{12} = +4\frac{5}{12}$$

$$\overline{\qquad 6\frac{14}{12}} \qquad \text{Add integers and fractions separately.}$$

$$6 + 1\frac{2}{12} \qquad \text{Write improper fractions as mixed numbers and add whole numbers.}$$

$$\text{So, } 2\frac{3}{4} + 4\frac{5}{12} = 7\frac{1}{6} \qquad \text{Write the fraction in lowest terms.}$$

▼ With subtraction, you may need to rename before subtracting.

Example 5 $5\frac{1}{6} - 2\frac{2}{3} = \blacksquare$

Solution

$$5\frac{1}{6} = \quad 5\frac{1}{6} = \quad 4\frac{7}{6} \qquad \text{Write equivalent fractions.}$$

$$-2\frac{2}{3} = -2\frac{4}{6} = -2\frac{4}{6}$$

$$\overline{\qquad\qquad\qquad = \quad 2\frac{3}{6}}$$

$$\text{So, } 5\frac{1}{6} - 2\frac{2}{3} = \quad 2\frac{1}{2} \qquad \text{Write the fraction in lowest terms.}$$

THINK AND DISCUSS

1. Is the sum or difference of two rational numbers also a rational number?

2. Do the commutative and associative properties also apply to rational numbers? Use examples to support your answer.

CLASS EXERCISES

Use a model to find the sum or difference.

1. $\frac{1}{3} + \frac{1}{6}$ **2.** $\frac{2}{3} - \frac{1}{6}$ **3.** $\frac{11}{12} + \frac{5}{6}$ **4.** $1\frac{3}{8} - \frac{7}{8}$

Find the sum or difference.

5. $\frac{1}{3} + \frac{3}{4}$ **6.** $\frac{4}{5} + 3\frac{7}{10}$ **7.** $\frac{3}{4} - \frac{2}{5}$ **8.** $5\frac{1}{3} - 2\frac{3}{4}$

9. $\frac{x}{3} + \frac{5}{6}$ **10.** $\frac{3}{4}x + \frac{2}{3} + \frac{1}{2}x$ **11.** $11\frac{3}{4} - \left(-19\frac{5}{8}\right)$ **12.** $5 - 3\frac{3}{4}$

Estimate the sum or difference.

13. $5\frac{5}{9} + 8\frac{2}{31}$ **14.** $21.76 - 15\frac{3}{41}$ **15.** $-\frac{11}{3} + (-3.25)$ **16.** $15\frac{3}{4} - 38\frac{1}{2}$

17. $2\frac{1}{3} + 7\frac{1}{8}$ **18.** $-\frac{7}{8} - \left(-\frac{1}{4}\right)$ **19.** $14.7 + 3\frac{1}{5}$ **20.** $8\frac{11}{12} + 4\frac{1}{12}$

WRITTEN EXERCISES

Use a model to find the sum or difference.

1. $\frac{3}{8} + \left(-\frac{1}{2}\right)$ **2.** $-\left(\frac{2}{3}\right) - \frac{1}{6}$ **3.** $\frac{3}{4} + \frac{1}{2}$ **4.** $1\frac{1}{2} - \frac{3}{4}$

Write a number sentence for each model shown.

5. 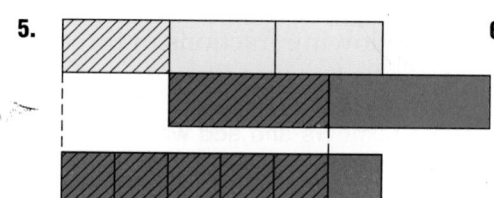   **6.**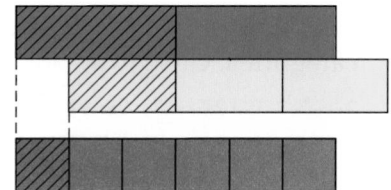

Find each sum or difference.

7. $\frac{7}{8} + \frac{5}{12}$ **8.** $\frac{5}{6} + \frac{-1}{8}$ **9.** $\frac{2}{3} - 1\frac{1}{9}$ **10.** $4\frac{3}{5} - 2\frac{7}{10}$

11. $\frac{2}{3} + 1\frac{5}{6}$ **12.** $\frac{x}{4} + \frac{x}{6}$ **13.** $14\frac{5}{9} - 5\frac{1}{3}$ **14.** $\frac{4x}{5} + \left(-\frac{6x}{10}\right)$

15. $\frac{5}{9}y - \frac{1}{6}y$ **16.** $2\frac{3}{5} + 4\frac{7}{15}$ **17.** $2\frac{1}{8} - 6\frac{3}{4}$ **18.** $\frac{3b}{4} - \frac{5b}{6}$

Estimate each sum or difference.

▼▼ *SAMPLE* $12\frac{3}{4} - 5\frac{3}{8} \approx 13 - 5 = 8$

19. $28\frac{5}{18} - 12\frac{7}{17}$ **20.** $-145.76 + \left(-76\frac{8}{19}\right)$ **21.** $52.097 - \left(-98\frac{5}{23}\right)$

22. $35.1 - 12\frac{8}{11}$ **23.** $52\frac{25}{48} + 22\frac{7}{16}$ **24.** $42\frac{3}{11} + 57\frac{9}{16}$

MENTAL MATH Find each sum or difference.

25. $5\frac{1}{4} + 19\frac{2}{3} + 4\frac{3}{4}$ **26.** $7\frac{2}{8} + 4\frac{5}{8} + \left(-6\frac{7}{8}\right)$

CALCULATOR Check whether the following are correct.

27. $25\frac{7}{12} - \left(-18\frac{13}{18}\right) = 44\frac{11}{36}$ **28.** $17\frac{11}{24} + \left(-11\frac{17}{30}\right) = 5\frac{107}{120}$

29. $23\frac{5}{8} - 12\frac{3}{5} = 11\frac{1}{3}$ **30.** $16\frac{7}{12} - \left(-14\frac{3}{8}\right) = 30\frac{23}{24}$

31. Which of the following are equal to $1\frac{1}{2}$?

   a. $4\frac{3}{8} - 3\frac{1}{4}$ **b.** $\frac{-3}{-2} - \frac{1}{2}$ **c.** $2\frac{1}{x} - \frac{3}{x}, x = 4$ **d.** $\frac{x - 1.5}{3.5 - x}, x = \frac{1}{2}$

32. Classify each statement as *sometimes*, *always*, or *never* true.

   a. $\left|\frac{4}{5}x\right| \geq \frac{4}{5}x$ **b.** $\frac{2x}{3} < x$ **c.** $\frac{1}{x} < x, x \neq 0$ **d.** $\frac{2}{x} < \frac{3}{x}, x > 0$

MIXED REVIEW
Calculate each answer.

1. Write the opposite and the absolute value of $3\frac{1}{5}$.

2. $5\frac{8}{11} + \blacksquare = 0$

3. Write the rational number $\frac{-7}{10}$ in two other ways.

4. $-6\frac{2}{3} = \frac{\blacksquare}{3}$

5. Compare $-\frac{13}{9}$ and $-\frac{30}{21}$.

6. When is $\frac{y}{8} > \frac{1}{2}$?

7. What is the LCM of 15 and 20?

8. Sara earns $4.95 an hour and works for 29 hours. Estimate her pay.

PROBLEM SOLVING HINT
Try guess and test.

Compare. Use >, <, or =.

33. $\dfrac{3^2}{5} \ \blacksquare\ \dfrac{17}{20}$

34. $-\dfrac{5}{14} \ \blacksquare\ -\dfrac{7}{15}$

35. $\dfrac{3}{8} + \dfrac{2}{3} \ \blacksquare\ \dfrac{4}{5}$

36. $\dfrac{a}{3} \ \blacksquare\ \dfrac{a}{4}$, $a > 0$

37. $\dfrac{a}{5} \ \blacksquare\ \dfrac{a^2}{5}$, $a < 0$

38. $\left|\dfrac{a}{b}\right| \ \blacksquare\ \dfrac{|a|}{|b|}$, $b \neq 0$

39. Lynn wishes to wallpaper her room. Estimate the perimeter of Lynn's room. The length is $9\frac{3}{8}$ ft and the width is $11\frac{7}{12}$ ft.

40. **MENTAL MATH** Make a chart. List the following fractions in three categories: close to 0, close to $\frac{1}{2}$, close to 1.

$$\frac{3}{5}, \ \frac{17}{21}, \ \frac{5}{14}, \ \frac{27}{53}, \ \frac{17}{15}, \ \frac{28}{59}, \ \frac{8}{55}$$

41. What fraction of an hour is fifteen minutes? What fraction is seventy-five minutes?

42. In the lower bass section of the band, 15 students play trombone and 4 play tuba. Two students play both instruments. What fraction of the group play tuba?

43. What numbers must be in the blanks to form a magic square?

PROBLEM SOLVING HINT
Use a Venn diagram.

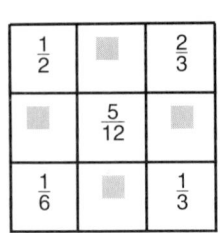

Critical Thinking

EXPLORING VISUALIZATION

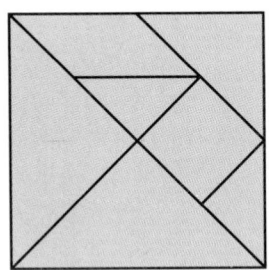

An ancient geometric puzzle known as the tangram divides a large square into seven pieces. You can use the pieces to create a variety of geometrical designs. The large triangles are $\frac{1}{4}$ of the tangram. Two of the large triangles equal half of the large square. Written in fractions this would be $\frac{1}{4} + \frac{1}{4} = \frac{1}{2}$.

1. Copy the tangram on graph paper. What fraction of the tangram does each piece represent?

Draw or model the tangram pieces that show each equation.

2. $\dfrac{1}{4} = \dfrac{1}{8} + \dfrac{1}{16} + \dfrac{1}{16}$

3. $\dfrac{1}{4} + \dfrac{1}{4} = \dfrac{1}{8} + \dfrac{1}{8} + \dfrac{1}{8} + \dfrac{1}{16} + \dfrac{1}{16}$

Create a figure to show each expression.

4. $\dfrac{1}{8} + \dfrac{1}{16}$

5. $\dfrac{1}{8} + \dfrac{1}{16} + \dfrac{1}{16}$

6. $\dfrac{1}{4} + \dfrac{1}{8} + \dfrac{1}{8}$

7. Compare your figures with those of other students in the class.

OBJECTIVE:
To solve problems by working backwards.

5-6 Working Backwards

■ With some problems, you have to work backwards from the given information to get an answer.

PROBLEM

The Tanaka family is planning a trip to the Grand Canyon. It will take 5 h of driving. In addition, they plan to make three half-hour rest stops. They plan on arriving at 3:30 P.M. What time should they plan to leave?

SOLUTION

READ ▶ Answer these questions to understand the given information:

What do you want to find?	The departure time for the trip.
What is the arrival time?	3:30 P.M.
How much time will be spent driving?	5 h
How much time will be spent resting?	$1\frac{1}{2}$ h

PLAN ▶ Add up the time needed for the trip.
Work back from the arrival time to find the departure time.

SOLVE ▶ Total time: $5 + 1\frac{1}{2} = 6\frac{1}{2}$
Work backwards from the arrival time:

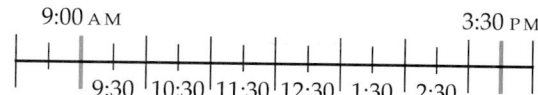

9:00 A.M.   3:30 P.M.

9:30 10:30 11:30 12:30 1:30 2:30

LOOK BACK ▶ Did you solve the problem? Count forward from 9:00 A.M. The elapsed time between 9:00 A.M. and 3:30 P.M. is $6\frac{1}{2}$ hours. ✓

CLASS EXERCISES

1. What other strategy could you use to solve this problem?

2. How could you use estimation to find the approximate departure time?

3. Suppose it will take $6\frac{1}{2}$ h of driving. At what time should the Tanakas leave?

4. The Tanakas will need $2\frac{1}{2}$ hours to get dressed and have breakfast. They will also need another $1\frac{1}{4}$ h to pack the car. At what time should the Tanakas get up in order to leave at 9:00 A.M.?

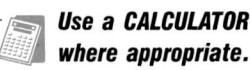

WRITTEN EXERCISES

Solve each problem by working backwards.

1. Solve this riddle: "I think of a number, add 5, multiply by 3, divide by 4, and subtract 1. The answer is 8." What is the original number?

2. Carla spent $\frac{1}{3}$ of her money at the amusement park. Afterward, she had $15 left. How much money did she have originally?

3. A ball is bouncing on the floor. After each bounce, the ball is $\frac{2}{3}$ as high as the previous bounce. On the fifth bounce, the ball is 2 ft off the floor. How high was the ball before the first bounce?

Solve each problem. Use an appropriate strategy.

4. Use the map at the left. It took the Tanakas 7 h to reach the Grand Canyon. If their average speed was 55 mi/h, could Seattle be their home town?

5. Joan is twice as old as her brother Harry. When Joan is twice as old as she is now, she will be six years older than Harry. How old is Joan now?

6. Look at the following list of numbers: {1, 1, 1, 2, 3, 5, 6}. How many combinations of numbers will make the following equation true?

$$\frac{\blacksquare}{\blacksquare} + \frac{\blacksquare}{\blacksquare} = \frac{\blacksquare}{\blacksquare}$$

You cannot use a number on the list more than once for each equation.

7. **CALCULATOR** Find the first three quotients. Predict the quotients for the remaining equations.
   a. $1 \div 9 = \blacksquare$
   b. $2 \div 9 = \blacksquare$
   c. $3 \div 9 = \blacksquare$
   d. $4 \div 9 = \blacksquare$
   e. $5 \div 9 = \blacksquare$
   f. $6 \div 9 = \blacksquare$

8. You have two nickels, three dimes, and a quarter. Using at least one of each coin, how many different amounts of money can you make?

9. Look for the number pattern and find the next three numbers.
   $\frac{2}{3}, 1\frac{5}{12}, 2\frac{1}{6}, 2\frac{11}{12}$

10. Alex, Bart, Clarence, and Dan enter a classroom. All four choose one of the four desks at the back. Each day they sit in a different order. How many days can they do this before they must repeat a previous pattern?

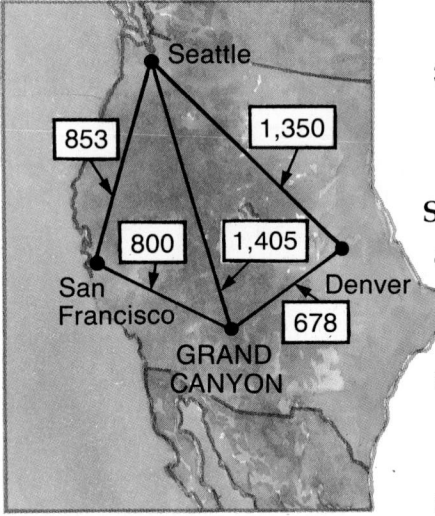

Driving distance in miles

Practice

Write in lowest terms.

1. $\dfrac{3}{15}$　　2. $\dfrac{4}{18}$　　3. $\dfrac{8}{12}$　　4. $\dfrac{20}{45}$

5. $\dfrac{9}{15}$　　6. $\dfrac{24}{42}$　　7. $\dfrac{15y^2}{35y}$　　8. $\dfrac{5m}{5m}$

9. $\dfrac{3a}{9a}$　　10. $\dfrac{6xy}{20x}$　　11. $\dfrac{12m}{18m^2}$　　12. $\dfrac{cd}{3c^2d}$

Write each mixed number as an improper fraction.

13. $2\dfrac{3}{5}$　　14. $1\dfrac{7}{8}$　　15. $4\dfrac{2}{3}$　　16. $5\dfrac{7}{9}$

17. $8\dfrac{1}{4}$　　18. $12\dfrac{5}{8}$　　19. $20\dfrac{7}{12}$　　20. $15\dfrac{3}{4}$

Write each improper fraction as a mixed number.

21. $\dfrac{12}{5}$　　22. $\dfrac{19}{2}$　　23. $\dfrac{25}{4}$　　24. $\dfrac{41}{12}$

25. $\dfrac{53}{8}$　　26. $\dfrac{35}{6}$　　27. $\dfrac{57}{7}$　　28. $\dfrac{28}{9}$

Write the opposite and absolute value of each number.

29. $2\dfrac{3}{8}$　　30. $-5\dfrac{4}{5}$　　31. $-18\dfrac{2}{3}$　　32. $24\dfrac{7}{15}$

33. $-13\dfrac{5}{9}$　　34. $22\dfrac{1}{6}$　　35. $-\dfrac{11}{15}$　　36. $31\dfrac{8}{9}$

Compare. Use >, <, or =.

37. $\dfrac{2}{3}$ ◻ $\dfrac{3}{4}$　　38. $-\dfrac{7}{15}$ ◻ $-\dfrac{3}{5}$　　39. $\dfrac{7}{8}$ ◻ $\dfrac{13}{16}$

40. $-\dfrac{5}{6}$ ◻ $-\dfrac{7}{8}$　　41. $\dfrac{11}{15}$ ◻ $\dfrac{7}{10}$　　42. $-\dfrac{5}{9}$ ◻ $\dfrac{7}{12}$

Find the sum or difference.

43. $\dfrac{5}{12} + \dfrac{7}{12}$　　44. $\dfrac{3}{8} - \dfrac{5}{8}$　　45. $\dfrac{8}{9} + \dfrac{2}{9}$

46. $\dfrac{3}{5} - \left(-\dfrac{7}{10}\right)$　　47. $-\dfrac{5}{8} + \dfrac{1}{4}$　　48. $\dfrac{7}{15} - \dfrac{2}{5}$

49. $-2\dfrac{1}{2} - 3\dfrac{3}{4}$　　50. $7\dfrac{5}{8} - 2\dfrac{1}{4}$　　51. $3\dfrac{5}{6} - 2\dfrac{3}{8}$

52. $3\dfrac{3}{8} - 2\dfrac{7}{12}$　　53. $4\dfrac{7}{15} + 2\dfrac{3}{10}$　　54. $-4\dfrac{2}{3} + 6\dfrac{5}{8}$

55. $10 - 3\dfrac{4}{7}$　　56. $4\dfrac{3}{8} - 5$　　57. $-5\dfrac{1}{2} - 5\dfrac{1}{2}$

58. $-14\dfrac{5}{8} + 2\dfrac{3}{5}$　　59. $18\dfrac{9}{16} + 11\dfrac{3}{4}$　　60. $15\dfrac{3}{8} - 8\dfrac{3}{4}$

CAREER

Help Wanted: Acoustical Physicist

Bachelor of Science degree in physics required.

For more information, write to American Institute of Physics, 1 Physics Ellipse, College Park, MD 20740-0843.

Acoustical physicists study sound to design concert halls, theaters, and auditoriums. Acoustical physicists consider the materials used to build and furnish a hall, the shape of the hall, and the placement of people and equipment. The acoustical physicist ensures that sound is distributed evenly so that each person in the theater or auditorium hears equally well.

PROJECT

Find out what kinds of materials absorb sound and what materials efficiently distribute sound.

5-7 *Multiplying and Dividing Rational Numbers*

▼ About $\frac{3}{4}$ of the world's fresh water is found in glaciers. Antarctica has $\frac{9}{10}$ of the world's glaciers. What fraction of the world's fresh water is in Antarctica? To find the solution, multiply $\frac{3}{4}$ by $\frac{9}{10}$.

$$\frac{3}{4} \cdot \frac{9}{10} = \frac{3 \cdot 9}{4 \cdot 10}$$
$$= \frac{27}{40}$$

Antarctica has more than half of the world's fresh water.

▼ You can also use a model to multiply rational numbers.

Example 1 $\quad \frac{4}{5} \cdot \frac{2}{3} = \blacksquare$

Solution

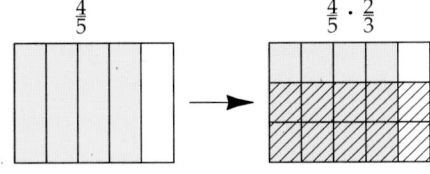

Count the number of rectangles that include both patterns.

So, $\frac{4}{5} \cdot \frac{2}{3} = \frac{8}{15}$.

▼ You can multiply fractions that have variables.

Example 2 $\quad -\frac{2}{3} \cdot \frac{x}{7} = \blacksquare$

Solution $\quad -\frac{2}{3} \cdot \frac{x}{7} = -\frac{2 \cdot x}{3 \cdot 7} \quad$ Multiply the numerator and denominator.

$$= -\frac{2x}{21}$$

THINK Why must you multiply both numerators and denominators?

Product of Two Rational Numbers	For any two rational numbers $\frac{a}{b}$ and $\frac{c}{d}$, $\quad \frac{a}{b} \cdot \frac{c}{d} = \frac{a \cdot c}{b \cdot d} \qquad b \neq 0, d \neq 0$

▼ You can multiply mixed numbers.

Example 3 $\quad 2\frac{1}{4} \cdot \left(-2\frac{2}{3}\right) = \blacksquare$

Solution $\quad 2\frac{1}{4} \cdot \left(-2\frac{2}{3}\right) = \frac{9}{4} \cdot \left(-\frac{8}{3}\right) \quad$ Write mixed numbers as improper fractions.

$$= -\frac{72}{12}$$
$$= -6$$

▼ You can sometimes simplify fractions before multiplying.

Example 4 $\frac{3}{14} \cdot \frac{2}{3} \cdot \left(-\frac{1}{2}\right) = $ ■

Solution $\dfrac{\overset{1}{\cancel{3}} \cdot \overset{1}{\cancel{2}} \cdot 1}{14 \cdot \underset{1}{\cancel{3}} \cdot (-\cancel{2})} = -\dfrac{1}{14}$ **Divide common factors from the numerator and denominator.**

▼ You can divide two rational numbers.

Example 5   Use pattern blocks to model $\frac{4}{6} \div \frac{1}{3}$.

Solution   Two $\frac{1}{3}$ pieces fit in $\frac{4}{6}$.

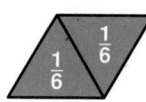 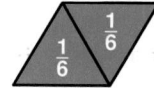

$\frac{4}{6} \div \frac{1}{3} = 2$

▼ You can divide two fractions by multiplying by the *reciprocal* of the second factor.

Example 6 $\frac{2}{5} \div \frac{3}{7} = $ ■

Solution   The reciprocal of $\frac{3}{7}$ is $\frac{7}{3}$.

$\frac{2}{5} \cdot \frac{7}{3} = \frac{14}{15}$ **Multiply by the reciprocal.**

Dividing Two Rational Numbers	For any two rational numbers $\frac{a}{b}$ and $\frac{c}{d}$, $$\frac{a}{b} \div \frac{c}{d} = \frac{a}{b} \cdot \frac{d}{c} \qquad b \neq 0,\ c \neq 0,\ d \neq 0$$

THINK What is the reciprocal of a whole number?

CLASS EXERCISES

Use a model to find the product or quotient.

1. $\frac{2}{3} \cdot \frac{3}{4}$ **2.** $\frac{1}{2} \cdot \frac{3}{8}$ **3.** $\frac{1}{2} \div \frac{1}{3}$ **4.** $2\frac{1}{2} \cdot \frac{1}{6}$

Find the product or quotient.

5. $\frac{1}{3} \cdot \frac{1}{2}$ **6.** $\frac{5a}{7} \cdot -\frac{3a}{5}$ **7.** $\frac{5a}{9} \div \frac{4a}{5}$ **8.** $1\frac{1}{2} \div \frac{3}{8}$

9. $-\frac{5}{8} \div \frac{3}{4}$ **10.** $1\frac{1}{5} \cdot \frac{3}{8}$ **11.** $-4\frac{1}{6} \cdot 1\frac{4}{5}$ **12.** $-3\frac{2}{3} \div \left(-2\frac{4}{9}\right)$

THINK AND DISCUSS

1. Is the product of two rational numbers a rational number? Is the quotient?

2. If two proper fractions are less than 1, is their product less than 1?

Solve.

1. $x - 7.2 = -5.8$

2. $y + (-6.2) = 3.7$

3. $3\frac{1}{3} + \left(-2\frac{5}{6}\right)$

4. $\frac{17}{24} \stackrel{?}{=} \frac{13}{18}$

5. Convert $\frac{13}{40}$ to a decimal.

6. What is the GCF of 30 and 24?

7. $\left|-2\frac{1}{2}\right| + \left|2\frac{1}{2}\right|$

8. Paul's height is $5\frac{11}{12}$ ft, Jim's height is $5\frac{13}{16}$ ft, and Sam's height is $5\frac{7}{8}$ ft. Who is the tallest?

WRITTEN EXERCISES

Use a model to find the product or quotient.

1. $\frac{1}{2} \cdot \frac{2}{3}$　　**2.** $\frac{5}{6} \cdot \frac{1}{6}$　　**3.** $4 \div \frac{1}{2}$　　**4.** $2\frac{1}{2} \div \frac{1}{2}$

Find the answer.

5. $\frac{1}{3} \cdot \frac{6}{11}$　　**6.** $\frac{8}{15} \div \frac{2}{3}$　　**7.** $\frac{3}{8} + \frac{9}{16}$　　**8.** $\frac{9}{10} \div \frac{5}{12} \div \frac{1}{2}$

9. $\frac{3a}{5} - \frac{7a}{10}$　　**10.** $\frac{5q}{8} \div \frac{3}{5}$　　**11.** $3\frac{1}{3} + 2\frac{1}{2}$　　**12.** $1\frac{3}{8} \div 2\frac{1}{16}$

13. $\frac{2}{5} \cdot 2\frac{1}{2}$　　**14.** $2\frac{1}{3} \cdot \frac{3}{7}$　　**15.** $\frac{-4}{9}\left(-2\frac{1}{4}\right) - \frac{1}{4}$　　**16.** $-1\frac{3}{5} \cdot \left(\frac{-5}{8}\right) + \frac{4}{5}$

Estimate the answer by rounding to the nearest integer.

17. $-12\frac{3}{4} \cdot \left(-3\frac{1}{3}\right)$　　**18.** $25\frac{1}{10} \div \left(-5\frac{2}{5}\right)$　　**19.** $-11\frac{7}{18} + 2\frac{7}{10}$

20. $45\frac{3}{8} \cdot \left(-2\frac{6}{7}\right)$　　**21.** $-75\frac{1}{12} - \left(-15\frac{1}{10}\right)$　　**22.** $-33\frac{1}{16} \cdot \left(-12\frac{5}{7}\right)$

23. $18\frac{2}{5} \div 11\frac{1}{2}$　　**24.** $-42\frac{2}{3} + 65\frac{3}{8}$　　**25.** $25\frac{3}{8} \cdot 4\frac{5}{7} + 5\frac{1}{3}$

Compare. Use >, <, or =.

26. $\frac{3}{4} \cdot \frac{4}{5}$ ▨ $\frac{3}{4} \div \frac{4}{5}$　　　　　　**27.** $\frac{9}{7} \cdot \left(-\frac{56}{3}\right)$ ▨ $-30 + 2\frac{1}{2}$

28. $\frac{1}{2} \cdot \frac{1}{2} \cdot \frac{1}{2}$ ▨ $\frac{1}{2^3}$　　　　　　**29.** $\frac{x}{4} \div 2\frac{1}{2}$ ▨ $\frac{2}{3}x,\ x > 0$

30. $-\frac{2a}{3} \cdot 1\frac{1}{8}$ ▨ $\frac{1a}{4} \cdot \left(-1\frac{3}{7}\right),\ a > 0$　　**31.** $3\frac{3}{10} \cdot \left(-3\frac{2}{11}\right)$ ▨ $-4\frac{2}{3} \cdot 2\frac{1}{4}$

Solve. Write each answer in simplest form.

32. $\frac{1}{2} \cdot \frac{1}{4} \cdot \left[\frac{1}{3} + \left(-\frac{1}{6}\right)\right]$　　　　　**33.** $\frac{4}{5} \div \left(\frac{-4}{9}\right) + \frac{4}{9} \cdot \frac{3}{5}$

34. $\frac{3}{10} - \frac{4}{5} \cdot \frac{8}{5} \div 2\frac{1}{2}$　　　　　**35.** $\frac{3}{5} + \frac{1}{4} \cdot \left(-\frac{4}{5}\right) \div \frac{2}{15}$

36. Classify the following as *sometimes*, *always*, or *never* true, assuming $a \neq 0$ and $b \neq 0$.

　　a. $\frac{5a}{b} \cdot \frac{4}{25} = \frac{20a}{b}$　　**b.** $\frac{5a}{3b} \div \frac{15a}{9b} = 1$　　**c.** $\frac{a}{b} \cdot \frac{a}{b} = \left|\frac{a}{b}\right| \cdot \left|\frac{a}{b}\right|$

37. **MENTAL MATH** Solve each problem.

　　a. How many quarters are there in $50?

　　b. How many nickels are there in $25?

　　c. How many $.75 drinks will $9 buy?

FLASHBACK

Order of operations:

1. grouping symbols

2. exponents

3. multiplication and division

4. addition and subtraction

OBJECTIVE:
To use a computer or calculator to study the concept of infinity.

MATERIALS

• Paper and pencil

• Computer and graphing software (optional)

• Math journal to record work

■ Using a computer or a graphing calculator, you can create a bar graph of the *unit fractions,* or fractions with a numerator of 1. The first six unit fractions are shown below.

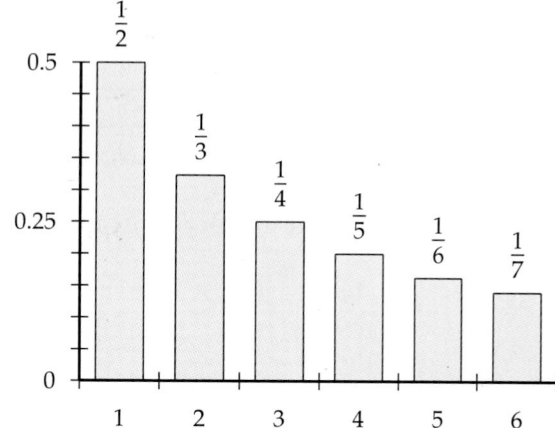

1. Continue the bar graph for the first 10 unit fractions.

2. What happens to the size of the bar for each new fraction?

3. What will the graph look like for 20 unit fractions?

4. Will this trend continue for 100 unit fractions? for 1,000?

5. Can a bar have a height of zero?

6. **Write** a description of the graph of the unit fractions for an increasing denominator.

■ The graphs of the unit fractions are equivalent to these equations:

$$\text{height of bar } 1 = 1 \cdot \frac{1}{2}$$

$$\text{height of bar } 2 = 1 \cdot \frac{1}{3}$$

$$\text{height of bar } 3 = 1 \cdot \frac{1}{4}$$

$$\text{height of bar } 4 = 1 \cdot \frac{1}{5}$$

$$\text{height of bar } 5 = 1 \cdot \frac{1}{6}$$

$$\text{height of bar } 6 = 1 \cdot \frac{1}{7}$$

7. Why does the height of the bars decrease as the denominator of the unit fraction increases?

8. Write an equation that shows the height for *any* bar.

■ You can also create a bar graph made up of the product of two unit fractions. For example, look at the spreadsheet shown below.

	A
1	= 1/2
2	= A1*A1
3	= A1*A1*A1
4	= A1*A1*A1*A1
5	= A1*A1*A1*A1*A1
6	

A bar graph of the spreadsheet data looks like this.

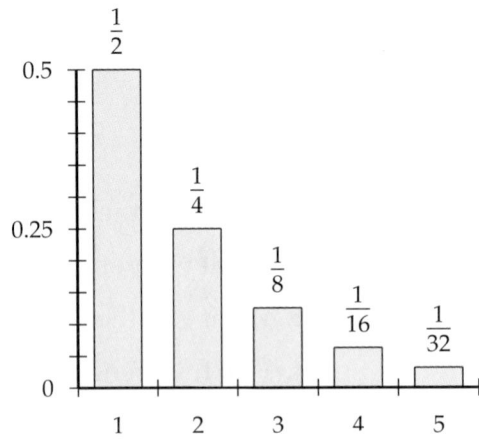

9. How would you continue the spreadsheet data for five more bars?

10. What happens to the bars in the graph? **Compare** this to the change in the graph for the unit fractions.

11. **Write** each of the five fractions on the bar graph using exponents. Then write an equation to show the height of any bar on the graph.

■ For each graph, the height of the bars approaches zero as the denominators become larger, or approach *infinity*. A number is said to approach infinity if the number increases without limit. The symbol for infinity is ∞.

12. Why does the value of a unit fraction approach zero as the denominator approaches infinity?

13. Decide which of the following expressions will approach zero as x approaches infinity. (Use a computer to create a bar graph for $x = 1$ to 5, if necessary.)

a. $\frac{1}{3}x$ **b.** $\frac{1}{3x}$ **c.** $\frac{x^2}{2x}$ **d.** $\frac{1}{3^x}$ **e.** $\frac{3}{x}$

5-8 Rational Numbers with Exponents

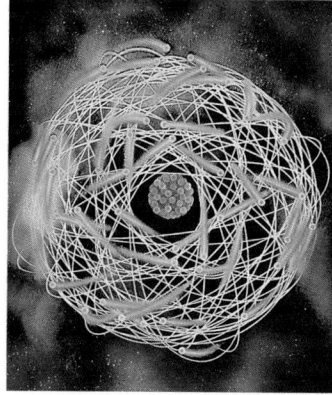

▼ The mass in grams of a proton is 1.67×10^{-24}. To understand numbers like this, you must learn about rational numbers with exponents.

▼ You can divide rational numbers with exponents.

Example 1 Simplify $7^8 \div 7^3$.

Solution
$$\frac{7^8}{7^3} = \frac{\overset{1}{\cancel{7}} \cdot \overset{1}{\cancel{7}} \cdot \overset{1}{\cancel{7}} \cdot 7 \cdot 7 \cdot 7 \cdot 7 \cdot 7}{\underset{1}{\cancel{7}} \cdot \underset{1}{\cancel{7}} \cdot \underset{1}{\cancel{7}}}$$ Divide common factors.

$$= \frac{7 \cdot 7 \cdot 7 \cdot 7 \cdot 7}{1} = \frac{7^5}{1}$$

$$= 7^5$$

Notice that $\frac{7^8}{7^3} = 7^{8-3}$, or 7^5. This suggests the following rule.

Rule of Exponents for Division	To divide numbers or variables with the *same* base, subtract exponents.
	Arithmetic **Algebra**
	$\frac{4^5}{4^2} = 4^{5-2} = 4^3$ $\frac{a^m}{a^n} = a^{m-n}$ $a \neq 0$

Example 2 Simplify.

    a. $\frac{x^6}{x^3}$ **b.** $\frac{a^4 b^2}{a^2 b}$

Solution   **a.** $x^{6-3} = x^3$ **b.** $\frac{a^4}{a^2} \cdot \frac{b^2}{b} = (a^{4-2})(b^{2-1}) = a^2 b$

▼ Sometimes the exponents in the numerator and denominator are equal.

Example 3 Simplify $\frac{3^4}{3^4}$.

Solution   **1.** $3^{4-4} = 3^0$ Use the rules of exponents for division.

          2. $\frac{3^4}{3^4} = 1$ Divide common factors.

Since $\frac{3^4}{3^4} = 3^0$ and $\frac{3^4}{3^4} = 1$, you know that $3^0 = 1$. This suggests the following definition of zero as an exponent.

FLASHBACK

Any nonzero number divided by itself is equal to one.

Zero as an Exponent	Any nonzero number with zero as an exponent equals 1.
	$a^0 = 1$ for all $a \neq 0$.

▼ Sometimes the exponent in the denominator is greater than the exponent in the numerator.

Example 4 Simplify $\frac{2^2}{2^3}$.

Solution   **a.** Use the rule.

$$\frac{2^2}{2^3} = 2^{2-3}$$

$$= 2^{-1}$$

b. Use the meaning of exponents.

$$\frac{2^2}{2^3} = \frac{\overset{1}{\cancel{2}} \cdot \overset{1}{\cancel{2}}}{\underset{1}{\cancel{2}} \cdot \underset{1}{\cancel{2}} \cdot 2}$$

$$= \frac{1}{2}$$

Since $\frac{2^2}{2^3} = 2^{-1}$ and $\frac{2^2}{2^3} = \frac{1}{2}$ you know that $2^{-1} = \frac{1}{2}$. This suggests the following about negative exponents.

THINK Why must 0^0 be undefined?

Negative Exponents	For any nonzero integers a and n: $a^{-n} = \frac{1}{a^n}$

Example 5 Simplify. Write with positive exponents.

   a. $\frac{m^2}{m^5}$ **b.** $4x^{-3}$

Solution   **a.** $\frac{m^2}{m^5} = m^{2-5}$ **b.** $4x^{-3} = 4 \cdot \frac{1}{x^3}$

$$= m^{-3} \qquad\qquad\qquad = \frac{4}{x^3}$$

$$= \frac{1}{m^3}$$

THINK AND DISCUSS

1. Can you simplify $\frac{x^3}{y^4}$?

2. How many ways can you write $-8x^{-3}$?

3. Explain why 3^{-2} is not a negative number.

CLASS EXERCISES

Evaluate.

1. 2^{-3} **2.** 5^{-2} **3.** 7^0 **4.** -3^0

5. $\frac{2^5}{2^2}$ **6.** $\frac{5^{-3}}{5^{-2}}$ **7.** $8^4 \div 8^2$ **8.** 0^0

Write with positive or negative exponents. Leave no exponents in the denominator.

9. $\frac{a^3}{a^7}$ **10.** $\frac{m^5}{m^2}$ **11.** $\frac{b^5}{c^2}$ **12.** $\frac{a^5 b^7}{a^6 b^{-3}}$

Write with positive exponents.

13. a^{-3} **14.** $5b^{-7}$ **15.** $\frac{6x^2}{x^4}$ **16.** $\frac{2y^5}{8y^3}$

17. $x^{-3}y^2$ **18.** 5^{-2} **19.** $4a^{-3}$ **20.** $15x^2 y^{-4}$

WRITTEN EXERCISES

Evaluate.

1. 6^{-2} **2.** 3^{-1} **3.** $(-2)^0$ **4.** $\dfrac{4^3}{4^5}$

5. $2^{-3} \cdot 3$ **6.** -7^0 **7.** $(-5)^{-2}$ **8.** $3^0 \cdot 5^2 \cdot 2^{-4}$

Write with positive or negative exponents. Leave no exponents in the denominator.

9. $\dfrac{1}{a^3}$ **10.** $\dfrac{b^5}{b^7}$ **11.** $\dfrac{5x^2}{10x^{-5}}$ **12.** $\dfrac{3y^4z}{y^6z^2}$

13. $\dfrac{x^5y^{-2}}{x^3y^8}$ **14.** $\dfrac{y^{-2}z^{-4}}{y^3z^{-2}}$ **15.** $\dfrac{15b^6c}{3b^2c^{-4}}$ **16.** $\dfrac{4xy^{-5}}{20x^7y^{-2}}$

Write with positive exponents.

17. $\dfrac{20m^5}{4m^3}$ **18.** $\dfrac{3b^2}{4b^7}$ **19.** $\dfrac{3x^2y^3}{x^5y}$ **20.** $\dfrac{b^{-3}c^7}{b^5c^{-2}}$

21. Write each of these numbers without an exponent.

　a. -5^2 **b.** $(-5)^2$ **c.** 5^{-2} **d.** $(-5)^{-2}$

Simplify.

22. $(3a)^2$ **23.** $(5a)^{-2}$ **24.** $-(2y^4)^0$ **25.** $(a^2b^{-3})^5$

26. $x^2 \cdot x^{-3}$ **27.** $\left(\dfrac{3a}{b^2}\right)^2 \cdot \left(\dfrac{a^2}{b^{-3}}\right)$ **28.** $(2x^2y^{-3}) \cdot (x^3y^4)$

29. Study the table at the right.

　a. Describe the pattern in the first column of the table.

　b. Describe the pattern in the second column. If this pattern continues, what will be the next three entries?

　c. How are these values related to 3?

　d. Create a similar table for values of n and 2^n. How are the values in the table related to 2?

4	81
3	27
2	9
1	3
0	
-1	
-2	

True or *false*? **Explain your answer.**

30. $\dfrac{a^3 \cdot a^4}{a^2} = \dfrac{a^3 + a^4}{a^2}$ **31.** $x^8 \cdot x^2 = x^5 \cdot x^5$ **32.** $1^0 = 1^{-1}$

33. $x^5 \cdot x^3 = x^{15}$ **34.** $x^3 \cdot y^4 = (xy)^7$ **35.** $5^0 = 7^0$

36. $(-r^3)^2 > 0$ **37.** $-(r^2)^3 < 0$ **38.** $1^8 = 1^{23}$

Write in standard notation.

39. The weight of all the ocean water on Earth is 1.58×10^{18} t.

40. The radius of Earth's orbit is 1.5×10^{11} m.

Use the article below to answer each question.

Future Glows for Natural Gas

As oil prices continue to rise, American investors look again at an abundant resource, natural gas. In the United States, natural gas now accounts for $\frac{1}{4}$ of daily energy use. Petroleum products account for about $\frac{2}{5}$.

Not only can gas replace oil for home heating, it can also fuel cars and power electric generating plants. Natural Gas burns more cleanly than oil, emitting less carbon dioxide.

When gas replaces coal in electric generating plants, sulphur emissions are immediately cut.

41. How much of the energy of the United States do natural gas and petroleum products provide?

42. _PROJECT_ Research natural gas. Find out how it can be used to fuel automobiles. What are the costs of converting from gasoline to natural gas?

Critical Thinking

EXPLORING PATTERNS IN SCIENTIFIC NOTATION

1. Continue the pattern and describe what happens when the exponents are negative.

$$1.2 \times 10^3 = 1{,}200$$
$$1.2 \times 10^2 = 120$$
$$1.2 \times 10^1 = 12$$
$$1.2 \times 10^0 = \blacksquare$$
$$1.2 \times 10^{-1} = \blacksquare$$
$$1.2 \times 10^{-2} = \blacksquare$$

2. $1.2 \times 10^{-3} = 0.0012$. Extend the pattern above to see if it agrees.

3. Write 3.7×10^{-4} in standard notation.

4. 1.67×10^{-24} g is the mass of a proton. How many zeros would follow the decimal point and come before the 1 if this were written in standard notation?

5. The mass of the sun is 1.00×10^{30} kg and the mass of an electron is 9.11×10^{-28} g. Why do scientists prefer scientific notation to standard notation for very large and very small numbers?

Addition and Subtraction Equations

▼ In four months Jules grew $\frac{2}{3}$ in. How could you represent his new height?

Let x = Jules' height four months ago. You can represent Jules' new height by the following variable expression.

$$x + \frac{2}{3}$$

▼ You can write an equation using a variable expression.

Example 1 **Write an equation to represent the situation.**

At high tide the water level rose $3\frac{1}{2}$ ft to a height of 25 ft.

Solution Let x = the previous height.
Then $x + 3\frac{1}{2} = 25$ is an equation to represent the water level at high tide.

▼ You can solve rational number equations by using or drawing a model.

Example 2 **Solve the equation using a model.**

$$x + \frac{1}{2} = \frac{11}{12}$$

Solution

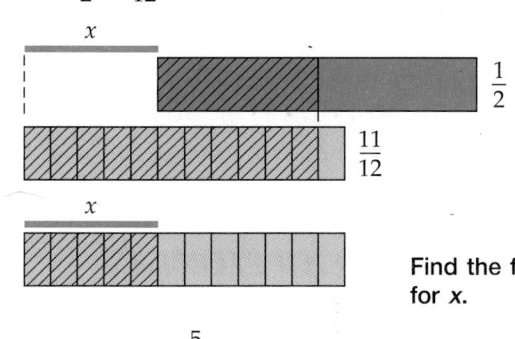

Find the fraction strip for *x*.

So, $x = \frac{5}{12}$.

▼ You know how to solve integer equations by isolating the variable. You can use the same procedure for solving equations with rational numbers.

Example 3 Solve $x + \frac{4}{15} = \frac{7}{10}$.

Solution

$$x + \frac{4}{15} - \frac{4}{15} = \frac{7}{10} - \frac{4}{15}$$ Subtract $\frac{4}{15}$ from each side to isolate *x*.

$$x = \frac{7}{10} - \frac{4}{15}$$

$$= \frac{21}{30} - \frac{8}{30}$$ Find a common denominator.

$$= \frac{13}{30}$$

NOTES & QUOTES

The ancient Egyptians represented all fractions, except $\frac{2}{3}$, as the sum of *unit fractions*. A unit fraction is a fraction with a numerator of 1, such as $\frac{1}{2}$. The Egyptians would write $\frac{2}{15}$ as $\frac{1}{10} + \frac{1}{30}$. They also used special symbols to denote unit fractions.

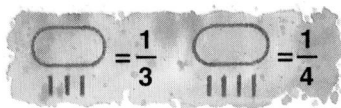

PROJECT Write $\frac{2}{7}$ and $\frac{3}{5}$ using unit fractions.

FLASHBACK

You isolate a variable by getting it alone on one side of the equal sign.

▼ You can also solve equations involving subtraction of rational numbers.

Example 4   Solve $z - \left(-3\frac{7}{10}\right) = -2\frac{1}{5}$.

Solution $z - \left(-3\frac{7}{10}\right) + \left(-3\frac{7}{10}\right) = -2\frac{1}{5} + \left(-3\frac{7}{10}\right)$ Add $-3\frac{7}{10}$ to each side.

$$z = -2\frac{1}{5} + \left(-3\frac{7}{10}\right)$$

$$= -2\frac{2}{10} + \left(-3\frac{7}{10}\right)$$ Find a common denominator.

$$= -5\frac{9}{10}$$

THINK AND DISCUSS

1. How is a rational number equation similar to an equation with integers?

2. How could you write the equation $x + \frac{1}{2} = 1\frac{5}{8}$ as an equation with decimals?

3. How could you write the equation $x + \frac{1}{2} = 10$ as an integer equation?

CLASS EXERCISES

Use a model to solve each equation.

1. $x + \frac{1}{4} = \frac{2}{3}$ **2.** $y + \frac{1}{3} = \frac{3}{4}$ **3.** $z + \left(-\frac{1}{3}\right) = 8$

Solve each equation.

4. $a + \frac{1}{8} = \frac{5}{6}$ **5.** $b + \left(-\frac{4}{5}\right) = 6$ **6.** $c - \frac{9}{10} = \frac{4}{3}$

7. $x + \left(-1\frac{1}{2}\right) = \frac{1}{4}$ **8.** $y - 4\frac{7}{8} = -2$ **9.** $z + \left(-7\frac{5}{9}\right) = -7\frac{5}{9}$

10. $g - \left(9\frac{2}{3}\right) = -10\frac{4}{5}$ **11.** $h + \left(-12\frac{1}{10}\right) = -12\frac{3}{10}$

WRITTEN EXERCISES

Write and solve an equation for each model.

1. 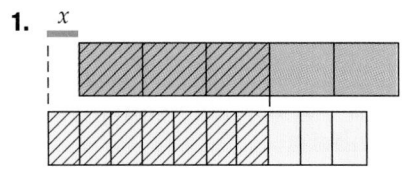   **2.**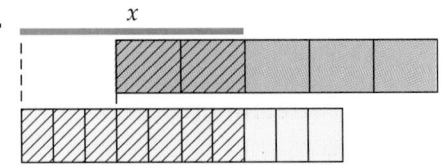

Solve each equation.

3. $m + \frac{3}{4} = \frac{1}{4}$ **4.** $p - \frac{2}{3} = 1\frac{1}{3}$ **5.** $n + \frac{5}{8} = 6$

6. $a + \frac{5}{8} = \frac{7}{12}$ **7.** $b + \left(-\frac{1}{6}\right) = \frac{3}{8}$ **8.** $c - \frac{3}{16} = -5$

9. $d - \left(\frac{-3}{10}\right) = \frac{-7}{8}$ **10.** $e - 6\frac{1}{4} = 3$ **11.** $f - \left(-4\frac{5}{12}\right) = 5\frac{3}{8}$

12. $g + 8\frac{1}{6} = 3\frac{4}{9}$ **13.** $h + \left|-2\frac{3}{4}\right| = 5\frac{7}{10}$ **14.** $k + 4.5 = 3.3$

15. $m + (-0.7) = |-5.4|$ **16.** $n - 7.23 = 10.88$

17. $p - 16.5 = -11\frac{1}{2}$ **18.** $z - 12.3 = 13\frac{1}{5}$ **19.** $q + 6.4 = 12\frac{2}{5}$

MENTAL MATH Solve each equation.

20. $a + \frac{3}{5} = \frac{4}{5}$ **21.** $b - \frac{9}{10} = -\frac{7}{10}$ **22.** $c + 2\frac{11}{12} = 3\frac{5}{12}$

23. $d + 5\frac{7}{16} = -2\frac{11}{16}$ **24.** $e - \frac{5}{8} = \frac{3}{4}$ **25.** $f + \frac{5}{6} = -\frac{7}{12}$

26. For which equations does $x = 3\frac{1}{2}$?

   a. $x + 3\frac{1}{2} = 0$ **b.** $x + \left(-\frac{7}{2}\right) = 0$ **c.** $x + \left(-\frac{4}{5}\right) = 3\frac{1}{2}$

27. WRITE Suppose you are solving the equation $x + \frac{1}{2} = \left(-3\frac{4}{5}\right)$. Without solving the equation, how can you tell that x is less than zero?

MENTAL MATH Which equations have a solution greater than 0?

28. $x + 4\frac{1}{5} = 5\frac{1}{2}$ **29.** $x - 5\frac{7}{9} = 6\frac{1}{4}$ **30.** $x + \left(-5\frac{3}{4}\right) = -5\frac{3}{4}$

Write an equation and solve.

31. Billie's tote bag weighed $3\frac{3}{16}$ lb when she left for school. When she returned home it weighed $5\frac{11}{16}$ lb. How much did she add to the weight of her tote bag? Let b represent the number of pounds she added to the weight in her tote bag.

32. On January 2, 0.26 in. of rain fell. The total rainfall for the year was 3.5 in. How much rain fell on January 1?

33. In June Jonathan's height was $68\frac{1}{2}$ in. During the school year he had grown $1\frac{5}{8}$ in. What was Jonathan's height the previous September?

Solve.

34. Some freshmen were trying out for the school track team.

After Round 1, $\frac{1}{2}$ were eliminated.

After Round 2, $\frac{1}{3}$ of those remaining were eliminated.

After Round 3, $\frac{1}{4}$ of those remaining were eliminated.

After Round 4, $\frac{1}{5}$ of those remaining were eliminated.

After Round 5, $\frac{1}{6}$ of those remaining were eliminated.

The 10 who remained became the track team. How many freshmen originally tried out?

PROBLEM SOLVING HINT
Try working backwards.

OBJECTIVE:
To solve equations involving multiplication of rational numbers.

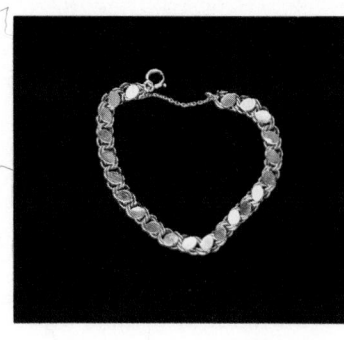

5-10 Multiplication Equations

▼ An 18-karat gold bracelet is three-fourths pure gold. Suppose a bracelet has $3\frac{1}{2}$ oz of gold. How could you represent the total weight of the bracelet with an equation?

Let x = the weight of the bracelet. Then, $\frac{3}{4} \cdot x = 3\frac{1}{2}$ is an equation that represents the situation.

▼ You can solve multiplication equations by isolating the variable and using the multiplication property of equality.

Example 1   Solve $\frac{7}{8}x = -\frac{4}{5}$.

Solution

$$\frac{8}{7} \cdot \frac{7}{8}x = \frac{8}{7} \cdot \left(-\frac{4}{5}\right)$$ Multiply both sides by the reciprocal of $\frac{7}{8}$.

$$\frac{\overset{1}{\cancel{8}} \cdot \overset{1}{\cancel{7}}}{\underset{1}{\cancel{7}} \cdot \underset{1}{\cancel{8}}}x = \frac{8 \cdot (-4)}{7 \cdot 5}$$

$$x = -\frac{32}{35}$$

▼ When equations involve mixed numbers, rewrite them as improper fractions. Then solve the equation.

Example 2   Solve $-\frac{5x}{9} = 3\frac{1}{2}$.

Solution

$$-\frac{5x}{9} = 3\frac{1}{2}$$

$$-\frac{5x}{9} = \frac{7}{2}$$ Write $3\frac{1}{2}$ as an improper fraction.

$$\left(-\frac{9}{5}\right) \cdot \left(-\frac{5}{9}\right)x = -\frac{9}{5} \cdot \frac{7}{2}$$ Multiply by the reciprocal.

$$x = -\frac{63}{10}$$

$$= -6\frac{3}{10}$$

FLASHBACK

$-\frac{5x}{9} = -\frac{5}{9}x$

▼ Some equations are false and do not have a solution.

Example 3   Solve $\frac{1}{2}|x| = -\frac{2}{9}$.

Solution

$$\frac{1}{2}|x| = -\frac{2}{9}$$

$$\frac{2}{1} \cdot \frac{1}{2}|x| = \frac{2}{1} \cdot \left(-\frac{2}{9}\right)$$ Multiply by the reciprocal.

$$|x| = -\frac{4}{9}$$

Since the absolute value of a number is never negative, $|x| \neq -\frac{4}{9}$. This is a false equation. It has no solution.

CLASS EXERCISES

Solve each equation.

1. $\frac{1}{5}x = \frac{2}{3}$

2. $-\frac{2}{7}x = \frac{3}{8}$

3. $\frac{7}{8}z = 2\frac{3}{4}$

4. $-1\frac{6}{7} \cdot x = \frac{9}{10}$

5. $4\frac{5}{8} \cdot z = 6\frac{2}{5}$

6. $\frac{2}{3}x = 2$

7. $\frac{2}{3} \cdot |x| = \frac{7}{12}$

8. $\frac{5}{9} \cdot |y| = -1\frac{1}{2}$

9. $1\frac{1}{3} \cdot |m| = 2\frac{2}{3}$

THINK AND DISCUSS

1. How would you solve the equation $\frac{3}{5} = \frac{x}{2}$?

2. How would you solve the equation $\frac{2}{3}x = 3x$? What is the value of x?

3. What is the reciprocal of x? of $\frac{1}{x}$?

WRITTEN EXERCISES

Solve each equation.

1. $\frac{2}{7}b = \frac{3}{8}$

2. $-\frac{5}{7}x = \frac{9}{10}$

3. $\frac{2}{9}z = 1\frac{4}{5}$

4. $6\frac{3}{5} \cdot x = \frac{1}{2}$

5. $\frac{2}{3}x = -8$

6. $1\frac{1}{2} \cdot m = \frac{3}{4}$

7. $\frac{3x}{4} = \frac{3}{8}$

8. $-\frac{7x}{8} = 1$

9. $\frac{1}{6}x = \frac{2}{3}$

10. $\frac{3}{4}x = -2\frac{1}{3}$

11. $\frac{1}{2}x = -0.4$

12. $\frac{-2}{3}x = 7$

Without solving, how do you know that $x < 0$?

13. $-\frac{3}{4}x = 6$

14. $\frac{-5}{-7}x = -\frac{3}{5}$

15. $\frac{5}{8}x = -1\frac{1}{2}$

For what values of x is each equation true?

16. $\frac{|x|}{5} = \frac{2}{3}$

17. $-\frac{3}{5}|x| = -1\frac{2}{3}$

18. $\frac{5}{8}|x| = -\frac{4}{5}$

19. $-2\frac{3}{4} \cdot |x| = 3\frac{1}{7}$

20. $-1\frac{2}{3} \cdot |x| = \frac{-25}{27}$

21. $4\frac{2}{5} \cdot |x| = -2\frac{1}{5}$

MIXED REVIEW

Calculate each answer.

1. $7\frac{1}{3} \cdot \left(-1\frac{3}{11}\right)$ **2.** $\frac{-5}{6} \cdot \left(-1\frac{7}{20}\right)$

3. $4\frac{1}{6} \div \frac{3}{8}$ **4.** $2.4 + 3.7$

5. $x + \left(\frac{-5}{12}\right) = \frac{7}{18}$

6. $y - (-1.6) = 3.8$

7. Compare $\frac{-7}{16}$ and $\frac{-5}{12}$.

8. Three-fifths of the freshman class intend to help with a fund raising project. There are 210 students in the class. How many will help?

Write an equation and solve each problem.

22. A sheet of plywood is $\frac{3}{4}$-in. thick. How many sheets would make a stack 9 in. high? Let s represent the number of sheets of plywood.

23. A fast-growing ivy plant grew $\frac{5}{8}$ in. each day. How many days did it take the plant to grow 12 in? Let d represent the number of days.

24. How many dimes are in $12.50? Let d represent the number of dimes.

Solve each equation. Is $a >$, $<$, or $=$ to b?

25. $\frac{2}{3}a = \frac{5}{9}$, $\frac{3}{5}b = \frac{8}{10}$

26. $1\frac{1}{2}a = -6\frac{2}{3}$, $\frac{-3}{8}b = 1\frac{2}{3}$

Solve.

27. One-fifth of the students at Lincoln High are graduating. This represents 70 students. How many students attend Lincoln High?

28. In a tree replanting project, $\frac{2}{3}$ of the trees planted survived the winter. There are 150 trees still living. Find the original number of trees planted.

29. Sara has a handful of coins. Three-fifths of the coins are dimes, one-third are nickels, and the rest are pennies. What fraction of the coins are pennies?

30. Two-thirds of the science club's members are older than fifteen. One-fifth of the members are younger than 15. Six members are exactly 15 years old. Find the number of students in the science club.

31. **PROJECT** While watching your favorite half-hour TV program, compute the number of minutes spent on commercials. Then count the number of different products advertised in each set of commercials.

    a. What fraction of the 30 min is program time?

    b. What fraction of the 30 min is spent on commercials?

    c. How many products are advertised?

    d. Write the number of products advertised compared to the minutes of commercial time as a fraction.

    e. Compare your results with others in the class.

Complete each analogy.

32. one-fifth : terminating decimal : : two-thirds : ▨

33. numerator : denominator : : part : ▨

34. multiplication : division : : addition : ▨

35. sum : product : : addition : ▨

36. $\frac{1}{10} : 0.10 : : \frac{1}{4} :$ ▨

37. $0.75 : \frac{3}{4} : : 0.875 :$ ▨

38. $11 : \text{prime} : : 20 :$ ▨

39. $3^4 : 81 : : 4^3 :$ ▨

40. $\frac{2}{4} : \frac{1}{2} : : \frac{3}{6} :$ ▨

41. $\frac{15}{8} : \frac{19}{7} : : 1\frac{7}{8} :$ ▨

42. $\frac{1}{3} : 0.\overline{3} : : \frac{2}{3} :$ ▨

43. $0.\overline{45} : \frac{5}{11} : : 0.\overline{63} :$ ▨

Use the article below and the data at the right to answer each question.

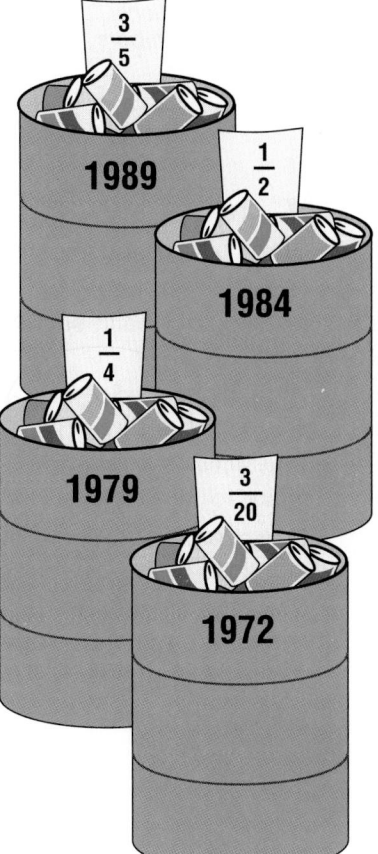

Aluminum Recycling on Rise

In 1989, Americans recycled about three-fifths of the aluminum cans produced. They returned 49 billion cans and earned $900 million. The trend toward recycling has steadily increased since 1972 when the number of recycled cans was only $\frac{3}{20}$ of the number produced. Recycling saves money and saves our environment.

44. Write each fraction as a decimal.

45. How much greater is the fraction recycled in 1989 than 1979?

46. One year $\frac{2}{5}$ of the cans produced were recycled. Would you predict the year was between 1979 and 1984 or between 1984 and 1989?

47. Would the data suggest that recycling doubled from 1979 to 1984? Why or why not?

48. *ESTIMATION* About how much is each recycled can worth?

49. The fraction of recycled cans in 1995 is predicted to be $1\frac{1}{2}$ times the number for 1989. What fraction of the cans produced would you expect to be recycled in 1995?

TEST YOURSELF

Solve each equation.

1. $\frac{2}{3} + x = 1\frac{5}{8}$

2. $a - 3\frac{1}{2} = 6\frac{3}{4}$

3. $m - (-2.5) = 1\frac{5}{8}$

4. $\frac{2}{3}x = 1\frac{5}{8}$

5. $-\frac{3}{8}y = \frac{7}{12}$

6. $2\frac{2}{3} \cdot p = -2\frac{1}{4}$

7. $\frac{x}{5} = 3\frac{3}{8}$

8. $\frac{9}{14} \cdot |x| = -4\frac{1}{2}$

9. $-\frac{2}{5} \cdot |x| = 3\frac{1}{5}$

Evaluate.

10. 3^{-2}

11. $(-1)^0$

12. $\frac{3^4}{3}$

13. $3^0 \cdot 5^{-1} \cdot 2^3$

Write with positive exponents.

14. $\frac{5n^3}{n^2}$

15. $\frac{9a^2}{3a^5}$

16. $\frac{8x^3y^2}{xy^5}$

17. $\frac{a^{-3}b^2}{a^2b^{-4}}$

OBJECTIVE:
To apply operations with rational numbers to stock market problems.

5-11 *The Stock Market*

Companies sell shares of stock to raise money. Stock prices appear as mixed numbers such as $3\frac{1}{8}$ for $3.125. When people buy stock, they usually use a broker who charges a commission for buying or selling stock.

KEY

• **Stock** name of company

• **Div** payment made to investors for each share held

• **High** highest price per share for the day

• **Low** lowest price per share for the day

• **Close** price of a share at the close of the day

• **Chg.** the amount of change from the previous day's closing price

Stock	Div	High	Low	Close	Chg.
DQ	1.02	$5\frac{5}{8}$	$5\frac{1}{2}$	$5\frac{1}{2}$	$-\frac{1}{8}$
MCJ	1.26	10	$9\frac{3}{4}$	$9\frac{7}{8}$	$-\frac{1}{8}$
EDL	.90	$11\frac{7}{8}$	$11\frac{5}{8}$	$11\frac{3}{4}$	$+\frac{1}{4}$
JMB	.68	$46\frac{7}{8}$	$45\frac{1}{4}$	$46\frac{5}{8}$	$+1\frac{3}{8}$
BBH	2.76	$53\frac{1}{4}$	$52\frac{3}{4}$	53	$+\frac{1}{4}$

Newspapers publish the results of stock trading daily in lists like the one at the left.

Example 1 Mr. Jitters bought 100 shares of MCJ for $9\frac{3}{4}$ per share plus a broker's fee of $19.50. He later sold the stock for $11\frac{1}{2}$ per share minus a $23 broker's fee. Did Mr. Jitters gain or lose money? How much?

Solution

$$100\left(9\frac{3}{4}\right) + 19.50 = 100(9.75) + 19.50 \qquad \text{buying price}$$
$$= 994.50$$

$$100\left(11\frac{1}{2}\right) - 23 = 100(11.50) - 23 \qquad \text{selling price}$$
$$= 1{,}127$$

$$1{,}127 - 994.50 = 132.50 \qquad \text{difference}$$

Mr. Jitters gains $132.50.

■■■■■■ Decision Making ■ *DECISION MAKING* ■ Decision Making ■ Decision Making ■ Decision Making ■

THE STOCK MARKET

■ **COLLECT DATA**

1. Assume you have $10,000 to invest. You must choose at least four stocks and buy at least 100 shares of each stock. Find out what a PE ratio is and how you might use it to choose a stock. Also consider whether or not the stock pays a dividend. Balance your portfolio by choosing stocks in different industries.

2. Use the financial pages of the newspaper to choose your stocks. Assume a broker's fee of 0.02. Determine the cost of your investment including the broker's fee. Make a table and keep track of your portfolio for three months.

CLASS EXERCISES

Write each share price as a decimal.

1. $9\frac{7}{8}$ **2.** $4\frac{1}{2}$ **3.** $27\frac{3}{8}$ **4.** $198\frac{1}{8}$ **5.** $76\frac{3}{4}$

Find each difference. Write the gain or loss in dollars and cents.

6. $22\frac{7}{8}$ to $29\frac{1}{2}$ **7.** $115\frac{1}{4}$ to $98\frac{3}{4}$ **8.** $33\frac{1}{8}$ to $29\frac{7}{8}$

9. $37\frac{5}{8}$ to $32\frac{1}{2}$ **10.** $49\frac{3}{4}$ to $52\frac{1}{8}$ **11.** $65\frac{1}{2}$ to $67\frac{3}{8}$

Solve.

12. An investor bought 2,500 shares of XYZ Company on Monday. She kept track of the daily changes and on Friday decided to sell. Use the table at the right to answer each question. Each change number is the change from the day before.

    a. What was the price at the end of the week for a share of XYZ stock?

    b. How much money did the investor pay for the 2,500 shares on Monday?

    c. How much will the 2,500 shares of stock sell for on Friday?

    d. What else do you need to know to find out whether the investor made or lost money on the stock?

13. A share of stock in the ABC Company has an average weekly change of $-\frac{5}{8}$ over 14 weeks. How much less is 100 shares worth at the end of the 14-week period than at the beginning?

XYZ Stock

Day	Opening Price	Change
Mon	$29\frac{1}{2}$	
Tues		$-\frac{1}{4}$
Wed		$+4\frac{1}{8}$
Thurs		$+2\frac{1}{2}$
Fri		$-\frac{3}{4}$

■ *Decision Making* ■ *Decision Making* ■ *Decision Making* ■ *Decision Making* ■ *Decision Making* ■ *Decision Making* ■

■ **ANALYZE DATA**

3. Which of your stocks increased in value? Which decreased?

4. How would factors such as an oil spill or news of a company's new product affect stock prices? What factors influenced the way your stocks changed?

■ **MAKE DECISIONS**

5. Stocks are risky investments because their value can increase or decrease. Suppose you invested $5,000 in stocks and $5,000 in a savings account. How might your financial position differ at the end of the three months? Do you think it's a good idea to invest all of your money in one stock? Why or why not?

WRITTEN EXERCISES

Write each share price as a decimal.

1. $62\frac{5}{8}$ **2.** $104\frac{3}{8}$ **3.** $77\frac{1}{8}$ **4.** $15\frac{3}{4}$ **5.** $88\frac{7}{8}$

Find each difference. Write the gain or loss in dollars and cents.

6. $17\frac{7}{8}$ to $12\frac{1}{2}$ **7.** $57\frac{3}{4}$ to $61\frac{3}{8}$ **8.** $96\frac{1}{2}$ to $95\frac{7}{8}$

9. Use the stock table on page 222.

    a. Determine the cost of buying 500 shares of each stock at the closing price. Assume a broker's commission of 0.02.

    b. Determine the dividend earned on 500 shares of each stock.

10. Use the **DATA** below to solve.

Stock	Price	Changes			
	Mon	**Tues**	**Wed**	**Thurs**	**Fri**
VEX	$9\frac{3}{8}$	$+\frac{1}{2}$	$-\frac{1}{8}$	$+2$	$+1\frac{7}{8}$
VYE	$36\frac{1}{2}$	$-1\frac{3}{8}$	$+\frac{3}{4}$	$+\frac{1}{2}$	$-\frac{1}{8}$
WITT	$111\frac{1}{4}$	$+\frac{5}{8}$	$+1\frac{1}{8}$	$+\frac{3}{4}$	$-\frac{1}{4}$
WKM	67	$-1\frac{1}{2}$	$-\frac{1}{8}$	$+\frac{1}{4}$	$-1\frac{7}{8}$
X-L	$101\frac{7}{8}$	$-3\frac{1}{4}$	$-1\frac{1}{2}$	$+3\frac{1}{8}$	$+\frac{3}{4}$

    a. What was the net change for each stock for the week?

    b. What was the closing price for each stock on Friday?

    c. Which stock showed the greatest change by Friday?

    d. Which stock had the greatest gain during the week? Explain.

    e. Which stock had the greatest loss during the week? Explain.

11. Why is the amount of a broker's commission different on the sale of stock than on the purchase when the rate is the same?

12. **WRITE** A stockholder in the ABC Company decides to sell all stock in the company based on the steady drop in market price. Is it certain that the investor is making the right move? Describe what things you think might influence the investor's decision.

13. **DATA FILE 3 (pp. 96–97)** Look at the value of the proof sets in 1965, 1968, and 1990. Which proof set seems to be the best investment? Why do you think the value of some sets increased while others decreased?

Problem Solving Practice

Solve. The list at the left shows some possible strategies you can use.

1. In science class there is a jar of bacteria that doubles each day. If the jar is full on the 28th day, on what day is it half full?

2. Phillip has 4 pairs of pants, 5 shirts, and 2 sweaters. How many different three-piece outfits can he make?

3. What is a four-digit number in which the first digit is half the second, the third digit is the product of the first two, and the last is the sum of the first two?

4. You check your coin collection. The total is $16. Surprisingly, you have an equal number of nickels, quarters, and half-dollars. How many coins do you have?

5. In a race Marie was faster than Sophie. Clara beat Lena but lost to Sophie. Who came in last?

6. RPM means the number of revolutions a record makes in one minute. How many more revolutions does a 45-rpm record make in 6 min than a $33\frac{1}{3}$-rpm record?

7. Clara had $30. She bought 3 packets of Morning Glory seeds at $1.98 each, 4 packets of Marigold seeds at $2.49 each, tomato plants for $5.95, and fertilizer for $2.89. How much change did she receive?

8. John found the following prices on a list of sports equipment: $3, $2, $6, $4, $9, $8. Although the list seemed a bit odd, John was sure there was a pattern. What are the next three numbers?

9. The magic square shown below has the sum of 15. An anti-magic square uses the numbers from 1–9, but the totals in any direction, including the diagonals, are different. Make an anti-magic square.

Magic Square

4	3	8
9	5	1
2	7	6

Anti-Magic Square

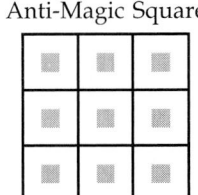

10. **DATA FILE 9 (pp. 360–361)** Create a data base of the different types of golf clubs. Include these field names: club, loft, and distance. Arrange the data by distance from least to greatest.

11. Ralph bought $3\frac{1}{2}$ lb of cheese. He used $2\frac{3}{4}$ lb for cheese spread. He used the rest for sandwiches. How much did he use for sandwiches?

Chapter 5 Review

Complete each statement. Use the vocabulary words given.

1. You can form ▓ by multiplying or dividing the numerator and denominator by the same nonzero factor.

2. When a fraction is in ▓ , the only common factor of the numerator and denominator is 1.

3. A ▓ is a number you write in the form $\frac{a}{b}$ where a is an integer and b is a nonzero integer.

4. The ▓ of two or more fractions is the LCM of the denominators.

5. To divide numbers or variables with the same base, subtract ▓ .

Equivalent Fractions 5-1

To form equivalent fractions, multiply or divide the numerator and denominator by the same nonzero factor.

Rename the variable to form equivalent fractions.

6. $\frac{3}{4} = \frac{a}{8}$

7. $\frac{2}{3} = \frac{4}{b}$

8. $\frac{3}{x} = \frac{12}{32}$

9. $\frac{y}{5} = \frac{16}{20}$

10. $\frac{5}{6} = \frac{c}{30}$

Fractions and Decimals 5-2

To write an improper fraction as a mixed number or as a decimal, divide the numerator by the denominator. To write a decimal as a fraction, write the decimal as a fraction with a denominator as a power of ten. Write the fraction in lowest terms.

Write each improper fraction as a mixed number and as a decimal.

11. $\frac{15}{4}$

12. $\frac{3}{2}$

13. $\frac{12}{5}$

14. $\frac{17}{6}$

15. $\frac{21}{8}$

Write each decimal as a fraction or a mixed number.

16. 0.6

17. 2.375

18. 5.25

19. 0.7

20. 0.35

Rational Numbers 5-3, 5-4

To compare rational numbers, write as fractions with a common denominator and compare the numerators, or write the fractions as decimals and compare.

Compare. Use >, <, or =.

21. $\frac{2}{3}$ ▓ $\frac{3}{4}$

22. 0.9 ▓ $\frac{8}{9}$

23. $-\frac{4}{5}$ ▓ -0.8

24. $\left|\frac{5}{9}\right|$ ▓ $\left|\frac{5}{11}\right|$

Adding and Subtracting Rational Numbers   5-5

To add or subtract rational numbers, write equivalent fractions with
the same denominator, and add or subtract the numerators.

Write each sum or difference.

25. $2\frac{1}{3} + \frac{3}{4}$ **26.** $16\frac{4}{5} - 9\frac{2}{3}$ **27.** $8\frac{1}{6} + 7\frac{3}{12}$ **28.** $11\frac{5}{6} - 5\frac{3}{8}$

Problem Solving   5-6, 5-11

To solve some problems, you have to work backwards.

To determine the price of 100 shares, multiply the number of shares
by the quoted price.

Solve.

29. It will take the Smiths 9 h to drive to
Washington. They plan to make five $\frac{1}{2}$-h
stops. They plan to arrive at 5:30 P.M.
At what time should they plan to
leave?

30. Ms. Nelson bought 500 shares of Plato
Publishing at $39\frac{7}{8}$ per share. Find the cost of
the 500 shares.

Multiplying and Dividing Rational Numbers   5-7

For any two rational numbers $\frac{a}{b}$ and $\frac{c}{d}$, $\frac{a}{b} \cdot \frac{c}{d} = \frac{a \cdot c}{b \cdot d}$ and $\frac{a}{b} \div \frac{c}{d} = \frac{a}{b} \cdot \frac{d}{c}$.

Find each product or quotient.

31. $\frac{3}{5} \cdot 1\frac{1}{2}$ **32.** $2\frac{2}{3} \cdot 3\frac{3}{8}$ **33.** $5\frac{1}{4} \div \frac{7}{8}$ **34.** $\frac{4}{5} \div 1\frac{3}{5}$

Simplifying Expressions with Exponents   5-8

To divide numbers or variables with the *same* base, subtract
exponents. For any nonzero integers a and n: $a^{-n} = \frac{1}{a^n}$.

Write with positive exponents.

35. x^{-5} **36.** $6a^{-1}$ **37.** $\frac{4m^6}{2m^2}$ **38.** $\frac{10b^2}{5b^3}$ **39.** $\frac{12x^2y^5}{4x^4y^2}$

Solving Equations   5-9, 5-10

To solve equations, use the properties of equality.

Solve each equation.

40. $x - \frac{4}{5} = \frac{1}{3}$ **41.** $\frac{3}{4}x = 2\frac{1}{2}$ **42.** $\frac{2}{5}x = -1\frac{1}{4}$ **43.** $x + 4\frac{2}{3} = 6$

Chapter 5   Test

Write a rational number for each point on the number line.

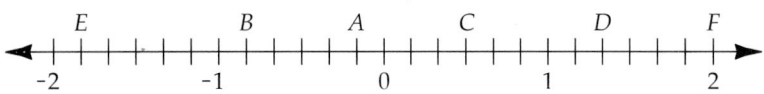

1. A **2.** B **3.** C **4.** D **5.** E **6.** F

ESTIMATION Tell whether each fraction is close to 0, $\frac{1}{2}$, or 1.

7. $\frac{7}{8}$ **8.** $\frac{7}{12}$ **9.** $\frac{21}{25}$ **10.** $\frac{2}{15}$ **11.** $\frac{16}{31}$ **12.** $\frac{5}{9}$

Write each fraction as a decimal. Write each decimal as a fraction.

13. $\frac{2}{5}$ **14.** $\frac{3}{4}$ **15.** $\frac{7}{8}$ **16.** 0.9   **17.** -0.4 **18.** 0.75

Compare. Use >, <, or =.

19. $\frac{4}{5}$ ☐ $\frac{2}{3}$ **20.** 0.66 ☐ $\frac{2}{3}$ **21.** $-\frac{7}{10}$ ☐ -0.07 **22.** 0.875 ☐ $\frac{7}{8}$

Find each answer.

23. $\frac{3}{8} + \frac{5}{6}$ **24.** $\frac{3}{4} \cdot 2\frac{5}{8}$ **25.** $3\frac{4}{5} - 2\frac{1}{2}$ **26.** $4\frac{2}{3} \div 1\frac{5}{6}$

27. $3\frac{7}{9} - \frac{5}{9}$ **28.** $-1\frac{1}{3} \div \left(-\frac{5}{9}\right)$ **29.** $-\frac{3}{5} - \left(-1\frac{1}{3}\right)$ **30.** $3\frac{3}{4} \cdot 2\frac{4}{5}$

31. $4\frac{3}{8} \cdot 2\frac{4}{5}$ **32.** $4\frac{3}{7} + 5\frac{4}{7}$ **33.** $-1\frac{5}{9} \cdot 2\frac{5}{8}$ **34.** $-1\frac{7}{8} + \left(-3\frac{5}{6}\right)$

Solve each equation.

35. $-\frac{7}{6} + x = \frac{5}{6}$ **36.** $\frac{3}{5}a = 9$ **37.** $n + \left(-\frac{7}{8}\right) = \frac{5}{6}$ **38.** $\frac{2}{3}k = -6$

39. $m - \left(-\frac{3}{4}\right) = 1\frac{1}{2}$ **40.** $\frac{3}{8}y = -15$ **41.** $-5b = -3\frac{1}{3}$ **42.** $r - 6.5 = -9.3$

Solve.

43. Suppose you take a number, subtract 8, multiply by 7, add 10, divide by 5, and the answer is 9. What is the original number?

44. Josie spent $\frac{3}{4}$ of her money on clothes. She had $21 left. How much money did she originally have?

45. Write a word problem for the equation $x - 1.70 = 3.50$.

46. Find the price of 1,000 shares of Universal Tractor stock at $21\frac{5}{8}$ per share.

Chapters 1–5   Cumulative Review

Choose the correct answer. Write A, B, C, or D.

1. Evaluate $(-1)^{27}$.
   - **A.** 1
   - **B.** 1×10^{27}
   - **C.** -1
   - **D.** not given

2. Write $\frac{3x^2y}{12xy^2}$ in lowest terms.
   - **A.** $\frac{1}{4}$
   - **B.** $\frac{2y}{4xy}$
   - **C.** $\frac{x}{4y}$
   - **D.** not given

3. Which number is written in scientific notation?
   - **A.** 0.5×10^6
   - **B.** 1.5×10^6
   - **C.** 1.5×6^6
   - **D.** not given

4. Solve $\frac{2}{3}x = 2\frac{2}{9}$.
   - **A.** $\frac{3}{10}$
   - **B.** $3\frac{1}{3}$
   - **C.** $2\frac{8}{9}$
   - **D.** not given

5. Write $\frac{28}{3}$ as a mixed number.
   - **A.** $3\frac{1}{3}$
   - **B.** $4\frac{1}{3}$
   - **C.** $7\frac{2}{3}$
   - **D.** not given

6. $(0.0056)(-3.5)$
   - **A.** -0.196
   - **B.** -0.00196
   - **C.** -0.0196
   - **D.** not given

7. Identify the property used.
   $$(x^2y^3)x^0 = x^2y^3$$
   - **A.** associative
   - **B.** identity
   - **C.** commutative
   - **D.** not given

8. The GCF of 25 and 50 is ▮.
   - **A.** 10
   - **B.** 5
   - **C.** 2
   - **D.** not given

9. Which number is divisible by 3 and 9?
   - **A.** 663
   - **B.** 879
   - **C.** 864
   - **D.** not given

10. Without computing, state the sign of $2(-4)(-9) + 100$.
    - **A.** positive
    - **B.** negative
    - **C.** zero
    - **D.** not given

11. Linda is 12 years older than Jill. The sum of their ages is 38. Find their ages.
    - **A.** 12 and 26
    - **B.** 12 and 38
    - **C.** 5 and 17
    - **D.** not given

12. Simplify $\frac{5a^3b^{-2}}{15a^2b^3}$.
    - **A.** $\frac{a}{3b^5}$
    - **B.** $3ab^{-1}$
    - **C.** $\frac{ab}{3}$
    - **D.** not given

13. Compare $|2\frac{1}{4}|$ ▮ $|-\frac{9}{4}|$.
    - **A.** $>$
    - **B.** $<$
    - **C.** $=$
    - **D.** not given

14. Find the number of times at bat in the formula $a = \frac{h}{n}$ for $a = 0.25$ and $h = 25$.
    - **A.** 625
    - **B.** 50
    - **C.** 100
    - **D.** not given

15. Find the LCD of $\frac{7}{12}$ and $\frac{5}{18}$.
    - **A.** 35
    - **B.** 6
    - **C.** 72
    - **D.** not given

16. $3\frac{1}{2} - 5\frac{3}{8} =$ ▮.
    - **A.** $-2\frac{1}{8}$
    - **B.** $-1\frac{7}{8}$
    - **C.** $-2\frac{7}{8}$
    - **D.** not given

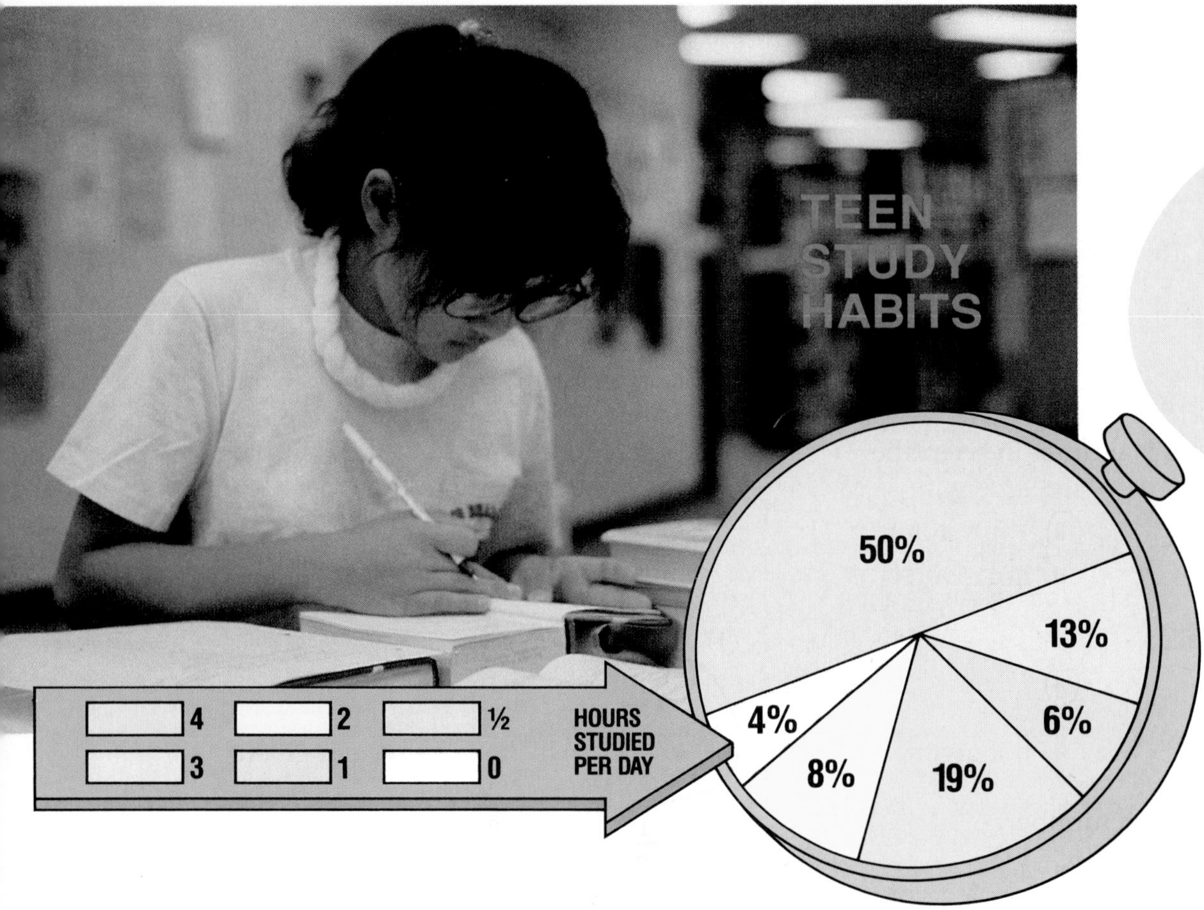

TEEN
STUDY
HABITS

50%

13%

4%

8%

19%

6%

4	2	½
3	1	0

HOURS
STUDIED
PER DAY

WHO'S GOING TO THE STORE?

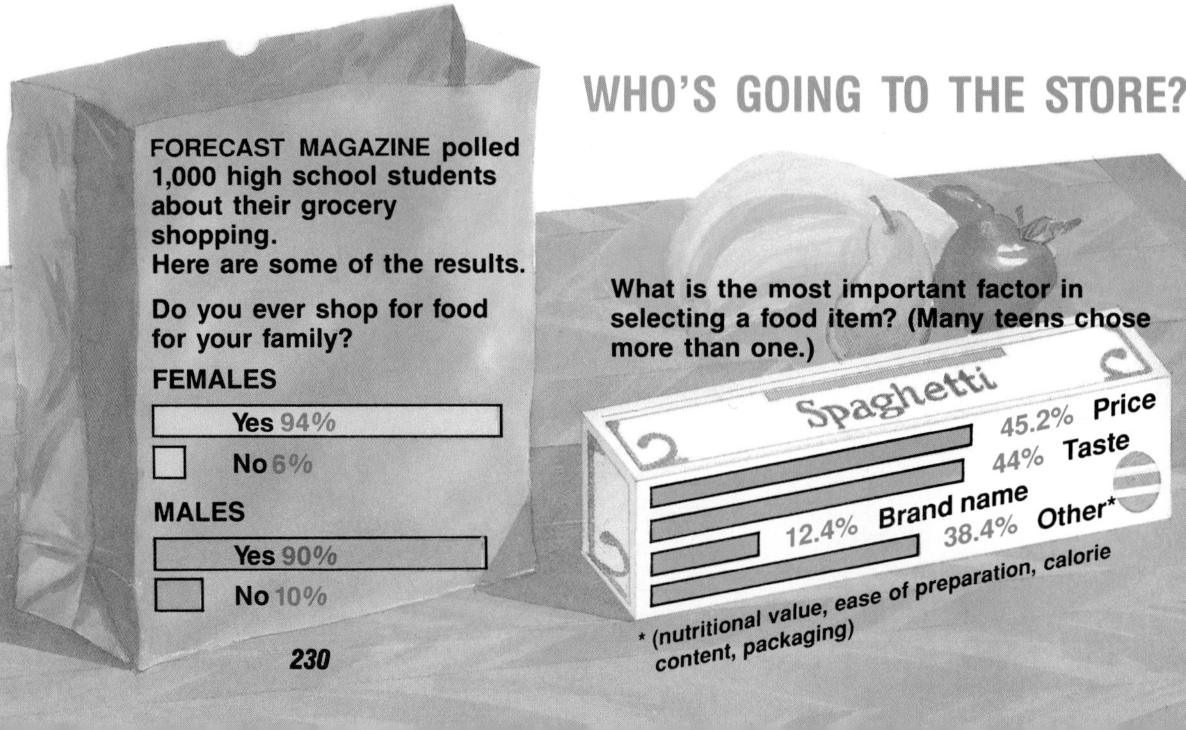

FORECAST MAGAZINE polled 1,000 high school students about their grocery shopping.
Here are some of the results.

Do you ever shop for food for your family?

FEMALES

Yes 94%

No 6%

MALES

Yes 90%

No 10%

What is the most important factor in selecting a food item? (Many teens chose more than one.)

45.2% Price

44% Taste

12.4% Brand name

38.4% Other*

* (nutritional value, ease of preparation, calorie content, packaging)

Ratios, Proportions, and Percent

▶ **TEENAGE RESEARCH UNLIMITED (TRU)** of Northbrook, IL, developed the Teenage Buying Control Index (TBC). TRU asked teens whether they or their parents make the buying decision for a list of products. An index number of 100 means the teen makes the decision. An index number of 0 means the parent makes the decision.

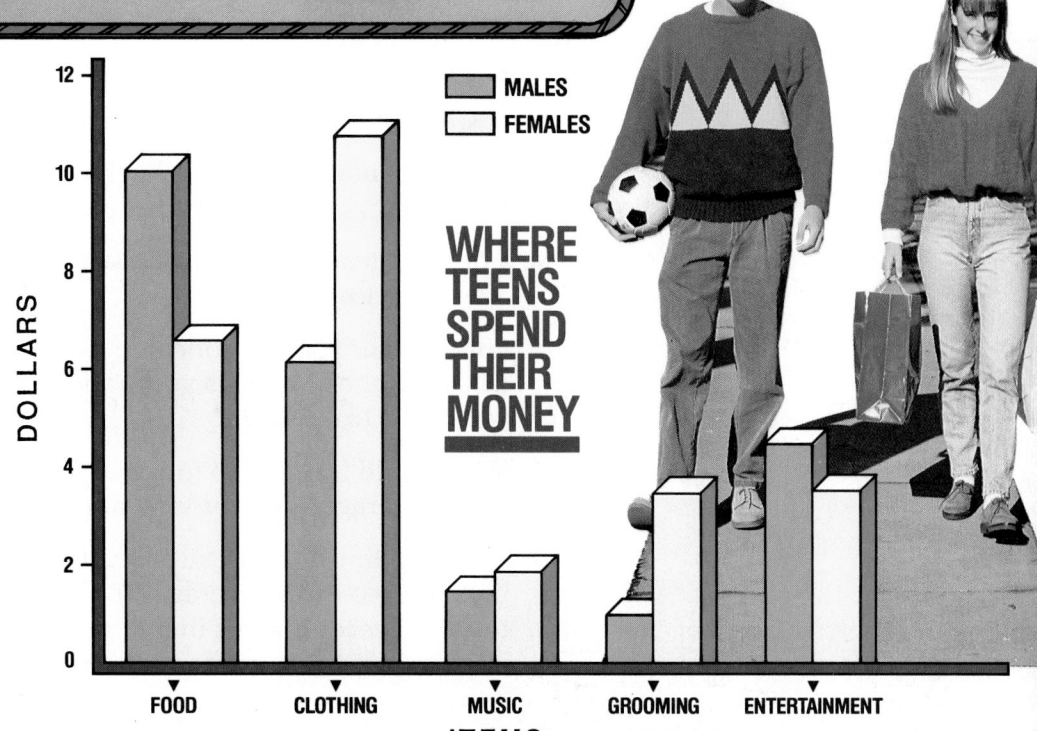

TEENAGE BUYING CONTROL INDEX (TBC)

ITEM	MALES	FEMALES
Book	63	63
Poster	78	78
Camera Film	54	53
Health and Beauty Aids	31	42
Food	39	39
Clothing	38	39
Audio/Video	55	48
School Supplies	46	52

WHERE TEENS SPEND THEIR MONEY

Think about it...

Look at the data from TRU. Why are some items on the TBC rated higher than others? How do you think advertisers might use the index?

MALES
FEMALES

DOLLARS

FOOD CLOTHING MUSIC GROOMING ENTERTAINMENT

ITEMS

OBJECTIVE:
Use activities to explore ratios.

Exploring Ratios

▼ What do batting averages, pass completions, first down statistics, and free-throw averages have in common? They are all *ratios*. Each statistic compares two numbers by division.

MATERIALS

- Waste basket

- Wadded up sheet of paper

- Math journal to record work

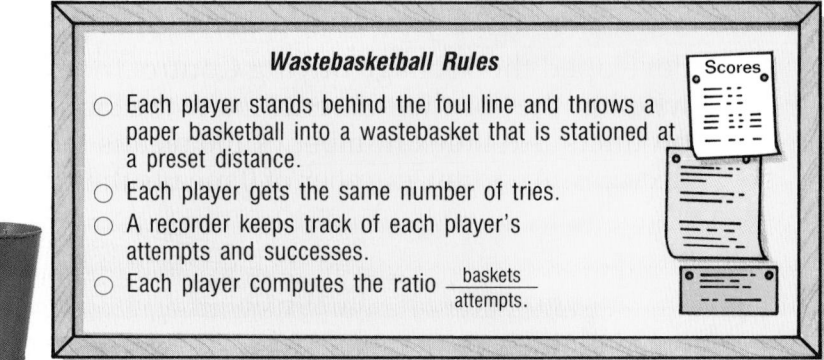

Wastebasketball Rules

○ Each player stands behind the foul line and throws a paper basketball into a wastebasket that is stationed at a preset distance.

○ Each player gets the same number of tries.

○ A recorder keeps track of each player's attempts and successes.

○ Each player computes the ratio $\frac{\text{baskets}}{\text{attempts}}$.

Play a game of wastebasketball and compute your own ratios.

Player	Attempts	Baskets	Free-throw Average (Ratio)

1. **Compare** with another group. Are the averages close?

2. Change the conditions. Then play more games.

   a. Change the distance to the basket.

   b. Change the number of attempts.

3. Compute new statistics. Which variable has the greatest impact? Is it different for different people?

4. Compute team statistics. **Compare** with other groups. Are the averages close?

5. **Discuss** what you can conclude from the statistics. If you make 2 baskets out of 2 tries, is your ratio better than someone who gets 7 out of 10? 15 out of 20?

6. **Write** Would it be fair to judge a player's ability on one game's free-throw average? Why or why not?

7. **PROJECT** How does the ratio relate to the number of tries? Look up lifetime free-throw averages for five basketball players. Compare to averages for players in one game and over a season. What impact does the number of attempts have on the average?

6-1 *Ratios, Proportions, and Rates*

▼ Statistics show that 10 out of 25 people in the United States have brown eyes. The numbers 10 and 25 form a *ratio*. You can write a ratio in three different ways:

$$10 \text{ to } 25; \quad 10 : 25; \quad \frac{10}{25}$$

You can express a ratio as a fraction in lowest terms.

$$\frac{10}{25} = \frac{2}{5}$$

READ 10 is to 25 as 2 is to 5. You can say that two out of five people have brown eyes.

Ratio	A ratio is a comparison of two quantities by division.
	Arithmetic **Algebra**
	$1 \text{ to } 2; 1 : 2; \frac{1}{2}$ $\quad a \text{ to } b; a : b; \frac{a}{b}$ $\quad b \neq 0$

▼ You can write ratios that compare $\frac{\text{part}}{\text{part}}$, $\frac{\text{part}}{\text{whole}}$, and $\frac{\text{whole}}{\text{part}}$.

Example 1 In a survey of 100 students, 60 reported having after school jobs. Write three ratios for the data.

THINK Why don't we write ratios as mixed numbers?

Solution

$$\frac{60 \quad \text{students with jobs}}{40 \quad \text{students without jobs}} \qquad \frac{\text{part}}{\text{part}}$$

$$\frac{60 \quad \text{students with jobs}}{100 \quad \text{all students surveyed}} \qquad \frac{\text{part}}{\text{whole}}$$

$$\frac{100 \quad \text{all students surveyed}}{60 \quad \text{students with jobs}} \qquad \frac{\text{whole}}{\text{part}}$$

▼ When two ratios are equal they form a *proportion*.

Proportion	A proportion is a statement that two ratios are equal. If two ratios are equal, their cross products are equal.
	Arithmetic **Algebra**
	6 is to 9 as 8 is to 12 $\quad a$ is to b as c is to d
	$\quad 6 : 9 : : 8 : 12$ $\qquad a : b : : c : d$
	$\quad \frac{6}{9} = \frac{8}{12}$ $\qquad \frac{a}{b} = \frac{c}{d}$ $\quad b \neq 0, d \neq 0$

Example 2 The directions for making orange juice from concentrate call for 4 cans of water to 1 can of concentrate. So, for 2 cans of concentrate you would need 8 cans of water. The following proportion describes the situation.

$$\frac{1}{4} = \frac{2}{8}$$

▼ You can write *rates* and *unit rates* to describe many situations.

THINK What rate describes money earned? mileage?

THINK What proportion would you write to describe the number of minutes it takes to blink once?

Rate	A rate is a ratio that compares quantities in different units. A unit rate compares a quantity to one.

Example 3 On average, a person blinks 100 times in 4 min. How many times does a person blink in one minute?

Solution $\dfrac{100}{4} = \dfrac{t}{1} = \dfrac{\text{number of blinks}}{\text{number of minutes}}$ Write a ratio to describe the the situation.

$4t = 100$ Write cross products.

$\dfrac{4t}{4} = \dfrac{100}{4}$ Divide both sides by 4.

$t = 25$

On average, a person blinks 25 times per minute.

Example 4 A car travels 264 mi on 12 gal of gas. Find the unit rate in miles per gallon.

Solution $\dfrac{264}{12} = \dfrac{x}{1}$

$264 \div 12 = 22$

$x = 22$ mi/gal

THINK AND DISCUSS

1. You know that 2 in 5 people have brown eyes. How many people do *not* have brown eyes? Explain.

2. The ratios $\frac{a}{b}$ and $\frac{c}{d}$ form a proportion. How can you use cross products to express the relationship between *a*, *b*, *c*, and *d* as an equation without using fractions?

3. A student claims that a ratio would remain unchanged if 1 is added to both the numerator and the denominator of the fraction as in $\frac{a}{b} = \frac{a+1}{b+1}$. Is the student correct? Explain your decision.

CLASS EXERCISES

Write each ratio as a fraction in lowest terms.

1. 9 : 27

2. 10 out of 16

3. 12 is to 8

4. 6 people in 50 are over 65 years of age.

5. 1 person in 18 plays the piano.

Write three ratios to describe each figure.

6. **7.** **8.**

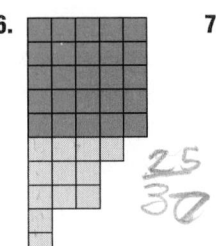 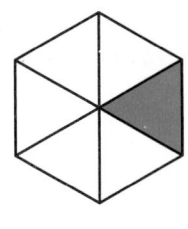 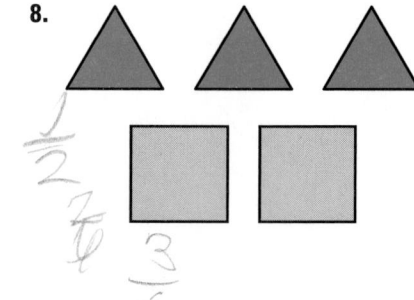

Write each ratio as a unit rate.

9. A bathtub contains 20 gal of water. The tub empties in 4 min. What is the rate of flow per minute?

10. A sprinter completes 200 m in 22 s.

11. A keyboarder types 1,575 words in 25 min.

WRITTEN EXERCISES

Write each ratio as a fraction in lowest terms.

1. 3 : 8 $\frac{3}{8}$ **2.** 7 is to 9 $\frac{7}{9}$ **3.** 8 out of 11   **4.** 14 out of 18 $\frac{7}{9}$

5. 15 : 25 $\frac{3}{5}$ **6.** 36 is to 48 $\frac{3}{4}$ **7.** 60 is to 24   **8.** 16 : 12

9. 25 homes out of 125 have a personal computer.

10. 3 out of 12 people live in a rural area. $\frac{1}{4}$

11. 4 people out of 24 attend school.

12. 20 homes in 25 have a TV. $\frac{4}{5}$

13. 6 of 24 people live in a household composed of three people.

14. 7 of 35 people live in a household composed of four people.

15. 6 of 42 people live in a household composed of five or more people. $\frac{1}{7}$

Write three ratios to describe each figure.

16. 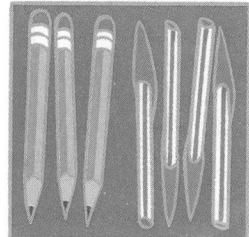   **17.** 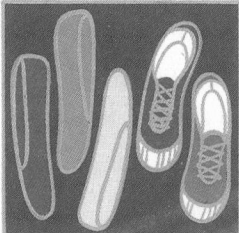   **18.**

3 : 4   3 : 2   1 : 2

Use graph paper to draw a model of each ratio.

19. $\frac{3}{6}$ **20.** 12 : 36   **21.** 5 out of 8   **22.** 9 : 10

23. PROJECT Survey at least ten people. Find the number of people living in each household. Use your data to write ratios showing the number of people who live in a household composed of three or fewer people, of four people, and of more than four people. Compare your ratios with the statistics in Exercises 13–15.

Compare. Write = or ≠. Then tell which pairs of ratios form a proportion.

24. $\frac{4}{7} = \frac{20}{35}$ **25.** $\frac{3}{2} \;\blacksquare\; \frac{16}{10}$ **26.** $\frac{3}{4} \;\blacksquare\; \frac{12}{15}$ **27.** $\frac{8}{3} \;\blacksquare\; \frac{56}{21}$

28. $\frac{9}{24} \;\blacksquare\; \frac{15}{40}$ **29.** $\frac{32}{20} \;\blacksquare\; \frac{20}{12}$ **30.** $\frac{40}{24} \;\blacksquare\; \frac{75}{45}$ **31.** $\frac{7}{8} \;\blacksquare\; \frac{8}{9}$

CALCULATOR Write = or ≠. Then tell which pairs of ratios form a proportion.

32. $\frac{75}{90} \;\blacksquare\; \frac{90}{108}$ **33.** $\frac{120}{144} \;\blacksquare\; \frac{145}{75}$ **34.** $\frac{215}{155} \;\blacksquare\; \frac{270}{165}$ **35.** $\frac{192}{144} \;\blacksquare\; \frac{256}{192}$

MIXED REVIEW

Find each answer.

1. Which fraction is closer to $\frac{1}{2}$, $\frac{5}{11}$ or $\frac{7}{13}$?

2. Compare the fractions $\frac{13}{19}$ and $\frac{19}{28}$. Use >, <, or =.

Solve for x.

3. $\frac{x}{7} = -2$

4. $2\frac{1}{3}x = -5\frac{1}{4}$

Are the fractions equivalent?

5. $\frac{4}{12}$ and $\frac{10}{30}$

6. $\frac{7}{8}$ and $\frac{14}{24}$

Solve.

7. On a trip, Mark drove 7 mi more than Craig. Craig drove five times as far as Brad. Brad drove 112 mi. How long was the trip?

Express each as a unit rate.

36. 20 mi in 5 h 4 mi/h

37. 42 gal in 7 min

38. a fall of 144 ft in 3 s 48 ft/s

39. 12 hits in 66 times at bat

40. 68 baskets in 119 throws

41. 245 mi in 56 h 4.375

42. 676 mi in 13 h

43. 78 hits in 260 times at bat

Write three ratios to describe each situation.

44. For every five victories, the baseball team lost one game.

45. For every fifty radios sold, two were returned for a refund.

46. A bookstore sells paperbacks, hardbacks, and magazines. For every three paperbacks sold, five hardbacks are also sold. For every ten hardbacks sold, twenty magazines are sold.

Write a ratio to describe each situation. Decide if the rates form a proportion. Solve each problem.

47. In one classroom, 4 of the 24 students are boys. In another classroom, 6 of the 30 students are boys. Is the ratio of boys to total number of students the same in both classes?

48. A subcompact car travels 196 mi on 7 gal of gas. A compact travels 336 mi on 12 gal of gas. Is the fuel economy of both cars the same?

49. Two cans of beans cost $1.69. Five cans cost $3.98. Is the ratio of cans to cost the same? If not, which is the better buy? Explain.

50. *DATA FILE 3 (pp. 96–97)* Suppose you turn in $\frac{1}{2}$ of a 20-dollar bill. How much will you get?

51. Use the article below to answer each question.
   a. Write the ratio of sap to syrup in three different ways.
   b. Write the cost of syrup per pint as a ratio.
   c. Write the cost of syrup per gallon as a ratio.

A Sappy Story

Vermont is renowned as a major producer of maple syrup. It is a little known fact, however, that more than 100 farms in Connecticut also produce maple syrup. Sugarers collect sap daily and boil it down to make syrup. In a good year, one small sugarer in Connecticut collects 300 gal of sap from 200 trees. The sap boils down to just 7 gal of syrup. The syrup is sold for $4.50 per half pint or $44 per gallon.

6-2 Solving Proportions

▼ An average adult's heart beats 8 times every 6 s. At this rate, how many times does it beat in 120 s? You can write a proportion to describe the situation. Let x = the number of heartbeats in 120 s.

$$\frac{8}{6} = \frac{x}{120} \quad \begin{matrix} \leftarrow \text{number of heartbeats} \\ \leftarrow \text{ number of seconds} \end{matrix}$$

$6x = 8 \cdot 120$ Write the cross products.

$6x = 960$ Divide both sides by 6.

$x = 160$

The average person's heart beats 160 times in 120 s.

▼ You can use cross products to solve a proportion.

Example 1   A canary's heart beats 130 times in 12 s. At this rate, how many times does it beat in 30 s?

Solution

$$\frac{130}{12} = \frac{x}{30} \qquad \text{Write a proportion.}$$

$130 \cdot 30 = 12x$ Write the cross products.

$3{,}900 \div 12 = 12x \div 12$ Divide both sides by 12.

$325 = x$

A canary's heart beats 325 times in 30 s.

▼ You can use a calculator to help you solve a proportion.

Example 2   Solve $\frac{x}{3.5} = \frac{35}{8.75}$ for x.

Solution

$$\frac{x}{3.5} = \frac{35}{8.75}$$

$8.75x = 3.5 \cdot 35$ Write the cross products.

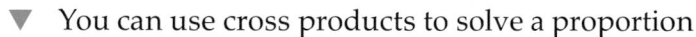 3.5 ⊗ 35 ⊘ 8.75 ⊜ 14   Use a calculator to solve.

$x = 14$

THINK How is writing cross products an application of the multiplication property of equality?

Solving Proportions	To solve a proportion:
	1. Write the cross products.
	2. Solve the equation.

▼ Express quantities in the same units before solving proportions.

Example 3   Ribbon costs $3 for 15 in. Find the cost of 3 ft of ribbon.

Solution

$$\frac{15 \text{ in.}}{\$3} = \frac{3 \text{ ft}}{d} \qquad \text{Write a proportion.}$$

$$\frac{15}{3} = \frac{36}{d} \qquad \text{Write 3 ft as 36 in.}$$

$15d = 108$ Solve the proportion for d.

$d = 7.20$

It costs $7.20 for 3 ft of ribbon.

THINK AND DISCUSS

1. If $\frac{a}{b} = \frac{c}{d}$, will $\frac{a}{b} = \frac{d}{c}$? Give examples to justify your answer.

2. Explain why it's important to express quantities in the same units before writing a proportion.

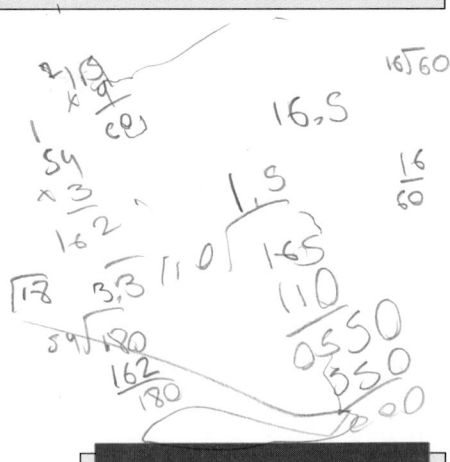

MIXED REVIEW

Tell if each equation is true or false.

1. $|-2\frac{1}{4}| + |2\frac{1}{4}| = 0$

2. $|-2\frac{1}{4}| - |2\frac{1}{4}| = 0$

Write each ratio as a fraction in lowest terms.

3. 30 to 55   **4.** 125 : 70

Tell whether or not these ratios form a proportion.

5. $\frac{80}{25}$ and $\frac{16}{5}$ **6.** $\frac{15}{42}$ and $\frac{25}{70}$

Solve.

7. On Saturday, a student bought two cassette tapes for $8.95 each and a sweater for $24.95. He received $20 for mowing a lawn. On Saturday night, he has $45.12. How much money did he have Saturday morning?

CLASS EXERCISES

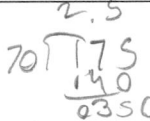

Solve.

1. $\frac{4}{11} = \frac{x}{16.5}$ **2.** $\frac{7}{12} = \frac{17.5}{y}$ **3.** $\frac{z}{5.4} = \frac{13}{18}$ **4.** $\frac{2}{v} = \frac{1}{8}$

Write a proportion to describe each situation. Then solve.

5. 3 oz of nuts cost $1.70; 5 oz cost x dollars.

6. A student runs 24 yd in $2\frac{1}{2}$ s; 100 yd in x seconds.

7. 50 calories in 4 oz of orange juice; x calories in 14 oz.

8. A lion's heart beats 12 times in 16 s; x times in 60 s.

Each pair of figures is in proportion. Find the missing length.

9.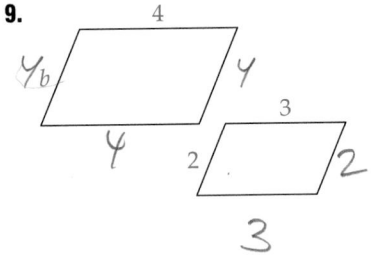

10.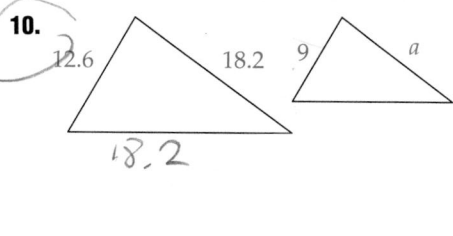

WRITTEN EXERCISES

Solve.

1. $\frac{4}{15} = \frac{a}{75}$ **2.** $\frac{4}{3} = \frac{b}{21}$ **3.** $\frac{13}{c} = \frac{39}{60}$ **4.** $\frac{3}{6} = \frac{7}{d}$

5. $\frac{6}{25} = \frac{e}{80}$ **6.** $\frac{4}{9} = \frac{f}{15}$ **7.** $\frac{3}{8} = \frac{50}{g}$ **8.** $\frac{24}{17} = \frac{108}{h}$

9. $\frac{7}{9} = \frac{j}{22.5}$ **10.** $\frac{11}{18} = \frac{k}{49.5}$ **11.** $\frac{6}{13} = \frac{7.8}{m}$ **12.** $\frac{20}{27} = \frac{1.1}{n}$

Each pair of figures is in proportion. Find the missing length.

13.

14.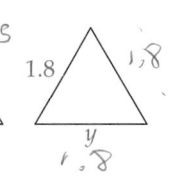

Write a proportion to describe each situation. Then solve.

15. 4 oz of cheese costs $1.85; $1\frac{1}{2}$ lb costs t dollars.

16. A baseball player gets 54 hits in 225 times at bat; x hits in 500 times at bat.

17. A student runs 5 km in 18 min 36 s; 8 km in v min.

18. 20 lb of dog food costs $27.50; 12 lb costs x dollars.

19. 96 oz costs $2.25; y pounds costs $10.

20. A rectangle measuring 20 cm by 28 cm is reduced to one measuring 9 cm by z cm.

21. Three tea bags are used to make a gallon of iced tea. How many tea bags are needed to make four gallons?

22. At the Copy Shoppe, 18 copies cost $1.08. At the same rate, how much will 40 copies cost?

23. The cost of 3 posters is $9.60. Find the cost of 15 posters.

24. *DATA FILE 10 (pp. 404–405)* What would be the home range, in acres, for a pack of 30 gray wolves?

25. A microchip inspector found three defects in a batch containing 750 chips. How many defects should the inspector find in a batch of 10,000 chips?

26. A truck driver estimated that it would take him 12 h to drive 1,160 km. After 5 h, he had driven 480 km. Is he on target? Explain.

27. *PROJECT* How would you describe your class? Use the list of questions at the right or questions of your own. Interview your classmates and tally all the responses. Write ratios to describe the results.

Use the relationship $x \blacktriangleright y = \frac{x+y}{x}$ **for exercises 28–35. Evaluate each expression.**

▼▼ *SAMPLE* $3 \blacktriangleright 5 = \frac{3+5}{3} = \frac{8}{3}$.

28. $2 \blacktriangleright 3$ **29.** $3 \blacktriangleright 4$ **30.** $5 \blacktriangleright -4$ **31.** $-7 \blacktriangleright 9$

Write *yes* **or** *no* **to tell if each is proportional to** $\frac{1}{3}$**.**

32. $-1 \blacktriangleright -3$ **33.** $2 \blacktriangleright 6$ **34.** $-15 \blacktriangleright 10$ **35.** $5 \blacktriangleright -3$

Solve.

36. If $\frac{y}{25} = \frac{6}{30}$, find the ratio of y to 6.

37. If $\frac{10}{100} = \frac{r}{30}$, find the ratio of r to 10.

38. If $\frac{15}{75} = \frac{30}{f}$, find the ratio of f to 75.

39. If $\frac{12}{p} = \frac{1}{3}$, find the ratio of p to 3.

40. An artist mixes red and blue paint to make purple paint in the ratio of 2 : 3. This tells you that for every 2 parts of red there are 3 parts of blue. What does each ratio tell you about the mixture of red and blue paint?

a. 6 : 9   **b.** 1 : 1.5   **c.** 10 : 15   **d.** 20 : 30

Complete.

41. $3 : 15 = 1 : 5$ because $15 = 3 \cdot 5$ and $\blacksquare = \blacksquare \cdot 15$

42. $15 : 6 = 5 : 2$ because $\blacksquare = 15 \cdot 2$ and $\blacksquare = 6 \cdot \blacksquare$

43. $8 : 2 = 16 : 4$ because $\blacksquare = \blacksquare \cdot 4$ and $\blacksquare = \blacksquare \cdot 2$

44. $6.5 : 2.5 = 19.5 : 7.5$ because $\blacksquare = 6.5 \cdot \blacksquare$ and $2.5 \cdot \blacksquare$

Human Heartbeats

Age (years)	Heartbeat
Newborn	140/min
1 y	120/min
6 y	100/min
10 y	90/min
12 y	85/min
Adult	80/min

Use the _DATA_ at the left to solve each problem.

45. In how many seconds will a newborn's heart beat 35 times?

46. In how many seconds will a 12-year-old's heart beat 25 times?

47. How many times does an adult's heart beat in 270 s?

48. How many more times does a newborn's heart beat in 45 s than a 6-year-old child's heart?

49. About how many times will an adult's heart beat in one year?

50. _PROJECT_ Find examples of heartbeat rates during different activities, such as sleeping, running, reading, and so on. Then take your pulse to determine your own heartbeat rate. Compare to see how close your rate is to the average heartbeat rates.

Critical Thinking

EXPLORING VENN DIAGRAMS

Study the numbers in each circle. How are they alike? How are they different?

Write a sentence to describe each.

1. the numbers in Circle A

2. the numbers in Circle B

3. the numbers in Circle C

4. Describe the numbers that fit in the intersection of A and B.

5. What numbers fit in the intersection of B and C?

6. Would 11 fit in B? in the intersection of B and C?

7. Are there other numbers that fit in the intersection of A and B? Why or why not?

8. Draw your own Venn diagram to classify sets of numbers. Trade with a classmate and describe each other's diagrams.

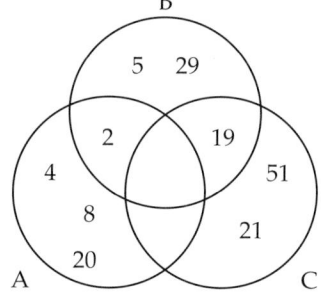

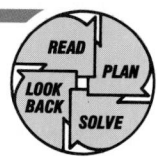

OBJECTIVE:
To apply proportional reasoning to problems involving scale plans.

6-3 Scale Drawing

■ Maps and floor plans are examples of *scale drawings*. Sizes in scale drawings are usually smaller than the actual sizes. However, if you sketch something you're observing through a microscope, your measurements will be greater than the actual measurements.

Example 1 On the map below, 1 cm represents about 84 km. What is the air distance between Lubbock and Abilene?

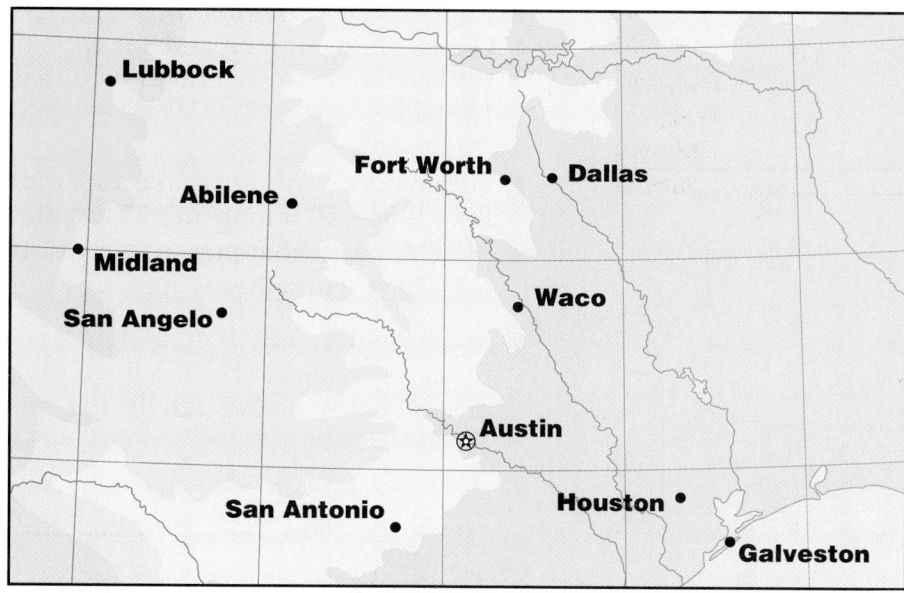

SCALE: 1 cm: 84 km

Solution Measure the distance on the map with a centimeter ruler. The map distance is about 2.9 cm. Write and solve a proportion.

$$\frac{1}{84} = \frac{2.9}{d} \qquad \text{Let } d = \text{actual distance.}$$

$$1 \cdot d = 84 \cdot 2.9 \qquad \text{Use cross products.}$$

$$d = 243.6$$

The air distance is about 244 km.

CLASS EXERCISES

Use the map above. Round to the nearest 5 km.

1. What is the air distance from Midland to Dallas?

2. Which city on the map is about 285 km from Ft. Worth?

3. A plane flies from San Angelo to Houston and then on to Galveston. About how far does it travel in all?

BEDROOM AND BATH AREA

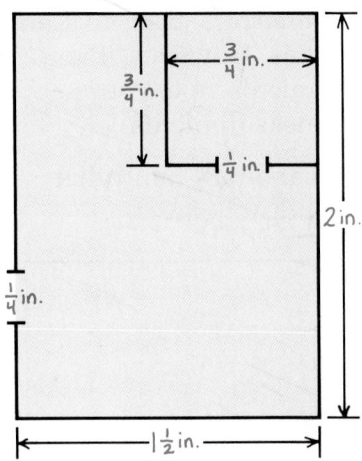

WRITTEN EXERCISES

The length of the bedroom and bath area in the diagram at the left is 2 in. The actual length is 20 ft. Use the diagram to solve.

1. What is the scale for the diagram?

2. How many feet wide are the doors leading into the bedroom and into the bath?

3. How wide is the widest part of the bedroom?

4. Could a bed 6 ft long and 3 ft wide fit into the narrow section of the bedroom? Does it matter along which wall the bed is placed? Explain.

5. Suppose you want to make a scale drawing of a rectangular dance floor that is 90 ft long and 75 ft wide. Can you fit the drawing on a piece of paper that measures $8\frac{1}{2}$ in. by 11 in. if your scale is 1 in. : 9 ft? Explain.

6. In a scale drawing, Marco plans to use $\frac{1}{2}$ in. to represent 1 ft. The room he wants to show in the drawing is 16 ft 3 in. long. To the nearest half-inch, what will be the length in the scale drawing?

■■■■■■ Decision Making ■ **DECISION MAKING** ■ Decision Making ■ Decision Making ■ Decision Making ■

SCALE DRAWING

■ COLLECT DATA

1. Choose a furnished room in your home. Measure its length and width to the nearest inch. Measure the width of each door and window. Then measure the distance that each door, window, and unmovable piece of furniture is from the nearest corner.

2. Measure the movable furniture so that you can tell how much floor space it occupies.

■ ANALYZE DATA

3. Make a scale drawing of the room, showing windows, doors, and any unmovable furniture. Then make and cut out a scale model for each piece of movable furniture. Position the cutouts on the scale drawing to show the location of each piece of furniture.

Each piece of a model railroad built on the HO scale is $\frac{1}{87}$ the size of an actual railroad part. The N scale, where models are $\frac{1}{160}$ the size of the real thing, is another popular scale.

7. Which models are smaller, HO or N scale models?

8. Each car on a full-size passenger train is 80 ft long.

   a. What is the length, in inches, of a model passenger car, using the HO scale? using the N scale?

   b. What is the length of a model train with eight cars, using the HO scale? using the N scale?

9. A diesel electric locomotive is 60 ft long. How long is the model locomotive using the N scale?

10. A boxcar on a freight train is 40 ft long. A model boxcar is $\frac{1}{4}$ ft long. In what scale was the model built, HO or N?

11. You are building a table for your HO-scale model train set. Your railroad includes a passenger train 12 cars long. Each car is 1.2 ft long. How long must your table be for the cars to fit end-to-end?

12. Toy trains are larger than most model trains. Using the O scale, a toy train is $\frac{1}{48}$ the size of an actual train. A toy locomotive is 1.04 ft long. How long is the real locomotive?

■ Decision Making ■ Decision Making ■ Decision Making ■ Decision Making ■ Decision Making ■ Decision Making ■

4. Look at the furniture in the room. Analyze the placement of each piece to make the most efficient use of light, traffic patterns, and so on.

5. Move your cutouts to try different furniture arrangements. What floor plan do you like the best? Why?

■ MAKE DECISIONS

6. Decide on two pieces of furniture that might be good additions to the room. Find out their dimensions as accurately as you can.

7. Make flat, to-scale cutouts for the new furniture. Work with the cutouts to decide on one or two good ways to arrange all the items in the room. You may remove two other pieces of furniture from the room if necessary. State some of the points you considered in making your decision.

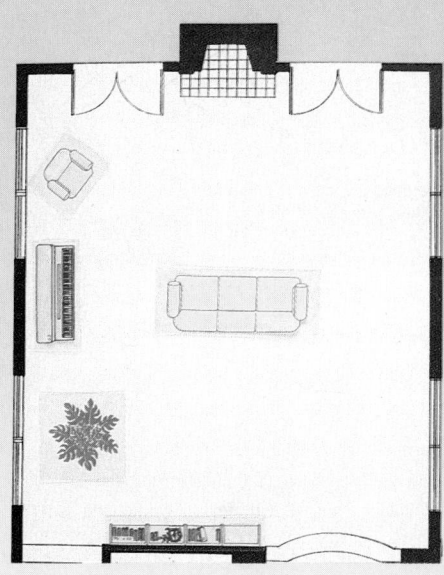

Exploring Percents

OBJECTIVE:
Use models to
explore percents.

MATERIALS

- Graph paper
- Math journal to record work

▼ A *percent* is a ratio that compares a number to 100. You can use a decimal model to show percents.

1. Each grid has 100 squares. Write a ratio and a percent to describe the shaded part.

  a. 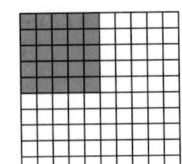 25% b. 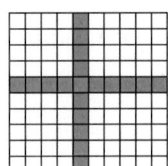 10% c. 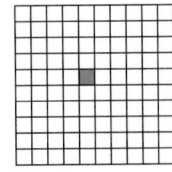 1%

2. Use graph paper to model each percent.

  a. 20%   **b.** 60%   **c.** 73%   **d.** 5%

3. Compare with others in your group. Do all your models look the same? Do they all show the same percents?

4. Write a ratio and a percent to describe the shaded part of each figure.

  a. 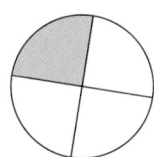 b. 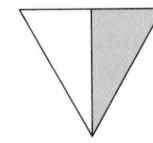 c. 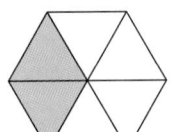 d.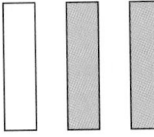

  e. **Discuss** how ratios and percents are like fractions.

▼ You can model percents greater than 100 and less than 1.

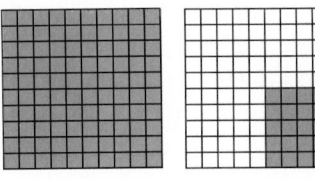 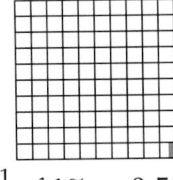

100%   +   25%   = 125% $\frac{1}{2}$ of 1% = 0.5%

5. Use graph paper to model each percent.

  a. 150% $1\frac{1}{2}$ **b.** 170% $1\frac{7}{10}$ **c.** 0.25% $\frac{1}{4}$ **d.** 0.75% $\frac{3}{4}$

▼ You can use number sense to estimate percents. You know that $\frac{1}{100}$ is 1% so $\frac{1}{200}$ is less than 1%.

6. Which fractions are less than 1%? **Write** a rule to tell when a fraction equals a percent less than 1%.

  a. $\frac{2}{400}$ **b.** $\frac{300}{500}$ **c.** $\frac{1}{1,000}$ **d.** $\frac{500}{1,000}$

OBJECTIVE:
To express ratios and
rates as percents.

6-4 Percent

▼ In a recent survey, 25 people out of 100 said they buy a newspaper every day. When you compare a number to 100, you are finding a *percent*.

Percent (%) means *per hundred*. You can express 25 out of 100 as 25% (25 percent). You can say that 25% of the people buy a daily newspaper.

Percent	A percent is a ratio that compares a number to 100.

▼ You can express a ratio as a percent.

Example 1 Express each ratio as a percent.

    a. 5 out of 100   **b.** 4 out of 5

Solution   **a.** $\frac{5}{100} = 5\%$ **b.** $\frac{4}{5} = \frac{x}{100}$ Write and solve a proportion.

$$= \frac{80}{100}$$
$$= 80\%$$

▼ You can write proportions to solve percent problems.

Example 2 In a survey, 57 out of 90 ninth graders said they received an allowance. What percent is this?

Solution

$\frac{57}{90} = \frac{n}{100}$ Write a proportion.

$90n = 5{,}700$ Write cross products.

$\frac{90n}{90} = \frac{5{,}700}{90}$ Divide both sides by 90.

$n = 63.\overline{3}$

$\approx 63\%$ Write a percent.

▼ You can write a decimal as a fraction with a denominator of 100 before writing as a percent.

Example 3 Write each decimal as a percent.

  a. 0.62   **b.** 0.03   **c.** 0.005   **d.** 1.25

Solution   **a.** $0.62 = \frac{62}{100}$ **b.** $0.03 = \frac{3}{100}$

             $= 62\%$ $= 3\%$

      c. $0.005 = \frac{0.5}{100}$ **d.** $1.25 = \frac{125}{100}$

             $= 0.5\%$ $= 125\%$

During the time of Columbus, the words *per cento*, derived from the Latin form *per centum*, were used to indicate *per hundred*. Later, the words were abbreviated and the term slowly changed its form to the symbol we use today.

Columbus's era

per cento

Today

▼ You can use the following rule to write decimals as percents.

Decimals to Percents	To write decimals as percents, move the decimal point two places to the right and write the percent sign.

▼ You can use a calculator to write fractions as decimals before writing as percents.

Example 4   Write as a percent.

  a. $\frac{3}{8}$ b. $\frac{5}{400}$ c. $1\frac{2}{3}$ d. $2\frac{1}{4}$

Solution   a. $3 \div 8 = 0.375$
              $= 37.5\%$

b. $5 \div 400 = 0.0125$
   $= 1.25\%$

c. $5 \div 3 = 1.6\ldots$
   $\approx 167\%$

d. $9 \div 4 = 2.25$
   $= 225\%$

CLASS EXERCISES

Write each fraction as a percent. Round to the nearest tenth.

1. $\frac{23}{100}$ 2. $\frac{1}{4}$ 3. $\frac{11}{20}$ 4. $\frac{1}{6}$

Write each ratio as a percent. Round to the nearest tenth.

5. $28:40$ 6. $60:150$ 7. $75:39$ 8. $20:36$

Write each decimal as a percent.

9. 1.68 10. 0.36 11. 0.70 12. 0.002

13. Write a percent to describe each situation.
   a. 4 out of 16 people live in a rural area.
   b. What percent do *not* live in a rural area?

1. Why is it possible to write a decimal as a percent by moving the decimal two places to the right? Justify your answer and give examples.

2. Which do you think is easiest to compare: ratios, decimals, or percents? Explain.

WRITTEN EXERCISES

Write each ratio as a percent. Round to the nearest tenth.

1. $15:20$ 2. $6:30$ 3. $30:48$ 4. $22:80$
5. $28:48$ 6. $32:56$ 7. $84:60$ 8. $72:54$

Write each decimal as a percent. Round to the nearest tenth.

9. 0.33 10. 0.35 11. 0.06 12. 0.0075

13. 0.045 *4.5%* **14.** 0.375 **15.** 1.88 *188%* **16.** 2.59

Write each fraction as a percent. Round to the nearest tenth.

17. $\frac{79}{100}$ *79%* **18.** $\frac{29}{50}$ **19.** $\frac{3}{10}$ *30%* **20.** $\frac{7}{20}$

21. $\frac{17}{25}$ *68%* **22.** $\frac{3}{50}$ **23.** $\frac{111}{100}$ *111%* **24.** $\frac{27}{80}$

CALCULATOR Write each fraction as a percent. Round to the nearest tenth.

25. $\frac{2}{9}$ *22.2%* **26.** $\frac{5}{6}$ **27.** $\frac{7}{16}$ *43.8%* **28.** $\frac{18}{11}$

ESTIMATION About what percent of each flag is red?

29. *80%*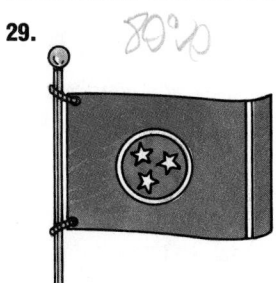
Tennessee

30.
North Carolina

31. *25%*
Arizona

Copy and complete the table.

	Fraction	Decimal	Percent
32.	$\frac{4}{5}$	0.80	80 %
33.	$\frac{1}{10}$	0.10	10%
34.	$\frac{1}{2}$	0.5	50%
35.	$\frac{3}{4}$	0.75	75%
36.	$\frac{67}{100}$	0.67	67
37.	$\frac{1}{4}$	0.25	25

Solve. Round to the nearest tenth.

38. Jamie scored 31 correct on a 45-item test. The passing grade is 70%. Did Jamie pass?

39. A scale drawing needs to be enlarged by a factor of 1.12. Express this as a percent. *112%*

40. A map was drawn to a scale of 0.725% of the original. Express this as a decimal.

41. A student committee has 15 members. Nine voted in favor of a smoking ban. What percent is this? *60%*

MIXED REVIEW
Solve for x.

1. $0.85x = 39.95$

2. $4.8x = -0.84$

3. $\frac{25}{48} = \frac{x}{132}$

4. $\frac{52}{x} = \frac{14}{490}$

Write a fraction and a percent for each ratio.

5. $42 : 168$

6. $176 : 224$

Solve.

7. The average of three test scores is 85. One test score is 90; another is 72. What is the third?

42. In a ball-throwing contest, Player A scores 30 hits out of 35 shots. Player B scores 0.85 of her throws and Player C's rate is 85.5%. Which player has the best record?

43. At a local high school, 560 out of 1,060 students voted to support a community fund drive. What percent of the students did not support the fund drive?

44. A crowd filled the 8,000 seats at a football stadium. There were 1,500 children and 5,600 men present. Write a ratio and a percent that describes how many seats were filled by:

a. men **b.** children **c.** women

45. A student is a member of a 4-person relay team. What percent of the distance will she run in a race?

Compare. Use >, <, or =.

46. $\frac{7}{12}$ ▦ 60% **47.** 0.0325 ▦ 32.5% **48.** $\frac{5}{8}$ ▦ 0.625

49. 0.05% ▦ 50% **50.** $\frac{7}{8}$ ▦ 68% **51.** 15 : 30 ▦ 85%

52. $\frac{3}{2}$ ▦ 1.5 **53.** 140 : 130 ▦ 104% **54.** 0.1756 ▦ 176%

WRITE Does each sentence makes sense? Explain why or why not.

55. A student ran 150% farther today than yesterday.

56. Since 15% of the students play tennis, 85% of the students do not play tennis.

57. A student got 200% of the items correct on a test.

58. A student missed 12 items on a test and got an A.

Complete each analogy.

59. dime : dollar : : 10 : ▦ **60.** foot : yard : : ▦ : 3

61. 50 : 20 : : 25 : ▦ **62.** 10 : decade : : 100 : ▦

63. 1 : 7 : : day : ▦ **64.** 1 : 365 : : ▦ : year

Use the **DATA** at the left. Write a ratio of pure gold to total karat weight for jewelry that has each marking.

65. 10 K **66.** 14 K **67.** 18 K **68.** 24 K

69. WRITE a sentence that tells what percent of gold each of the markings indicate.

70. a. Which label indicates that less than 50% of the item consists of gold?

b. Which label indicates that an item is 100% gold?

NOTES & QUOTES

The proportion of gold to other metals is marked in karats. Pure gold is marked 24 K. This is read as 24 karats. Gold is often mixed with other metals to make it more durable.

Karats	Gold	Other	Total
24 K	24	0	24
18 K	18	6	24
14 K	14	10	24
10 K	10	14	24

Practice

Write as a fraction in lowest terms.

1. 18 is to 45　　　　　**2.** 17 : 24　　　　　　**3.** 24 out of 60

4. 92 : 38　　　　　　　**5.** 21 out of 49　　　　**6.** 14 is to 52

Compare. Use = or ≠. Then tell if the pair of ratios form a proportion.

7. $\frac{11}{9}$ ▇ $\frac{55}{54}$　　**8.** $\frac{5}{15}$ ▇ $\frac{3}{9}$　　**9.** $\frac{6}{9}$ ▇ $\frac{24}{36}$　　**10.** $\frac{52}{4}$ ▇ $\frac{26}{2}$

11. $\frac{4}{5}$ ▇ $\frac{20}{25}$　　**12.** $\frac{12}{4}$ ▇ $\frac{9}{3}$　　**13.** $\frac{7}{28}$ ▇ $\frac{4}{16}$　　**14.** $\frac{16}{26}$ ▇ $\frac{8}{12}$

Solve.

15. $\frac{a}{7} = \frac{1}{3.5}$　　**16.** $\frac{6}{7.2} = \frac{5}{b}$　　**17.** $\frac{3}{c} = \frac{2}{8}$　　**18.** $\frac{7}{5} = \frac{d}{45}$

19. $\frac{22}{18} = \frac{2.75}{e}$　　**20.** $\frac{3a}{39} = \frac{3}{6}$　　**21.** $\frac{8}{5g} = \frac{16}{20}$　　**22.** $\frac{2.4}{3} = \frac{12}{h}$

Write as a percent. Round to the nearest tenth.

23. $\frac{9}{5}$　　　**24.** $\frac{1}{3}$　　　**25.** $\frac{3}{8}$　　　**26.** $\frac{125}{100}$

27. $\frac{46}{60}$　　**28.** $\frac{7.5}{10}$　　**29.** $\frac{11}{20}$　　**30.** $\frac{5}{6}$

Write as a percent. Round to the nearest tenth.

31. 2 : 30　　　**32.** 15 : 5　　　**33.** 34 : 40　　　**34.** 2 : 3

35. 5 : 8　　　**36.** 1 : 25　　　**37.** 4 : 32　　　**38.** 7 : 35

Write as a decimal.

39. $22\frac{1}{2}\%$　　**40.** 165%　　**41.** 73.6%　　**42.** 9%

Express as a fraction in lowest terms, as a decimal, and as a percent. Round to the nearest tenth of a percent.

43. 15 : 45　　　**44.** 6 : 10　　　**45.** 3 : 9　　　**46.** 13 : 10

47. 48 : 72　　　**48.** 19 : 95　　　**49.** 32 : 54　　　**50.** 16 : 28

Compare the following. Use >, <, or =.

51. $\frac{24}{36}$ ▇ 65%　　**52.** $\frac{11}{12}$ ▇ 90%　　**53.** $0.45\frac{1}{3}$ ▇ $45\frac{1}{3}\%$

54. 0.52 ▇ $\frac{13}{25}$　　**55.** 19.6% ▇ 0.195　　**56.** 5 : 18 ▇ 28%

57. 0.75 ▇ $\frac{3}{4}$　　**58.** 0.25 ▇ $\frac{1}{5}$　　**59.** 38% ▇ 0.038

CAREER

Help Wanted: Chef

High school diploma required. Vocational training or 2–4 years of college desirable.

For more information, write to American Culinary Federation, P.O. Box 3466, St. Augustine, FL 32085.

Preparing food for others is a delicate yet rigorous undertaking. A chef must know how to combine ingredients to create the desired taste. Will the meal serve 10 or 100? Chefs must understand proportions to adjust a recipe. They also need to use ratios if they need to substitute ingredients. Chefs even use percents to help determine what types and quantities of food to prepare.

PROJECT

Find a recipe for your favorite food. Rewrite the recipe so that it will serve your entire class.

OBJECTIVE:
To explore number relationships.

Exploring Number Relationships

■   At a homecoming dance, two-thirds of the ninth-grade boys have dates with a ninth-grade girl. Half of the ninth-grade girls have dates with a ninth-grade boy. What part of the entire ninth-grade class are boys who do *not* have dates with ninth-grade girls?

You can organize and analyze the data to make it easier to decide on a strategy to solve the problem.

1. *Analyze* the data and answer these questions.

   a. Do you know the number of ninth-grade students that are in the school?

   b. Do you know whether there are more boys or girls in the ninth grade at the school? *Explain* how you know and use a model to justify your answer.

2. List some strategies you think might help you solve the problem.

■   Sometimes substituting a number in a problem can help you understand the relationships in a problem.

3. Is this technique like any of the strategies you listed? If so, describe the ones that are similar.

4. a. Choose a possible number of ninth-grade boys and substitute this number into the problem. *Compare* with another group.

   b. Could there be a total of exactly ten boys in the ninth grade? exactly twelve boys? *Explain.*

5. *Analyze* the data after you substitute a number into the problem.

   a. How many ninth-grade boys have dates with ninth-grade girls?

   b. How many ninth-grade girls have dates with ninth-grade boys? *Explain* how you found the number of girls when you know the number of boys. Use a model if necessary.

   c. What is the total number of ninth-grade girls at the school?

   d. What is the total number of ninth-grade students?

   e. How many ninth-grade boys do *not* have a date with a ninth-grade girl? *Describe* how you found this answer. *Compare* with another group.

   f. What fractional part of the entire ninth grade is boys who do not have a date with a ninth-grade girl?

   g. *Write* a ratio in three different forms to describe your answer.

6. Choose a *different* possible number of ninth-grade boys and try substituting this number into the problem.

   a. Complete each step in Exercise 5 using your new chosen number.

   b. *Compare* the results you get from Exercises 5 and 6. What do you notice about the ratios?

7. Refer to the problem. *Write* a ratio that describes each of the following.

   a. the part of the entire ninth-grade class that are girls who do *not* have a date with a ninth-grade boy

   b. the part of the entire ninth-grade class that are boys who do have dates with a ninth-grade girl

   c. the part of the entire class that are girls who do have a date with a ninth-grade boy

   d. a ratio of boys to girls

■ You can often use more than one strategy to solve a problem.

8. Try using some of the other strategies you listed to solve the same problem.

9. *Describe* how you might use a diagram or draw a picture to help you solve the problem.

   a. What kind of picture would be appropriate?

   b. How can your picture display the ratio of boys to girls?

10. *Summarize* your findings.

   a. *Explain* how substituting numbers can sometimes help to clarify the relationships within the problem.

   b. List the strategies that were effective in solving the problem. *Discuss* which ones were helpful and which ones were not. *Explain.*

   c. *Write* a similar problem. Trade with a partner and solve each other's problem.

6-5 Using Proportions to Find Percent

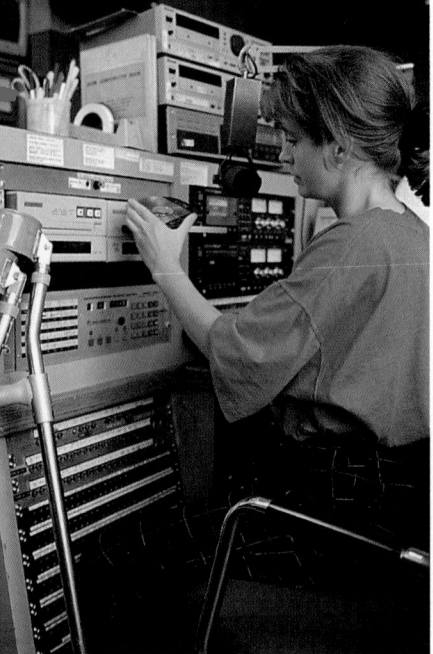

▼ In a recent year, there were 8,763 commercial radio stations in the United States. Of these, 295 stations had a rock format. To find the percent of stations with a rock format, you can find the ratio of some number to 100.

You can write a proportion to solve the problem.

$$\frac{295}{8,763} = \frac{n}{100}$$ Write a proportion.

$$8,763n = 29,500$$ Write cross products.

$$\frac{8,763n}{8,763} = \frac{29,500}{8,763}$$ Divide both sides by 8,763.

$$n = 3.366$$ Solve for *n*.

$$= 3\%$$ Round to the nearest whole number. Write as a percent.

Proportions and Percents	To find the ratio of a number to 100, use the formula. $$\frac{part}{whole} = \frac{n}{100}$$

▼ You can use proportions to solve other percent problems.

Example 1 About 5% of the 8,763 radio stations had a golden oldie format. How many stations played golden oldies?

Solution

$$\frac{p}{8,763} = \frac{5}{100}$$ Write a proportion.

$$8,763\left(\frac{p}{8,763}\right) = 8,763\left(\frac{5}{100}\right)$$ Multiply both sides by 8,763.

$$p = \frac{43,815}{100}$$

$$= 438.15 \approx 438$$

About 438 radio stations played golden oldies.

Example 2 Memphis, TN, had 12 AM radio stations in one year. These stations accounted for 60% of the AM and FM stations in Memphis. How many AM and FM stations did Memphis have at this time?

Solution

$$\frac{12}{b} = \frac{60}{100}$$ Write a proportion.

$$60b = 1,200$$ Write the cross products.

$$\frac{60b}{60} = \frac{1,200}{60}$$ Divide both sides by 60.

$$b = 20$$ Solve for *b*.

Memphis had 20 AM and FM radio stations.

▼ To compare ratios and percents, write both in the same form.

Example 3 At Pineapples, all books and posters are marked down 30%. At Avocados, the same items are marked $\frac{1}{3}$ off. Which store offers the greater markdown?

Solution To compare the sale prices, write $\frac{1}{3}$ as a percent.

$$\frac{1}{3} = \frac{x}{100}$$

$$x = 100\left(\frac{1}{3}\right)$$

$$x = 33\frac{1}{3}\%$$

Since $33\frac{1}{3}\% > 30\%$, Avocados offers the greater markdown.

CLASS EXERCISES

Write and solve a proportion. Round to the nearest tenth.

1. What percent of 40 is 30? 75
2. What percent of 20 is 40? 200%
3. Find 80% of 20. 16
4. Find 300% of 50. 150
5. What is $33\frac{1}{3}\%$ of 75? 24.9975
6. What is 40% of 60? 24
7. 25% of f is 8. What is f? 32
8. 250% of t is 50. What is t?

THINK AND DISCUSS

1. Is $a\%$ of b the same as $b\%$ of a? Explain.

2. When might it be easier to solve a percent problem by writing it as a fraction with a denominator other than 100?

Solve.

9. A bank account balance of $400 earns $24 interest in one year. What is the rate of interest?

10. A bicycle cost $200 last year. The same bike costs $250 this year. What percent of last year's cost is this year's cost?

11. A student pole vaulted 5 ft yesterday. Today she vaulted 20% higher. How high was her vault today?

WRITTEN EXERCISES

Write a proportion to solve. Round to the nearest tenth.

1. What percent of 25 is 13?
2. Find 18% of 150.
3. 116% of a is 125. What is a?
4. Find 116% of 75.
5. What percent is 40 of 120?
6. 49% of b is 31.85. What is b?
7. Find 60% of 15.
8. $12\frac{1}{2}\%$ of n is 6. What is n?

9. Find $58\frac{1}{3}\%$ of 54. **10.** What percent of 250 is 75?

11. What percent of 20 is 7? **12.** What percent of 80 is 130?

13. Find 125% of 16. **14.** Find 92% of 625.

15. What percent of 40 is 70? **16.** 35% of x is 52.5. What is x?

Compare. Use >, <, or =.

17. $\frac{14}{25}$ ▨ 56% **18.** 0.3125 ▨ 32.5% **19.** $\frac{1}{9}$ ▨ 0.111

20. 0.4205 ▨ 42.5% **21.** 30 : 36 ▨ 85% **22.** $\frac{8}{7}$ ▨ 114%

23. $\frac{13}{8}$ ▨ 1.625 **24.** 125 : 120 ▨ 104% **25.** $\frac{7}{8}$ ▨ 75%

26. **WRITE** a paragraph explaining why a proportion is frequently set up with at least one ratio having a denominator of 100.

MIXED REVIEW

Find each answer.

1. $x^2 + 3$ for $x = 7$

2. $a + b^2$ for $a = 3$ and $b = 6$

Write each as a percent.

3. $2\frac{7}{12}$ **4.** 4.523

5. 0.08 **6.** 45.6

7. The ski club has 50 members. There are 19 students going on a ski trip. What percent of the club members are going on the trip?

MENTAL MATH Solve.

27. What percent of 50 is 10? **28.** What percent of 10 is 15?

29. What percent is 6 of 24? **30.** What percent is 18 of 9?

31. Find 120% of 20. **32.** Find 9% of 300.

33. 200% of p is 24. What is p? **34.** $\frac{1}{4}\%$ of n is 3.75. What is n?

CALCULATOR Write a proportion and solve. Round to the nearest tenth.

35. What percent of 92 is 17? **36.** What percent of 68 is 89?

37. Find 93% of 47.89. **38.** Find 53% of 76,550.

39. Find 138% of 61. **40.** Find 189% of 82.

41. Find 80 increased by 65%. **42.** Find 36 reduced by $16\frac{2}{3}\%$.

43. 43% of q is 18.06. What is q? **44.** 2.5% of z is 912.5. What is z?

Solve.

45. The interest on an account of $1,500 is $120 for one year. What is the rate of interest?

46. The population of a city was 28,000 in 1950 and 70,000 in 1990. What percent is the 1990 population of the 1950 population?

47. A salesperson gets an 8% commission on sales after the first $5,000 per month. What commission would the salesperson receive on sales of $20,000?

48. **DATA FILE 4 (pp. 138–139)** About what percent of the world's population speaks Chinese? what percent speaks English?

WRITE a sentence telling whether or not the statement makes sense.

49. Sam got a 25% markdown on the price of a new car. Pat got $2,500 off. Pat got a better deal.

50. On a recent math test, 15 students passed in one class and 22 passed in another. The second class did better on the test.

51. The human body is about 60% water by weight. That means that a person who weighs 100 lb is about 60 lb water.

To Insure Proper Service

Some say TIPS means *To Insure Proper Service.* No matter what your translation, you need to know the rules. On a long awaited cruise vacation, you just want to have fun. You think you've accounted for everything. Everything, that is, except for the small print that reads GRATUITIES NOT INCLUDED. Don't despair. Follow these simple guidelines for tipping and you'll be in for a smooth sailing vacation!

Resort Tipping Guidelines

Restaurants	15%-20% of the check before taxes
Caddies	$4-$5 per bag or 15% of the greens fees
Hairdresser	15%
Laundry	15%-20%
Taxis	15% of the fare ($.25 minimum)
Bellhops and porters	$.50-$1 per bag

Use the chart at the right to solve.

52. What would be the tip for a $25 haircut?

53. You tipped your server $4.50. About what was the cost of your meal?

TEST YOURSELF

Write each ratio as a fraction in lowest terms.

1. 7 out of 21 students have a TV in their bedroom.

2. 5 out of 100 students plan to be doctors.

Write a proportion to describe each situation. Then solve.

3. One pint of paint costs $2.89. Find the cost of a quart of paint.

4. Three light bulbs cost $5.25. Find the cost of one light bulb.

Write each as a percent.

5. $\frac{3}{4}$ **6.** 0.89   **7.** $\frac{7}{8}$ **8.** 0.03   **9.** 0.007

Write and solve a proportion.

10. Find 18% of 30.   **11.** 25% of n is 25. Find n.

OBJECTIVE:
To evaluate percents
using models and
equations.

6-6 Percents and Equations

▼ You can use a triangle diagram to relate the parts of a percent problem.

You know that 12 is 50% of 24. You can read this from the diagram as $\frac{12}{50\%} = 24$. You can also see the following relationships from the diagram.

50% of 24 is 12 → 50% · 24 = 12

50% equals 12 divided by 24 → 50% = $\frac{12}{24}$

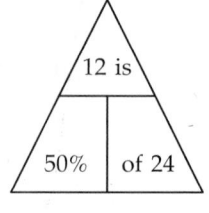

▼ You can draw a diagram to model the parts of any percent problem. The diagram always has the same form. To use the diagram, decide which part of the problem fits in each section. Then write and solve the appropriate equation.

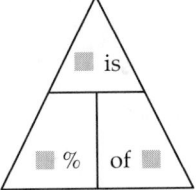

Example 1 In a recent survey, about 28% of the households surveyed were watching the top-rated TV program. Researchers used the information to estimate that about 25,312,000 households were watching the program. This assumes how many households in the total viewing population?

Solution Let x = the number of households

Draw a diagram and use it to write an equation.

$\frac{25,312,000}{28\%} = x$

25,312,000 ÷ 0.28 = 90,400,000

There are about 90,400,000 households in the viewing population.

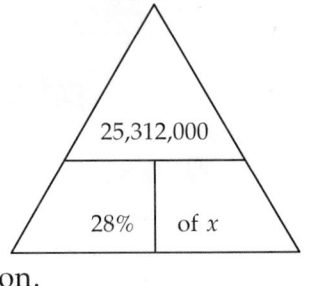

Example 2 About 18% of the 90,400,000 households in the viewing population watched the thirteenth-place program. About how many households watched this program?

Solution Let x = the number of households. that watched the program.

Draw a diagram and use it to write an equation.

18% of 90,400,000 = x
0.18 × 90,400,000 ÷ 16,272,000

About 16,272,000 households watched the thirteenth-place program.

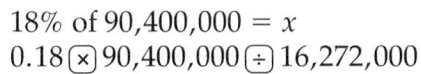

Example 3 About 21,114,600 households in the viewing population watched the eighth-place program. What percent of the 90,400,000 households watched this program?

Solution Let x = the percent viewing the program. Draw a diagram and use it to write an equation.

$$x = \frac{21,114,600}{90,400,000}$$
$$\approx 0.234$$

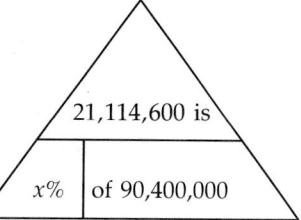

About 23.4% of the households saw the program.

CLASS EXERCISES

Write and solve an equation for each triangle diagram.

1.
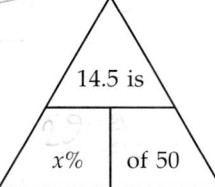

2.
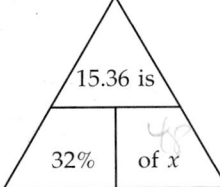

Draw a triangle diagram and use it to solve.

3. What percent of 25 is 40?

4. Find 30% of 30.

5. What is $66\frac{2}{3}$% of 63? 42

6. Find 150% of 90. 135

7. Sneakers are on sale for 60% of their regular price. They are selling for $36. What is their regular price? 60

8. A banker loaned $650 last year. The balance is $400 this year. What percent of the original loan is still outstanding? 62%

9. **WRITE** In your own words, describe how to use a triangle diagram to solve percent problems.

THINK AND DISCUSS

1. When might it be easier to use the proportion method than the equation method to solve a percent problem?

2. Describe a shortcut for finding the sale price of an item marked 20% off.

$\dfrac{30}{100}$

WRITTEN EXERCISES

Write and solve an equation for each triangle diagram.

1.
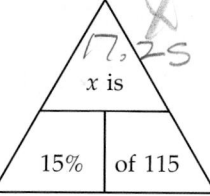

2.
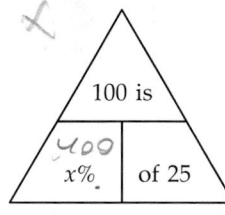

Draw a triangle diagram and use it to solve.

3. What percent of 20 is 11? _55%_   **4.** Find 56% of 75. _42_

5. 135% of t is 63. What is t? _46⅔_   **6.** What percent of 25 is 17? _68_

7. Find 500% of 12. _60_   **8.** 85% of z is 106,250. What is z?
                                           _125000_

Solve. Round to the nearest tenth.

9. What percent of 4 is 9? _225%_   **10.** $33\frac{1}{3}\%$ of s is $7\frac{1}{2}$. What is s? _67_

11. Find $26\frac{2}{3}\%$ of 81. _21.6_   **12.** $12\frac{1}{4}\%$ of b is 9.1875. What is b? _8_

13. Find 5.5% of 44. _2.4_   **14.** $16\frac{2}{3}\%$ of m is 6. What is m? _36_

15. What percent of 150 is 96? _64 %_   **16.** What percent of 45 is 24? _106.52_

17. Find 15% of 150. _22.5_   **18.** What percent of 8 is 20? _2.4%_

19. Find 225% of 36. _81_   **20.** 35% of d is 105,000. What is d?
                                      _14_

MENTAL MATH Solve.

21. What percent of 60 is 30? _50%_   **22.** Find 20% of 20. _20_

23. 100% of t is 100. What is t? _100_   **24.** What percent of 3 is 30? _10%_

25. Find $33\frac{1}{3}\%$ of 66. _22_   **26.** 200% of g is 24. What is g? _12_

27. What percent of 55 is 11? _20%_   **28.** Find 5% of 10. _½_

29. 18% of n is 18. What is n? _100_   **30.** What percent of 100 is 35? _35%_

31. Find 10% of 125. _12.5_   **32.** 25% of z is 200. What is z? _40_

33. What percent of 9 is 3? _33⅓%_   **34.** Find 20% of 80. _16_

CALCULATOR Solve. Round to the nearest tenth.

35. What percent of 117 is 54? _46.2_   **36.** 18% of a is 15. What is a? _101_

37. Find 16% of 83. _13.3_   **38.** What percent of 59 is 176? _43%_

39. 23% of a is 23. What is a? _100_   **40.** Find 86% of 29. _7.83_

Solve.

41. The rate of interest on a savings account is $5\frac{1}{4}\%$. What is the simple interest for a year on $750? _39.38_

42. An item on sale for $7.50 is 70% of the original price. What was the original price? _9.25_

43. **DATA FILE 6 (pp. 230–231)** Is it accurate to say that females spend about 50% more per week on clothes than males do? _no_

44. Identical sweaters are on sale in two different stores. In the first store, the sweater is on sale at 70% of the list price of $25. In the second store, the sweater is on sale at 60% of the list price of $30. Which sweater is the better buy?

$\frac{80}{100}$

45. A tie and a wallet were originally the same price. The tie is now 75% of its original price; the wallet is now 70% of its original price. The wallet has a sale price $17.50. What was the original price of each item? What is the sale price of the tie?

DATA Use the table at the right.

46. True or false? Write *T* or *F*.

   a. The number of households with VCRs increased more than 100% from 1978 to 1980.

   b. The number of households with VCRs in 1978 is less than 1% of the number of households with VCRs in 1986.

47. ESTIMATION Suppose the average cost of a VCR was $1,200 in 1978. Estimate the value of the sales of VCRs in 1978.

48. Use the data to make a bar graph.

49. The number of households with VCRs in 1981 was about 57% of the households with VCRs in 1982. How many households had VCRs in 1981?

50. Which of the following could you *not* conclude from the data?

   a. VCRs are very popular in the United States.

   b. More VCRs are produced in the United States than in any other country.

   c. The number of movies available on videotape probably increased from 1978 to 1986.

United States Households with VCRs	
year	households
1978	200,000
1980	840,000
1982	2,530,000
1984	8,880,000
1986	30,920,000

Critical Thinking

EXPLORING VISUAL PERCEPTION

1. Study the unfolded pattern. Then decide which, if any, of the three-dimensional figures would result if you fold the pattern.

  a. 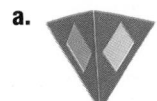   **b.**    **c.**

2. Use graph paper to make a pattern for a visual perception problem like the one above. Trade with a classmate and try to solve the problem.

OBJECTIVE:
To find percent of
increase or decrease.

6-7 Percent of Change

▼ Over a ten-year period, the average tuition at a private four-year college increased from $2,476 to $7,693. You can write and solve an equation to find the *percent of change.*

1. Subtract to find the amount of change. $\qquad 7{,}693 - 2{,}476 = 5{,}217$

2. Write an equation.

$$\text{percent of change} = \frac{\text{amount of change}}{\text{original amount}} \qquad\qquad n = \frac{5{,}217}{2{,}476}$$

3. Solve the equation. Round to the nearest hundredth. $\qquad 5{,}217 \,\boxed{÷}\, 2{,}476 \,\boxed{=}\, 2.107 \ldots$
$$n \approx 2.11$$

4. Write as a percent. $\qquad\qquad\qquad\qquad\qquad\qquad\qquad 211\%$

Tuition rose by about 211% over the ten-year period.

Percent of Change	Use the following equation to find percent of change. $\text{percent of change} = \dfrac{\text{amount of change}}{\text{original amount}}$

▼ You can use the same approach to find the percent of decrease.

Example 1 High school enrollment fell from 13.3 million students to 11.4 million in 20 y. Find the percent of change.

Solution
$$13.3 - 11.4 = 1.9 \qquad \text{Find the amount of change.}$$
$$d = \frac{1.9}{13.3} \qquad\qquad \text{Write an equation.}$$
$$1.9 \,\boxed{÷}\, 13.3 \,\boxed{=}\, 0.1428 \ldots \qquad \text{Solve the equation.}$$
$$d \approx 0.14 \qquad\qquad\qquad \text{Round to the nearest}$$
$$\text{hundredth.}$$
$$14\% \qquad\qquad\qquad \text{Write as a percent.}$$

High school enrollment fell about 14%.

▼ Always use the same units when working with measures.

Example 2 An animal weighed 5 lb at birth. A week later it weighed 5 lb 6 oz. What was the percent of change?

Solution
$$86 - 80 = 6 \qquad \text{Write measures in the same}$$
$$\text{units. Find the amount of change.}$$
$$c = \frac{6}{80} \qquad\qquad \text{Write an equation.}$$
$$6 \,\boxed{÷}\, 80 \,\boxed{=}\, 0.075 \qquad \text{Solve the equation.}$$
$$c = 0.075$$
$$7.5\% \qquad\qquad \text{Write as a percent.}$$

The animal had a 7.5% gain in weight.

▼ The percent of change may be part of a multi-step problem.

Example 3   An investment grew from $100 to $110 in the past year because of interest earned. The investment will earn interest at the same rate for the next year. What will be the value of the investment at the end of next year?

Solution   1. Find the percent of increase: $\frac{10}{100} = 10\%$.

2. Find the interest for the next year: 10% of $110 = $11.

3. Find the value of the investment:
   $110 + $11 = $121.

At the end of next year, the investment will be worth $121.

▼
THINK Why is the denominator always the original amount in percent of change problems?

CLASS EXERCISES

Find the percent of increase.

1. 30 is increased to 39.

2. 45 is increased to 144.

Find each percent of decrease.

3. 60 is decreased to 48.

4. 96 is decreased to 78.

Find each percent of change.

5. 72 to 99   **6.** 64 to 40   **7.** 144 to 300   **8.** 400 to 120

Find the percent of change for the first set of numbers. Use the same percent of change to complete the second set of numbers.

9. 50 to 60 : : 60 to ▨ .

10. 250 to 200 : : 200 to ▨ .

▼

THINK AND DISCUSS

1. 100 is increased by 10%. Then the result is decreased by 10%. Is the final result 100? Explain.

2. 100 is decreased by 10%. Then the result is increased by 10%. Is the final result 100? Explain.

3. Are the values of the answers to Questions 1 and 2 the same? Explain.

WRITTEN EXERCISES

Find each percent of increase. Round to the nearest tenth.

1. 50 is increased to 66.

2. 80 is increased to 95.

3. 32 is increased to 76.

4. 45 is increased to 105.

Find each percent of decrease. Round to the nearest tenth.

5. 90 is decreased to 75.

6. 64 is decreased to 24.

7. 120 is decreased to 95.

8. 280 is decreased to 126.

Find each percent of change. Round to the nearest tenth.

9. 38 to 95   **10.** 111 to 74   **11.** 27 to 72   **12.** 180 to 54

MENTAL MATH Find each percent of change. Label your answer as increase or decrease.

13. 25 to 30   **14.** 40 to 45   **15.** 50 to 45   **16.** 40 to 30

Find the percent of change from the first number to the second. Use the same rate of change to find the next number in the pattern. Round each answer to the same number of decimal places.

17. 38, 57, ▨   **18.** 70.6, 105.9, ▨   **19.** 103.6, 77.7, ▨

Item	Price ($)	
	1980	1990
calculator	13	4
110 camera	40	28
radio with headphones	100	35
video game system	29	99
sneakers	29	52
candy bar	0.25	0.50
movie ticket	2	4.50
cassette tape	8.98	9.99
basic watch	16	20
ballpoint pen	0.29	0.39

DATA Use the table at the left.

20. a. Find the percent of change for each item. Round each answer to the nearest hundredth. Label your answer as increase or decrease.

   b. WRITE Which items increased in price? Which items decreased in price? Why do you think some items increased in price and some decreased?

CALCULATOR Find each percent of change. Label your answer as increase or decrease. Round to the nearest tenth.

21. 87 to 108   **22.** 59 to 127   **23.** 77 to 13

24. 132.8 to 93.3   **25.** 131.75 to 40.45   **26.** 18 to 47.69

Solve. Round each answer to the nearest tenth.

27. A stock increased in value from $130 to $166. What was the percent of change?

28. The value of artwork appreciated from $295 to $495. What was the percent of change?

29. Investments decreased in value from $1,750 to $1,232. What was the percent of change?

30. A stock traded at the following prices each day for a week: Monday, $846; Tuesday, $819; Wednesday, $838; Thursday, $864; Friday, $850.

   a. Find the percent of change for each day.

   b. On which day was the percent of change the greatest?

   c. On which day was the percent of change the least?

   d. What was the percent of change from the value on Monday to the value on Friday?

31. A worker received a raise from $22,000 to $25,000. What is the percent of change?

32. A family bought a house for $78,000 in 1985. In 1991, the family sold the house for $88,900. Find the percent of change.

MIXED REVIEW

Evaluate.

1. $|-3| + |x|$ for $x = -5$

2. $[(3 + 12)(8 \div 2)]^2$

Compare. Use >, <, or =.

3. $42 : 54$ ▨ $56 : 64$.

4. $\frac{3}{11}$ ▨ $27\frac{1}{4}\%$

5. Find 45% of 45.

6. There are about 20,000 human-made objects in orbit around Earth. All but 300 are junk. What percent are junk?

33. A gallon of gas cost $.32 in 1972. In 1991, a gallon of gas cost $1.58. What is the percent of change?

34. The population of Growtown increased from 10,000 to 13,000 in one year, while the population of Slowtown decreased from 30,000 to 24,000 in one year.

   a. Find the respective rates of increase or decrease.

   b. If both towns maintain the same rate of change, when will the population of Growtown exceed that of Slowtown?

35. *DATA FILE 3 (pp. 96–97)* Find the percent of change for the value of each proof set from 1965 to 1968.

36. *DATA* Use the table on page 259. Find the percent of change for each time period.

   a. from 1978 to 1980   **b.** from 1980 to 1982

   c. from 1982 to 1984   **d.** from 1984 to 1986

37. *DATA* Use the table at the right to solve.

   a. Find the percent of change for each occupation from 1986 to 2000. Round to the nearest whole percent.

   b. Is the percent of change the only factor that you would consider when making a career decision?

   c. *WRITE* What impact might these projections have on a person's career planning?

38. *PROJECT* Research the expected employment demands in the profession of your choice. Find out what training and education is necessary to qualify for this position.

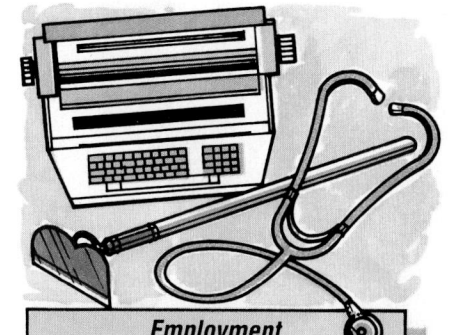

Employment (in thousands)		
Career	*1986*	*2000*
Nurse	1,406	2,018
Cashier	2,165	2,740
Medical asst.	132	251
Farmer	1,182	850
Typist	178	128

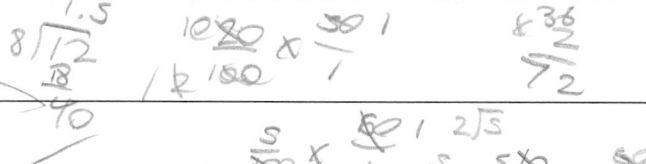

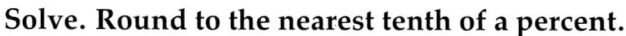

TEST YOURSELF

Write and solve an equation.

1. Find 33% of 120. *39.6*   **2.** Find 125% of 42. *60*

3. What percent of 50 is 10? *20*   **4.** 15% of q is 9.75. What is q?

5. What percent of 12 is 8?   **6.** 80% of w is 120. What is w?

Solve. Round to the nearest tenth of a percent.

7. A pair of sneakers was reduced from $125 to $85. What was the percent of change? *67.77%*

8. Tickets to regular season games are $36. Tickets to playoff games are $50. What is the percent of change? *72*

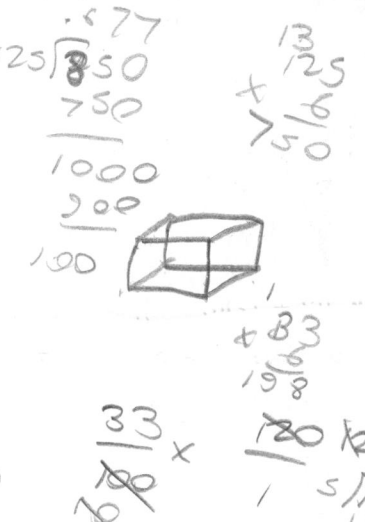

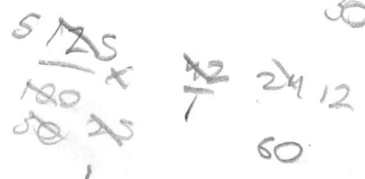

OBJECTIVE:
To solve problems by drawing a diagram.

6-8 Draw a Diagram

■ You can solve many types of problems using diagrams.

PROBLEM

A sales representative travels by train from Salt Lake City, Utah, to Boise, Idaho. This distance is about 30% of her entire trip. She then flies 400 mi to Spokane, Washington. She completes the remaining 300 mi of her trip to Seattle, Washington, by bus. What percent of her trip did she cover by bus?

SOLUTION

Answer these questions to understand the given information.

READ ▶ What facts do you have?

Salt Lake City to Boise → 30% by train

Boise to Spokane → 400 mi by air

Spokane to Seattle → 300 mi by bus

What do you want to find?

What percent of the trip (the part covered by bus) does 300 mi represent?

PLAN ▶ Make a diagram to organize the information.

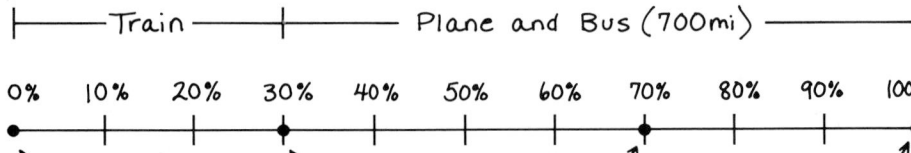

SOLVE ▶

How far did she travel by air and by bus?	700 mi
What percent represents the total she traveled by air and bus?	70%
The distance between two marks on your diagram represents what percent of the total distance?	10%
How many miles does the distance between two marks represent?	100 mi (700 ÷ 7)
How many miles did she travel in all?	1,000 mi (100 · 10)
What percent of the trip did she cover by bus?	$\frac{300}{1,000} = 30\%$

LOOK BACK ▶ Does your answer make sense? Look at the problem another way to check.

Think of a proportion.

70% : 700 as 30% : 300. So, 300 mi by bus is 30%.

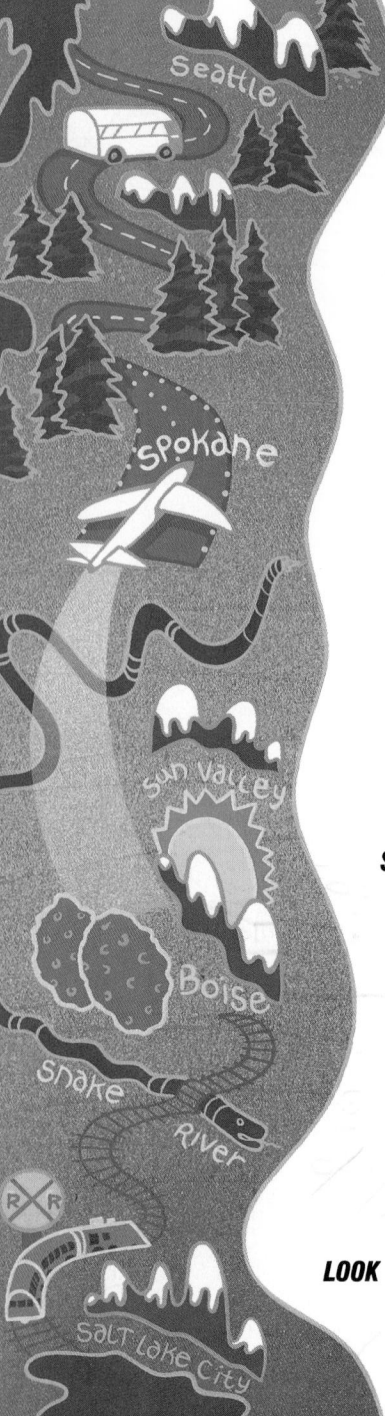

CLASS EXERCISES

1. Refer to the problem in the example on page 264.

   a. What percent of the trip was covered by plane?

   b. How many miles were covered by train?

2. A student has 80 miles to walk. She walks 50% of the distance the first day and 25% of the remaining distance the second day. How far does she have to walk to finish her trip?

3. A student put points P and Q on a line to the right of point X. Three times the distance from point X to point P is four times the distance from point X to point Q. What is the ratio of $PQ : XQ$?

4. There are 25 students in an algebra class. Ten students are members of the math club. Twelve students are members of the chess club. Five students are members of both clubs. How many of the students in the algebra class are members of neither club?

WRITTEN EXERCISES

Use a CALCULATOR where appropriate.

Solve using a diagram.

1. Container A has twice the capacity of container B. Container A is full of sand and container B is empty. Suppose $\frac{1}{8}$ of the sand in container A is poured into container B. What fractional part of container B will contain sand?

2. Six students are in the finals of the chess tournament. Each student plays one game against every other student. How many games will be played?

3. Points P, Q, R, and S appear in that order on a line. The ratio of $PQ : QR$ is $3 : 4$, and the ratio of $QR : RS$ is $2 : 5$. The length of $PQ = 6$ in. Find the length of PS.

4. A wooden cube that measures 5 cm along each edge is painted blue. The painted cube is then cut into centimeter cubes. How many of the small cubes are painted on three faces?

5. A homeowner is building a fence around a rectangular lot that measures 48 ft by 60 ft. He digs a post hole at each corner and one every 4 ft in between corners. How many post holes must he dig?

Solve. Use any strategy you wish.

6. After George poured 48 gal of water into an empty tank, the tank was 75% full. How many gallons does the tank hold? *12*

7. Maureen cut a 20-cm wire into exactly three pieces. The first piece is 3 cm shorter than the second piece. The third piece is 4 cm shorter than the second piece. Find the length of the shortest piece.

8. At a local high school, 60% of the students are girls. Of these girls, 75% own a cassette player. What percent of all the students are girls who do *not* own cassette players? *45%*

9. Twelve of Ms. Brown's students tried out for both the gymnastics and the baseball teams. Half of the students made the baseball team. One-third made the gymnastics team. One-fourth made neither team. How many students made both teams? *1*

10. Belinda takes the bus $\frac{2}{5}$ of the distance from home to school. She then walks 2 blocks to her friend's house and rides with her friend the remaining 7 blocks to school. What fractional part of the trip did Belinda ride with her friend? *$\frac{3}{4}$*

11. A student has 5 mi to walk. The student walks half the distance the first hour and a fourth of the remaining distance the next hour. How far does the student have to walk to finish the trip? *$1\frac{7}{8}$ mi*

12. On Saturday, a student pays off a loan of $12.50. He then earns $20 mowing a lawn. At the mall, he buys two pairs of socks for $3.98 each and a pair of shoes for $45.79. He has $24.32 left. How much money did he have to start with?

13. A student was standing in the middle of a line. Twenty-three students were ahead of him. How many students were in the line?

14. A board is cut in half. Then each piece is cut in half again. Then each of these pieces is cut in half.

　a. How many cuts are made?

　b. How many pieces are there?

15. A chain fence encloses a square pen. The 8 posts on each side of the pen are spaced 6 ft apart and are 6 in. in diameter. There is a post at each corner of the pen.

　a. How many posts are there?

　b. What are the dimensions of the pen?

16. *DATA FILE 9 (pp. 360–361)* Suppose you are teeing off on the 8th hole at St. Andrew's golf club. Would you be more likely to use a 1 wood or a 3 wood?

Problem Solving Practice

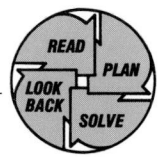

Solve. The list at the left shows some strategies you may use.

PROBLEM SOLVING STRATEGIES

Look for a Pattern
Guess and Test
Simplify the Problem
Account for All Possibilities
Make an Organized List
Work Backwards
Make a Table
Write an Equation
Solve by Graphing
Draw a Diagram
Make a Model
Simulate the Problem

1. What is the maximum possible number of digits in the product of two positive integers each having two digits?

2. To make an orange dye, 3 parts of red dye are mixed with 2 parts of yellow dye. To make a purple dye, 2 parts of blue dye are mixed with 1 part of red dye. Suppose equal amounts of orange and purple are mixed. What fractional part of the mixture is red dye?

3. When n is divided by 7, the remainder is 4. What is the remainder when $2n$ is divided by 7?

4. The ratio of Clark's weight to Kim's weight is 3 : 2. The ratio of Kim's weight to Janine's weight is 1 : 2. Compare Clark's weight with Janine's weight.

5. Working together, two painters earned $1,000 for painting a new house. The first painter worked for seven days. The second painter worked for three days. What is the first painter's fair share of the $1,000?

6. Refer to the two circle graphs at the left.

   a. What percent of Earth's water supply is fresh water?

   b. What percent of Earth's fresh water is found in rivers, lakes, and streams?

   c. What percent of Earth's total water supply is found in rivers, lakes, and streams? How did you find the answer?

   d. What is the ratio of salt water to fresh water? the ratio of salt water to the water from icecaps and glaciers?

7. **DATA FILE 4 (pp. 138–139)**

   a. In 1989, the world population was about 5 billion. Approximately what percent of the population spoke Japanese?

   b. Is this more than the percent of the population that spoke both English and Spanish?

8. **DATA FILE 10 (pp. 404–405)**

   a. What is the total area (in mi²) of the earth covered by oceans? Of the total area, approximately what percent is the Pacific Ocean? the Atlantic Ocean?

   b. The total surface area of Earth is 1.96951×10^8 mi². Approximately what percent of Earth's surface area do the oceans cover?

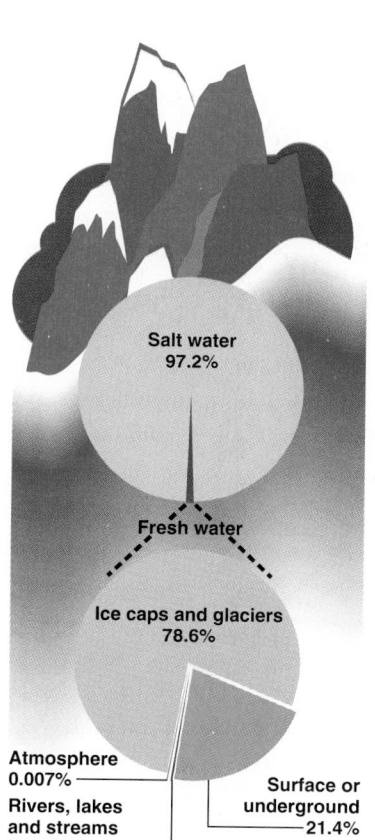

Salt water
97.2%

Fresh water

Ice caps and glaciers
78.6%

Atmosphere
0.007%

Rivers, lakes
and streams
0.03%

Surface or
underground
21.4%

Chapter 6 Review

Write true or false. If false, change the underlined word to make the statement true.

1. A <u>proportion</u> is a comparison of two quantities by division.

2. If two ratios are equal, their <u>cross products</u> are equal.

3. $\frac{\text{miles}}{\text{hour}}$ is an example of a <u>ratio</u>.

4. A <u>rate</u> is a ratio that compares a number to 100.

5. The percent of change is the amount of change divided by the <u>original amount</u>.

Ratios, Proportions, and Rates   6-1

To compare two quantities, write a ratio. To determine if two ratios form a proportion, multiply the cross products. If the cross products are equal, the ratios form a proportion.

To compare quantities measured in different units, use a rate.

Compare. Write = or ≠. Then tell whether or not the ratios form a proportion.

6. $\frac{3}{8} \blacksquare \frac{9}{24}$ 7. $\frac{5}{7} \blacksquare \frac{20}{35}$ 8. $\frac{3}{4} \blacksquare \frac{15}{20}$ 9. $\frac{2}{3} \blacksquare \frac{18}{17}$ 10. $\frac{5}{6} \blacksquare \frac{100}{130}$

Write each ratio as a unit rate.

11. 150 mi in 3 h   12. 115 mi on 5 gal   13. 270 words in 3 min   14. $9.45 for 5 lb

Solving Proportions   6-2

To solve a proportion, write the cross products, then solve.

Solve.

15. $\frac{5}{6} = \frac{n}{42}$ 16. $\frac{3}{2} = \frac{18}{x}$ 17. $\frac{15}{a} = \frac{30}{98}$ 18. $\frac{y}{9} = \frac{30}{90}$ 19. $\frac{21}{25} = \frac{m}{150}$

Scale Drawing   6-3

To use a scale drawing, measure the distance on the drawing. Then use the scale given to write and solve a proportion.

Use the scale 1 cm : 75 km.

20. The distance on the map from Centerville to Toptown is 2.5 cm. What is the actual distance?

21. The actual distance from Summit to Crown Heights is 37.5 km. What is the map distance?

Writing Percents

To write decimals as percents, move the decimal point two places to the right and write a percent sign. To write a fraction as a percent, first write the fraction as a decimal. Then write the decimal as a percent.

Write each decimal as a percent.

22. 0.05   **23.** 0.98   **24.** 1.45

Write each fraction as a percent.

25. $\frac{3}{4}$ **26.** $\frac{5}{8}$ **27.** $\frac{3}{25}$

Using Proportions to Find Percent

To find the ratio of a number to 100, use the following formula.

$$\frac{\text{part}}{\text{whole}} = \frac{n}{100}$$

Write and solve a proportion.

28. Find $12\frac{1}{2}\%$ of 48.

29. 20% of x is 30. What is x?

30. What percent is 90 of 270?

Using Equations to Find Percent

Use a triangle diagram to relate the parts of a percent problem.

Write and solve an equation. Round to the nearest tenth.

31. 35% of a is 70. What is a?

32. Find 68% of 300.

33. What percent is 9 of 180?

34. What percent of 55 is 10?

35. Find 3% of 89.

36. 125% of y is 100. What is y?

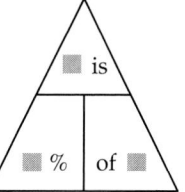

Finding Percent of Change

$$\text{percent of change} = \frac{\text{amount of change}}{\text{original amount}}$$

Find the percent of change.

37. 18 to 24   **38.** 120 to 90   **39.** 148 to 37   **40.** 285 to 342   **41.** 1,000 to 250

Problem Solving

To solve a problem, draw a diagram to represent the information.

Solve.

42. Alicia rides 25% of a 100-mi trip the first day. She rides $33\frac{1}{3}\%$ of the remaining distance the second day. What percent of the original distance does she have to ride to finish her trip?

43. *DATA* Refer to the circle graphs on page 267. What percent of Earth's fresh water supply is on the surface or underground?

Chapter 6   Test

Write each ratio as a unit rate.

1. A car travels 84 mi on 3 gal of gas.

2. A car travels 220 mi in 4 h.

Compare. Write = or ≠.

3. $\dfrac{7}{8}$ ▓ $\dfrac{42}{40}$

4. $\dfrac{3}{5}$ ▓ $\dfrac{45}{75}$

5. $\dfrac{12}{18}$ ▓ $\dfrac{18}{12}$

6. $\dfrac{5}{9}$ ▓ $\dfrac{25}{81}$

Write a proportion to describe each situation. Then solve.

7. Three cans of dog food sell for 99¢. Find the cost of 15 cans.

8. A photo that measures 5 in. by 7 in. is enlarged to 7.5 in. by b.

9. A student reads 45 pages in 2 h; x pages in 3 h.

The length of the kitchen in the diagram at the right is $1\frac{1}{4}$ in. The actual length is 20 ft. Use the diagram to solve.

10. What is the scale of the diagram?

11. What is the actual size of the dining area?

12. How wide is the kitchen at its narrowest part?

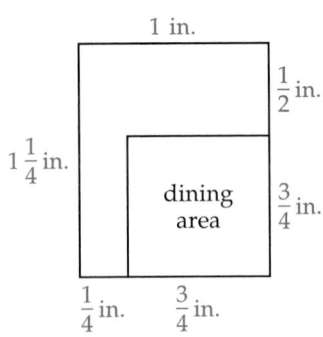

Write each decimal as a percent.

13. 0.37

14. 0.005

15. 1.02

Write each fraction as a percent.

16. $\dfrac{5}{8}$

17. $\dfrac{2}{3}$

18. $\dfrac{7}{9}$

19. WRITE a paragraph describing how to use a triangle diagram to solve a percent problem.

Solve.

20. What percent of 400 is 20?

21. Find $33\frac{1}{3}\%$ of 12.

22. 20% of c is 24. What is c?

23. What percent of 3 is 15?

24. Find 125% of 50.

25. 60% of y is 75. What is y?

Find each percent of change. Round to the nearest tenth.

26. 60 to 36

27. 18 to 24

28. 15 to 25

29. 85 to 50

30. 88 to 300

Solve.

31. Suppose you have posts of length 6 in., 9 in., and 11 in. How can you use the posts to measure a 4-in. length?

32. Two oranges weigh the same as an apple and a grape. An apple weighs the same as 11 grapes. How many grapes equal the weight of an orange?

Chapters 1–6　　Cumulative Review

Choose the correct answer. Write A, B, C, or D.

1. Which number is divisible by 3 and 5?
   A. 725　　　　　　　　B. 726
   C. 720　　　　　　　　D. not given

2. Write $\frac{7}{8}$ as a percent.
   A. $87\frac{1}{2}\%$　　　　　B. 70%
   C. 78%　　　　　　　　D. not given

3. Which is *not* a ratio that describes
   □□□□ △△△?
   A. 4:3　　　　　　　　B. 4:7
   C. 4 + 3　　　　　　　D. not given

4. Simplify $\frac{5a^3b^4}{10a^2b^3}$.
   A. $\frac{a}{2b^{-1}}$　　　　　B. $\frac{1}{2}ab$
   C. $\frac{1}{2}a^{5b-1}$　　　　D. not given

5. Evaluate $\frac{2x^3 - 0.01}{x^2}$ for $x = -0.2$.
   A. 0.65　　　　　　　B. -0.41
   C. 0.065　　　　　　　D. not given

6. The figures are in proportion. Find the missing length.

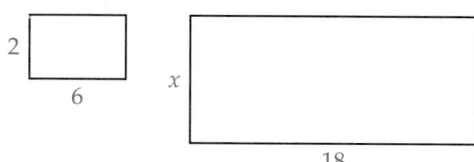

   A. 6　　　　　　　　　B. 10
   C. 12　　　　　　　　D. not given

7. Solve $1.5 = 0.2x - 0.5$.
   A. 1　　　　　　　　　B. 5
   C. -10　　　　　　　　D. not given

8. Compare $\frac{\sqrt{25}}{2^3}$ ▇ $\frac{\sqrt{9}}{2^2}$.
   A. >　　　　　　　　　B. <
   C. =　　　　　　　　　D. not given

9. Find the LCM of $6x^3y^2$ and $8x^2y^5$.
   A. $2x^2y^2$　　　　　　B. $24x^3y^5$
   C. $48x^5y^7$　　　　　D. not given

10. Evaluate $3 + 4 \cdot 5 - 5 + 6 \div 3$.
    A. 20　　　　　　　　B. 12
    C. 8　　　　　　　　　D. not given

11. The sum of two numbers is 9. The product is 20. What are the numbers?
    A. 3 and 6　　　　　　B. 2 and 10
    C. 4 and 5　　　　　　D. not given

12. Identify the model.

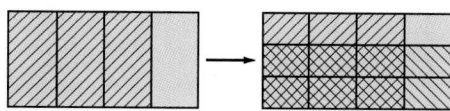

    A. $\frac{3}{4} + \frac{2}{3}$　　　　　B. $\frac{3}{4} - \frac{6}{12}$
    C. $\frac{3}{4} \cdot \frac{2}{3}$　　　　　D. not given

WHEN STANDARD TIME was first established in 1884, there were 24 time zones—one for every 15° of longitude. The prime meridian at 0° longitude is used to determine noon. Time for other zones depends on the number of zones east or west of the prime meridian.

The line opposite 0° at 180° (called the international date line) is used to determine midnight. To make standard time practical for daily use, many nations, states, and cities changed the time zones to include local boundaries.

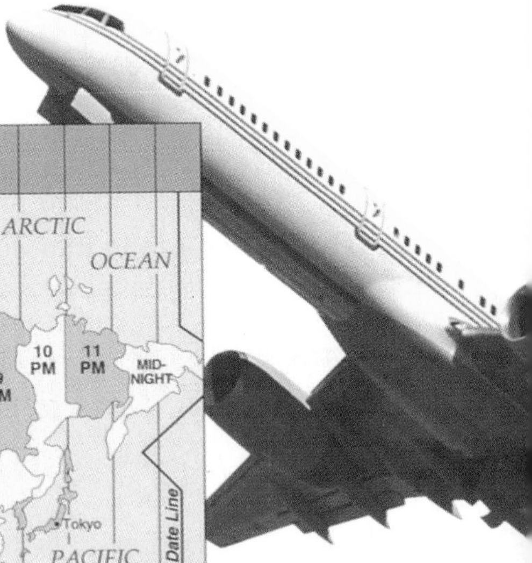

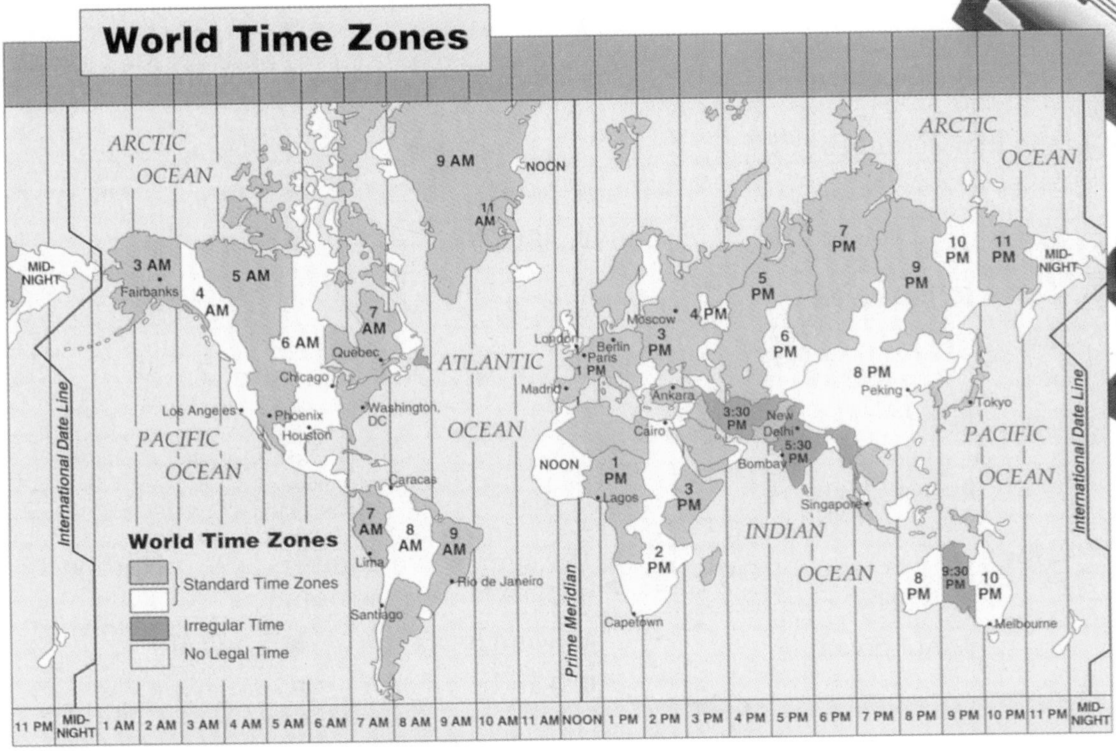

World Time Zones

World Time Zones

- Standard Time Zones
- Irregular Time
- No Legal Time

11 PM | MID-NIGHT | 1 AM | 2 AM | 3 AM | 4 AM | 5 AM | 6 AM | 7 AM | 8 AM | 9 AM | 10 AM | 11 AM | NOON | 1 PM | 2 PM | 3 PM | 4 PM | 5 PM | 6 PM | 7 PM | 8 PM | 9 PM | 10 PM | 11 PM | MID-NIGHT

Federal regulations ban smoking on all domestic flights.

Passengers 11 years of age, or younger, and 62 years of age, or older, are eligible for discounts on most major airlines. Children under two fly for free.

Air Travel Information

Equations and Inequalities

Think about it...

Look at the data about passenger boardings. What factors might make one airport busier than another? What might happen to increase or decrease the passenger boardings from year to year?

UNITED STATES BUSIEST AIRPORTS	PASSENGER BOARDINGS (Millions of Passengers)		RANK	
AIRPORT	1987	2000	1987	2000
Chicago O'Hare	27.5	43.6	1	1
Atlanta	23.9	34.6	2	3
Los Angeles	21.2	27.1	3	4
Dallas/Ft. Worth	20.8	23.6	4	5
Denver	16.1	35.7	5	2
New York/Kennedy	14.4	17.6	6	12
San Francisco	14.0	20.3	7	7
Newark	12.2	23.4	8	6
New York/La Guardia	11.6	16.0	9	15
Miami	11.6	18.9	10	9

OBJECTIVE:
Use models to explore and solve two-step equations.

___

MATERIALS

___

- Algebra tiles

- Math journal to record work

___

Exploring Two-step Equations

▼ You can use algebra tiles to model a two-step equation.

a. $2x + 3 = 5$

b. $2x - 4 = 6$

1. **Describe** what each tile represents in each equation. **Analyze** how these equations and models are different from the ones you have seen before.

2. **Model** each equation. **Compare** your models with those of another group.

   a. $3n + 4 = 7$ **b.** $4x - 2 = 6$ **c.** $5r - 2 = 8$

▼ You can also use algebra tile models to help you solve a two-step equation.

3. **Analyze** the model for $2x + 3 = 5$. To solve the equation, you must isolate the variable.

   a. **Discuss** what isolating a variable means.

   b. **Describe** the first step you would take in isolating the variable expression $2x$. What operation did you perform?

   c. **Discuss** what you need to do to solve the resulting equation for x. What is the value of x?

4. **Analyze** the model for $2x - 4 = 6$.

   a. **Discuss** why it is helpful to think of this equation as $2x + (-4) = 6$.

   b. **Describe** the two steps needed to solve the equation.

   c. What is the solution of $2x - 4 = 6$?

5. Use models to solve each equation.

   a. $3r + 4 = 10$ **b.** $2b - 7 = 3$ **c.** $4n - 6 = -2$

6. **Analyze** your solutions for Exercise 5.

   a. What was the first thing you did to solve each equation?

   b. **Summarize** Write a rule describing the steps you used to solve a two-step equation.

7-1 Two-step Equations

▼ A student pays \$.86 for three school stickers and a school emblem. An emblem costs \$.29. What is the price for each sticker? If we represent the price of one sticker with variable p, we can write the following equation.

$$3p + 29 = 86$$

FLASHBACK

You can use inverse operations to solve an equation.

You can solve this equation by using the subtraction and division properties of equality.

$$3p + 29 = 86$$
$$3p + 29 - 29 = 86 - 29 \quad \text{Subtract 29 from both sides.}$$
$$3p = 57$$
$$\frac{3p}{3} = \frac{57}{3} \quad \text{Divide both sides by 3.}$$
$$p = 19$$

Check $3p + 29 = 86$

$3 \boxed{\times} 19 \boxed{+} 29 \boxed{=} 86 \checkmark$ \quad Replace p with 19.

Each sticker costs \$.19.

Julia B. Robinson (1920–1985), a mathematics researcher at the University of California, Berkeley, showed that there was no automatic method of determining whether or not an equation had a whole number solution.

▼ You can also solve two-step equations using the addition and multiplication properties of equality.

Example 1 **Write an equation to describe the situation. Solve.**

Suppose you divide a number by 4 and then subtract 5 to get 8. What is the original number?

Solution Let n = the original number.
Then the equation $\frac{n}{4} - 5 = 8$ describes the situation.

$$\frac{n}{4} - 5 = 8$$
$$\frac{n}{4} - 5 + 5 = 8 + 5 \quad \text{Add 5 to both sides.}$$
$$\frac{n}{4} = 13$$
$$4\left(\frac{n}{4}\right) = 13(4) \quad \text{Multiply both sides by 4.}$$
$$n = 52$$

Check $\frac{n}{4} - 5 = 8$

$52 \boxed{\div} 4 \boxed{-} 5 \boxed{=} 8 \checkmark$ \quad Replace n with 52.

Solving a Simple Two-step Equation	To solve a simple two-step equation:
	1. Undo addition or subtraction.
	2. Undo multiplication or division.

CANOE
RENTALS

Example 2 **Choose the correct equation. Solve.**

Three friends rent a canoe. Each person also rents a paddle for $4. Each person pays a total of $20. What is the cost of renting the canoe without the paddles?

a. $3n - 4 = 20$ **b.** $3n + 12 = 20$

c. $\frac{n}{3} + 4 = 20$ **d.** $\frac{n}{3} - 4 = 20$

Solution Let $n =$ the total cost of the canoe rental.
Then the correct equation is c.

$$\frac{n}{3} + 4 = 20$$

$$\frac{n}{3} + 4 - 4 = 20 - 4 \qquad \text{Subtract 4 from each side.}$$

$$\frac{n}{3} = 16$$

$$3\left(\frac{n}{3}\right) = 16(3) \qquad \text{Multiply both sides by 3.}$$

$$n = 48 \qquad \text{The check is left for you.}$$

The cost of renting a canoe without the paddles is $48.

CLASS EXERCISES

State the first step in solving each equation. $46-6+6=2+6$

1. $\frac{a}{6} + 9 = 13$ $\frac{a}{6}+9-9=13-9$ **2.** $4b - 6 = 2$

3. $2c + 1 = 5$ $2c+1-1=5-1$ **4.** $\frac{d}{3} - 10 = 5$

Choose the correct equation. Solve.

a. $3x + 1 = 14$ **b.** $x - 1 = 14$

c. $\frac{x}{3} + 1 = 14$ **d.** $\frac{x}{3} - 1 = 14$

5. Sarita, Clara, and Joe baked muffins, which they shared equally. Clara ate one on the way home. She had 14 muffins left. How many muffins did Sarita, Clara, and Joe bake?

6. Kyle sent away for three tapes. The cost of the order, with $1 for shipping, was $14. What was the price of each tape?

Solve each equation.

7. $9x - 15 = 39$ **8.** $\frac{y}{7} - 6 = 8$ **9.** $\frac{2}{3}n + \frac{3}{8} = \frac{15}{16}$

10. $4 - \frac{z}{3} = 13$ **11.** $-35 = 4x + 1$ **12.** $2.4r - 5.6 = 11.2$

THINK AND DISCUSS

1. What is the first step in solving the equation $ax - b = c$ for x?

2. How can you solve the equation $5x + 2 = -28$ using addition and multiplication?

3. Is the solution of the equation $18n - 1 = 402$ a negative number? Explain.

13. $6n - 5 = 55$ **14.** $\frac{x}{3} + 2 = 14$ **15.** $16d - 28 = 174$

WRITTEN EXERCISES

Solve each equation.

1. $3n + 5 = 23$ **2.** $18 = 4t + 2$ **3.** $-86 + 4k = 102$

4. $30 = 18 + 2b$ **5.** $5 + \frac{k}{9} = -31$ **6.** $2 + \frac{m}{3} = 0$

7. $12d - 6 = 138$ **8.** $4x - 2 = 28.4$ **9.** $15 = 6 + \frac{m}{6}$

10. $-19 = 4 + 3x$ **11.** $4 - \frac{k}{5} = 18$ **12.** $15 = -11c + 4$

13. $12 - 11s = 45$ **14.** $10 = 3 + \frac{d}{2}$ **15.** $\frac{-3}{4}n + \frac{1}{4} = 1\frac{3}{4}$

16. $\frac{x}{-6} + 7 = 0$ **17.** $0 = 91 + 13t$ **18.** $5p - 0.48 = 0.12$

19. $\frac{2n}{5} - 23 = 11$ **20.** $2.1 + 3b = 1.8$ **21.** $\frac{t}{8} - \frac{3}{4} = \frac{1}{2}$

MENTAL MATH Solve each equation.

22. $2n + 3 = 15$ **23.** $\frac{y}{5} - 2 = 10$ **24.** $4x - 1 = 27$

25. $\frac{m}{10} + 3 = 6$ **26.** $2x - 7 = 11$ **27.** $3a - 2 = 13$

CALCULATOR Solve each equation.

28. $31.5 - 4.2x = -65.1$ **29.** $238.7 + 1.8k = 3.02 \cdot 10^5$

30. $0 = -5.67x + 0.25$ **31.** $47.2 = \frac{4r}{5} + 81.9$

Write a situation for each equation.

32. $3g + 4 = 16$ **33.** $\frac{r}{4} + 0.35 = 5.15$

Choose the correct equation. Solve.

34. A student bought some pencils for $.39 each and a pad of drawing paper for $1.19. The total cost for the supplies was $3.92. How many pencils did the student buy?

   a. $39x + 1.19 = 3.92$ **b.** $1.19x + 39y = 3.92$

   c. $0.39x + 1.19 = 3.92$ **d.** $0.039x + 1.19 = 3.92$

35. A student is saving $15 each week from earnings and already has $150. In how many weeks will the balance be $210?

   a. $150 + 210 = 15n$ **b.** $150 - 15n = 210$

   c. $150 + 15n = 210$ **d.** $15n - 150 = 210$

MIXED REVIEW

Solve each equation.

1. $12n + 60 = 300$

2. $25n - 30 = 70$

Find each answer.

3. Solve $\frac{12}{x} = \frac{18}{27}$.

4. What is 15% of $42?

5. 24 is 25% of what number?

Simplify each expression.

6. $4m + 5 - m$

7. $13 - 5x + 2$

8. How much warmer is it when the temperature is 90° than when the temperature is -6°?

Write a two-step equation with each number as its solution.

36. −2 $\frac{x}{3} + 4 = 12$　　　　**37.** 7 $z + u = 11$　　　　**38.** 0.3

$n + 0.7 = 1$

Write an equation to describe the situation. Do not solve.

39. Seven less than three times a number equals 19. Find the number. $3n - 7 = 19$

40. Linda had $235 in her savings account. She withdrew the same amount each week for 15 weeks. Her balance was then $55. How much money did Linda withdraw each week? $75

Write an equation to describe the situation. Solve.

41. Two is twelve times a number less four. Find the number. $2 = 12n - 4$ $\frac{1}{2}$

42. Phillip wants to buy a bicycle for $189. He has $24 and plans to save $15 each week. In how many weeks will he be able to buy the bicycle? $189

43. Phyllis wants to buy a camera for $78. She has already saved $36. She plans to save $8 each week. In how many weeks will she be able to buy the camera? $8d + 36 = 78$

44. A taxi ride costs $.40 for each quarter-mile and $.85 for each additional passenger. Yolanda and Cara paid $5.25 altogether. How far did they travel?

45. Thirty is three times a number less nine. Find the number. $30 = 3n$

46. Greg bought four greeting cards, all at the same price, and a package of wrapping paper for $1.79. He spent a total of $5.19. How much was each greeting card? $4.59x =$

Solve each equation for x.

47. $ax + b = c$ $x = \frac{6 - 6}{a}$　　　　**48.** $\frac{x}{a} - b = c, \; a \neq 0$

49. *DATA FILE 3 (pp. 96–97)* Nicholas turned in five halves of one-dollar bills that had accidentally been torn, along with $6 worth of pennies. How much money will he receive? $8.50

Simplifying and Solving Equations

▼ A bowler scores 20 points more in her second game than in her first game. Her total for both games is 310. What is her score in the first game? Let s represent the score in the first game and $s + 20$ represent the score in the second game. Then the following equation describes the situation.

$$s + s + 20 = 310$$

THINK What if we let s represent the score in the second game. How would the score of the first game be expressed? What would be the new equation?

You can solve this equation by combining like terms.

$s + s + 20 = 310$	
$2s + 20 = 310$	Combine like terms.
$2s + 20 - 20 = 310 - 20$	Subtract 20 from both sides.
$2s = 290$	
$\dfrac{2s}{2} = \dfrac{290}{2}$	Divide both sides by 2.
$s = 145$	

Check $s + s + 20 = 310$

$145 \boxed{+} 145 \boxed{+} 20 \boxed{=} 310 ✓$ Replace s with 145.

▼ Sometimes you need to use the distributive property before combining like terms.

Example 1 $2(x + 7) - 4x = 8$

Solution

$2x + 14 - 4x = 8$	Distributive property
$-2x + 14 = 8$	Combine like terms.
$-2x + 14 - 14 = 8 - 14$	Subtract 14 from each side.
$-2x = -6$	
$\dfrac{-2x}{-2} = \dfrac{-6}{-2}$	Divide both sides by -2.
$x = 3$	

Check $2(x + 7) - 4x = 8$ Replace x with 3.

$$2(3 + 7) - 4(3) = 8$$
$$2(10) - 12 = 8$$
$$20 - 12 = 8$$
$$8 = 8 ✓$$

Solving a Multi-step Equation	To solve a multi-step equation:
	1. Remove parentheses using the distributive property.
	2. Combine like terms.
	3. Undo addition or subtraction.
	4. Undo multiplication or division.

▼ You can use an equation to solve word problems.

Example 2 The sale price of a sweater is $48. The price is 20% less than the original price. What was the original price?

THINK How would you write the equation in Example 2 using a fraction instead of a decimal for 20%?

Solution Let p = the original price.
Then $p - 0.2p = 48$ describes the situation.

$p - 0.2p = 48$

$0.8p = 48$ Combine like terms.

$\dfrac{0.8p}{0.8} = \dfrac{48}{0.8}$ Divide both sides by 0.8.

$p = 60$

Check $p - 0.2p = 48$

$60 \ominus 0.2 \otimes 60 \boxminus 48$ ✓   Replace p with 60.

THINK AND DISCUSS

1. How can you solve the equation $25x + 2 = -73$ using addition and multiplication?

2. Is the solution of the equation $14(2x - 1) = 56$ a negative number? Explain.

CLASS EXERCISES

Simplify the left side of each equation. Do not solve.

1. $4x + 5x = 45$

2. $-2(x - 7) = 8$

3. $5 + x - 2x = 8$

4. $\dfrac{x}{3} \cdot \dfrac{x}{6} = -7$

Solve and check each equation.

5. $9x - 2x = -42$

6. $4x + 1 - x = 19$

7. $15 = x - 7x$

8. $3(n - 2) = 36$

9. $1.2x + 2.6x = 4.56$

10. $\dfrac{x}{2} - \dfrac{x}{4} = -\dfrac{1}{8}$

Choose the equation that describes the situation. Solve.

11. This year's soybean crop of 224,000 t represents an increase of 40% over last year's crop. How many tons of soybeans were produced last year?

   a. $n = 224,000 - 0.4n$ **b.** $n = 224,000 + 0.4n$

   c. $n + 0.4n = 224,000$ **d.** $n - 0.4n = 224,000$

12. Sally paid $22.40 for a sweatshirt. It had been discounted by 30%. What was the original price of the sweatshirt?

   a. $x + 0.30x = 22.40$ **b.** $x + 30x = 22.40$

   c. $x - 0.30x = 22.40$ **d.** $x = 22.40(0.30x)$

13. Joe bought 2 cartons of milk on Monday and 3 cartons on Tuesday. He spent $1.75. How much was each carton of milk?

   a. $2c + 2c = 1.75$ **b.** $2c + 3c = 0.175$

   c. $5c = 17.5$ **d.** $1.75 = 2c + 3c$

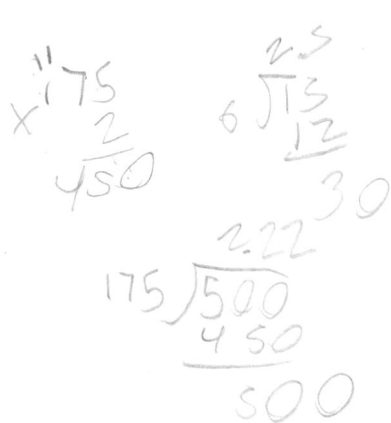

WRITTEN EXERCISES

Solve and check each equation.

1. $5x - x = 11$
2. $-4(y - 1) = 28$
3. $7 = 2(y + 6)$
4. $4(y + 2) = 2$
5. $9 = \frac{1}{3}(h - 4)$
6. $0.9t + 2.3t = -6.4$
7. $16 = 2(y - 1) - 6$
8. $6 = a + a + 4$
9. $n + 2 - 3n = -8$
10. $9 - b + 8b = 23$
11. $9(2m + 5) = -14$
12. $2x + 4 + 3x = -26$
13. $36 = y - 5y - 12$
14. $\frac{1}{5}(x + 2) = 2$
15. $8 - 3(x - 4) = 6$
16. $21 = 9 - 2(4a + 2)$
17. $7(2k - 1) + 4 = 7$
18. $15 = -8(c - 1) + 9$
19. $-0.5x + 4 + 2x = 9$
20. $\frac{2}{3}n + \frac{3}{8}n = \frac{15}{16}$

MENTAL MATH **Find each value.**

21. If $\frac{1}{6}(4x + 5) = 0.5$, find the value of $4x + 5$.
22. If $3(x + 5) = 18$, find the value of $3x$.
23. If $21 = 2(4 + x) + 7$, find the value of $2x$.

CALCULATOR **Solve each equation.**

24. $25.8x + 17.3 - 4.2x = -65.1$
25. $238.7 + 1.8(k - 0.2) = 371.9$
26. $0 = 2.4x + 9.8x - 0.25$
27. $-13.5 = 0.8x + 6.7 - 1.3x$
28. $12.3 + 18.6x - 3.5(2.8x + 8.5) = 7(2.55 + 2.5)$
29. $2.34(2.2x - 4.66) + 2.352x + 2.4044 = 0.25 + 1.25$

Write a situation for each equation.

30. $x + 2x + 3x = 18$
31. $5(x - 1) = 10$

Choose the equation which describes the situation. Solve.

32. Julio bought some pencils for $.39 each and the same number of erasers for $.19 each. The total for his supplies was $4.06. How many pencils did Julio buy?
    a. $39x + 19 = 4.06$
    b. $0.39x + 0.19x = 4.06$
    c. $0.39 + 0.19x = 4.06$
    d. $0.39x + (0.39)(0.19) = 4.06$

33. Use the table at the right. What was the original price of a pair of running shoes?
    a. $0.3p = 21$
    b. $30p = 21$
    c. $\frac{p}{30} = 21$
    d. $\frac{p}{0.3} = 21$

SALE ATHLETIC SHOES 30% OFF	
Shoe Type	**Savings**
Basketball	$15
Track	$ 9
Running	$21

NOTES & QUOTES

The procedure for solving an equation is known as an *algorithm*. The term is based on the name of a Persian mathematician, al-Khowârizmî (c. 780–850).

Write an equation to describe the situation. Solve.

34. I'm thinking of a number. If I subtract 7 and multiply the result by 3, I get 18. What is the number?

35. Team A defeated Team B by 13 points. The total number of points scored by both teams was 171. How many points were scored by Team B?

$P + P + 13 = 171$

36. Find two consecutive integers whose sum is -39.

37. Bill paid $53 for a sweater. It was 20% off the original price. What was the original price of the sweater?

66.25 $P - 0.2P = 53$

38. Jo Ann paid $16.25 for an alarm clock. The original price was $25. What was the percent discount?

39. I'm thinking of a number. If the number is decreased by 8 and the result is tripled, I get 36. What is the number?

$3n - 7 = 18$

Each of these solutions contains a common error. Find each error. State the correct solution.

$3x - 3 - 5 = 14$

40. $7x - 1 = 15$
$$7x = 14$$
$$x = 2$$

41. $3(x - 1) - 5 = 14$
$$3x - 1 - 5 = 14$$
$$3x - 6 = 14$$
$$3x = 20$$
$$x = \frac{20}{3}$$

$x = 7\frac{1}{3}$

42. *DATA FILE 3 (pp. 96–97)* An employee at the United States Mint worked 3.2 h on Monday, 6.8 h on Tuesday, and 6 h on Wednesday. How many sheets of one-dollar bills were produced in this time? How many one-dollar bills were produced?

TEST YOURSELF

Solve each equation.

1. $4a - 7 = -15$

2. $52 = \frac{b}{3} - 2$

3. $8.35 + 0.12s = 9.07$

4. $3x + 3x + 9 = -9$

5. $-8 = -2(y + 5)$

Write an equation to describe the situation. Solve.

6. Carmen had $185 in her account. She withdrew the same amount each week for 11 weeks. She then deposited $40. At that time, her balance was $93. How much money did Carmen withdraw each week?

Problem Solving Practice

Solve. Use an appropriate strategy or a combination of strategies.

1. A student is building a square pen 21 ft long on each side. He puts one post at each corner and one post every 3 ft in between. How many posts will he use?

2. Find two whole numbers whose sum is 125 and whose difference is 23.

3. There are six basketball teams in a tournament. Each team will compete twice against each of the other teams. What is the total number of games to be played?

4. A student counts 18 legs on the chairs and three-legged stools at the Science Fair exhibit booth. How many chairs are there? how many stools?

5. The perimeter of a rectangle is 340 cm. The length is 20 more than twice the width of the rectangle. Find the length.

6. A supermarket clerk stacks cans of beans for a display. The clerk puts 10 cans on the bottom row, 9 cans on top of them, and so on. How many cans does the clerk use if the top layer has one can?

7. A student bought some cassette tapes for $7.95 each and a cassette player for $45.98. The total is $77.78. How many cassette tapes did the student buy?

8. A ninth-grade student rides her bike every other day for exercise. Her friend rides his bike every third day. They both rode their bikes on January 2. How many other days in January will they both ride their bikes on the same day?

9. In a competition, one runner runs 280 m farther than another. Together they run 2,870 m. How many meters did each run?

10. A student bought a skirt for $21.49 and two blouses for $18.98 each. She then had $23.15. How much money did she have before she made the purchases?

11. The sum of the numbers on two facing pages is 149. Their product is 5,550. What are the page numbers?

12. There are 156 students at band practice. There are twice as many females as males at the practice session. How many males are there?

13. A painter can paint a square wall that measures 100 ft on a side in 1 h. How long will it take to paint a square wall that measures 50 ft on a side?

OBJECTIVE:
To solve problems by
writing equations.

7-3 *Writing Equations*

■ You can solve many types of problems using equations.

PROBLEM

The Standard Oil Building has eight times as many stories as the first
skyscraper. The Sears Tower has 110 stories, which is 20 more than
the total number of stories of the other two skyscrapers. How many
stories does the first skyscraper have?

SOLUTION

READf ▶ Answer these questions to understand the given information:

What do you want to find?	how many stories are in the first skyscraper
How many stories are in the Standard Oil Building?	eight times as many as are in the first skyscraper
How many are in the Sears Tower?	110 stories
How many more stories are in the Sears Tower than in the other two skyscrapers?	20 more stories

PLAN ▶ Write an equation.

Let n = the number of stories in the first skyscraper.
Then $8n$ = the number of stories in the Standard Oil Building.
The equation $n + 8n + 20 = 110$ describes the situation.

SOLVE ▶ Solve the equation.

$$n + 8n + 20 = 110$$
$$9n + 20 = 110 \qquad \textbf{Combine like terms.}$$
$$9n + 20 - 20 = 110 - 20 \qquad \textbf{Subtract 20 from each side.}$$
$$9n = 90$$
$$\frac{9n}{9} = \frac{90}{9} \qquad \textbf{Divide both sides by 9.}$$
$$n = 10$$

The first skyscraper has 10 stories.

LOOK BACK ▶ How many stories are in the Standard Oil Building? 80 stories

---

CLASS EXERCISES

Write an equation for each sentence. Do not solve.

1. Two-thirds of a number is decreased by 7 to obtain 13.

2. 45 less twice a number is equal to 15.

WRITTEN EXERCISES

Write an equation. Do not solve.

1. The difference between 8 times a number and $\frac{1}{2}$ of the number is 16. Find the number.

2. When half of n is added to three times n, the sum is thirty-five. Find n.

Write an equation. Solve.

3. A pair of boots cost $5 more than a pair of shoes. The total cost for both is $114.90. Find the price of the boots.

4. A coin bank contains $2.80 in dimes and quarters. The bank contains the same number of each coin. How many of each coin does the bank contain? *Hint:* Let n = the number of dimes. Since each dime has a value of $.10, the value of n dimes is $.10$n$. Since the number of quarters is also n, the value of n quarters is $.25$n$.

5. A pencil and an eraser together cost $.95. The pencil costs $.45 more than the eraser. Find the cost of the eraser.

6. A piggy bank contains the same number of pennies, dimes, and quarters for a total of $13.32. How many of each kind of coin is in the bank?

7. A cheese pizza costs $8.75. Each additional topping costs $1.25. If a pizza costs $12.50, how many toppings are on the pizza?

8. A wire of uniform thickness and composition weighs 48 lb. The wire is cut into two pieces. The piece that is 120 yd long weighs 32 lb. Find the original length of the wire.

9. The booster club sold 75% of the tickets printed for the raffle. They did not sell 175 tickets. How many tickets did they have printed?

10. A car rental agency charges $27.95 a day plus $.14/mi. Pat's bill for 3 days was $154.83. How many miles did she drive?

11. Jan has $240 in the bank to pay for her tuba lessons. A lesson costs $15. How many lessons can she afford with her savings?

12. The perimeter of a rectangle is 64 cm. The length is 4 cm less than twice the width. Find the length and width.

13. A number s is multiplied by $\frac{2}{3}$. Then $\frac{2}{5}$ is subtracted from the product. The result is $\frac{11}{45}$. What number is s?

14. Water flows over the Niagara Falls at a rate of 1.5 million gal/s. How many gallons flow over the falls in 1 h 15 s?

Solve.

15. Miss Zawtocki teaches a total of 40 students. The ratio of female students to male students is 1 to 4. How many female students does she teach?

16. The weight of an object on the moon is about $\frac{1}{6}$ of its weight on Earth. If an astronaut weighs 134 lb on Earth, how much would she weigh on the moon to the nearest tenth of a pound?

17. **DATA FILE 1 (pp. 2–3)** What is the danger of frostbite if the air temperature is 10°F and the wind speed is 25 mi/h?

18. Approximately 27 million acres of rain forest are cut and burned each year. If this rate continues, how many acres will be destroyed in the next decade?

19. Mr. Macintosh has 42 rows of apple trees in his orchard. Each row contains 24 trees. Mr. Macintosh is expecting to harvest 18,144 bu of apples this year. On the average, how many bushels of apples does each tree produce?

Critical Thinking
EXPLORING CLOCK ARITHMETIC

Visualize a 12-hour clock face. Start at 10:00. Count forward 16 h. What time will it be?

To find the time using clock arithmetic, follow these steps.

1. To find the *clock time*, add the starting time to the number. $10 + 16 = 26$

2. Use the following formula to determine what the time will be.

   clock time − (hours on clock face)(groups of 12 in clock time)
   $26 - (12)(2) = 2$, so the time will be 2 o'clock.

Solve.

1. It is 3:00. What time will it be in 7 h?

2. It is 6:00. What time will it be in 17 h?

3. It is 4:00. How many hours ago was it 9 o'clock?

4. **a.** Suppose a clock shows five hours on its face. How could you adapt the formula so that you could use clock arithmetic? Write the formula.

   b. It is 4 o'clock. What time will it be in 17 h?

   c. It is 1 o'clock. What time was it 29 hours ago?

OBJECTIVE:
To solve equations
with an unknown on
both sides.

7-4 Equations with Variables on Both Sides

▼ The Ricardos have three children whose ages are consecutive even integers. The sum of the children's ages is equal to four times the youngest child's age. What are the ages of the Ricardos' children?

Let a = the youngest child's age.
Then $a + 2$ = the middle child's age.
Then $a + 4$ = the oldest child's age.

We can write the following equation to describe this situation.

$$a + a + 2 + a + 4 = 4a$$

You can solve this equation by using a model.

 Model the equation.

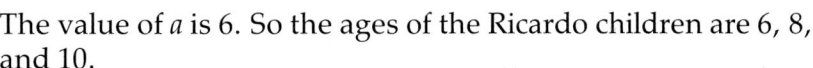 Combine like terms.

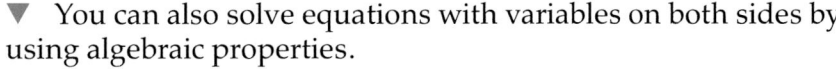 Subtract 3a from each side of the equation.

The value of a is 6. So the ages of the Ricardo children are 6, 8, and 10.

▼ You can also solve equations with variables on both sides by using algebraic properties.

Example 1 Solve $3x + 7 = 5x - 1$.

Solution
$$3x + 7 = 5x - 1$$
$$3x + 7 - 3x = 5x - 1 - 3x \qquad \text{Subtract } 3x \text{ from each side.}$$
$$7 = 2x - 1$$
$$7 + 1 = 2x - 1 + 1 \qquad \text{Add 1 to each side.}$$
$$8 = 2x$$
$$\frac{8}{2} = \frac{2x}{2} \qquad \text{Divide each side by 2.}$$
$$4 = x$$

Check $3x + 7 = 5x - 1$
$$3(4) + 7 = 5(4) - 1 \qquad \text{Replace } x \text{ with 4.}$$
$$12 + 7 = 20 - 1$$
$$19 = 19 \checkmark$$

▼ When more than one term on a side of an equation contains a variable, you need to combine like terms before you add or subtract.

Example 2 Solve $5x - 2 - 3x = 2x + 7 - x$.

Solution

$$5x - 2 - 3x = 2x + 7 - x$$
$$2x - 2 = x + 7 \qquad \text{Combine like terms.}$$
$$2x - 2 - x = x + 7 - x \qquad \text{Subtract } x \text{ from each side.}$$
$$x - 2 = 7$$
$$x - 2 + 2 = 7 + 2 \qquad \text{Add 2 to each side.}$$
$$x = 9$$

Check $5x - 2 - 3x = 2x + 7 - x$
$$5(9) - 2 - 3(9) = 2(9) + 7 - 9 \qquad \text{Replace } x \text{ with 9.}$$
$$45 - 2 - 27 = 18 + 7 - 9$$
$$16 = 16 ✓$$

▼ You may need to use the distributive property to remove parentheses before combining like terms.

Example 3 Solve $n + 2(n + 2) = n + 16$.

Solution

$$n + 2(n + 2) = n + 16$$
$$n + 2n + 4 = n + 16 \qquad \text{distributive property}$$
$$3n + 4 = n + 16 \qquad \text{Combine like terms.}$$
$$3n + 4 - n = n + 16 - n \qquad \text{Subtract } n \text{ from each side.}$$
$$2n + 4 = 16$$
$$2n + 4 - 4 = 16 - 4 \qquad \text{Subtract 4 from each side.}$$
$$2n = 12$$
$$\frac{2n}{2} = \frac{12}{2} \qquad \text{Divide both sides by 2.}$$
$$n = 6 \qquad \text{The check is left for you.}$$

Solving Equations with Variables on Both Sides	To solve equations with variables on both sides:
	1. Use the distributive property to remove parentheses.
	2. Combine like terms.
	3. Use the addition and/or subtraction properties so that variables are on one side and constants on the other.
	4. Use the multiplication or division property.

THINK How is adding and subtracting variables similar to adding and subtracting numbers from both sides of an equation?

THINK AND DISCUSS

1. To solve the equation $6x = x - 10$, what should you do first?

2. How are the steps for solving equations related to the strategy, *Simplify the Problem?*

CLASS EXERCISES

State the first step in solving each equation.

1. $4x = 9x + 50$

2. $2x - 9 = 27$

3. $4 - x + 6x = 10 + x - 1$

4. $3(2x - 0.3) = 15 - (x + 2)$

Write an equation for each diagram. Solve.

5.

x	3

| 6 | |

6.

x	x	7

| $x + 9$ | | |

Solve and check each equation.

7. $n + 12 = 5n$

8. $-2r + 7 = r - 8$

9. $9 - (x - 4) = 3(x - 1)$

10. $\frac{1}{4}(d + 2) = \frac{3}{4}d - 6$

WRITTEN EXERCISES

Write an equation for each diagram. Solve.

1.

m	m	m	m	5

| 21 | | | | |

2.

3	y	4

| $2y - 6$ | | |

MENTAL MATH Solve.

3. $x + x + x = x + 6$

4. $3x + 20 = 8x$

5. $x + 7 = 2x + 6$

6. $2(x + 4) = 3x$

Solve each equation.

7. $5x + 8 = 7x$

8. $3a = a + 22$

9. $8.6 + 2.1x = -0.05x$

10. $m + m + 18 = 4m$

11. $4w + 8 = 6w - 4$

12. $7r = 2(r - 10)$

13. $6(h + 3) = -2(h + 31)$

14. $-2(y + 6) = y + 3 + 2y$

15. $9 - (2y - 3) = y$

16. $4 - 7t = 2(t - 7)$

17. $2g + 6 = -g - 8$

18. $5(n - 3) = 2n - 6$

19. $7b = b + 16 + 2b$

20. $0.3k + 1.4 = 4.2 - 0.1k$

21. $4(8 - k) = 2k + 16$

22. $m - 16 = 3m + 18 + 2m$

23. $\frac{1}{5}(x + 8) = \frac{4}{5}x - \frac{1}{5}$

24. $\frac{1}{2}(2h + 4) = \frac{1}{3}(h - 4)$

Is the given number a solution of the equation?

25. $b + 6 = 3(b - 4)$, $b = 9$

26. $10 - 6m = 2(m - 3)$, $m = -3$

27. $-f + 3f = f + 27$, $f = 27$

28. $a - 8 - 2 = \frac{1}{2}(a - 2)$, $a = 18$

CALCULATOR Solve.

29. $3.6a - 6.2 - 0.1a = 1.5 + 0.2(a + 6)$

30. $4 - 0.6a = 3(1.5a + 0.9) + 7.93$

MIXED REVIEW

Write an algebraic expression.

1. twice the result of increasing a number by 4

2. $14 more than the cost of a cassette

Write an equation. Solve.

3. Six less than three times a number is twelve.

4. Fifty-six is eight more than six times a number.

Replace each ▓ with <, >, or =.

5. $\frac{12}{-4}$ ▓ $-2 - 1$

6. 3 ▓ $\sqrt{9}$

7. A student pays $168 for a coat and jacket. The jacket costs $18 less than the coat. What is the price of the coat?

Write an equation to describe the situation. Solve.

31. Find three consecutive integers whose sum is 165.

32. Find three consecutive odd integers whose sum is 87.

33. One more than one-half of a number is one less than two-thirds of the number. What is the number?

34. If a number is subtracted from 18, the result is four less than the number. What is the number?

35. Twice a number less eight is 16 less than three times the number. What is the number?

36. Find four consecutive integers whose sum is negative two.

37. *DATA FILE 9 (pp. 360–361)* Twice the measure of the loft of a 6 iron minus *x* is equal to the measure of the loft of a 9 iron.

Use the article below.

38. a. Use Diophantine symbols. Write the numerals 56, 129, and 683.

    b. *WRITE* Will a letter in any number written in Diophantine symbolism ever come before a letter of later rank in the alphabet? Explain.

    c. Determine how many years Diophantus lived. *Hint:* Let his age *a* equal the expression in the article below. Simplify the expression and solve for *a*.

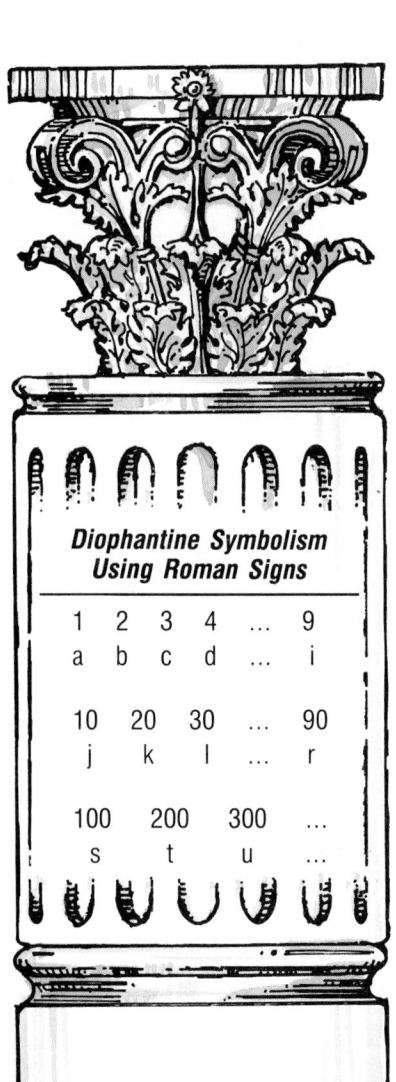

Diophantine Symbolism Using Roman Signs

1	2	3	4	...	9
a	b	c	d	...	i

10	20	30	...	90
j	k	l	...	r

100	200	300	...
s	t	u	...

The Father of Algebra

Diophantus was a Greek mathematician who lived in the third century. He is called the father of algebra because he was the first mathematician to use symbols. For example, Diophantus expressed numerals as shown in the table at the left. The number 234 would have been written as *tld*.

We know how long Diophantus lived from a description of his life in terms of an algebraic riddle. The riddle states, "Diophantus' youth lasted one sixth of his life. He grew a beard after one twelfth more. After one seventh more of his life he married. Five years later he had a son. The son lived exactly one-half as long as his father and Diophantus died four years after his son. All of this adds up to the years Diophantus lived."

Adding the parts of Diophantus' life results in the following expression:

$$\frac{1}{6}a + \frac{1}{12}a + \frac{1}{7}a + 5 + \frac{1}{2}a + 4$$

OBJECTIVE:
Use models to explore inequalities.

Exploring Inequalities

▼ Study the number line models to see what happens to each inequality sign for $-2 < 4$ when you multiply each side of the inequality by a positive or negative number.

MATERIALS

- Paper
- Ruler
- Math journal to record work

a. Add 3, a positive number.

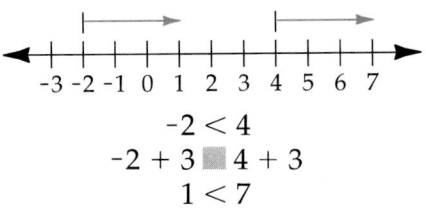

$$-2 < 4$$
$$-2 + 3 \ \blacksquare\ 4 + 3$$
$$1 < 7$$

b. Add -3, a negative number.

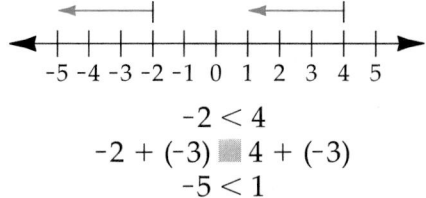

$$-2 < 4$$
$$-2 + (-3) \ \blacksquare\ 4 + (-3)$$
$$-5 < 1$$

c. Multiply each side by 2, a positive number.

d. Multiply each side by -1, a negative number.

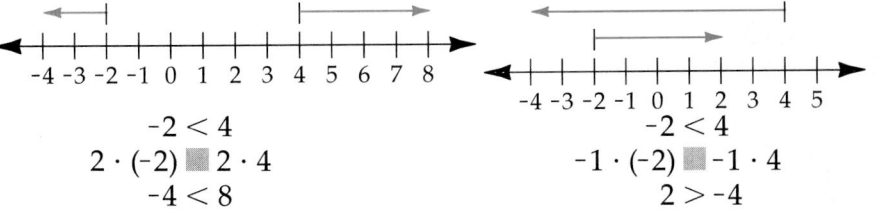

$$-2 < 4$$
$$2 \cdot (-2) \ \blacksquare\ 2 \cdot 4$$
$$-4 < 8$$

$$-2 < 4$$
$$-1 \cdot (-2) \ \blacksquare\ -1 \cdot 4$$
$$2 > -4$$

1. **Describe** what you notice about the direction of the arrows in the inequalities modeled above.

2. Try adding other positive and negative numbers to the inequality $-2 < 4$. **Model** on the number line. **Explain** what happens to the inequality sign.

3. **Explore** what happens to the inequality sign if you subtract the same number from each side of an inequality.

4. Try multiplying each side of $-2 < 4$ by other positive and negative numbers and model on the number line. **Explain** what happens to the inequality sign.

5. **Explore** what happens if you divide each side of the inequality $-2 > 4$ by 2 and by -2.

6. **Summarize** Write a rule that tells what happens to an inequality sign if you perform the following operations on each side of the inequality.

   a. Add or subtract either a positive number or a negative number.

   b. Multiply or divide by a positive number.

   c. Multiply or divide by a negative number.

7. How are the rules for inequalities similar to the rules for equations? How are they different?

OBJECTIVE:
To write and graph simple inequalities with one variable.

7-5 Inequalities and Their Graphs

▼ No one under 17 is admitted to theaters showing R-rated films unless they are accompanied by an adult. If you let *a* represent age, you can write the *inequalities* $a < 17$ and $a > 0$ to describe this situation.

Inequality	An inequality is a statement that two expressions are not equal.

▼ You can graph an inequality on a number line.

Example 1 **Graph each inequality.**

    a. $y < 3$ **b.** $x > -1$

Solution   **a.**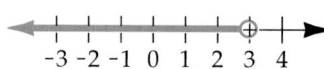
-3 -2 -1 0 1 2 3 4

The value for *y* is any real number less than 3. We place an open dot above 3 to show that 3 is not a solution.

  b.
-3 -2 -1 0 1 2 3

The value for *x* is any real number greater than -1. We place an open dot above -1 to show that -1 is not a solution.

THINK Why is graphing an inequality an easier way to show the solutions than listing them?

▼ You can also graph inequalities that include an equal sign.

Example 2 **Graph each inequality.**

    a. $a \leq -2$ **b.** $g \geq -6$

Solution   **a.**
-4 -3 -2 -1 0 1 2

The value for *a* is -2 or any real number less than -2. We place a solid dot above -2 since -2 is a solution.

  b.
-7 -6 -5 -4 -3 -2 -1

The value for *g* is -6 or any real number greater than -6. We place a solid dot above -6 since -6 is a solution.

FLASHBACK

$\leq$ *is less than or equal to*

$\geq$ *is greater than or equal to*

Example 3 **State whether the endpoint of the graph of each inequality would be a solid dot or an open dot.**

    a. $y + 3 > 12$ **b.** $3a \geq -21$ **c.** $6x \leq 18$

Solution   **a.** open   **b.** solid   **c.** solid

▼ You can write an inequality for a graph.

Example 4   **Write an inequality for each graph.**

a.

b.

Solution   **a.** $x > 0$ **b.** $x \leq -1$

▼ You can write an inequality for a sentence or a sentence for an inequality.

Example 5   **a.** Write an inequality for p is greater than -2.

b. Write a sentence for the inequality $b \leq 8$.

Solution   **a.** $p > -2$ **b.** b is less than or equal to 8.

▼ You can write an inequality to describe a situation.

Example 6   **Write an inequality to describe the situation.**

There are more than 15 girls in the class.
Let g = the number of girls in the class.

Solution $g > 15$

CLASS EXERCISES

Read each inequality aloud.

1. $t > -16$ **2.** $57 \leq n$ **3.** $y < 28$

Tell whether each inequality is true or false.

4. $-2 + 7 > 6$ **5.** $0.03 > 0.1$ **6.** $-2^4 < (-2)^4$

Match each inequality with the appropriate graph.

7. $x \geq -4$ **a.**

8. $x \leq -4$ **b.**

9. $x > 0.4$ **c.**

10. $t \geq -0.4$ **d.**

THINK AND DISCUSS

1. Is the inequality $a > b$ equivalent to $b < a$?

2. How is an inequality with one variable different from an equation?

Write an inequality for each word phrase.

11. x is less than 5.   **12.** y is more than -3.

WRITTEN EXERCISES

Tell whether each inequality is true or false.

1. $-5 + 2 < -2$

2. $|-8 \times 2| \geq 10$

3. $\sqrt{16} \leq 4$

4. $3(-5) + 1 > -2(-6) - 18$

5. $(0.5)(2 + 8) < -2^2 + 2$

CALCULATOR True or false.

6. $-8.46 - 4.51 < 5(1.13) - 1.76$

7. $3(-0.04 + 7.12) > -2.87(-2.35)$

8. $-0.8(8.3 + 6.8) \geq 4.3(-3)$

9. $|-14.3 + 4.9| < 4.47(2.1)$

Write each inequality as a word sentence.

10. $2.5 > m$

11. $6.2 \leq j$

12. $5 \leq k$

13. $|x| \geq 2$

14. $8r < 29$

15. $72 \geq g$

State an inequality for each graph.

16.
```
◄——|—⊕—|—|—|—|—|—|—|——►
   -5 -4 -3 -2 -1  0  1  2  3
```

17.
```
◄——|—|—|—|—|—|—|—●—|——►
   -5 -4 -3 -2 -1  0  1  2  3
```

18.
```
◄——|—|—|—|—●—|—|—|—|——►
   -5 -4 -3 -2 -1  0  1  2  3
```

Graph each inequality on a number line.

19. $x < 7$

20. $y > 2$

21. $a \geq -2$

22. $j \leq 0$

23. $x > -1$

24. $a < 2$

25. $m > -5$

26. $b \geq 6$

27. $p \leq 4$

28. $x > 1$

29. $j \geq -1$

30. $c < 1$

Write an inequality for each sentence.

31. Three is less than ten.

32. The total t is greater than seven.

33. A number p is positive.

34. A number c is at least a dozen.

35. The price p is not more than $30.

36. The number of seats s in the auditorium is no more than 3,500.

37. *DATA FILE 4 (pp. 138–139)* Three times x is less than the population of Monaco per square kilometer.

State two inequalities for each graph.

38.
```
◄——|—|—|—●—⊕—|—|—|——►
   -3 -2 -1  0  1  2  3
```

39.
```
◄——|—|—⊕—●—|—|—|——►
  -15 -10 -5  0  5  10 15
```

MIXED REVIEW

Solve.

1. $2x - 5 = 29$

2. $x - 3(5 - x) = 2 + 7x$

Write as an expression.

3. 4 less than twice a number

4. 14 less a number

Simplify.

5. $\sqrt{16} - |-4|$

6. $n + (n + 2) + (n + 4)$

Solve.

7. A recipe calls for $\frac{2}{3}$ c of milk. Jane needs to triple the recipe. How much milk will she need?

Replace ▨ **with <, >, or = to make the statement**
$3 + x$ ▨ $7 + x$ **true.**

40. if $x = 4$ **41.** if $x = 0$ **42.** if $x = \text{-}5$ **43.** if $x < 0$

Replace ▨ **with <, >, or = to make the statement** $3x$ ▨ $7x$ **true.**

44. if $x = 7$ **45.** if $x = 0$ **46.** if $x = \text{-}2$ **47.** if $x < \text{-}1$

Replace ▨ **with < or > to make each statement true.**

48. If $a < b$, then b ▨ a.   **49.** If $x > y$, and $y > z$, then x ▨ z.

Write an inequality to describe each situation.

50. Fewer than 45 people attended the show. Let n equal the number of people who attended the show.

51. A student has $5 but does not have enough money to purchase three pairs of socks. Let m equal the cost of three pairs of socks.

52. At least 127 students attended the rock concert. Let s equal the number of students.

53. A student picked at least 15 bushels of apples. Let b equal the number of bushels picked.

54. A student pays for three movie tickets with a twenty-dollar bill. The change is less than $1. Let t equal the cost of a movie ticket.

55. No more than 50 students walked in the walkathon. Let s equal the number of students.

56. *DATA FILE 7 (pp. 272–273)* Let h equal the flight time in hours.

   a. On flights of how many hours is smoking not permitted?

   b. On flights of how many hours is smoking permitted?

COMPUTER You can use a computer to compare data. The table at the right shows yearly salaries for six people. Each person's tax is based on salary. Let s equal salary.

57. a. Run the following BASIC program. Use the data in the table for S.

```
10 PRINT "SALARY";
20 INPUT S
30 IF S < 20000 THEN PRINT "TAX = ";S*.15
40 IF S > 20000 THEN PRINT "TAX = ";S*.2
```

   b. *CALCULATOR* Did the program calculate the correct tax for each employee?

   c. The IF command allows the program to decide which tax rate to use. What role do the inequalities play in the program?

Name	Salary
Smith, J.	$25,700
Chien, H.	32,500
Garcia, R.	22,000
O'Malley, M.	19,500
Jones, K.	38,500
Strauss, J.	17,000

Tax Rates
If $s < 20,000$, 15%
If $s > 20,000$, 20%

Solving One-step Inequalities

NOTES & QUOTES

Dimitri Ivanovich Mendeleev (1834–1907) was a Russian chemist. He classified the elements by their similarities. Mendeleev left gaps in his periodic table for elements that would be discovered in later years.

▼ In 1869, Dimitri Mendeleev arranged the 63 known elements into the first *periodic table*. By 1984, advances in science had gradually increased the size of the table to 109 elements. How many elements could have been added to Mendeleev's table by 1982?

We can let n equal the number of elements added to the periodic table. Then the following inequality represents the number of elements that could have been added to the table by 1982.

$$63 + n < 109$$
$$-63 + 63 + n < 109 - 63$$
$$n < 46$$

Fewer than 46 elements could have been added to the table by 1982.

▼ You can solve inequalities by using the *addition properties for inequalities.*

Example 1 Solve the inequality $n - 15 < 73$.

Solution
$$n - 15 < 73$$
$$n - 15 + 15 < 73 + 15 \qquad \text{Add 15 to each side.}$$
$$n < 88$$

Addition Properties for Inequalities	Arithmetic
	1. $7 > 3$, so $7 + 4 > 3 + 4$.
	2. $2 < 5$, so $2 + 6 < 5 + 6$.
	Algebra
	1. If $a > b$, then $a + c > b + c$.
	2. If $a < b$, then $a + c < b + c$.

▼ You can solve inequalities by using the *subtraction properties for inequalities.*

Example 2 Solve the inequality $-26 > y + 15$.

Solution
$$-26 > y + 15$$
$$-26 - 15 > y + 15 - 15 \qquad \text{Subtract 15 from each side.}$$
$$-41 > y$$

Subtraction Properties for Inequalities	Arithmetic
	1. $12 > 4$, so $12 - 3 > 4 - 3$.
	2. $8 < 9$, so $8 - 2 < 9 - 2$.
	Algebra
	1. If $a > b$, then $a - c > b - c$.
	2. If $a < b$, then $a - c < b - c$.

▼ You can solve inequalities which involve multiplication using the *multiplication properties for inequalities*.

Multiplication Properties for Inequalities	**Arithmetic**
	1. $3 < 4$, so $3(5) < 4(5)$.
	2. $7 > 2$, so $7(4) > 2(4)$.
	3. $6 < 7$, so $6(-2) > 7(-2)$.
	4. $7 > 5$, so $7(-3) < 5(-3)$.
	Algebra
	1. If c is positive and $a < b$, then $ac < bc$.
	2. If c is positive and $a > b$, then $ac > bc$.
	3. If c is negative and $a < b$, then $ac > bc$.
	4. If c is negative and $a > b$, then $ac < bc$.

Example 3 Solve the inequality $\frac{x}{6} > -4$.

Solution
$$\frac{x}{6} > -4$$
$$6\left(\frac{x}{6}\right) > -4(6) \quad \text{Multiply each side by 6.}$$
$$x > -24$$

THINK How are the rules for solving inequalities similar to those for solving equations? How are they different?

▼ You can solve inequalities which involve division using the *division properties for inequalities*.

Division Properties for Inequalities	**Arithmetic**
	1. $3 < 6$, so $3 \div 3 < 6 \div 3$.
	2. $6 > 2$, so $6 \div 2 > 2 \div 2$.
	3. $6 < 12$, so $6 \div (-3) > 12 \div (-3)$.
	4. $16 > 8$, so $16 \div (-4) < 8 \div (-4)$.
	Algebra
	1. If c is positive and $a < b$, then $\frac{a}{c} < \frac{b}{c}$.
	2. If c is positive and $a > b$, then $\frac{a}{c} > \frac{b}{c}$.
	3. If c is negative and $a < b$, then $\frac{a}{c} > \frac{b}{c}$.
	4. If c is negative and $a > b$, then $\frac{a}{c} < \frac{b}{c}$.

Example 4 Solve the inequality $-5x < 20$.

Solution
$$-5x < 20$$
$$\frac{-5x}{-5} > \frac{20}{-5} \quad \text{Divide each side by -5. Change the direction of the inequality symbol.}$$
$$x > -4$$

You need to change the direction of the inequality sign only when multiplying or dividing by a negative number.

CLASS EXERCISES

State whether the inequality symbol remains the same or is reversed when you do the following to each side of an inequality.

1. add -5   **2.** multiply by -7   **3.** divide by 3

4. subtract 12   **5.** divide by -1   **6.** add 8

What was done to both sides of the first inequality to obtain the second?

7. $x - 5 \geq 6; x \geq 11$ **8.** $8 > -4x; -2 < x$

Tell whether each number is a solution of $3 - x > 1$.

9. 3   **10.** 2   **11.** 0   **12.** -4

Solve each inequality.

13. $\frac{x}{-6} > 3$ **14.** $-3.2x < 14.4$ **15.** $x - 8.4 > -2.7$

WRITTEN EXERCISES

State whether the inequality symbol remains the same or is reversed when you do the following to each side of an inequality.

1. A negative number is subtracted from both sides.

2. Both sides are multiplied by a positive number.

3. Both sides are divided by a negative number.

What was done to both sides of the first inequality to obtain the second?

4. $x + 8 \leq 11; x \leq 3$ **5.** $9 > -3x; -3 < x$

6. $4x \geq 48; x \geq 12$ **7.** $\frac{1}{3}x \leq 18; x \leq 54$

Tell whether each number is a solution of $5 - 2x \leq 1$.

8. 3   **9.** 2.5   **10.** 0   **11.** -4

Solve each inequality.

12. $x + 6 \geq 7$ **13.** $3 \leq x - 5$ **14.** $\frac{x}{3} \geq -5$

15. $-3x < 0$ **16.** $-4x \leq -16$ **17.** $x - 9 > -5$

18. $\frac{1}{2}x \geq -3$ **19.** $x - 7 < -15$ **20.** $9x \leq 27$

21. $5 + x > -7$ **22.** $\frac{b}{3} \leq -31$ **23.** $-3 \geq \frac{g}{-7}$

THINK AND DISCUSS

1. The rules for multiplying and dividing both sides of an inequality do not mention zero. Discuss these cases.

2. Is -6 a solution of the inequality $x \div 3 > 2$? Explain.

MIXED REVIEW

Find the GCF of each set of numbers.

1. 10, 35

2. 4, 7, 8

Graph each inequality.

3. $x < 2$

4. $x \geq -5$

Solve each equation.

5. $3x - 5 = 4 - 2x$

6. $3(1 - x) = 6x + 11$

7. Find two whole numbers whose sum is 164 and whose difference is 12.

24. *DATA FILE 7 (pp. 272–273)* Write each as an inequality.

a. Use two inequalities to describe the passengers eligible for discounted airline fares. Let p = the age of passengers eligible for discounted fares.

b. Two times the number of passengers boarding in Miami in 1987 is less than the number boarding in Chicago/O'Hare in 1987.

DATA The circle graph at the right shows the source of energy for every 100 kilowatts (kw) of energy produced in the United States.

25. Let x and y be two sources of energy from the graph. Determine the source related to x and y based on the inequalities: $x < y$; $x + y > 10$; $xy > 200$; $y - x \geq 35$.

26. What percent of the energy is obtained from oil and natural gas?

27. *COMPUTER* How many more kilowatts of nuclear energy would be required to increase nuclear energy's share to at least 25%? Assume that the other sources of energy have the same number of kilowatts shown on the circle graph. *Hint:* use a spreadsheet and a graphics program.

28. *PROJECT* What sources of energy are not included in the graph?

Sources of Energy in the United States for Every 100 kw

Coal ⬚   Oil ⊞
Natural Gas ▨
Hydroelectric ⠿
Nuclear ⬚   Other ■

TEST YOURSELF

Solve each equation.

1. $12w = 7w + 25$

2. $8 - 3t = t - 2t - 6$

3. $(y + 6)3 + 2y = 2y + 6$

4. $12 - 2x = -(x - 4)$

Solve each inequality.

5. $y - 3 > -7$

6. $y + 4 < 8$

7. $\frac{s}{-6} > -7$

8. $7h > \frac{1}{3}$

9. $64 \leq -8k$

10. $y - (-5) > -7$

Write an inequality to describe the situation. Solve.

11. Seven less than a number is greater than negative two. Find the number.

12. When this number is divided by negative four, the result is at least 30. Find the number.

13. Negative eight is greater than or equal to a number divided by negative three. Find the number.

7-7 Solving Two-step Inequalities

▼ A research company budgeted $1,000 for an on-line computer information service. The service charges a $250 monthly service fee plus $75 for each hour of use. How many hours can the research company use the service and stay within budget?

Let h = the number of hours.
Then $250 + 75h \leq 1,000$ describes the situation.

The steps for solving a two-step inequality are similar to the steps for solving a two-step equation.

$$250 + 75h \leq 1,000$$
$$250 + 75h - 250 \leq 1,000 - 250 \qquad \text{Subtract 250 from each side.}$$
$$75h \leq 750$$
$$\frac{75h}{75} \leq \frac{750}{75} \qquad \text{Divide each side by 75.}$$
$$h \leq 10$$

The company can use the computer service for, at most, 10 h.

FLASHBACK

When multiplying by a negative number, the inequality symbol is reversed.

Example 1 Solve each inequality.

a. $6 - x > 3$

b. $\frac{1}{2}y - 3 \leq -5$

Solution **a.** $6 - x - 6 > 3 - 6$
$$-x > -3$$
$$(-1)(-x) < (-1)(-3)$$
$$x < 3$$

b. $\frac{1}{2}y - 3 + 3 \leq -5 + 3$
$$\frac{1}{2}y \leq -2$$
$$(2)\left(\frac{1}{2}y\right) \leq (2)(-2)$$
$$y \leq -4$$

▼ You can use inequalities to describe situations.

Example 2 Divide a number by -5. Then add 4 to the quotient. The result is no more than 7. Find the number.

Solution Let n = the original number.
Then $\frac{n}{-5} + 4 \leq 7$ describes the situation.

$$\frac{n}{-5} + 4 \leq 7$$

$$\frac{n}{-5} + 4 - 4 \leq 7 - 4 \qquad \text{Subtract 4 from each side.}$$

$$\frac{n}{-5} \leq 3$$

$$-5 \cdot \frac{n}{-5} \geq -5 \cdot 3 \qquad \text{Multiply each side by -5.}$$

$$n \geq -15$$

The number is greater than or equal to -15.

▼ Sometimes you will use an inequality to solve a problem with only one correct answer.

Example 3 Find the two smallest consecutive integers whose sum is greater than 55.

Solution Let i = the lesser of the two integers.
Then $i + 1$ = the next consecutive integer.
The inequality $i + i + 1 > 55$ describes the situation.

$$i + i + 1 > 55$$
$$2i + 1 > 55 \qquad \text{Combine like terms.}$$
$$2i + 1 - 1 > 55 - 1 \qquad \text{Subtract 1 from each side.}$$
$$2i > 54$$
$$\frac{2i}{2} > \frac{54}{2} \qquad \text{Divide each side by 2.}$$
$$i > 27$$

The two consecutive integers are 28 and 29.

CLASS EXERCISES

What was done to each side of the first inequality to obtain the second?

1. $2 + x \le 9;\ x \le 7$

2. $16 + x > \text{-}5;\ x > \text{-}21$

3. $\text{-}3x > 24;\ x < \text{-}8$

4. $8x - 3 \le 19;\ 8x \le 22$

Solve each inequality for x.

5. $\frac{2x}{3} + 1 > 3$

6. $4x - 1 \le 3$

7. $6x + 2 \ge 0$

8. $\frac{1}{2}x - 3 < 1$

9. $20 - 3x > 2$

10. $3x - 1 < 11$

11. $5 - (x - 1) \ge 9$

12. $\text{-}4(2x + 7) < \text{-}12$

13. $3 + x > \text{-}6$

Write an inequality to describe the situation. Solve.

14. Find the two greatest consecutive odd integers whose sum is less than -11.

WRITTEN EXERCISES

What was done to each side of the first inequality to obtain the second?

1. $8 - x \le 11;\ \text{-}x \le 3$

2. $6 + 3x > 5;\ 3x > \text{-}1$

3. $4x + 7 > 0;\ 4x > \text{-}7$

4. $\frac{2x}{5} < 2;\ x < 5$

MIXED REVIEW

**Write an equation.
Solve.**

1. Two times a number is 5 more than the number.

2. Five less than double the number is 121.

Solve and check.

3. $-2x \geq 6$

4. $\frac{1}{2}x \leq 16$

Solve for x if y is 2.

5. $x - y = 16$

6. $3x + y = 17$

7. The length of a rectangle is 5 m longer than the width. The perimeter is 40 m. What are the length and width?

Solve each inequality for variable x.

5. $\frac{x}{3} + 2 > 3$

6. $9x + 3 \geq 21$

7. $\frac{1}{2}x - 4 \geq -1$

8. $\frac{1}{2}x - \frac{1}{4} < -\frac{3}{4}$

9. $-3x + 15 < 0$

10. $2x - 9 > -7$

11. $5x \leq 15 - 8$

12. $11 - 3x > 5$

13. $6x - 10 - x > 14$

14. $8 + 2x \leq 10$

15. $-5x + 3 \geq 28$

16. $2x + x + 5 > 18$

17. $1 + 8x > 25$

18. $4 + 7x \geq 32$

19. $\frac{1}{9}x + 13 \geq 5$

20. $2x + \frac{1}{2} > \frac{3}{2}$

21. $-21 - 3x < 0$

22. $10x - 8 - x < 19$

23. $19 - 8x > -5$

24. $7 + 2x - x \geq 9$

25. $18x - 5x - 4 > 22$

26. $6 - 4x > 14$

27. $\frac{1}{3}x + 11 < 31$

28. $\frac{1}{6}x - 2 < 4$

29. $2x + 2x + 2 < 18$

30. $11x + 13 > -86$

Choose the inequality which describes the situation. Solve.

31. You divide a number by -3. Then you subtract 1 from the quotient. The result is at most 5. Find the number. (Let x = the number.)

   a. $\frac{-3}{x} - 1 < 5$
      b. $\frac{x}{-3} - 1 \leq 5$

   c. $\frac{x}{3} - 1 \leq -5$
      d. $\frac{x}{-3} - 1 > 5$

32. Laura has $16 in her savings account. She earns $4.50 per hour babysitting. Laura wants to purchase a sweater for $55. What is the least number of hours Laura must babysit in order to buy the sweater? Let x = the number of hours Laura must babysit.

   a. $16x + 4.50 \geq 55$
      b. $4.50x \geq 55 + 16$

   c. $4.50x + 16 \geq 55$
      d. $55 \geq 16 + 4.50x$

Write an inequality to describe the situation. Solve.

33. Five less than twice a number is at least 13. Find the number.

34. An artist withdrew $14 from a bank in each of the last three weeks and still has more than $65. How much did he start with?

35. Students in a math class need an average test score of at least 90 points to earn an A. A student's test scores are 88, 91, and 85. What could the student score on the next test to have an A average?

36. A salesperson earns a salary of $600 per month, plus a commission of 2% of sales. How much must the salesperson sell to have a monthly income of at least $1,700?

37. Find the least whole number solution of $6x - 19 > -7$.

38. Find the greatest integer solution of $-5x + 7 > 22$.

Write a problem that could be solved using the inequality.

39. $n + n + 2 < 15$ **40.** $50h + 40h > 360$

41. DATA FILE 10 (pp. 404–405)

    a. What is the least number of acres of rain forests cut down in an eight-hour working day?

    b. How many eight-hour days would it take to destroy an area of rain forest equivalent to the home range of a grizzly bear?

Critical Thinking

EXPLORING QUANTITATIVE COMPARISONS

▼ A *quantitative comparison* is a type of question that appears on some standardized tests. This type of question requires that you evaluate two quantities, compare them, and choose the correct lettered response. Common answer choices are listed below.

(A) The number in Column A is greater.

(B) The number in Column B is greater.

(C) The two numbers are equal.

(D) The relationship cannot be determined based on the available information.

Compare each pair of expressions. The first one is done for you.

	Column A	Column B	Response Choice
1.	$x + 2$	$x + 5$	B, no matter what replacement you choose for x, $x + 5 > x + 2$.
2.	$2x$	$5x$	▨
3.	$|-5 - 2|$	$|5| - |2|$	▨
4.	$3x$	$\frac{x}{3}$	▨
5.	$5(x - 3)$	$5x - 15$	▨
6.	$\frac{x-2}{2-x}; x \neq 2$	$4 - \sqrt{16}$	▨

Practice

Solve and check each two-step equation.

1. $6x + 4 = 40$

2. $7x - 10 = 25$

3. $57 - 11x = 13$

4. $6 + 5x = 66$

5. $\frac{2}{9}x - 9 = 45$

6. $7 - \frac{3}{5}x = 13$

7. $19 + 2x = 57$

8. $7x - 17 = -3$

9. $-21 = -6t - 3$

Solve and check each multi-step equation.

10. $8x - 20 + 2x = 60$

11. $42 = -6(5 - x)$

12. $\frac{2}{7}(x + 5) = 8$

13. $\frac{2}{3}x - \frac{1}{12}x = 4$

14. $5x - 2x + 11 = 59$

15. $19 = x + x - 7$

16. $3(3x - 8) = 21$

17. $1.5x - 0.7x = 8$

18. $18 - 3x = 4(x + 8)$

19. $6.5 - (0.1x + 2) = -1.6x$

20. $2(6 + x) = 17 - 3x$

21. $x + 9 = 2x - 43 + x$

22. $\frac{3}{4}(x - 4) = \frac{1}{4}x + 23$

23. $\frac{1}{2}(6x - 6) = \frac{1}{4}(x + 54)$

24. $8x - 7 = 2x - 1$

25. $7x + 5 = 8x - 3$

Graph each inequality.

26. $x \le -3$

27. $x < 6$

28. $x > 0$

29. $x \ge 5$

30. $x > -4$

31. $x \le 10$

Solve each inequality for x.

32. $x + 6 > 2$

33. $-2x < 8$

34. $x - 7 \le 6$

35. $\frac{1}{3}x > -6$

36. $x - \frac{1}{5} < \frac{4}{5}$

37. $6x \le 18$

38. $10 > 5x$

39. $8x \ge 32$

40. $x - 2 > 5$

41. $6 + 3x > 12$

42. $18 - 5x < -2$

43. $x + x - 7 \le 21$

44. $\frac{1}{2}x - 9 < 27$

45. $\frac{4}{5}x + 4 \ge 16$

46. $8x + 54 < 53$

Write an equation to describe the situation. Solve.

47. Martha is saving $22 each week from her paycheck. She already has $47 in her account. In how many weeks will her balance be $201?

48. Fifty-three is four times a number minus nineteen. Find the number.

49. Find four consecutive integers whose sum is -490.

50. Four times the sum of a number and five is equal to 100. Find the number.

7-8 Buying a Car

OBJECTIVE:
To apply mathematical skills when purchasing a car.

Option	Price
Air Conditioning	$744
AM/FM Radio-cassette	$155
Automatic Transmission	$732
Metallic Color	$91
Sunroof	$549

THINK What must a dealership do to a car to prepare it for sale?

■ Buying a car is one of the first major purchases an individual makes. There are several things to consider when making such an expensive purchase.

A car dealership will give you a *base price* on a car. This is the price of the car without any additional features. Additional features, or *options*, have an additional charge. The table at the left lists the cost of several options that dealers frequently offer.

Example 1 Mr. Perry wants to buy a car with automatic transmission, an AM/FM radio-cassette, and a sunroof. What is the total cost of these options?

Solution $732 + 155 + 549 = 1,436$ Add the cost of the options.

The total cost of these options is $1,436.

■ You will automatically pay a *destination* and *delivery charge* on a new car. This charge pays for the cost of shipping the car from the manufacturer and for preparing the automobile for sale. Most states require you to pay a *sales tax* on a new car.

Example 2 James is purchasing a car for $8,667. The sales tax is 6%. How much sales tax will James pay?

Solution $6\% = 0.06$ Write 6% as a decimal.
$8,667(0.06) = 520.02$ Multiply the cost of the car by 0.06.

James will pay $520.02 in sales tax.

■ Many people take out a loan to help pay for a car. They then make monthly payments. To determine the monthly payment, multiply the number of thousands of dollars being borrowed by a factor which can be found in an *amortization table* like the one shown below.

Amortization Table (per $1,000)

number of months	interest rate		
	10%	11%	12%
12	87.92	88.39	88.85
24	46.15	46.61	47.08
36	32.27	32.74	33.22
48	25.37	25.85	26.34

Example 3 What is the factor for a 10% loan over 36 mo?

Solution Find the number of months. Read across to the 10% column. The factor is 32.27.

Example 4 Lynn wants to borrow $12,000 from her bank. The bank is offering an 11% interest rate. Lynn plans to take out a 36-mo loan. What will be her monthly payment?

Solution
1. Determine the number of thousands of dollars that are being borrowed on $12,000.

   12,000 is the same as 12 thousands.

2. Find the factor on an 11% interest rate over 36 mo using the amortization table.

   32.74

3. Multiply the number of thousands of dollars being borrowed by the factor.

   $12 \cdot 32.74 = 392.88$

Lynn's monthly payment will be $392.88.

CLASS EXERCISES

Refer to the options list on page 305.

1. What would a sunroof and an AM/FM radio-cassette cost?

2. How much sales tax must you pay on a $10,000 car at 6%?

3. How many thousands are in $14,500?

4. What is the factor on a loan at 12% interest over 48 mo?

■■■■■■ Decision Making ■ **DECISION MAKING** ■ Decision Making ■ Decision Making ■ Decision Making ■

BUYING A CAR

■ **COLLECT DATA**

1. Choose a car you would like to own. Interview salespeople at three dealerships. Organize your data in a chart.

Dealership	base price	options	price of options	dest/del charge

2. Find out the sales tax in your state.

3. Contact three banks in your area and find out what interest rates they offer on new car loans.

■ **ANALYZE DATA**

The base price of a car includes the dealership's profit.

4. Did the base prices on the car you chose vary?

WRITTEN EXERCISES

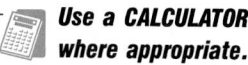
Use a **CALCULATOR**
where appropriate.

Determine the sales tax on each amount at a rate of 6%.

1. $8,675   **2.** $7,988   **3.** $16,654   **4.** $12,560

Determine how many thousands each amount represents.

5. $9,000   **6.** $8,500   **7.** $11,750   **8.** $14,250

Determine each factor using the amortization table on page 305.

9. a loan at 12% over 24 mo   **10.** a loan at 11% over 48 mo

11. Gerald wants to buy a car with a base price of $9,518. The car is metallic black. Gerald is having a sunroof installed. The destination and delivery charge is $342.

    a. Gerald has enough money saved to pay for the sales tax. How much sales tax will Gerald pay at a rate of 6%?

    b. Gerald took out a loan at 10% over 48 mo for the remaining cost of the car. What will he pay per month?

12. Alicia bought a car with a base price of $14,670. She had an AM/FM radio-cassette installed. The destination and delivery charge was $397. Alicia paid 5% sales tax. She withdrew $4,483.10 from her savings and took out a 12% loan over 36 mo for the rest. What does Alicia pay per month?

■ *Decision Making* ■ *Decision Making* ■ *Decision Making* ■ *Decision Making* ■ *Decision Making* ■ *Decision Making* ■

5. Why might one dealership offer a lower base price than another?

6. Did the prices on the options you chose vary from place to place?

7. Is there a relationship between the base price that a dealership offered and the price that they charged for the options?

8. Why might loan rates differ at different banks?

■ **MAKE DECISIONS**

Suppose you are buying the car of your choice. You may add any options. You have enough money saved for sales tax.

9. What is the price of the car, including the options you chose, the destination and delivery charge, and sales tax?

10. Determine what your monthly payment would be if you took out a loan for the full amount needed at 11.5% over 48 mo.

11. How much did you pay the bank for their loan service?

7-8 Buying a Car

Complete each statement. Use the vocabulary words given.

VOCABULARY

negative
combine
operations
distributive
equation
not equal

1. A two-step equation involves two ▪.

2. To solve $3(x + 2) - 2x$, first remove the parentheses using the ▪ property.

3. To solve $2x - 3 + 4x = x + 2 - 3x$, first ▪ like terms.

4. An inequality is a statement that two expressions are ▪.

5. If c is ▪ and $a > b$, then $ac < bc$.

6. The steps for solving a two-step inequality are similar to the steps for solving a two-step ▪.

Two-step Equations 7-1

To solve a two-step equation,   **1.** undo addition and subtraction;
   2. undo multiplication and division.

Solve each equation.

7.

8.

9. $5a + 3 = 28$

10. $\frac{x}{4} - 9 = -6$

11. $7n - 2 = 19$

12. $\frac{5b}{6} + 7 = 22$

Simplifying and Solving Equations 7-2

To solve a multi-step equation,   **1.** remove parentheses using the distributive property;
   2. combine like terms;
   3. undo addition and subtraction;
   4. undo multiplication and division.

Solve each equation.

13. $3(x - 5) + 2x = 20$

14. $2x - 8 - 3x = 2$

15. $(2x - 1)2 + 5x = 1$

16. $9 - 5x + 1 = 15$

17. $5(x + 2) - 3x = 38$

18. $8x + 5 - 5x = 3$

Problem Solving Strategy: Writing Equations 7-3

To write an equation for a word problem, you need to recognize words that imply the variable(s), the operation(s), and the equality.

Solve.

19. The difference between 3 times n and 2 times the quantity $n + 5$ is 3. Find n.

20. A sweater cost $12 more than a shirt. The total cost of two sweaters and three shirts is $144. Find the cost of the shirt.

Equations with Variables on Both Sides   7-4

To solve equations with variables on each side,

    1. use the distributive property to remove parentheses;
    2. combine like terms;
    3. use the addition and subtraction property so that all variables
       are on one side and constants on the other;
    4. use the multiplication and division property.

Solve each equation.

21.

22. $3x + 5 = 7x - 11$

23. $n + 3(n - 2) = 5n + 4$

Inequalities and Their Graphs   7-5

To graph an inequality, use an open dot for $>$ and $<$, use a closed
dot for $\geq$ and $\leq$. If the symbol is $>$ or $\geq$, graph all points to the right
of the boundary. If the symbol is $<$ or $\leq$, graph all points to the left
of the boundary.

Match each inequality with the appropriate graph.

a. 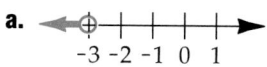   **b.** 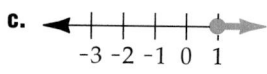   **c.** 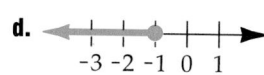   **d.**

24. $x \geq 1$ **25.** $x < -3$ **26.** $x > -3$ **27.** $x \leq -1$

Solving One-step Inequalities   7-6

To solve an addition or subtraction inequality, add or subtract the
same value from both sides of the inequality.

To solve a multiplication or division inequality, multiply or divide
both sides of the inequality by the same nonzero value. If the value is
positive, keep the inequality symbol. If the value is negative, reverse
the inequality symbol.

Solve each inequality.

28. $x - 3 < -8$ **29.** $x + 2 \geq -1$ **30.** $-3x > 12$ **31.** $\frac{x}{4} \leq -2$

Solving Two-step Inequalities   7-7

To solve a simple two-step inequality,   **1.** undo addition and subtraction;
                                                2. undo multiplication and division.

Solve each inequality.

32. $5x - 7 \leq 18$ **33.** $2y + 4 > 12$ **34.** $\frac{b}{-3} + 5 > 8$ **35.** $\frac{2a}{3} - 1 < 7$

Chapter 7   Test

Solve each equation.

1.

2.

3.

4. $5x + 9 = -6$

5. $0.5 + 2n = 3$

6. $\frac{3}{4}y - 5 = 7$

7. $7p - 3 = 18$

8. $-3(b - 6) = 27$

9. $1.5(c + 2) = 6$

10. $7z + 8 - 2z = 23$

11. $5x - 9 = 3x$

12. $2(6 - 2x) = 5x - 6$

Write an equation to describe each situation. Solve.

13. Kendra bought a scarf for $35.75. The original price was $55. What was the percent discount?

14. The perimeter of a rectangle is 132 cm. The length is 3 cm more than twice the width. Find the length and width.

Match each inequality with the appropriate graph.

15. $x \geq 2$

   a. ![number line with closed circle at 2 shaded left, -3 to 3]

16. $x > -2$

   b. ![number line with open circle at -2 shaded right, -3 to 3]

17. $x > 2$

   c. ![number line with closed circle at 2 shaded right, -3 to 3]

18. $x \leq -2$

   d. ![number line with open circle at 2 shaded right, -3 to 3]

Solve each inequality.

19. $5 \leq x + 1$

20. $3a > 4$

21. $y - 6 < 9$

22. $-2n \leq 10$

23. $\frac{b}{3} \geq \frac{1}{3}$

24. $\frac{p}{-2} < -5$

25. $-2x + 14 < 6$

26. $9y - 8 > -17$

27. $\frac{1}{5}c - 1 \geq 2$

28. $-9 + 6r \leq -33$

29. $-7m + 6 < 48$

30. $9k + 5 > -67$

Write an inequality for each sentence. Graph each inequality.

31. The total, t, is greater than 5.

32. The perimeter, p, is less than 64.

33. The number of passengers, p, on the bus is less than or equal to 45.

34. The number of students, s, that ran in the road race was not less than 55.

35. The number of questions, q, answered correctly is less than or equal to 35.

Chapters 1–7 Cumulative Review

Choose the correct answer. Write A, B, C, or D.

1. Write an equation for the model.

    A. $2x + 3 = 4$ **B.** $2x - 3 = 4$

    C. $2x = 3 - 4$ **D.** not given

2. What is the prime factorization of 108?

    A. $2 \cdot 3$ **B.** $2^3 \cdot 3^2$

    C. $2^2 \cdot 3^3$ **D.** not given

3. Solve $\frac{10}{15} = \frac{x}{3}$.

    A. 2   **B.** $\frac{1}{2}$

    C. 5   **D.** not given

4. Write $\frac{3a^3b}{12ac^2}$ in lowest terms.

    A. $\frac{3ab}{4ac}$ **B.** $\frac{ab}{4c}$

    C. $\frac{a^2b}{4c^2}$ **D.** not given

5. Solve $3x - 1 + 2x = x + 11$.

    A. 3   **B.** 2

    C. 0   **D.** not given

6. Write 0.0050 as a percent.

    A. 50%   **B.** 5%

    C. 0.5%   **D.** not given

7. Find the next number.
0.5, 1.2, 2, 2.9, 3.9, . . .

    A. 4.9   **B.** 4

    C. 5   **D.** not given

8. Count the number of squares.

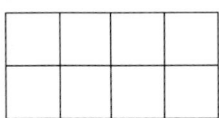

    A. 8   **B.** 11

    C. 10   **D.** not given

9. Simplify $x^2(x - 24)$.

    A. $x^3 - x^2y$ **B.** $x^3 - 2x^2y$

    C. $x^3 - 2y^2$ **D.** not given

10. Find a number between $-1\frac{1}{2}$ and -2.

    A. $-\frac{3}{4}$ **B.** $-1\frac{1}{4}$

    C. $-1\frac{3}{4}$ **D.** not given

11. What percent is 35 of 105?

    A. 3%   **B.** 33%

    C. $33\frac{1}{3}\%$ **D.** not given

12. If c is negative and $a < b$, then

    A. $ac > bc$ **B.** $ac < bc$

    C. $ac \leq bc$ **D.** not given

13. Simplify $(a^2b^3)^2(ab^2)$.

    A. a^5b^7 **B.** a^5b^8

    C. a^3b^5 **D.** not given

14. There are 12 students that belong to the Math Club and 18 that belong to the Science Club. There are 5 students that belong to both clubs. How many notices need to be printed for a joint meeting?

    A. 30   **B.** 13

    C. 7   **D.** not given

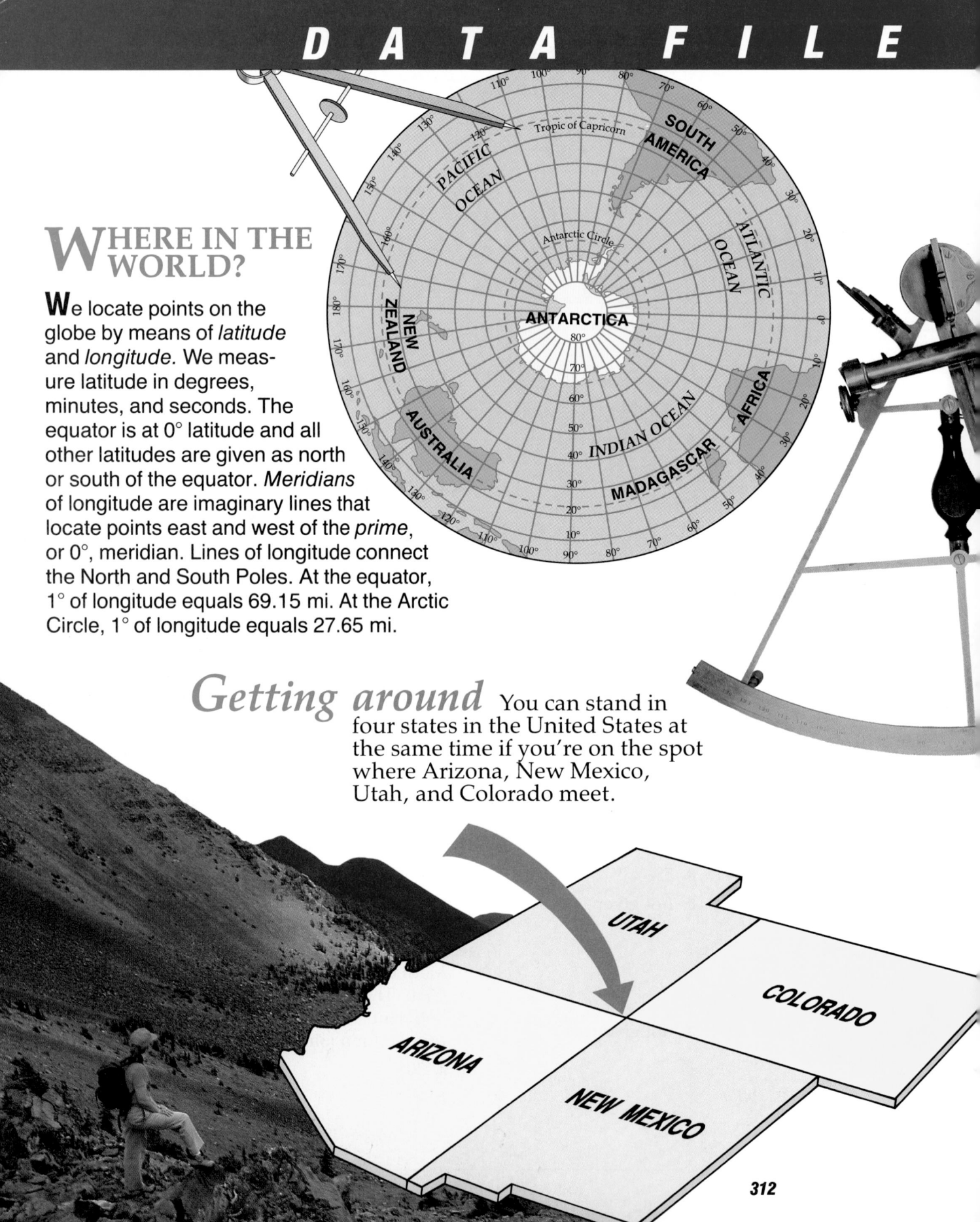

WHERE IN THE WORLD?

We locate points on the globe by means of *latitude* and *longitude.* We measure latitude in degrees, minutes, and seconds. The equator is at 0° latitude and all other latitudes are given as north or south of the equator. *Meridians* of longitude are imaginary lines that locate points east and west of the *prime*, or 0°, meridian. Lines of longitude connect the North and South Poles. At the equator, 1° of longitude equals 69.15 mi. At the Arctic Circle, 1° of longitude equals 27.65 mi.

Getting around You can stand in four states in the United States at the same time if you're on the spot where Arizona, New Mexico, Utah, and Colorado meet.

Graphing in the Coordinate Plane

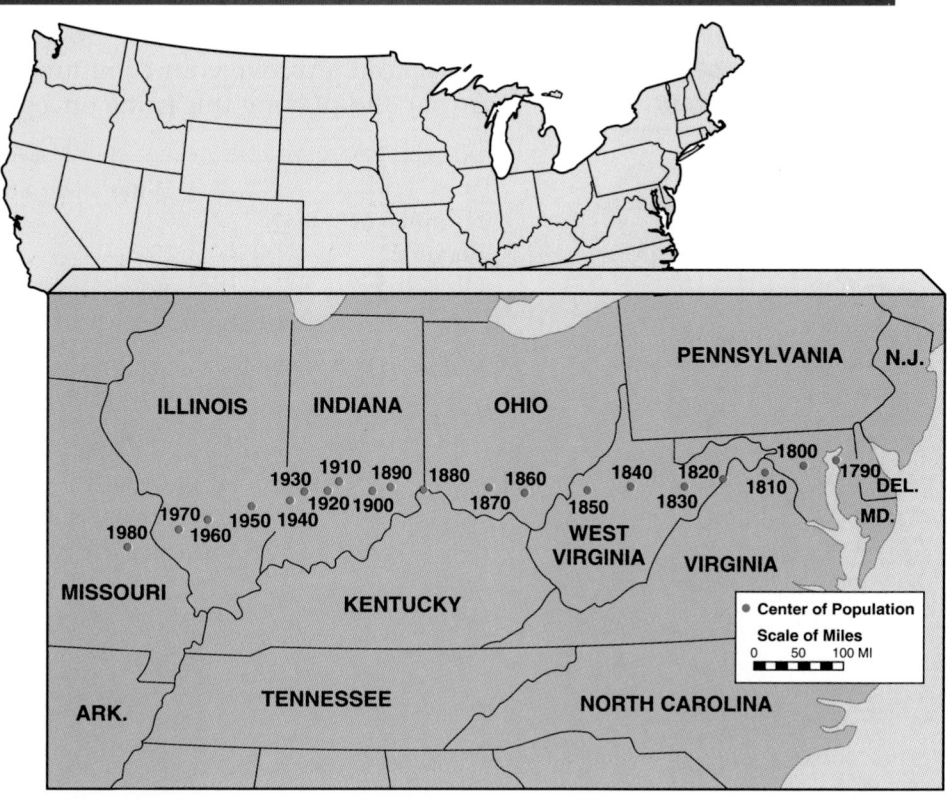

UNITED STATES CENSUS DATA	
YEAR	POPULATION
1790	3,929,214
1800	5,308,483
1810	7,239,881
1820	9,638,453
1830	12,866,020
1840	17,069,453
1850	23,191,876
1860	31,443,321
1870	39,818,449
1880	50,155,783
1890	62,947,714
1900	75,994,575
1910	91,972,266
1920	105,710,620
1930	122,775,046
1940	131,669,275
1950	150,697,361
1960	179,323,175
1970	203,302,031
1980	226,545,805
1990	249,632,692

THE CENTER OF POPULATION is the point in the United States at which the population is evenly balanced. This means that if the country were flat, and everyone had the same weight, the country would exactly balance at the center of population.

Think about it...

Look at the Center of Population map. Why do you think the center of population moves? Do you think the center of population will ever stop moving west?

OBJECTIVE:
To explore communication problems.

Exploring Verbal Communication

▼   Oral communication is an important tool. It involves an accurate portrayal of a situation by the speaker and careful analysis by the listener.

MATERIALS

• Geoboard

• Math journal to record work

▼   You can improve your communication skills by choosing a partner and playing this game on a geoboard.

What's My Shape?

Number of Players:	2
Objective:	Each player will end up with the same shape in the same location on their geoboard.
Rules:	**1.** Players sit back-to-back so that neither player can see the other's geoboard.

2. Player 1 creates a shape on the geoboard using a rubber band. The rubber band may not intersect itself and it may not double back. Examples are shown below.

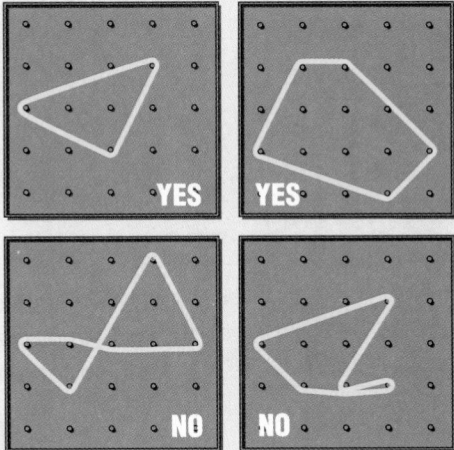

3. Player 1 describes the shape to player 2.

4. Player 2 listens carefully to the description and tries to duplicate the shape in the correct location on his or her geoboard.

5. Player 2 may ask player 1 to repeat the instructions, but may not ask any other questions.

6. After player 2 has completed the shape, both players turn around and compare the shapes on their geoboards.

1. **Write** a description of the method player 1 used to communicate the location of the points on the geoboard. Include answers to the following questions in your description.

   a. Did player 1 give instructions to move right or left?

   b. Did player 1 give instructions to move up or down?

   c. Did player 1 refer to columns and rows?

2. a. **Describe** some of the problems player 1 had in describing the shape and location.

   b. **Explain** how player 1 could improve his or her oral communication skills.

3. **Describe** some of the problems player 2 had in interpreting player 1's instructions.

4. Together, write a set of clear instructions so that the shape and location can be duplicated without any problem.

5. Reverse roles and repeat the activity. Answer Questions 1–4.

▼ Good communication skills are necessary when you are giving directions to someone.

6. a. **Explain** how playing this game is similar to giving directions to get from your school to your home.

   b. **Explain** how it is different.

   c. **Write** a clear set of instructions telling someone how to get from your school to your home.

   d. **DATA FILE 1 (pp. 2–3) Write** a clear set of instructions telling someone how to use the wind chill chart to determine the degree of danger of frostbite if the air temperature is -15°F and the wind speed is 25 mi/h.

▼ You can try other games to improve listening skills.

7. One student reads a short news article to the listener. The listener writes a short paragraph describing what he or she heard.

   a. **Compare** what is written with the original article.

   b. **Explain** how the listener can improve his or her listening skills.

8. Form a group of ten students. One student whispers the contents of a short newspaper story to another. That student whispers to another what he or she heard. Repeat the process until the last student has heard the story. That student then relates the story he or she heard to the group.

   a. **Compare** the accuracy of the last story with the original.

   b. **Describe** how the group can improve its communication skills.

OBJECTIVE:
To locate and graph a point given the coordinates and to identify the coordinates of a given point.

8-1 The Coordinate Plane

▼ Mapmakers use letters and numbers to designate regions on maps. According to the index, Southeastern Avenue in Indianapolis, Indiana, is in Region B2.

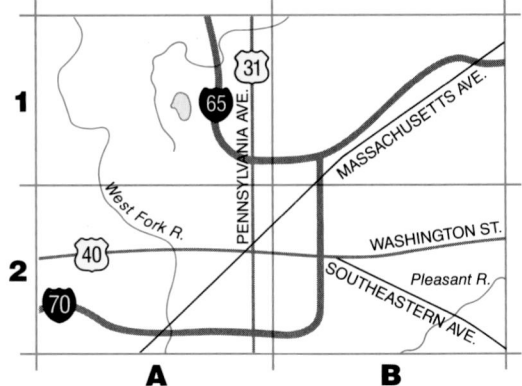

Benjamin Banneker (1731–1806) was a famous mathematician, astronomer, and surveyor. In 1791 he was asked by President George Washington to help plan the streets and buildings of the nation's new capital, Washington, D.C.

▼ Mathematicians represent a region using a *coordinate plane*.

Coordinate Plane	A coordinate plane is the plane which results when two perpendicular number lines intersect at their zero points. The number lines form a grid on the plane.

▼ We call the horizontal number line the *x-axis*, with the positive direction to the right. We call the vertical number line the *y-axis*, with the positive direction upward. The *x*- and *y*-axes intersect at the *origin*. The *x*- and *y*-axes divide the coordinate plane into four *quadrants*.

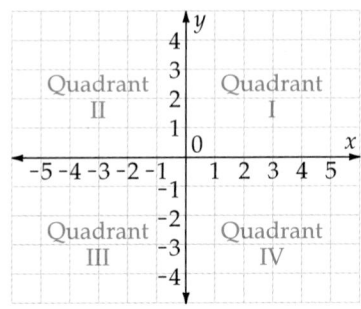

▼ We use *ordered pairs* to locate points in the coordinate plane.

Ordered Pair	An ordered pair is a pair of numbers (x,y) assigned to a point on a coordinate plane.

In the ordered pair (x,y), the value that corresponds with x is called the *x*-coordinate. The value that corresponds with y is called the *y*-coordinate. You can locate a point on the coordinate plane when given an ordered pair.

FLASHBACK

The absolute value of a number is its distance from zero on a number line.

Locating a Point on the Coordinate Plane	To locate $P(x,y)$ on the coordinate plane: 1. Begin at origin. 2. Locate x on the *x*-axis. 3. Move up or down the absolute value of y units.

▼ Use the coordinate plane below for the examples.

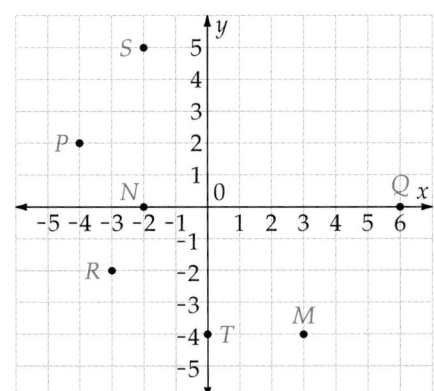

Example 1 **Locate each point on the coordinate plane. State the letter of the point.**

    a. $(-2,5)$ **b.** $(0,-4)$ **c.** $(-3,-2)$ **d.** $(6,0)$

Solution   **a.** Start at the origin. Move 2 units left and up 5. S

    b. Start at the origin. Move zero units left or right and 4 units down. T

    c. Start at the origin. Move 3 units left and 2 units down. R

    d. Start at the origin. Move 6 units right and zero units up or down. Q

▼ Identifying the quadrant in which a point falls is similar to identifying a region on a map.

Example 2 **In which quadrant or on which axis does each point fall?**

    a. $(2,6)$ **b.** $(-4,0)$ **c.** $(0,0)$

    d. $(3,-1)$ **e.** $(-5,-2)$ **f.** $(0,5)$

Solution   **a.** quadrant I   **b.** x-axis   **c.** both axes

    d. quadrant IV   **e.** quadrant III   **f.** y-axis

▼ You can use an ordered pair to locate a point on the coordinate plane.

Example 3 **Name the coordinates of each point.**

    a. point M **b.** point P **c.** point N

Solution   **a.** Point M is 3 units to the right (positive) of the origin and 4 down (negative). The ordered pair is $(3,-4)$.

    b. Point P is 4 units to the left (negative) of the origin and 2 units up (positive). The ordered pair is $(-4,2)$.

    c. Point N is 2 units to the left (negative) of the origin and zero units up or down. The ordered pair is $(-2, 0)$.

CLASS EXERCISES

State the letter of the point
named by each ordered pair.

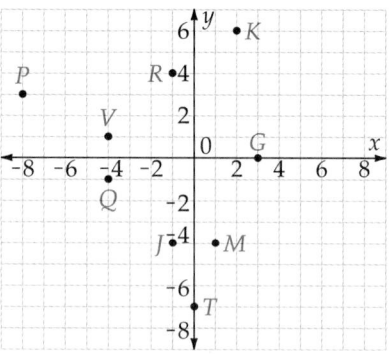

1. $(-1,-4)$ **2.** $(3,0)$

3. $(-1,4)$ **4.** $(-4,-1)$

State the coordinates of each point.

5. T **6.** V

7. M **8.** K

MENTAL MATH State the coordinates of each point described.

9. the point which is 5 units to the left of the y-axis and down
2 units from the x-axis

10. the point on the y-axis that is 4 units below the x-axis

In which quadrant or on which axis does each point fall?

11. $(-2.6, 3.4)$ **12.** $\left(5\frac{1}{4}, 2\frac{1}{2}\right)$ **13.** $\left(0, -4\frac{2}{3}\right)$ **14.** $(1.36, 19.41)$

15. $P(-1,3)$, $Q(4,3)$, and $R(4,-2)$ are three vertices of a square. Find the
coordinates of the fourth vertex.

THINK AND DISCUSS

1. What ordered pair
names the origin?

2. Describe how to locate
point $Q(4,-3)$.

3. Do (a,b) and (b,a)
describe the same point?
Assume that a and b are
not the same number.
Explain.

4. Complete: $P(a,b)$ is in
quadrant II. The value of a
must be ▦. The value of b
must be ▦.

WRITTEN EXERCISES

State the letter of the point
named by each ordered pair.

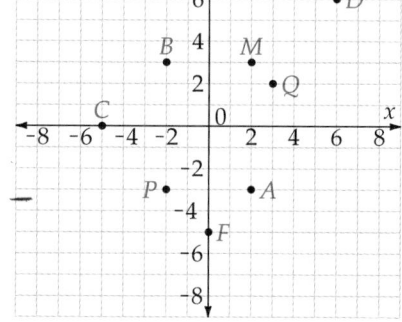

1. $(3,2)$ **2.** $(0,-5)$

3. $(2,3)$ **4.** $(-2,-3)$

State the coordinates of each point.

5. A **6.** B

7. C **8.** D

Draw a coordinate plane. Graph each point.

9. $F(-3,2)$ **10.** $G(-1.5,0)$ **11.** $H(1,7)$ **12.** $J(-3.5,-4)$

13. $K(5,-6)$ **14.** $L(0,0)$ **15.** $M\left(\frac{1}{2},3\right)$ **16.** $N(7,0)$

17. State the coordinates of four points in the coordinate plane that
are 3 units from the origin.

MENTAL MATH State in which quadrant or on which axis $P(x,y)$ lies if the following conditions are true.

18. x is negative and y is zero.

19. x is positive and y is negative.

20. x is positive and y is positive.

21. x is negative and y is positive.

22. x is negative and y is negative.

In which quadrant or on which axis does each point fall?

23. $(13,25)$

24. $(-17.654,-0.02)$

25. $(0,|-2|)$

26. (x,y) if $x > 0$, $y < 0$

27. (x,y) if $x < 0$, $y < 0$

28. (x,y) if $x = 0$, $y > 0$

Graph and connect each point in the order given. Connect the last point to the first. Name the figure.

29. $(-1,2)$, $(1,5)$, $(7,5)$, $(5,2)$

30. $(2,2)$, $(2,-1)$, $(-5,-1)$, $(-5,2)$

31. $(-4,1)$, $(1,1)$, $(-3,-1)$

32. $(2,-4)$, $(7,-1)$, $(4,4)$, $(-1,1)$

33. $P(0,5)$, $Q(5,0)$, and $R(-5,0)$ are three vertices of a square. Find the coordinates of the fourth vertex.

34. PROJECT Draw a dot-to-dot picture on a coordinate grid. Write the coordinates of each point in order. Exchange with a classmate and draw each other's picture.

MIXED REVIEW

Solve for y.

1. $4.5 + 7y = 18.5$

2. $5a - 10 = 30$

Solve for x.

3. $-3x + 8 > 29$

4. $\frac{2}{3}x - 19 \leq -13$

Solve for y if x = 3.

5. $7x + y = 24$

6. $21x + 2y = -7$

Solve.

7. The perimeter of a rectangle is 62 in. Its length is twice its width, less 5 in. Find the actual length and width.

Critical Thinking

EXPLORING GRAPHING

1. *Describe* what you think will happen to a figure if you perform an operation on one or both coordinates of each point.

2. Graph the points $(-2,1)$, $(-2,3)$, $(1,3)$, $(1,1)$. Connect them in the order given. Connect the last point to the first.

3. Find the new coordinates and graph.

  a. Multiply each x-coordinate by -1.

  b. Multiply each y-coordinate by -1.

  c. Multiply each coordinate by -1.

  d. Multiply each coordinate by 2.

4. *Compare* the figures in Exercise 3. ***Write*** a short paragraph describing your results.

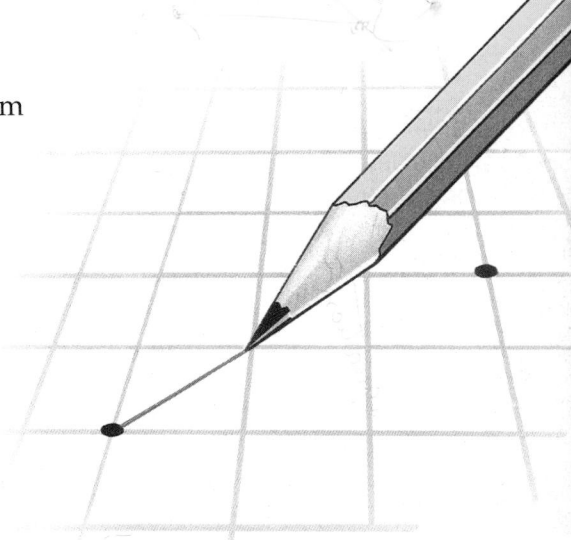

OBJECTIVE:
To solve linear
equations in two
variables.

8-2 Solving Equations

▼ The normal low temperature at the base of Mt. Rushmore in July is 21°C. The temperature drops an average of 1°C for every 100 m of vertical ascent. You can write an equation using two variables to describe this situation. Let y = temperature and let x = meters above the foot of the mountain.

$$y = 21 - 0.01x$$

▼ An ordered pair that makes an equation in two variables a true statement is a *solution* of the equation.

Example 1 **Tell whether each ordered pair is a solution for the equation $y = 21 - 0.01x$.**

    a. (300,18)   **b.** (500,15)

Solution Substitute the first number of each ordered pair for x and the second number for y.

a.	b.
$y = 21 - 0.01x$	$y = 21 - 0.01x$
$18 = 21 - 0.01(300)$	$15 = 21 - 0.01(500)$
$18 = 21 - 3$	$15 = 21 - 5$
$18 = 18$ ✓	$15 = 16$ ✗

True, so the ordered pair (300,18) is a solution.

False, so the ordered pair (500,15) is not a solution.

What is the average temperature 300 m above the base of Mt. Rushmore in July?

THINK Why is it sometimes helpful to choose 0 as a value for x?

▼ You can find solutions for an equation with two variables by using a table to organize your data.

Example 2 **Find three solutions to the equation $y = 3x + 6$.**

Solution
1. Choose three values for x. Try -3, 0, and 4.
2. Use a table to organize your data.
3. Substitute x values into the equation to find y values.

x	y	(x,y)
-3	▓	(▓,▓)
0	▓	(▓,▓)
4	▓	(▓,▓)

$y = 3x + 6$	$y = 3x + 6$	$y = 3x + 6$
$y = 3(-3) + 6$	$y = 3(0) + 6$	$y = 3(4) + 6$
$y = -9 + 6$	$y = 0 + 6$	$y = 12 + 6$
$y = -3$	$y = 6$	$y = 18$

The ordered pairs (-3,-3), (0,6), and (4,18) are solutions.

▼ You may need to solve an equation for y in order to find solutions of the equation.

Example 3 Solve the equation $3x + 5y = 30$ for y in terms of x.

Solution

$$3x + 5y = 30$$
$$3x + 5y - 3x = 30 - 3x \qquad \text{Subtract 3x from each side.}$$
$$5y = 30 - 3x$$
$$\frac{5y}{5} = \frac{30 - 3x}{5} \qquad \text{Divide each side by 5.}$$
$$y = \frac{30}{5} - \frac{3x}{5}$$
$$y = 6 - \frac{3}{5}x$$
$$y = -\frac{3}{5}x + 6 \qquad \leftarrow \textit{linear equation}$$

> **FLASHBACK**
>
> Solving an equation for a specific variable means to isolate that variable on one side of the equation.

Example 4 Find three solutions of the equation $4x - \frac{2}{3}y = 6$.

Solution

1. Solve for y in terms of x.

$$4x - \frac{2}{3}y = 6$$
$$3\left(4x - \frac{2}{3}y\right) = 6(3) \qquad \text{Multiply each side by 3.}$$
$$12x - 2y = 18$$
$$12x - 2y - 12x = 18 - 12x \qquad \text{Subtract 12x from each side.}$$
$$-2y = 18 - 12x$$
$$\frac{-2y}{-2} = \frac{18 - 12x}{-2} \qquad \text{Divide each side by -2.}$$
$$y = \frac{18}{-2} + \frac{-12x}{-2}$$
$$= -9 + 6x$$
$$= 6x - 9$$

2. Find three solutions of the equation $y = 6x - 9$.

   a. Choose three values for x. Try -3, 0, and 2.

   b. Use a table to organize your data.

x	y	(x,y)
-3	▨	(▨,▨)
0	▨	(▨,▨)
2	▨	(▨,▨)

   c. Substitute x values into the equation to find y values.

$y = 6x - 9$	$y = 6x - 9$	$y = 6x - 9$
$y = 6(-3) - 9$	$y = 6(0) - 9$	$y = 6(2) - 9$
$y = -18 - 9$	$y = 0 - 9$	$y = 12 - 9$
$y = -27$	$y = -9$	$y = 3$

   The ordered pairs $(-3,-27)$, $(0,-9)$, and $(2,3)$ are solutions of the equation $y = 6x - 9$.

THINK AND DISCUSS

1. How is a table helpful in determining ordered pair solutions?

2. How can you clear the decimals in $0.25x + 0.75y = 6.75$?

3. Find the value of k that makes the given point a solution of the equation:

a. $x + ky = 6$; $(-3,3)$

b. $x - ky = 12$; $(4,2)$

CLASS EXERCISES

Tell whether each ordered pair is a solution of $4x - 3y = 6$.

1. $(5,7)$ 2. $(3,2)$ 3. $(0.5,-1.3)$

Find the value of y that corresponds to each value of x for the equation $6x + 2y = 12$.

4. $x = -3$ 5. $x = 2.5$ 6. $x = 0$

Solve for y in terms of x.

7. $-5x + \frac{y}{3} = 9$ 8. $-4x - 0.5y = -2$ 9. $\frac{1}{4}x + \frac{1}{4}y = \frac{1}{2}y$

Find four solutions for each equation.

10. $x - y = 9$ 11. $3x + y = 12$ 12. $3x + y = 24$

MIXED REVIEW

Solve.

1. $5x + 9 = 6x + 25$

2. $12 - \frac{3}{4}y = 34 + 2y$

3. Graph $(-1,3)$, $(2,0)$, and $(1,1)$ in the coordinate plane.

4. In the third quadrant, the x-coordinate is always ■ and the y-coordinate is always ■.

5. Write three ordered pairs whose y-coordinate is twice the x-coordinate.

6. Name the coordinates of the point on the y-axis 8 units above the x-axis.

7. A student gets out of bed and spends 48 min getting ready for school, 25 min walking to school, and 55 min in her first class. The class ends at 9:25 A.M. At what time did the student get up?

WRITTEN EXERCISES

MENTAL MATH Is each ordered pair a solution of $x + 2y = 57$?

1. $(5,0)$ 2. $(-1,28)$ 3. $(57,0)$

MENTAL MATH Is each ordered pair a solution of $x + 2y = 5$?

4. $(-1,2)$ 5. $(-3,4)$ 6. $(2,-3)$

CALCULATOR Is each ordered pair a solution of $x + 2y = 5$?

7. $(1.2,1.9)$ 8. $(-4.5,4.5)$ 9. $(13.2,4.1)$

Find the value of y that corresponds to each value of x.

10. $3x - 4y = 24$ if $x = -2$ 11. $5 - y = \frac{1}{2}x$ if $x = 12$

12. $2x + y = 5$ if $x = 2$ 13. $x + 8y + 6 = 0$ if $x = -22$

14. $2.9x + 2y = 5$ if $x = 0$ 15. $0.25x + 0.5y = 6.75$ if $x = 4$

Solve for y in terms of x.

16. $x = 11 - 3y$ 17. $x + y - 5 = 4x$

18. $5x + 3y = 2x - 10$ 19. $2(x - y) = -x + 10$

20. $x - y - 8 = 6(2x + 4)$ 21. $7y - x - 1 = y - (2x + 1)$

Solve for y in terms of x. Find four solutions of each equation.

22. $4x + \frac{1}{2}y = 3$ 23. $x + 2y = -5$ 24. $3x - y = -1$

25. $2x - 3y = 12$ 26. $x + y = 32$ 27. $x + 4y = 16$

28. PROJECT Many situations rely on coordinate systems. As you press B5 in a vending machine, the letter refers to a row of items and the number to a position in the row. Find other examples in which a coordinate system is used to locate positions. Write the results in your math journal.

Use the article below to answer each question.

Mountains Under the Sea

A mountain range exists in the Pacific Ocean, far, far beneath the surface of the water. In 1960, Jacque Piccard and Donald Walsh made a record dive in these mountains at the site of the Marianas Trench. Piccard and Walsh descended to 10,916 m. The depth of the dive is remarkable because of the tremendous amount of pressure that exists at these depths. The pressure of the air at sea level is 1 kg/cm², but it increases 0.1 kg/cm² for every meter an object descends in salt water.

29. The equation $P = 1 + 0.1x$ gives the pressure in kg/cm² at x m below sea level.

  a. Find four possible solutions for this equation.

  b. Find the pressure at the record-breaking depth achieved by Piccard and Walsh.

  c. *DATA FILE 10 (pp. 404–405)* Find the pressure at the greatest known depth of the Atlantic Ocean.

TEST YOURSELF

State the letter of the point named by each ordered pair.

1. (–3,3)

2. (0,–2)

3. (–2,1)

4. (–3,0)

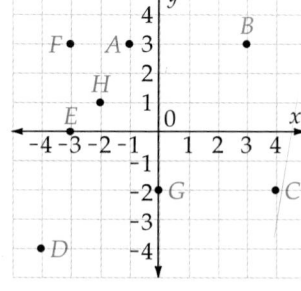

State the coordinates of each point.

5. A

6. B

7. C

8. D

Solve for y in terms of x. Find three solutions of each equation.

9. $3x + 2y = 4$

10. $\frac{1}{2}x + y = -3$

11. $x + 3y = 7$

8-3 Graphing Linear Equations

ph a linear
ation and find x
nd y-intercepts.

▼ You can graph an equation to show the solutions.

Example 1 **Graph the equation $2x + y = 3$.**

Solution **1.** Solve for y in terms of x.

$$2x + y = 3$$
$$2x + y - 2x = 3 - 2x$$
$$y = 3 - 2x$$
$$y = -2x + 3$$

2. Find three solutions to the equation.

a. Choose three values. Try -1, 0, and 2.

b. Use a table to organize your data.

x	y	(x,y)
-1	▨	(▨,▨)
0	▨	(▨,▨)
2	▨	(▨,▨)

c. Substitute each x value into the equation to find y.

$y = -2x + 3$	$y = -2x + 3$	$y = -2x + 3$
$y = -2(-1) + 3$	$y = -2(0) + 3$	$y = -2(2) + 3$
$y = 2 + 3$	$y = 0 + 3$	$y = -4 + 3$
$y = 5$	$y = 3$	$y = -1$

Three solutions are $(-1,5)$, $(0,3)$, and $(2,-1)$.

3. Graph the points. Draw a line connecting them.

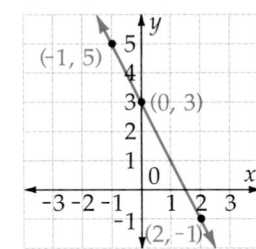

Each ordered pair on the graph is a solution of the linear equation $2x + y = 3$.

THINK How many points must you have to draw a line?

▼ We call the equations you have been solving *linear equations*.

Linear Equation	A linear equation is an equation for which the graph is a line. The standard form of a linear equation is $Ax + By = C$, where A, B, and C are real numbers and A and B are not both equal to zero.

Example 2 **Write each linear equation in standard form.**

a. $x = 12 - 2y$ **b.** $x + y - 2 = 0$

Solution

a.
$$x = 12 - 2y$$
$$x + 2y = 12 - 2y + 2y$$
$$x + 2y = 12$$

b.
$$x + y - 2 = 0$$
$$x + y - 2 + 2 = 0 + 2$$
$$x + y = 2$$

Example 3   Is the point (6,1) on the graph of $x - 2y = 4$?

Solution

$$x - 2y = 4 \qquad \text{Substitute 6 for } x \text{ and 1 for } y.$$
$$6 - 2(1) = 4$$
$$6 - 2 = 4$$
$$4 = 4\checkmark$$

True, so (6,1) is on the graph of $x - 2y = 4$.

▼ You can use the x- and y-intercepts when graphing an equation.

x-intercept	The x-intercept is the x-coordinate of a point where a graph crosses the x-axis.

y-intercept	The y-intercept is the y-coordinate of a point where a graph crosses the y-axis.

Example 4   **Find the x-intercept and the y-intercept for the equation $2x - 3y = 12$. Use the intercepts to sketch the graph.**

Solution

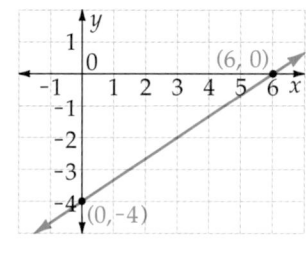

To find the x-intercept, substitute 0 for y.

$$2x - 3y = 12$$
$$2x - 3(0) = 12$$
$$2x - 0 = 12$$
$$2x = 12$$
$$\frac{2x}{2} = \frac{12}{2}$$
$$x = 6$$

The x-intercept is 6.

To find the y-intercept, substitute 0 for x.

$$2x - 3y = 12$$
$$2(0) - 3y = 12$$
$$0 - 3y = 12$$
$$-3y = 12$$
$$\frac{-3y}{-3} = \frac{12}{-3}$$
$$y = -4$$

The y-intercept is -4.

▼ You can graph an equation which contains only one variable.

Example 5   **Graph each equation on the same coordinate plane.**

a. $4x = 12$ **b.** $3y = -6$

Solution

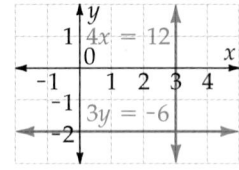

a. When you solve this equation for x, you get $x = 3$. Any ordered pair having an x-coordinate equal to 3 will be a solution.

b. When you solve this equation for y, you get $y = -2$. Any ordered pair having a y-coordinate equal to -2 will be a solution.

▼
THINK What are two solutions of the equation $4x = 12$? of the equation $3y = -6$?

CLASS EXERCISES

The figure at the right shows the graph of the equation $y = 3x - 2$.

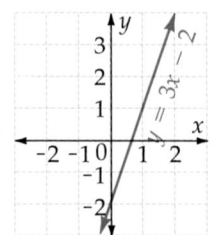

1. Write the equation in standard form.

2. Tell whether each point is on the graph.

    a. $(0,-2)$ **b.** $(1,0)$

    c. $\left(\frac{4}{3},2\right)$ **d.** $(-0.5,-3.5)$

3. What are the x-intercept and the y-intercept?

Find the x-intercept and y-intercept for each equation.

  4. $4x - 3y = 12$ **5.** $2x + \frac{1}{2}y = -3$

  6. $\frac{1}{3}x = 2$ **7.** $1.5y + 6 = 0$

Solve for y in terms of x. Graph each equation.

  8. $8x + 4y = 16$ **9.** $9.3x + 3.1y = 15.5$

 10. $\frac{1}{4}x - 3y = 6$ **11.** $6x + \frac{2}{3}y = 8$

WRITTEN EXERCISES

The figure at the right shows the graph of the equation $3 + y = -\frac{1}{2}x$.

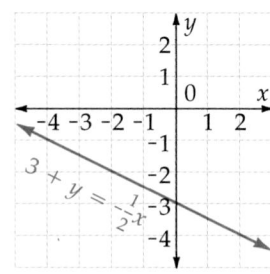

1. Write the equation in standard form.

2. Tell whether each point is on the graph.

    a. $(1,2.5)$ **b.** $(-2,2)$

    c. $(-4,-1)$ **d.** $(-2,-2)$

3. What are the x-intercept and the y-intercept?

Find the x-intercept and y-intercept for each equation.

  4. $3x + 5y = 15$ **5.** $0.75x - 0.25y + 1 = 0$

  6. $6x + 8 = 0$ **7.** $y = \frac{2}{3}x$

▼

THINK AND DISCUSS

1. Describe and give an example of an equation of a line with

a. no y-intercept.

b. no x-intercept.

2. Is the graph of $y = x^2 - 4$ a line? Use intercepts to help you decide. Explain.

3. Is the graph of the equation $xy = 12$ a line? Use guess and test to find four ordered pairs that are solutions. Graph the points.

4. Explain how the x- and y-intercepts can be helpful when graphing.

Solve for y in terms of x. Graph each equation.

8. $2x - \frac{1}{3}y = 1$

9. $10 - 2(x + 2y) = -3y - (x - 8)$

10. $y : x = 3 : 2$

11. $y - 3(0.25x + 1) = -8 - \frac{3}{4}x$

Graph each equation on a separate set of coordinate axes.

12. $3x - 5y = 15$

13. $3x + \frac{1}{2}y = -3$

14. $\frac{1}{3}x + 1 = -2$

15. $y = 0$

16. $|x| = 2$

17. $|y| = 3$

18. $|x| + |y| = 3$

19. $|x + y| = 3$

MENTAL MATH Write an equation for each line described.

20. the line parallel to the y-axis and 2 units to the left of the y-axis

21. the line 2 units to the right of the line $x = -3$

22. the line 7 units below the line $y = 2$

23. the line parallel to the x-axis and 6 units below the x-axis

24. the line perpendicular to the x-axis and passing through the point $(-3, 0)$

Write an equation using two variables for each situation. Graph the equation on a coordinate plane. Use the graph to find one solution of the word problem.

25. Find two numbers whose difference is 3.

26. Find two numbers such that one is three times the other.

27. Louis buys six pieces of fruit. Some are apples and some are oranges. Let x equal the number of oranges and y equal the number of apples.

28. A collection of nickels and dimes is valued at $1. Let x equal the number of nickels and y equal the number of dimes.

29. Ben cut a ribbon so that one piece was twice as long as the other. Let x equal the shorter piece and y equal the longer piece.

30. Gina's sister earned $6 at her lemonade stand. She sold small cups of lemonade for $.25 and large cups for $.40. Let x equal the number of small cups sold and y equal the number of large cups sold.

31. A 12-m fence encloses a rectangular garden. Let x equal the width of the garden and y equal the length of the garden.

32. **DATA FILE 3 (pp. 96–97)** A collection of 1936 and 1961 proof sets was valued at $20,264 in 1990. Let x equal the number of 1936 proof sets and y equal the number of 1961 proof sets.

THINK In Exercise 27, can the values of x and y be negative numbers? fractions? Why or why not?

FLASHBACK

perimeter of a rectangle $= 2l + 2w$

OBJECTIVE:
To use coordinate graphs to explore linear equations, intercepts, and slope.

MATERIALS

- Graph paper

- Math journal to record work

Standard form	Solved for y	y-intercept	Ratio

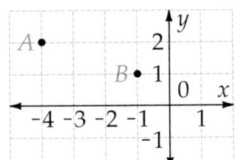

Exploring Slope

▼ The graph below shows the linear equation $-2x + y = 4$.

Copy and complete a table like the one at the left.

1. a. In what form is the equation written? Write the equation in the table.

 b. Solve the equation for y in terms of x. Write the equation in the table.

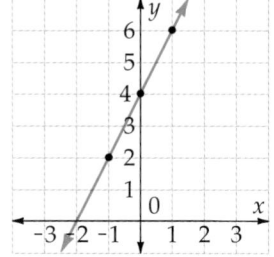

2. a. *Describe* what a y-intercept is.

 b. Determine from the graph what the y-intercept of the equation $y = 2x + 4$ is. Write the y-intercept in the table.

3. a. *Write* the coordinates of three points found on the line.

 b. *Explain* how to get from the first point to the second. Use only two sentences. Give vertical directions first using the words *up* and *down*. Then give horizontal directions, using *left* and *right*. What is the ratio in fraction form of the vertical change to the horizontal change?

Example To get from B to A: To get from A to B:

 1. Go up 1. (+1)   **1.** Go down 1. (-1)

 2. Go left 3. (-3)   **2.** Go right 3. (+3)

 3. The ratio is $\frac{1}{-3}$ or $-\frac{1}{3}$.   **3.** The ratio is $\frac{-1}{3}$ or $-\frac{1}{3}$.

 c. *Explain* how to get from the second point to the third. What is the ratio of the vertical change to the horizontal change?

 d. *Explain* how to get from the third point to the first. What is the ratio of the vertical change to the horizontal change?

 e. *Discuss* how the ratios in (b), (c), and (d) are alike. How are they different?

 f. *Write* the ratio of the vertical change to the horizontal change in simplest form. Write the result in your table.

4. Repeat Steps 1–3 for each equation shown.

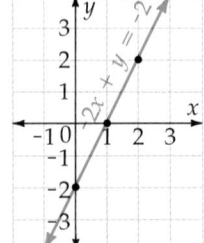 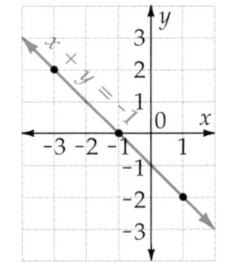 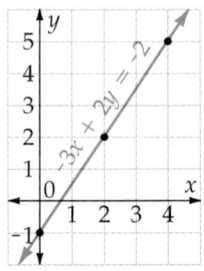

▼ We call the ratio of the vertical change to the horizontal change the *slope* of the line.

5. **a.** ***Analyze*** the table and discuss the relationship between each equation when it is solved for y in terms of x and its y-intercept.

   b. ***Analyze*** the table and discuss the relationship between each equation when it is solved for y in terms of x and its slope.

   c. Is the y-intercept the same for the equation $y = 3x - 4$ and $y = 3x + (-4)$?

6. Name the y-intercept and slope of each linear equation.

   a. $y = 12x - 4$ **b.** $y = 2x + 14$

▼ Knowing the y-intercept and the slope are useful when sketching the graph of a line.

7. **a.** ***Discuss*** why solving an equation for y is helpful when graphing the equation.

8. Sketch each equation by using the y-intercept and slope.

   a. $-4x + y = 10$ **b.** $-5x + y = -10$

▼ You can write the equation of a line by studying its graph.

9. **a.** What is the y-intercept?

   b. What is the slope?

   c. ***Write*** an equation for the line graphed at the right.

   d. ***Discuss*** how you could check that the equation is correct.

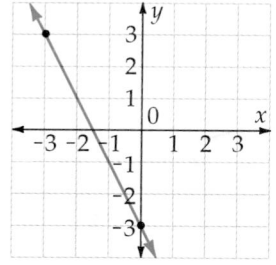

▼ You can write the equation of a line when you know the y-intercept and the slope.

10. ***Write*** the equation of each line described.

   a. The y-intercept is 7 and the slope is 8.

   b. The y-intercept is -1 and the slope is 6.

OBJECTIVE:
*Find the slope and
y-intercept for the
graph of a linear
equation.*

8-4 *Slope and y-intercept*

▼ The ski hill pictured at the left has a vertical rise of 4 m for every 20 m of horizontal run. You can find the steepness or *slope* of the ski hill by using the ratio of the vertical change to the horizontal change. The ratio for the ski hill is $\frac{4}{20}$ or $\frac{1}{5}$.

Slope	The slope of a line is the ratio of the vertical change in *y* to the corresponding horizontal change in *x*.

▼ You can also find the slope of a straight line in the coordinate plane by counting the units of vertical change and the units of horizontal change from one point to another.

Example 1 **Find the slope of the line shown on each graph.**

a. 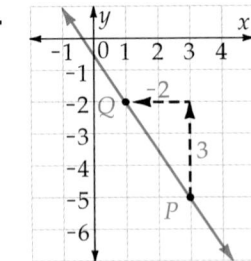 **b.**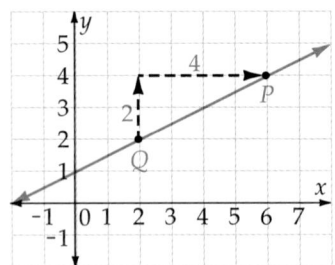

▼
THINK What is the slope if
you begin at point *Q*?

Solution **a.** Choose any two points on the line. Try $P(3,-5)$ and $Q(1,-2)$. If you begin at *P*, and move three units up and two units to the left, you reach *Q*.

$$\text{slope} = \frac{\text{vertical change}}{\text{horizontal change}} = \frac{3}{-2} \text{ or } -\frac{3}{2}$$

b. Choose any two points on the line. Try $P(6,4)$ and $Q(2,2)$. If you begin at *Q*, and move 2 units up and 4 units to the right, you reach *P*.

$$\text{slope} = \frac{\text{vertical change}}{\text{horizontal change}} = \frac{2}{4} \text{ or } \frac{1}{2}$$

▼
THINK What is the slope if
you begin at point *P*?

▼ You can use a formula to find the slope if you know the coordinates of any two points on the line.

Slope Formula	Use the following formula to calculate slope. $$\text{slope} = \frac{\text{difference in } y\text{-coordinates}}{\text{difference in } x\text{-coordinates}}$$

Example 2 **Find the slope of a line that contains the points $R(-2,1)$ and $S(4,3)$.**

Solution $$\text{slope} = \frac{\text{difference in } y\text{-coordinates}}{\text{difference in } x\text{-coordinates}} = \frac{3-1}{4-(-2)} = \frac{2}{6} \text{ or } \frac{1}{3}$$

Example 3 Determine the slope of the line containing the given points. Graph the line on a coordinate plane.

a. (2,4) and (-3,4) **b.** (3,2) and (3,-1)

Solution **a.** slope $= \dfrac{4-4}{-3-2} = \dfrac{0}{-5} = 0$

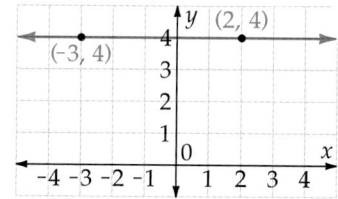

The slope of a horizontal line is zero.

b. slope $= \dfrac{-1-2}{3-3} = \dfrac{-3}{0}$

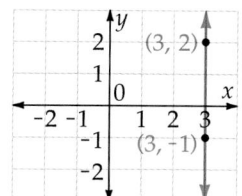

Because division by zero is undefined, a vertical line has no slope.

▼ You can draw the graph of a line if you know the slope of the line and a point on the line.

Example 4 Graph the line with slope $\dfrac{3}{4}$ and y-intercept -4.

Solution Locate the point (0,-4) and label it *P*. Move 3 units up and 4 units to the right. You are now at (4,-1), or *Q*. Draw the line containing *P* and *Q*.

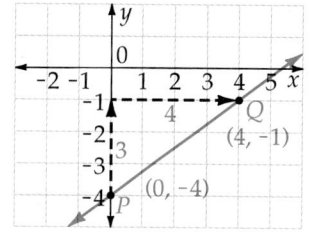

FLASHBACK

The *y*-intercept is the *y*-coordinate of a point where a graph crosses the *y*-axis.

▼ When you solve an equation for *y* it is in *slope-intercept* form.

Slope-intercept Form

A linear equation in the form $y = mx + b$ is in slope-intercept form. The slope is *m* and the *y*-intercept is *b*.

Example 5 Sketch the graph of the equation $y = 3x + 1$.

Solution The slope is 3 or $\dfrac{3}{1}$. The *y*-intercept is 1. Locate the point (0,1) and label it *P*. Move 3 units up and 1 unit to the right. You are now at (1,4), or *Q*. Draw the line containing *P* and *Q*.

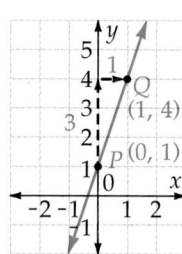

THINK AND DISCUSS

True or false?

1. The greater the absolute value of *m*, the greater the steepness of the line.

2. A line with a positive slope runs downward from left to right.

3. If a line has a *y*-intercept of zero, it does not cross the *x*-axis.

4. Given $y = mx + b$, the slope of the line is *m* and the *y*-intercept is *b*.

CLASS EXERCISES

Find the steepness and *y*-intercept of each line.

1. 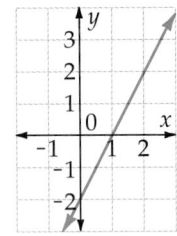   **2.** 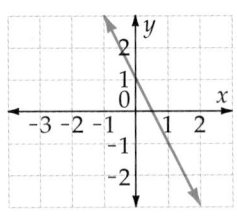   **3.**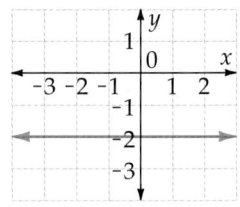

Find the slope of the line containing the given points.

4. (4,5) (6,13)   **5.** (-3,5) (-4,-1)   **6.** (-10,-6) (-13,-10)

Write each linear equation in slope-intercept form. Name the slope and *y*-intercept.

7. $3x + y = 3$ **8.** $2y + 4x = 12$ **9.** $-10 + y = -2x$

10. Graph the line with slope -2 and containing the point (1,-3).

MIXED REVIEW

Find the LCM.

1. 4, 10, 16

2. 7, 12, 18

Tell whether or not each equation is linear. Explain how you know.

3. $Ax + By + C = 0$

4. $y = -2$

5. $xy = -12$

6. $x + y = -6$

7. $3(x - 2y) + y = 7 - x$

8. $x = y^2$

Solve.

9. The price of gold per oz increases from $350 to $420. Find the percent of increase.

WRITTEN EXERCISES

MENTAL MATH **Find the steepness and *y*-intercept of each line.**

1. 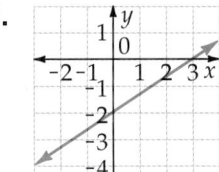   **2.** 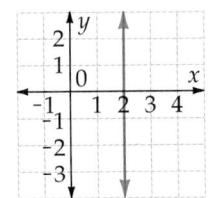   **3.**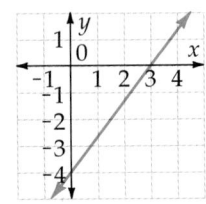

Plot each pair of points. Draw the line containing them. Then find its slope and *y*-intercept.

4. (-1,3), (1,-1)   **5.** (-6,2), (0,4)   **6.** (0,3), (5,0)

Find the slope of the line containing the given points.

7. (2,1) (3,1)   **8.** (-2,5) (-2,-1)   **9.** (3,5) (6,15)

10. (-5,-2) (1,4)   **11.** (1,-2) (2,-4)   **12.** (-1,15) (3,5)

Graph each line described.

13. the line having slope -3 and containing the point (-6,5)

14. the line having slope 5 and containing the point (-4,-5)

15. the line having slope $\frac{2}{3}$ and containing the point (0,-4)

Graph each line described.

16. the line having slope 0 and containing the point (5,3)

17. the line having no slope and containing the point (4,-2)

18. the line having slope -3 and containing the origin

Write each linear equation in slope-intercept form. Name the slope and y-intercept.

19. $-2x + y = 1$ **20.** $6x + y = \frac{1}{6}$ **21.** $3 + y = -2x$

22. $-2x + 3y = 18$ **23.** $-3x + 4y - 1 = 0$ **24.** $4y = 2x$

Sketch the graph of each equation.

25. $y = 2x + 4$ **26.** $y = \frac{1}{2}x$ **27.** $y = -5x - 3$

28. $y = -x + 1$ **29.** $y = -\frac{2}{5}x - 2$ **30.** $y = x - \frac{3}{4}$

31. a. Graph each pair of lines on one coordinate grid.

Pair 1   Pair 2

$y = 2x - 5$ $y = -3x + 1$

$y = 2x + 3$ $y = -3x - 2$

b. Describe the lines.

c. Compare the slopes of each pair of equations.

d. Draw a conclusion.

Write an equation in standard form for each line described. *Hint: First write the equation in slope-intercept form.*

32. having slope 3 and y-intercept -4

33. having slope 0 and y-intercept 6

34. having slope -2 and y-intercept -1.

35. having no slope and containing the point (-3,0).

36. having slope -8 and y-intercept $\frac{1}{2}$

37. PROJECT Call a local taxi company to find out the rates for trips of distances up to 1.5 mi. Make a table and draw the graph. Find the slope and the y-intercept. Compare with other members of your group.

38. The table at the right shows a student's savings between the sixth and tenth weeks. The student saved at the same rate during this time.

a. Find the rate of savings per week.

b. Find the slope of the line passing through points (6,5) and (10,11). How does the slope compare with the savings?

Student's Savings	
Weeks (x)	**Savings (y)**
6	$5
10	$11

8-5 Solve by Graphing

OBJECTIVE:
To solve problems using a graph.

■ You can solve many types of problems using graphs.

PROBLEM

Two years ago the value of a new car was $12,000. Its current value is $9,000. Predict the value of the car three years from now if it continues to depreciate at the same rate.

SOLUTION

READ ▶ What do you want to find?

the value of the car in three years

PLAN ▶ Decide on a strategy.

Make a graph.
Let x = the age of the car and y = the dollar value.

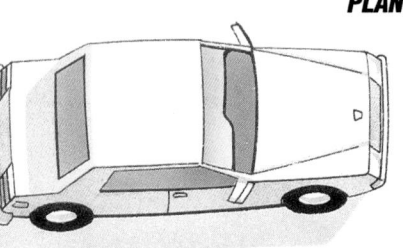

What was the value of x when the car was new? the value of y?

$x = 0$
$y = 12,000$

What is the current value of x when y is 9,000?

$x = 2$

SOLVE ▶ What will be the value of x in three years?

$x = 2 + 3 = 5$

Use the information to write two ordered pairs.

$(0, 12,000)$ and $(2, 9,000)$

Plot the points. Connect them. Extend the line so that you can find other values.

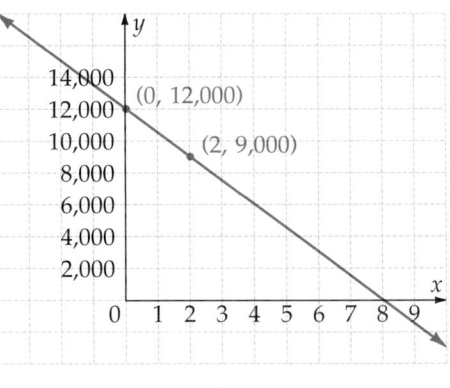

Find the value of y when $x = 5$

$y = 4,500$

The value of the car in three years will be $4,500.

LOOK BACK ▶ Check your answer by solving another way.

In two years the car depreciates $3,000, or $1,500 per year. If it drops at the same rate for three more years, it would be worth $9,000 - 3(1,500)$ or $4,500.

CLASS EXERCISES

Refer to the problem on page 334.

1. What will the car be worth five years from now?

2. When the car is worth $6,000, how old will the car be?

3. How old must the car be before its value has depreciated to $0? Explain why this is probably not an accurate prediction.

WRITTEN EXERCISES

Use a CALCULATOR where appropriate.

Solve by using the strategy of graphing.

1. The relationship between the Fahrenheit and Celsius temperature scales is linear. The freezing point of water is 32°F or 0°C. The boiling point of water is 212°F or 100°C.

   a. Make a graph showing this information.

   b. What is the approximate Fahrenheit temperature that is equivalent to 10°C?

   c. What is the approximate Celsius temperature that is equivalent to 70°F?

2. The Jackson family bought a house in 1968 for $32,000. In 1988 they sold it for $192,000. Assume that the increase in value was constant over the 20-year period.

   a. Make a graph showing this information.

   b. What was the value of the house in 1980?

   c. Assume the value of the house continues to increase at the same rate. Predict the value of the house in the year 2000.

   d. Is it reasonable to assume that the increase in value over time is constant? Explain.

Solve using any strategy.

3. The temperature at 6:00 A.M. was 48°F. At 9:00 A.M. it was 60°F. The temperature climbed at a constant rate from 6:00 A.M. to 11:00 A.M. What was the temperature at 10:00 A.M.?

4. An airplane flying at an altitude of 30,000 ft begins its descent at the rate of 1,500 ft/min. Assume the plane continues to descend at the same rate. In how many minutes will the plane be on the ground?

5. If 4 is subtracted from three times a number, the result is two more than the number. Find the number.

6. A supermarket charges $1.19 for a 12-oz jar of salsa and $1.89 for a 20-oz jar. The manufacturer has just come out with a 16-oz size. What would you suggest the supermarket should charge for the new size? Justify your answer.

7. The sales tax on an item costing $17.50 is $1.23. Find the sales tax on an item that costs $30. Round your answer to the nearest cent.

8. A shoe store employs high-school students as part-time salespeople. The starting pay is $3.85/h. Every six months a worker is eligible for a raise of $.35 an hour, if the work has been satisfactory. What can a good salesperson expect to be earning per hour two years after starting at the store?

9. A slope of $\frac{1}{10}$ is suitable for a ramp to allow wheelchair access to a building. How far from a doorway will a ramp extend if the doorway is $3\frac{1}{2}$ ft above the ground?

10. A delivery van travels 240.8 mi using 10.6 gal of gas. The tank holds 13.6 gal. How many miles can the van expect to travel on a full tank of gas? Round your answer to the nearest mile.

11. A store is holding its annual 30% off sale.

   a. What will you save on an item if the regular price is $89.95? Round your answer to the nearest dollar.

   b. A student saved $50 on a dress she bought at the sale. Estimate its original price.

12. The high school hired a rock band for a concert. The school guaranteed the band a fee of $1,500, plus $4.50 for each ticket sold. There are 1,132 seats in the auditorium. What is the greatest possible amount of money the band can earn for its single concert performance? the least amount?

13. A student has $5.90 in dimes and quarters. There are 32 coins altogether. How many of each coin does the student have?

14. *PROJECT* Look up record times for the 100-m dash in the Olympics for the years 1980 and 1984.

   a. Assume that the record time continues to decrease at the same rate. Graph the data from the first two years. Use the horizontal axis to represent the year. Use the vertical axis to represent the time.

   b. Extend the graph to predict the record time for the 1988 Olympic games. Compare your result with the actual Olympic record in 1988.

   c. *WRITE* a paragraph about your findings in your journal.

15. *DATA FILE 9 (pp. 360–361)* Ron played eighteen holes of golf at St. Andrew's golf club for five consecutive days. About how many miles did Ron walk on the golf course?

Problem Solving Practice

READ
PLAN
LOOK BACK
SOLVE

Look for a Pattern
Guess and Test
Simplify the Problem
Make an Organized List
Work Backwards
Account for All Possibilities
Make a Table
Write an Equation
Solve by Graphing
Draw a Diagram
Make a Model
Solve Another Way
Simulate the Problem

Solve. Use an appropriate strategy or a combination of strategies.

1. In a collection of dimes and quarters, there are seven more quarters than there are dimes. How many dimes and quarters are there if the collection is worth $3.50?

2. Anna has $75 in the bank. She saves $5 the first week, $10 the second week, and $15 the third week. At this rate, how much money will she have in the bank at the end of 12 weeks?

3. A landscaper wants to plant a bush every 1.5 ft around the edge of a circular garden. It is 72 ft around the edge of the garden. How many plants should the landscaper purchase?

4. A student withdraws $15 from his bank account. He then buys lunch for $4.75, a ticket to the movies for $7.50, and a snack after the movie for $3.45. He has $14.23 left. How much money did he have before he withdrew the $15?

5. The sum of three consecutive integers is 111. What are the integers?

6. A plumber charges $35 for a service call, plus $60 per hour for her time.

    a. Find the cost of a two-hour service call.

    b. How much time was spent on a call if the bill was $125?

7. The height of a toddler is 36 in. The mother's height is double the toddler's height, less 7 in. How tall is the mother?

8. You can buy 12 pencils for $.80. How much will you pay for 27 pencils?

9. One square has sides four times as long as the sides of a second square. The combined area of the squares is 272 ft². Find their dimensions.

10. The sum of the squares of two consecutive integers is 145. Find the integers.

11. Mr. Harrow earns $22,500 a year. He gets paid weekly. He pays 6.3% of his salary to social security. How much money is taken out of each pay check for social security?

12. There are four candidates running for president of the student council. Three candidates are running for vice-president. How many different ways can the two offices be filled?

13. A grocery store sells apples at $1.92 a dozen. Oranges are $2.16 a dozen. What is the cost of 4 apples and 3 oranges?

Exploring Simulations

OBJECTIVE:
To study computer-simulated motion.

MATERIALS

- Computer and graphing software or a graphing calculator
- Measuring tape or ruler
- Rubber ball or tennis ball
- Stopwatch
- Math journal to record work

DATAPOINT

Keep track of your data in a table.

d	D	h	t
⋮	⋮	⋮	⋮

■ Scientists and engineers use computers to *simulate*, or re-create the motion of an object such as rolling a ball off a table.

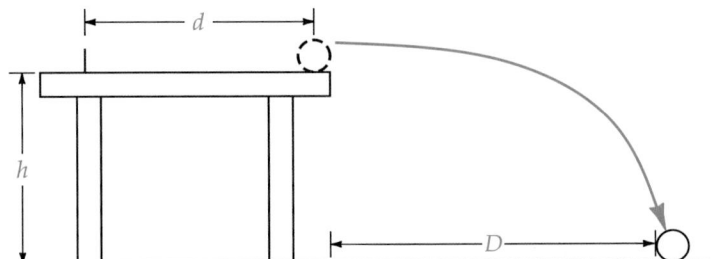

1. **Model** the situation shown above. Measure the distances *d* and *h*. Roll a ball off a table along distance *d*. Use a stopwatch to measure *t*, the time it takes the ball to hit the ground after it rolls off the table. Measure *D*, the distance from the table to where the ball hits the ground.

   a. Continue the experiment, but each time increase the speed of the ball. What happens to the time it takes the ball to hit the ground? What happens to *D*?

   b. When does *D* = 0? Is there a limit to the value of *D*?

2. Increase the value of *h* by using a higher table. Repeat the experiment.

   a. How does increasing *h* affect *t*? How does increasing *h* affect *D*?

   b. How does increasing the speed of the ball affect *D*?

Sonya Kovalevsky (1850–1891) was a mathematical genius. In 1888 she wrote the brilliant essay "On the Problem of the Rotation of a Solid Body about a Fixed Point," which won the highest award of the French Academy of Sciences.

■ You can use a computer or graphing calculator to graph the *trajectory*, or path, of the ball. The equation for this trajectory is $y = -16x^2 + 10$. The figure below shows the part of the graph that simulates the ball's trajectory.

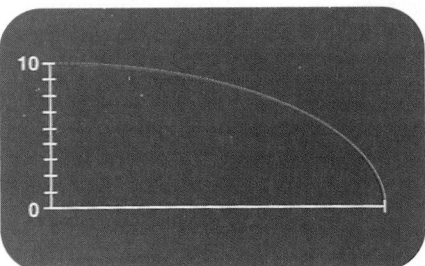

3. In the equation $y = -16x^2 + 10$, the value 10 indicates the height of the table. Write equations for table heights of 15 ft, 20 ft, and 35 ft.

4. Graph the equations from Exercise 3. What do you notice about the trajectory as *h* increases?

■ The equation $y = -16x^2 + 10$ assumes a speed of 1 ft/s. The equation for *any* speed is $y = -\frac{16}{v^2}x^2 + h$, where h is the height of the table and v is the speed of the ball.

5. a. *Write* equations for each speed and height.

Speed (ft/s)	1	2	3	4	4	4	6	7	8
Height (ft)	10	10	10	10	15	20	20	20	20

b. Graph each equation.

c. *Analyze* what happens to D as the speed of the ball increases but the height remains the same. Is this what you would expect to happen?

d. What happens to D as the height of the table increases but the speed of the ball remains the same? Is this what you would expect to happen?

e. What happens to D as both the table height and the speed of the ball increase? Is this what you would expect to happen?

6. *Explore* What happens to D for very large values of v? What happens to the ball's trajectory for large values of v?

■ A computer or graphing calculator simulation can help you predict the outcome of an experiment. The three trajectories below are for a ball moving with speeds 1 ft/s, 2 ft/s, and 3 ft/s off a 4-ft high table.

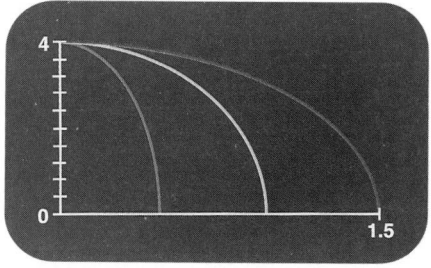

7. a. *Estimation* What are the values for D in each case?

b. *Model* each situation in the graph. To get the right speed, measure d and use a stopwatch. Time the motion of the ball to 1 s, 2 s, or 3 s, depending on the speed.

c. How do your results compare to those of the computer simulation? How do they differ?

d. *Discuss* the advantages to using a computer to simulate an experiment.

OBJECTIVE:
To solve two
equations in two
variables by
graphing.

8-6 Solving Systems of Linear Equations

▼ Two linear equations using the same variables form a *system of linear equations.*

System of Linear Equations	A system of linear equations is two or more linear equations using the same variables.

Example 1 State whether each pair of linear equations is a system of linear equations.

a. $2x + y = 8$
$x - 3y = -9$

b. $x + 8y = 12$
$6a + b = -3$

Solution **a.** Yes, this is a system of linear equations. Both equations contain variables x and y.

b. No, this is not a system of linear equations. The equations do not contain the same variables.

▼ A *solution* of a system of linear equations makes all of the equations in the system true.

Solution	A solution of a system of linear equations is any ordered pair of numbers that satisfies all equations in the system.

Example 2 Tell whether the ordered pair (2,5) is a solution for the system of linear equations $2x + y = 9$ and $4x - y = 3$.

Solution Substitute the ordered pair into each equation.

$$2x + y = 9 \qquad 4x - y = 3$$
$$2(2) + 5 = 9 \qquad 4(2) - 5 = 3$$
$$4 + 5 = 9 \qquad 8 - 5 = 3$$
$$9 = 9 ✓ \qquad 3 = 3 ✓$$

Since (2,5) makes both equations true, it is a solution of the system of linear equations.

FLASHBACK

Every point on the graph of an equation represents an ordered pair of numbers that is a solution of the equation.

▼ You can solve a system of linear equations by graphing.

Example 3 Solve the system $2x + 3y = 6$ and $3x - y = -2$ by graphing.

Solution Graph each equation on the same set of axes. The lines intersect at (0,2). The point (0,2) is the only solution of the system.

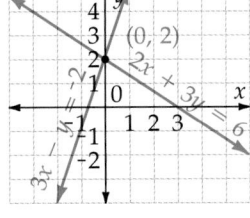

▼ Some systems of linear equations have no solution.

Example 4 Solve the system of linear equations $x + y = 1$ and $x + y = 4$ by graphing.

Solution Graph each equation on the same set of axes. The lines are parallel and do not intersect. There is no solution to this system.

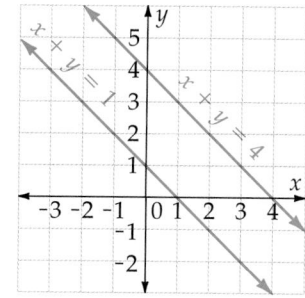

▼ Some systems of equations have infinitely many solutions.

Example 5 Solve the system of linear equations $x - 2y = 4$ and $2x - 4y = 8$ by graphing.

Solution Graph each equation on the same set of axes. The graph of each equation is the same line. Therefore, every point on the line satisfies both equations. There are infinitely many solutions to this system.

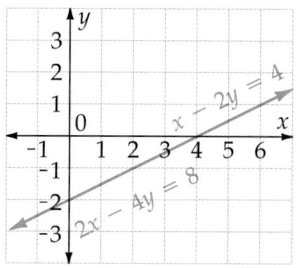

▼ Systems of equations can help you solve word problems.

Example 6 Find two numbers whose sum is 6 and difference is 4.

Solution Let x represent the first number and y represent the second number. Write a system of linear equations.

$x + y = 6$ ←**Sum**
$x - y = 4$ ←**Difference**

Graph each equation on the same set of axes. The lines intersect at (5,1). The numbers are 5 and 1.

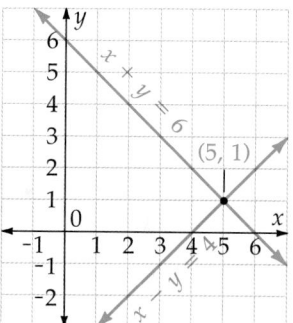

Check $x + y = 6$ $x - y = 4$
         $5 + 1 = 6$ $5 - 1 = 4$
              $6 = 6$ ✓ $4 = 4$ ✓

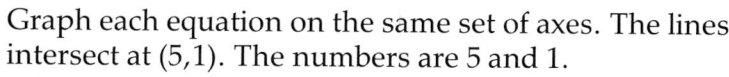

CLASS EXERCISES

Find the solution for each system.

1. $y = x + 1$ and $y = 3x - 7$

2. $x + y = -3$ and $y = 3x - 7$

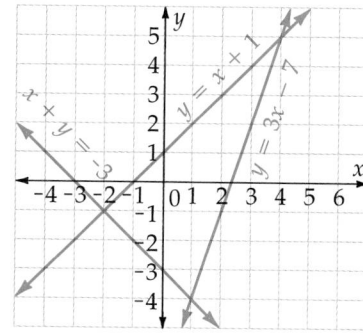

Write the coordinates of each point.

3. a point that satisfies $y = x + 1$ but not $y = 3x - 7$

4. a point that satisfies $y = 3x - 7$ but not $x + y = -3$

THINK AND DISCUSS

1. All the examples had integer solutions. When do you think graphing might not be useful for solving a system of equations?

2. A system of two linear equations in two variables has no solution. Describe the graphs of the equations.

3. Two distinct ordered pairs are solutions of a system of two linear equations. Describe the graphs of the equations.

Tell whether the ordered pair is a solution of the system.

5. $3x - 2y = 8$
$x = -3y$
$(3, -1)$

6. $x - 2y = 0$
$2x + y = 4$
$(2, 1)$

7. $x + 2y = 3$
$y = 2x - 1$
$(1, 1)$

Solve each system by graphing. Check your solutions.

8. $2x - y = 4$
$y = -2x$

9. $3y - 2x = 6$
$y = x + 1$

10. $2x + 3y = 6$
$y + 2 = 0$

Write a system of linear equations. Solve by graphing.

11. The sum of two numbers is 19. Their difference is 5.

12. The sum of two numbers is 10. Twice the larger decreased by three times the smaller is 5. Find the two numbers.

WRITTEN EXERCISES

Tell whether the ordered pair is a solution of the system.

1. $y = x + 2$
$x - 3y = 4$
$(-5, -3)$

2. $y = x - 1$
$x = 4y$
$\left(\dfrac{4}{3}, \dfrac{1}{3}\right)$

3. $x + y = 2$
$-x + y = -4$
$(3, 1)$

Solve each system by graphing. Check your solutions.

4. $y = x + 5$
$2x + y = 8$

5. $x = y - 4$
$x + y = 6$

6. $2x - y = 2$
$2y = 4x - 4$

7. $x + 4y = 6$
$x - 2 = 0$

8. $x + y = 3$
$2x = 10 - 2y$

9. $x = y$
$x + y = 4$

10. $y = x - 8$
$y = 3x$

11. $y = x - 2$
$x + 3y = 6$

12. $2x + 3y = 6$
$2x + y + 2 = 0$

13. $x + y = 1$
$y = -x - 1$

14. $y = 2x - 4$
$4x - 2y = 8$

15. $y = 2x - 2$
$x = 3$

Write a system of linear equations. Solve by graphing.

16. The sum of two numbers is 120. Their difference is 20. Find the numbers.

17. The sum of two numbers is 55. Their difference is 15. Find the numbers.

18. The difference of two numbers is 5. The greater number decreased by twice the lesser number is 9. Find the numbers.

19. A 144-m rope is cut into 2 pieces. One piece is three times as long as the other. How long is each piece of rope?

MIXED REVIEW

Simplify.

1. $\dfrac{15x^3}{5x}$

2. $\dfrac{20x^2y^6}{8xy^3}$

Find the slope and y-intercept.

3. $x = y$

4. $2x + 3y = 12$

Solve each inequality.

5. $2x + 3 < 9$

6. $3 - (2x + 1) \leq 8$

Solve.

7. A coat regularly sells for $125. It is on sale for 40% off. What is the sale price?

20. Cliff is 6 years older than Claire. In two years, Cliff will be twice Claire's age. Find their present ages.

21. Questions on a 16-item test are worth either 5 points or 10 points each. There are a total of 100 points on the test. How many items of each point value appear on the test?

Describe the nature of each system of linear equations without graphing. Note that they are all written in the form $y = mx + b$.

22. $y = x + 2$
$y = -x + 2$

23. $y = -x + 2$
$y = -x + 5$

24. $y = x - 1$
$3y = 3x - 3$

25. *DATA FILE 8 (pp. 312–313)* In what year was the United States population approximately one fourth of the population in 1910?

26. The unit of distance a boat uses to navigate is called a *nautical mile*. One nautical mile is 6,076.1 ft. Saona Island and Mona Island are located in the Caribbean Sea. They are 45 mi apart from each other.

a. To the nearest tenth, how many nautical miles apart are Saona Island and Mona Island? *Hint:* 5,280 ft is 1 mi.

b. A boat measures its speed in knots. One knot is equal to one naut mi/h. If your boat is traveling at a rate of 12 naut mi/h, how long will it take, to the nearest hour, to go from Saona Island to Mona Island?

TEST YOURSELF

Find the x-intercept and the y-intercept for each equation.

1. $2x + 5y = 20$

2. $3y = 6 + 9x$

3. $5x + 15 - y = 5$

Find the slope of the line containing the given points.

4. $(7,-3)$ $(7,4)$

5. $(-12,6)$ $(4,-2)$

6. $(-5,-3)$ $(6,-1)$

Write each equation in slope-intercept form. Name the slope and y-intercept. Sketch the graph of the equation.

7. $4x + 2y = 14$

8. $3y = -2$

9. $-4 + 6y = -2x$

Solve each system of linear equations by graphing.

10. $2x + y = 4$
$y = \dfrac{-1}{2}x + 7$

11. $2x - 3y = 12$
$4x - 24 = 6y$

12. $2x - 3y = 12$
$x - 3 = 0$

OBJECTIVE:
To solve linear
inequalities in two
variables.

8-7 *Solving Linear Inequalities*

▼ The radiator of a car requires a 40% solution of antifreeze to protect it to -24°F. You can write an equation in two variables to describe the amount of antifreeze needed for your car. Let x represent the capacity of your radiator and y represent the amount of antifreeze solution needed.

$$y = 0.4x$$

You may put more antifreeze in the radiator than is needed to be sure your car is protected. You can describe the situation with an inequality in two variables.

$$y \geq 0.4x$$

▼ An ordered pair that makes an inequality in two variables a true statement is a solution of the inequality.

Example 1 **Tell whether each ordered pair is a solution of the inequality $y \geq 0.4x$.**

   a. (4,5)　　　　　**b.** (5,1)　　　　　**c.** (-5,-2)

Solution

a. $y \geq 0.4x$
$5 \geq 0.4(4)$
$5 \geq 1.6$ ✓

True, so (4,5) is a solution.

b. $y \geq 0.4x$
$1 \geq 0.4(5)$
$1 \geq 2$ ✗

False, so (5,1) is not a solution.

c. $y \geq 0.4x$
$-2 \geq 0.4(-5)$
$-2 \geq -2$ ✓

True, so (-5,-2) is a solution.

▼ You can find solutions for a linear inequality in two variables by solving for y in terms of x.

Example 2 **Find three solutions of the inequality $x - y > 1$.**

Solution Solve for y in terms of x.

$$x - y > 1$$
$$x - y - x > 1 - x \qquad \text{Subtract } x \text{ from each side.}$$
$$-y > 1 - x$$
$$-1(-y) < -1(1 - x) \qquad \text{Multiply each side by -1.}$$
$$y < -1 + x$$
$$y < x - 1 \qquad \text{Substitute a value, say 0, for } x.$$
$$y < 0 - 1$$
$$y < -1$$

When x is 0, y can be any number less than -1. So, (0,-2), (0,-3), and (0,-4) are three solutions of the inequality. There may be infinitely many solutions of an inequality.

FLASHBACK

When both sides of an inequality are multiplied by a negative number, the inequality sign is reversed.

▼ You can solve inequalities to find solutions for real world problems.

Example 3 William has $36. He wants to buy some tropical fish. Red Oscars are $6 each. Blue Acaras are $12 each. How many of each can William buy if he wants to buy at least one of each?

Solution 1. Write an inequality to describe the situation.

Let x equal the number of Red Oscars.
So, $6x$ equals the amount of money for Red Oscars.
Let y equal the number of Blue Acaras.
So, $12y$ equals the amount of money for Blue Acaras.
The inequality $6x + 12y \leq 36$ describes William's situation.

2. Solve the inequality for y.

$$6x + 12y \leq 36$$
$$6x + 12y - 6x \leq 36 - 6x \qquad \text{Subtract 6x from each side.}$$
$$12y \leq 36 - 6x$$
$$\frac{12y}{12} \leq \frac{36 - 6x}{12} \qquad \text{Divide each side by 12.}$$
$$y \leq \frac{36}{12} - \frac{6x}{12}$$
$$\leq 3 - \frac{1}{2}x$$

3. Substitute values for x. Use a chart to organize the data.

x	y	(x,y)
0	3	(0,3)
1	2.5	(1,2.5)
2	2	(2,2)
3	1.5	(3,1.5)
4	1	(4,1)
5	0.5	(5,0.5)
6	0	(6,0)
7	-0.5	(7,-0.5)

4. Analyze the chart to make reasonable conclusions.

The ordered pairs (2,2) and (4,1) are solutions. William can buy 2 Red Oscars and 2 Blue Acaras or 4 Red Oscars and 1 Blue Acara.

The ordered pairs (0,3) and (6,0) are *not* solutions. William wants to buy *at least* one of each type.

The ordered pairs (1,2.5), (3,1.5), and (5,0.5) are *not* solutions. William cannot buy a fraction of a fish.

The ordered pair (7,-0.5) is *not* a solution. William can only buy positive numbers of items.

Tell whether each ordered pair is a solution of the inequality.

1. $|x + y| > 3$; $(0,-5)$
2. $2x + y \leq -1$; $(2,3)$
3. $3x - 5y \geq 36$; $(7,-4)$
4. $|x| - |y| > 0$; $(-1,-11)$

Solve each inequality for y in terms of x. Write three ordered pairs that are solutions of the inequality.

5. $3x - 2y > -12$
6. $4x + 5y \geq 15$
7. $x \leq -3y$
8. $x - 2y < -1$
9. $-6x + 8y > 48$
10. $x - y < 1$

11. Students are selling tickets for a play. Student tickets cost $3. General admission tickets cost $5. How many of each kind must the students sell to raise at least $200 for costumes?

   a. Suppose only student tickets are sold. How many must the students sell to purchase costumes?

   b. Suppose only general admission tickets are sold. How many must the students sell to purchase costumes?

   c. Let x equal the number of student tickets sold and y equal the number of general admission tickets sold. Write an inequality that describes the situation.

   d. Find three solutions. Assume at least one of each type of ticket must be sold.

GENERAL ADMISSION $5

STUDENT $3

1. List three ordered pairs that satisfy the inequality $y > 2x$.

2. Describe the solution set of the inequality $|x + y| < 0$.

3. Describe the solution set of the inequality $|x| + |y| \leq 0$.

WRITTEN EXERCISES

Tell whether each ordered pair is a solution of the inequality.

1. $|x + y| > 3$; $(-2,1)$
2. $2x + 3y \leq 12$; $(-2,5)$
3. $x - 5y < 0$; $(7,-3)$
4. $|x| + |y| > |x + y|$; $(-4,10)$

CALCULATOR Tell whether each ordered pair is a solution of the inequality.

5. $|x| - 6.8y < -27.09$; $(-3.75,4.5)$
6. $2x - 9.4y \geq 3.7x$; $(8.96,-1.73)$
7. $3.2x + y < 0.35$; $(-1.25,4.5)$
8. $13.85x + 7.94y > 0$; $(3.91,-6.72)$

Solve each inequality for y in terms of x. Write three ordered pairs that are solutions of the inequality.

9. $5x - 2y < 10$
10. $x + 2y + 13 \geq 5x - y - 6$

11. $(x - 2y) > x + y + 1$

12. $6 - (3x - y) \leq 12$

13. $|x| - y \geq 4$

14. $11 - 2\left(x - \frac{1}{2}y\right) - 3y < 0$

15. $3 - y \geq x - 2$

16. $-x > 3y - 5(2y - 3)$

Solve.

17. Ray bought five identical pencils and two identical pens. He spent not more than $2. What could be the cost of each item?

18. A collection of nickels and dimes is worth less than $1.70. Determine how many coins of each type are in the collection.

   a. Suppose the collection contains only nickels. How many nickels could there be?

   b. Suppose the collection contains only dimes. How many dimes could there be?

   c. Let x equal the number of nickels in the collection and y equal the number of dimes in the collection. Write an inequality that describes the problem situation.

   d. Find ten possible solutions. Assume there is at least one nickel and one dime in the collection.

19. Write a journal entry explaining how you know how many solutions each inequality has.

   a. $|x| + |y| \geq 0$ **b.** $|x - y| < 0$

Critical Thinking

EXPLORING GRAPHING

▼ Classify each graph.

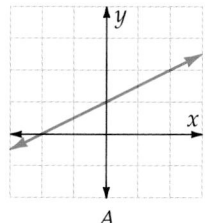 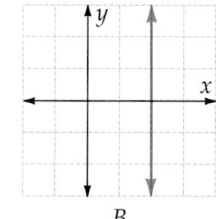 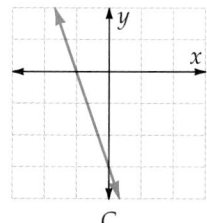 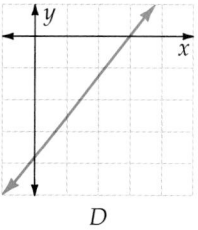

     A   B   C   D

1. a. Which graphs have a positive slope?

   b. Which graphs have a negative slope?

2. a. Which graphs have a positive y-intercept?

   b. Which graphs have a negative x-intercept?

OBJECTIVE:
To graph a linear
inequality in two
variables and to
explore simple
systems of
inequalities.

8-8 Graphing Linear Inequalities

▼ You can use the graph of the equation $x + y = 5$ to solve the inequality $x + y \leq 5$.

The line shows the solutions for $x + y = 5$.

The shaded region of the graph shows the solutions for $x + y < 5$.

The line and the shaded region show the solutions for $x + y \leq 5$.

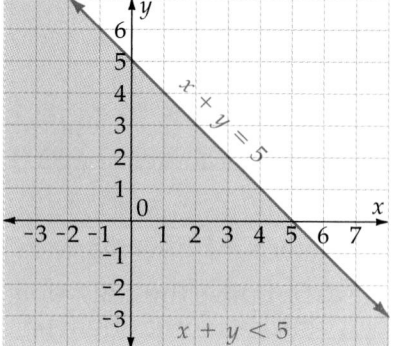

▼ Sometimes the line may include points that are not solutions to the inequality.

Example 1 Graph the inequality $2x - 3y > 6$.

Solution

1. Substitute $=$ for $>$.

$$2x - 3y > 6$$
$$2x - 3y = 6$$

2. Solve the equation for y.

$$2x - 3y - 2x = 6 - 2x$$
$$-3y = 6 - 2x$$

$$\frac{-3y}{-3} = \frac{6 - 2x}{-3}$$

$$y = \frac{6}{-3} - \frac{2x}{-3}$$

$$y = -2 + \frac{2}{3}x$$

$$y = \frac{2}{3}x - 2$$

3. Graph the equation. The inequality does not include *is equal to*, so use a dotted line to show that the line itself is not part of the solution set.

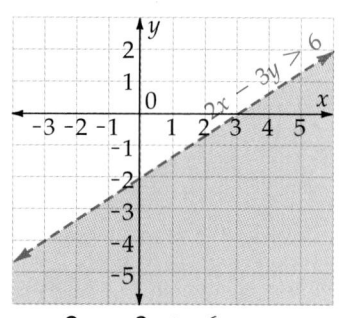

Check Choose any point above or below the line. Determine if the point is a solution. Try (0,0).

$$2x - 3y > 6$$
$$2(0) - 3(0) > 6$$
$$0 - 0 > 6$$
$$0 > 6 \text{ False}$$

Since (0,0) is not a solution, shade the area below the line.

Any point that is shaded is a solution of the inequality.

▼ When you graph linear inequalities in two variables, the line is part of the solution if the inequality symbol is $\leq$ or $\geq$. The line is not part of the solution if the inequality symbol is $<$ or $>$.

Example 2 Write the equation of the line you would graph for each inequality. Tell whether the graph of the equation would be drawn as a solid or a dotted line.

    a. $y > 4x + 3$ **b.** $3x - 7y \leq -21$ **c.** $3x \geq 2y + 1$

Solution **a.** Graph the equation $y = 4x + 3$. The graph is a dotted line.

    b. Graph the equation $3x - 7y = -21$. The graph is a solid line.

    c. Graph the equation $3x = 2y + 1$. The graph is a solid line.

▼ You can show the solution of a *system of linear inequalities* by graphing both inequalities on the same set of coordinate axes.

System of Linear Inequalities	A system of linear inequalities is two or more linear inequalities using the same variables.

Example 3 Solve the system of linear inequalities $y > x$ and $y \leq 2$.

Solution **1.** Graph $y > x$. Shade the region above the dotted line.

2. Graph $y \leq 2$ on the same set of axes. Shade below the solid line.

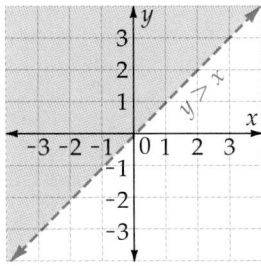
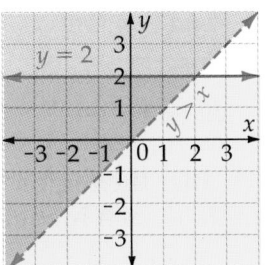

The graph of the solution is the part shaded in both colors.

THINK AND DISCUSS

1. Is $(-2,-1)$ a solution of the inequality $y > x$?

2. If (p,q) is a solution of $y > x$, what must be true about $\frac{p}{q}$?

3. State whether $(0,0)$ is a solution.

a. $4x - 11y \leq 15$

b. $-x + y > -1.45$

c. $x \geq -3$

CLASS EXERCISES

Write the equation of the line you would graph for each inequality. Tell whether the graph would be a solid or a dotted line.

1. $x + 2y > 5$ **2.** $3x - y \leq 1$ **3.** $x < 6$

4. $y + 2x \leq -1$ **5.** $x - 3y \geq 9$ **6.** $y > 7$

7. $x + 2y > 5$ **8.** $3x - y \leq 1$ **9.** $x < 6$

Graph each inequality.

10. $x + 2y > 5$ **11.** $3x - y \leq 1$ **12.** $x < 6$

Write an inequality for each word sentence. Graph the inequality.

13. The sum of two numbers is greater than 3.

14. A number is greater than or equal to three times another.

15. The y-coordinate of a point is less than twice the x-coordinate.

Write two inequalities. Graph the system of inequalities.

16. Find two numbers such that one is greater than four times the other and their sum is greater than 14.

17. Find two numbers such that the sum is greater than 3 and the difference is less than 5.

WRITTEN EXERCISES

Write the equation of the line you would graph for each inequality. Tell whether the graph would be a solid or a dotted line.

1. $2x + y \geq 3$ **2.** $\frac{1}{2}x - y < 4$ **3.** $y \geq -2$

4. $-3x < 6$ **5.** $x - 4y > 1$ **6.** $3x + 2y > 4$

7. $5x - 3y < 2$ **8.** $2x - y \geq 7$ **9.** $x \geq 9$

10. $x - 2y \leq 4$ **11.** $3x + y < 2$ **12.** $x + 4y \leq 5$

Tell whether the region containing the origin would be shaded in the graph of each inequality.

13. $2x + y \geq 6$ **14.** $\frac{1}{2}x - 2y < 4$ **15.** $y \geq -4$

16. $-3x < 18$ **17.** $x > y$ **18.** $2x - 2y \leq 1$

19. $y > -2x - 1$ **20.** $x + 2y > 4$ **21.** $y > 3x + 1$

Graph each inequality.

22. $2x - y \geq -4$ **23.** $\frac{3}{4}x + 4y < -8$ **24.** $y \geq 2$

25. $-2x < 6$ **26.** $-1 \leq x - 3$ **27.** $10 - y \leq 1$

28. $y + 4 < 3x$ **29.** $y > x + 4$ **30.** $2x + 3y < 9$

31. $x + 6 < 3y$ **32.** $x - y \leq 4$ **33.** $2x - y \geq -2$

34. $x < 6$ **35.** $y > 0$ **36.** $3x > 4y$

MIXED REVIEW

Determine whether each system has one solution, no solution, or infinitely many solutions.

1. $4x - 2y = 6$
$2x - y = 3$

2. $4x - 2y = 6$
$2x - y = 1$

3. $4x - 2y = 6$
$2x + y = 1$

Write three ordered pairs that are solutions of each inequality.

4. $4x - y \leq 6$

5. $5 - 2x - y > x$

Solve.

6. A student has $120 to spend on clothes. Shirts cost $15 and sweaters cost $24.

a. What is the maximum number of shirts she can buy?

b. What is the maximum number of sweaters she can buy?

c. Assume she wants to buy at least one shirt and one sweater. How many of each can she buy?

Write an inequality for each word sentence. Graph the inequality.

37. Find two numbers whose difference is greater than 3.

38. Find two numbers where one is at least three times the other.

39. Timothy has a collection of nickels and dimes valued at less than $1. Let x equal the number of nickels and y equal the number of dimes.

40. A gift wrapper cut a ribbon so that one piece was more than twice as long as the other. Let x equal the shorter piece and y equal the longer piece.

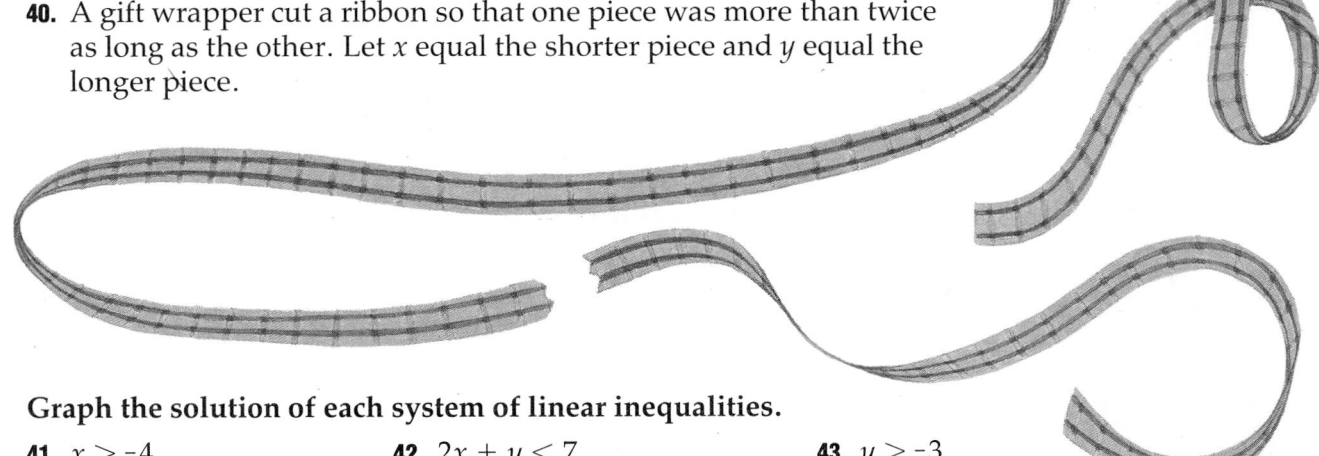

Graph the solution of each system of linear inequalities.

41. $x > -4$
$y \le 0$

42. $2x + y < 7$
$x - y \le 2$

43. $y > -3$
$x < 5$

Use the system of linear inequalities $2x - y \ge 5$ and $\frac{1}{3}x + y < 2$ to find each point described.

44. a point which satisfies the first inequality but not the second

45. a point which satisfies the second inequality but not the first

Write two inequalities. Graph the system of inequalities.

46. Find two numbers where one is more than three times the other and their sum is greater than 12.

47. Find two numbers such that their sum is not more than 10 and the larger is greater than twice the smaller. Let y equal the larger number.

48. A student has a collection of more than 18 dimes and quarters. It is valued at more than $2.80. Let x equal the number of dimes and y equal the number of quarters.

49. **WRITE** two different situations that you could represent by the inequality $y \ge x + 3$.

50. **PROJECT** *Linear programming* is an interesting topic related to inequalities that has numerous real world applications. Research this topic and give some examples of situations where linear programming might be useful.

Practice

In which quadrant or on what axis does each point fall?

1. $(4,5)$ **2.** $(-3,0)$ **3.** $(11,-7)$ **4.** $(-6,-2)$

State the coordinates of each point described. Begin at the origin.

5. the point which is 4 units to the left of the y-axis and down 3 units from the x-axis

6. the point which is 3 units to the right of the y-axis and up 7 units from the x-axis.

Solve for y in terms of x. Find three solutions of each equation.

7. $3x + y = -10$ **8.** $2x + 4y = 8$ **9.** $4x + 2y - 8 = 0$

Find the x-intercept and y-intercept for each equation.

10. $3x - 4y = 12$ **11.** $y = 6x$ **12.** $\frac{4}{5}x - y = 20$

Graph each equation on a separate set of coordinate axes.

13. $x = 8$ **14.** $-4x + y = 16$ **15.** $2y + 6 = -4x$

16. $y = -\frac{1}{2}$ **17.** $2y = -6$ **18.** $|y| = 5$

Find the slope of the line containing the given points.

19. $(1,-1)(-1,1)$ **20.** $(2,-5)(2,4)$ **21.** $(2,-9)(12,3)$

Graph each line described.

22. the line having slope -5 and containing the point $(-3,2)$

23. the line having no slope and containing the point $(6,-1)$

Write each linear equation in slope-intercept form. Name the slope and y-intercept. Sketch the graph of each equation.

24. $6x + y = 24$ **25.** $x - 4y = 12$ **26.** $-x - y = -1$

Solve each system by graphing. Check your solutions.

27. $y = x + 2$ **28.** $x = y - 8$ **29.** $2x + 3y = 8$
    $3x + 4y = 22$ $x - y = 2$ $y = 2x$

Solve each inequality for y in terms of x. Write three ordered pairs that are solutions of each.

30. $7x - 2y < 20$ **31.** $4x + 5y > -6$ **32.** $12x + 2y - 8 > 0$

Graph each inequality.

33. $y > -x + 3$ **34.** $x - y \leq -6$ **35.** $2x + y \geq 1$

8-9 Direct and Indirect Variation

OBJECTIVE:
To solve problems involving direct and indirect variation.

FLASHBACK

Volume is the amount of space an object occupies.

■ The temperature and volume of a gas vary *directly*.

Direct Variation	Direct variation means that as one factor increases the other factor also increases. We represent direct variation by an equation in the form $y = kx$, where k is not zero. k is the constant of variation.

■ *Charles's law* states the relationship between the temperature in degrees Kelvin and volume of a gas.

NOTES & QUOTES

Jacques Charles (1746–1823) was a French scientist. He discovered the relationship between the temperature of a gas and its volume in the late 1700s.

Charles's Law	The volume of a fixed amount of gas varies directly with the temperature of the gas.

Example 1   A gas has a volume of 250 mL at 300°K. The temperature of the gas decreases to 240°K. What is its volume?

Solution   Let x = temperature.
Let y = volume.

$$y = kx \qquad \text{Find } k \text{, the constant of variation.}$$
$$250 = k(300)$$
$$\frac{250}{300} = k$$
$$\frac{5}{6} = k$$
$$y = \frac{5}{6}x \qquad \text{Rewrite the formula.}$$
$$= \frac{5}{6}(240) \qquad \text{Substitute 240 for } x.$$
$$= 200$$

The volume of the gas is 200 mL.

■ The volume and pressure of a gas vary *indirectly*.

NOTES & QUOTES

Robert Boyle (1627–1691) was an Irish scientist. In 1662, he reported the relationship between the pressure and volume of a gas. This is now known as Boyle's law.

Indirect Variation	In indirect variation, one factor increases as the other factor decreases. The equation $xy = k$ represents an indirect variation. k is the constant of variation.

■ *Boyle's law* states the relationship between the volume and pressure of a gas.

Boyle's Law	The volume of a fixed amount of gas varies indirectly with the pressure of the gas.

Example 2   The volume of a gas is 60 ft³ under 5 lb of pressure. What is the gas's volume under 10 lb of pressure?

Solution   Let x = pressure
Let y = volume

$xy = k$ Find k, the constant of variation.
$5(60) = k$
$300 = k$

$xy = 300$ Rewrite the formula.
$10y = 300$ Substitute 10 for y.
$\dfrac{10y}{10} = \dfrac{300}{10}$
$y = 30$

The volume of the gas is 30 ft³.

CLASS EXERCISES

State whether the data varies directly or indirectly. Write an equation to describe each variation. State the constant of variation.

1.
x	y
2	4
3	6
4	8

2.
x	y
6	3
2	9
1	18

3.
x	y
40	120
60	180
80	240

■ ■ ■ ■ ■ ■ ■ Decision Making ■ **DECISION MAKING** ■ Decision Making ■ Decision Making ■ Decision Making ■

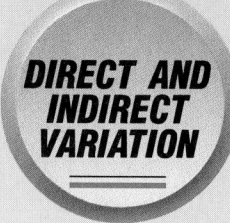

DIRECT AND INDIRECT VARIATION

■   A product is packaged under pressure by inserting a gas into the container.

■ **COLLECT DATA**

1. Find five products that are packaged under pressure.

2. Read each warning label. Write a paragraph telling how the labels are similar to each other.

3. What does packaging a product under pressure allow the contents to do?

■ **ANALYZE DATA**

Support each answer using either Charles's law or Boyle's law.

4. What do you think will happen to a container that is stored above the recommended temperature?

5. When pressure is applied to the container, what will happen to the contents of the container?

WRITTEN EXERCISES

Use a **CALCULATOR** where appropriate.

State whether each equation is a direct or indirect variation. For each variation, state the constant of variation.

1. $y = 30x$

2. $xy = 58$

3. $8.5x = y$

4. $x = \dfrac{10}{y}$

Assume that y varies directly as x.

5. An object weighs 6 times more on Earth than it does on the moon. Ian weighs 165 lb on Earth. What would he weigh on the moon?

6. A gas has a volume of 150 mL at 320°K. The gas's temperature is increased to 360°K. What is its volume to the nearest tenth?

Assume that y varies indirectly as x.

7. A piano string 40 in. long vibrates at a frequency of 520 cycles/s. Find the frequency of the string if it were shortened to 18 in. Round to the nearest whole unit.

8. Pressure acting on 12 m³ of a gas is 20 atmospheres. The pressure is reduced until the volume is 15 m³. What is the new pressure acting on the gas?

9. Amy drove for 4 h at a rate of 40 mi/h. To the nearest hour, how long would it have taken Amy if she drove at 55 mi/h?

Dr. Maria Mayer (1906–1972), Nobel Prize winner in physics, wrote the classic textbook *Statistical Mechanics* along with her husband. They developed the book from their lectures on this branch of physics, which deals with the study of molecules and their atomic makeup.

■ Decision Making ■ Decision Making ■ Decision Making ■ Decision Making ■ Decision Making ■ Decision Making ■

6. Why do container labels suggest that you use pressurized products in well-ventilated areas?

7. Why do airlines recommend that you not bring contents that are under pressure on board a plane?

8. Do you think that there is a minimum temperature that pressurized products must be stored under? Explain.

■ **MAKE DECISIONS**

■ Some products that are packaged under pressure contain gases that are harmful to the environment.

9. What environmental concerns arise from the use of chlorofluorocarbons in a container stored under pressure?

10. What are alternative packaging methods that manufacturers could use?

11. What can we do as individuals to promote these alternatives?

Chapter 8 Review

Write *true* or *false*. If false, change the underlined word(s) to make a true statement.

1. A <u>coordinate</u> pair is a pair of numbers (x,y) assigned to a point on a coordinate plane.

2. A linear equation is an equation for which the graph is a <u>line</u>.

3. The x-intercept is the x-coordinate of the point at which the graph of a linear equation intersects the <u>y-axis</u>.

4. A linear equation in the form $y = mx + b$ is in slope-intercept form. The slope is <u>b</u>, and the y-intercept is <u>m</u>.

5. When you graph a linear inequality in two variables, the line <u>is part of</u> the solution if the inequality symbol is $<$ or $>$.

The Coordinate Plane   8-1

To locate $P(x,y)$ on the coordinate plane,

    1. Begin at the origin.

    2. Move x units along the x-axis.

    3. Move $|y|$ units up or down.

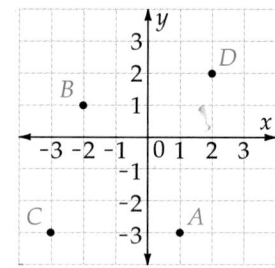

State the coordinates of each point.

6. A **7.** B **8.** C **9.** D

Solving Equations   8-2

To solve an equation in two variables, choose a value for x. Then substitute the x value into the equation to find the y value. Write the solution as an ordered pair.

Write the solution for the given value of x.

10. $2x + 5y = 12;\ x = 1$ **11.** $3x = -\frac{1}{2}y + 5;\ x = 2$ **12.** $3(x - 1) = 2y;\ x = 3$

Graphing Linear Equations   8-3

To graph a linear equation,

    1. Solve for y in terms of x.

    2. Find three solutions to the equation.

    3. Plot the points and draw a straight line.

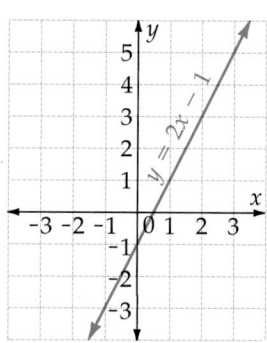

Determine whether each point is on the graph.

13. $(1,1)$ **14.** $(2,2)$ **15.** $(-1,-3)$ **16.** $(3,5)$

Slope and y-intercept

To find the slope of a line when you know the coordinates of any two points on the line, use the slope formula.

$$\text{slope} = \frac{\text{difference in } y\text{-coordinates}}{\text{difference in } x\text{-coordinates}}$$

An equation in the form $y = mx + b$ is in slope-intercept form. The slope is m and the y-intercept is b.

Find the slope of the line containing the given points.

17. $(1,3)(2,5)$ **18.** $(-1,0)(1,3)$ **19.** $(2,-2)(3,-3)$ **20.** $(-6,7)(4,7)$

Write each linear equation in slope-intercept form. Name the slope and y-intercept.

21. $y - 2x = 3$ **22.** $\frac{1}{2}x + y = -2$ **23.** $2x + 2y = 10$ **24.** $5 - 2y = 10x$

Problem Solving

To solve a word problem using a graph, write the given information as ordered pairs, plot the points, and draw a line. Find the missing information by reading the graph.

25. A car uses 10 L of gasoline to travel 90 km. How much gasoline will the car use to travel 198 km?

Solving Systems of Linear Equations

To solve a system of linear equations, graph both equations on the same coordinate plane. A solution is any ordered pair that satisfies all equations in the system.

Tell whether the ordered pair is a solution of the system.

26. $y = 2x - 1$
$3y + 2x = 13$
$(2,3)$

27. $3x - 2y = 10$
$x + y = 0$
$(-2,-8)$

28. $\frac{1}{3}x + 2y = 1$
$\frac{3}{4}x + \frac{1}{4}y = -2$
$(-3,1)$

Solving and Graphing Linear Inequalities

A solution of a linear inequality is an ordered pair that makes the inequality true.

To graph a linear inequality, graph the related equation. Determine if the line should be solid or dotted and whether the solutions are above or below the line. Shade in the appropriate region.

Graph each inequality. Give three ordered pair solutions.

29. $y \geq x + 2$ **30.** $y < x - 3$ **31.** $y > x + 3$ **32.** $y < x + 3$

Chapter 8   *Test*

In which quadrant or on which axis does each point fall?

1. $(-5, 7)$ **2.** $(0, -4)$ **3.** $(-8, -6)$

Write an equation using two variables. Find three solutions.

4. Mrs. Jones bought eight cans of juice. Some were orange juice and some were apple juice. Let x = the number of cans of orange juice and let y = the number of cans of apple juice.

5. A collection of nickels and dimes is valued at $2.50. Let x = the number of nickels and y = the number of dimes.

Find the slope of the line containing the given points.

6. $(5, 1)(8, -2)$ **7.** $(6, 3)(-2, 4)$ **8.** $(-4, 3)(6, -5)$

Write each linear equation in slope-intercept form. Name the slope and y-intercept.

9. $x + \frac{1}{2}y = 4$ **10.** $6x - 3y = 6$ **11.** $3x = 4y + 1$

Graph each equation on a separate set of coordinate axes.

12. $3x + y = 4$ **13.** $2x - y = 1$ **14.** $y = 3x + 1$

Write a system of linear equations. Find the solution.

15. A piece of ribbon 30 in. long is cut into 2 pieces. One piece is 5 times as long as the other. How long is each piece of ribbon?

16. The sum of two numbers is 35. When the greater number is decreased by 3 times the lesser number, the result is 15.

Solve each system by graphing. Check your solutions.

17. $x + y = 3$ **18.** $x + 3y = 6$ **19.** $y = 2x + 3$
     $x - y = 1$ $x + 3y = 9$ $3y - 6x = 9$

Write an inequality. Find three solutions.

20. Find two numbers whose sum is less than 5.

Graph each inequality or system.

21. $x + y > 1$ **22.** $x - y < 2$ **23.** $y + 2 < x$
                                                       $y - 3x > 2$

Chapters 1–8   Cumulative Review

Choose the correct answer. Write A, B, C, or D.

1. In which quadrant does $\left(-1\frac{1}{2}, 2\right)$ fall?

  A. I   **B.** II

  C. III   **D.** not given

2. Find a solution of $2x + y = 3$.

  A. $(-1, 2)$ **B.** $(-1, 1)$

  C. $(2, -1)$ **D.** not given

3. State the inequality of which $(3,1)$ is a solution.

  A. $2x - y \geq 5$ **B.** $2x - y < 5$

  C. $2x - y > 5$ **D.** not given

4. Find the missing digit so that the resulting number is divisible by 9.

  $5,76\boxed{},239$

  A. 1   **B.** 9

  C. 4   **D.** not given

5. Evaluate $\frac{3}{7} \div 1\frac{2}{5}$.

  A. $\frac{3}{5}$ **B.** $3\frac{4}{5}$

  C. $\frac{5}{7}$ **D.** not given

6. Compare $\frac{5}{8} \ \blacksquare \ \frac{3}{5}$.

  A. $>$ **B.** $<$

  C. $=$ **D.** not given

7. 37.5% of a is 36. What is a?

  A. 96   **B.** 48

  C. 64   **D.** not given

8. Write the inequality.

  $\xleftarrow{\quad}\overset{\displaystyle\circ}{\underset{-3\ -2\ -1\ \ 0\ \ 1}{\rule{0pt}{0pt}}}$

  A. $x < -2$ **B.** $x > -2$

  C. $x \geq -2$ **D.** not given

9. Solve $-2(x - 1) \leq -6$.

  A. $x \leq 3$ **B.** $x \leq -3$

  C. $x \geq 3$ **D.** not given

10. Write 132% as a decimal.

  A. 0.132   **B.** 13.2

  C. 1.32   **D.** not given

11. Find the slope of the line containing the points $(3,2)$ and $(1,-2)$.

  A. -2 **B.** 2

  C. 1   **D.** not given

12. Write an inequality to describe the situation. A movie costs \$5. A drink costs \$1. Aaron did not spend more than \$7.

  A. $5x + 1y = 7$ **B.** $5x + 1y \leq 7$

  C. $5x + 1y < 7$ **D.** not given

13. Write 0.28 as a fraction in lowest terms.

  A. $\frac{28}{100}$ **B.** $\frac{7}{25}$

  C. $\frac{2}{25}$ **D.** not given

14. Write 9.05×10^8 in standard notation.

  A. 905,000,000   **B.** 90,500,000

  C. 90,500,000,000   **D.** not given

15. Simplify $\frac{8a^2b^{-3}c}{24a^3bc^{-2}}$.

  A. $\frac{c^3}{3ab^4}$ **B.** $3a^5b^{-2}c$

  C. $\frac{b^{-2}}{3ac}$ **D.** not given

16. Find the y-intercept of the equation $x + 2y = -4$.

  A. -4 **B.** -2

  C. $-\frac{1}{2}$ **D.** not given

*T*here are two different types of golf clubs—woods and irons. Woods have a bit more weight in the head and thus hit the ball farther. Irons are used for accuracy.

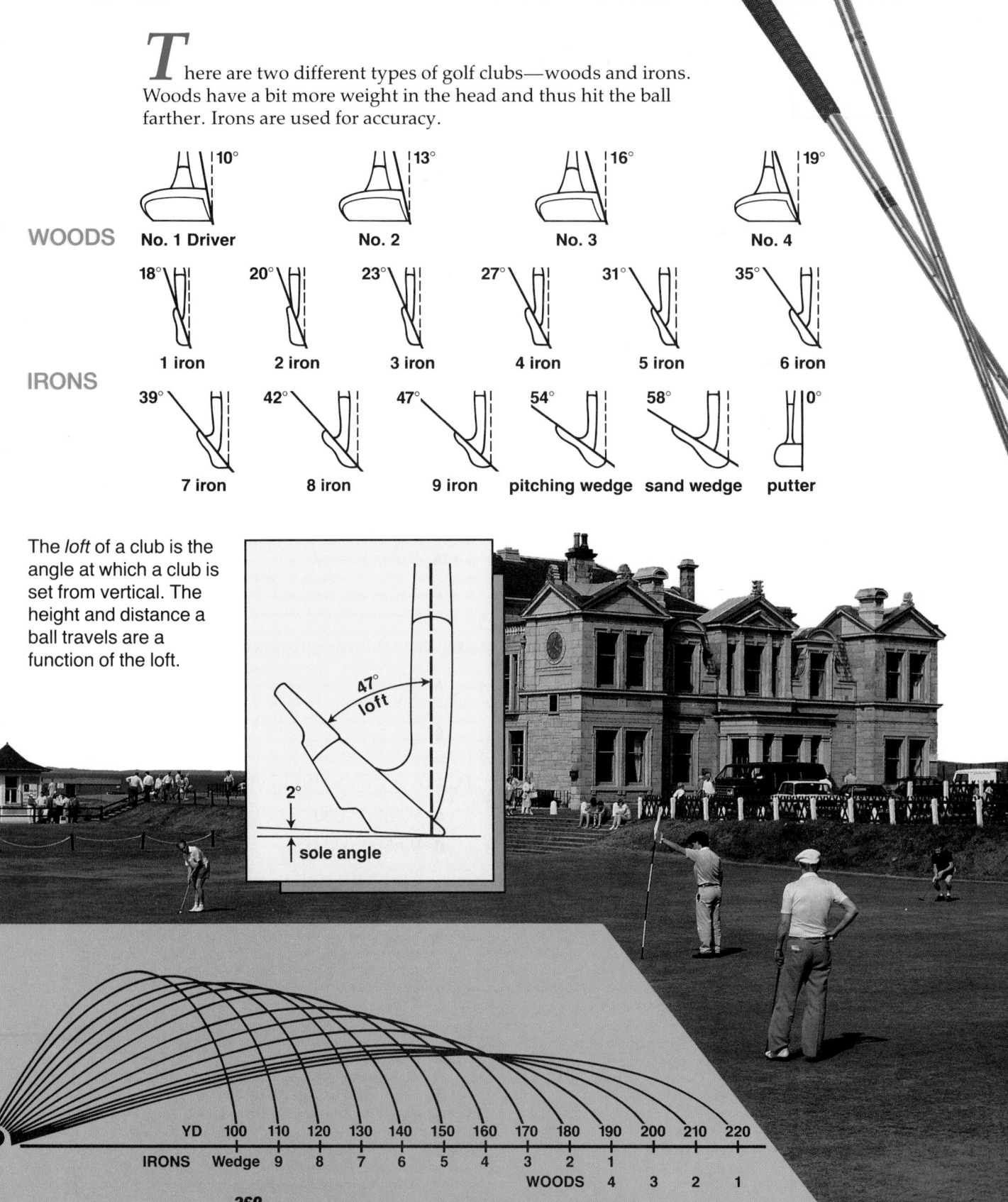

WOODS

10°	13°	16°	19°
No. 1 Driver	No. 2	No. 3	No. 4

IRONS

18°	20°	23°	27°	31°	35°
1 iron	2 iron	3 iron	4 iron	5 iron	6 iron

39°	42°	47°	54°	58°	0°
7 iron	8 iron	9 iron	pitching wedge	sand wedge	putter

The *loft* of a club is the angle at which a club is set from vertical. The height and distance a ball travels are a function of the loft.

47° loft

2°

↑ sole angle

YD	100	110	120	130	140	150	160	170	180	190	200	210	220
IRONS Wedge		9	8	7	6	5	4	3	2	1			
								WOODS			4	3	2	1

360

Algebra in Geometry and Measurement

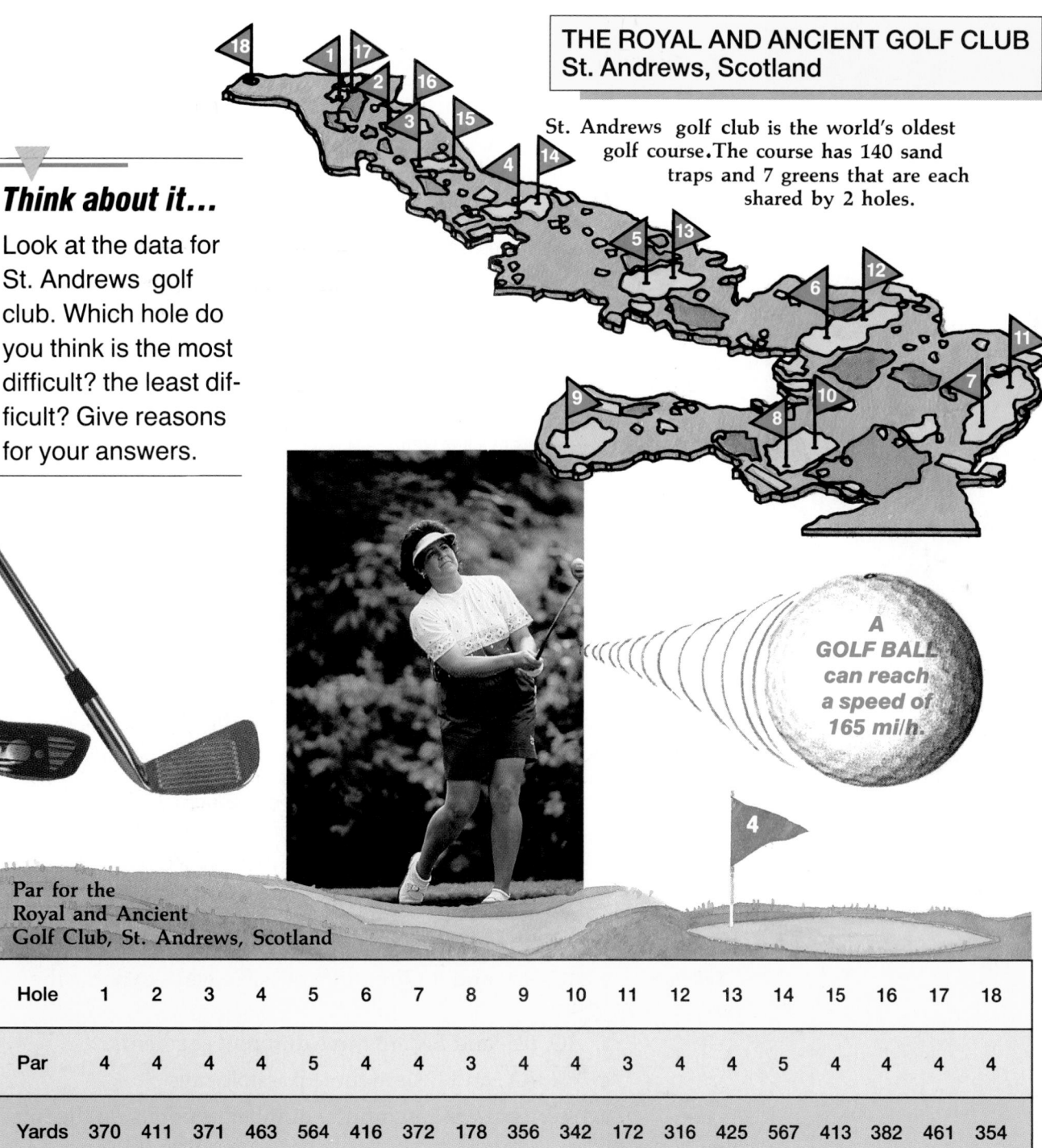

THE ROYAL AND ANCIENT GOLF CLUB
St. Andrews, Scotland

St. Andrews golf club is the world's oldest golf course. The course has 140 sand traps and 7 greens that are each shared by 2 holes.

Think about it...

Look at the data for St. Andrews golf club. Which hole do you think is the most difficult? the least difficult? Give reasons for your answers.

A **GOLF BALL** can reach a speed of 165 mi/h.

Par for the
Royal and Ancient
Golf Club, St. Andrews, Scotland

Hole	1	2	3	4	5	6	7	8	9	10	11	12	13	14	15	16	17	18
Par	4	4	4	4	5	4	4	3	4	4	3	4	4	5	4	4	4	4
Yards	370	411	371	463	564	416	372	178	356	342	172	316	425	567	413	382	461	354

9-1 Introduction to Geometry

▼ Geometric shapes are evident in many man-made and natural structures. The hexagonal design of the snowflake or honeycomb and the spiral design of the snail are but two examples of geometry in nature.

▼ The table illustrates some basic geometric figures.

Figure	Properties	Example	Symbol	Read as
Point	• represents a position in space	• *A*	*A*	*point A*
Line	• continues without end in opposite directions	*A* *B*	$\overleftrightarrow{AB}$	*line AB*
Plane	• is a flat surface with no thickness that continues without end in all directions	*A* *B* *M* *D* *C*	*ABCD* *M*	*plane ABCD* or *plane M*
Segment	• is part of a line with two endpoints	*A* *B*	$\overline{AB}$	*segment AB*
Ray	• is part of a line with only one endpoint • continues without end in one direction	*A* *B*	$\overrightarrow{AB}$	*ray AB*

▼ You can name a line by any two points on the line.

NOTES & QUOTES

One need not know the profoundest mysteries of geometry to be able to discern its usefulness.
–Robert Boyle (1627–1691)

Example 1 **Use the figure at the right.**

a. Give three ways, other than line *AB*, to name the line.

b. Name three different segments.

c. Name three different rays.

d. Are there points other than *A*, *B*, *C*, and *X* on the line?

Solution a. $\overleftrightarrow{AC}$, $\overleftrightarrow{BA}$, and $\overleftrightarrow{BX}$ are three possible ways to name the line.

b. $\overline{AC}$, $\overline{BC}$, and $\overline{BX}$ are three different segments.

c. $\overrightarrow{AX}$, $\overrightarrow{BX}$, and $\overrightarrow{CA}$ are three possible rays.

d. Yes. There are an infinite number of points on the line.

▼ When lines, rays, and segments intersect, the intersection is a point. *Parallel lines* (∥ lines) are lines that are always the same distance apart and never intersect.

Parallel Lines	Two lines are parallel if they lie in the same plane and do not intersect.
Parallel Planes	Two planes are parallel if they do not intersect.
Skew Lines	Skew lines are lines that do not lie in the same plane and do not intersect.

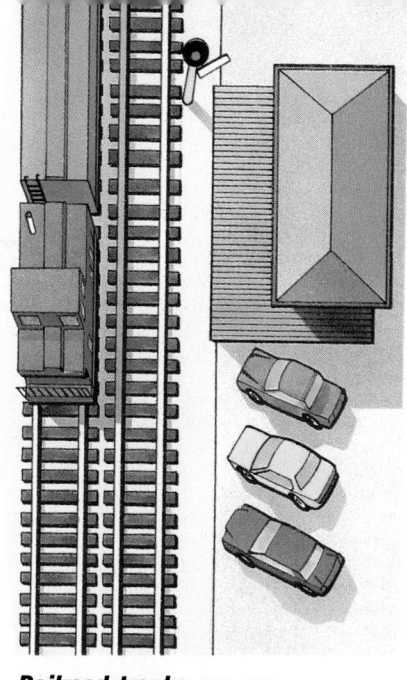

Railroad tracks are an example of parallel lines. Can you think of an example of parallel planes?

▼ Unless you are given other instructions, you will be judging the geometric properties of figures in this book by appearance.

Example 2 Use graph paper to draw and label a figure containing three lines. Make two of the lines parallel.

Solution

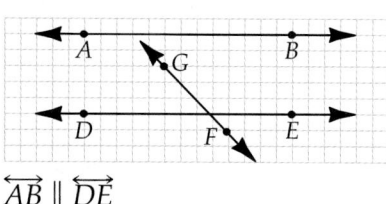

$\overleftrightarrow{AB} \parallel \overleftrightarrow{DE}$

CLASS EXERCISES

Use the figure at the right.

1. Name the line in three ways. ꙅ꙳ꙏꙊ/Ꙍꙍꙅ, ꙌꙊꙅꙏ
2. Name three different segments. ꙅꙊ, ꙏꙌ, ꙏꙌ
3. Name three rays.

Use dot paper or graph paper to draw and label a figure to fit each description.

4. intersecting lines $\overleftrightarrow{AB}$ and $\overleftrightarrow{CD}$
5. parallel rays $\overrightarrow{MN}$ and $\overrightarrow{OP}$
6. point Q on $\overline{MN}$ and $\overline{XY}$
7. $\overleftrightarrow{CD}$ containing point X

8. **WRITE** a description of the streets in your neighborhood. Use the street names and the terms *parallel* and *intersecting* as appropriate. Could streets in a town form skew lines? Why or why not?

THINK AND DISCUSS

1. Look around your classroom. Give an example of a point, a line, skew lines, and a plane.

2. Describe how parallel lines would look on a sphere.

3. Why would a three-legged table stand firmly on the ground while a four-legged table might wobble?

4. If lines are not parallel, must they intersect?

WRITTEN EXERCISES

1. Name all possible segments in the figure below using the points labeled.

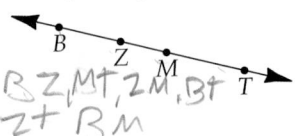

BZ,MT,ZM,Bt T
Z+ BM

2. Name four different rays in the figure below.

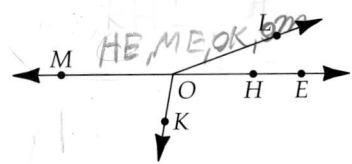

3. Points A, B, C, and D are collinear (all on a line) and in the same order. Name $\overrightarrow{DA}$ three different ways. DA DA DA

4. Draw a figure in which $\overleftrightarrow{ZR}$ contains P and $\overline{PQ}$ contains R.

   a. Is only one figure possible? If *no*, show an alternate figure.

   b. Is R between Q and P? Yes

   c. Must $\overleftrightarrow{ZR}$ contain P? N

   d. Could $\overrightarrow{ZR}$ contain P? y

5. How many lines can you draw that contain a given point Q? that contain two given points X and Y? 2, S

6. a. Suppose a town installs a mailbox at point M. How many straight roads can the town build leading to M? 8

   b. Suppose a town installs mailboxes at points M and A. How many straight roads might the town build that pass by both mailboxes? 16

7. WRITE Remember to use complete sentences.

   a. Describe the intersection of two planes.

   b. Give a physical example of the intersection of two planes.

8. Planes M and N do not intersect. What can you conclude?

M and N are Parallel lines

Write an equation and then find the length of each segment.

9. 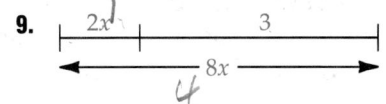   4

10. 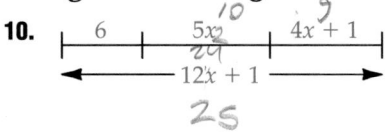   25

True or false?

11. Skew lines never intersect. F

12. A ray has two endpoints. T

13. A line has no endpoints. T

14. A segment has two endpoints. T

15. PROJECT Collect at least five pictures from magazines and catalogs that show geometry in the real world. **WRITE** a sentence for each picture to explain the connection.

MIXED REVIEW

1. Graph the points $A(5,0)$, $B(6,3)$, $C(1,1)$. Connect A to B and B to C.

2. $a = \frac{b}{2} + c - 2$. Find a if $b = 11$ and $c = 3$.

3. What percent of 73 is 25?

4. A 12-oz can of juice costs 69¢. What would you expect to pay for a 16-oz can?

Solve.

5. $2x + 8 = 12$

6. $3 + \frac{a}{8} = 11$

7. How many three-digit numbers, greater than 500, can you form using the digits 2, 6, and 8 exactly once each?

9-2 Angles

▼ When lines or parts of lines intersect, they form angles. Different angles contribute to designs on quilts, tile floors, stained glass windows, and other forms of art and architecture.

▼ You can name an angle by the vertex and points on the sides, by a number, or by the vertex alone. When using three letters, the middle letter always names the vertex.

Angle	Two rays with a common endpoint form an angle.

Example 1 **Name the angle shown in four different ways.**

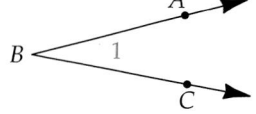

Solution $\angle ABC$, $\angle 1$, $\angle B$, $\angle CBA$

FLASHBACK

The symbol ∟ indicates a right angle. Perpendicular lines form right angles.

▼ We classify angles by their measure in degrees (°). The notation $m\angle ABC$ means *the measure of angle ABC.*

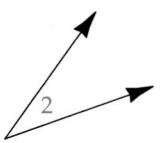

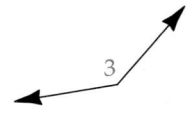

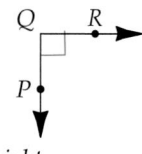

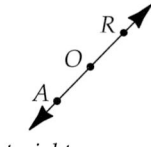

acute	*obtuse*	*right*	*straight*
less than 90°	between 90° and 180°	equals 90°	equals 180°
$m\angle 2 < 90°$	$90° < m\angle 3 < 180°$	$m\angle PQR = 90°$	$m\angle AOR = 180°$

▼ We use a protractor to measure and draw angles.

Example 2 **Use a protractor to measure $\angle XYZ$.**

1. Place the center point of the protractor on Y, the vertex of the angle.

2. Position the protractor so that $\overrightarrow{YZ}$ passes through zero on the protractor scale. Estimate to decide which scale to read. Is $\angle XYZ$ acute or obtuse?

3. Read the angle measure at the point where $\overrightarrow{YX}$ passes through the protractor scale.

Solution $m\angle XYZ = 29°$

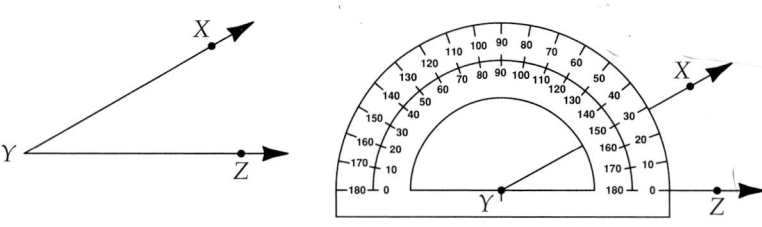

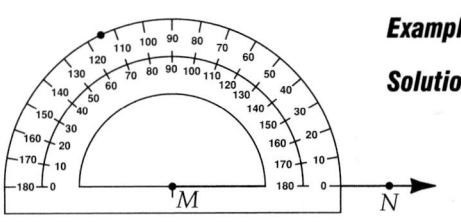

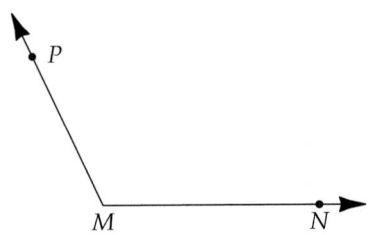

Example 3 Use a protractor to draw an angle with measure 115°.

Solution 1. Draw and label a ray.

2. Place the center point of the protractor on the endpoint of the ray. Line up the ray so that it passes through zero.

3. Mark a point at 115° on the protractor scale.

4. Remove the protractor. Draw a ray connecting the endpoint of the ray and the point marked at 115°.

5. $m\angle PMN = 115°$

▼ You can add or subtract the measures of *adjacent angles*.

Adjacent Angles	Two angles that have the same vertex and have a common side but no interior points in common form adjacent angles.	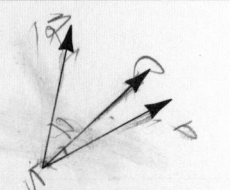
Supplementary Angles	Two angles are supplementary angles if the sum of their measures is 180°.	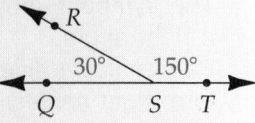
Complementary Angles	Two angles are complementary angles if the sum of their measures is 90°.	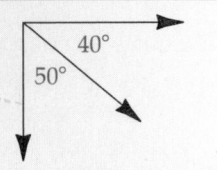

Example 4 $m\angle XOZ = 180°$. Find $m\angle YOX$.

Solution
$$35° + m\angle YOX = 180°$$
$$35° + m\angle YOX - 35° = 180° - 35°$$
$$m\angle YOX = 145°$$

$\angle XOY$ and $\angle YOZ$ are supplementary. Subtract 35° from each side.

▼ When segments, rays, or lines intersect, they form vertical angles.

Vertical Angles	Two intersecting lines form two pairs of vertical angles. The measures of vertical angles are equal.

Example 5 **Find the value of x and y.**

Solution $x = 28$ $y = 152$

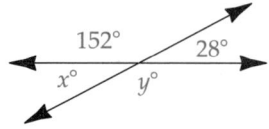

Example 6 Find the measure of each numbered angle.

Solution $m\angle 1 = 90° - 26° = 64°$
$m\angle 2 = 180° - 90° = 90°$
$m\angle 3 = 26°$
$m\angle 4 = m\angle 1 = 64°$
$m\angle 5 = m\angle 2 = 90°$

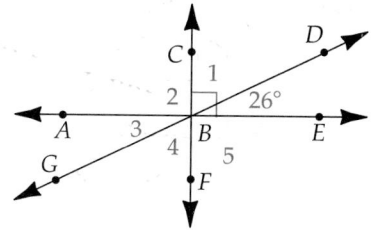

THINK AND DISCUSS
1. Describe a real world example of vertical angles.
2. How can you measure an angle if one ray is not on the base line of the protractor?
3. Can a pair of vertical angles be adjacent? Why or why not?

CLASS EXERCISES

Refer to the figure at the right.

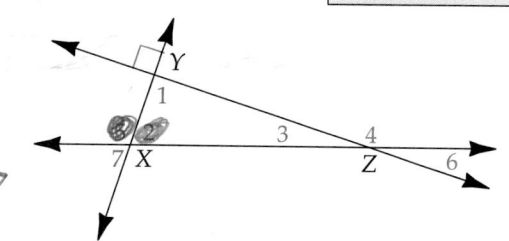

1. Give another name for $\angle 1$. $\angle Y$
2. Find $m\angle 5 + m\angle 2$.
3. Name a pair of supplementary angles. $\times, 7$
4. Name a pair of adjacent angles. $4, 3$
5. Is $\angle Y$ acute, obtuse, or right? right
6. State the relationship between $\overleftrightarrow{XZ}$ and $\overleftrightarrow{ZY}$. both line segments
7. Name two pairs of vertical angles. $\times, z y$
8. $m\angle 3 = t°$ and $m\angle 4 = 9t°$. Find the value of t.
   2

WRITTEN EXERCISES

Classify each angle as acute, obtuse, right, or straight.

1. 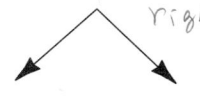 right
2. 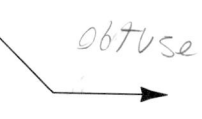 obtuse
3. 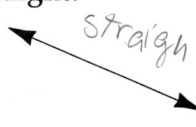 straight
4.  right
5.  acute
6. acute 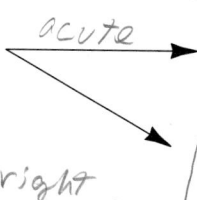 right

7. Under what conditions are two angles supplementary?
8. Use a drawing to illustrate vertical angles.

Name two pairs of vertical angles in each figure. RT

9. 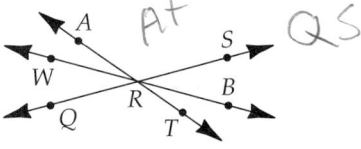 At QS
10. 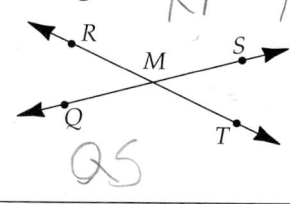 QS

Describe the angles in the photograph.

Find the measure of each indicated angle.

11. ∠ACD and ∠ACB

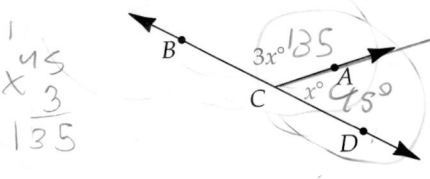

12. ∠QRT and ∠QRU

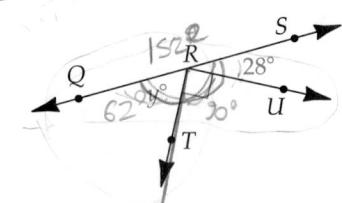

13. ∠TMX

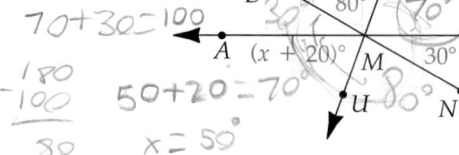

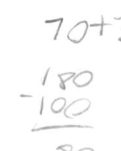

14. ∠AMT and ∠TMH

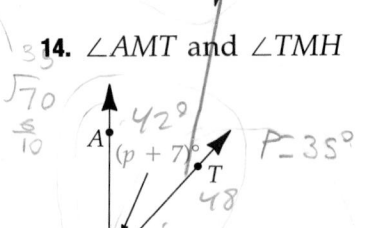

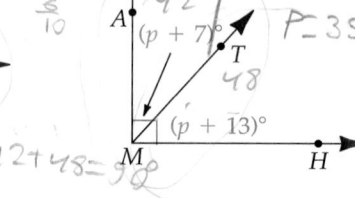

PROBLEM SOLVING HINT
Try guess and test.

15. Find an angle with a measure that is twice as great as a supplement.

16. Find a pair of supplementary angles such that the difference of their measures is 56°.

Use a protractor to measure each angle.

17.

18.

19.

20.

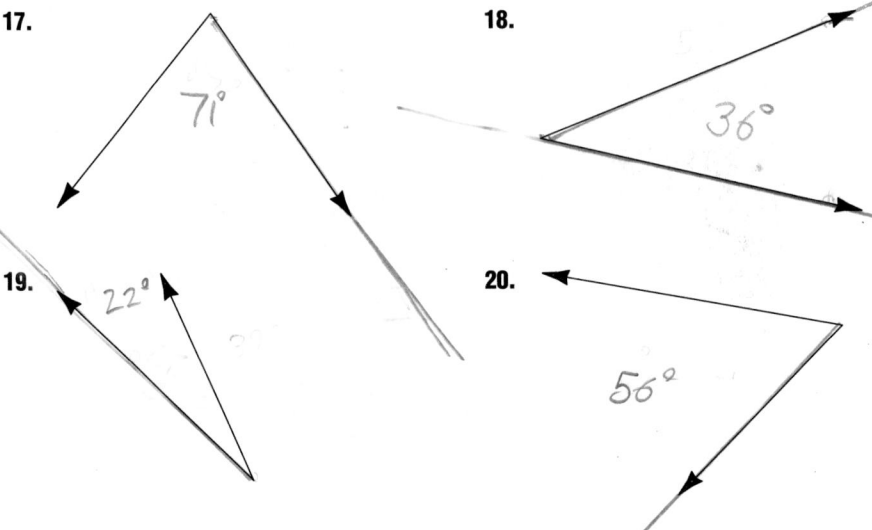

MIXED REVIEW
Solve for y in terms of x.
1. x = 4y − 8
2. x − y + 12 = 2x

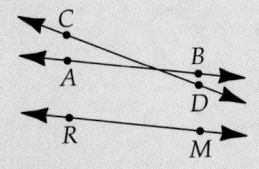

3. Name one pair of parallel segments.

4. $\overline{CD}$ and $\overline{AB}$ are called ▨ segments.

5. The Jones' monthly mortgage payment is $1,237. There is a 2% penalty if the payment is late. How much is the penalty?

Tell whether each angle is acute, right, obtuse, or straight.

21. 65°   **22.** 45°   **23.** 90°   **24.** 180°

25. 125°   **26.** 27°   **27.** 21°   **28.** 108°

Find the measure of a complement and a supplement of each angle, if possible.

29. 90°   **30.** 18°   **31.** 115°   **32.** 89°

33. 43°   **34.** x°   **35.** (y − 20)°   **36.** (3a)°

Exploring Segments and Angles

▼ You can use a geoboard to explore many geometric concepts. As you complete the activities that follow, think about the ideas of segments and angles. The geoboard at the right shows a segment *one unit in length.*

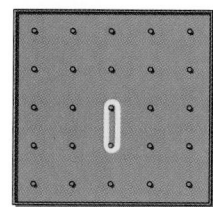

MATERIALS

- Geoboards and colored rubber bands or
- Dot paper and colored pencils
- Math journal to record work

1. Use your geoboard or dot paper to represent a segment of the given length.

   a. 2 units   **b.** 4 units   **c.** 5 units

2. What is the longest segment you can show? Explain how you know you have the longest possible segment.

▼ In geometry, the word *congruent* means *same size and same shape.*

3. **Model** the following on your geoboard or draw on dot paper.

   a. two or more congruent segments

   b. two intersecting segments that are not congruent
   Discuss the ways your segments might intersect.

   c. two parallel segments; three parallel segments
   Discuss the ways your segments might be parallel.

   d. two perpendicular segments
   Discuss the ways your segments might be perpendicular.

4. Show each figure below on your geoboard or on dot paper. **Classify** each angle as acute, obtuse, right, or straight.

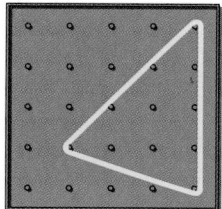 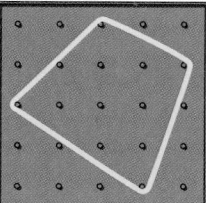 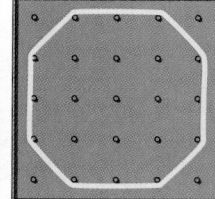 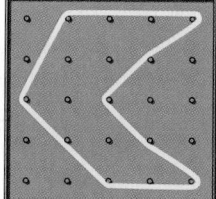

▼ Shapes you make with one rubber band in which edges do not cross or touch are called *polygons.* A place where the band turns a corner (or is hooked on a peg) is called a *vertex.* The segment joining two vertices is called a *side.*

5. Make several polygons on your geoboard or dot paper. Make each one a different color. State the number of vertices and sides for each polygon you made.

6. What are some limitations you experience when modeling figures on a geoboard?

9-3 Polygons and Quadrilaterals

▼ Many of the shapes you see in the world around you and in art are examples of *polygons*.

Describe the polygons you see in the picture of the pyramidal entrance to the Louvre Museum.

Polygon	A polygon is a closed plane figure such that no two segments with a common endpoint are collinear and segments intersect only at the endpoints.

Example 1 State whether or not each figure is a polygon.

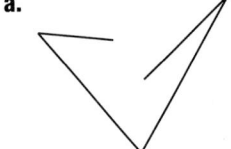 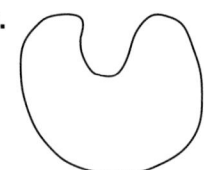 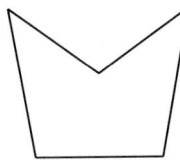

a.   b.   c.

Solution   **a.** no (not closed)   **b.** no (not segments)   **c.** yes

▼ Polygons may be *convex* or *concave*.

Convex and Concave Polygons	A polygon is convex if all points on the diagonals are inside the polygon. Otherwise, the polygon is concave.

FLASHBACK

A *diagonal* is a segment that joins two nonconsecutive vertices.

Example 2 Determine whether each polygon is convex or concave.

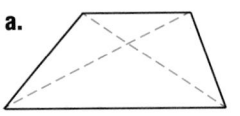 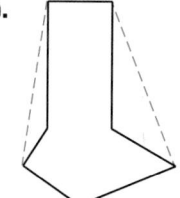 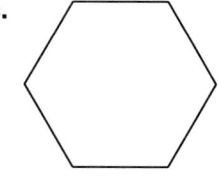

a.   b.   c.

Solution   **a.** convex   **b.** concave   **c.** convex

▼ A polygon is *regular* if the measures of all sides and all angles are equal.

Example 3 Decide if the polygon is regular.

a.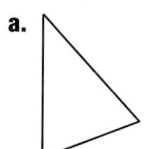

b.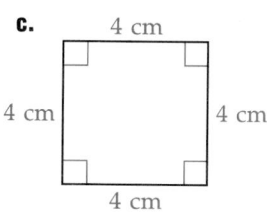

c.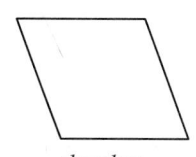

Solution a. no   b. no   c. yes

Number of Sides	Polygon
3	triangle
4	quadrilateral
5	pentagon
6	hexagon
7	heptagon
8	octagon
9	nonagon
10	decagon
12	dodecagon
n	n-gon

▼ Some quadrilaterals have special names and properties.

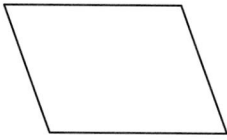

parallelogram
two pairs of opposite parallel sides

rectangle
parallelogram with four right angles

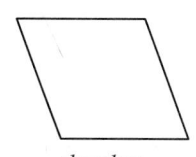

rhombus
parallelogram with all sides equal

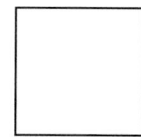

square
a parallelogram that is both a rectangle and a rhombus

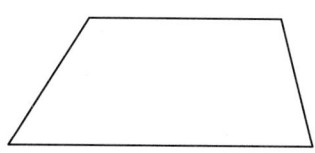

trapezoid
exactly one pair of parallel sides

▼
THINK Is a trapezoid a parallelogram?

CLASS EXERCISES

State whether or not the figure is a polygon.

1.

2.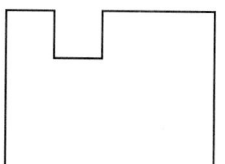

3.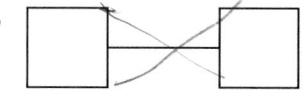

Give three correct names for each figure. Choose from polygon, quadrilateral, parallelogram, rectangle, square, or trapezoid.

4.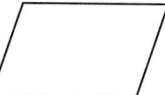

5.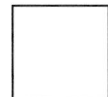

6.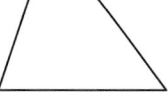

▼
THINK AND DISCUSS

1. Use a Venn diagram to show the relationship between quadrilaterals, squares, parallelograms, trapezoids, rhombuses, and rectangles.

2. Can a regular polygon be concave?

3. Which quadrilateral is a regular polygon?

WRITTEN EXERCISES

True or false? Write _T_ or _F_.

1. Every rhombus is a regular quadrilateral.
2. All quadrilaterals are parallelograms.
3. Some trapezoids are squares.
4. All squares are rectangles.
5. All rectangles are squares.
6. Some rectangles are rhombuses.
7. Some parallelograms are squares.
8. All parallelograms are quadrilaterals.

Give two other correct names for each figure.

9. square _ABCD_

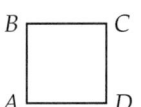

10. parallelogram _BASE_

11. trapezoid _QRTS_

Determine whether the polygon is concave or convex. Then classify the polygon by the number of sides.

12.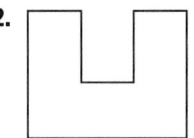

13.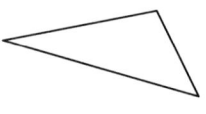

14.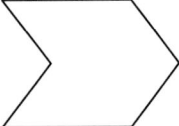

Draw a figure to fit each description.

15. a convex quadrilateral
16. a concave hexagon
17. a pentagon
18. a rhombus

19. Look at convex hexagon _ABCDEF_. How many diagonals can you draw from vertex _A_? How many triangles are formed?

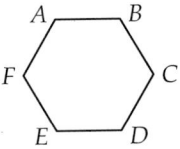

20. **_PROJECT_** Use or make a tangram.

   a. Classify the pieces in as many ways as possible.

   b. Use any number of pieces to form a square, a hexagon, a pentagon, a trapezoid, and a parallelogram.

   c. Record the number of pieces used to make each figure.

   d. Compare with a classmate. Did you both use the same pieces to make the figures? Is there more than one way to make each figure?

MIXED REVIEW

Simplify.

1. x^2 for $x = 2.5$
2. $2y^3$ for $y = 0.8$
3. Find a supplement to a 120° angle.
4. Find a complement to a 43° angle.
5. Name the vertex in angle _ABC_.

Solve.

6. $3a - 4 > 7$
7. $4y = 17 + 3y$
8. Joe bought 7 more tickets than Ellen. Together they bought 19 tickets. How many tickets did each buy?

Exploring with LOGO

MATERIALS

• graph paper

• LOGO software and a computer (optional)

• Math journal to record work

LOGO COMMANDS

FD	forward
BK	back
RT	right turn
LT	left turn
PU	pen up
PD	pen down

■ You can use LOGO to draw segments, angles, and polygons.

1. a. Sketch what you think the following commands will produce. Then, if possible, try them on a computer.

FD 25
RT 45
FD 25
RT 45

b. Classify the angle from part(a).

c. What command determines the measure of the angle? What numbers would give an acute angle? an obtuse angle?

d. Suppose you change the second and fourth lines from RT to LT. Does this change your angle measure?

e. Write a procedure to make an animal from segments and angles. Use the commands at the left.

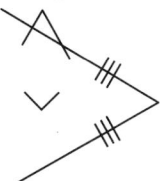

2. a. Sketch what you think the following commands will produce. Then, if possible, try them on a computer.

FD 65 RT 90 FD 65 RT 90
FD 65 RT 90 FD 65 RT 90

b. What would you change to make a larger square?

c. What would you change to draw a rectangle that is not a square?

d. What would you change to draw a rhombus?

■ You can use the REPEAT command to shorten your procedures.

3. Type in the following POLYGON procedure.

TO POLYGON :LENGTH :SIDES

REPEAT :SIDES [FD :LENGTH RT 360 / :SIDES]

END

a. Choose a value for LENGTH. Replace SIDES with 3 and then with 4. What types of polygons did you get?

b. What would SIDES be for a hexagon?

c. Try greater and greater values for SIDES. ***Describe*** what happens to your polygon.

9-4 Triangles

▼ The framework of a geodesic dome is made up of triangles. Engineers use triangles to lend stability to bridges and other structures.

▼ We classify triangles by their angles or sides.

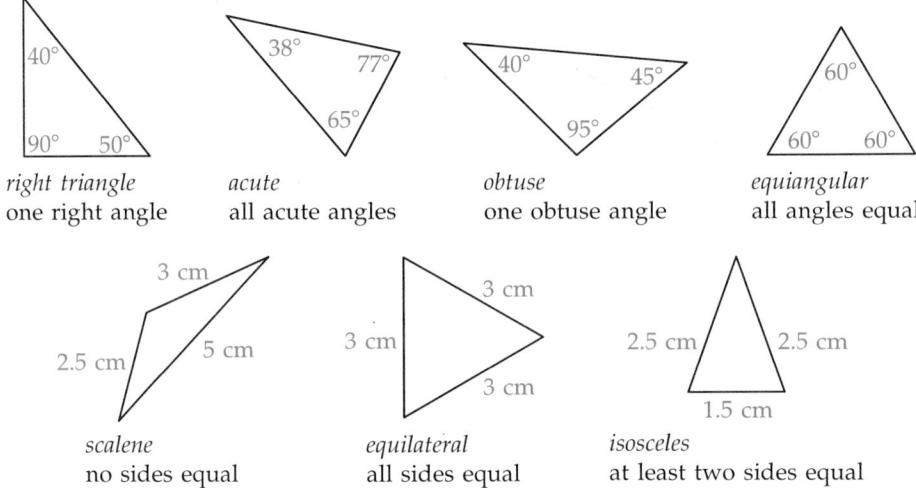

right triangle
one right angle

acute
all acute angles

obtuse
one obtuse angle

equiangular
all angles equal

scalene
no sides equal

equilateral
all sides equal

isosceles
at least two sides equal

THINK How could you use a protractor to find the sum of the measures of the interior angles of a triangle?

▼ You can do an experiment to show that the sum of the measures of the interior angles of a triangle is 180°.

a. Draw and label any triangle *ABC*. Tear off any two angles. (*B* and *C* for example)

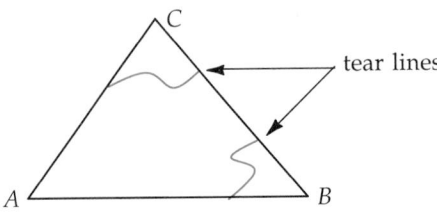

tear lines

b. Position *B* and *C* next to *A*, bringing vertices together. Notice that the angles form a straight angle.

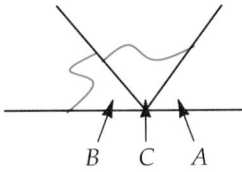

$$m\angle A + m\angle B + m\angle C = 180°$$

Example Find $m\angle 1$.

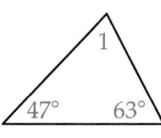

Solution
$$m\angle 1 + 47° + 63° = 180°$$
$$m\angle 1 + 110° = 180°$$
$$m\angle 1 = 180° - 110°$$
$$= 70°$$

CLASS EXERCISES

Classify each triangle as acute, obtuse, or right.

1.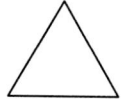

2.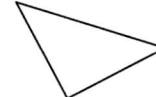

3.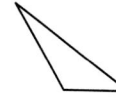

Draw a figure to fit each description.

4. right triangle *ABC*

5. an obtuse scalene triangle

6. isosceles triangle *TRI*

7. a regular triangle

THINK AND DISCUSS

1. Does a triangle have diagonals? Explain.

2. Are all equilateral triangles isosceles? Are all isosceles triangles equilateral? Explain.

3. What is a common name for a regular triangle?

WRITTEN EXERCISES

Classify each triangle by its angles or its sides.

1.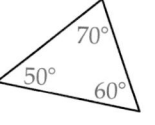

2.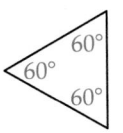

3.

4.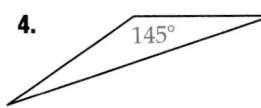

5.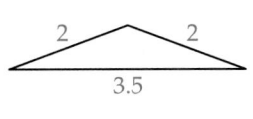

6.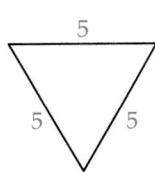

True or false? Write *T* or *F*.

7. No equilateral triangles are scalene.

8. All right triangles are isosceles.

9. Some right triangles are isosceles.

10. Some right triangles are obtuse.

11. All triangles have three angles.

12. Some triangles are regular.

13. Some parallelograms are triangles.

14. All triangles are equilateral.

MIXED REVIEW

Insert parentheses to make each equation true.

1. $6^2 + 18 + 9 \cdot -2 = -18$

2. $150 + 17 \cdot 10 = 1,670$

Draw a figure to fit each description.

3. a regular triangle

4. a pentagon

Write as a decimal.

5. 23.5%   6. 5.9%

7. A mail-order catalog offers computer disks at 100 for $121.50 or 50 for $62.50. Which is the lower price per disk?

Draw a figure to fit each description.

15. a convex parallelogram   16. a trapezoid

17. an obtuse scalene triangle   18. a triangle with one obtuse angle

Find the measure of each numbered angle.

19. 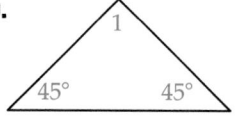   20. 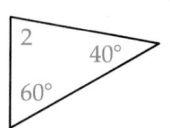   21.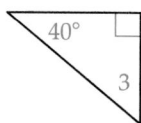

CALCULATOR Find the measure of the third angle of a triangle that has two angles with the given measures.

22. $110°, 35°$ 23. $25°, 65°$ 24. $45°, 45°$ 25. $30°, 60°$

26. $126°, 20°$ 27. $42°, 78°$ 28. $(2y)°, 60°$ 29. $(x + 4)°, 96°$

Classify each triangle as acute, right, or obtuse.

30. $\triangle MNO$ with $m\angle M = 35°$, $m\angle N = 70°$, and $m\angle O = 75°$

31. $\triangle ABC$ with $m\angle A = 104°$, $m\angle B = 46°$, and $m\angle C = 30°$

Critical Thinking

EXPLORING INDUCTIVE REASONING

▼ You use *inductive reasoning* to draw conclusions based on specific examples.

1. Does the expression $n^2 + n + 5$ always produce a prime number when n is a positive integer?

   a. Try several values of n.

   b. A *counterexample* is an example that proves your conclusion is false. What value of n is a counterexample?

n	$n^2 + n + 5$
1	7
2	
3	
4	

Use inductive reasoning to tell whether the statement is true or false. If false, give a counterexample.

2. All squares are rectangles.

3. All rectangles are squares.

4. All equilateral triangles are equiangular.

5. **DISCUSS** How do you know when you have tried enough examples to make an inductive conclusion?

9-5 Circles

▼ Compact disks are shaped like circles. The circular shape allows the disk to store thousands of bits of information on a spiral track. If unraveled, the hair-thin track could stretch for several miles.

Circle	A circle (⊙) is the set of all points the same distance from a given point called the center.

▼ The table shows some parts of circles and their properties.

Term	Description
chord	a segment that has endpoints on the circle
diameter	a chord that passes through the center of the circle; The diameter (d) is the length of such a chord.
radius	a segment that has endpoints at the center of the circle and on the circle; The radius (r) is the length of such a segment.
central angle	an angle with vertex at the center of the circle

▼ We usually name a circle by its center.

Example 1 Name all the radii, diameters, chords, and central angles shown in ⊙*O*.

Solution

radii $\overline{OT}(\overline{TO})$; $\overline{OQ}(\overline{QO})$; and $\overline{OR}(\overline{RO})$

diameter $\overline{RQ}(\overline{QR})$

chord $\overline{AB}(\overline{BA})$; $\overline{RQ}(\overline{QR})$

central angles $\angle TOQ(\angle QOT)$; $\angle ROT(\angle TOR)$

▼ In any circle, the diameter d is twice the radius r.

Example 2 In a given circle, $\overline{YZ}$ and $\overline{XW}$ are diameters.

  a. If $OZ = 10$ cm, find YZ.

  b. If $WX = 25$ cm, find OX.

Solution Draw a figure to show the given information.

  a. $YZ = 2(OZ)$
         $= 2(10) = 20$ cm

  b. $OX = \dfrac{WX}{2}$

         $= \dfrac{25}{2} = 12.5$ cm

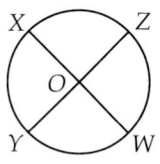

Metals in Gold Jewelry

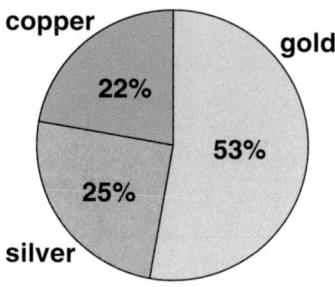

copper
gold
22%
53%
25%
silver

▼ There are 360° in any circle. You can use this fact to construct circle graphs.

Example 3 **Construct a circle graph for the data at the left.**

Solution

1. Write the data in decimal form.

   $22\% = 0.22$
   $25\% = 0.25$
   $53\% = 0.53$

2. Multiply each decimal by 360 to determine the measure of each central angle. Round to the nearest degree. Make sure the total is 360.

   $360 \,\boxed{\times}\, 0.22 \,\boxed{=}\, 79.2 \approx 79$
   $360 \,\boxed{\times}\, 0.25 \,\boxed{=}\, 90$
   $360 \,\boxed{\times}\, 0.53 \,\boxed{=}\, 190.8 \approx 191$

3. Draw a circle with a compass and any radius. Draw each angle with a protractor.

4. Label each section. Give your graph a title.

THINK AND DISCUSS

1. Is every chord a diameter? Explain.

2. How many chords, radii, and diameters does a circle have?

CLASS EXERCISES

1. Name all chords, radii, diameters, and central angles in the circle at the right.

2. If $PO = 15$ in., find PB.

3. If $LM = 37.5$ in., find OM.

4. $\angle MOP$ is $\frac{1}{5}$ of circle O. Find $m\angle MOP$.

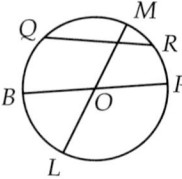

NOTES & QUOTES

The ancient Sumerians believed that Earth revolved around the sun. The Sumerians assumed that Earth traveled in a circular path that took 360 days (one year) to complete. They used this relationship to define the degree as the distance traveled in one day, or $\frac{1}{360}$ of the circle.

WRITTEN EXERCISES

True or false? Write *T* or *F*.

1. If a chord of a circle is 20 cm long, the radius is 10 cm.

2. The longest chord in any circle is the diameter.

3. All radii of a given circle are the same length.

4. All chords of a circle are the same length.

5. If two circles have the same radius, they have the same diameter.

MENTAL MATH **For each length, find the radius or the diameter.**

6. $r = 50$ cm
   $d = \blacksquare$

7. $r = 42.5$ in.
   $d = \blacksquare$

8. $d = 100$ cm
   $r = \blacksquare$

9. $d = 70$ cm
   $r = \blacksquare$

10. $r = 36$ ft
   $d = \blacksquare$

11. $d = 500x$ ft
   $r = \blacksquare$

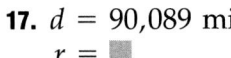**CALCULATOR** For each length, find the radius or the diameter.

12. $r = 32.2$ mm
$d = $ ▨

13. $r = 15.75$ in.
$d = $ ▨

14. $d = 17.09$ cm
$r = $ ▨

15. $d = 0.58$ cm
$r = $ ▨

16. $r = 7{,}832$ ft
$d = $ ▨

17. $d = 90{,}089$ mi
$r = $ ▨

18. Circle O has a diameter of 12 in. Point A is 6 in. from point O.

  a. Is point A inside, outside, or on the circle?

  b. Is $\overline{OA}$ a radius of $\odot O$?

  c. Point B is on $\odot O$. Is $\overline{AB}$ a chord?

  d. What must be true of $\overline{OB}$ for $\overline{AB}$ to be a diameter?

> **PROBLEM SOLVING HINT**
> Drawing a diagram may help.

19. Draw $\odot O$, with $r = 3$ cm. Label two points as C and D inside the circle.

  a. Is $\overline{CD}$ a chord of $\odot O$?

  b. Can $\overline{CD}$ be a diameter of $\odot O$? why or why not?

20. In $\odot O$ at the right, $\overline{OA}$ and $\overline{OB}$ are radii. What kind of triangle is $\triangle AOB$? How do you know?

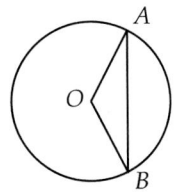

CALCULATOR Use the data to construct a circle graph.

21.

Recommended Diet Components	
Carbohydrates	48%
Refined sugars	10%
Saturated fats	10%
Monosaturated fats	10%
Polyunsaturated fats	10%
Protein	12%

22.

Teens' Career Choices	
Health care	16%
Trade	8%
Teacher	7%
Performer	6%
Sports	6%
Business/law	6%
Other	20%
Undecided	31%

> **MIXED REVIEW**
> Solve.
> **1.** $\frac{6}{8} = \frac{n}{12}$ **2.** $\frac{a}{24} = \frac{30}{48}$
> Evaluate.
> **3.** $y^2 + 5$ for $y = 12$
> **4.** $5a^4 - a$ for $a = 10$
> **5.** Find $m\angle 1$ and $m\angle 2$.
>
>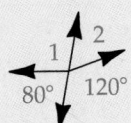
>
> Use the formula $d = rt$.
>
> **6.** A satellite orbiting Earth travels at a rate of 28,000 km/h. How far will it travel in 24 h?

23. CALCULATOR In a survey about favorite colors, 28% responded that blue was their favorite color. Another 56% chose red. All other respondents chose yellow. Draw a circle graph to display the results of the survey.

24. PROJECT Choose a topic from the list below, or one of your own. Collect data in your class and construct a circle graph to display the results.

  a. career choice

  b. favorite sport

  c. favorite subject

  d. own TV, camera, phone, computer

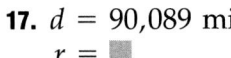

OBJECTIVE:
To identify congruent
figures and figures
with line symmetry.

9-6 Congruence and Symmetry

▼ Two figures with the same size and shape are *congruent*. We use the symbol ≅ to mean *is congruent to*. When two figures are congruent their *corresponding* parts are equal. The symbol ↔ means *corresponds to*.

▼ Think of sliding one figure on top of the other. You can see the following correspondences.

$S \leftrightarrow T$	$\angle S \leftrightarrow \angle T$
$L \leftrightarrow I$	$\angle L \leftrightarrow \angle I$
$O \leftrightarrow M$	$\angle O \leftrightarrow \angle M$
$W \leftrightarrow E$	$\angle W \leftrightarrow \angle E$

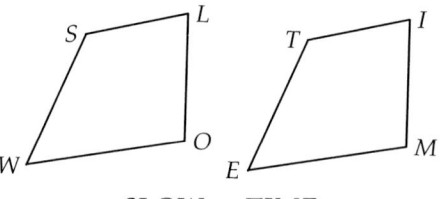

$$SLOW \cong TIME$$

Describe figures in the kaleidoscope picture that appear to be congruent.

▼ The definition of congruent figures follows.

Congruent Polygons	Two polygons are congruent if there is a correspondence between their vertices such that the corresponding sides and corresponding angles are congruent.

Example 1 Do the figures appear to be congruent? Explain.

a. 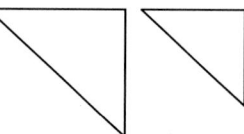   b. 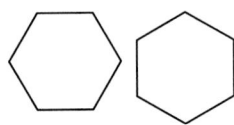   c.

Solution a. no; not the same size

b. yes; same size and same shape

c. no; not the same shape

Example 2 △*ABC* ≅ △*XYZ*. Write congruence statements for corresponding parts.

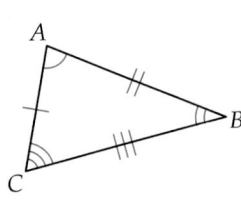   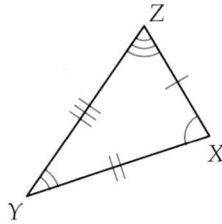

Solution

$\overline{AB} \cong \overline{XY}$	$\angle A \cong \angle X$
$\overline{BC} \cong \overline{YZ}$	$\angle B \cong \angle Y$
$\overline{CA} \cong \overline{ZX}$	$\angle C \cong \angle Z$

▼ If you can draw a line through a figure so that one side is a reflection of the other, the figure is said to have *line symmetry*. Some figures have more than one line of symmetry. Some figures have no lines of symmetry.

Example 3 Is each dotted line a line of symmetry?

a. 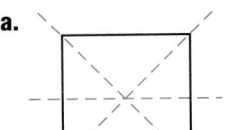 **b.** 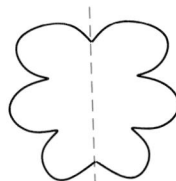 **c.**

Solution **a.** yes   **b.** yes   **c.** no

CLASS EXERCISES

Write congruence statements for corresponding parts.

1. 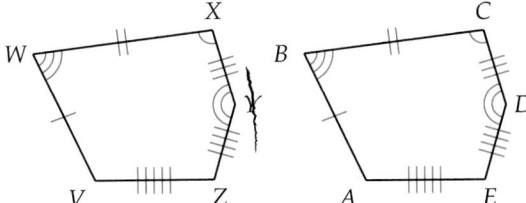   **2.**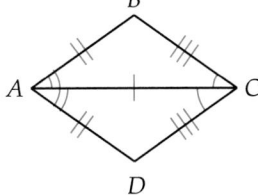

Trace each figure and draw all lines of symmetry.

3. 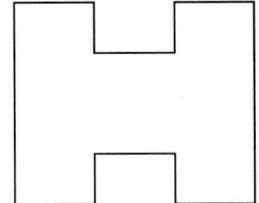   **4.**

5. **WRITE** Why would it be important for machines to produce congruent parts?

THINK AND DISCUSS

1. Do congruent figures have to be polygons? Can segments, angles, circles, curves, or shapes from nature be congruent?

2. Are all right angles congruent? all acute angles?

3. How many lines of symmetry does a circle have?

WRITTEN EXERCISES

1. Which figure appears not to be congruent to the other three?

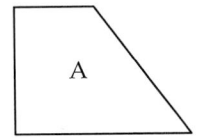 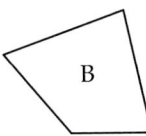 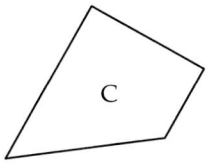 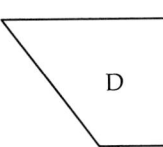

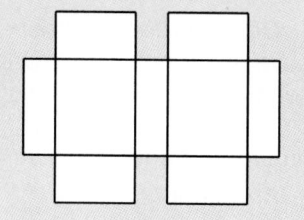
Write congruence statements for corresponding parts.

2.
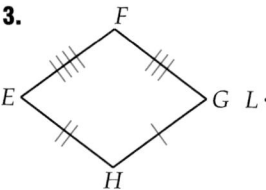

3.
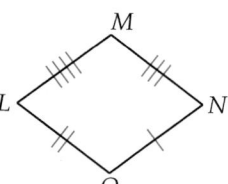

$\triangle XYZ \cong \triangle ABC$. **Write each angle measure or segment length.**

4. $\angle C$ 5. $\angle A$ 6. $\angle B$

7. XZ 8. XY 9. YZ

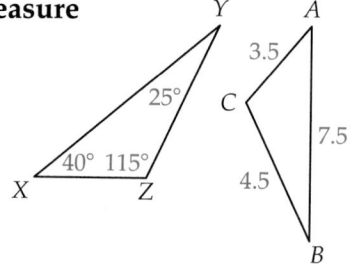

Suppose $RSTU \cong WXYZ$. Which congruence statements must be true?

10. $\angle R \cong \angle W$

11. $\overline{ST} \cong \overline{XY}$

12. $\angle R \cong \angle Z$

13. $\overline{UT} \cong \overline{ZY}$

14. $\overline{RS} \cong \overline{XY}$

15. $\angle T \cong \angle W$

Find the measure of each numbered angle.

16. $\triangle ABC \cong \triangle XYZ$

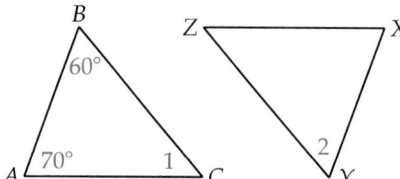

17. $\triangle PQR \cong \triangle MNO$

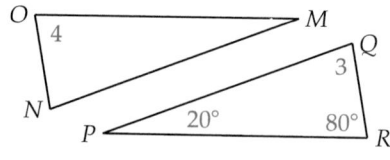

Trace each pair of symmetric figures. Fold to find the line of symmetry.

18.
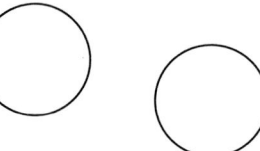

19.

The dotted line is a line of symmetry for each figure. Trace the figure and complete the drawing.

20.
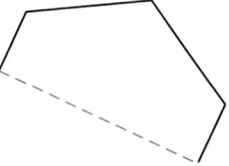

21.
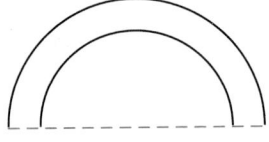

Which figures have line symmetry?

22.

23.

24.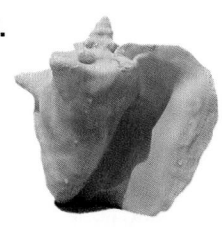

25. Fold a plain sheet of paper in half lengthwise. Write your name along the fold. Turn the paper over and trace your name through the paper. Is the fold a line of symmetry? Are the two names congruent?

26. Which letters of the alphabet have only one line of symmetry when written in capital block form? Sketch your responses with the symmetry lines.

27. *PROJECT* Carpenters and artisans use a tool called a level to insure that a surface is flat. You can make a level that uses the properties of congruent triangles.

Cut three congruent rectangles out of oak tag. Join the rectangles at the short edges to form a triangle. Mark the midpoint of the triangle's base. Attach a string weighted with a button to the vertex at the top of the triangle. When you stand the level on a flat surface, $\triangle FLT \cong \triangle ALT$. Rest the triangle on a non-level surface. Do you still see congruent triangles? Explain.

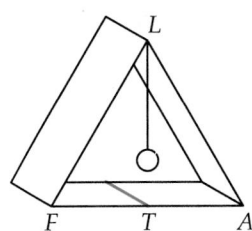

TEST YOURSELF

1. Name three lines, three rays, three segments, and three angles in the figure at the right.

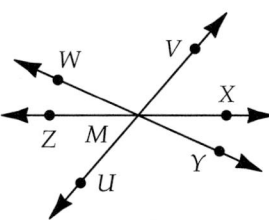

Use the figure at the right.

2. Classify *ABCD* as a square, a rectangle, or a parallelogram.

3. Classify $\triangle ABD$ as *acute*, *obtuse*, or *right*.

4. Write a congruence statement for corresponding parts in $\triangle ABD$ and $\triangle CDB$.

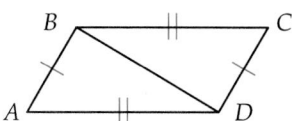

For each given length, find the radius or diameter.

5. $r = 26$ ft
  $d = $ ▨

6. $d = 60$ in.
  $r = $ ▨

7. $r = 15.5$ m
  $d = $ ▨

8. $d = 22.2$ cm
  $r = $ ▨

9-7 Similar Figures

▼ Designers often make scale models of new products. The models are the same shape but not the same size as the final product. We say the models and the real product are *similar*.

Similar Figures	Two figures are similar (∼) if corresponding angles are congruent and corresponding sides are in proportion.

Example 1   Do the pairs of figures appear to be similar?

a.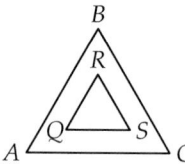

b.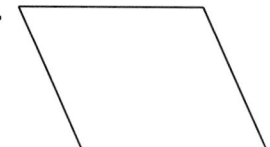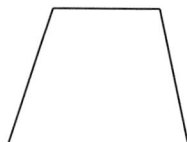

Solution   **a.** yes   **b.** no; not the same shape

▼ In similar figures, the lengths of the sides may change but the measures of the angles remain the same. You can use proportions to find an unknown length when two figures are similar.

Example 2 $ABCDE \sim VWXYZ$. **Find** AB.

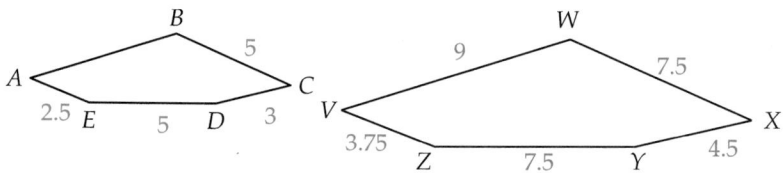

Solution   Since the figures are similar, corresponding sides are in proportion.

$$\frac{AB}{VW} = \frac{BC}{WX}$$ Write a proportion.

$$\frac{AB}{9} = \frac{5}{7.5}$$ Substitute values.

$$AB = \frac{5}{7.5} \cdot 9$$ Solve.

$$= 5 \; \boxed{\div} \; 7.5 \; \boxed{\times} \; 9 \; \boxed{=} \; 6$$

$$AB = 6$$

▼ When you know the measures of the angles, you can determine whether or not two triangles are similar.

Similar Triangles	Two triangles are similar if two angles of one are congruent to two angles of another.

Example 3 **Determine whether or not the triangles are similar. If *yes*, write a similarity statement.**

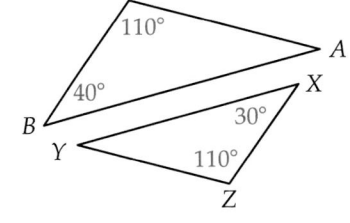

Solution $m\angle Y = 180° - (110° + 30°)$ since $m\angle B = m\angle Y$
$\qquad\quad = 40°$ and $m\angle C = m\angle Z$
$\qquad\triangle ABC \sim \triangle XYZ$

Two angles of one triangle are congruent to two angles of the other. The triangles are similar.

▼ You can use similar triangles to measure distances that you would be unable to measure directly.

Example 4 A 6-ft tall man, standing near a tree, casts a shadow 14 ft long. The tree casts a shadow 40 ft long. Use similar triangles to find the height of the tree to the nearest tenth of a foot.

Solution Draw a sketch to display the information in the problem.

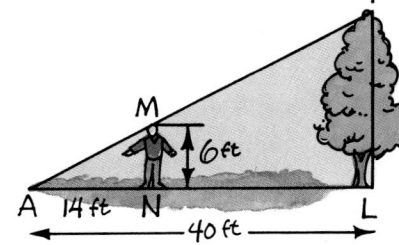

$\qquad m\angle N = m\angle L$ Right angles are congruent.
$\qquad m\angle A = m\angle A$ An angle is congruent
$\qquad \triangle TAL \sim \triangle MAN$ to itself.
$\qquad \dfrac{AL}{AN} = \dfrac{TL}{MN}$

$\qquad \dfrac{40}{14} = \dfrac{TL}{6}$

$\qquad 40 \cdot 6 = 14 \cdot TL$ Cross multiply to solve.
$\qquad 240 \;÷\; 14 \;=\; 17.142 \ldots$
$\qquad\qquad TL \approx 17.1 \text{ ft}$ Round to the nearest tenth.

CLASS EXERCISES

1. Draw three different equilateral triangles. Are all your triangles similar?

2. In similar figures, what ratios are always equal?

HGFE ~ MNOP.

3. Find *EF*.

4. Find *MN*.

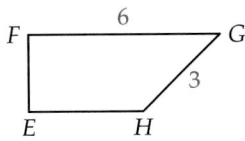
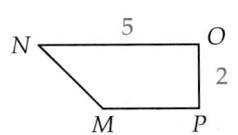

THINK AND DISCUSS

1. Are all circles similar? Explain.

2. Are all right angles similar? All right triangles? Explain.

3. Are congruent figures always similar? Explain.

WRITTEN EXERCISES

Use graph paper to sketch a figure similar to, but not congruent to, each figure.

1.

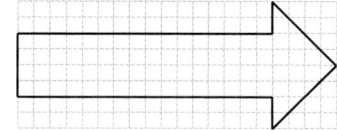

2.

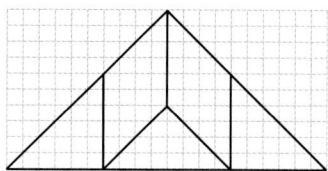

3. *MORE ~ TRYS*. Name four equal ratios.

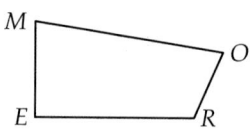
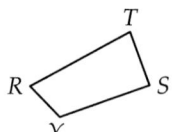

4. △*HOT ~*△*PIE*. Name three equal ratios.

Assume each pair of triangles is similar. Find the missing length.

5.

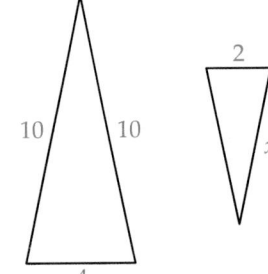

6.

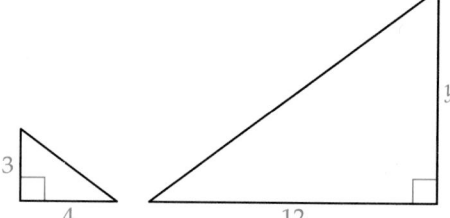

7.

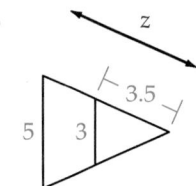

8.

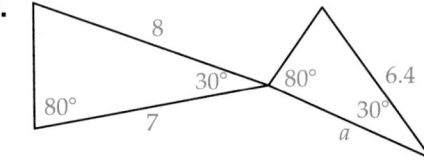

Is each pair of triangles similar? If *yes*, identify three pairs of corresponding sides.

9.

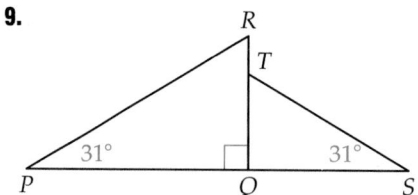

10.

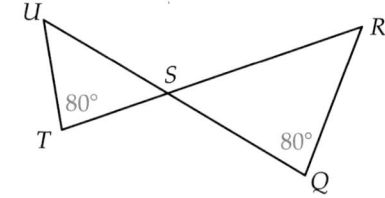

11. Suppose you wish to make a mailbox which is a model of your home. **WRITE** a paragraph which describes your plan. Include as many details as possible.

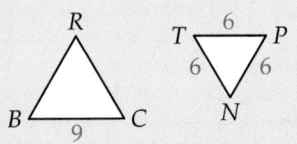

Solve.

12. A tree casts a shadow 10 ft long. A 5-ft tall person casts a shadow 3 ft long. How tall is the tree?

PROBLEM SOLVING HINT
Draw a diagram.

13. A photographic slide is 35 mm wide and 22 mm high. The projected image is 85 cm wide. How high is the image?

14. **PROJECT** Use similar triangles to measure the height of your school, flagpole, or a tall tree.

15. **DATA FILE 3 (pp. 96–97)** Find the dimensions of a dollar bill. What are the possible dimensions for a sheet of bills?

Check Your Proportions

What do paintings by Leonardo DaVinci, buildings of ancient Greece, and your physical proportions have in common? They all reflect the *Golden ratio*. The golden ratio (calculated as approximately 1.61) is the ratio of the length to the width of a golden rectangle, which is thought to be the most pleasing to the eye. Examples of the golden ratio are found in art, architecture, nature, and in the human skeleton. An American researcher found that the ratio of a person's height to the distance from the ground to his waist approaches the golden ratio. How do you measure up?

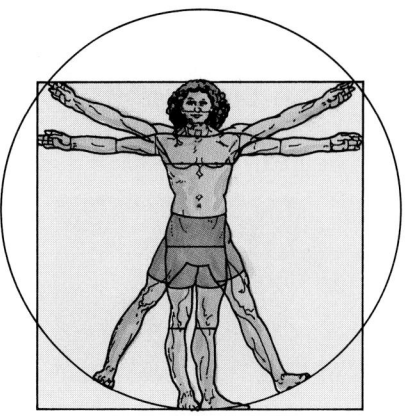

16. Use the article above. Measure, then compute each ratio. Do your ratios approach the golden ratio?

a. $\dfrac{\text{head to ground}}{\text{waist to ground}}$

b. $\dfrac{\text{shoulder to finger tips}}{\text{elbow to finger tips}}$

Critical Thinking
EXPLORING DEDUCTIVE REASONING

▼ When you reach conclusions after reasoning from accepted information, you are using *deductive reasoning*.

1. Each card has either a triangle, circle, or square on the back. Use the given information to decide the figure on each card.

   a. The figure on card 1 is not a quadrilateral.

   b. The figure on the even-numbered card is not a polygon.

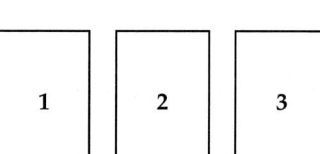

2. **WRITE** a problem of your own that requires deductive reasoning. Give it to a classmate to solve.

Practice

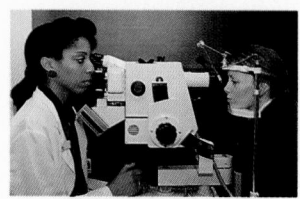
Find the measure of each indicated angle.

1. ∠*PNM*

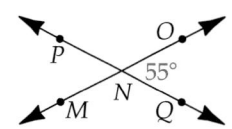

2. ∠*CBD*

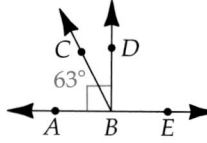

3. ∠*UEN*

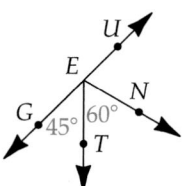

Find the measure of a complement and a supplement of each angle, if possible.

4. 12°   **5.** 57°   **6.** 101°   **7.** 43°

8. 128°   **9.** 16°   **10.** 92°   **11.** 179°

Find the measure of the third angle of a triangle that has two angles with the given measures.

12. 55°, 65°   **13.** 45°, 45°   **14.** 60°, 70°   **15.** 80°, 28°

16. 58°, 65°   **17.** 110°, 25°   **18.** 78°, 19°   **19.** 103°, 33°

For each length, find the radius or the diameter.

20. $r = 17$ in.   **21.** $r = 56.8$ m   **22.** $d = 85.5$ cm
    $d = $ ▨ $d = $ ▨ $r = $ ▨

23. $d = 0.38$ km   **24.** $r = 28.6$ mi   **25.** $r = 67{,}385$ mi
    $r = $ ▨ $d = $ ▨ $d = $ ▨

Name all chords, diameters, radii, and central angles shown in each circle.

26.
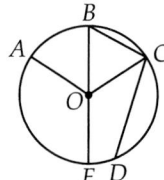

27.

28.
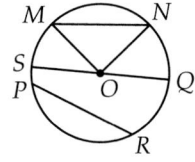

Write congruence statements for the corresponding parts of each pair of polygons.

29.
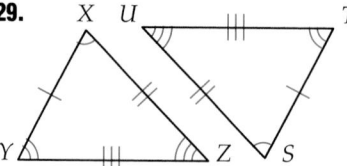

30.
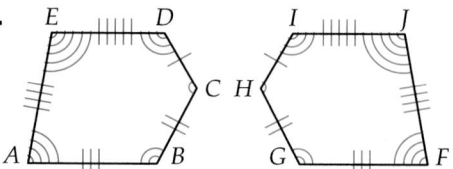

OBJECTIVE:
To explore pi as a ratio.

MATERIALS

- String and a measuring stick or a measuring tape

- Several circular objects (cans, records, CDs, etc.)

- Large grid paper

- Coin or other marker

- Calculator

- Math journal to record work

Exploring Pi

▼ Pi (π) is a fascinating ratio. You may use it in many calculations with circles. The activities that follow will help you discover pi.

1. Choose at least five circular objects. Complete steps (a–c) and record your data in a chart.

   a. Measure the circumference of each object.

   b. Measure the diameter of each object.

Object	Circumference (C)	Diameter (d)	$\frac{C}{d}$

   c. Use a calculator to find the ratio $\frac{C}{d}$ for each object. What is the approximate value for the ratio?

▼ Here is another experiment that approximates pi.

2. Use a penny and a large grid like the one below. Toss the coin so that it lands on the grid. Count only tosses that land completely on the grid.

Tosses						
1–10	h	m	m	h	h	h
11–20						

	h	t	$\frac{4h}{t}$
20 tosses		20	
40 tosses		40	
60 tosses			
80 tosses			
100 tosses			

   a. Make a 10 × 10 chart to record your tosses. Count a hit when the coin touches or covers a dot. Make an *h* in a box on your chart. When the coin misses, mark an *m* on your chart. Continue filling in your grid for 100 tosses.

   b. Use your data from (a) to complete a chart like the one at the left.

   c. Combine your data with data from other groups. Use your data to complete the formula $\frac{4h}{t} = \blacksquare$.

3. Is your result close to 3.1416? Do you think more tosses will result in a closer approximation of π?

OBJECTIVE:
To find the perimeter
or circumference of a
figure.

9-8 Perimeter and Circumference

▼ A seamstress buying lace for the bottom of a dress needs to know the *perimeter* of the hem.

Perimeter	Perimeter is the distance around a figure.

▼ You may need to find the perimeter of a common shape.

Example 1 A homeowner wants to buy a wallpaper border for a rectangular room. The room is 9 ft 2 in. long and 12 ft 3 in. wide. There is a 3-ft wide doorway. Borders are sold in 11-yd lengths. How many rolls of border does the homeowner need?

Solution
1. Find the perimeter. $P = 2l + 2w$
$P = 2(9 \text{ ft } 2 \text{ in.}) + 2(12 \text{ ft } 3 \text{ in.})$
$= 42 \text{ ft } 10 \text{ in.}$

2. Subtract the width   42 ft 10 in. $-$ 3 ft = 39 ft 10 in.
of the doorway.

3. Round to the   39 ft 10 in. $\approx$ 40 ft
nearest foot.

4. Compare.   11 yd = 33 ft

Since one roll is not enough, the homeowner must purchase two rolls of border paper.

▼ We call the distance around a circular figure *circumference*. The ratio of the circumference to the diameter is pi (π).

Circumference	The circumference (C) is the distance around a circle. Use the formula $C = \pi d$ to compute circumference.

Example 2 **Find each circumference.**

a.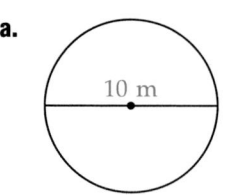
10 m

b.
6 in.

c.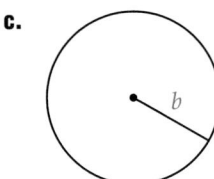
b

Solution   a. $C = \pi d$
$= 10\pi \text{ m}$

b. $C = \pi d$
$= \pi(2r)$
$= \pi(2 \cdot 6)$
$= 12\pi \text{ in.}$

c. $C = \pi d$
$= \pi(2r)$
$= \pi(2b)$
$= 2b\pi \text{ units}$

▼ If you know the circumference of a circle, you can find the radius and diameter.

Example 3 The circumference of a circle is 43π ft. Find the diameter and the radius.

Solution

$$C = \pi d$$
$$43\pi = \pi d$$
$$\frac{43\pi}{\pi} = \frac{\pi d}{\pi} \qquad \text{Divide both sides by } \pi.$$
$$43 = d$$
$$d = 2r$$
$$43 = 2r \qquad \text{Substitute 43 for } d.$$
$$43 \boxed{\div} 2 \boxed{=} r \qquad \text{Divide both sides by 2.}$$
$$21.5 = r$$

▼ We frequently use 3.14 or $\frac{22}{7}$ as approximations for π. Unless you are asked to approximate your answer, or given a value for π, leave answers in terms of π.

Example 4 Find the circumference of a circle with the given radius or diameter. Round measures to the nearest tenth.

  a. $d = 12$ mi (Use 3.14 for π.)

  b. $r \approx 7$ ft $\left(\text{Use } \frac{22}{7} \text{ for } \pi.\right)$

Solution

a.
$$C = \pi d$$
$$\approx (3.14)(12)$$
$$= 37.68$$
$$\approx 37.7 \text{ mi}$$

b.
$$C = \pi \, 2r$$
$$\approx \frac{22}{7}(2)(7)$$
$$= \frac{22}{7}(14)$$
$$= 2(22)$$
$$= 44 \text{ ft}$$

NOTES & QUOTES

Using only paper and pencil, William Shanks (1812–1882) spent 20 years calculating π to 707 decimal places. In 1945 it was discovered that Mr. Shanks had made an error in the 528th place. Today, supercomputers can calculate the value of π to millions of places in seconds.

THINK AND DISCUSS

1. Describe a method for finding the perimeter of some irregularly shaped objects such as a leaf or an oil spill.

2. Suppose you are asked to find the perimeter of your math book. Would you rather measure in inches or feet? Explain your choice.

CLASS EXERCISES

1. Choose five objects or areas in the classroom. Estimate and then measure the perimeter of each object. Choose an appropriate unit for measuring each item. Record your results in a table like the one below.

Item	Unit	Estimate	Measure	Difference	% Error

Estimate the circumference of each circle in centimeters. Then measure each diameter and compute the circumference. Use 3.14 for π.

2.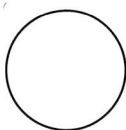

3.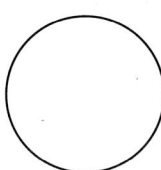

WRITTEN EXERCISES

Find the perimeter of each figure.

1. a square with side 9 ft *36 ft*

2. an equilateral triangle with side 5 yd *15 yd*

3. a trapezoid with bases 3 ft and 3 yd, and sides 5 ft *17 ft*

4. a regular hexagon with side 3.7 in. *22.2 in*

Find the perimeter of each polygon.

5. 60 *240* 30 30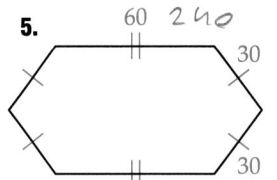

6. 2 *22* 2 2 1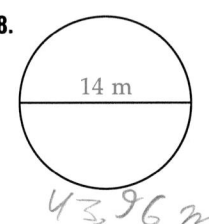

7. 7 2 3 1 6 *19*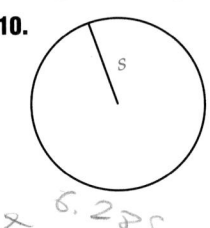

Find the amount of tape needed to wrap each figure. Use 3.14 for π.

8. 14 m *43.96 m*

9. 9 ft *56.52 ft*

10. *s* *6.28s*

11. $3\frac{2}{7}$ mi *5.15 mi*

Find the diameter and the radius of a circle with the given circumference.

12. $C = 15\pi$ m *7.5, 15*

13. $C = 5a\pi$ yd *2.5 a yd*

14. $C \approx 19$ in. *≈ 9.5 in 19*

15. $C \approx 2.5x$ units *1.25x, 2.5*

CALCULATOR Find the circumference to the nearest tenth of a unit. Use 3.14 for π. *21.98*

16. $r = 5$ *31.4*

17. $r = 3.5$

18. $d = 17.8$ *55.892*

19. $d = 0.625$ *1.9625*

Find the circumference. Use $\frac{22}{7}$ for π.

20. $r = \frac{1}{4}$ *1.57*

21. $r = \frac{3}{11}$ *1.7*

22. $d = 49$ *153.86*

23. $d = 181$ *568.34*

Find the unknown length.

24. $P = 75$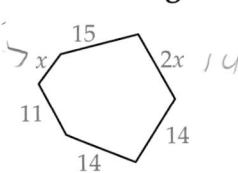
15 x 2x 14
11
14
14

25. $P = 91$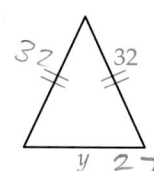
32 32
y 27

26. $P = 10$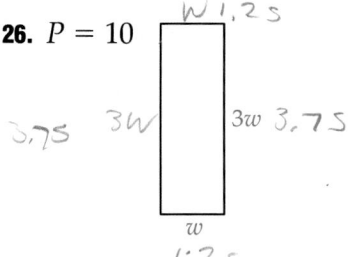
W 1.25
3.75 3w 3w 3.75
w
1.25

27. $P = 37$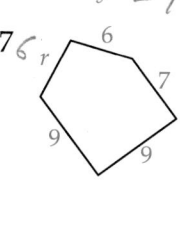
6 r 6
7
9 9

Write an expression for the perimeter of each polygon.

28. 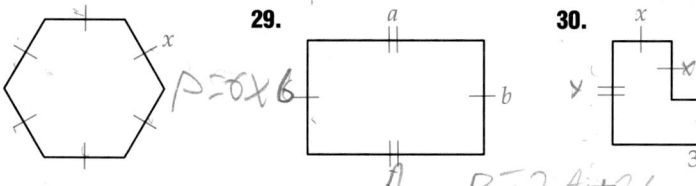 x
P=6×6

29. a
b
P=2A+2b

30. x
x x
y y
$3x$
P= 7x+2y

Use graph paper to draw a polygon that fits each description.

31. a rectangle with a perimeter of 12 units

32. a square with a perimeter of 60 units

33. a hexagon with a perimeter of 8 units

34. *DATA FILE 3 (pp. 96–97)* Find two possible perimeters for a sheet of dollar bills.

TEST YOURSELF

1. Find BC. $\triangle ABC \sim \triangle DEF$.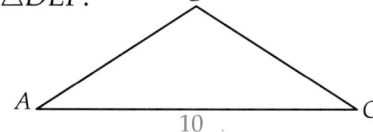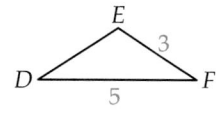
B
A 10 C
E 3
D 5 F

Find the perimeter or circumference. Use 3.14 for π.

2.
6.2
10.5

3.
15

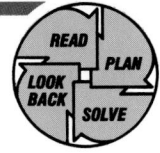

9-9 Draw a Diagram

OBJECTIVE:
To solve problems by
drawing a diagram.

■ For many geometric problems it helps to draw a diagram to
represent the given information.

PROBLEM

The wheels of a bicycle have a diameter of 60 cm. How many
revolutions do the wheels make during a 4,000 m race?

SOLUTION

READ ▶ What information do you have?

> The wheels have a diameter of
> 60 cm.
> The race is 4,000 m long.

What do you want to find?

> How many revolutions (turns)
> do the wheels make in a race?

PLAN ▶ Decide on a strategy.

> Draw a picture to represent the
> information.

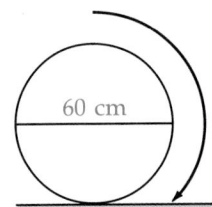

60 cm

What is a complete turn?

> the circumference of the wheel

What units will you use?

> Find the circumference in
> centimeters. Then write the
> circumference in meters.

SOLVE ▶ Use the formula $C = \pi d$. Use
3.14 for π.

$$C = \pi d$$
$$\approx 3.14(60)$$
$$= 188.4 \text{ cm}$$
$$= 1.884 \text{ m}$$

Divide the total distance by the
distance of one revolution.
Round to the nearest whole
number.

$4,000 \div 1.884$

$$= 2,123.142 \ldots$$
$$\approx 2,123$$

LOOK BACK ▶ Estimate to check your answer.

> Each revolution was 1.8 m or
> about 2 m. The race was
> 4,000 m, so each wheel turned
> about 2,000 times.

> The answer of 2,123 turns is
> reasonable.

CLASS EXERCISES

Refer to the problem on page 394. Use 3.14 for π.

1. Suppose the race was 6,000 m long. Estimate the number of revolutions for the tires.

2. Suppose a race car has tires with diameter of 34 in.

   a. How far would the tires turn in one complete revolution?

   b. How many revolutions would the tires make in a 500 mi race?

WRITTEN EXERCISES

Use a CALCULATOR where appropriate.

Solve using a picture. Use 3.14 for π. Round to the nearest whole number.

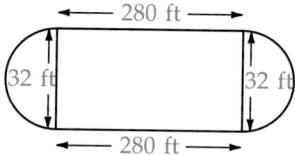
← 280 ft →
32 ft   32 ft
← 280 ft →

1. How many laps must you run on the track pictured at the right to cover 1 mi?
   Hint: 5,280 ft = 1 mi

2. Sam is building a circular table for eight people. Each person needs 2 ft of table edge. What is the diameter of the table?

3. Two intersecting circles can form two or three regions. Three intersecting circles can form from three to seven regions. What is the greatest number of regions you can form with four intersecting circles?

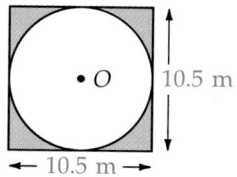
• O   10.5 m
← 10.5 m →

Solve using any strategy.

4. Find the circumference of circle *O*. Use 3.14 for π.

5. Suppose you want to make a scale model of Earth, the sun, and the moon. Use the **DATA** at the right to determine the dimensions of the model. Assume that Earth will have a diameter of 3 in.

   a. What will be the diameter of the sun and the moon?

   b. In the model, how far from Earth must each be?

	d (mi)	distance from Earth (mi)
Earth	8,000	0
Sun	864,000	93,000,000
Moon	2,200	240,000

6. The figures shown are all composed of equal size squares. Figure *A* has a perimeter of 36. Find the perimeter of each figure.

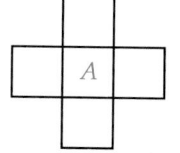
A

a.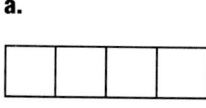

b.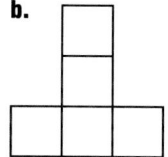

c.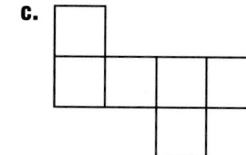

Problem Solving Practice

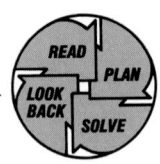

Solve. The list at the left shows some strategies you might use.

PROBLEM SOLVING STRATEGIES

Look for a Pattern
Guess and Test
Simplify the Problem
Account for All Possibilities
Make an Organized List
Work Backwards
Make a Table
Write an Equation
Solve by Graphing
Draw a Diagram
Make a Model
Simulate the Problem

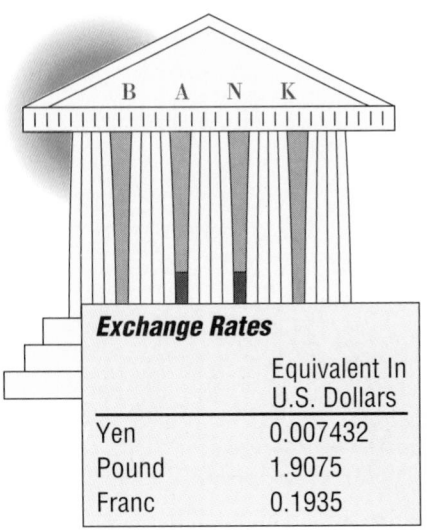

Exchange Rates

	Equivalent In U.S. Dollars
Yen	0.007432
Pound	1.9075
Franc	0.1935

1. The scores in a game were -7, 8, 7, 15, -6, 12, and -6. Was the final score positive or negative?

2. State sales tax on new car purchases is 5%. Find the sales tax on a car costing $22,489.

3. The Blazers lost 35% of the 20 games they played this season. How many games did they win?

4. You open a book and the product of the page numbers is 16,002. To what pages have you opened?

5. Two buses leave a terminal at the same time and travel in opposite directions. One bus travels at 55 mi/h. The other travels at 48 mi/h. How far apart will the buses be in 3 h?

6. Sabrina can run 5 km in 1 h. In the same time, Lucy can run a 3-km distance. How much of a head start does Lucy need for both girls to finish an 8-km course at the same time?

7. A stamp collector has 53 rare stamps. This is 12 less than 5 times the number he had a year ago. How many stamps did the collector have a year ago?

8. Suppose you want to find the thickness of one sheet of paper. Describe a method that uses a ruler.

9. ***DATA*** Use the data at the left. How many yen would you get for $100? how many pounds? how many francs?

10. At a track meet, finishers received 5 points for blue ribbons and 3 points for red ribbons. How many and what color ribbons were won for the following points?

    a. 12   **b.** 14   **c.** 18   **d.** 15

11. A real estate agent earns a 6% commission on the sale of a house. Find the commission on a $289,000 house.

12. ***DATA FILE 10 (pp. 404–405)*** Find the circumference of the circular home range for a snowshoe hare.

13. Two friends rented a canoe for 10 days. One friend used the canoe for 6 days. The other friend used the canoe for 4 days. How much of the $150 rental fee should each friend pay?

14. José bought two posters for $9. The posters were on sale at one for full price and the second at half price. How much was the full price poster?

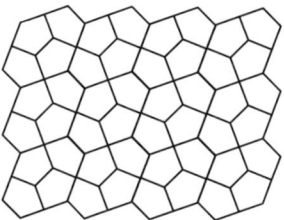

OBJECTIVE:
To understand and create tessellations.

9-10 Tessellations

■ The *tessellation* at the right is made from congruent pentagons. You could see this tessellation in the street tiling of portions of Cairo, Egypt. When a tessellation uses only one shape, we call it a *pure tessellation.*

NOTES & QUOTES

"All my works are games. Serious games."

M. C. Escher

Maurice Cornelius Escher (1898–1972), a Dutch artist, used tessellations in many of his sketches. He created at least 150 different tessellations without ever having any formal mathematics training.

| **Tessellation** | A tessellation is a design that covers a plane with no gaps and no overlaps. |

■ You can determine if a figure forms a pure tessellation by using graph paper to represent a plane.

Example 1 **Determine whether the figure at the right forms a pure tessellation.**

Solution

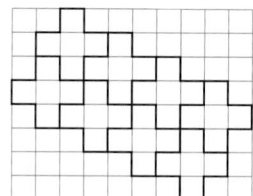

Yes, the figure forms a pure tessellation.

■ Tiled floors often use a pattern in which two figures tessellate. The patterns are *semiregular tessellations.* You can use a pattern to determine whether two figures form a semiregular tessellation.

| **Semiregular Tessellation** | A semiregular tessellation is a design that covers a plane using more than one shape. |

Example 2 **Determine whether the figures at the right form a semiregular tessellation.**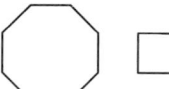

Solution

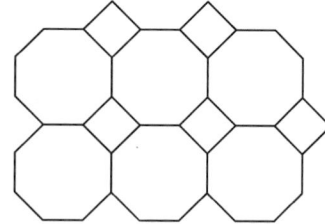

Yes, the figures form a semiregular tessellation.

■ You can create a tessellating figure by beginning with a shape that is known to tessellate.

THINK What are four shapes that will tessellate?

Example 3 **Create a tessellating figure using a square.**

Solution 1. Begin with a square.

2. Cut a shape out of one side. Slide the shape to the opposite side. Tape the shape in place.

3. Use the new shape as a pattern. Trace the shape in different places to form a tessellation.

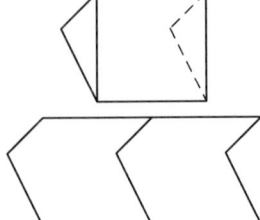

THINK The Greeks proved that only three *regular* polygons will tessellate a plane. Which regular polygons tessellate?

CLASS EXERCISES

Use graph paper to determine whether each figure forms a pure tessellation.

1.

2.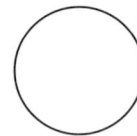

3.

■■■■■■■ Decision Making ■ **DECISION MAKING** ■ Decision Making ■ Decision Making ■ Decision Making ■

TESSELLATIONS

Tessellations are frequently found in nature. Architects and designers often use nature as a model for their work.

■ **COLLECT DATA**

1. List three places in nature where tessellations occur.

2. List three places where you see man-made tessellations in your home and community.

3. Visit a store that sells floor tiles. In what shapes do the tiles come? Write down the cost of each tile.

■ **ANALYZE DATA**

4. a. Why do you think bees use a hexagon shape for their honeycombs instead of an octagon?

WRITTEN EXERCISES

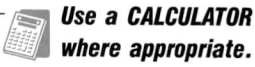 Use a **CALCULATOR** where appropriate.

Use a pattern to determine whether the figures form a pure tessellation.

1.    **2.** 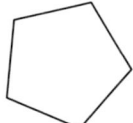   **3.**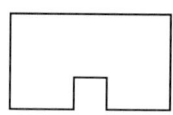

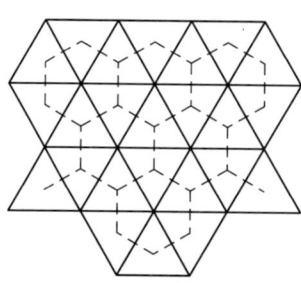

THINK Some patterns will tessellate around a sphere rather than a plane. What shapes tessellate on a soccer ball?

4. A triangle tessellates six times around point *P*. What must be the size of each angle around point *P*?

5. Create a pure tessellation on graph paper.

Use a pattern to determine whether the figures form a semiregular tessellation.

6. 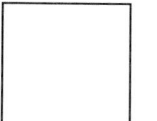   **7.**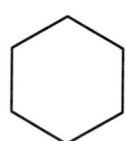

8. Create a semiregular tessellation on graph paper.

9. PROJECT A tessellation of equilateral triangles is shown at the right. You can form another tessellation when you connect the center of each triangle across the common sides of the tessellating triangles. The new tessellation is called a *dual*. Every tessellation of regular polygons has a dual. Create a dual using any regular polygon. Describe your results.

■ *Decision Making* ■ *Decision Making* ■ *Decision Making* ■ *Decision Making* ■ *Decision Making* ■ *Decision Making* ■

b. Each hexagon in a honeycomb can be broken down into smaller regular polygons. What kind of regular polygons are they?

5. What is the sum of the measures of all the angles that come together at a point in a pure tessellation? in a semiregular tessellation?

6. Why do you think architects frequently use a triangular truss to build bridges?

■ **MAKE DECISIONS**

7. A customer wants you to design a tiling pattern for a rectangular foyer. The foyer is 15 ft by 15 ft. Create two designs on graph paper. Make the first a pure tessellation and the second a semiregular tessellation. For each design, determine how many of each shape tile the customer will need. Then find the total cost of each design.

Chapter 9 Review

1. Classify the following words. Use the categories basic geometric figures, angles, triangles, quadrilaterals, polygons, or circles. Some words belong in more than one category.

acute	diameter	obtuse	ray	square
adjacent	equiangular	parallelogram	rectangle	straight
chord	equilateral	pentagon	rhombus	supplementary
circumference	hexagon	plane	right	triangle
complementary	isosceles	point	scalene	trapezoid
convex	line	radius	segment	vertical

Introduction to Geometry   9-1

The basic geometric figures include point, line ($\overleftrightarrow{AB}$), segment ($\overline{AB}$), ray ($\overrightarrow{AB}$), and plane.

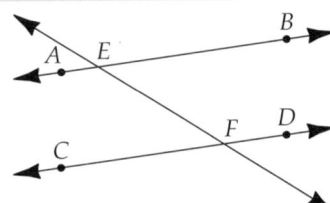

Refer to the figure at the right.

2. Name two parallel lines.

3. Name three lines.

4. Name five different segments.

5. Name eight different rays.

Angles   9-2

We classify angles by their measures. Acute angles have measures greater than 0° and less than 90°. Obtuse angles have measures greater than 90° and less than 180°. Right angles measure 90°.

Two angles are supplementary if the sum of their measures is 180. Two angles are complementary if the sum of their measures is 90.

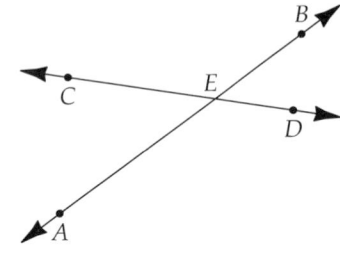

Refer to the figure at the right.

6. ∠AEC is an ▓ angle.

7. ∠AEC and ∠BEC are ▓ angles.

8. ∠AEC ▓ ∠BED.

9. If $m\angle CEB = 120°$, $m\angle AED = $ ▓.

10. If $m\angle BED = 55°$, $m\angle AED = $ ▓.

Polygons and Quadrilaterals   9-3

Some quadrilaterals have special names and special properties.

True or *false*? **Write *T* or *F*.**

11. A trapezoid is a parallelogram.

12. All squares are rhombuses.

13. A rhombus is a rectangle.

14. Some rhombuses are rectangles.

15. All rectangles are parallelograms.

16. A rhombus can be a square.

Triangles

We classify triangles by angles and by sides. The sum of the measures of the interior angles of a triangle is 180°.

Classify each triangle by its angles.

17. 30°, 60°, and 90°   **18.** 40°, 37°, and 103°   **19.** 55°, 55°, and 70°

20. A triangle has two angles with measures of 50° and 70°. What is the measure of the third angle?

Circles

In any circle, the diameter d is twice the radius r.

For each length, find the radius or the diameter.

21. $r = 25$ cm
$d = $ ▨

22. $d = 40$ cm
$r = $ ▨

23. $r = 3\frac{1}{2}$ in.
$d = $ ▨

24. $r = 4.2$ cm
$d = $ ▨

25. $d = 30$ ft
$r = $ ▨

26. $d = 9$ ft
$r = $ ▨

Congruent Figures

Two figures are congruent if their corresponding angles and corresponding sides are congruent.

27. $ABCD \cong WXYZ$. Write congruence statements for corresponding parts.

Similar Figures

Two figures are similar if the corresponding angles are congruent and the corresponding sides are in proportion.

Assume each pair of triangles is similar. Find the missing length.

28.

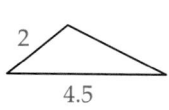

29.

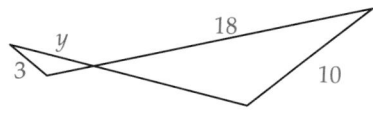

Perimeter and Circumference

To find the perimeter of a polygon, add the lengths of the sides.

To find the circumference of a circle, use the formula $C = \pi d$.

Find the perimeter or the circumference. Use 3.14 for π.

30. rectangle with sides 24 in. and 18 in.   **31.** circle with $d = 150$ cm

Chapter 9   *Test*

Use the figure at the right.

1. Name $\overleftrightarrow{AB}$ in three ways.

2. Name three different segments on $\overleftrightarrow{CD}$.

3. Name three rays on $\overleftrightarrow{GH}$.

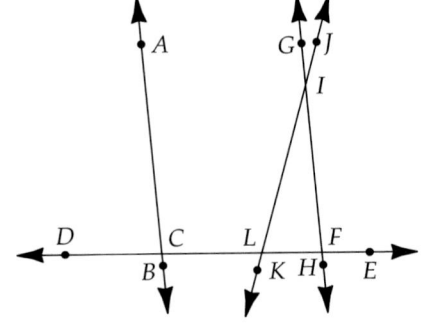

Complete each sentence.

4. $\angle ACL$ is an ▨ angle.

5. $\angle ACD$ and $\angle LCB$ are ▨ angles.

6. $m\angle GIL$ ▨ $m\angle JIF$.

7. $\overleftrightarrow{AB}$ is ▨ to $\overleftrightarrow{GH}$.

8. $\angle JLF$ is an ▨ angle.

9. $m\angle GFL = 85°$, $m\angle GFE = $ ▨.

10. **WRITE** Describe the intersection of two lines.

Draw a figure to fit each description.

11. a regular quadrilateral

12. a hexagon

13. an acute triangle

Find the measure of each numbered angle. Then classify each triangle by its angles and its sides.

14.
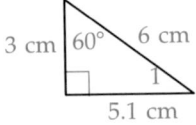

15.
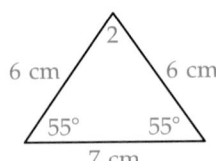

16.
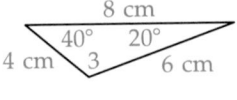

Find the radius or diameter for each given length.

17. $r = 12$ in.

$d = $ ▨

18. $d = 15$ cm

$r = $ ▨

19. $r = 30$ mm

$d = $ ▨

20. Which figure appears *not* to be congruent to the other three?

a.
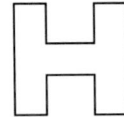

b.
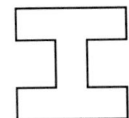

c.
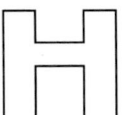

d.
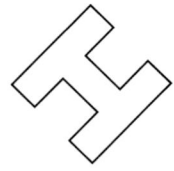

Each pair of triangles is similar. Find the missing length.

21.
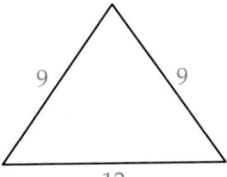
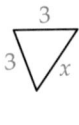

22.
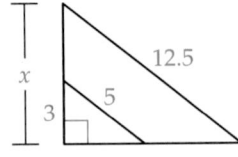

Find each perimeter or circumference. Use 3.14 for π.

23. a rectangle with length 12 in. and width 8 in.

24. a circle with radius 0.5 cm

25. an isosceles triangle with side 60 mm and base 30 mm

Chapters 1–9   Cumulative Review

Choose the correct answer. Write A, B, C, or D.

1. Order $\frac{1}{2}, \frac{5}{6}, \frac{2}{3}, \frac{3}{8}$ from least to greatest.

    A. $\frac{1}{2}, \frac{2}{3}, \frac{3}{8}, \frac{5}{6}$ **B.** $\frac{3}{8}, \frac{2}{3}, \frac{1}{2}, \frac{5}{6}$

    C. $\frac{3}{8}, \frac{1}{2}, \frac{2}{3}, \frac{5}{6}$ **D.** not given

2. Write $\frac{5}{8}$ as a decimal.

    A. 0.58   **B.** 0.625

    C. 0.875   **D.** not given

3. Solve.

    A. 3   **B.** -4

    C. -2   **D.** not given

4. $d = 4.5$. What is the radius?

    A. 9   **B.** 2.25

    C. 3.14   **D.** not given

5. $|\text{-}0.5| - |1.5| = $ ▨

    A. -1   **B.** 2

    C. -2   **D.** not given

6. $b(2b + 3) - b^2 = $ ▨

    A. $5b - b^2$ **B.** $2b^2 + 3b - b^2$

    C. $3b^2 + 3b$ **D.** not given

7. Describe the solution to the system.

    $2y - x = 3; 3y = \frac{3}{2}x + 9$

    A. no solution   **B.** one solution

    C. infinite   **D.** not given

8. Classify the triangle.

    A. obtuse isosceles

    B. right scalene

    C. acute isosceles

    D. not given

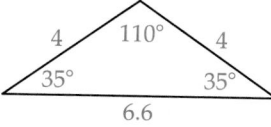

9. Write $1\frac{2}{3}$ as a percent.

    A. $16\frac{2}{3}\%$ **B.** 123%

    C. $166\frac{2}{3}\%$ **D.** not given

10. 3,256,134 is divisible by ▨ .

    A. 8   **B.** 2, 3

    C. 2, 3, 6   **D.** not given

11. Name the figure.

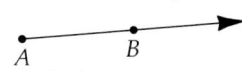

    A. $\overleftrightarrow{AB}$ **B.** $\overrightarrow{AB}$

    C. $\overline{AB}$ **D.** not given

12. $3x - 2y = 8$. What is the slope?

    A. 3   **B.** $\frac{3}{2}$

    C. -2   **D.** not given

13. $ABCD \sim EFGH$. Find x.

    A. 8   **B.** 10

    C. 4   **D.** not given

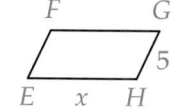

14. What percent of 80 is 20?

    A. 20%   **B.** 80%

    C. 60%   **D.** not given

15. The 6 members of a chess club play each other once. How many games are played?

    A. 6   **B.** 12

    C. 15   **D.** not given

16. A plane climbs to 30,000 ft then descends 5,000 ft. The plane then climbs another 7,000 ft. What is the plane's altitude?

    A. 6,000 ft   **B.** 32,000 ft

    C. 28,000 ft   **D.** not given

EARTH'S TROPICAL RAIN FORESTS AND OCEANS

Costa Rica's Diminishing Rain Forests

1940   1985

Tropical rain forests cover only about 2% of the earth's surface and yet are home to half the world's wild plant and animal life. Though many of the rain forest's plants are vital to medical research, the rain forests are being cut down at the rate of 50 acres per minute.

Corcovado, Costa Rica Rain Forest

area	163 mi^2
average rainfall	220 in./y
species of trees	500
species of mammals	140
species of insects	6,000
species of butterflies	123

EARTH'S OCEANS

OCEAN	AREA (mi^2)	GREATEST WIDTH (mi)	GREATEST KNOWN DEPTH (ft)	AVERAGE DEPTH (ft)
Arctic	5,105,700	2,630	17,880	4,360
Indian	28,350,500	6,200	25,344	12,780
Atlantic	31,820,000	4,150	28,374	14,000
Pacific	63,820,000	11,000	36,198	14,050

Area and Volume Formulas

WILLDLIFE HOME RANGES

WILDLIFE HOME RANGES ■ An animal's home range is the amount of space the animal needs to fulfill its requirements for food, breeding, and so forth. Home range can be expressed in acres or by the radius of a circular area.

Home Ranges for Mammals in Oregon and Washington

MAMMAL	HOME RANGE (Acres)	CIRCULAR HOME RANGE (Radius in Meters)
Black bear	4,382.4	2,370
Cougar	123,753	12,600
Gray wolf (pack of five)	380,970	22,100
Grizzly bear	938,730	34,600
Mule deer	1,045.8	1,160
Northern flying squirrel	0.082	32
Otter	7,494.9	3,100
Porcupine	86.9	333
Red fox	154.38	718
Snowshoe hare	6.35	90
Striped skunk	251.49	567

▼ Think about it...

Look at the home range data. Do you think there is a relationship between the size of an animal and the size of its home range?

10-1 Area of Rectangles and Parallelograms

▼ Geoboards and dot paper are helpful models for understanding area. Each figure at the left takes up 12 square units of area.

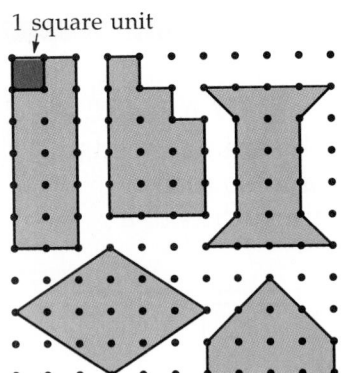

1 square unit

Area	Area is the amount of surface inside a region.

▼ You can find the area of a rectangle on a geoboard by counting the square units within the figure.

Example 1 **Find the area of each rectangle.**

a. 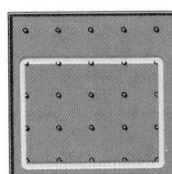   b.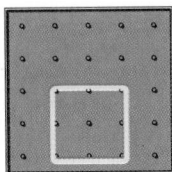

Solution   **a.** The area is 12 square units.   **b.** The area is 4 square units.

▼ You can find the area of a rectangle by multiplying the base length (b) by the height (h). Either side may be the base or the height.

Area of a Rectangle	The area (A) of a rectangle equals the product of its base length (b) and its height (h). $$A = bh$$

Example 2 **Find the area of each rectangle.**

a.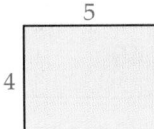
5
4

b.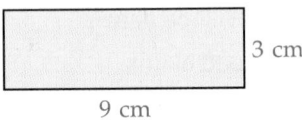
3 cm
9 cm

Solution   **a.** $A = bh$
$\quad = 4 \cdot 5$
$\quad = 20$

   b. $A = bh$
$\quad = 9 \cdot 3$
$\quad = 27$

The area is 20 square units.   The area is 27 cm^2.

▼
THINK How many rectangles can you form that have an area of 48 ft^2?

Example 3 **Use the area formula to find the missing information.**

   a. b is x and h is $5x$. Find A.

   b. A is 21 cm^2 and h is 7 cm. Find b.

Solution   **a.** $A = bh$
$\quad = x \cdot 5x$
$\quad = 5x^2$

   b. $A = bh$
$\quad 21 = b \cdot 7$
$\quad\quad b = 3$

The area is $5x^2$ square units.   The base is 3 cm.

▼ A rectangle is a special kind of parallelogram. You can make a parallelogram into a rectangle by rearranging the pieces.

Example 4 Use a geoboard or dot paper. Show that a parallelogram and a rectangle with height 3 and base length 7 have the same area.

Solution

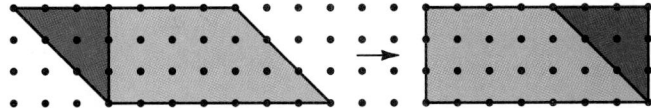

Copy the triangle formed on the left. Place the same shape on the right.

$A = bh$ **Find the area of the rectangle.**
$\quad = 7 \cdot 3$
$\quad = 21$ square units

The parallelogram and rectangle each have an area of 21 square units.

▼ Example 4 illustrates that you find the area of a parallelogram the same way you find the area of a rectangle.

Area of a Parallelogram	The area of a parallelogram equals the product of its base length (*b*) and its height (*h*). $A = bh$

THINK When is the height of a parallelogram equal to the length of each of the sides?

▼ The height of a parallelogram is the length of an *altitude*.

Altitude	An altitude is a segment from one vertex perpendicular to the line containing the opposite side, called the base.

Example 5 State the height and the measure of the base. Find the area.

a.
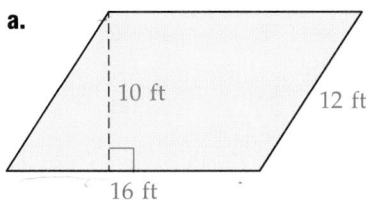

b.
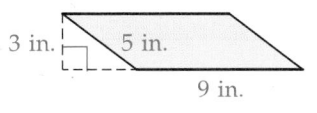

Solution

a. $h = 10$ ft,   **b.** $h = 3$ in.
$\quad b = 16$ ft $b = 9$ in.
$\quad A = bh$ $A = bh$
$\quad\quad = 16 \cdot 10$ $= 9 \cdot 3$
$\quad\quad = 160$ ft^2 $= 27$ in.^{2}

CARPET SALE $9.99 per square yard, including pad. Buy today and we will install tomorrow.

CLASS EXERCISES

Find the area of each figure.

1.    4 ft   14 ft   *56*

2. 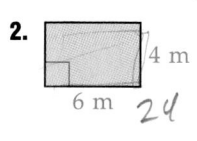   4 m   6 m   *24*

3. 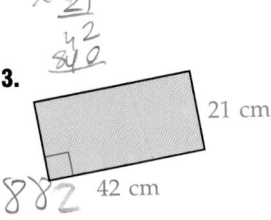   21 cm   42 cm   *882*

State the height and the measure of the base. Find the area.

4. 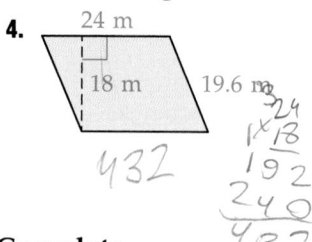   24 m   18 m   19.6 m   *432 192 240 432*

5. 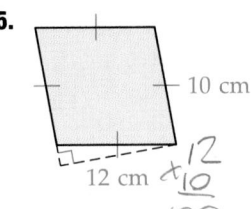   10 cm   12 cm   *120 129*

6. 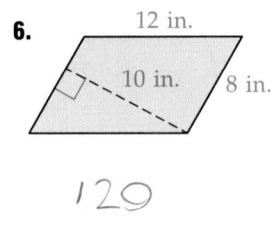   12 in.   10 in.   8 in.   *129*

Complete.

7. parallelogram,
Area = 8 m²
$b = 3$ m, $h = $ ▨ *2.6*

8. rectangle,
Area = $75x^2$
$h = 15x$, $b = $ ▨ *5x*

9. parallelogram,
Area = 525 cm²
$b = 25$ cm, $h = $ ▨ *21*

10. Use the advertisement at the left. What would it cost for both carpet and pad for your classroom?   *19.98*

WRITTEN EXERCISES

Name something you would measure with the given unit.

1. 1 square centimeter
2. 1 square foot
3. 1 square meter

4. 1 square millimeter
5. 1 square inch
6. 1 square mile

CALCULATOR Find the area of each figure.

7. 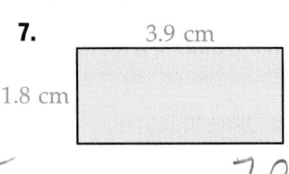   3.9 cm   1.8 cm   *7.02*

8. 23 ft   17.3 ft   13.8 ft   *321.44*

9. 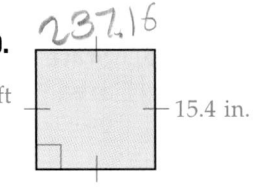   237.16   15.4 in.

10. 22.4 in.   8.4 in.   5.7 in.   *105.28*

11. 17.2 cm   10.5 cm   9 cm   *154.8*

12. 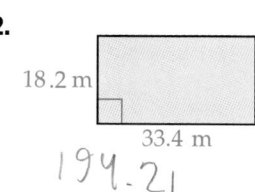   18.2 m   33.4 m   *194.21*

Complete.

13. rectangle,
$A = 22$ cm²
$b = 4$ cm, $h = $ ▨   *5.5*

14. parallelogram,
$A = 24.8$ ft²
$h = 16$ ft, $b = $ ▨

15. parallelogram,
$A = 120x^2$
$b = 8x$, $h = $ ▨

CALCULATOR **Find the area of each parallelogram with the given base and height. Round to the nearest hundredth.**

16. $b = 8.2$ cm, $h = 11.4$ cm

17. $b = 15$ ft, $h = 36$ ft

18. $b = 7.4$ m, $h = 0.008$ m

19. $b = 5.879$ km, $h = 10$ km

20. $b = 29.9$ in., $h = 32.67$ in.

21. $b = 55$ cm, $h = 10.5$ cm

22. $b = 3x + 7, h = 3x$

23. $b = 6x, h = 7x$

24. Find the area of each parallelogram.

a.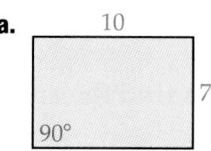

b.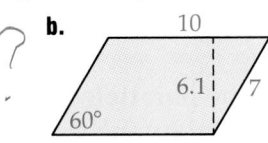

c.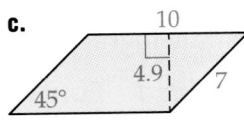

d. Does the angle measure affect the area measure? *no?*

e. Two parallelograms have sides of lengths 10 and 7. The parallelograms have altitudes to the same base. One height is 5 and the other is 4.99. Without calculating, which parallelogram has the greater area? *B*

25. The area of a square is 64 ft². What is its perimeter? *32*

26. The area of a square is $144x^2$ m². What is its perimeter? *?*

27. The perimeter of a square is 28 cm. What is its area? *49*

28. The area of a parallelogram is 36 ft². Its height is 4 ft. Find its perimeter. *26*

29. The base length of a rectangle is 5 times as great as its height. The area is 320 ft². What is the perimeter of the rectangle? *96*

30. The area of a rectangle is 56 cm². Name three different dimensions that the rectangle could have. *?*

31. How many square feet are in a square yard? Draw a diagram to illustrate your answer. *36*

32. **PROJECT** Cut the label from any cylindrical can. Make sure the cut is perpendicular to the ends. Tape the label to your paper and find the area to the nearest square centimeter.

Use the article at the right.

33. You wish to erect a political sign that is 6 ft high. What is the greatest width it can be?

34. Draw and label the dimensions for three different political signs that use the maximum possible area.

35. **PROJECT** Research the sign laws in your community. Design a political campaign sign for a candidate of your choice.

MIXED REVIEW

1. DATA FILE 1 (pp. 2–3) Write the freezing point of salt in scientific notation.

2. Simplify $2^2 \cdot 3^{-4}$.

3. $3^4 \blacksquare 4^3$.

4. Between what two integers is the square root of 41?

5. Find the circumference of a circle with $r = 8$.

6. What is the sum of the measures of the angles of a triangle?

7. A 3-ft tall child casts an 8-ft long shadow. How high is the tree next to the child if the tree's shadow is 60 ft?

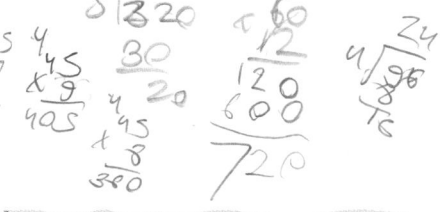

Sign Regs for Politicos

The city council issued the following regulations for political signs:

1. Only one sign may be posted on a single parcel of land.

2. Signs may not exceed 32 ft².

3. Detached signs cannot be more than 6 ft high.

4. All signs must be removed within 15 days after the election.

10-2 *Area of Triangles and Trapezoids*

▼ You can form two congruent triangles by drawing a diagonal in any parallelogram.

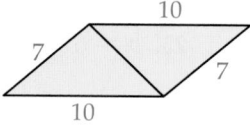 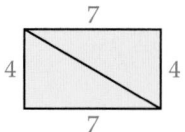

The figures suggest that the area of a triangle is half the area of a parallelogram.

THINK Why are the triangles formed by the diagonal of a parallelogram congruent?

Example 1 **Find the area of the parallelogram. Then find the area of each triangle formed by the diagonal.**

Solution $A = bh$
$\quad\quad = 9 \cdot 4$
$\quad\quad = 36$

4 in.

9 in.

The area of the parallelogram is 36 in.^{2}.
The area of each triangle is $\frac{1}{2} \cdot 36$ or 18 in.^{2}.

THINK Are $\frac{1}{2}bh$, $\frac{bh}{2}$, $b \cdot \frac{h}{2}$, and $h \cdot \frac{b}{2}$ equal?

Area of a Triangle	The area of a triangle equals half the product of the base length (b) and the height (h). $A = \frac{1}{2}bh$

▼ The height (*h*) of a triangle is the measure of an altitude. You can draw an altitude from each vertex of a triangle. An altitude may be inside, outside, or on the triangle.

Example 2 **State the height and the measure of the base. Find the area.**

a.

11x   8x   16x

20x

b.

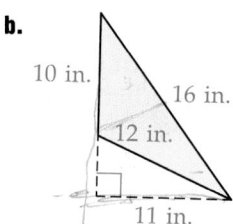

10 in.   16 in.

12 in.

11 in.

Solution **a.** $h = 8x; b = 20x$

$\quad A = \frac{1}{2}bh$

$\quad\quad = \frac{1}{2} \cdot 20x \cdot 8x$

$\quad\quad = 80x^2$ square units

b. $h = 11$ in.; $b = 10$ in.

$\quad A = \frac{1}{2}bh$

$\quad\quad = \frac{1}{2} \cdot 10 \cdot 11$

$\quad\quad = 55$ in.^{2}

▼ A diagonal through a trapezoid forms two triangles having different areas.

Example 3   Find the area of each triangle and of the trapezoid.

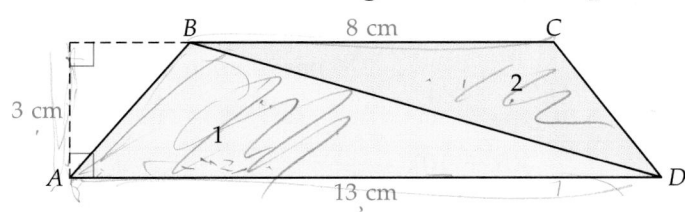

THINK Why is the height of both triangles the same?

Solution   Area of $\triangle ABD$

$A = \frac{1}{2}bh$

$= \frac{1}{2} \cdot 13 \cdot 3$

$= 19.5$ cm^2

Area of $\triangle BCD$

$A = \frac{1}{2}bh$

$= \frac{1}{2} \cdot 8 \cdot 3$

$= 12$ cm^2

The area of the trapezoid is $19.5 + 12 = 31.5$ cm^2.

▼ The area of a trapezoid is the sum of the areas of the two triangles formed by a diagonal. In a trapezoid, we label the bases (the parallel sides) as b_1 and b_2.

$$A = \frac{1}{2}b_1h$$

$$+ \ A = \frac{1}{2}b_2h$$

Area of trapezoid $\quad = \frac{1}{2}b_1h + \frac{1}{2}b_2h$

$$= \frac{1}{2}h(b_1 + b_2)$$

Area of a Trapezoid	The area of a trapezoid equals half the product of the height (h) and the sum of the bases (b_1 and b_2). $A = \frac{1}{2}h(b_1 + b_2)$

Example 4   Use the formulas to find the missing information.

a. triangle, $h = 9$ mm, $A = 67.5$ mm^2 Find b.

b. trapezoid, $b_1 = 12$ cm, $b_2 = 16$ cm, $A = 112$ cm^2 Find h.

Solution   **a.** $A = \frac{1}{2}bh$

$67.5 = \frac{1}{2}b \cdot 9$

$67.5 = 4.5b$

$b = 15$ mm

b. $A = \frac{1}{2}h(b_1 + b_2)$

$112 = \frac{1}{2}h(12 + 16)$

$112 = \frac{1}{2}h \cdot 28$

$112 = 14h$

$h = 8$ cm

▼ When you find the area of a figure, all units must be the same.

Example 5 Find the area of a trapezoid with $b_1 = 5$ mm, $b_2 = 1$ cm, and $h = 4$ mm.

Solution $b_2 = 1$ cm $= 10$ mm   Write 1 cm as 10 mm so the bases are in the same units.

$$A = \frac{1}{2}h(b_1 + b_2)$$

$$= \frac{1}{2} \cdot 4(5 + 10)$$

$$= 30 \text{ mm}^2$$

THINK AND DISCUSS

1. Are $\left(\frac{1}{2} \cdot 3\right) \cdot 8$ and $3 \cdot \left(\frac{1}{2} \cdot 8\right)$ equal? How can this help in finding the area of a triangle?

2. Find the area pictured. Is there more than one method?

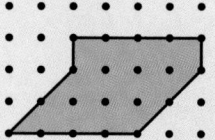

3. Why can the sides be the altitude and base in a right triangle?

CLASS EXERCISES

Find the area of a triangle with the given base and height.

1. $b = 12$ cm
  $h = 7$ cm

2. $h = 3$ in.
  $b = 1$ ft

3. $b = 2.5$ mm
  $h = 5$ mm

4.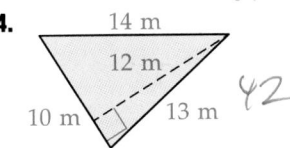

5.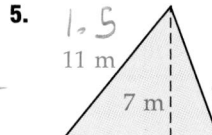

6.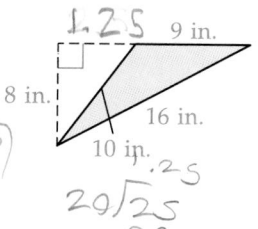

Find the area of a trapezoid with the given base lengths and height.

7. $b_1 = 6$ cm
  $b_2 = 10$ cm
  $h = 5$ cm

8. $b_1 = 6$
  $b_2 = 2$
  $h = 5$

9. $h = 3$
  $b_1 = x$
  $b_2 = x + 2$

10.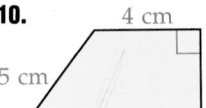

11.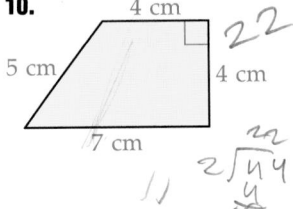

12.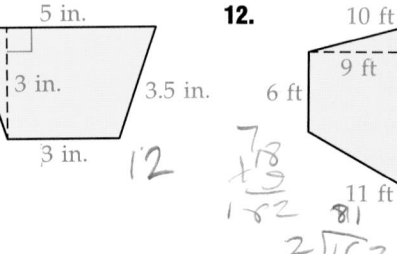

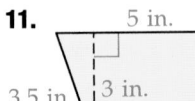

WRITTEN EXERCISES

CALCULATOR Find the area of a triangle with the given base and height.

1. $b = 8.2$ m
  $h = 9.6$ m

2. $h = 35$ mm
  $b = 20$ mm

3. $b = 49$ in.
  $h = 18$ in.

4.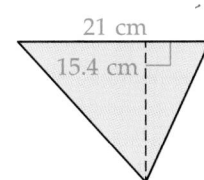
3.6 in.
3.3 in.
4.8 in.

5.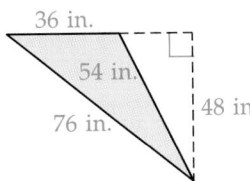
21 cm
15.4 cm

6.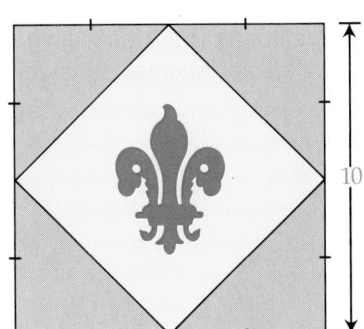
36 in.
54 in.
76 in.
48 in.

CALCULATOR Find the area of a trapezoid with the given base lengths and height.

7. $b_1 = 40$ cm
$b_2 = 35$ cm
$h = 20$ cm

8. $b_1 = 54$ m
$b_2 = 80$ m
$h = 15$ m

9. $h = 62.4$ ft
$b_1 = 30.5$ ft
$b_2 = 14.2$ ft

10.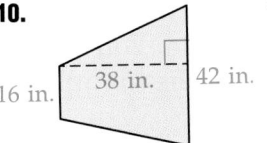
16 in.
38 in.
42 in.

11.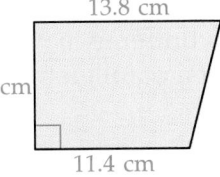
13.8 cm
9.5 cm
11.4 cm

12.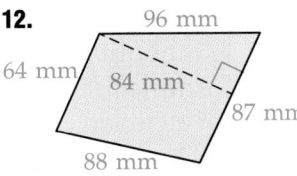
96 mm
64 mm
84 mm
87 mm
88 mm

Measure each figure to the nearest tenth of a centimeter and find the area.

13.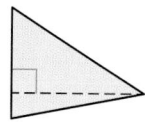

14.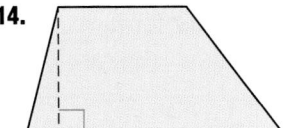

15.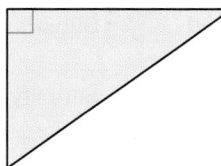

Find the missing values.

	Figure	h	b_1	b_2	A
16.	triangle	0.1 m	4 cm	—	▨
17.	square	$9x$	—	—	▨
18.	trapezoid	▨	8 ft	2 ft	15 ft²
19.	parallelogram	▨	10 ft	10 ft	15 ft²

20. Find the area of the yellow square tile at the right.

True or false? Write T or F.

21. A triangle has three altitudes.

22. A square is always a parallelogram.

23. A trapezoid and a parallelogram can never have the same area.

24. A square crossed by two diagonals will form four congruent triangles.

25. An altitude is always perpendicular to a side of a triangle.

26. Two rectangles with the same perimeter always have the same area.

MIXED REVIEW

Find the area.

1. rectangle,
$b = 15$ cm
$h = 12$ cm

2. parallelogram,
$b = 38.2$ mm
$h = 20$ mm

3. *DATA FILE 7 (pp. 272–273)* Find the percent change, to the nearest tenth, of passenger boardings in Denver from 1987 to 2000.

4. Write $3{,}120{,}000 \times 4{,}600$ using scientific notation.

5. Find the circumference of a circle with radius $3x$.

Solve.

6. $-8x - 12 = 28$

7. $\frac{2}{3}x = \frac{5}{8}$

8. A rectangular yard is 20 ft by 40 ft. Your lawn mower will mow a 2-ft wide path. What is the least number of paths you must make to mow the lawn?

10-3 Area of Circles

▼ Notice what happens when you cut a circle into several equal size
pieces and then rearrange the pieces.

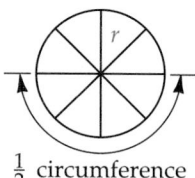 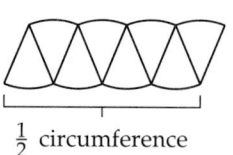

$\frac{1}{2}$ circumference

$\frac{1}{2}$ circumference

The new shape closely resembles a parallelogram where the
height, h, is about the same as the radius of the circle. The base
length, b, is about half the circumference (C) of the circle. You can
use the formula for the area of a parallelogram to find the formula for
the area of a circle.

$b = \frac{1}{2}C$ Substitute the formula for circumference.

$\quad = \frac{1}{2}2\pi r$

$\quad = \pi r$

$A = bh$ Substitute πr for b and r for h.

$\quad = \pi r \cdot r$

$\quad = \pi r^2$ Simplify.

Area of a Circle	The area of a circle equals the product of π and the square of the radius (r). $$A = \pi r^2$$

Example 1 Find the area of a circle with diameter 12 cm. Give both
an exact and an approximate answer. Use 3.14 for π.

THINK Why does
substituting 3.14 for π give
you an approximate answer?

Solution
$d = 12, r = 6$ The radius is half the
$A = \pi r^2$ diameter.
$\quad = \pi(6)^2$
$\quad = 36\pi$ cm^2, exact answer
$\quad \approx 36 \cdot 3.14$ Substitute 3.14 for π.
$\quad = 113.04$ cm^2

▼ If you know the area of a circle, you can find the radius.

Example 2 Find the radius of a circle with area 452.16 cm^2. Use 3.14
for π.

Solution
$\qquad A = \pi r^2$
$452.16 = 3.14 \cdot r^2$ Divide each side by 3.14.
$\quad\ \ 144 = r^2$ Find the square root of 144.
$\qquad\ \ r = 12$ cm

CLASS EXERCISES

Find the area of each circle. Give an exact answer and an approximate answer. Use 3.14 for π.

1. $r = 3$ ft

2. $d = 10$ m

3. $r = 20$ cm

4.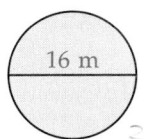
16 m

5.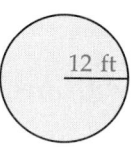
12 ft

6.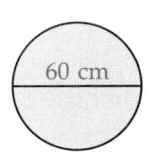
60 cm

Find the radius of a circle with the given area. Use 3.14 for π.

7. 49π cm^2

8. 254.34 yd^2

9. $225x^2\pi$ square units

> **THINK AND DISCUSS**
>
> **1.** Name two real world situations where area of a circle is important.
>
> **2.** Suppose you didn't know the formula for the area of a circle. How could you approximate the number of square units in a circle?

WRITTEN EXERCISES

Find the area of each circle. Give an exact answer and an approximate answer. Use 3.14 for π. Round to nearest hundredth.

1. $r = 11$ mi

2. $r = \frac{1}{2}$ m

3. $d = 1.2$ in.

4. $d = 12$ in.

5. $d = 3.2$ ft

6. $d = 8.4$ mm

7. $r = 5x$

8. $d = 6\sqrt{2}$

9. $d = 4.2x$

Match the item listed with the most reasonable area.

	Item	Area
10.	dinner plate	**a.** 3.14 cm^2
11.	quarter	**b.** 113.04 in.^{2}
12.	circle on basketball floor	**c.** 28.26 cm^2
13.	jar lid	**d.** 36π ft^2
14.	shirt button	**e.** 452.16 mm^2
15.	12-in. pizza	**f.** 78.5 in.^{2}

16. Which has a greater area, a circle with a radius of 2 or a square with side of length 2? Explain your answer.

17. Which has a greater area, four circles with the radius of 1 or one circle with the radius of 4? Explain your answer.

18. Write a formula for the area of a circle that uses the diameter instead of the radius.

19. What is the area of the largest circle that will fit in a square with area 64 cm^2?

20. DATA FILE 10 (pp. 404–405) Find the approximate area of the circular home range for each animal. Use 3.14 for π.

a. cougar   b. red fox   c. Northern flying squirrel

r (units)	A (square units)
1	▦
3	▦
5	▦
7	▦

21. Copy and complete the table at the left. Round to the nearest tenth. Use 3.14 for π.

a. Graph the results. Use the x-axis for radius and the y-axis for area.

b. Predict the radius of a circle with area 125 square units.

Find the radius of a circle with the given area. Use 3.14 for π.

22. 81π cm^2 **23.** 803.84 in.^{2} **24.** 7.065 mm^2

Find the circumference and area of each circle. Use 3.14 for π. Round to the nearest tenth.

25. $r = 5.2$ cm   **26.** $d = 7.8$ in.   **27.** $r = 18.6$ m

28. $r = \dfrac{3}{4}$ cm   **29.** $r = 8.7$ m   **30.** $d = 15xy$

Find the area of each shaded portion. Use 3.14 for π.

31.
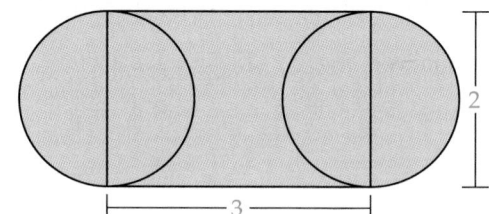
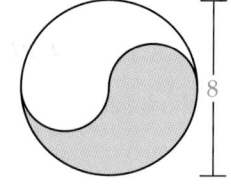

32.

33. Find the area of the outer ring of the figure at the left.

34. Manufacturers of tin cans stamp the lids from rectangular sheets of tin.

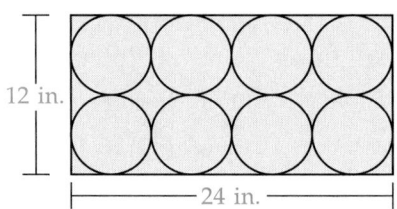

a. What is the radius of each lid?

b. What is the total area used by the lids?

c. How much of the sheet of tin is wasted?

35. You wish to carpet the border of the pool at the left.

a. How many square feet do you need for the border?

b. Carpets are sold by the square yard. How many square feet are in a square yard?

c. How many square yards of carpet should you purchase?

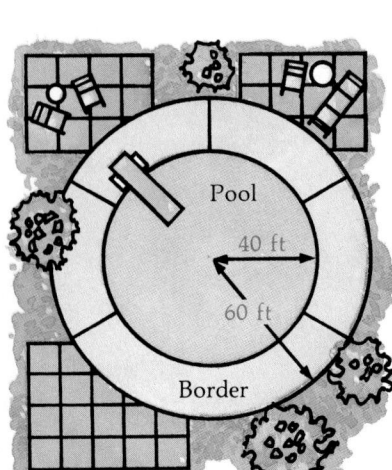

36. a. What is the area of each pizza pictured below?

b. What is the price per square inch?

c. Is the largest pizza always the best buy?

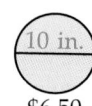 10 in. $6.50

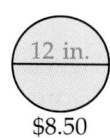 12 in. $8.50

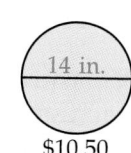 14 in. $10.50

37. *COMPUTER* Use a spreadsheet to compare the radius, circumference, and area of different circles. Use the format shown below.

	A	B	C
1	Radius	Circumference	Area
2	1	=2*A2*3.14	=3.14*A2^2
3	2	=2*A3*3.14	=3.14*A3^2
4	3	=2*A4*3.14	=3.14*A4^2
5			

Complete cells A2 to A10 for radii from 1 to 9.

a. What happens to the circumference of a circle if the radius is doubled? if the radius is tripled?

b. If you double the radius of a circle, do you double the area?

TEST YOURSELF

State the formula for the area of each figure.

1. circle   **2.** triangle   **3.** rectangle

4. trapezoid   **5.** parallelogram

Find the area of each figure. Use 3.14 for π.

6. 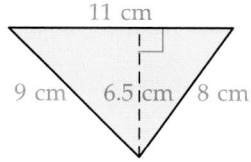 11 cm, 9 cm, 6.5 cm, 8 cm

7. 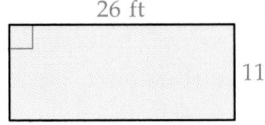 26 ft, 11 ft

8. 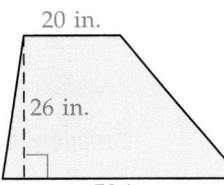 20 in., 26 in., 50 in.

9.  35 mm

10. 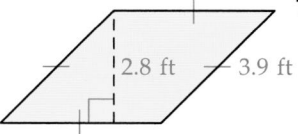 2.8 ft, 3.9 ft

11. 24 ft

Exploring Pick's Theorem

▼ You can use a geoboard to develop a formula or rule about area. Each square on the geoboard represents 1 square unit of area. Use dot paper to copy the shapes shown.

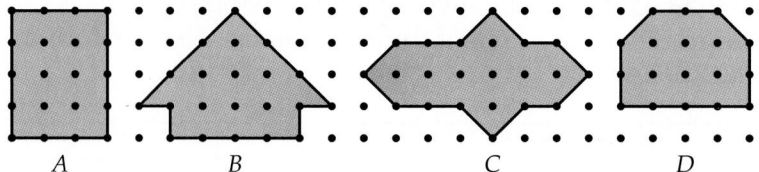

A   B   C   D

1. Find the area of each shape.

2. Copy and complete the chart for each shape. Interior dots are those inside the shape. Boundary dots are those on the side or at corners of the shape.

	Boundary Dots	Interior Dots	Area
A	14	6	▨
B	▨	▨	▨
C	▨	▨	▨
D	▨	▨	▨

3. **Describe** the relationship between the number of interior dots, the number of boundary dots, and the area.

4. **Model** several figures with five boundary dots and up to four interior dots. Find the area of each figure. **Discuss** how the dots are related to the area.

5. Copy the shapes below on a geoboard or dot paper.

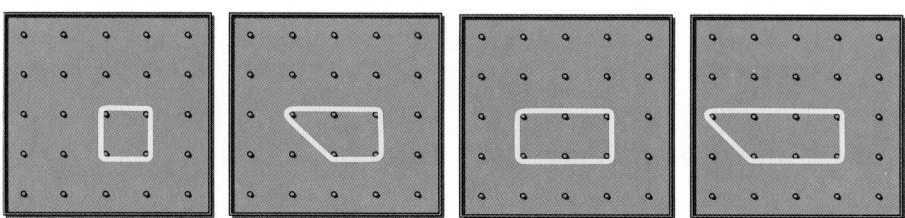

a. Copy and complete the chart.

Boundary Dots	Interior Dots	Area
4	0	▨
5	0	▨
6	0	▨
7	0	▨

b. Which rule relates boundary dots (B) to area when the number of interior dots is zero?

I. $\frac{B}{2} + 1$ II. $\frac{B}{2}$ III. $\frac{B}{2} - 1$

6. Copy the shapes below on a geoboard or dot paper.

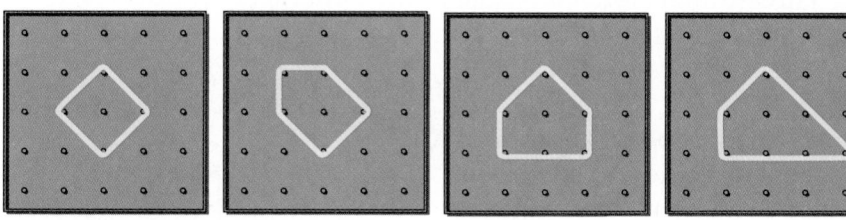

    a. Complete a chart for one interior dot.

    b. *Predict* the area of a shape with 12 boundary dots and one interior dot.

    c. *Write* a rule that relates boundary dots to area when there is one interior dot.

7. Copy the shapes below on a geoboard or dot paper.

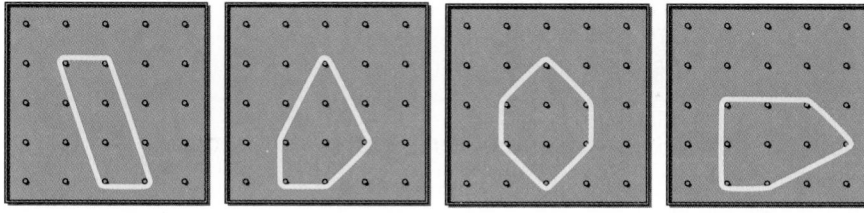

    a. Complete a chart for two interior dots.

    b. *Predict* the area of a shape with 12 boundary dots and two interior dots.

    c. *Write* a rule that relates boundary dots to area when there are two interior dots.

8. *Write* a rule for finding area for each number of dots.

    a. three interior dots   **b.** four interior dots   **c.** n interior dots

9. Test your rule. Find the area of each figure using area formulas. Then use your rule.

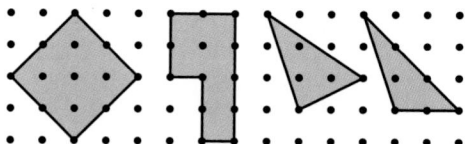

10. Use Pick's theorem to find the area of each shaded region.

Exploring Pick's Theorem   **419**

10-4 Space Figures

▼ An interior designer must be aware of the interplay of shapes in a room. Three-dimensional or space figures interact to produce different effects.

▼ *Prisms* are a type of *polyhedron*. An unsharpened six-sided pencil is in the shape of a prism. The diagram shows some of the terms we use to describe the parts of a prism.

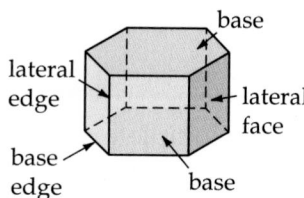

| **Polyhedron** | A polyhedron is a space figure in which all faces are polygons. |

| **Prism** | A prism is a polyhedron with two parallel bases that are congruent polygons and sides that are parallelograms. |

We name a prism by the shape of its bases.

Example 1

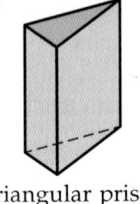

triangular prism

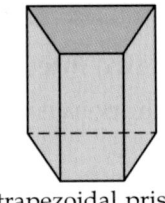

trapezoidal prism

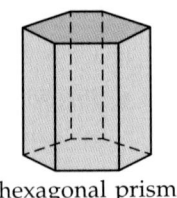

hexagonal prism

▼ *Pyramids* are a type of polyhedron. The ancient Egyptians built pyramids for tombs. You can also find a pyramid on a dollar bill. The diagram at the left shows the parts of a pyramid.

| **Pyramid** | A pyramid is a polyhedron with triangular sides that meet at a vertex. The base of a pyramid is a polygon. |

We name a pyramid by the shape of its base.

Example 2

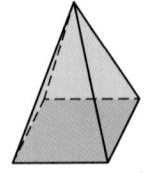

square pyramid

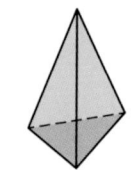

triangular pyramid

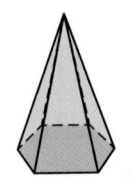

hexagonal pyramid

THINK Why do we use dashed lines when drawing space figures?

▼ Cylinders, cones, and spheres are space figures that contain circles.

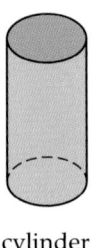
cylinder

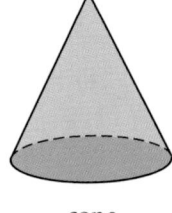
cone

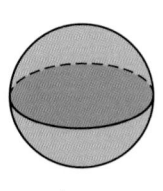
sphere

Cylinder	A cylinder is a space figure with two circular, parallel, and congruent bases.
Cone	A cone is a space figure with one circular base and one vertex.
Sphere	A sphere is the set of all points in space that are the same distance from a given point called the center.

▼ **THINK** How is the definition of a sphere similar to the definition of a circle?

▼ A *net* is a pattern you can fold into a space figure.

Example 3 Name the space figure you can form from each net.

a.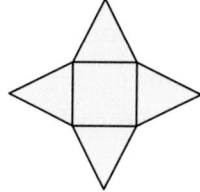

b.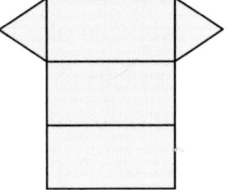

Solution **a.** square pyramid   **b.** triangular prism

CLASS EXERCISES

1. Give another name for a cube.
2. What polyhedron is a cone most like?
3. What polyhedron is a cylinder most like?
4. How many faces of a regular hexagonal pyramid are congruent? What is the name of the shape of a face?
5. Draw a net for a pentagonal pyramid.
6. Draw a net for a hexagonal prism.
7. Draw a net for a cylinder.

▼ **THINK AND DISCUSS**

1. How many nets can you draw for a cube? Draw them.

2. How do the bases of a cylinder look when they are drawn? Draw a cylinder and a cone.

3. What is a mathematical name for a brick?

WRITTEN EXERCISES

Name each polyhedron.

1. 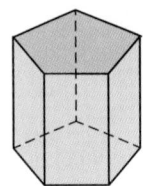   **2.** 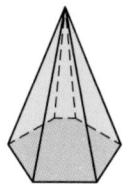   **3.**

Name the space figure you can form from each net.

4. 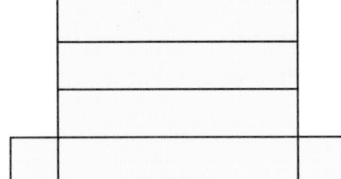   **5.**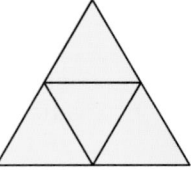

Draw a net for each space figure named.

6. hexagonal pyramid   **7.** octagonal prism

True or false? Write T or F.

8. A cone has two bases.

9. A square pyramid has four triangles.

10. The lateral faces of a prism are parallelograms.

11. A cylinder is an example of a polyhedron.

12. The lateral faces of a regular pyramid are isosceles triangles.

13. A pyramid can have a circular base.

Complete each statement.

14. A triangular prism has ▦ triangles.

15. An octagonal prism has 8 ▦ and 2 ▦.

16. A hexagonal prism has ▦ lateral edges.

17. A square pyramid has ▦ base edges.

18. A cone has ▦ vertex.

19. A ▦ has 5 parallelograms for faces and 2 ▦ for bases.

Write the mathematical name for each object.

20. soup can   **21.** shoe box   **22.** tepee   **23.** basketball

24. *WRITE* Examine a soccer ball. Describe it using mathematical names.

25. *PROJECT* A tetrahedron, octahedron, hexahedron, dodecahedron, and icosahedron are regular polyhedra.

    a. Find out how many faces each regular polyhedron has and what polygons make the faces.

    b. These shapes are often called Platonic solids. Research what each solid represented for Plato.

Copy each of the figures below on graph paper and write the mathematical name for each.

26.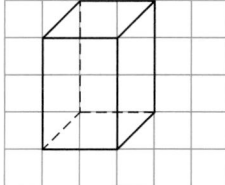

27.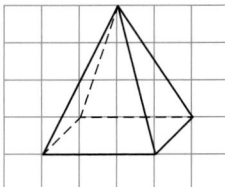

28. *PROJECT* Draw the nets for four polyhedra on heavy paper or cardboard. Fold to form the polyhedron and label with the mathematical name.

Critical Thinking
EXPLORING VISUALIZATION

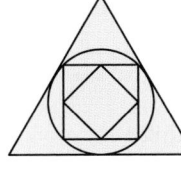
    A

    B

    C

    D

1. Guess the pattern for *D*.

2. Name each shape in pattern *A* in order from greatest area to least. Do this for pattern *B* and pattern *C*.

3. Predict the pattern for *D* and draw it.

4. Select the pattern that best completes the series below.

                                         A   *B*   *C*

Exploring Patterns in a Cube

OBJECTIVE:
To explore spatial visualization and patterns in a cube.

MATERIALS

• Graph paper

• Math journal to record work

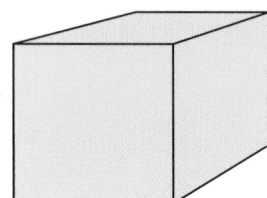

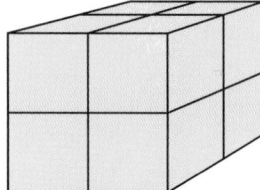

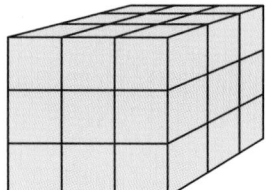

■ You can explore the characteristics of three-dimensional objects by thinking about how they appear and by sketching them.

1. Consider a cube.

   a. How many faces does it have?

   b. You tie a string to the cube and dip it into paint. How many faces have you painted?

2. Suppose you cut the painted cube in half vertically and horizontally to make smaller cubes. Each edge is half the length of the original cube.

   a. How many smaller cubes do you have?

   b. How many cube faces have painted surfaces?

   c. How many faces of each of the smaller cubes would be painted?

3. Complete the chart and extend it for a cube cut into smaller cubes of equal size.

Number of Segments on Each Edge	Total Number of Cubes	Total Expressed as a Number Cubed	Number of Cubes with the Given Number of Sides Painted			
			0	1	2	3
2	8	2^3	0	0	0	8
3						
4						
5						
6						

4. **Discuss** the patterns you find in each column of the chart.

5. **Predict** the total number of cubes if there are 12 smaller cubes on each edge.

6. There are 100 cubes on each edge. How many will be painted on three sides?

7. **Predict** the number that have two sides painted if there are 10 cubes on each edge. How many will have no paint at all?

8. **Analyze** Suppose you could paint only the sides of the cube that you can see without moving it. How many sides of the original cube would be painted? How will this change all of your results?

9. **Write** Was it necessary to draw a sketch of each cube? Explain when you were able to anticipate the results of the next row.

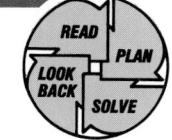

OBJECTIVE:
To solve problems by
making a model.

10-5 *Make a Model*

■ Sometimes solving a problem is made simpler by a model.

PROBLEM

A delivery person is unloading drums of oil along a ramp. In order to prevent the drums from being damaged, the ramp is not too steep. The more slowly a moving drum rolls, the less likely it is that it will be damaged. What kind of drum is better to use, one with a large or small radius?

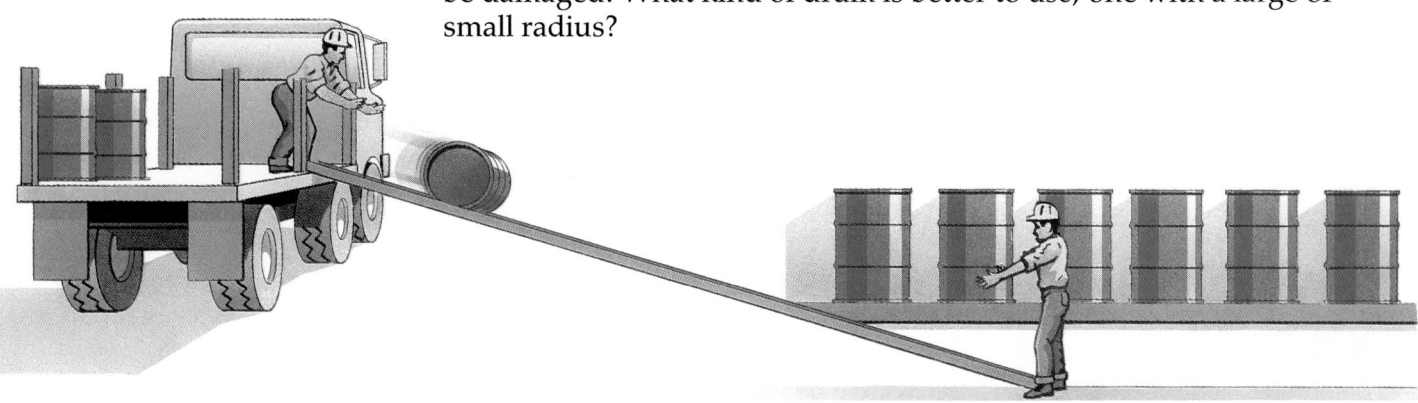

SOLUTION

READ ▶ What do you want to find?

which size of cylindrically shaped drum travels more slowly down an inclined plane

PLAN ▶ Use a wooden plank as an inclined plane.
Take some cylinders such as an oatmeal box or the cardboard center from paper towels. Make sure that the cylinders have different radii but the same height. Roll the object down the inclined plane. Determine which cylinder takes longer to roll down the plane.

SOLVE ▶ What do you notice?

Cylinders with a greater radius take longer to travel down the plane.

LOOK BACK ▶ What can you conclude?

Cylindrical drums with a greater radius should be used because they travel down a ramp more slowly.

CLASS EXERCISES

Answer each question.

1. How might the area touching the ramp affect the speed at which a cylinder rolls down the ramp?

2. How can you find the area of the part of the cylinder that touches the ramp?

3. Use cylinders with the same radii but with different lengths. What affect does length have on the rate a cylinder travels down a ramp?

WRITTEN EXERCISES

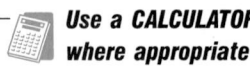
Use a CALCULATOR where appropriate.

Explain how a model could be made for each situation.

1. You wish to find out the effect the length of a pendulum has on the amount of time the pendulum will swing.

2. You must decide which bridge design will be the strongest for a new bridge across Niagara Falls.

Use any strategy to solve each problem.

3. The junior class sold tickets for a pancake breakfast. One hundred twenty people came to the breakfast. This amount accounted for 60% of the tickets sold. How many tickets were sold?

4. The length of a rectangle is twice the width. The perimeter of the rectangle is 42 cm. What are the length and width?

5. *DATA FILE 2 (pp. 52–53)* A treasure hunter must determine the depth of a sunken ship. She sends a sonar wave towards the location of the ship. It takes 9.2 s for the sound to return. How far beneath the ocean is the sunken ship?

6. The difference between two numbers is 18. The sum of the two numbers is 34. What are the two numbers?

7. Eight teams are in a soccer tournament. When a team wins, it goes on to play another team. A team that loses is out of the tournament. How many games must be played in this tournament?

8. You fill a container $\frac{3}{4}$ full of water. The amount of water now in the container is 6 quarts. How much can the container hold?

9. A number n is multiplied by $\frac{5}{8}$. Then the result is subtracted from $\frac{2}{3}$. The answer is $\frac{7}{12}$. What is n?

10. Sara rented a car for two days. The rate was $22.50 per day and $.32 per mile. Sara traveled 150 mi. How much was she charged?

11. Troy is digging post holes for his ranch. He has a triangular plot that is 100 yd by 300 yd by 250 yd. He digs a hole every 10 yd. How many holes must he dig?

OBJECTIVE:
To use a model to
find surface area of
prisms and cylinders.

10-6 Surface Area—Prisms and Cylinders

▼ The packages for most food items are prisms and cylinders. The cost of the package is part of the price of the item. Manufacturers consider the surface area of a package when calculating the price.

Surface Area	Surface area (*SA*) is the sum of the areas of the base(s) and the side(s).

▼ You can use a net to help you find the surface area.

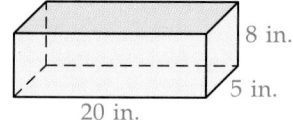

Example 1 **Find the surface area of the rectangular prism at the left using a net.**

Solution

40 in.² ├── 20 ──┤ 40 in.²

8	160 in.²
5	100 in.²
8	160 in.²
5	100 in.²

Draw and label a net.

Write the area of each rectangle on the net.

$40 + 40 + 160 + 100 + 160 + 100 = 600$ Add the areas.

The surface area is 600 in².

▼ You can use formulas to find the surface area.

Lateral Area of a Prism	The lateral area (*LA*) of a prism is the product of the perimeter of the base (*P*) and the height of the prism (*h*). $A = Ph$

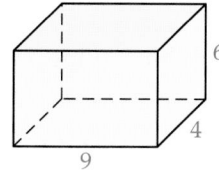

Example 2 **Find the surface area of the rectangular prism at the left using formulas.**

Solution

1. State each dimension. $b = 4, h = 6$
                              height of prism = 9

2. Find the perimeter. $P = 2(b + h) = 2(4 + 6) = 20$

3. Find the lateral area. $LA = Ph = 20 \cdot 9 = 180$

4. Find the base area. $A = bh = 4 \cdot 6 = 24$

5. Find the sum of the two $SA = 2 \cdot 24 + 180 = 228$
   base areas and the lateral
   area.

The surface area is 228 square units.

By the year 2,000 B.C., the Babylonians and Egyptians had fairly accurate calculations for π.

Babylonian value $\quad 3\frac{1}{8}$

Egyptian value $\quad 4\left(\frac{8}{9}\right)^2$

What is the decimal equivalent for each calculation of π?

▼ You can cut a label from a can of soup to see that it is a rectangle. The height of the rectangle is the height of the can. The base length of the rectangle is the circumference of the can. The area of the rectangle is the *lateral area* of the can.

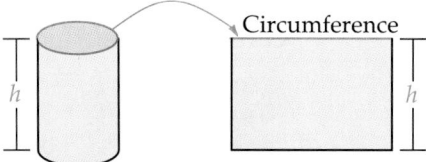

Lateral Area of a Cylinder	The lateral area (*LA*) of a cylinder is the product of the circumference of the base (*C*) and the height of the cylinder (*h*).
	$A = Ch$

Example 3   Find the surface area of the oatmeal box at the left to the nearest square centimeter. Use 3.14 for π.

Solution

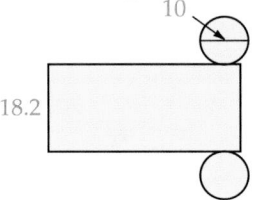

Draw and label a net.

$$\text{Area of bases} = 2(\pi r^2) = 2(\pi \cdot 5^2) \approx 50(3.14) = 157$$
$$LA = Ch = \pi \cdot 10 \cdot 18.2 \approx 182(3.14) = 571.48$$
$$\text{Total} = 728.48$$

The surface area of the oatmeal box is about 728 cm².

10 cm

18.2 cm

1. Name a real world situation where you need to know surface area.

2. Explain the difference between the height of a base and the height of a prism.

CLASS EXERCISES

1. Find the surface area of a cube that is 10 ft on each edge.

2. Draw and label a net for a hexagonal prism with base edge 7 and height 13.

3. Draw and label a net and find the surface area for a cylinder with radius 8 and height 12. Use 3.14 for π.

4. Draw and label a net and find the surface area of a rectangular prism. The base is 3 in. × 5 in. and the height is 11 in.

5. Draw and label a net and find the surface area of a cylindrical water tank with radius 20 ft and height 30 ft. Use 3.14 for π.

6. Use formulas to find the surface area of a square prism with base edge 7 m and height 15 m.

WRITTEN EXERCISES

Find the surface area of the space figure shown in each net.

1.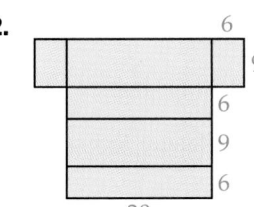

2.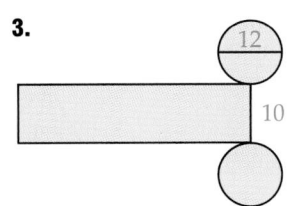

3.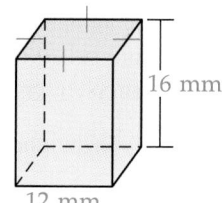

CALCULATOR Find the surface area of each space figure.

4.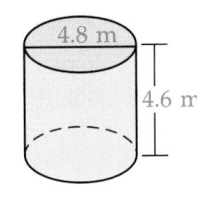

5.

6.

Find the surface area.

7. a triangular prism with all base edges 9 cm, base height 7.8 cm, and height of the prism 15 cm

8. a cylinder with radius 8 cm and height 10 cm; Use 3.14 for π.

9. Use cubes of base 1, 2, and 3 units to answer the following questions.

   a. Find the surface area of each cube.

   b. If the length of the cube is doubled, the surface area is ▨. If the length is tripled, the surface area is ▨.

10. The neighborhood swimming pool needs to be resurfaced. The pool is 40 ft by 60 ft. The depth of the pool is 6 ft.

   a. How many sides need to be resurfaced? how many bases?

   b. What is the total number of square feet to be resurfaced?

   c. The materials for resurfacing the pool cost $1.75/ft². What is the cost of resurfacing the pool?

11. A cylindrical storage tank needs painting. The radius of the tank is 18 ft and its height is 30 ft. The paint covers 350 ft²/gal. How many gallons of paint are needed? Use 3.14 for π.

12. Which cylinder at the right will be the more expensive to paint? Explain your answer.

13. *PROJECT* Draw and label a net and find the number of square feet in the surface area of a room in your home.

MIXED REVIEW

1. $(x)(2x)(3x)$

2. $a(4a + 7)$

3. Solve for x. $\frac{3x}{4} = \frac{5}{6}$

4. $\sqrt[2]{144}$

5. 16^2

Find the area.

6. circle, $r = 12$

7. parallelogram, $b = 8$ and $h = 14$

8. *DATA FILE 2 (pp. 52–53)* Express the sound intensity of a rocket launch in bels.

9. The wheels of a racing bike are about 70 cm in diameter. What is the circumference of a wheel?

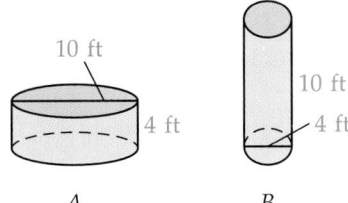

A   *B*

OBJECTIVE:
To use a model to
find surface area of
pyramids, cones, and
spheres.

10-7 Surface Area—Pyramids, Cones, Spheres

▼ To find the surface area of pyramids and cones, you must use the height of a face, called the *slant height* (*l*), to find the area of the lateral faces.

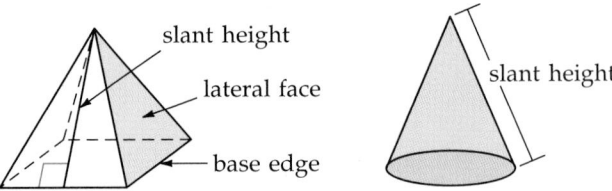

slant height

lateral face

base edge

slant height

▼ You can draw a net to help find the surface area of a pyramid.

Example 1 A pyramid has a base edge of 720 ft. The slant height is 584 ft. Find the surface area.

Solution

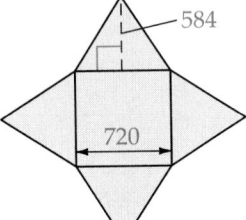

584

720

Draw and label a net.

$$\text{Area of lateral faces} = 4\left(\frac{1}{2}bl\right)$$

$$= 4\left(\frac{1}{2} \cdot 720 \cdot 584\right) = 840{,}960 \text{ ft}^2$$

$$\text{Area of base} = (bh) = \quad (720 \cdot 720) \quad = 518{,}400 \text{ ft}^2$$

$$\text{Total} \qquad\qquad\qquad\qquad = 1{,}359{,}360 \text{ ft}^2$$

The surface area is 1,359,360 ft².

▼ The curved surface of a cone is its *lateral area*. A cone that is cut and flattened may remind you of a triangle with the height of *l* and the base equal to the circumference of the circular base. If you substitute *C* for *b* and *l* for *h* in the triangle area formula, the result is the formula for the lateral area of a cone.

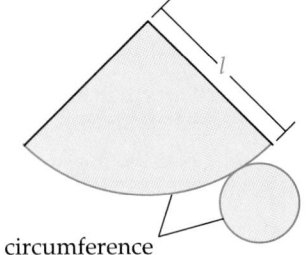

circumference

$$\text{Triangle Area} = \frac{1}{2}bh$$

$$\text{Lateral Area} = \frac{1}{2}Cl$$

Lateral Area of a Cone	The lateral area (*LA*) of a cone equals half the product of the circumference (*C*) and slant height (*l*).
	$LA = \frac{1}{2}Cl$

Example 2 Find the surface area of the cone. Use 3.14 for π.

Solution Draw and label a net.

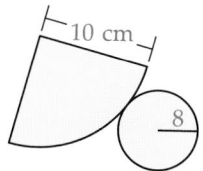

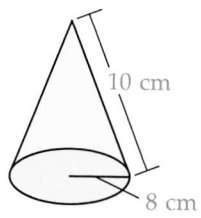

$$\text{Lateral area} = \tfrac{1}{2}Cl = \tfrac{1}{2} \cdot 16\pi \cdot 10 \approx 80(3.14) = 251.2$$

$$\underline{\text{Base area} \quad = \pi r^2 = \quad \pi \cdot 8^2 \quad \approx 64(3.14) = 200.96}$$

$$\text{Total} \qquad\qquad\qquad\qquad\qquad\qquad\quad = 452.16 \text{ cm}^2$$

The total surface area of the cone is about 452.16 cm².

> **FLASHBACK**
> $C = \pi d$

▼ Many sports, including basketball, tennis, soccer, and golf rely on spheres.

Surface Area of a Sphere	The surface area of a sphere equals the product of 4π and the square of the radius (r). $$A = 4\pi r^2$$

Example 3 Calculate the surface area of a basketball. Use 3.14 for π.

Solution
$$A = 4\pi r^2$$
$$= 4\pi(12)^2$$
$$\approx 576(3.14)$$
$$= 1{,}808.64$$

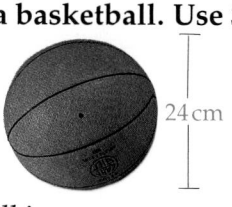

24 cm

The surface area of a basketball is about 1,808.64 cm².

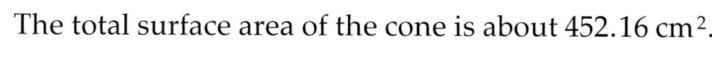

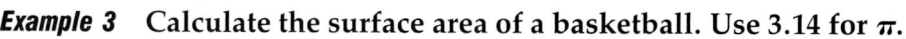

CLASS EXERCISES

Draw and label a net and find the surface area. Use 3.14 for π.

1.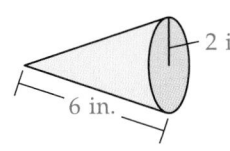
2 in. · 6 in.

2.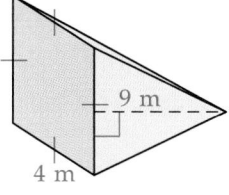
9 m · 4 m

3.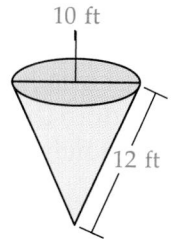
10 ft · 12 ft

4. Find the surface area of a cone with radius 3 and slant height 8. Use 3.14 for π.

5. Find the surface area of a square pyramid with base 5 and slant height 8.

> **THINK AND DISCUSS**
>
> **1.** Name two uses of cones.
>
> **2.** How is the slant height of a pyramid different from the height of a prism?
>
> **3.** Could you find the lateral area of a pyramid in a way that is similar to finding the lateral area of a cone? Explain.

6. Which has the greater surface area, a cylinder with radius 2 and height 2 or a sphere with radius 2?

7. Which has the greater surface area, a square prism with base edge 4 and height 5 or a square pyramid with base edge 4 and slant height 5?

8. Find the surface area of a tennis ball with diameter of 2.5 in.

MIXED REVIEW

Solve.

1. $2x - 5 = 39$

2. $18 - 3x = 42$

3. DATA FILE 5 (pp. 180–181) The list price on a CD is $11.97. How much will the artist receive in royalties, to the nearest cent, on each CD sold?

4. $\frac{x}{12} = \frac{4}{15}$

Find the perimeter.

5. a regular hexagon with side 13.2 cm

6. an equilateral triangle with side 8.6 in.

7. Use scientific notation to find $(3.2 \times 10^4)(3.2 \times 10^4)$.

8. Explain how a hexagonal pyramid and a hexagonal prism are alike and how they are different.

WRITTEN EXERCISES

Draw and label a net and find the surface area. Use 3.14 for π.

1.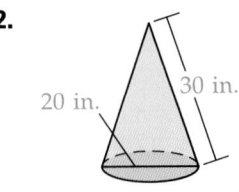
40 ft
50 ft

2.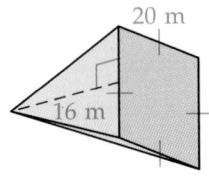
20 in.   30 in.

3.
20 m
16 m

4. square pyramid,
$s = 35$ in.
$l = 42$ in.

5. cone,
$r = 14$ m
$l = 25$ m

6. cone,
$d = 22$ cm
$l = 34$ cm

CALCULATOR Find the surface area. Use 3.14 for π.

7. a sphere with radius 15 in.   **8.** a sphere with diameter 18 m

9. a hemisphere (half of a sphere) with radius 27 m

10. a hemisphere with diameter 42 cm

11. Find the surface areas of a sphere, $r = 2$, and a sphere, $r = 5$. How do the ratios of the surface areas compare with the ratios of the radii?

12. Which is greater, the surface area of a cone with radius 5 and slant height 10 or the surface area of a sphere with radius 5?

13. A spherical satellite is 3 m in diameter. What is the approximate area of the material covering its surface?

14. Find the surface area of a triangular pyramid that has a base congruent to the lateral faces. The base edge is 24 cm and the slant height is 16 cm.

15. PROJECT Research the radius of both Earth and the moon. Calculate the surface area of each.

16. Spaceship Earth at Epcot Center in Florida is a 180-ft geosphere. Estimate the approximate surface area by assuming it is a sphere with diameter 180 ft.

OBJECTIVE:
To use area formulas
to plan parade floats.

10-8 Parade Floats

■ Thousands of dollars are spent each year to construct the spectacular floats that appear in the Rose Bowl Parade. Many months of planning and building go into each one of these elaborate floats.

Example Sunnydale Farms is going to have a float in a parade. On the float they plan to have a large sun symbol like the one at the left. The interior circle will have a diameter of 4 ft. Each triangle will have a height of 4 ft. The base will be 1.25 ft. What will be the total area of the sun symbol?

Solution Use the formulas for the area of a circle and the area of a triangle to find the total area of the sun symbol. Use 3.14 for π.

$$A = \pi r^2 \qquad \text{Find the area of a circle.}$$
$$\approx 3.14 \cdot 2^2$$
$$= 3.14 \cdot 4$$
$$= 12.56 \text{ ft}^2$$

$$A = \frac{1}{2}bh \qquad \text{Find the area of a triangle.}$$
$$= \frac{1}{2} \cdot 1.25 \cdot 4$$
$$= 2.5 \text{ ft}^2$$
$$2.5 \cdot 10 = 25 \text{ ft}^2 \qquad \text{Find the area of 10 triangles.}$$
$$12.56 + 25 = 37.56 \text{ ft}^2 \qquad \text{Find the total area.}$$

The total area of the sun symbol is 37.56 ft².

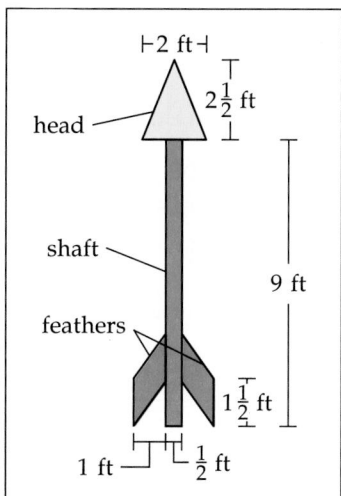

CLASS EXERCISE

Use the DATA in the figure at the left to solve.

1. A float will have a child holding a large arrow. All parts of the arrow will be made from heavy cardboard.

   a. What is the area of the head of the arrow?

   b. What is the area of the shaft of the arrow?

   c. What is the area of each section of feathers in the arrow?

   d. What is the total area of the arrow?

   e. The cardboard costs $.27/ft². What is the cost to build the arrow?

   f. Covering the arrow with flowers will cost $3.60/ft². What is the cost of the flowers? What is the total cost?

WRITTEN EXERCISES

Use the *DATA* below to solve.

1. A float will have a large heart made of plywood. To make the heart, builders will take a circle with a diameter of 5 ft and cut it in half. They will then attach both pieces to one side of an equilateral triangle. The triangle has height 8.6 ft and side 10 ft. The builders will cover the heart with red roses. To control expenses, they do not want the area covered to exceed 275 ft².

   a. Make a sketch of the way the heart will look when it has been constructed as described. Include measurements in your sketch.

   b. How many square feet of plywood will have to be covered with roses if both sides are covered? Will this be within the limit of 275 ft²?

   c. The cost of covering the float with red roses is $10/ft². What is the cost for covering one side of the heart with flowers? both sides?

■■■■■■ Decision Making ■ **DECISION MAKING** ■ Decision Making ■ Decision Making ■ Decision Making ■

PARADE FLOATS

■ **COLLECT DATA**

1. You are on the committee to design a float for your school's homecoming parade. You want an imaginative design that is simple to build. You also want to use real flowers.

   a. Decide what kind of float platform you will use. Find the dimensions of the platform.

   b. Sketch several figures that you could build for the float.

   c. Find the cost of a square foot of building materials.

   d. Survey local florists. Find the cost of various flowers. Determine which flowers will stay fresh the longest. Record your results in a chart like the one below.

Types of Flowers	Number of Blossoms to Cover 1 ft²	Life Expectancy of Flowers
Roses		
Daisies		
Carnations		

Use the *DATA* below to solve.

2. Every year near the end of November, Chicago has a parade. A department store plans to build a large gift box for the middle of its float. The gift box will measure 6 ft by 9 ft by 5 ft. The platform of the float will be the bottom of the box. This will save the cost of materials for one side of the box.

   a. Make a sketch of the gift box that the store plans to build. Include measurements.

   b. To save as much building material as possible, which side of the box should be the bottom? Give its length, width, and area.

   c. What will be the total area of the sides that need to be decorated?

   d. Building materials cost $.55/ft². What is the cost of building the box?

   e. The cost of decorations is $2.25/ft². What is the cost of decorating the gift box?

   f. What is the total cost of the gift box?

■ *Decision Making* ■ *Decision Making* ■ *Decision Making* ■

■ ANALYZE DATA

2. Calculate the areas of the shapes you plan to build. Find the cost of the building materials.

3. Calculate the areas of the shapes you plan to cover with each type of flower.

4. Calculate the cost of flowers for each part of the float you are designing.

5. Find the total cost of the design.

■ MAKE DECISIONS

6. What is the cost of decorating your float? What changes can you make to lower the cost?

7. Suppose you have an unlimited budget. What design would you use for your float? What would be the total cost?

Practice

Find each area. Round to the nearest tenth.

1. trapezoid: $b_1 = 2.5$ m; $b_2 = 3.4$ m; $h = 9.9$ m
2. triangle: $b = 5$ in.; $h = 7.2$ in.
3. rectangle: $b = 3\frac{1}{2}$ ft; $h = 8\frac{3}{4}$ ft
4. square: $s = 87\frac{7}{8}$ cm
5. parallelogram: $b = 4.8$ yd; $h = 9.2$ yd
6. circle: $d = 6.5$ cm
7. trapezoid: $b_1 = 3.8$ m; $b_2 = 5.2$ m; $h = 2{,}800$ cm
8. circle: $r = 3.25$ cm

9.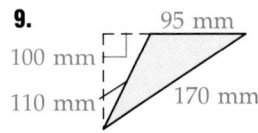

10.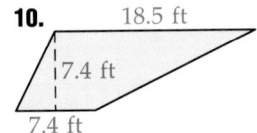

11.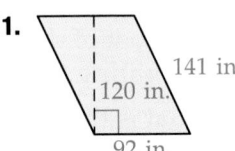

Name the space figure that each net can form.

12.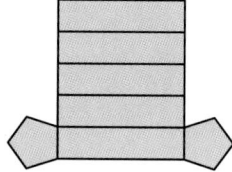

13.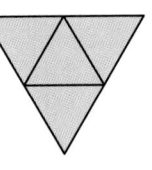

14.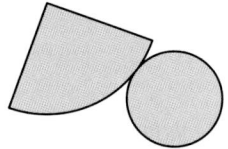

Find each surface area. Use 3.14 for π.

15.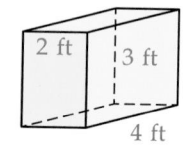

16.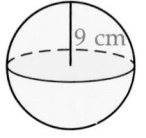

17.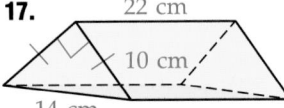

18.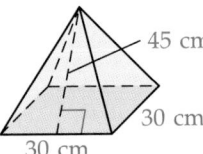

19.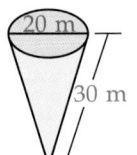

20.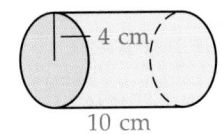

21.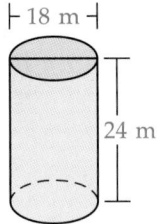

22.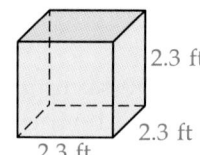

23.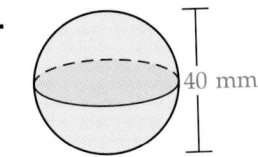

OBJECTIVE:
To find the volume of
prisms and cylinders.

10-9 Volume—Prisms and Cylinders

▼ A gallon and a liter are liquid measures, but they also measure volume. A gallon of milk occupies 231 in.³ of space. A liter of milk occupies 1,000 cm³ of space.

Volume	Volume is the measure of the space inside a space figure. We measure volume in cubic units.

▼ The figure below shows a rectangular prism. The base is covered by 12 cubes. The height is 2, allowing for 2 layers of 12 cubes. The volume of the prism is 24 cubic units.

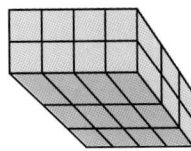

This example suggests the following formula.

Volume of a Prism or Cylinder	The volume (V) of a prism or a cylinder is base area (B) times the height (h). $$V = Bh$$

▼ In formulas for volume, B represents the base area, while b is the length of the base edge.

Example 1 Find the volume of the triangular prism.

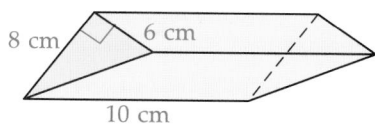

Solution

$$B = \frac{1}{2}bh \qquad \text{Find the area of the base.}$$

$$= \frac{1}{2}(8 \times 6) \qquad \text{Substitute 8 for } b \text{ and 6 for } h. \text{ Simplify.}$$

$$= 24$$

$$V = Bh \qquad \text{Find the volume.}$$

$$= (24)10 \qquad \text{Substitute 24 for } B \text{ and 10 for } h.$$

$$= 240 \qquad \text{Simplify.}$$

The volume is 240 cm³.

3 cm

12.5 cm

355 ml

▼ Finding the volume of a cylinder is similar to finding the volume of a prism.

Example 2 Find the volume of a juice can in centimeters. Use 3.14 for π.

Solution $B = \pi r^2$ Find the area of the base.
      $= \pi \cdot 3^2$
      $= 9\pi$

      $V = Bh$ Use the formula for volume.
      $= 9\pi \cdot 12.5$
      $= 112.5\pi$
      $\approx 3.14 \times 112.5$
      $= 353.25 \text{ cm}^3$

The volume is about 353.25 cm^3.

THINK AND DISCUSS

1. Why is volume usually labeled in gallons or liters rather than cubic inches or cubic centimeters?

2. In metric units, volume and mass are easily changed from one unit to another. For water, $1 \text{ ml} = \blacksquare \text{ cm}^3 = \blacksquare \text{ g}$.

3. When finding the volume of a rectangular prism with dimensions $5 \times 8 \times 9$, does it matter which two dimensions represent the base of the figure?

4. Name at least one prism and one cylinder where you need to know the volume.

CLASS EXERCISES

MENTAL MATH Calculate the volume of each rectangular prism.

1.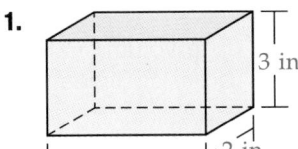
3 in.
5 in. 2 in.

2.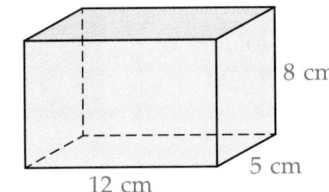
8 cm
12 cm   5 cm

Find the volume of each prism.

3.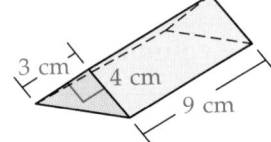
3 cm 4 cm
9 cm

4.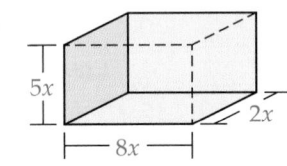
5x
8x   2x

Find the volume of each cylinder. Use 3.14 for π.

5.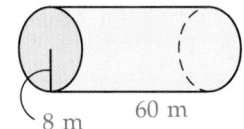
8 m   60 m

6.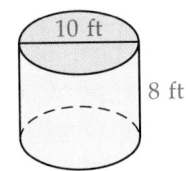
10 ft
8 ft

Complete.

7. $1 \text{ ft}^2 = \blacksquare \text{ in.}^2$

8. $1 \text{ yd}^2 = \blacksquare \text{ ft}^2$

9. $1 \text{ cm}^2 = \blacksquare \text{ mm}^2$

10. $1 \text{ m}^2 = \blacksquare \text{ cm}^2$

11. $1 \text{ ft}^3 = \blacksquare \text{ in.}^3$

12. $1 \text{ yd}^3 = \blacksquare \text{ ft}^3$

13. $1 \text{ cm}^3 = \blacksquare \text{ mm}^3$

14. $1 \text{ m}^3 = \blacksquare \text{ cm}^3$

WRITTEN EXERCISES

Find the volume of a prism with the given dimensions.

1. square base:
7 in. by 7 in.
height: 13 in.

2. rectangular base:
9 ft by 5 ft
height: 36 in.

3. cube:
sides: $3a$

4.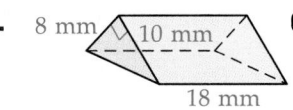

5.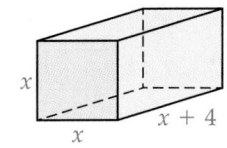

6.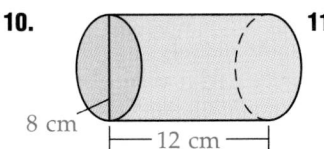

CALCULATOR Find the volume of a cylinder with the given dimensions
to the nearest hundredth. Use 3.14 for π.

7. radius: 12 ft
height: 15 ft

8. diameter: 3.8 m
height: 18 m

9. radius: 7.6 cm
height: 32 cm

10.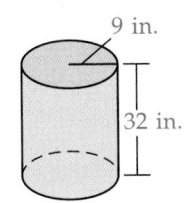

11.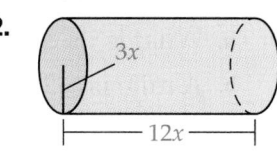

12.

13. Wood for wood-burning stoves is sold by the cord. A cord is
8 ft × 4 ft × 4 ft. How many cubic feet is a cord?

14. When purchasing concrete, the price quoted is *per yard*, which
means per cubic yard. Concrete costs $52 a yard. How much
would it cost to pour a 14 ft × 16 ft × 6 in. slab for a patio?

15. Cylinder A has radius 1 and height 3. Cylinder B has radius 1 and
height 6. What is the ratio of the volumes of the two cylinders?
How does doubling the height affect the volume?

16. Cylinder A has radius 1 and height 3. Cylinder B has radius 2
and height 3. What is the ratio of the volumes of the two
cylinders? How does doubling the radius affect the volume?

17. How much juice can a drinking straw hold? A straw has a
diameter of 6 mm and a length of 208 mm.

18. Write a formula for the volume of a cube that has side x.

19. Write a formula for the volume of a cylinder with
radius x and height x.

20. **PROJECT** Pop half a cup of popcorn.

   a. How many cups of popped corn do you have?

   b. What is the ratio of popped to raw popcorn?

Sailing Across the Prairie

American pioneers traveled west of the Mississippi in prairie schooners, or covered wagons. For two thousand miles and several months, the wagon was home for the pioneer family. A prairie schooner was about 4 ft wide and 10 ft long. Most wagons were about 8 ft high. In this small space, pioneer families carried all of the supplies needed to survive the trip and to start new lives.

Use the article at the left to answer each question.

21. What is the volume of a rectangular prism the dimensions of a prairie schooner?

22. A wagon wheel is about 4 ft in diameter.

   a. What is its circumference? Use 3.14 for π.

   b. A mile is 5,280 ft. About how many turns would a wheel make in a mile? in 2,000 mi?

TEST YOURSELF

Find the surface area of each figure.

1.
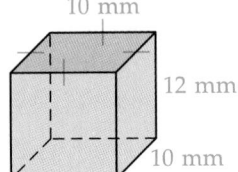
10 mm · 12 mm · 10 mm

2.
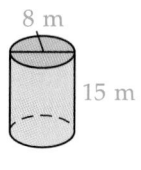
8 m · 15 m

3.
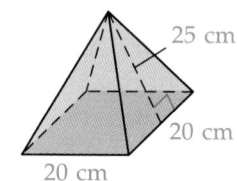
25 cm · 20 cm · 20 cm

Find the volume of each figure.

4.
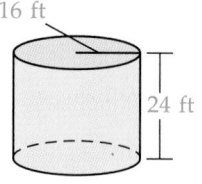
16 ft · 24 ft

5.
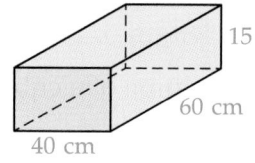
15 cm · 60 cm · 40 cm

6.
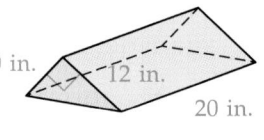
10 in. · 12 in. · 20 in.

7.
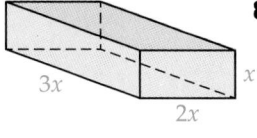
3x · x · 2x

8.
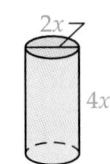
2x · 4x

9.
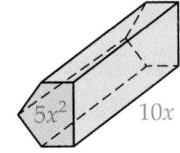
5x² · 10x

OBJECTIVE:
To find the volume of
pyramids, cones, and
spheres.

10-10 *Volume—Pyramids, Cones, and Spheres*

▼ You can fill three cones
with water and pour the
contents into a cylinder
with the same height and
radius. The cylinder will
be completely filled.

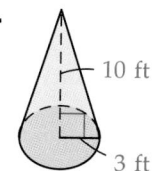

The volume of the cone is $\frac{1}{3}$ the volume of the cylinder. The same
relationship is true of a pyramid and a prism with the same base and
height.

Volume of a Cone and a Pyramid	The formula for the volume of a cone and pyramid is $\frac{1}{3}$ the base area (*B*) times the height (*h*). $$V = \frac{1}{3}Bh$$

▼ The height of a regular pyramid or cone is the measure of the
altitude from the vertex to the center of the base.

Example 1 **Find the volume of each figure.**

a.

b.

10 ft

10 ft

3 ft

6 ft

Solution

a. $B = \pi r^2$
$\quad = \pi \cdot 3^2$
$\quad = 9\pi$

$V = \frac{1}{3}Bh$

$\quad = \frac{1}{3} \cdot 9\pi \cdot 10$
$\quad = 30\pi$
$\quad \approx 30 \cdot 3.14$
$\quad = 94.2$

b. $B = bh$
$\quad = 6 \cdot 6$
$\quad = 36$

$V = \frac{1}{3}Bh$

$\quad = \frac{1}{3} \cdot 36 \cdot 10$
$\quad = 120$

The volume of the cone is about 94.2 ft³.
The volume of the square pyramid is 120 ft³.

▼ Below is the formula for the volume of a sphere.

Volume of a Sphere	The volume (*V*) of a sphere with radius *r* is $$V = \frac{4}{3}\pi r^3.$$

Example 2 Find the volume of a spherical scoop of ice cream with radius 3 cm.

Solution

$$V = \frac{4}{3}\pi r^3$$

$$\approx \frac{4}{3} \cdot 3.14 \cdot 3^3 \quad \textbf{Use 3.14 for } \boldsymbol{\pi}.$$

$$= \frac{4}{3} \cdot 3.14 \cdot 27$$

$$= 113.04 \text{ cm}^3$$

The volume is about 113.04 cm³.

THINK AND DISCUSS

1. Does $\frac{1}{3}Bh = \frac{1}{3}hB = \frac{Bh}{3}$? How can this help in finding volume of a pyramid or a cone?

2. Compare the formula for the surface area of a sphere to the formula for the volume of a sphere. How are they alike? How are they different?

3. In a sphere, if the radius is doubled, how is the volume changed?

CLASS EXERCISES

Find the volume of each figure. Use 3.14 for π.

1.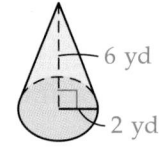
6 yd
2 yd

2.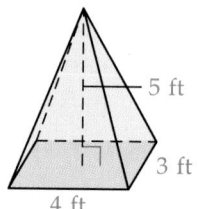
5 ft
3 ft
4 ft

3.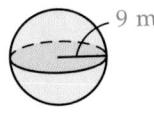
9 m

4. A cone has a radius 1 and height 1. What is the exact volume of the cone?

5. The volume of a pyramid is 25 m³. What is the volume of a prism with the same base and same height?

Complete each analogy.

6. square : cube :: circle : ▩

7. pyramid : cone :: polygonal base : ▩

8. volume : cubic units :: area : ▩

9. cylinder : prism :: cone : ▩

10. perimeter : area : volume :: cm : ▩ : ▩

11. Cone A has $h = 5$ and $r = 3$. Cone B has $h = 5$ and $r = 6$. What is the ratio of the volumes? How does doubling the radius affect the volume?

12. Cone A has $h = 5$ and $r = 3$. Cone B has $h = 10$ and $r = 3$. What is the ratio of the volumes? How does doubling the height affect the volume?

13. How many cones of radius 1 and height 1 equal the volume of a sphere with radius 1?

WRITTEN EXERCISES

CALCULATOR Find the volume. Use 3.14 for π.

1. sphere,
   $r = 6$ cm

2. square-based
   pyramid,
   $s = 12$ m, $h = 15$ m

3. cone,
   $r = 9$ ft, $h = 10$ ft

4.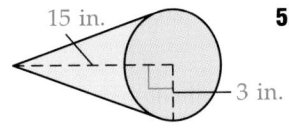

5.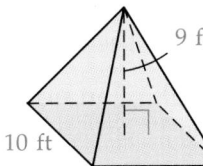

6.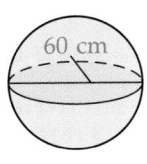

7. Theater A sells popcorn in prism-shaped boxes. Theater B sells popcorn in pyramid-shaped boxes. The base and height of both popcorn boxes are the same. Which box holds more popcorn? How much more?

8. Find the volume of a square-based pyramid with base edge 9 in. and height 1 ft.

Find the radius of a sphere for each volume.

9. $\frac{256}{3}\pi$ m^3

10. $\frac{4}{3}\pi$ cm^3

11. $\frac{500}{3}\pi$ ft^3

12. CALCULATOR The diameter of Earth is about 7,926.6 mi.

  a. Find the surface area.

  b. Find the volume of Earth. You may need to use scientific notation.

  c. Find the surface area and volume of Earth in the encyclopedia. Compare your answers.

13. Tennis balls with a diameter of 2.5 in. are sold in cans of three. The can is a cylinder. What is the volume of the space in the can not occupied by tennis balls? Assume the balls touch the can on the sides, top, and bottom.

14. You place a steel ball with diameter 4 cm, in a water-filled cylinder that is 5 cm in diameter and 10 cm high. How much water will spill?

15. The diameter of the world's largest ball of string is 12 ft 9 in. Francis A. Johnson of Darwin, Minnesota, collected the ball of string between 1950 and 1978.

  a. What is the circumference of the ball of string?

  b. What is the surface area?

  c. What is the volume?

MIXED REVIEW

1. Find the volume of a compact disc with diameter 14 cm and thickness 4 mm.

2. Find the circumference of a circle that has $d = 13.8$ in.

3. Find the surface area of a cylinder with $r = 5$ in. and $h = 12$ in.

4. $(3 \times 10^2)(4 \times 10^2) = $ ▧

Solve.

5. $-4.2y + 3.4 = 7.6$

6. $2.8x - 5.6 = 16.8$

7. $3x - \frac{3}{8} = 1\frac{5}{12}$

8. A box is 25.5 cm by 17 cm by 5 cm. What volume of dishwasher detergent can it hold?

16. _WRITE_ Which is the better buy on oranges? Explain how you made your selection.

4/$1.00   3/$1.00

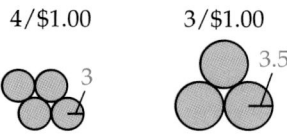

17. A pyramid is 460 ft high. It is 760 ft on each side of its square base. What is the volume of the pyramid?

18. You want to fill the top half of an hourglass $\frac{2}{3}$ full of salt. The height of the hourglass is 12 cm and the radius is 3 cm. Find the volume of salt needed.

Critical Thinking
EXPLORING A HYPOTHESIS

A hypothesis is an educated guess. To find if a hypothesis is true, you must test it.

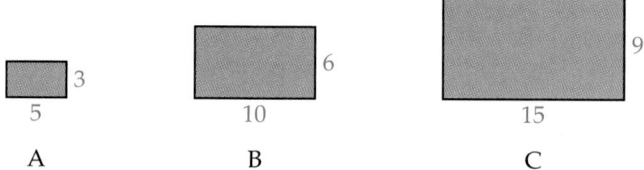

A   B   C

1. Write a hypothesis about the ratio of the perimeters and areas of two similar figures.

2. Make a table with entries for base, height, perimeter, and area and find this information for similar figures A, B, and C.

3. Use the information in your chart for figures B and C to answer the following questions. Write all fractions in lowest terms.

   a. What is the ratio of the heights?

   b. What is the ratio of the bases?

   c. What is the ratio of the perimeters?

   d. What is the ratio of the areas?

4. Do you need to revise your hypothesis? Do so, if necessary. Test it on figures A and C.

5. Predict the ratio of the perimeters and areas of two triangles if the ratio of their heights is $\frac{5}{8}$.

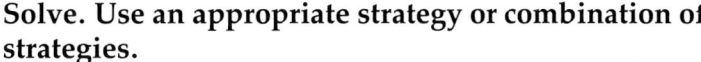

Solve. Use an appropriate strategy or combination of strategies.

1. A rectangular piece of tin measures 26 in. × 20 in. A square measuring 2 in. × 2 in. is cut out of each corner and the sides are folded to form a box. What is the volume of the box?

2. Susan and Karen are in a marathon race. Susan's average speed is 5 mi/h and Karen's is 8 mi/h. If they start at 10 A.M., when will they be $4\frac{1}{2}$ mi apart?

3. Frank Goodshot usually hits his mark when throwing free throws. However, in the last few games he has made only 15 shots out of 24. How many consecutive free throws must Frank make to raise his record to 80%?

4. A 12-m by 15-m rectangular garden has a walk 1 m wide around it. What is the area of the walk?

5. Three boys, Jack, Jim, and Jay, planned to share a bag of apples equally. Jack found the bag on the doorstep first and took his share. Jim came along later and took what he thought was his share. Later yet, Jay arrived, taking what he thought was his share. He left 8 apples. How many apples were there to start with?

6. Five economically minded girls decided to share wardrobes. Each bought a different three-piece outfit, a skirt, a blouse, and a vest. Then they traded pieces around. How many different outfits can they make?

7. Juan and his younger brother Kimo picked apples. The average of what they picked was 10 bushels. Juan picked three times as many apples as Kimo. How many bushels did each pick?

8. *DATA (p. 128)* Use the formula for cricket chirps and temperature. How many chirps does a cricket make per minute when the temperature is 56°?

9. Six girls ran a 100-yd race. Fran beat Clara by 8 yd. Clara finished 12 yd behind Teresa. Marie finished 16 yd behind Fran but 2 yd ahead of Cindy. Vivian finished exactly between the first and last runner. In what order did the girls finish the race?

10. *DATA FILE 10 (pp. 404–405)* About how many Arctic Oceans could fit into the Pacific Ocean? Consider the volume of water in each, based on the average depth.

11. A rectangle is 8 ft longer than it is wide. The area of the rectangle is 240 ft². What are the dimensions?

Chapter 10 Review

Complete each statement. Use the vocabulary words given.

1. The ▨ is the amount of surface inside a region.
2. A polyhedron is a space figure that has ▨ for all faces.
3. The sides of a pyramid are ▨ that meet at a common point.
4. The sides of a ▨ are parallelograms.
5. A ▨ has two circular bases that are parallel and congruent.
6. A ▨ has one circular base and one ▨.
7. A ▨ is the set of all points in space that are the same distance from a given point called the ▨.
8. Surface area is the sum of the area of the ▨.
9. The ▨ ▨ is the height of a face.
10. ▨ is the measure of the space inside a space figure.

VOCABULARY

area
cone
volume
cylinder
sphere
polygons
prism
faces
slant height
vertex
triangles
center

Finding Areas of Polygons   10-1, 10-2

To find the area of a polygon, use the appropriate formula.

parallelogram   triangle   trapezoid

$A = bh$ $A = \frac{1}{2}bh$ $A = \frac{1}{2}(b_1 + b_2)h$

Find the area of each figure.

11.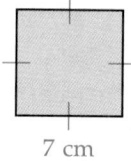
7 cm

12.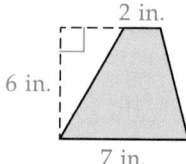
2 in.
6 in.
7 in.

13.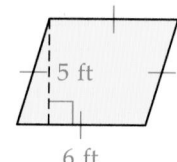
5 ft
6 ft

14.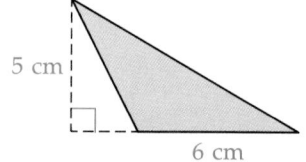
5 cm
6 cm

Finding the Area of a Circle   10-3

To find the area of a circle, multiply π by the square of the radius.
$A = \pi r^2$.

Find the area of each figure. Use 3.14 for π.

15.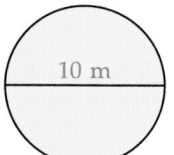
10 m

16.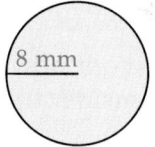
8 mm

17.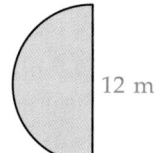
12 m

18.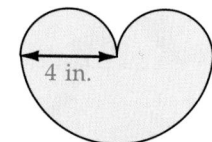
4 in.

Space Figures

We name pyramids and prisms by the shape of their bases.

Name the space figure that each net can form.

19.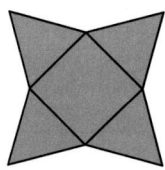

20.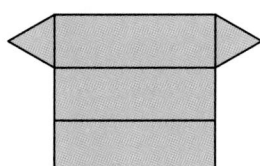

21.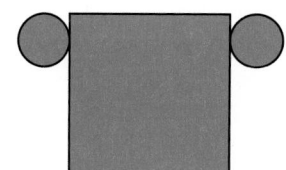

Problem Solving

To solve some problems, make a model.

22. What are the dimensions of a rectangular sheet of wrapping paper that will cover a 6 in. × 6 in. × 6 in. gift box with no more than a $\frac{1}{2}$ in. overlap?

Finding Surface Area

To find the surface area of a prism or a cylinder, add the areas of the base(s) and the side(s).

To find the surface area of a cone or a pyramid, use the slant height. The surface area is the sum of the lateral area and the base area.

The surface area of a sphere is $A = 4\pi r^2$.

Find the surface area. Use 3.14 for π.

23.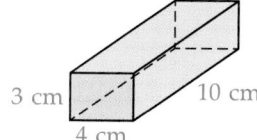

24.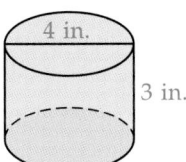

25.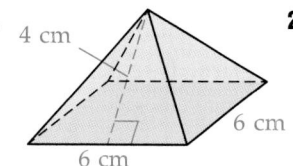

26.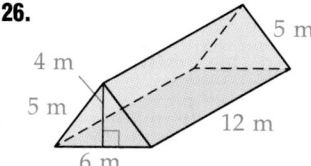

Finding Volume

To find the volume of a space figure, use the appropriate formula.

prisms and cylinders	pyramids and cones	spheres
$V = Bh$	$V = \frac{1}{3}Bh$	$V = \frac{4}{3}\pi r^3$

Find the volume. Use 3.14 for π.

27.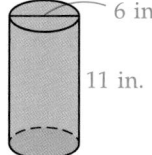

28.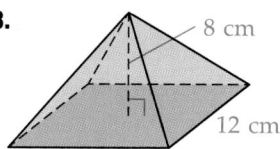

29.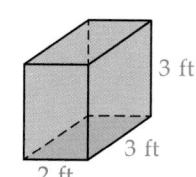

30.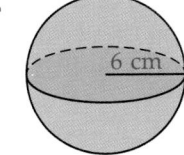

Chapter 10   *Test*

Find the area of each figure. Use 3.14 for π.

1.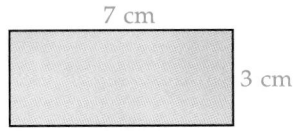
7 cm

3 cm

2.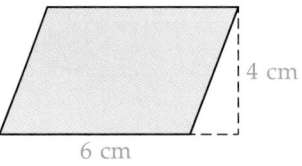
4 cm

6 cm

3.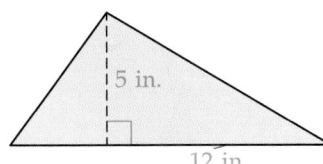
5 in.

12 in.

4.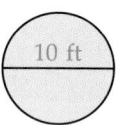
10 ft

5.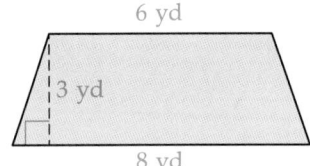
6 yd

3 yd

8 yd

6.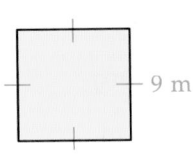
9 m

Find the missing measures.

7. a square
$A = 121\ m^2$
$b = $ ▨

8. a triangle
$A = 28\ m^2$
$b = 7\ m$
$h = $ ▨

9. a circle
$A = 64\pi\ cm^2$
$r = $ ▨

10. a parallelogram
$A = 48\ in.^2$
$b = 16\ in.$
$h = $ ▨

Find the surface area of each figure. Use 3.14 for π.

11.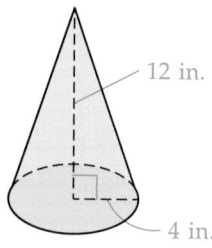
2 cm

8 cm

12.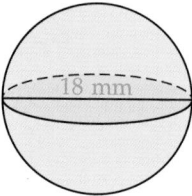
12 m

10 m

10 m

13.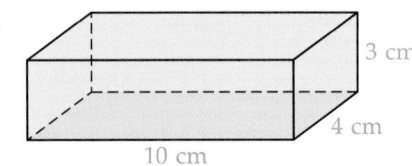
6 cm

6 cm

6 cm

Find the volume of each figure. Use 3.14 for π.

14.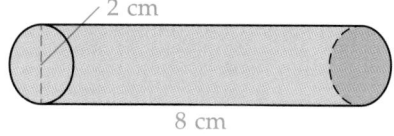
12 in.

4 in.

15.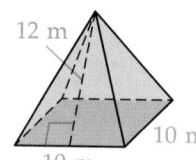
18 mm

16.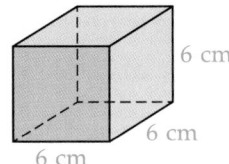
3 cm

4 cm

10 cm

Solve.

17. The height of a rectangle is doubled. How does this affect the area?

18. What is the surface area of a sphere with radius 5 ft?

19. How much greater is the volume of a cone with radius 6 ft and height 10 ft than the volume of a square pyramid with base edge 6 ft and height 10 ft? Use 3.14 for π.

20. ***WRITE*** How is the formula for the volume of a prism or cylinder the same as the formula for volume of a pyramid or cone? How are they different?

Chapters 1–10   Cumulative Review

Choose the correct answer. Write A, B, C, or D.

1. What is the volume?

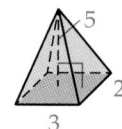

- **A.** 30
- **B.** 10
- **C.** 15
- **D.** not given

2. $\triangle ABC \sim \triangle DBE$. Find x.

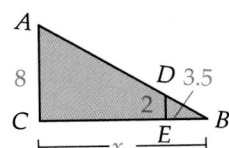

- **A.** 14
- **B.** 5
- **C.** 12.5
- **D.** not given

3. $\triangle ABC \cong \triangle DEF$. Which is not true?

- **A.** $\angle A \cong \angle D$
- **B.** $\overline{AC} \cong \overline{FD}$
- **C.** $\angle B \cong \angle F$
- **D.** not given

4. Simplify $\frac{3x^5y^3z^{-2}}{24x^6y^2z}$.

- **A.** $\frac{y}{8xz^3}$
- **B.** $8xyz^{-3}$
- **C.** $\frac{y^5}{8xz^3}$
- **D.** not given

5. What is the prime factorization of 84?

- **A.** $2^3 \cdot 7$
- **B.** $2 \cdot 3^2 \cdot 7$
- **C.** $2 \cdot 3 \cdot 7$
- **D.** not given

6. A $250 coat was on sale for $200. What was the percent decrease?

- **A.** 25%
- **B.** 80%
- **C.** 20%
- **D.** not given

7. Marcia has 13 dimes and quarters worth $2.80. How many of each does she have?

- **A.** 10 d, 3 q
- **B.** 6 d, 7 q
- **C.** 3 d, 10 q
- **D.** not given

8. Find the area of the shaded region.

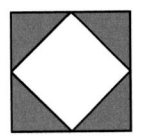

- **A.** 32
- **B.** 64
- **C.** 16
- **D.** not given

9. Name the space figure the net will form.

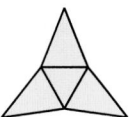

- **A.** prism
- **B.** pyramid
- **C.** cylinder
- **D.** not given

10. Solve $5 - 3x > 17$.

- **A.** $x < 4$
- **B.** $x > -4$
- **C.** $x < -4$
- **D.** not given

11. What percent of 23 is 4.6?

- **A.** 80%
- **B.** 20%
- **C.** 46%
- **D.** not given

12. Find the LCM of 18 and 24.

- **A.** 6
- **B.** 72
- **C.** 42
- **D.** not given

13. What is the equation for a line having slope -2 and y-intercept 3?

- **A.** $2x + y = 3$
- **B.** $y - 2x = 3$
- **C.** $3x + y = -2$
- **D.** not given

14. Which point lies on the line $2y - 3x = 14$?

- **A.** (-4,1)
- **B.** (1,-4)
- **C.** (0,-7)
- **D.** not given

PARACHUTING TERMS

TERM	DEFINITION
HOLDING	facing canopy into the wind to minimize ground speed
FREE FALL	a jump in which the parachute is activated manually
TARGET	the landing area
TERMINAL VELOCITY	the greatest speed at which a body falls through the air; about 176 ft/s which a jumper reaches after 12 s of free fall
WIND DRIFT INDICATOR	determines the strength and direction of the wind; usually a windsock that is 19.5 ft long with a diameter that varies from 36.25 in. to 12 in.
RUNNING	directing the canopy downwind to maximize ground speed

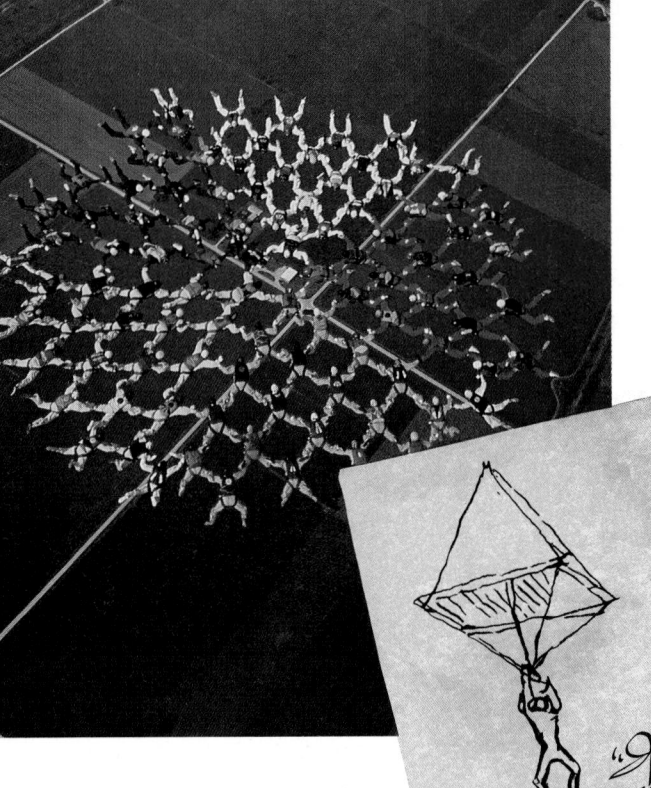

"If a man have a tent made of linen of which the apertures have all been stopped up, and it be twelve braccia across and twelve in depth, he will be able to throw himself down from any great height without sustaining any injury".

Leonardo daVinci

designed a parachute, called a *tent roof* in 1495. Today, parachuting is a popular sport in the United States and Europe. The first sport parachute championships were held in 1951.

11

Right Triangles in Algebra

IF A PARACHUTIST descends at a rate of 10 ft/s, and travels 2,460 ft straight down, it takes 4.1 min to reach the ground.

You can use right triangles to determine the angle the parachutist makes with the ground, the distance traveled in the jump, and the time it takes to reach the ground.

Up, up, and away

You can use the tangent ratio and the table of trigonometric ratios on page 580 to find the angle the jumper makes with the ground.

$$\tan x = \frac{2,460}{5,280} \approx .46591$$
$$x \approx 25°$$

2,460 ft

Holding all the way

Running all the way

1 mi **GROUND MARKER** 1 mi **TARGET** 1 mi 1 mi

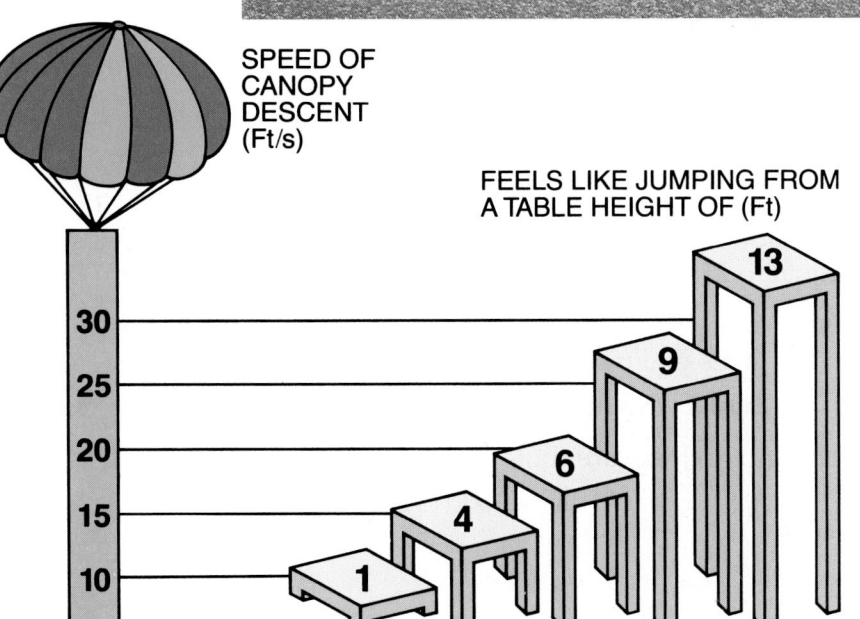

SPEED OF CANOPY DESCENT (Ft/s)

FEELS LIKE JUMPING FROM A TABLE HEIGHT OF (Ft)

13

9

6

4

1

30

25

20

15

10

Think about it...

Do you think the size and shape of the parachute canopy affect the rate at which a parachute descends? Describe an experiment to test your hypothesis.

451

MATERIALS

- Algebra tiles or graph paper
- Standard calculator
- Math journal to record work

Exploring Square Roots

▼ Suppose you build a square having length of 5 tiles.

1. **Model** the square using algebra tiles.

2. How many tiles make up the length of each side of the square?

3. How many tiles do you need to build the square?

4. **a. Write** an equation using an exponent to describe the relationship between the number of tiles on each side of the square and the total number in the square.

   b. Model other squares using algebra tiles. Write an equation for each square as you did in (a).

5. What part of the equation corresponds to the number of tiles on each side of the square?

6. **Discuss** how you can determine the number of tiles in a square, given the number of tiles on each side.

▼ The opposite of squaring a number is finding its *square root*. We refer to the number of tiles on each side of the square as the square root of the total number of tiles in the square.

7. **a. Model** a square with 9 tiles.

   b. How many tiles are on each side?

   c. What is the square root of 9?

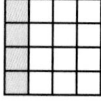

$4^2 = 16$
4 is a square root of 16

8. **Model** the square represented by each equation using graph paper. Shade in the square root. State the square root of the product.

   a. $6^2 = 36$ **b.** $49 = 7^2$ **c.** $1^2 = 1$ **d.** $3.5^2 = 12.25$

   e. Describe the position in each equation of the square root of the product.

   f. Write a sentence relating your answers in (5) and (8e).

▼ We say *five is a square root of twenty-five* and write $\sqrt{25} = 5$. The notation $\sqrt{25}$ means to find a positive number that when squared is equal to 25. We call the symbol $\sqrt{}$ the square root sign.

9. **a.** Is there a number other than positive five, that when squared gives you twenty-five?

   b. Explain why this number is not a correct value of $\sqrt{25}$.

10. Find each square root.

   a. $\sqrt{81}$ **b.** $\sqrt{100}$ **c.** $\sqrt{144}$ **d.** $\sqrt{20.25}$

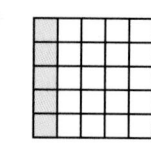

5 is a square root of 25
$\sqrt{25} = 5$

▼ Suppose you are given 21 tiles with which to build a square.

11. a. *Model* the square. Describe your results.

   b. Does 21 have a whole number square root? Explain.

12. Complete each statement.

   a. If I could eliminate ▧ tiles, I would have a ▧ × ▧ square.

   b. If I could add ▧ more tiles, I would have a ▧ × ▧ square.

13. a. Between what two positive integers does the $\sqrt{21}$ lie?

   b. To what integer is $\sqrt{21}$ closer? Base your answer on the number of squares you need to add or subtract.

14. Each square root lies between what two integers? Circle the integer to which it is closer.

   a. $\sqrt{5}$ **b.** $\sqrt{76}$ **c.** $\sqrt{147}$

▼ You can use a standard calculator to estimate a square root.

Estimate the value of $\sqrt{76}$ to the nearest tenth. You already know that $\sqrt{76}$ lies between the integers 8 and 9.

Try 8.3	8.3	⊗	8.3	⊜	68.89	**too low**
Try 8.6	8.6	⊗	8.6	⊜	73.96	**too low**
Try 8.7	8.7	⊗	8.7	⊜	75.69	**very close**

So, to the nearest tenth, $\sqrt{76}$ is approximately 8.7.

15. Use a calculator to find an approximate value, to the nearest tenth, for each square root. Do not use the square root key.

   a. $\sqrt{75}$ **b.** $\sqrt{29}$ **c.** $\sqrt{94}$ **d.** $\sqrt{186}$

16. a. *Describe* a method for finding an approximate value of a square root to the nearest hundredth.

   b. Find the value of $\sqrt{131}$ to the nearest hundredth.

▼ You can also use a square root key on a calculator.

17. *Explore* how to find the square root of a number using a square root key. Start with a square root you already know, such as $\sqrt{9}$.

18. Use a calculator to find the value of each square root.

   a. $\sqrt{25}$ **b.** $\sqrt{19}$ **c.** $\sqrt{0}$ **d.** $\sqrt{-36}$

19. a. *Describe* the result when you took the square root of -36.

   b. Is it possible to take the square root of a negative number?

11-1 *Finding Square Roots*

▼ Each of the quadrilaterals in the puzzle is a square, except the surrounding quadrilateral. Here are two possible ways to find the length of a side of the shaded square if its area is 81.

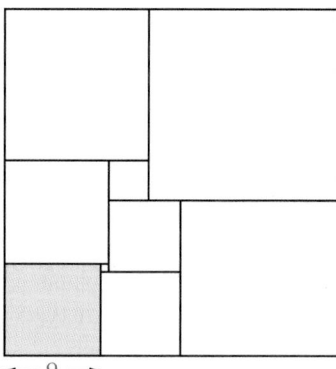

1. Think, *What number squared gives me 81?* Use guess and test with several numbers until you arrive at the correct answer, which is 9.

2. Think, *What is the square root of 81?* The result is also 9.

▼ The inverse of squaring a number is finding its *square root.*

Square Root	The square root of a number, *n*, is *a* if $a^2 = n$.

Example 1 Find the square root of 64.

Solution **a.** $(-8)^2 = 64$, so -8 is a square root.

b. $8^2 = 64$, so 8 is also a square root.

▼ We use the symbol $\sqrt{}$ to denote the positive square root or *principal square root* of a number.

Principal Square Root	The principal square root of a number is its positive square root. The principal square root is denoted by the symbol $\sqrt{}$.

Example 2 Find the principal square root of each expression.
   a. 10,000   **b.** $121x^2$

Solution **a.** $100^2 = 10,000$, so the principal square root is 100.

b. $(11x)^2 = 121x^2$, so the principal square root is $11x$.

Example 3 Evaluate.
   a. $\sqrt{196}$ **b.** $\sqrt{225p^6}$

Solution **a.** $14^2 = 196$, so 14 is the value of the expression.

b. $(15p^3)^2 = 225p^6$, so $15p^3$ is the value of the expression.

▼ Rational numbers such as 144, 64, and 1 are all perfect squares. They have whole number square roots of 12, 8, and 1, respectively. Rational numbers such as 27 and 65 are not perfect squares. They do not have whole number square roots. We call the square roots of these numbers *irrational numbers*. The set of *real numbers* is made up of the rational numbers and the irrational numbers.

NOTES & QUOTES

We use the term *radical* to refer to the square root sign. The term comes from the Latin word *radix*, which means root.

Irrational Numbers	Irrational numbers are numbers which we cannot express as either terminating or repeating decimals.

Example 4 Determine whether each number is rational or irrational. Use a calculator, if necessary.

  a. 15   **b.** 0.1212 . . .   **c.** π **d.** $\sqrt{1.21}$

Solution   **a.** rational; 15 terminates

   b. rational; the decimal has a repeating pattern

   c. π 3.1415927 . . . ; irrational; the decimal does not terminate or repeat

   d. 1.21 ☑ 1.1; rational; 1.1 terminates

▼ You can use a table of square roots to find an approximate value for irrational square roots.

Example 5 Find the approximate value of $\sqrt{29}$. Use the table on p. 579.

Solution $\sqrt{29} \approx 5.385$

THINK Why does a table of square roots only show approximate values?

CLASS EXERCISES

Complete.

1. The name for the mathematical symbol $\sqrt{}$ is ▧.

2. *The square root of forty-nine* can be written using mathematical symbols as ▧.

3. A ▧ number is implied by the symbol $\sqrt{}$.

4. The set of real numbers is made up of ▧ and ▧ numbers.

5. A repeating decimal is a(n) ▧ number.

6. If a square has an area of 49 in.², each side has length of ▧.

7. The two square roots of 100 are ▧ and ▧. The principal square root is ▧.

8. $\sqrt{92}$ is between the integers ▧ and ▧.

9. The decimal 0.121231234 . . . is a(n) ▧ number.

THINK AND DISCUSS

1. Are the solutions for $x^2 = 16$ and $x = \sqrt{16}$ different? Why?

2. Do the expressions $\sqrt{25}$ and $-\sqrt{25}$ have the same value? Explain.

3. Rewrite the equation $3^2 + -4^2 = 5^2$ to make it true.

4. What number results when you square a square root?

Find each square root. Use the square root table on p. 579 or a calculator, if necessary. Round answers to the nearest thousandth.

10. $\sqrt{100}$ **11.** $\sqrt{1}$ **12.** $\sqrt{13}$ **13.** $\sqrt{50}$

14. $\sqrt{\frac{4}{9}}$ **15.** $\sqrt{12.25}$ **16.** $\sqrt{15^2}$ **17.** $\sqrt{m^2}$

State whether each number is rational or irrational. Use a calculator, if necessary.

18. $\sqrt{0}$ **19.** $\sqrt{87}$ **20.** $-\sqrt{16}$ **21.** 4.1010010001 . . .

WRITTEN EXERCISES

True or false.

1. All real numbers are integers.

2. All integers are real numbers.

3. The principal square roots of 36 are −6 and 6.

4. $\sqrt{36} + \sqrt{64} = 14$

5. $\sqrt{36 + 64} = \sqrt{100} = 10$

6. $\sqrt{79}$ is between 8 and 9.

7. If a square has an area of 225 cm², the side is 15 cm.

8. An approximation for $\sqrt{3}$ is 1.723.

MENTAL MATH Square each term.

9. 16 **10.** −8 **11.** $\frac{2}{3}$ **12.** 11

13. $5x^3$ **14.** $\sqrt{2}$ **15.** $\sqrt{9^2}$ **16.** $\sqrt{2x}$

MENTAL MATH Evaluate.

17. $\sqrt{10,000}$ **18.** $\sqrt{169}$ **19.** $\sqrt{59 + 5}$ **20.** $\sqrt{p^2}$

Find each square root. If necessary, use your calculator. Round decimal answers to the nearest thousandth.

21. $\sqrt{49}$ **22.** $\sqrt{81}$ **23.** $\sqrt{\frac{16}{25}}$ **24.** $\sqrt{(r + 3)^2}$

25. $\sqrt{49.49}$ **26.** $\sqrt{196x^6}$ **27.** $\sqrt{8y^5 \cdot 2y^5}$ **28.** $\sqrt{3 \cdot 12x^{16}}$

29. $\sqrt{256}$ **30.** $\sqrt{7y^4}$ **31.** $\sqrt{100 \div 5}$ **32.** $\sqrt{a^4b^6c^8}$

Between what two integers does each square root lie? Circle the integer to which the square root is closer.

33. $\sqrt{51}$ **34.** $\sqrt{93}$ **35.** $\sqrt{5}$ **36.** $-\sqrt{22}$

37. $-\sqrt{5}$ **38.** $\sqrt{132}$ **39.** $\sqrt{7 + 11}$ **40.** $\sqrt{99}$

MIXED REVIEW

1. Find the surface area of a cube whose side is 8.2 cm.

2. Find the volume of a cylinder with $r = 0.03$ m and $h = 0.9$ m.

Solve and check.

3. $8n - 2 \leq 5$

4. $\frac{1}{3}x + 5 \geq \frac{1}{2}$

5. Find the slope of the line $-4x - 7y = 10$.

6. Solve the proportion $\frac{x}{7} = \frac{7}{3}$.

7. DATA FILE 8 (pp. 312–313) What is the percent increase in the United States population from 1790 to 1890?

8. Laura bought two sweaters for $36. The sweaters were on sale at one for full price and the second at half price. How much was the half-price sweater?

State whether each term is rational or irrational. Use a calculator, if necessary.

41. $\sqrt{625}$ **42.** $-\sqrt{36}$ **43.** $\sqrt{32}$ **44.** $\sqrt{0}$

45. 198.94762 **46.** $\sqrt{53}$ **47.** $4.33333\ldots$ **48.** $\sqrt{5+11}$

Use the square root table on p. 579 to approximate each value.

49. $\sqrt{50}$ **50.** $\sqrt{77}$ **51.** $\sqrt{99}$ **52.** $\sqrt{2}$

53. $\sqrt{43}$ **54.** $\sqrt{17}$ **55.** $\sqrt{54}$ **56.** $\sqrt{87}$

Critical Thinking

EXPLORING PATTERNS

Sir Isaac Newton devised a method for finding a square root. It is often referred to as the *divide and average method*.

Problem   Approximate the value of $\sqrt{47}$.

Solution   Use the *divide and average method:*

1. Trap between two integers. $6 < \sqrt{47} < 7$
2. Identify the closer integer. $\sqrt{47}$ is closer to 7
3. Estimate to the nearest tenth.   6.8
4. Divide the number that you are taking the square root of by the estimate. Carry to whatever place accuracy is desired in the answer. $47 \div 6.8 \approx 6.91$
5. Find the mean average of the quotient and the divisor. $(6.8 + 6.91) \div 2 \approx 6.86$
6. Use the mean as the new divisor. $47 \div 6.86 \approx 6.85$
7. If necessary, repeat Steps 4, 5, and 6 until the divisor is very close to the quotient.

You can use a BASIC program to simulate Newton's method.

```
10 PRINT "Square root of
   what number";
20 INPUT A
30 PRINT "How many
   averages";
40 INPUT B
50 PRINT "What is your first
   estimate";
60 INPUT C
70 FOR X = 1 to B
80 PRINT (A/C + C)/2
90 NEXT X
```

1. Continue this pattern for $\sqrt{47}$. Explain your results. How can you get the answer?

2. Use Newton's method to find the approximate value of $\sqrt{19}$.

3. Why do you think people no longer use Newton's method?

4. **PROJECT** Use the computer program shown at the right to find the square roots of various numbers.

OBJECTIVE:
To solve a problem
by simulation.

11-2 *Simulating a Problem*

■ Sometimes when solving a problem, it is helpful to act out or *simulate* the problem.

PROBLEM

A class of 25 seated students counted off by ones beginning with the number one. Each student who counted a multiple of four stood up. Then the students who were still seated counted off by ones again. Each student who counted a multiple of four stood up. This process was repeated one more time. How many students were standing after the third counting?

SOLUTION

READD ▶ What do you want to find?   The number of students standing after the third counting

PLAN ▶ Start out with 25 students. Act out each step of the problem.

SOLVE ▶ Have 25 students sit in their seats.

Students Sitting	Students Standing
🧍🧍🧍🧍🧍🧍🧍🧍🧍🧍🧍🧍🧍 🧍🧍🧍🧍🧍🧍🧍🧍🧍🧍🧍🧍	None

First Counting
1. All students count off by ones.
2. All students who counted a multiple of four stand up.

Students Sitting	Students Standing
🧍🧍🧍🧍🧍🧍🧍🧍🧍🧍🧍🧍🧍 🧍🧍🧍🧍🧍🧍	🧍🧍🧍🧍🧍🧍

Second Counting
1. All students seated count off by ones.
2. All students who counted a multiple of four stand up.

Students Sitting	Students Standing
🧍🧍🧍🧍🧍🧍🧍🧍🧍🧍🧍🧍🧍🧍🧍	🧍🧍🧍🧍🧍🧍🧍🧍🧍🧍

Third Counting
1. All students seated count off by ones.
2. All students who counted a multiple of four stand up.

Students Sitting	Students Standing
🧍🧍🧍🧍🧍🧍🧍🧍🧍🧍🧍🧍	🧍🧍🧍🧍🧍🧍🧍🧍🧍🧍🧍🧍🧍

LOOK BACK ▶ There will be 13 students standing after the third counting.

CLASS EXERCISES

Refer to the problem on page 458.

1. How many students will be standing after the fifth counting?

2. After how many countings will three students be sitting?

WRITTEN EXERCISES

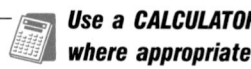 *Use a CALCULATOR where appropriate.*

Solve by simulating the problem.

1. Suppose you purchase a rare coin for $15, sell it for $23, and then buy it back for $31. How much money did you make or lose in selling and repurchasing this coin?

2. Jim is hosting a dinner party. Jim greets the first guest and they shake hands. The second guest arrives and shakes hands with Jim and the first guest. The third guest arrives and shakes hands with Jim, the first guest, and the second guest. This pattern continues. How many handshakes have taken place after the ninth guest arrives?

Solve. Use any strategy.

3. Sandy and Toby are 18 mi apart. They begin to walk toward one another. Sandy walks at 3 mi/h and Toby walks at 2 mi/h. After 1 h of walking Toby decides to rest for 1 h. In how many hours will they meet? How far will Sandy have walked? Toby?

4. Jon's bicycle license is a three digit number. The product of the digits is 140. The sum of the digits is 16. The numbers appear in descending order. What is Jon's license number?

5. Chris was thinking of a number. He added 4, multiplied the sum by -5, then subtracted 12. He then doubled the result to get -34. Of what number was Chris thinking?

6. There are 180 children standing around a parachute (assume this is a circle). The children are spaced evenly and numbered consecutively from 1 to 180. Ann is number 7. Tara is standing directly opposite Ann. What is Tara's number?

7. A hot air balloon is 2,200 ft in the air. It is scheduled to land at 3:22 P.M. The balloon descends at a rate of 110 ft/min. At what time should the descent begin?

8. **DATA FILE 12 (pp. 486–487)** Milwaukee, WI, has an altitude of 635 ft. Boston, MA, has an altitude of 21 ft. About how much farther will an average home run travel in Milwaukee than in Boston?

Exploring Right Triangles

OBJECTIVE:
To explore properties
of right triangles.

MATERIALS

- Graph paper
- Math journal to record work

■ Look at the right triangle shown. We call the side opposite the right angle the *hypotenuse*. We call the other two sides *legs*.

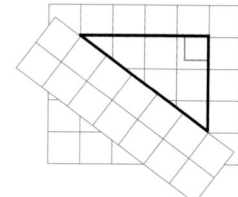

1. How many units long is each leg?

2. a. How many units long is the hypotenuse?

   b. *Explain* how the length of the hypotenuse was determined using graph paper.

■ A square is drawn on each side of the right triangle.

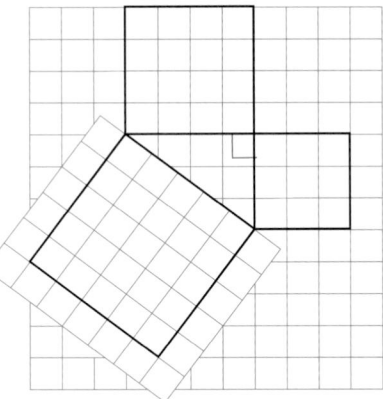

Egyptian rope stretchers used right triangles to relocate property lines after the annual flooding of the Nile river.

3. What is the length of a side on each square? *Describe* what it means to square a side of a triangle.

4. a. What are the areas of the squares on each leg?

   b. What is the area of the square on the hypotenuse?

   c. *Explain* how to draw the square on the hypotenuse.

   d. *Discuss* the relationship between your findings in (a) and (b).

■ A right triangle has side lengths 6, 8, and 10.

5. *Model* the right triangle and square each side.

6. a. What are the areas of the squares on each leg?

   b. What is the area of the square on the hypotenuse?

   c. *Discuss* the relationship between your findings in (a) and (b).

■ The sides of a right triangle share a special relationship.

7. *Describe* the relationship between the sides of any right triangle.

Pythagorean Theorem

OBJECTIVE:
*To use the rule of
Pythagoras to verify
right triangles and to
find missing values of
right triangles.*

NOTES & QUOTES

Pythagoras was a Greek
mathematician born about
500 B.C. He founded a
school to promote the
study of philosophy,
mathematics, and natural
science.

▼ Pythagoras is most famous for discovering the relationship
between the lengths of the sides of a right triangle. This relationship
is known as the *Pythagorean theorem.*

Pythagorean Theorem	In any right triangle with legs *a* and *b*, and hypotenuse *c*, $a^2 + b^2 = c^2$.

▼ You can model the Pythagorean theorem using graph paper. The
sum of the squares on each side equals the number of squares on the
hypotenuse.

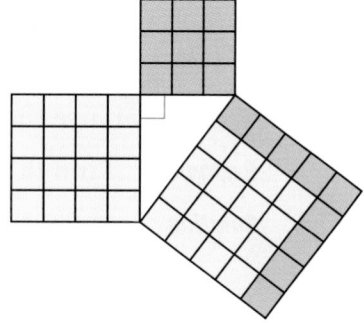

▼ You can use the Pythagorean theorem to find unknown lengths
of a triangle.

Example 1 Find *c*, the length of the hypotenuse.

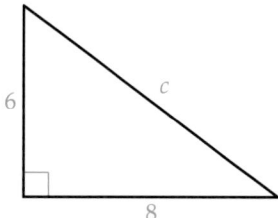

Solution

$$a^2 + b^2 = c^2 \qquad \text{Write the theorem.}$$
$$6^2 + 8^2 = c^2 \qquad \text{Substitute values for the variables.}$$
$$36 + 64 = c^2$$
$$100 = c^2$$
$$\sqrt{100} = \sqrt{c^2} \qquad \text{Find the square root of each side.}$$
$$10 = c$$

The hypotenuse, *c*, has length 10.

Check $\quad a^2 + b^2 = c^2 \qquad$ Substitute values.
$$6^2 + 8^2 = 10^2$$
$$36 + 64 = 100$$
$$100 = 100 \checkmark$$

▼ The converse of the Pythagorean theorem is also true.

Converse of Pythagorean Theorem	If $a^2 + b^2 = c^2$, then the triangle with sides a, b, and c is a right triangle.

THINK When given three side lengths of a right triangle, how do you know which one is the length of the hypotenuse?

Example 2 Determine if the triangle with the given side lengths is a right triangle.

    a. 12, 16, 20   **b.** 7, 8, 9

Solution

a. $12^2 + 16^2 = 20^2$
$144 + 256 = 400$
$400 = 400$ ✓
This is a right triangle.

b. $7^2 + 8^2 = 9^2$
$49 + 64 = 81$
$113 = 81$ ✗
This is not a right triangle.

We say that a set of integers such as 12, 16, 20 is a *Pythagorean triple*.

▼ You can use the Pythagorean theorem to help solve a problem.

Example 3 Find the area of *ABCED*.

Solution

1. Find *CD* using the Pythagorean theorem.

$6^2 + 8^2 = CD^2$
$36 + 64 = CD^2$
$100 = CD^2$
$\sqrt{100} = \sqrt{CD^2}$
$10 = CD$

2. Find the area of the triangle.

$A = \frac{1}{2}bh$

$24 = \frac{1}{2}(6)(8)$

3. Find the area of the rectangle.

$A = lw$
$80 = (10)(8)$

4. Find the total area. Add areas together.

$24 + 80 = 104$

The area of *ABCED* is 104 square units.

THINK AND DISCUSS

1. How could the Pythagorean theorem be used to find the altitude of an equilateral triangle with side length 12?

2. Is it possible for all three numbers in a Pythagorean triple to be even? odd?

3. A cube has a side length of 5. Find the length of the diagonal on one of the faces to the nearest hundredth.

CLASS EXERCISES

Name the legs and the hypotenuse.

1.

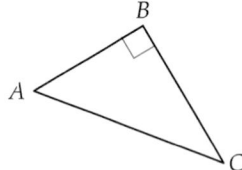

2.

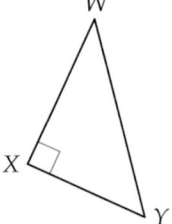

Write an equation. Solve for x.

3.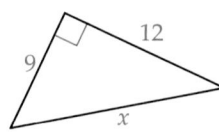

4.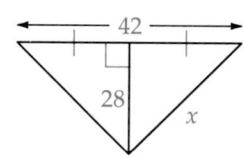

5.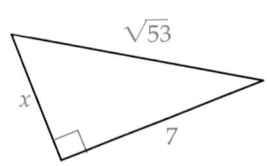

6. Is 1, 1, $\sqrt{2}$ a Pythagorean triple?

7. Two hikers started their trip from base camp by walking 15 m due east. They then turned due north, walking 17 m to a large pond. How far is the pond from base camp to the nearest tenth of a meter?

WRITTEN EXERCISES

MENTAL MATH **Simplify.**

1. $\sqrt{5^2}$

2. $\sqrt{144}$

3. $\left(\frac{3}{5}\right)^2$

4. $(2\sqrt{3})^2$

CALCULATOR **Find each value to the nearest thousandth.**

5. $\sqrt{63}$

6. $\sqrt{12}$

7. $\sqrt{32}$

8. $\sqrt{95}$

Name the legs and the hypotenuse.

9.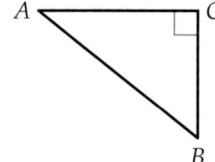

10.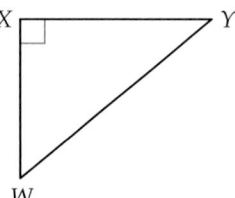

State which value is the length of the hypotenuse.

11. 10, 6, 8

12. $\sqrt{9}$, $\sqrt{25}$, $\sqrt{16}$

13. 5, $\sqrt{56}$, 9

Write an equation. Solve for x. Round to the nearest hundredth.

14.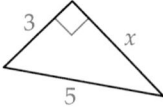

15.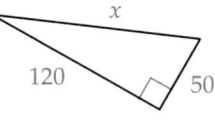

16.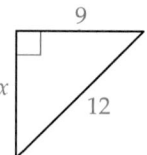

17.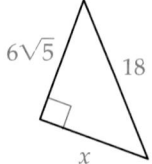

18.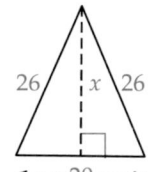

19.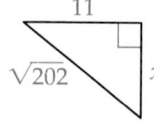

Write an equation. Solve for x. Round to the nearest hundredth.

20.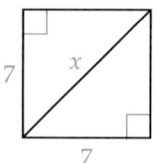

21.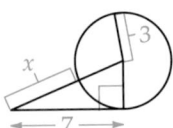

22.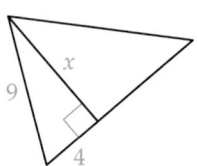

Determine whether each is a Pythagorean triple.

23. 7, 24, 25   **24.** 5, 12, 13   **25.** 1, 2, $2\sqrt{3}$ **26.** 1, 0.24, 0.26

27. 4, 5, 6   **28.** $1\frac{3}{5}$, $1\frac{1}{5}$, 2   **29.** $3p$, $4p$, $5p$ **30.** $\sqrt{5}$, $\sqrt{3}$, $\sqrt{2}$

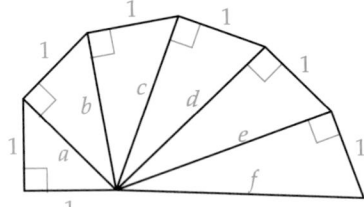

31. Find the lengths of the sides, a, b, c, d, e, f. Your answer may contain radical signs.

32. A carpenter was building a square deck. He measured the sides and the diagonal of the deck and got measures of 8 ft, 9 ft, and 12 ft. Did the carpenter fulfill his contract?

33. The recommended dimensions for a basketball court are 94 ft long and 50 ft wide. To the nearest foot, how long is the diagonal of the basketball court?

34. **CALCULATOR** A desk top is 75 cm wide and 130 cm long. How long is the diagonal of the desk top to the nearest hundredth?

35. Each side of a square is 15 in. long. Find the length of the diagonal to the nearest hundredth.

36. You are working for a landscaping company and you must plant and stake a tree. The stakes must be 2 ft from the base of the tree and the wires must extend 5 ft up the trunk. How long will the wires be to the nearest tenth?

37. Each side of a cube is 10 ft long. Find the length of the diagonal on one of the faces to the nearest tenth.

38. A ladder is 6 ft away from the base of a building. The ladder is 18 ft long. How many feet above the ground is the top of the ladder to the nearest hundredth?

39. The base of a pyramid is square. Each side of the base is 8 in. The slant height of the pyramid is 22 in.

    a. Find the height of the pyramid to the nearest hundredth.

    b. Find the volume of the pyramid to the nearest hundredth.

40. A cone has a diameter of 10 in. and a slant height of 16 in.

    a. Find the height of the cone to the nearest thousandth.

    b. Find the volume of the cone to the nearest thousandth. Use 3.14 for π.

OBJECTIVE:
To use parts of
similar triangles in
problem solving.

11-4 Similar Right Triangles

▼ Jack plans to cut down a tree. Since he does not want the tree to land on his house, pool, or shed, he must fell the tree towards the fence. To make sure the tree does not damage the fence, which is 49 ft away, Jack must know the height of the tree. Jack is 6 ft tall and casts a shadow 17 ft long. The tree casts a shadow 102 ft long. Using these measures and his knowledge of similar triangles, Jack finds the height of the tree.

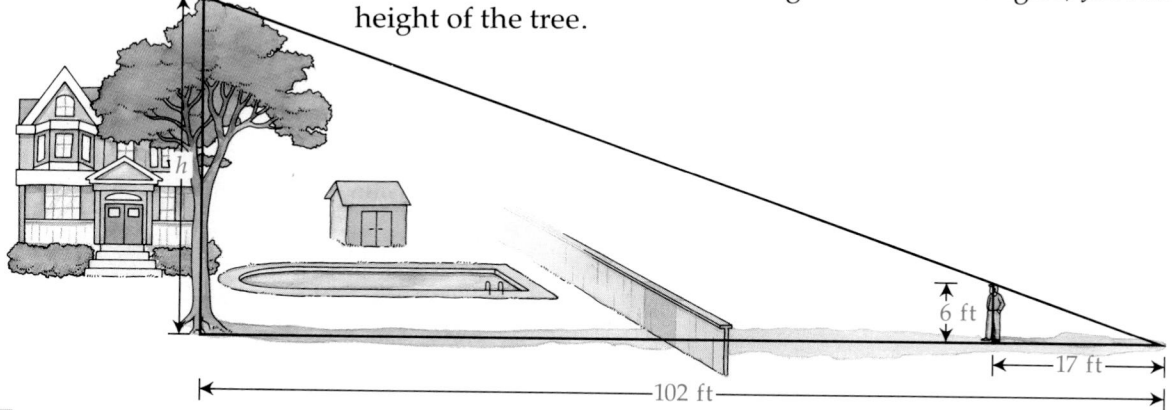

THINK What would be the proportion if Jack's height were 5 ft 9 in?

You can use similar triangles to set up a proportion.

$$\frac{\text{height of tree } (h)}{\text{length of tree shadow}} = \frac{\text{Jack's height}}{\text{length of Jack's shadow}}$$

Solve the proportion for h.

$$\frac{h}{102} = \frac{6}{17}$$ Substitute values.

$$17h = 6(102)$$ Cross multiply.

$$17h = 612$$

$$\frac{17h}{17} = \frac{612}{17}$$ Divide each side by 17.

$$h = 36$$

The tree is 36 ft tall. Since $36 < 49$, the fence will not be damaged.

▼ There is often more than one way to solve a problem.

Example 1 Find x using two different methods. The right triangles are similar.

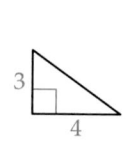
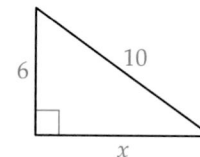

Solution   **Method 1**   Use the Pythagorean theorem.

$$a^2 + b^2 = c^2$$ Write the theorem.
$$6^2 + x^2 = 10^2$$ Substitute values.
$$36 + x^2 = 100$$
$$36 + x^2 - 36 = 100 - 36$$
$$x^2 = 64$$
$$\sqrt{x^2} = \sqrt{64}$$ Take each square root.
$$x = 8$$

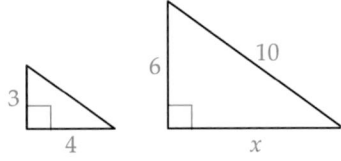

Method 2 Use similar triangles.

$$\frac{3}{4} = \frac{6}{x}$$ Write a proportion.

$$24 = 3x$$ Cross multiply.

$$\frac{24}{3} = \frac{3x}{3}$$ Divide each side by 3.

$$8 = x$$

The value of x is 8 no matter what method you use.

▼ You may need to use both methods to solve a problem.

Example 2 Find FB. $\overline{FC}$ and $\overline{CB}$ are altitudes of the triangles.

Solution

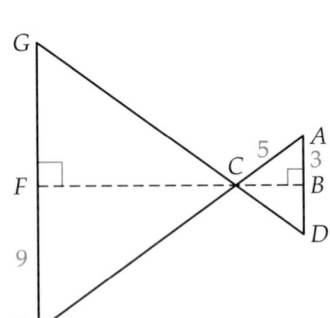

1. Find CB using the Pythagorean theorem.

$$a^2 + b^2 = c^2$$ Write the theorem.

$$3^2 + CB^2 = 5^2$$ Substitute values.

$$9 + CB^2 = 25$$

$$9 + CB^2 - 9 = 25 - 9$$ Subtract 9 from each side.

$$CB^2 = 16$$

$$\sqrt{CB^2} = \sqrt{16}$$ Find each square root.

$$CB = 4$$

2. Find FC using similar triangles.

$$\frac{9}{3} = \frac{FC}{4}$$ Write a proportion.

$$4 \cdot \frac{9}{3} = \frac{FC}{4} \cdot 4$$ Multiply each side by 4.

$$\frac{36}{3} = FC$$

$$12 = FC$$

3. $FB = CB + FC$

$$= 4 + 12$$

$$= 16$$

CLASS EXERCISES

Solve for x.

1. $\frac{x}{5} = \frac{12}{30}$

2. $\frac{2.5}{x} = \frac{7}{6}$

3. $\frac{9}{22} = \frac{x}{154}$

4. $\frac{a}{b} = \frac{x}{y}$

Complete each proportion. $\triangle ABC \sim \triangle DEC$.

5. $\frac{BC}{EC} = \frac{AC}{\blacksquare}$

6. $\frac{\blacksquare}{CB} = \frac{DC}{AC}$

7. $\frac{EC}{BC} = \frac{\blacksquare}{AB}$

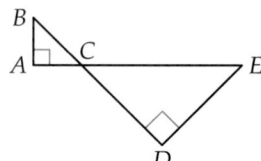

8. a. Find x using the Pythagorean theorem.

   b. Find y using the Pythagorean theorem.

   c. $\triangle ABC \sim \blacksquare \sim \blacksquare$

   d. $\triangle DBC \sim \blacksquare \sim \blacksquare$

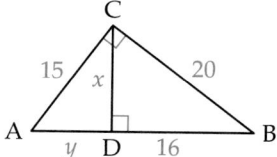

WRITTEN EXERCISES

MENTAL MATH Solve for variable x.

1. $\dfrac{4}{9} = \dfrac{12}{x}$

2. $\dfrac{x}{9} = \dfrac{7}{6}$

3. $\dfrac{1.5}{4} = \dfrac{x}{8}$

4. $\dfrac{y}{x} = \dfrac{a}{b}$

Solve for x using the Pythagorean theorem. Use the square root table on p. 579 to find the length to the nearest thousandth.

5.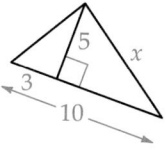

6.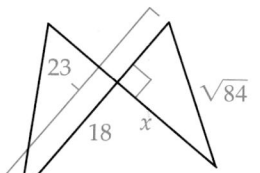

7.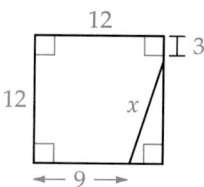

Solve for x using similar triangles. Each pair of triangles is similar.

8.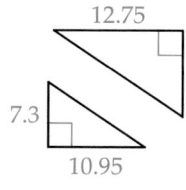

9.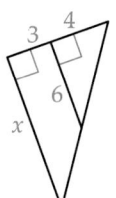

10.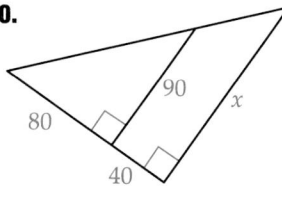

CALCULATOR Solve for x and y. Round to the nearest hundredth.

11.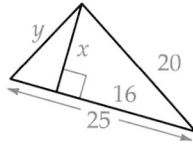

12.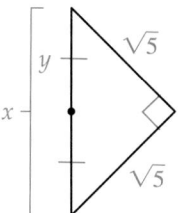

13.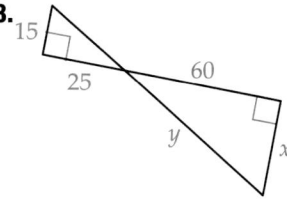

Solve.

14. A ladder is leaning against a building in such a way that the ladder touches the top of an 8-ft fence. The bottom of the ladder is 4 ft from the base of the fence. The fence is 8 ft from the building. How high up the building is the top of the ladder?

PROBLEM SOLVING HINT

Draw a diagram to help visualize the problem.

15. A radio tower is 25 ft high and casts a shadow of 40 ft. At the same time, a taller tower casts a shadow of 70 ft. What is the height of the taller radio tower?

16. Ian is 160 cm tall. His image on the film of a camera is 1.6 cm. Suppose the film is 2 cm from the camera lens. How far is Ian from the camera?

Use the article at the left to answer each question.

The Great Pyramid

The Great Pyramid of Khufu near Gîza was built about 2700 B.C. The pyramid has a square base. The Egyptians were able to form right angles by using an instrument called a gromma. The base length of each of the pyramid's four sides is 755 ft. Its height originally reached 481 ft but has grown smaller over the years from erosion. The pyramid is built from 2.3 million blocks of sandstone. Each block weighs about 2.5 t.

17. a. Determine the slant height of the faces of the pyramid to the nearest hundredth.

b. Find the area of the base of the pyramid.

c. *PROJECT* Research the gromma. Tell how Egyptians used this instrument to construct right angles.

TEST YOURSELF

Solve for variable *x*. Round to the nearest tenth.

1.

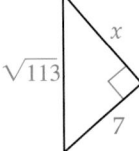

2.

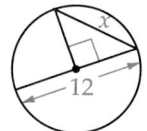

3.

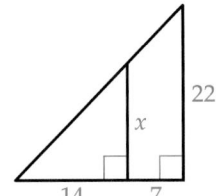

4. A rectangular box has a square base with area 16 cm². The height of the box is 7 cm. Find the length of the diagonal of a rectangular side. Use the square root table on p. 579.

5. A 42-ft tree casts a shadow of 63 ft. How long is the shadow cast by a 5-ft tall girl?

11-5 Special Right Triangles

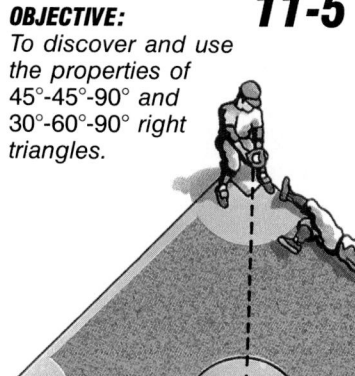

▼ A baseball diamond is a square. The distance between the bases is 90 ft. How long is a throw from home plate to second base? You can use a special right triangle and the Pythagorean theorem to find the distance.

$$a^2 + b^2 = c^2 \quad \text{Write the theorem.}$$
$$90^2 + 90^2 = c^2 \quad \text{Substitute values.}$$
$$8{,}100 + 8{,}100 = c^2$$
$$16{,}200 = c^2$$
$$\sqrt{16{,}200} = \sqrt{c^2} \quad \text{Take each square root.}$$
$$\sqrt{16{,}200} = c \quad \text{Simplify the right side.}$$
$$\sqrt{8{,}100 \cdot 2} = c$$
$$\sqrt{8{,}100} \cdot \sqrt{2} = c$$
$$90\sqrt{2} = c$$

A throw from home plate to second base is $90\sqrt{2}$ ft long.

▼ The triangle formed by the diagonal of a square is an *isosceles right triangle*. Each base angle has a measure of 45°.

45°-45°-90° Triangle	In a 45°-45°-90° right triangle, the lengths of the sides have the following relationships.
	$\text{hypotenuse} = \sqrt{2} \cdot \text{leg}$
	$\text{leg} = \dfrac{\text{hypotenuse} \cdot \sqrt{2}}{2}$

▼ You can use the properties of a 45°-45°-90° triangle to determine missing lengths.

Example 1 **Find x. The answer may contain a square root sign.**

a.

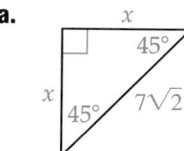

b.

THINK Why is $\dfrac{x\sqrt{2}}{\sqrt{2}}$ equal to x?

Solution

a. $\text{hypotenuse} = \sqrt{2} \cdot \text{leg}$
$$7\sqrt{2} = x\sqrt{2}$$
$$\frac{7\sqrt{2}}{\sqrt{2}} = \frac{x\sqrt{2}}{\sqrt{2}} \quad \text{Divide each side by } \sqrt{2}.$$
$$7 = x$$

b. $\text{leg} = \dfrac{\text{hypotenuse} \cdot \sqrt{2}}{2}$
$$x = \frac{1}{2}(16)(\sqrt{2})$$
$$x = 8\sqrt{2}$$

▼ The 30°-60°-90° right triangle is another special right triangle.

THINK In a 30°-60°-90° right triangle, how do you know which leg is longer?

30°-60°-90° Triangle	In a 30°-60°-90° triangle, the lengths of the sides have the following relationships.
	hypotenuse = 2(shorter leg)
	longer leg = shorter leg($\sqrt{3}$)

You can use these relationships to determine missing lengths.

Example 2 **Find *x* and *y*. The answer may have a square root sign.**

a.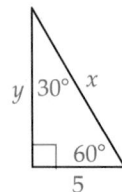

b.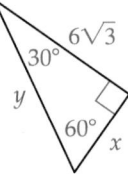

Solution **a.** hypotenuse = 2(shorter leg)   Solve for *x*.
$$x = 2(5)$$
$$x = 10$$
longer leg = shorter leg($\sqrt{3}$)   Solve for *y*.
$$y = \text{shorter leg}(\sqrt{3})$$
$$y = 5\sqrt{3}$$

b. longer leg = shorter leg($\sqrt{3}$)   Solve for *x*.
$$6\sqrt{3} = (x)(\sqrt{3})$$
$$\frac{6\sqrt{3}}{\sqrt{3}} = \frac{\sqrt{3}x}{\sqrt{3}}$$
$$6 = x$$
hypotenuse = 2(shorter leg)   Solve for *y*.
$$y = 2(6)$$
$$y = 12$$

THINK AND DISCUSS

1. In a 45°-45°-90° triangle, by what do you multiply each leg to get the length of the hypotenuse?

2. In a 30°-60°-90° triangle, what operation do you perform on the hypotenuse to get the length of the side opposite the 30° angle?

3. In a 30°-60°-90° triangle, what operation do you perform on the side opposite the 60° angle to get the length of the side opposite the 30° angle?

CLASS EXERCISES

Use the triangle at the right.

1. Which side is opposite ∠A?

2. Which side is opposite ∠B?

3. Which side is opposite ∠C?

4. Which side is the hypotenuse?

5. Which sides are the legs?

6. Which side of the triangle is the longest?

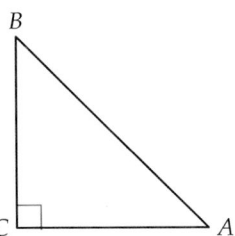

Tell whether a triangle with sides of the given lengths is 45°-45°-90°, 30°-60°-90°, or neither.

7. 6, 8, 10   **8.** 5, 5, 5√2   **9.** 15, 7.5√3, 7.5

Find each value. Answers may contain square root signs.

10.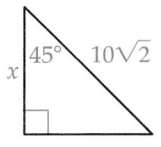

11.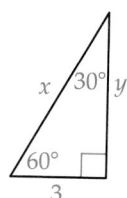

12.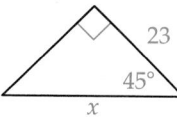

WRITTEN EXERCISES

The length of one side of the triangle is given. Find the missing measures. Answers may contain square root signs.

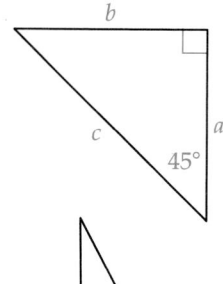

	a	b	c
1.	9	▨	▨
2.	▨	5.4	▨
3.	▨	▨	4√2
4.	▨	▨	3

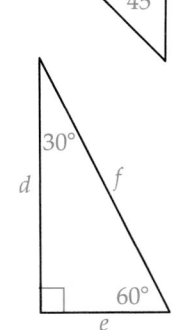

	d	e	f
5.	▨	2	▨
6.	▨	▨	10
7.	▨	7	▨
8.	8√3	▨	▨

Find each value. Answers may contain square root signs.

9.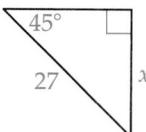

10.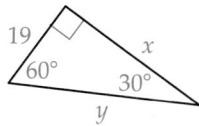

11.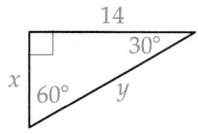

12. MENTAL MATH A square has a diagonal 6√2 in. long.

   a. Find the length of a side of the square.

   b. Find the perimeter of the square.

13. Each face on a cube has a diagonal 12 in. long.

   a. Find the length of a side of the cube to the nearest tenth.

   b. Find the surface area of the cube to the nearest hundredth.

MIXED REVIEW
Solve and check.
1. $\frac{x}{4} - 2 = 7 + x$
2. $-3.5x - 4x + 85 = x$

Solve the proportion.
3. $\frac{9.5}{x} = \frac{1.5}{0.75}$
4. Simplify $-(4x^3)^2$.
5. $-12 - (-18)$
6. A polygon with five sides is a ▨.

7. DATA FILE 6 (pp. 230–231) What percent of teens study for 2 or more hours each night?

8. All books are on sale for 40% off. Judy paid $19.99 for the new best seller. What was the original price?

14. The base of a cone has a diameter of 8. The cone slants on a 60° angle and has a slant height of 8. Find the height of the cone to the nearest thousandth. Use the square root table.

15. △*ABC* is equilateral. Each side has a length of 52 in. Find the altitude. The answer may contain a square root sign.

16. The length of the hypotenuse of a 30°-60°-90° triangle is 20*a*. What is the length of the shorter leg? What is the length of the longer leg? Your answers may contain square root signs.

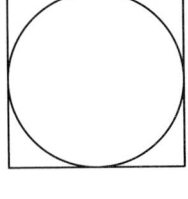

17. Use the diagram at the left. The diameter of the circle is 16 cm. How much larger is the area of the square than the area of the circle? Use 3.14 for π.

18. **CALCULATOR** A 15-ft ladder is leaning against a wall at a 45° angle. To the nearest tenth, how high above the ground is the ladder touching the wall?

19. Janet is building a kite in the shape of a square. Each side of the square is 18 in. To the nearest inch, how much wood does Janet need to make the diagonals?

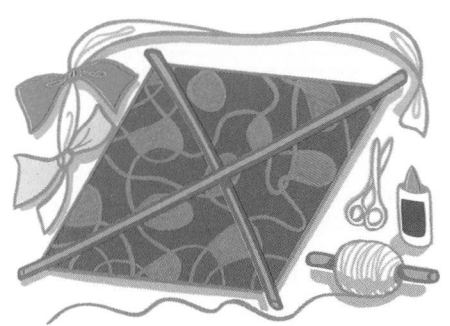

20. **DATA FILE 11 (pp. 450–451)** A skydiver jumps out of a plane at 2,750 ft. He wants to hit a marker 1.25 mi away. He falls at a rate of 10 ft/s. To the nearest tenth of a minute, how long will it take the jumper to hit the marker?

Critical Thinking
EXPLORING LOGIC

▼ To solve a logic problem, organize the information in a chart like the one at the left. Each of Mrs. Stephan's five children cleans one room each week. The rooms cleaned are the living room, family room, kitchen, bathroom, and a bedroom. Who cleans each room?

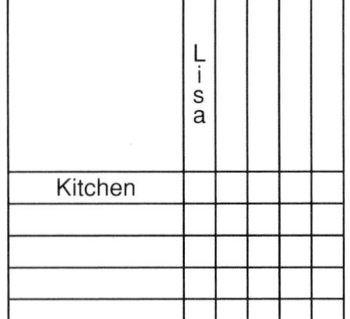

Copy and complete the chart to solve.

1. Lisa does not have to scrub the kitchen floor.

2. Nicole never makes her bed.

3. Robert and Eric always vacuum under the couches.

4. The family room joins the kitchen. Eric and Jo Ann enjoy talking to each other while they clean.

5. Only the living room and family room contain couches.

11-6 *Trigonometric Ratios*

▼ *Trigonometry* means triangle measurement. A *trigonometric ratio* is a ratio of the measures of two sides of a right triangle.

Example 1 Find each ratio.

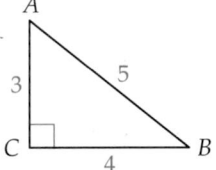

a. $\frac{CA}{CB}$ **b.** $\frac{CA}{AB}$ **c.** $\frac{CB}{AB}$

Solution   **a.** $\frac{3}{4}$ **b.** $\frac{3}{5}$ **c.** $\frac{4}{5}$

▼ Trigonometric ratios have special names.

Trigonometric Ratios	$\text{tangent of } \angle A = \dfrac{\text{length of side opposite } \angle A}{\text{length of side adjacent to } \angle A}$
	$\text{sine of } \angle A = \dfrac{\text{length of side opposite } \angle A}{\text{hypotenuse}}$
	$\text{cosine of } \angle A = \dfrac{\text{length of side adjacent to } \angle A}{\text{hypotenuse}}$

You can write the terms tangent, sine, and cosine using the abbreviations *tan, sin,* and *cos.* A shorter version of the trigonometric ratios follows.

$$\tan = \frac{\text{opposite}}{\text{adjacent}} \qquad \sin = \frac{\text{opposite}}{\text{hypotenuse}} \qquad \cos = \frac{\text{adjacent}}{\text{hypotenuse}}$$

Example 2 Find each trigonometric ratio.

     a. $\tan Y$ **b.** $\cos X$

Solution   **a.** $\tan Y = \dfrac{\text{opposite}}{\text{adjacent}} = \dfrac{12}{5}$

           b. $\cos X = \dfrac{\text{adjacent}}{\text{hypotenuse}} = \dfrac{12}{13}$

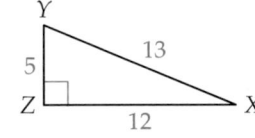

Angle	Sin	Cos	Tan
51°	.7771	.6293	1.2349
52°	.7880	.6157	1.2799
53°	.7986	.6018	1.3270
54°	.8090	.5878	1.3764
55°	.8192	.5736	1.4281

▼ If you know the measure of an acute angle of a right triangle, you can use a table of trigonometric ratios to approximate values of the tangent, sine, and cosine of the angle.

Example 3 Find the tangent, sine, and cosine of 42° using the table on p. 580.

Solution $\tan 42° \approx 0.9004$ $\sin 42° \approx 0.6691$ $\cos 42° \approx 0.7431$

▼ You can use a table of trigonometric ratios to approximate the measure of an angle when you know the sine, cosine, or tangent.

Example 4 Sin A = .7986. Find $m\angle A$.

Solution   Use the table. Find .7986 in the sin column.
       $m\angle A = 53°$.

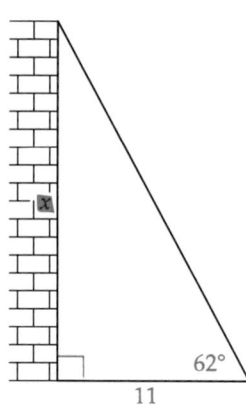

Example 5 A carpenter needs a ladder to do repair work on a building. The base of the ladder is 11 ft away from the building and forms a 62° angle with the ground. To the nearest foot, how high up on the building must the ladder rest?

Solution Draw a diagram.

$$\tan 62° = \frac{x}{11}$$ Use the tangent ratio.

$$1.8807 \approx \frac{x}{11}$$

$$11(1.8807) = \left(\frac{x}{11}\right)(11)$$ Multiply each side by 11.

$$20.6877 = x$$

$$21 \approx x$$ Round to the nearest whole number.

The ladder must rest about 21 ft up on the building.

▼ You may need to use more than one trigonometric ratio to find measures in a triangle.

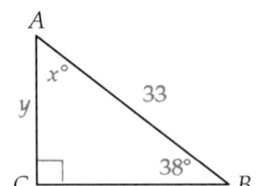

Example 6 **Use the triangle at the left. Find x, y, and z in $\triangle ABC$. Round to the nearest hundredth.**

Solution **1.** Find x.

$$x = 90 - 38$$ $\angle A$ and $\angle B$ are complementary.

$$= 52$$

2. Find y.

$$\sin 38° = \frac{y}{33}$$ $\sin = \frac{\text{opposite}}{\text{hypotenuse}}$

$$0.6157 \approx \frac{y}{33}$$ Substitute the value from the table.

$$33(0.6157) \approx \left(\frac{y}{33}\right)(33)$$ Multiply each side by 33.

$$20.3181 \approx y$$ Round.

$$20.32 \approx y$$

3. Find z.

$$\tan 38° = \frac{20.3181}{z}$$ $\tan = \frac{\text{opposite}}{\text{adjacent}}$

$$0.7813 \approx \frac{20.3181}{z}$$ Substitute the value from the table.

$$z(0.7813) = \left(\frac{20.3181}{z}\right)(z)$$ Multiply each side by z.

$$0.7813\,z = 20.3181$$

$$\frac{0.7813\,z}{0.7813} = \frac{20.3181}{0.7813}$$ Divide each side by 0.7813.

$$z = 26.005504$$

$$\approx 26.01$$ Round.

Angle	Sin	Cos	Tan
36°	.5878	.8090	.7265
37°	.6018	.7986	.7536
38°	.6157	.7880	.7813
39°	.6293	.7771	.8098
40°	.6428	.7660	.8391

CLASS EXERCISES

Use the table of trigonometric ratios on p. 580 to find each value.

1. sin 86°   **2.** cos 16°   **3.** tan 53°

Find $m\angle A$.

4. sin A = 0.8480   **5.** tan A = 3.7321   **6.** cos A = 0.5

State a trigonometric equation using the given values.

7. 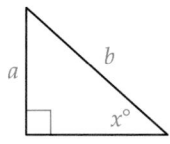   **8.** 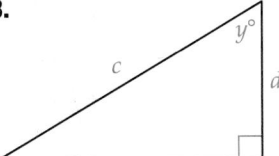   **9.**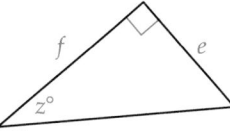

Find x, y, **and** z **for each triangle. Round to the nearest hundredth. Use the table of trigonometric ratios on p. 580.**

10. 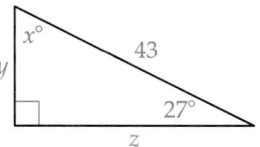   **11.** 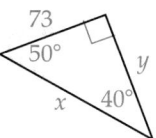   **12.**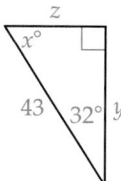

WRITTEN EXERCISES

Use the table of trigonometric ratios on p. 580 to find each value.

1. sin 10°   **2.** cos 80°   **3.** tan 15°

4. tan 55°   **5.** sin 78°   **6.** cos 60°

Find $m\angle B$. **Use the table of trigonometric ratios on p. 580.**

7. sin B = 0.9945   **8.** cos B = 0.7660   **9.** tan B = 1.9626

MENTAL MATH **Use 45°-45°-90° and 30°-60°-90° right triangles to find each value. Your answer may contain a square root sign.**

10. tan 45°   **11.** tan 60°   **12.** sin 30°

State a trigonometric equation using the given values.

13. 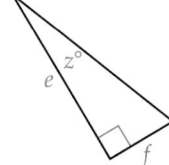   **14.** 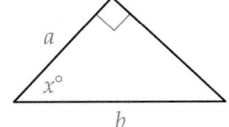   **15.**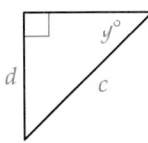

THINK AND DISCUSS

1. Why does the trigonometric table only go to 89°?

2. No angle has sine 0.638. If you compute that ratio, how do you decide which angle to use? Do angles have measure in divisions smaller than degrees?

MIXED REVIEW

A square has a diagonal 3.4√2 ft long.

1. Find the length of a side of the square.

2. Find the area of the square.

3. The angles of a triangle are 30°, 60°, 90°. The hypotenuse is 16 in. long. Find the lengths of the other two sides.

4. Simplify $(-x)^2 - (x)^2$.

5. A triangle with all angles less than 90° is called a(n) ▨ triangle.

6. Find the radius of a circle with area 25 πm^2.

7. Find three consecutive integers with a sum of -42.

Find x, y, and z for each triangle. Round to the nearest hundredth. Use the table of trigonometric ratios on p. 580.

16.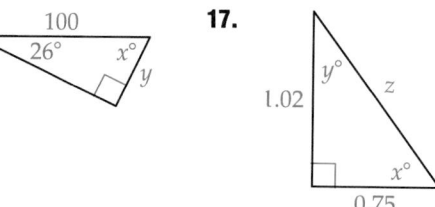

17.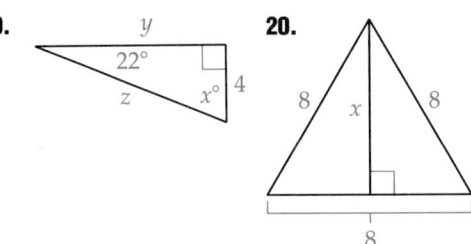

18.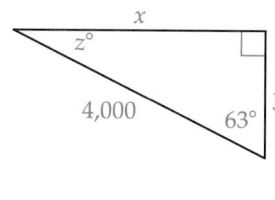
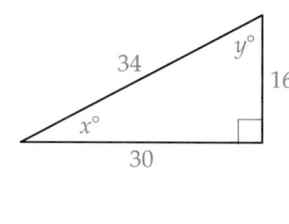

19.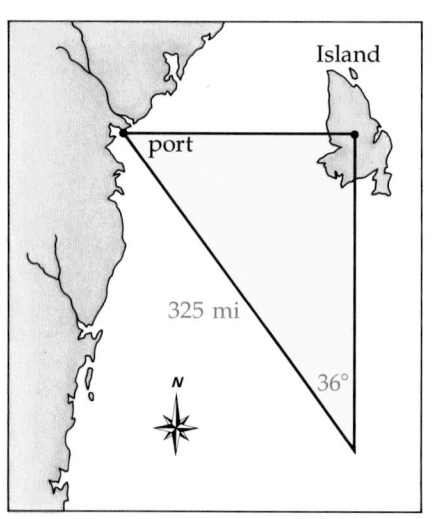

20.

21.

22. A navigator brings you a map charting a ship's course. She wants to know how far it is, to the nearest mile, from the island to the mainland port. Use the diagram at the left.

23. A Boeing 747 climbs continuously at a 30° angle to a height of 35,000 ft. To the nearest tenth of a mile, how far has the plane traveled to reach that elevation? *Hint:* 5,280 ft = 1 mi.

24. *DATA FILE 11 (pp. 450–451)* A skydiver jumps from 22,500 ft. He hits a marker 10,224 ft away. To the nearest degree, what angle does the skydiver make with the ground?

25. A man 6 ft tall paces 75 ft from the base of a tree. He uses a protractor to approximate the angle from his eye to the top of the tree. He finds that this angle is about 25°. Find the height of the tree to the nearest foot.

TEST YOURSELF

Tell whether a triangle with sides of the given lengths is 45°-45°-90°, 30°-60°-90°, or neither.

1. 10, 5, $5\sqrt{3}$ **2.** 8, $8\sqrt{2}$, 8   **3.** 6, 8, 10

Find x, y, and z for each triangle. Round to the nearest hundredth.

4.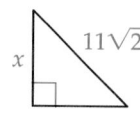

5.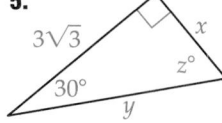

6.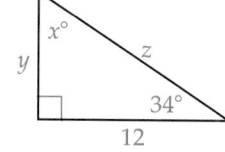

OBJECTIVE:
To apply right triangle concepts and trigonometric ratios to precision drawings.

11-7 Precision Drawing

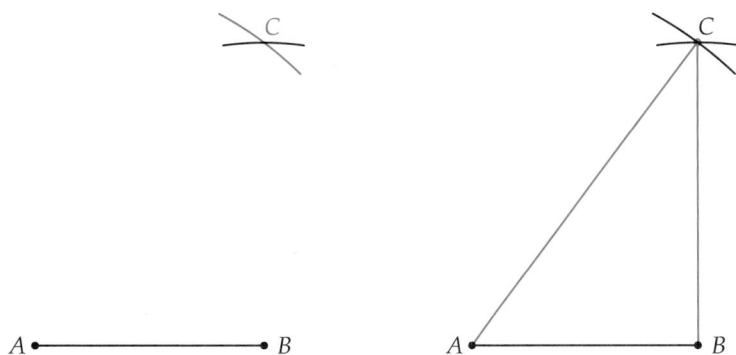

READ
PLAN
LOOK BACK
SOLVE

■ Architects and designers often require accurate plans and drawings. Professionals frequently use computers with graphic capability to help them with their work. Even so, there are many occasions when precision drawing must be done by hand.

THINK What are some professions that require precision drawing?

■ You can draw an angle accurately using a compass and a ruler.

Example 1 Draw a right angle using a ruler and a compass.

Solution A triangle whose sides measure 3 units, 4 units, and 5 units is a right triangle. Draw a right triangle with these dimensions.

1. Draw $\overline{AB}$, 3 cm long. $A \bullet\!\!-\!\!-\!\!-\!\!-\!\!-\!\!-\!\!\bullet B$

2. Use a compass with a radius of 4 cm. With center at B, draw an arc above B.

$A \bullet\!\!-\!\!-\!\!-\!\!-\!\!-\!\!-\!\!\bullet B$

3. Use a compass with a radius of 5 cm. With center at A, draw an arc that crosses the arc above B. Label the point of intersection as C.

Connect the three points to form $\triangle ABC$. By the converse of the Pythagorean theorem, $\triangle ABC$ is a right triangle. Therefore, $\angle ABC$ is a right angle.

■ You can draw any angle by finding the tangent of the angle and by predetermining the length of the adjacent side.

Example 2 **Draw a 23° angle. Use a protractor, a ruler, and the table of trigonometric ratios on p. 580.**

Solution

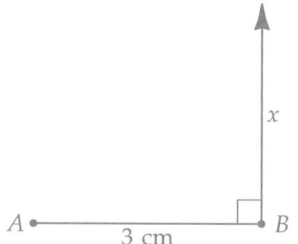

1. Choose a length, say 3 cm, for the side adjacent to the 23° angle. Draw $\overline{AB}$ with length 3 cm. Use a protractor to draw $\angle B$ with measure 90°. Let x represent the unknown length.

2. Solve for x to determine the length of the side opposite the 23° angle.

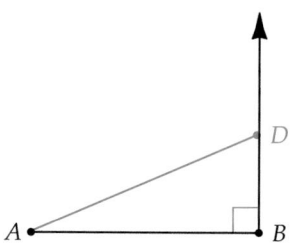

$$\tan = \frac{\text{opposite}}{\text{adjacent}} \qquad \text{Use the tangent ratio.}$$

$$\tan 23° = \frac{x}{3} \qquad \text{Substitute values.}$$

$$0.4245 = \frac{x}{3} \qquad \text{Find tan 23° in the table.}$$

$$3(0.4245) = \frac{x}{3}(3) \qquad \text{Multiply each side by 3.}$$

$$1.2735 = x \qquad \text{Round to the nearest tenth.}$$

$$x \approx 1.3$$

3. Mark a point 1.3 cm from B. Label the point as D. Then draw $\overline{AD}$.

$\angle A \approx 23°$.

■■■■■■ Decision Making ■ **DECISION MAKING** ■ Decision Making ■ Decision Making ■ Decision Making ■

PRECISION DRAWING

■ **COLLECT DATA**

1. Visit a store that sells drafting supplies. Take along the compass, ruler, and protractor that you use in school.

a. Do the inch and centimeter marks on your ruler perfectly match those on the best quality ruler found in the store?

b. Is your protractor the same size as the best one in the store?

■ **ANALYZE DATA**

2. Can the quality of the instruments you use affect the accuracy of the drawings you make? Explain.

3. Can the width of the markings on a ruler or compass affect the accuracy of a drawing? Explain.

4. Can the fineness of your pencil point affect the accuracy of a drawing? Explain.

CLASS EXERCISES

Find the tangent of each angle. Use the table of trigonometric ratios on p. 580.

1. $87°$ **2.** $15°$ **3.** $72°$

Solve for x. Use the table of trigonometric ratios on p. 580.

4. $\tan 47° = \frac{x}{4}$ **5.** $\tan 63° = \frac{x}{7}$ **6.** $\frac{x}{5} = \tan 36°$

WRITTEN EXERCISES

 Use a CALCULATOR where appropriate.

Use a compass, a ruler, and the table of trigonometric ratios to draw an angle with the given measure. Check using a protractor.

1. $20°$ **2.** $25°$ **3.** $85°$ **4.** $50°$ **5.** $76°$

6. $35°$ **7.** $145°$ **8.** $176°$ **9.** $138°$ **10.** $121°$

11. Use a compass and a ruler to draw a right triangle with sides of measure 5 units, 12 units, and 13 units.

    a. Label the triangle as shown. Use the table of trigonometric ratios on p. 580 to find $m\angle A$ and $m\angle B$.

    b. Check your results using a protractor.

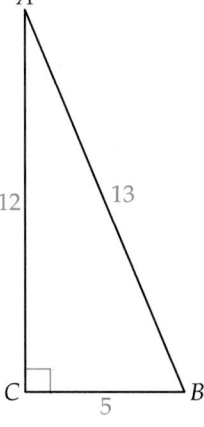

■ Decision Making ■ Decision Making ■ Decision Making ■ Decision Making ■ Decision Making ■ Decision Making ■

5. Would inaccuracies in angles and lengths in a drawing be more easily detected in small or in large drawings? Explain.

■ MAKE DECISIONS

6. Do you think it would be more accurate to draw a right triangle using a compass and ruler with the measurements in the ratio $3 : 4 : 5$, $6 : 8 : 10$, or $9 : 12 : 15$? Explain.

7. Suppose you are using a compass, ruler, and trigonometric ratios to draw angles. Would a table that expresses the ratios to hundredths or one that rounds ratios to the nearest tenth help you make a more accurate drawing? Explain.

Practice

Find each square root.

1. $\sqrt{169}$ **2.** $\sqrt{4x \cdot 4x}$ **3.** $\sqrt{\frac{81}{4}}$ **4.** $\sqrt{a^2 b^2}$ **5.** $\sqrt{\frac{x^2}{y^2}}$

6. $\sqrt{625x^{10}y^8}$ **7.** $\sqrt{400x^6}$ **8.** $\sqrt{529c^2}$ **9.** $\sqrt{121c^4}$ **10.** $\sqrt{2{,}500}$

Approximate each square root to the nearest integer.

11. $\sqrt{2}$ **12.** $-\sqrt{5}$ **13.** $\sqrt{10}$ **14.** $\sqrt{47}$ **15.** $\sqrt{96}$

State whether each number is rational or irrational.

16. $\sqrt{11}$ **17.** $-\sqrt{9}$ **18.** $4.1472\ldots$ **19.** $\sqrt{0.04}$ **20.** $\sqrt{81}$

Determine whether each is a Pythagorean triple.

21. 10, 11, 12   **22.** 2, 3, 4   **23.** 1.2, 0.5, 1.3   **24.** 30, 40, 50

25. $\sqrt{16}, \sqrt{25}, \sqrt{36}$ **26.** 5, 12, 13   **27.** 17, 8, 15   **28.** 1, 3, 5

Identify each triangle as 45°-45°-90°, 30°-60°-90°, or neither.

29. 5.2, $5.2\sqrt{2}$, 5.2   **30.** 8, 4, $4\sqrt{3}$ **31.** 15, 20, 25

Use the Pythagorean theorem to find x.

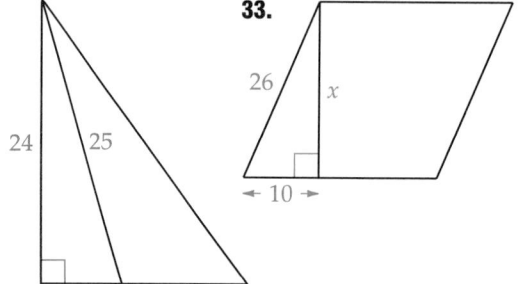

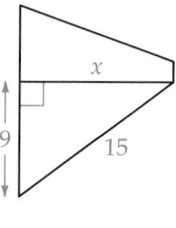

Use similar triangles to find y.

35.

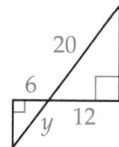

36.

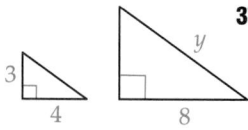

37.

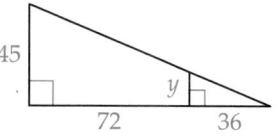

Find each missing length. Answers may contain square root signs.

38.

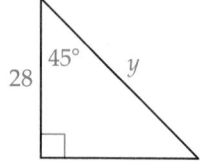

39.

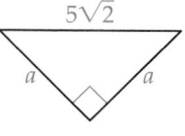

40.

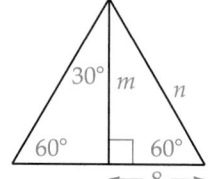

Problem Solving Practice

Solve. Use an appropriate strategy or a combination of strategies.

1. A car manufacturer offers exterior colors of white, blue, red, black, and silver. The manufacturer offers the same colors, plus tweed, for the interior. The manufacturer offers pinstripes, but only for cars with black or silver exteriors. How many different styles are there to choose from?

2. *The Battle of Gettysburg* is the largest painting in the world. The painting is 410 ft. long and 70 ft. wide. A tennis court is 78 ft. by 27 ft. How many tennis courts can fit inside the world's largest painting?

3. In $\triangle XYZ$, $m\angle X$ is 29° less than $m\angle Y$, and $m\angle Z$ is 52° less than $m\angle Y$. Find the measure of each angle.

4. Mt. Vesuvius is a volcano in Italy. Its crater is 7,920 ft in diameter. What is the area of the crater?

5. **CALCULATOR** The length of the Golden Gate Bridge in San Francisco, California, is 4,200 ft. How long, to the nearest hundredth of a minute, would it take a car driving at a continuous rate of 35 mi/h to cross the bridge? *Hint:* 5,280 ft = 1 mi.

6. **DATA FILE 10 (pp. 404–405)** How much more circular area, to the nearest square meter, does a snowshoe hare require than a Northern flying squirrel requires? Use 3.14 for π.

7. First-class letters cost $.29 for the first ounce and $.23 for each additional ounce. Warren spent $2.82 to send a first-class letter. How many ounces did his letter weigh?

8. I am a number less than 100. I am the product of two prime numbers. If you reverse my digits I am prime. The sum of my digits is a one-digit prime. One of my digits is a square number. What number am I?

9. Each face of cube A has a diagonal of $10\sqrt{2}$ cm. Each face of cube B has a diagonal of $7\sqrt{2}$ cm. How much more liquid will cube A hold than cube B?

10. Madison Square Garden in New York City is built in the shape of a circle. Its diameter is 404 ft. The stadium accommodates 20,234 spectators. To the nearest hundredth square foot, how much area does this allow for each person? Use 3.14 for π.

11. Three integers have a sum of 48. The greater integer is four more than the middle integer. The least integer is ten less than the middle integer. Find the integers.

Chapter 11 Review

Match each word with the example that illustrates its meaning.

1. square root symbol
2. principal square root
3. irrational number
4. Pythagorean theorem
5. in a 45°-45°-90° triangle
6. in a 30°-60°-90° triangle
7. tangent A
8. cosine A
9. sine A

a. hypotenuse = $\sqrt{2}$(length of leg)

b. $a^2 + b^2 = c^2$

c. $\dfrac{\text{opposite}}{\text{adjacent}}$

d. $\sqrt{4} = +2$

e. $\dfrac{\text{opposite}}{\text{hypotenuse}}$

f. 2.6457513 . . .

g. $\sqrt{}$

h. hypotenuse = 2(shorter side)

i. $\dfrac{\text{adjacent}}{\text{hypotenuse}}$

Finding Square Roots   11-1

To find the square root, think of the squares. You can also use a calculator or a table of squares.

Find each square root. Use the square root table on p. 579.

10. $\sqrt{196}$ 11. $\sqrt{64p^2}$ 12. $\sqrt{3}$ 13. $\sqrt{(x-2)^2}$ 14. $\sqrt{625}$ 15. $\sqrt{31+5}$

Problem Solving   11-2

To solve a problem, sometimes it is helpful to act it out.

16. A class of 31 students counted off by 1s beginning with the number one. Each student who counted a multiple of 5 stood up. This process was repeated. Those who were standing were skipped. After the fourth counting, how many students were standing?

Pythagorean Theorem   11-3

To use the Pythagorean theorem to find unknown parts of a right triangle, substitute the known values in the formula $a^2 + b^2 = c^2$, and solve for the unknown.

Write an equation. Solve for x.

17.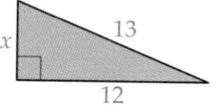

18.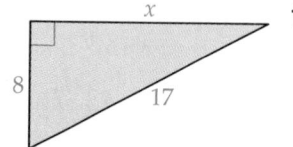

19.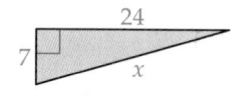

20.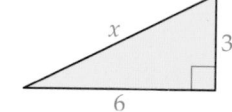

Similar Right Triangles

To find values in similar right triangles, you can use the Pythagorean theorem or write a proportion. Sometimes you will use both.

Solve for x. Each pair of triangles is similar.

21.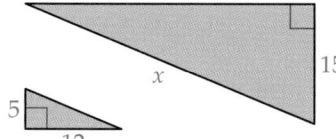

22.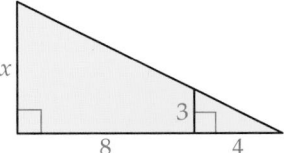

23.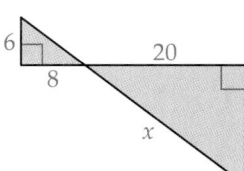

Special Right Triangles

To find missing lengths in a 45°-45°-90° triangle, use the relationships

$$\text{hypotenuse} = \sqrt{2} \cdot \text{leg} \qquad \text{leg} = \frac{\text{hypotenuse} \cdot \sqrt{2}}{2}.$$

To find missing lengths in a 30°-60°-90° triangle, use the relationships

$$\text{hypotenuse} = 2(\text{shorter leg}) \qquad \text{longer leg} = \text{shorter leg}\,(\sqrt{3}).$$

Find each value. Answers may contain square root signs.

24.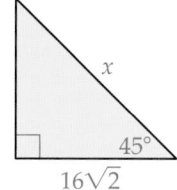

25.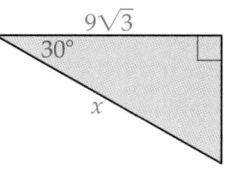

26.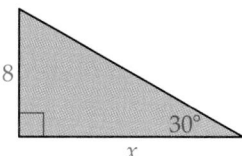

27.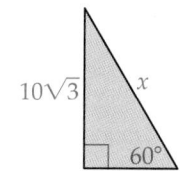

Trigonometric Ratios

To find measures in a right triangle, use a trigonometric ratio.

$$\tan A = \frac{\text{opposite}}{\text{adjacent}} \qquad \cos A = \frac{\text{adjacent}}{\text{hypotenuse}} \qquad \sin A = \frac{\text{opposite}}{\text{hypotenuse}}$$

Find each missing length or angle measure. Round to the nearest thousandth. Use the table of trigonometric ratios on p. 580.

28.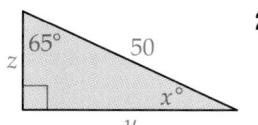

29.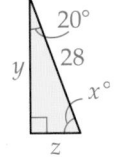

30.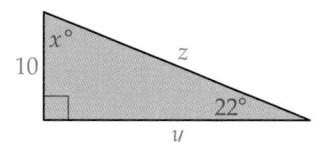

31.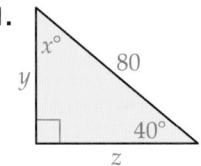

32. A ladder is 8 ft away from a building and forms a 54° angle with the ground. What is the length of the ladder?

33. A train in the mountains rises 8 ft for every 200 ft it moves along the track. Find the angle of elevation of the tracks.

Find each square root.

1. $\sqrt{64}$ **2.** $\sqrt{169}$ **3.** $\sqrt{\dfrac{36}{49}}$ **4.** $\sqrt{(x+5)^2}$

Solve for x. Calculate each length to the nearest hundredth.

5. 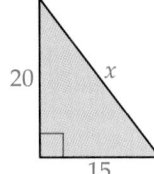   **6.** 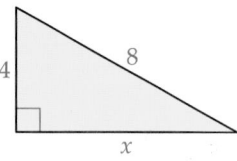   **7.** 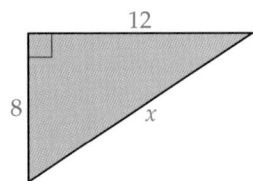   **8.**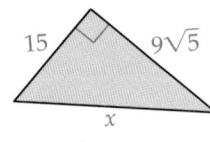

Determine if the lengths can be the sides of a right triangle.

9. 9, 12, 14   **10.** 1.1, 6.0, 6.1   **11.** $\dfrac{3}{5}, \dfrac{4}{5}, 1$ **12.** 8.1, 15.2, 18.6

Solve for x. Answers may contain square root signs.

13. 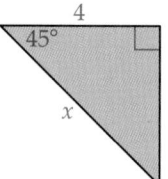   **14.** 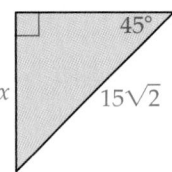   **15.** 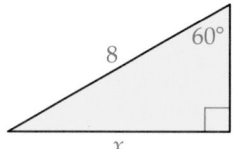   **16.**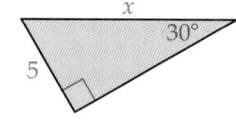

Use the table of trigonometric ratios on p. 580 to find each value.

17. $\cos 25°$ **18.** $\tan 40°$ **19.** $\sin 73°$ **20.** $\tan 88°$

Find each missing length or angle measure. Round angles to the nearest whole number and lengths to the nearest thousandth. Use the table of trigonometric ratios on p. 580.

21. 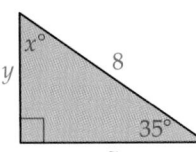   **22.** 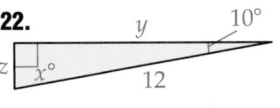   **23.** 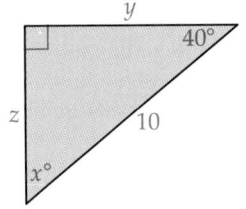   **24.**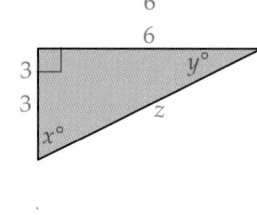

Solve.

25. A square is 6 in. on each side. What is the measure of the diagonal of the square?

26. The captain of a ship sights a lighthouse. The angle of elevation is 12°. The captain knows that the lighthouse is 24 m above sea level. What is the distance from the ship to the lighthouse?

Choose the correct answer. Write A, B, C, or D.

1. Solve $\frac{2}{3}x - 5 = 3x + 9 - \frac{1}{3}x$.

   A. -7   **B.** 7

   C. $3\frac{1}{2}$ **D.** not given

2. Solve.

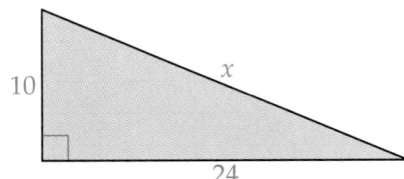

   A. 17   **B.** 26

   C. 28   **D.** not given

3. Find the y-intercept.
$2x + 3y = 12$

   A. 2   **B.** 12

   C. 3   **D.** not given

4. Solve.

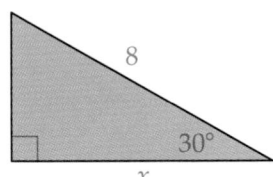

   A. 4   **B.** $4\sqrt{3}$

   C. $8\sqrt{3}$ **D.** not given

5. $\angle ABC$ and $\angle CBD$ are complementary angles. $m\angle ABC = 73°$. Find $m\angle CBD$.

   A. 107°   **B.** 17°

   C. 27°   **D.** not given

6. Simplify $\sqrt{32x^3 \cdot 2x^5}$.

   A. $64x^8$ **B.** $16x^2\sqrt{2}$

   C. $8x^4$ **D.** not given

7. Solve $\frac{a}{16} = \frac{15}{48}$.

   A. 5   **B.** 10

   C. 24   **D.** not given

8. Find the area.

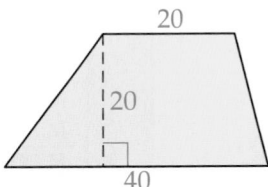

   A. 400 sq. units   **B.** 300 sq. units

   C. 600 sq. units   **D.** not given

9. The area of a triangle is 20 cm². The height is 5 cm. What is the base?

   A. 4 cm   **B.** 8 cm

   C. 10 cm   **D.** not given

10. Solve.

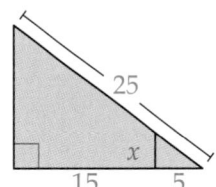

   A. 3.75   **B.** 5

   C. 8.5   **D.** not given

11. Name the inequality for the model.

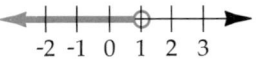

   A. $x < 1$ **B.** $x \geq 1$

   C. $x \leq 1$ **D.** not given

12. Determine the slope of the line containing (-2,3) and (5,-1).

   A. $\frac{5}{6}$ **B.** $-\frac{4}{7}$

   C. 2   **D.** not given

BASEBALL STADIUMS

TEAM	STADIUM	SEATING CAPACITY
ATLANTA BRAVES	Atlanta–Fulton County Stadium	52,003
BALTIMORE ORIOLES	Memorial Stadium	54,017
BOSTON RED SOX	Fenway Park	34,182
CALIFORNIA ANGELS	Anaheim Stadium	64,593
CHICAGO CUBS	Wrigley Field	39,600
CHICAGO WHITE SOX	Comiskey Park	44,087
CINCINNATI REDS	Riverfront Stadium	52,392
CLEVELAND INDIANS	Cleveland Stadium	74,483
DETROIT TIGERS	Tiger Stadium	52,416
HOUSTON ASTROS	Astrodome	45,000
KANSAS CITY ROYALS	Royals Stadium	40,625
LOS ANGELES DODGERS	Dodger Stadium	56,000
MILWAUKEE BREWERS	Milwaukee County Stadium	53,192
MINNESOTA TWINS	Hubert H. Humphrey Metrodome	55,883
MONTREAL EXPOS	Olympic Stadium	59,149
NEW YORK METS	Shea Stadium	55,300
NEW YORK YANKEES	Yankee Stadium	57,545
OAKLAND A's	Oakland Coliseum	49,219
PHILADELPHIA PHILLIES	Veterans Stadium	64,538
PITTSBURGH PIRATES	Three Rivers Stadium	58,727
SAN DIEGO PADRES	Jack Murphy Stadium	58,433
SAN FRANCISCO GIANTS	Candlestick Park	58,000
SEATTLE MARINERS	Kingdome	58,150
ST. LOUIS CARDINALS	Busch Stadium	54,224
TEXAS RANGERS	Arlington Stadium	43,508
TORONTO BLUE JAYS	Skydome	53,000

A t higher altitudes where the air is thinner, a baseball faces less resistance. A 275-ft rise in altitude adds about 2 ft to the distance an average home run will travel.

+ 2 ft

+275 ft Altitude

+ 2 ft

+275 ft Altitude

There is a 30% chance that a base runner will be caught if trying to steal a base.

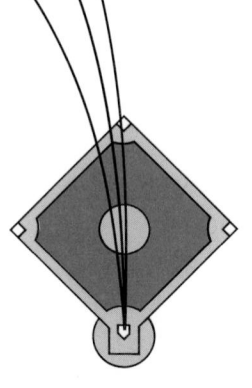

12 *Statistics and Probability*

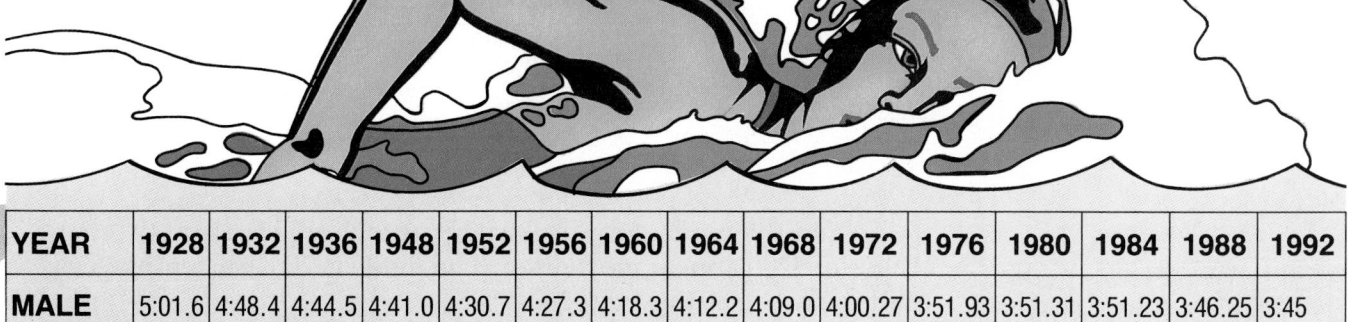

YEAR	1928	1932	1936	1948	1952	1956	1960	1964	1968	1972	1976	1980	1984	1988	1992
MALE	5:01.6	4:48.4	4:44.5	4:41.0	4:30.7	4:27.3	4:18.3	4:12.2	4:09.0	4:00.27	3:51.93	3:51.31	3:51.23	3:46.25	3:45
FEMALE	5:42.8	5:28.5	5:26.4	5:17.8	5:12.1	4:54.6	4:50.6	4:43.3	4:31.8	4:19.44	4:09.89	4:08.76	4:07.10	4:03.85	4:07.18

OLYMPIC RECORD TIMES FOR 400-m FREESTYLE SWIMMING (min.)

Think about it...

Look at the data for the Olympic records in the 400-m freestyle swimming competition. Why do you think the times for this Olympic event have gone down since 1928? Do you think the times will continue to go down?

USA

1988 WINTER OLYMPICS

Brian Boitano's scores for Technical Merit in Men's Figure Skating:

5.9
5.9
5.9
5.9
5.9
5.8
5.8
5.8
5.8

OBJECTIVE:
To calculate the
measures of central
tendency and select
the most appropriate
measure for a given
situation.

12-1 Mean, Median, and Mode

▼ A company's employees stated that average weekly wages were $200. Owners argued that wages averaged $300. The personnel department insisted that wages were $250. Each group is correct.

In statistics we use three *measures of central tendency* to describe data characteristics: *mean*, *median*, and *mode*. The company's weekly salary data are shown below.

Employee Wages (in dollars)	200, 200, 200, 200, 200, 200, 200, 200, 200
	250, 250, 250, 250, 250, 250
	350, 350
	500, 500
	1,000

THINK Why does it help to group wages of the same amount together?

▼ To find the mode, group all wages of the same amount together. Wages of $200 appear most often. The mode is 200. The employees used the mode as the average.

Mode	The mode is the data item that occurs most often.

▼ The owners divided the total wages by the total number of employees, $6{,}000 \div 20 = 300$, to get the mean.

▼ To find the median, order the wages for all the employees. Find the middle number. If there is an even number of data items, add the two middle numbers. Then divide by 2 to find the midpoint. The median is 250. Personnel used the median as the average.

Median	The median is the middle value in a set of data.

THINK The best average in a situation is the one that best reflects what is most typical. Which average reflects a typical salary? Why?

▼ Some data have more than one mode. Some data have no mode.

Example 1 Find the mode for each set of data.

　　　　a. 2 5 3 3 4 5 6 5 3 4 2 7

　　　　b. 6 3 2 5 6 4 4 2 3 5

Solution　**a.** 7 6 5 5 5 4 4 3 3 3 2 2　　Group like numbers.

Bimodal data have two modes. The modes of these data are 5 and 3.

　　　　b. 6 6 5 5 4 4 3 3 2 2　　Group like numbers.

There is no mode.　　　　All numbers are listed the same number of times.

▼ You can use the measures of central tendency to describe various situations.

Example 2 **Is the mean, median, or mode the best average for each situation? Explain.**

    a. the favorite rock group of the Freshman class

    b. the time it takes each student to get to school

    c. the cost of houses in your community

Solution **a.** Mode; The mode is useful in determining the most frequently chosen category. Mode is the preferred statistic when the data are not numerical.

    b. Mean; The mean is useful in situations that do not use unusually large or small numbers that distort the results.

    c. Median; This measure tells that half the data items are above and half below the average. The median is used when extreme measures distort the mean.

▼ *Range* is a measure of data dispersion.

Range	The range of a set of data is the difference between the greatest and least values in the set.

Example 3 **Find the range in the following set of data.**

car prices: $8,750; $24,560; $16,230; $26,990; $12,400

Solution $26,990 − $8,750 = $18,240   Subtract the least value from the greatest.

CLASS EXERCISES

Find the mean, median, mode, and range of each of the following.

1. 1 1 2 2 3 3 4 4 4 4 5 5 6 7 8 *5/.5 3̄, 4, 4 7*

2. 10 13 15 15 16 16 *7 /.67 15, 15 and 16 6*

3. 50 50 50 50 60 70 70 70 90 90 100 100 100 100 *80 70, 50 /80 /50*

4. 3 3 3 3 3 *3, 3, 3 0*

5. 59 63 48 50 85 *237, 48 No, 26*

What is the best average for each situation? Explain.

6. the average height of the students in the class *66 in*

7. the average scores of candidates on a scholarship examination
        84

THINK AND DISCUSS

The greatest number and the least number are eliminated from a set of data.

1. How will this affect the median? Explain.

2. How could this affect the mode? Explain.

3. How could this affect the mean? Explain.

8. the average scores of candidates on a driver's education test

9. the average earnings of 14-year-old students *69*

12

WRITTEN EXERCISES

Find the mean, median, mode, and range for each set of data.

1. golf scores   5 5 5 6 3 3 4 7 *3 /.37s, 4.s, 5, 4*

2. diving scores   9.7 9.8 9.2 9.9 8.9 8.7 8.8 *7.4s, 9.3, NO, 1.2*

3. miles per gallon   17.8 22.5 27.0 23.5 18.9 16.7 24.8 19.0 23.0 *71.96 2 ...*

4. allowance   3.50 5.50 2.00 5.00 2.75 3.00 4.00 4.50 3.00 3.50 *12.6, 2.7s, 3, 3.50*

MENTAL MATH **Find the mean, median, mode, and range for each set of data.**

5. 0 0 1 1 2 2 2 3 3 4 4 *2, 2, 2, 4*

6. 1 1 2 2 3 3 3 4 5 6 *24.6, 2.5, 3, 5*

7. 2 2 2 3 4 5 6 6 7 8 *37.8, 3.5, 2, 6*

8. 1 3 3 4 6 6 6 8 8 *37.9, 6, 6, 7*

CALCULATOR **Find the mean, median, mode, and range for each set of data.**

9. 76 84 88 90 78 80 84 88 92 80 86 84 *933, 80, 80*80, 14*

10. 135 170 165 170 185 165 170 175 160 150 145 *1658 18, 170, 170, 50*

11. 98 97 101 104 105 102 103 100 101 99 *920.9, 104, 101, 8*

Solve.

12. A student timed the length of telephone calls made over one weekend.

Minutes of calls   10 2 11 4 20 12 16 9 14 2
                    16 13 35 5 18 4

187.25

   a. Find the mean, median, and mode for the length of the calls.

   b. Which average best reflects the typical phone call? Explain.

   18

   c. Find the range of the length of the calls.

13. A basketball player made the following points per game.
   10 5 8 15 7 9 3 30 3

   a. Find the mean, the median, and the mode. *10, 8, 3*

   b. Which average best reflects a typical game? Explain.

   30, usually They get around 30 pts

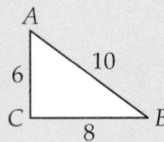

14. In a classroom experiment each student estimated when one minute had elapsed. The results of their estimates, in seconds, are listed below.

57 59 56 54 61 60 63 55 59 51 65 58 69 62 63
57 54 64 58 55 64 61 63 60

  a. Find the mean, the median, and the mode. *59.5, 55, 63*

  b. Which average best reflects a typical estimate? Explain.
    60.

Would you use the mean, the median, or the mode for each situation? Explain.

15. the heights of the members of the basketball team

16. the distance members of your class live from the school

17. the rainfall for the month of August in your community

18. the number of times each class member went to a mall last week

19. the cost of new cars

20. the amount of TV each student watches each week

21. the amount of time spent doing homework by the members of your class

Yes, you can find the mean, median, and mode with all of them.

22. *WRITE* a paragraph describing three situations in which the mode, the mean, and the median would each be the most appropriate measure of central tendency.

23. *PROJECT* Record the age of each member of your class in years and months. Find the mean, the median, and the mode. Which measure is the most representative?

24. *DATA FILE 12 (pp. 486–487)* Use the score for Brian Boitano to calculate each of the following.

  a. Find the mean, the median, and the mode of his scores. *5.86, 5.9, 5.9*

  b. Which average best reflects a typical score? Explain. *5.9, its the mode*

25. A student had the following scores on exams in her history class: 83, 76, 92, 76, 93.

  a. The teacher allows the student to decide which measure of central tendency to use as an average. Which measure do you recommend? Explain. *cm, its helpful*

  b. There is one more exam. What score must the student make to raise her average to 85 if using median as the average? *get a 95*

  c. What score must the student make to raise the average to 85 if using the mean as the average? *get 90*

  d. *WRITE* a paragraph explaining which measure of central tendency you consider the most representative of the student's grades. What measure would you choose for your grades?

OBJECTIVE:
To arrange data into
line plots and
frequency tables.

12-2 Line Plots and Frequency Tables

▼ In a survey, 25 students were stopped in the hallway and asked how many books they were carrying. Their responses were:
2, 0, 4, 1, 2, 3, 1, 0, 1, 6, 4, 1, 0, 2, 5, 1, 4, 3, 1, 6, 2, 5, 4, 3, 1.

THINK What does more than one x in a column represent?

The *line plot* shows the data.
An × represents one student.

The greatest number of ×s are above the number 1. The mode is 1.

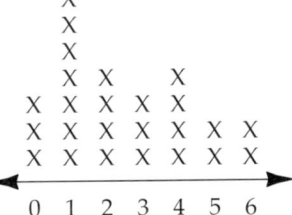

```
                    X
                    X
                    X
          X  X      X
       X  X  X  X  X
       X  X  X  X  X  X  X
       X  X  X  X  X  X  X
    ◄──────────────────────►
       0  1  2  3  4  5  6
```

Line Plot	A line plot shows data on a number line. You place an x for each response above the category of the response.

▼ A *frequency distribution* is another way to organize data. Instead of the ×s of the line plot, you write the frequency of a particular response to correspond to the type of response.

The table shows the frequency distribution for the book survey.

Number of books	n	0	1	2	3	4	5	6
Number of students	f	3	7	4	3	4	2	2

You can see that three students carried no books, seven carried 1 book, and so on. The greatest frequency is seven, so 1 is the mode.

Frequency Distribution	A frequency distribution is a listing of data that pairs each data item with the number of times it occurs.

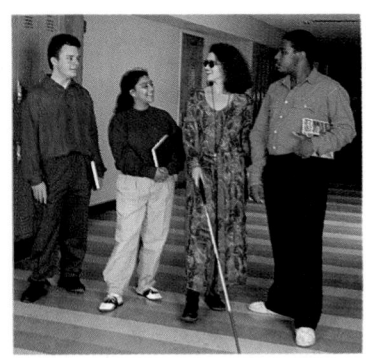

▼ You can construct a frequency table from a tally.

Example 1 Arrange the data in a frequency table.

7 2 5 4 1 6 5 2 5 1
3 6 2 3 4 5 2 6 3 4

Solution 1. Determine the values for *n*. Then prepare a tally chart.

2. Count the tally marks for each value. Record that number as the frequency.

n	1	2	3	4	5	6	7
Tally	//	////	///	///	////	///	/
f	2	4	3	3	4	3	1

▼ Sometimes you need to find the mean, median, and mode from a frequency distribution.

Example 2 Find the mean, median, and mode.

n	0	1	2	3	4
f	2	3	5	4	1

Solution **a.** To find the mean, multiply the number (n) times the frequency (f) for all n. Add the products. Divide by the total of the f.

$$\frac{2(0) + 3(1) + 5(2) + 4(3) + 1(4)}{2 + 3 + 5 + 4 + 1} = \frac{29}{15} = 1.9\overline{3}$$

The mean is $1.9\overline{3}$.

b. To find the median, list each number (n) f times. Then find the middle number.

0 0 1 1 1 2 2 2 2 2 3 3 3 3 4

There are 15 items. The eighth one is in the middle. The median is 2.

c. The mode is 2, the number with the highest frequency.

CLASS EXERCISES

Draw a line plot for each set of data. Find the mean, median, and mode.

1. 7 11 10 10 8 11 9 7 9 8 11 11   9, 5, 9, 11

2. 5 0 2 1 4 3 4 0 2 5 4 3 2 0 4   2.6, 2, 4

Find the mean, median, and mode for each.

3. x	f		**4.** x	f		**5.** x	f		**6.** x	f
0	3		16	2		2	1		1	1
1	2		17	5		4	3		2	2
2	2		18	4		6	2		3	2
3	1		19	2		8	3		4	2
4	2		20	1		10	1		5	2
						12	3		6	1

3.9, 22, no   40, 184, no   29, 72.5, no   14, 37, no

Make a frequency table for each set of data. Determine the mode of each distribution, if one exists.

7. 25 29 28 28 30 25 26 28 27 29 26 30   28

8. 10 30 20 30 50 10 40 30 50 40 30 50   30

9. 1 4 0 3 0 1 3 2 2 4   0~4~3

10. 6 2 8 7 9 3 5 4 8 2 4 6 4 1   4

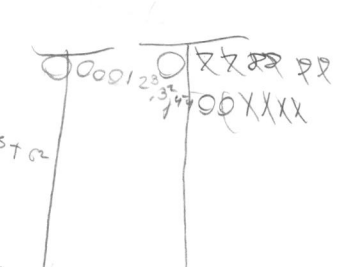

▼ **THINK AND DISCUSS**

1. Would you expect a set of exam scores to have more than one mode? Explain.

2. Describe the line plot of a distribution with no mode.

Draw a line plot for each frequency distribution. Find the median and the mode. _37_

1.

x	1	2	3	4	5	6
f	2	5	7	8	4	3

2. _85_

x	1	2	3	4	5	6
f	1	3	5	8	8	5

no mode

3.

x	1	2	3	4	5	6
f	7	5	3	2	6	7

4.

x	1	2	3	4	5	6
f	5	5	5	5	5	5

5.

x	1	2	3	4	5	6
f	1	8	6	7	5	3

6.

x	1	2	3	4	5	6
f	1	2	9	8	9	1

Make a frequency table for each set of data. Find the mean, the median, and the mode.

7. baseball scores   9 6 6 7 10 6 8 6 8 7   _16.2, 10 6_

8. the ages of club members   14 16 14 16 14 16 13 12 15 16 12 12 15 14 15 15   _20, 16, 14_

9. the heights of test plants   25 25 20 25 20 25 30 25 31 26 28 30   _20, 27.5, 25_

10. a class set of test scores   100 90 70 60 95 65 85 70 70 75 80 85 75 70 100 90   _39, 70, 70_

Construct the frequency table from each line plot. Find the median and the mode.

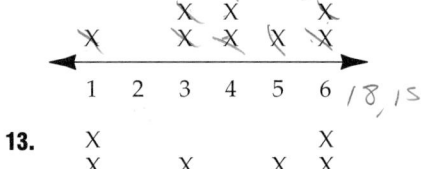

11.

```
              X    4 4
           X  X      X
     X     X  X  X  X  X
  ───────────────────────►
     1  2  3  4  5  6   18, 15-20
```

12. _4 1/6_

```
     X
     X        X  X  X
     X        X  X  X  X
  ───────────────────────►
     1  2  3  4  5  6
```

13.

```
  X                 X
  X     X        X  X
  X  X  X  X     X  X
  X  X  X  X  X  X
  ───────────────────────►
  15 16 17 18 19 20
```

14. _85, 79, 75_

```
  X        X              X
  X  X  X  X  X  X
  X  X  X  X  X  X
  X  X  X  X  X  X
  ───────────────────────►
  70 75 80 85 90 95
```

15. The number of letters in each of the first twenty-five words in a given passage of text are shown below.

2 7 6 3 1 2 7 6 3 2 2 6 9
5 3 2 2 4 5 4 3 2 3 2 11

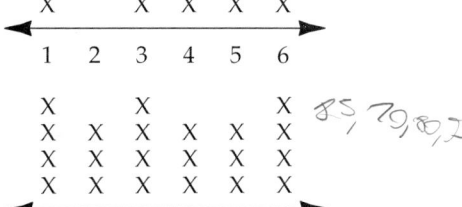

a. Draw the line plot for the data.   _22.8, 4, 2_

b. Make a frequency table.

c. Find the mean, the median, and the mode for the data.

16. The following figures represent the weekly earnings in dollars of the employees at Yanktown Industrial Enterprise.

160 160 160 200 200 200 200 200
200 240 240 240 360 360 360 520

a. Draw a line plot.

b. Draw a frequency table.

c. Find the mean, median, mode, and range.

17. Use the **DATA** at the right.

a. Draw a frequency table.

b. Find the mean, median, and mode.

c. Which measure of central tendency best reflects the average number of gold medals won? Explain your choice.

18. Babe Ruth's home runs from 1920 to 1934 are shown below.

54 59 35 41 46 25 47 60 54
46 49 46 41 34 22

a. Draw a frequency table.

b. Find the mean, median, and mode.

c. Which average best reflects a typical year? Explain your choice.

19. PROJECT Select a 50-word passage from a reading of your choice.

a. Tally the number of times each letter of the alphabet is used.

b. Draw a frequency table.

c. Find the mean, the median, and the mode of the distribution.

d. *E* is the most frequently used letter in English. Is this true of your data?

20. PROJECT Survey car usage. Count the number of people in each vehicle that passes a given point for a half-hour each weekday. Repeat at the same time on a weekend day. Construct two frequency tables. Are the results the same during the weekend as they are during the week? How could you use this information to determine the need for a traffic light?

21. Use the **DATA** at the right.

a. What age has the highest frequency for each group?

b. ANALYZE How would you find the median age for a large set of data? Find the median for men and women.

22. DATA FILE 12 (pp. 486–487) Round the seating capacity for each baseball stadium to the nearest thousand. Use the rounded data to draw a frequency table and to find the median and the mode of the data.

Distribution of Gold Medals 1988 Winter Games

Country	Medals
Soviet Union	11
East Germany	9
Switzerland	5
Austria	3
West Germany	2
Finland	4
Netherlands	3
Sweden	4
United States	2
Italy	2
Norway	0
Canada	0
Yugoslavia	0
Czechoslovakia	0
France	1
Japan	0
Liechtenstein	0

1990 Boston Marathon

Age	Number Entered	
	Male	Female
Under 20	19	3
20–24	251	96
25–29	828	330
30–34	1,318	396
35–39	1,533	371
40–44	1,681	297
45–49	1,026	147
50–54	605	76
55–59	266	16
60 & over	140	11

OBJECTIVE:
To draw valid conclusions from statistical data.

Exploring Misuse of Statistics

▼   Statistics is a powerful tool when used to influence the way a person perceives a situation. You might cite statistics to influence a friend's opinion. In a similar manner, companies often use statistics to present their best image. Advertisers also use statistics to influence you to select their product.

▼   When you use statistics, you must analyze the problem before choosing the data that meet your needs.

1. A toy manufacturer wants to sell more toys. The manufacturer decides to advertise on the most frequently watched television program. Using data collected by a rating company, the manufacturer determines that an adult comedy program is the most popular.

   a. *Analyze* Did the manufacturer find the group of people that might want to own the toy (the target market)?

   b. *Discuss* What factors need to be considered when deciding where to advertise?

   c. *Decide* Who is in the target market? What types of shows would reach more people in the target market?

▼   The most accurate way to collect data is to get everyone's opinion. This is usually impractical. A *sample* of the target group can often provide sufficient information from which to make decisions.

2. Suppose you want to find the number of boys in your school who watch football on Sunday.

   a. *Describe* the group about which you want information.

   b. Suppose your sample includes all the boys in your class. Does your sample represent the boys in the school? *Explain.*

   c. *Discuss* What might be a better sample? Do you think the size of the sample has any effect on the outcome? Would ten boys be enough? *Explain.*

   d. *Discuss* Where would you take the survey? When would be a good time to take the survey?

   e. *Discuss* methods of sampling. Would an interview survey be as accurate as a written survey? How would you word your survey?

   f. Would the time of year in which you took the survey make a difference? the part of the country? *Explain.*

   g. What other factors could influence your results?

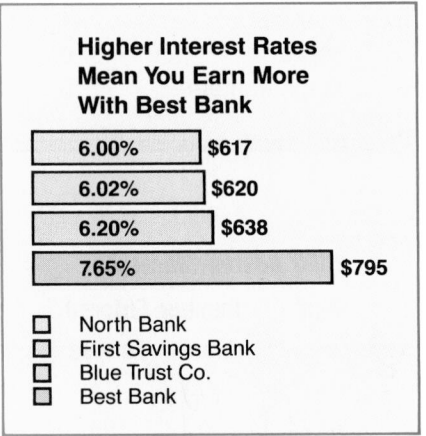

**Higher Interest Rates
Mean You Earn More
With Best Bank**

6.00%	$617
6.02%	$620
6.20%	$638
7.65%	$795

☐ North Bank
☐ First Savings Bank
☐ Blue Trust Co.
☐ Best Bank

Explain how the graph is misleading.

▼ Sometimes people present accurate data in a misleading manner to encourage the conclusions they support.

3. **Compare** and analyze the data in the graphs below.

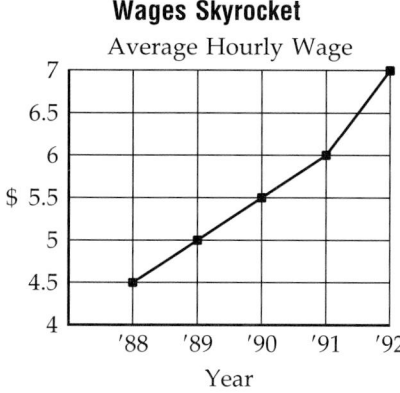

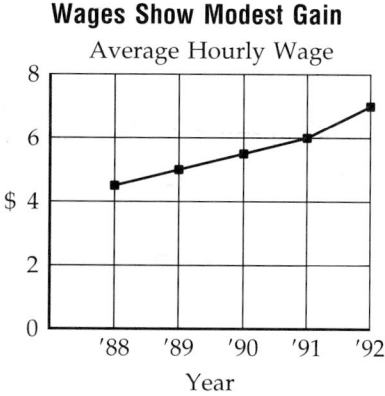

a. **Discuss** What is the difference in the way the vertical scales are used?

b. Do you think the information was presented accurately by each graph? **Explain.**

c. **Write** a short paragraph telling which graph you think was prepared by the personnel department of the company and which was prepared by the workers. Support your viewpoint.

4. An ad stated that 3 out of 4 dentists recommend *Smile* toothpaste.

a. **Decide** Do you need to know how many dentists were included in the sample?

b. **Decide** How could the city where the survey was taken affect the validity of the sample?

c. **Discuss** whether the dentists also recommend other brands. **Explain** why this might affect your opinion of the data.

5. **PROJECT** Find examples in a newspaper or a magazine where statistical data is used.

a. **Explain** Does the collection of data appear to be accurate?

b. Is the information presented in a distorted manner?

c. **Discuss** How could you present the data more fairly?

6. **PROJECT** Write a survey question.

a. **Decide** What is your target market?

b. Can you survey the entire target market or is it more practical to take a sample? Take the survey.

c. **Analyze** How can you accurately present the survey results? Make a presentation with a graph.

12-3 Stem and Leaf Plots

Fat Content in One Serving

Food	Fat Content in Grams
Deluxe, large hamburger	33
Plain, small hamburger	10
Cheeseburger	17
Roast beef sandwich	15
Beef and cheese sandwich	22
Fish sandwich	26
Fried chicken pieces	21
Deluxe pizza	26
Cheese pizza	12
Taco	26
Apple turnover	24
French fries	12

▼ The table at the left gives the fat content in one serving of various foods. How does the fat content for a cheese pizza compare with other items in the list?

It is difficult to compare the fat content from the table. You can reorganize the data by constructing a *stem and leaf plot.*

Choose the value for the *stem* by finding the least value and the greatest value for the fat content totals. The least value is 10. The greatest value is 33. Both numbers have two digits. The tens' digits will become the stem. Therefore, the stems for this data will be the digits 1 through 3.

Write the digits from 1 to 3 in a column. Draw a line to their right.

```
1 |
2 |
3 |
```

The *leaves* are the ones' digits associated with the tens' values. For a cheeseburger with the fat content of 17 g, the stem is 1 and the leaf is 7. For an apple turnover with fat content of 24 g, the stem is 2 and the leaf is 4. Record each food's fat content to obtain the plot below.

```
1 | 0 7 5 2 2
2 | 2 6 1 6 6 4
3 | 3
```

Arrange the leaves on each stem in order from least to greatest.

```
1 | 0 2 2 5 7
2 | 1 2 4 6 6 6
3 | 3
```

The mode is the greatest number of repeated leaves. For this data the mode is 26. Since the data are in order, the median is the midpoint of the twelve items. The median is the average of the sixth item, 21, and the seventh item, 22. The median is 21.5.

Now it is easier to evaluate the data. A cheese pizza, with fat content of 12 g for a serving, is below the median and the mode for fat content of the foods listed.

▼ In summary, to make a stem and leaf plot:

1. Choose a stem.

2. Write all values between and including the least stem and the greatest stem in order in a column. Draw a line to their right.

3. Write the leaf values to the right of the stem values.

4. Rewrite the plot, putting the values in order.

▼ The stem may be more than one digit. It can be any number that will provide a useful way to organize the data.

Example 1 Use the table at the right to construct a stem and leaf plot to compare the Olympic times for the 80-m hurdles from 1932–1968. Then find the mode.

Solution The stem will be the whole number of seconds. The leaves will be the tenths of a second.

10	3 5 7 8 9
11	2 7 7

The mode is 11.7 s.

▼ A back-to-back stem and leaf plot records two sets of data. The side-by-side display makes the data easier to compare.

Example 2 Draw a back-to-back stem and leaf plot for the times in the 100-m dash in the Olympic Games from 1928–1968. Find each median and mode.

Solution Use seconds for the stem and tenths of seconds for the leaves.

Men's Time (tenths of seconds)	Stem (seconds)	Women's Time (tenths of seconds)
9	9	
8 5 4 3 3 3 2 0	10	
	11	0 0 4 5 5 5 9 9
	12	2

Men's Scores		Women's Scores
10.3 s	Median	11.5 s
10.3 s	Mode	11.5 s

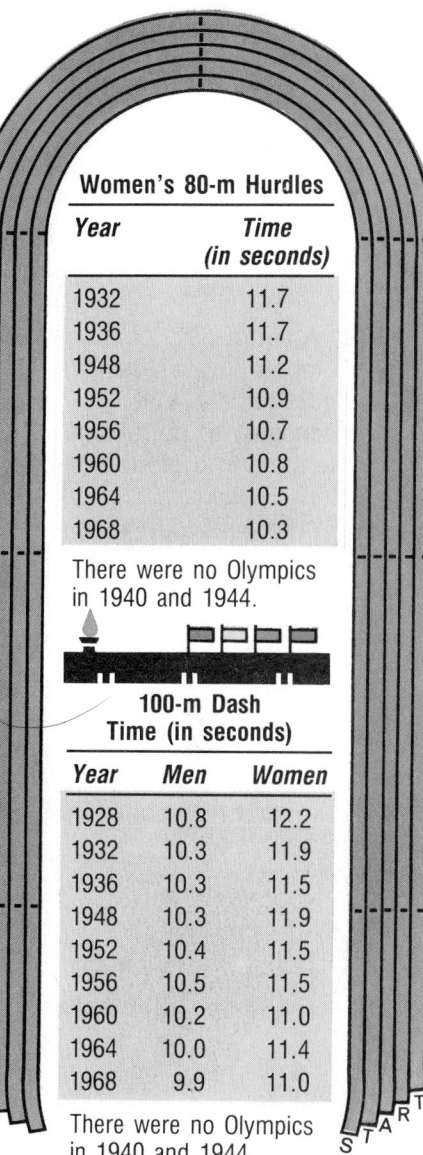

Women's 80-m Hurdles

Year	Time (in seconds)
1932	11.7
1936	11.7
1948	11.2
1952	10.9
1956	10.7
1960	10.8
1964	10.5
1968	10.3

There were no Olympics in 1940 and 1944.

100-m Dash Time (in seconds)

Year	Men	Women
1928	10.8	12.2
1932	10.3	11.9
1936	10.3	11.5
1948	10.3	11.9
1952	10.4	11.5
1956	10.5	11.5
1960	10.2	11.0
1964	10.0	11.4
1968	9.9	11.0

There were no Olympics in 1940 and 1944.

CLASS EXERCISES

Use the stem and leaf plot below to answer each question.

6	1 1 3 5 5
7	0 2 2 4
8	4 5 8 9
9	3 6 7 9 9 9

1. What numbers make up the stem?

2. What numbers make up the leaves for the first stem?

3. What is the mode?

4. What is the median?

5. **WRITE** Describe a situation for which the data in the stem and leaf plot might apply.

1. Is the stem and leaf plot a useful method of organizing data if you only want to find the mean? Explain.

2. A set of data contains numbers in the 20s, 30s, and 50s only. Is it necessary to put a 4 on the stem in a stem and leaf plot? Explain.

3. In a stem and leaf plot, can a leaf have no stem? Explain.

Make a stem and leaf plot from each set of data. Then find the median and the mode.

6. 15, 22, 25, 10, 36, 15, 28, 35, 18

7. 105, 115, 95, 97, 86, 89, 102, 107, 114, 113, 113, 113

8. 786, 789, 791, 777, 771, 781, 796, 797, 800, 801, 781

Make a back-to-back stem and leaf plot from each of the sets of data. Then find the median and the mode for each set of data.

9. Set A: 25, 23, 33, 36, 42, 44   Set B: 19, 16, 23, 34, 26

10. Set C: 236, 237, 241, 250, 242   Set D: 262, 251, 248, 243, 257

11. Set E: 9.1, 8.2, 7.3, 6.4, 7.3, 8.5   Set F: 7.6, 9.2, 8.2, 8.3, 9.7, 7.6

WRITTEN EXERCISES

Make a stem and leaf plot for each set of data. Then find the median and the mode.

1. 785, 785, 776, 772, 792, 788, 761, 768, 768, 750

2. 4.5, 4.3, 0.8, 3.5, 2.6, 1.4, 0.2, 0.8, 4.3, 6.0

3. 89, 70, 102, 82, 74, 74, 78, 105, 108, 107, 75

4. 47, 41, 60, 75, 85, 53, 57, 76, 79, 81, 84, 86

5. 11.5, 11.8, 10.6, 10.4, 9.5, 12.2, 11.8, 11.8, 11.8, 10.6

6. 225, 220, 221, 222, 231, 231, 219, 219, 215, 229, 236

Make a back-to-back stem and leaf plot for each set of data. Then find the median and the mode.

7. Set A: 63, 62, 63, 52, 58, 63   Set B: 45, 48, 53, 57, 61, 58, 65

8. Set C: 156, 158, 142, 142, 147   Set D: 141, 145, 148, 156, 157

9. Set E: 5.2, 5.8, 6.7, 6.3, 5.9, 4.1   Set F: 7.1, 6.4, 6.5, 6.8, 5.1, 5.2

10. Set G: 206, 205, 210, 215, 222   Set H: 218, 219, 228, 208, 209

11. Use the **DATA** at the left to solve.

   a. What number will make up the stem for the kangaroo and the opossum?

   b. Construct a stem and leaf plot.

   c. Find the mode.

   d. Find the median.

12. **DATA FILE 7 (pp. 272–273)** Draw a stem and leaf plot for the passenger boardings in 2000. Find the median.

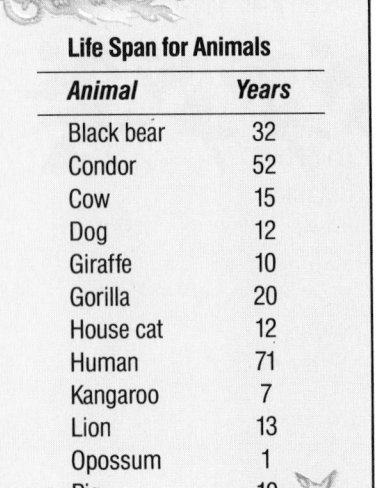

Life Span for Animals	
Animal	**Years**
Black bear	32
Condor	52
Cow	15
Dog	12
Giraffe	10
Gorilla	20
House cat	12
Human	71
Kangaroo	7
Lion	13
Opossum	1
Pig	10
Zebra	15

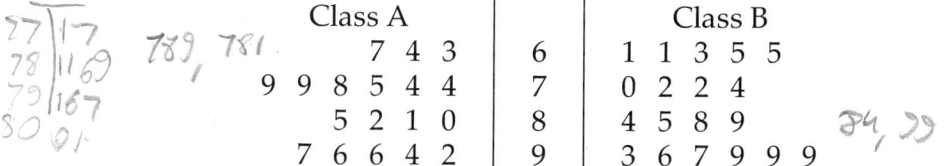

Use the stem and leaf plot below to answer each question. The plot is for the length of time, in minutes, two classes spent on homework.

Class A		Class B
7 4 3	6	1 1 3 5 5
9 9 8 5 4 4	7	0 2 2 4
5 2 1 0	8	4 5 8 9
7 6 6 4 2	9	3 6 7 9 9 9

13. What numbers make up the stem?

14. What is the lowest time for each set of data?

15. What is the median and the mode for each set of data?

Critical Thinking

EXPLORING HISTOGRAMS

▼ A *histogram* uses rectangles to show frequency data. You can make a histogram from a stem and leaf plot. The horizontal axis corresponds to the stem. The vertical axis reflects the number of items in the leaf (the frequency).

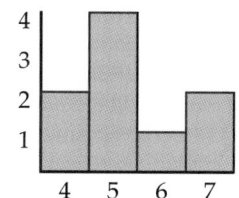

4	8 9
5	2 5 6 7
6	3
7	4 5

▼ You can divide the information on the horizontal scale of the histogram into smaller groupings.

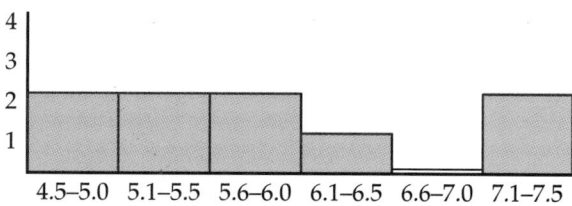

1. How does a change in the horizontal scale of a histogram affect the vertical scale?

2. How can the change in scales affect how people understand the information on the histogram?

3. Draw two histograms with different horizontal scales for the data at the right. Which scale more accurately reflects the information? Explain.

Record High Temperatures in Western States (°F)

State	Temperature
Alaska	100
Arizona	127
California	134
Colorado	118
Hawaii	100
Idaho	118
Montana	117
Nevada	122
Oregon	119
Utah	116
Washington	118
Wyoming	114

Box and Whisker Plots

OBJECTIVE:
To present data in box and whisker plots.

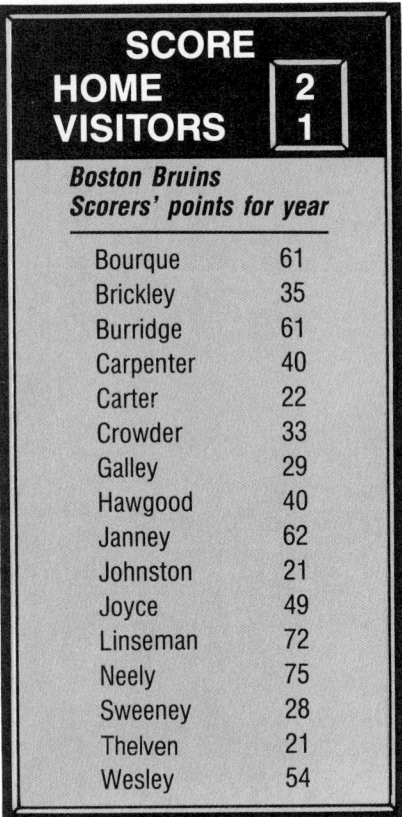

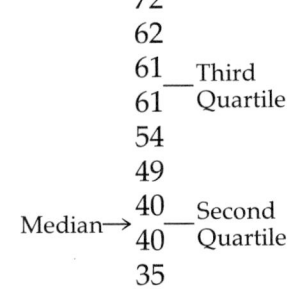

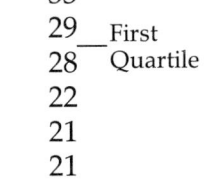

▼ The chart at the left shows the top sixteen scorers for the Boston Bruins during a recent hockey season. You can make a *box and whisker plot* to show the data. A box and whisker plot is especially useful in showing the distribution of data in each *quartile*, that is, in each 25% of the data.

1. Arrange the data in order from least to greatest. Then find the median. For these data, the median is 40.

2. Separate the data into four groups. Find the medians of the lower and upper halves. The median of the lower half is 28.5, and the median of the upper half is 61. These values are the first and third quartiles.

3. Draw a number line to display the data. Mark the number line with the quartile values.

4. Draw a box that extends from the first to the third quartiles. Mark the median with a vertical line across the box. Then draw whiskers from the box to the highest and lowest scores.

```
75
72
62
61 ── Third
61    Quartile
54
49
40 ── Second
40    Quartile
35
33
29 ── First
28    Quartile
22
21
21
```
Median→

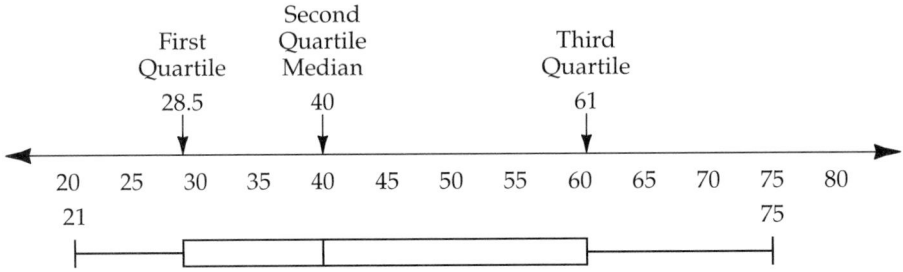

THINK Why aren't the quartiles marked at $\frac{1}{4}$ of the distance on the number line?

▼ Some trends are easy to recognize in a box and whisker plot.

Example 1 Describe the data in the plot below.

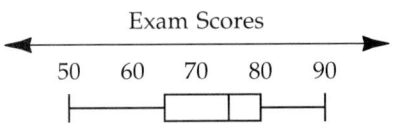

Solution The highest score is 90 and the lowest is 50. Of the scores, 25% are greater than 80 and 25% are less than 65. The plot has a small box indicating that half of the scores are clustered around the median, which is 75.

▼ You can use a box and whisker plot to compare two sets of data, such as scores for teams or individual players.

Example 2 Use the box and whisker plots to compare the leading scores for the Los Angeles Kings and the New York Islanders. What conclusions can you draw?

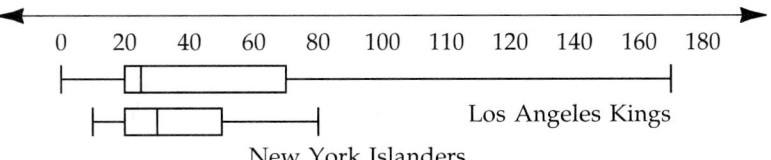

Los Angeles Kings

New York Islanders

Solution The first and second groups for both teams look fairly similar. The New York Islanders have a slightly higher median score. The top half is very different. The Kings have 25% of their scores between 70 and 170. The top 25% for the Islanders is between 50 and 80. The top group shows that the Kings outscore the Islanders by a large margin.

THINK AND DISCUSS

1. Explain how you can find the quartiles for a set of data.

2. Describe a set of data that has a long box and short whiskers.

3. How is a box and whisker plot like a stem and leaf plot? How is it different?

4. Can you tell what the mean, median, and mode of a set of data would be by looking at a box and whisker plot? Explain.

CLASS EXERCISES

Make a box and whisker plot for each set of data.

1. 16, 18, 59, 75, 29, 34, 25, 49, 27, 16, 21, 58, 71, 19, 31, 50

2. 138, 149, 200, 101, 128, 196, 186, 150, 129, 176, 192, 190, 107, 175, 171, 163

Use the box and whisker plot below to answer each question

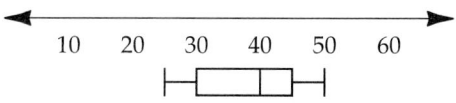

3. What is the median?

4. What percent of the numbers are contained in the box?

5. Are the data evenly distributed? Explain.

Make a box and whisker plot for each set of data. Use a single number line.

6. 1st set: 12, 16, 62, 48, 16, 59, 43, 39
2nd set: 34, 92, 73, 71, 59, 68, 49, 84

7. 1st set: 36, 9, 4, 3, 12, 29, 50, 16, 25, 21
2nd set: 18, 22, 7, 4, 11, 16, 40, 18, 33, 9

1. $29\frac{1}{2}\%$ of 400 is what number?

2. What percent of 48 is 18?

Use the set of test scores: 92, 84, 76, 68, 90, 67, 82, 71, 79, 85, 79.

3. Find the median and range.

4. Find the mean.

5. Find the mode.

6. Make a stem and leaf plot.

Solve.

7. Find $5 \cdot 4 \cdot 3 \cdot 2 \cdot 1$

8. *DATA FILE 12 (pp. 486–487)* Draw a back-to-back stem and leaf plot for the Olympic records for 400-m freestyle swimming. Round the time to the nearest second.

Maximum Speed of Animals for a Quarter Mile (mi/h)

Cheetah	70
Lion	50
Quarter horse	47.5
Coyote	43
Hyena	40
Rabbit	35
Giraffe	32
Grizzly bear	30
Cat (domestic)	30
Man	27.89
Elephant	25
Squirrel	12

WRITTEN EXERCISES

Make a box and whisker plot for each set of data.

1. 4, 6, 9, 4, 5, 12, 16, 21, 38, 5, 2, 27

2. 4, 5, 3, 2, 1, 6, 7, 8, 4, 5, 5, 6, 2, 1, 9, 3

3. 38, 49, 16, 21, 48, 36, 29, 52, 31, 25, 49, 36

4. 47, 19, 98, 16, 25, 38, 55, 49, 86, 79, 15, 91, 57

Use the box and whisker plot to answer each question.

Prices of 20 Walk-around Stereos

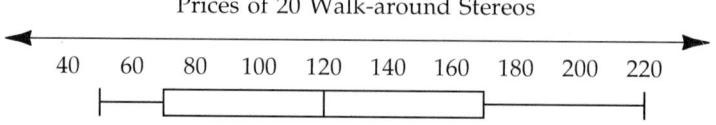

5. What are the highest and lowest prices for stereos?

6. What is a median price for a stereo?

7. What percent of prices are greater than $70?

8. What percent of stereos cost more than $170?

9. Are the data evenly distributed?

WRITE **Make a box and whisker plot for each set of data. Use a single number line. Then write a comparison.**

10. 1st Set: 3, 7, 9, 12, 2, 1, 6, 5, 4, 3, 7, 10, 13, 8, 1, 9
2nd Set: 9, 8, 1, 7, 6, 3, 7, 9, 8, 6, 4, 7, 8, 9, 10, 10

11. 1st Set: 34, 25, 19, 38, 49, 16, 38, 49, 56, 24, 42, 36
2nd Set: 38, 49, 52, 39, 50, 55, 46, 45, 40, 39, 51, 42

12. Use the data at the left to make a box and whisker plot for the maximum speed of animals.

13. **PROJECT** Measure the heights of the students in your class. Make a box and whisker plot of the data, by gender, to compare the heights of male and female students.

14. **WRITE** Make a box and whisker plot for each set of data on a single number line. Compare. Then write your conclusions.

National Hockey League High Scorers

Buffalo Sabres	18, 88, 57, 44, 1, 18, 70, 28, 6, 60, 16, 41, 18, 52, 49, 52, 20, 43, 44, 17
St. Louis Blues	7, 67, 13, 70, 84, 34, 29, 26, 45, 17, 52, 55, 23, 24, 25, 26, 19, 43, 42, 20

15. *DATA FILE 13 (pp. 534–535)* Make a box and whisker plot for the global carbon emissions per person.

16. *PROJECT* Find scores for your two favorite teams for the past season. Make a box and whisker plot for each set of scores on a single number line. Compare. Then write your conclusions about the data.

Use the article below and the chart at the right.

Earthquake!

A scientific journal recently reported that earthquakes can occur even in areas considered stable, far away from the edges of the earth's rigid plates. Stable regions make up about two-thirds of the continental crust.

The journal reported that the most reliable gauge of an earthquake's size is the moment-magnitude scale (M). The moment-magnitude scale is based directly on the physical process in the center of an earthquake.

Earthquakes in Stable Areas

Place	M
New Madrid, 1812	8.3
New Madrid, 1811	8.2
New Madrid, 1812	8.1
Kutch, 1819	7.8
Baffin Bay, 1933	7.7
Taiwan Straits, 1604	7.7
South Carolina, 1886	7.6
Nanai, 1918	7.4
Grand Banks, 1929	7.4
Basel, 1356	7.4

17. What is the mean, median, and mode of the magnitude of the earthquake? Which measure is the most representative?

18. Draw a line plot for the information in the chart.

19. Make a frequency table of the information in the chart.

20. Explain why a box and whisker plot is not helpful in understanding the information in the chart.

TEST YOURSELF

Use the data below for Exercises 1–3.

Average Monthly Temperatures(°F) for Washington, DC

44, 45, 55, 65, 75, 83, 86, 84, 78, 67, 56, 45

1. Find the mean, median, mode, and range.

2. Draw a stem and leaf plot.

3. Draw a box and whisker plot.

Use the data below for each exercise.

3, 2, 5, 7, 2, 4, 3, 1, 2, 5, 3, 4

4. Draw a line plot.

5. Make a frequency table.

OBJECTIVE:
To explore whether a game is fair or unfair.

MATERIALS

- Number cubes
- Spinners
- Counters
- Coins
- Math journal to record work

Exploring Fair and Unfair Games

▼ Playing a game is fun if the game is fair. It helps to analyze the rules of a game to see if each player has an equally likely chance of winning. Read the rules of the game below.

The Good Times and the Bad Times

Players:	Player A and Player B
Materials:	Two number cubes
Rules:	• Players take turns tossing the number cubes and then finding the product of the numbers on the two cubes.
	• If the product of the numbers is even, Player A scores a point. If the product of the numbers is odd, Player B scores a point.
	• The player with the most points at the end of 20 rounds is the winner. A round consists of each player tossing the number cubes once.

---

1. ***Discuss*** Is one player more likely to win the game than the other player? ***Explain***.

2. Choose a partner and play the game four times. Record your results.

3. ***Discuss*** Which player won more games? Based on your results, do you think each player has an equal chance of winning?

4. Make a list or draw a diagram to find all possible outcomes.

   a. How many possible outcomes are there?

   b. In how many ways can a player toss a product that is even? a product that is odd?

5. ***Analyze*** Is the game fair or unfair? ***Explain***.

6. ***Discuss*** How could you change the game to make it fair? Use lists or diagrams to support your conclusions.

7. ***Discuss*** How do other factors, such as the age and experience of the players, contribute to making a contest fair or unfair? Is a game of basketball fair as long as all players play by the same rules? Is a spelling bee always fair?

8. **Analyze** each game. Make a conjecture about whether the game is fair or unfair. Explain your reasoning. Then play each game.

Match or Not

Players: Player A and Player B

Materials: Two counters. One counter with both sides labeled **X** and the other with one side labeled **X** and the other side labeled **Y**.

Rules:
- Each player takes turns tossing the counters.
- If both counters match, Player A gets one point. If the counters do not match, Player B gets the point.
- The first player to get 20 points wins.

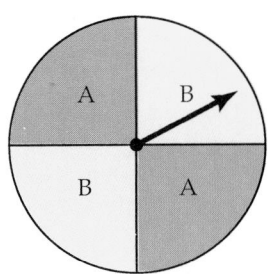

Spin Around

Players: Player A and Player B

Materials: Spinner

Rules:
- Each player spins the spinner twice.
- Player A scores if the spinner lands on the same letter both times. Player B scores if the spinner lands on different letters each time.
- The player with the most points after each player has had 50 spins is the winner.

A Lucky Trio of Coins

Players: Player A and Player B

Materials: Three coins

Rules:
- Each player takes turns tossing three coins.
- If all three coins show tails or all three coins show heads, Player A gets one point. If not, Player B gets the point.
- The player with the most points after 20 tosses is the winner.

9. **Summarize** Which of the three games is the most fair? the most unfair? **Explain**. Support your conclusions with lists or diagrams.

10. **PROJECT** Make up a fair game and an unfair game. Use number cubes, coins, or spinners. Trade with a partner. **Analyze** the rules of each game. Decide which is fair and which is unfair. Play the games to test your conjectures.

Exploring Fair and Unfair Games   **507**

OBJECTIVE:
To calculate the
number of outcomes
generated by a given
event.

12-5 *Counting Principle*

▼ Suppose you can fulfill your English requirement by taking Literature (L), Poetry (P), or Drama (D) first semester and Composition (C), Speech (S), Grammar (G), or Creative Writing (W) second semester. How many different ways can you choose?

You can draw a tree diagram to display the possible choices.

THINK How could you make a tree diagram with the branches spreading down rather than across?

1st Semester	2nd Semester	Possible Choices
	C	LC
L	G	LG
	S	LS
	W	LW
	C	PC
P	G	PG
	S	PS
	W	PW
	C	DC
D	G	DG
	S	DS
	W	DW

▼ You can also use the *counting principle.*

Number of Choices First Semester		Number of Choices Second Semester		Possible Choices
3	×	4	=	12

THINK Could you use the counting principle for more than two events? Explain.

Counting Principle	The number of outcomes for an event with two or more stages equals the product of the number of outcomes at each stage.

▼ You can use the counting principle when you must make choices in an ordered arrangement.

Example 1 Four Olympic gold medalists will pose together for a promotional photograph. How many different ways can they stand side-by-side in the photo?

Solution

1st Position	2nd Position	3rd Position	4th Position
4 choices	3 choices	2 choices	1 choice

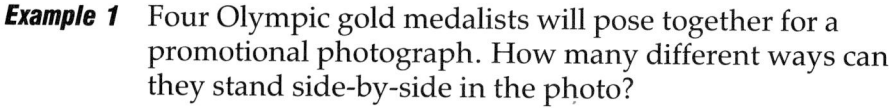
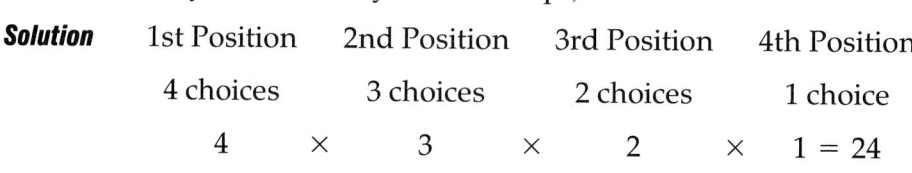

4 × 3 × 2 × 1 = 24

▼ *Factorials* are a mathematical shorthand for situations such as finding the product of numbers in an ordered arrangement.

Example 2   Find the value of 6 factorial.

Solution $6! = 6 \times 5 \times 4 \times 3 \times 2 \times 1 = 720$

Factorial	A factorial is the product of all whole numbers from n to 1. We write this as $n!$

▼
THINK Will 10^n be greater than or less than $n!$?

▼ You can use factorial expressions for products of all whole numbers from n to m, where m is a whole number less than n. Algebraically, this is $n(n - 1)(n - 2)(n - 3) \ldots (m)$.

Example 3   Express $9 \cdot 8 \cdot 7 \cdot 6 \cdot 5$ as a factorial.

Solution $\dfrac{9 \times 8 \times 7 \times 6 \times 5}{1}$ Express as a fraction.

$\dfrac{9 \times 8 \times 7 \times 6 \times 5 \times 4 \times 3 \times 2 \times 1}{4 \times 3 \times 2 \times 1} = \dfrac{9!}{4!}$ Multiply numerator and denominator by $4 \cdot 3 \cdot 2 \cdot 1$.

$9 \cdot 8 \cdot 7 \cdot 6 \cdot 5 = \dfrac{9!}{4!}$

Example 4   Evaluate $\dfrac{10!}{6!}$.

Solution $\dfrac{10!}{6!} = \dfrac{10 \times 9 \times 8 \times 7 \times 6 \times 5 \times 4 \times 3 \times 2 \times 1}{6 \times 5 \times 4 \times 3 \times 2 \times 1}$ Divide common terms.

$\dfrac{10!}{6!} = \dfrac{10 \times 9 \times 8 \times 7}{1}$ Simplify.

$\dfrac{10!}{6!} = 5,040$

CLASS EXERCISES

Find the value of each factorial.

1. $4!$ **2.** $8!$ **3.** $\dfrac{11!}{8!}$ **4.** $\dfrac{22!}{17!}$

Write each expression as a factorial.

5. $5 \cdot 4 \cdot 3 \cdot 2 \cdot 1$ **6.** $12 \cdot 11 \cdot 10 \cdot 9 \cdot 8 \cdot 7$

7. $15 \cdot 14 \cdot 13 \cdot 12$ **8.** $8 \cdot 7 \cdot 6$

Solve. Make a tree diagram to check your answer.

9. There are 6 roads leading from Seymour to Clarksville and 3 roads leading from Clarksville to Belleview. How many possible routes are there from Seymour to Belleview through Clarksville?

▼
THINK AND DISCUSS

1. When is it impractical to make a tree diagram?

2. How is using factorials a modification of the counting principle?

3. Does $6! - 2! = 4!$?

10. A student has 4 blouses and 5 skirts. How many different blouse skirt combinations can she wear?

MIXED REVIEW
Write using scientific notation.

1. 100,000,000,000

2. 0.0001

Use the data to solve the problem: 11, 15, 18, 19, 22, 27, 30, 8, 45.

3. Find the median.

4. Draw a box and whiskers plot for the data.

Simplify.

5. $\frac{9}{27}$ **6.** $\frac{40}{88}$

Solve.

7. A storekeeper marks a $38 sweater 25% off. What is the new price?

WRITTEN EXERCISES

Find the value of each factorial.

1. 5!   **2.** 7!   **3.** 10!   **4.** 2!

5. $\frac{5!}{2!}$ **6.** $\frac{6!}{3!}$ **7.** $\frac{10!}{5!}$ **8.** $\frac{13!}{7!}$

CALCULATOR Find the value of each factorial.

9. 12!   **10.** 8! × 3!   **11.** $\frac{15!}{10!}$ **12.** 9! · 9

MENTAL MATH Find the value of each factorial.

13. $\frac{6!}{5!}$ **14.** $\frac{100!}{99!}$ **15.** $\frac{10!}{8!}$ **16.** 3!

Tell whether each is true or false. If it is false, explain why.

17. 5! × 2! = 5! + 5!   **18.** 5! × 2! = 10!

19. $\frac{12!}{4!} = 3!$ **20.** $\frac{5!}{4!} = 5$

Solve using a tree diagram.

21. There are 3 ways of performing Task A. There are 4 ways of performing Task B. How many ways are there of performing Task A and then Task B?

22. There are 8 roads leading from Marsh to Taft and 5 roads leading from Taft to Polk. How many possible routes are there to take from Marsh to Polk through Taft?

Solve using the counting principle.

23. A student has 5 pairs of pants, 8 shirts, and 2 ties. How many different outfits does he have to choose from? Each pant/shirt/tie combination is considered a different outfit.

24. You can buy a pizza with thin crust or thick crust. You have a choice of six toppings. How many different combinations can you make if you choose one type of crust and one type of topping for your pizza?

25. An automobile manufacturer makes 4 different car styles. Each style comes in 11 different colors. Each car can have 5 different interior styles and automatic or standard transmission. Jamal wishes to order one of each kind of car for his car lot. How many cars must Jamal order?

26. You wish to have your picture taken with 5 friends. In how many ways can you line up for the photograph?

27. There are seven people eligible for three different positions on the student council. Their names have been placed in a paper bag.

    a. How many people are eligible for the first position?

    b. How many people are eligible for the second position once the first has been selected?

    c. How many people are eligible for the third position once the first two have been selected?

    d. In how many ways can three people out of seven be selected for three positions on the student council?

28. *WRITE* a paragraph defining the counting principle. Give an example of a situation that uses the principle to solve a problem.

Use the *DATA* at the right to determine how many different costumes each character could wear in the class play.

29. A hobo must wear a hat, a jacket, and carry a suitcase.

30. A scarecrow must wear a hat, a scarf, and a jacket.

31. The mystery person must wear a hat, a scarf, and carry a suitcase.

Costume Props	
hat	**scarf**
straw	knit
baseball	kerchief
derby	
Jacket	**Suitcase**
denim	satchel
plaid	briefcase
striped	duffel bag
leather	

EXPLORING VISUAL THINKING

1. Look at the three views of a number cube shown below. What number is opposite the number 6?

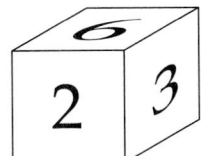 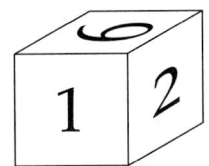 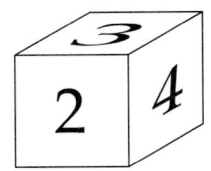

PROBLEM SOLVING HINT
1. Draw a net.
2. A number may be repeated.

2. Look at the cube below. Side A is red, side B is blue, side C is green, and side D is yellow. What color is opposite side A?

OBJECTIVE:
To calculate the
probability of
occurrence of a
given event.

12-6 Probability

▼ Car owners pay insurance premiums to protect against loss or damage. If there is an accident, the insurance company pays damages. Usually the premium is less than the value of the car.

To set the fee, mathematicians use *probability* theory to review past claims payouts and estimate future payouts. Then they use the expected payout to determine insurance rates.

Probability	Probability is the likelihood that a certain *event*, or set of outcomes, will occur. $$P(E) = \frac{\text{number of favorable outcomes}}{\text{total number of possible outcomes}}$$

Sample Space	The set of possible outcomes is the sample space.

THINK How many favorable outcomes are there for the event of tossing an even number?

Example 1 When tossing a number cube, there are six possible outcomes, 1, 2, 3, 4, 5, and 6.

▼ Probability relies on events occurring *randomly*. All outcomes must be equally likely to occur for the calculations to be valid.

Example 2 What is the probability that a letter chosen at random from the word **MISSISSIPPI** is the letter I?

Solution
1. Find the size of the sample space.
   Number of letters → 11
2. Find the number of favorable outcomes.
   Number of I's → 4
3. Find the probability.
   $P(I) = \dfrac{\text{Number of I's}}{\text{Number of letters}} = \dfrac{4}{11}$

The probability of choosing the letter I is $\frac{4}{11}$.

NOTES & QUOTES

In the small number of things we are able to know with any certainty, the principal means of ascertaining truth are based on probabilities.
—Pierre Simon de Laplace
(1749–1827)

▼ You can find the probability for more than one favorable outcome.

Example 3 You draw a card at random from a hat containing cards numbered 1–6. Find the probability that the card is even.

Solution
1. Find the size of the sample space.
   Cards → 6
2. Find the favorable outcomes for the event.
   Even cards, (2, 4, 6) → 3.
3. Find the probability.
   $P(\text{even}) = \dfrac{\text{Even cards}}{\text{All cards}} = \dfrac{3}{6} = \dfrac{1}{2}.$

The probability of drawing an even card is $\frac{1}{2}$.

▼ You can determine the probability of an event *not* occurring.

Example 4   There are 3 blue marbles, 2 yellow marbles, and 4 red marbles in a bag. What is the probability that a marble chosen at random is *not* a red marble?

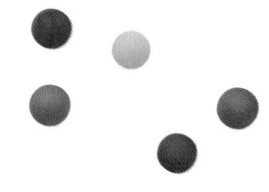

Solution   **1.** Find the size of the sample space.   Number of marbles → 9

2. Find the favorable outcomes.   Number of not red marbles → 5

3. Find the probability. $P(\text{not red}) = \dfrac{\text{not red}}{\text{all marbles}} = \dfrac{5}{9}$

The probability of *not* drawing a red marble is $\frac{5}{9}$.

▼ **THINK** The probability of getting a red marble is $\frac{4}{9}$. Why is $P(\text{not red}) = 1 - P(\text{red})$?

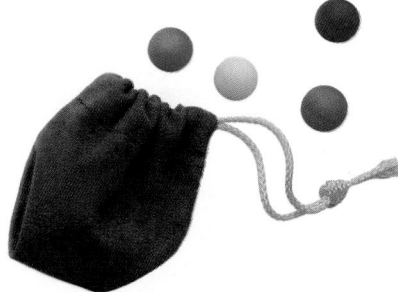

CLASS EXERCISES

Use the word ARKANSAS to answer each question.

1. You wish to know the probability of selecting the letter A.

   a. What is the number of possible outcomes in the sample space for selecting the letter A?

   b. What is the number of favorable outcomes for the event of selecting the letter A?

   c. What is the probability of selecting the letter A?

   d. What is the probability of *not* selecting the letter A?

2. What is the probability of selecting a vowel?

3. What is the probability of selecting the letter C?

Find each sample space.

4. choosing a Monday from all the days of the week

5. choosing the letter X from all the letters in the alphabet

Find each probability.

6. What is the probability that a digit selected at random from the number 364,892 is a multiple of 3?

7. A math class has 10 boys and 15 girls. What is the probability that a student chosen at random is a girl?

8. In a class of 24 students, 8 are saving to buy a camera. What is the probability that a randomly selected student is *not* saving to buy a camera?

9. Find the probability that a student chosen at random from your math class has blue eyes.

▼ **THINK AND DISCUSS**

1. What is the probability of an event that is certain to occur? Give an example of such an event.

2. What is the probability of an event that is impossible? Give an example of such an event.

3. Can a probability be greater than 1? Explain.

4. Can a probability be less than 0? Explain.

WRITTEN EXERCISES

Find the probability of each event.

1. that a digit selected at random from the number 164,743 is a multiple of 2

2. that a randomly chosen month has 30 days

Find each probability when a letter is chosen at random from the word MATHEMATICS.

3. choosing a consonant   4. choosing the letter M

5. choosing a letter that occurs more than once

6. choosing the letter K.

Find each probability.

7. What is the probability that a state selected at random from a list of the 50 United States begins with the letter M?

8. A lab class has 8 boys and 10 girls. What is the probability that a student chosen at random is a boy?

9. Students in a class were asked to name their preferred type of motor vehicle. Eight students preferred a pickup, 12 preferred a sports car, and eight preferred a convertible. What is the probability that a randomly selected student preferred a sports car?

10. What is the probability that any letter of the alphabet is not included in the sentence "*The quick brown fox jumps over the lazy dog*"?

11. There are 14 boys and 12 girls in a math class. There are 60 boys and 65 girls in the freshman class. In the school there are 375 boys and 360 girls. Find the probability that a female student is chosen at random.

    a. from the math class

    b. from the freshman class

    c. from the school

    d. Are the answers for (a), (b), and (c) different? Why or why not?

12. Find the probability of each event when a day of the week is chosen at random.

    a. a day of the week has six letters

    b. the day of the week has more than six letters

    c. What is the sum of the answers to parts (a) and (b)? Explain.

13. Find the probability of each event when a prime number less than 100 is chosen.

   a. It has one digit.   **b.** It has more than one digit.

   c. Why is the sum of parts (a) and (b) equal to 1?

14. The figure at the right illustrates a pattern of floor tiling. You drop a coin onto this portion of the floor tile. Find the probability for each event.

   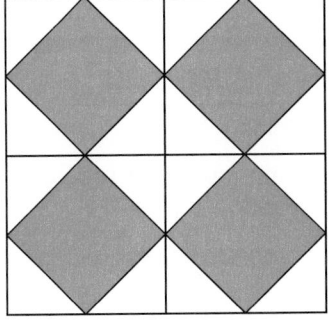

   a. The coin lands on a red tile.   **b.** The coin lands on a white tile.

15. A group of students was polled to find out their favorite sports. Four of the students chose skiing, eight chose baseball, ten chose basketball, four chose football, and two chose track. Find the probability of a randomly chosen student preferring each event.

   a. skiing   **b.** baseball   **c.** basketball

   d. football   **e.** track

   f. What is the sum of the five probabilities? Explain.

16. A set of flash cards is numbered from 1 to 36. A card is chosen at random. Find the probability for each event.

   a. an even number   **b.** a multiple of 3

   c. a multiple of both 2 and 3   **d.** a multiple of 2 or 3

   e. a prime number   **f.** a square number

17. A number is chosen at random. Find the probability of the last digit of its square being each number listed below.

   a. 1   **b.** 4   **c.** 5   **d.** 6   **e.** 9

   f. Why is the sum of these answers not equal to 1?

18. **PROJECT** What is the probability that a coin will land with the head face up? Record your answer.

   a. Toss a coin 100 times. Record the number of times the coin lands face up. Find the probability of the coin landing face up.

   b. Do the results of tossing the coin agree with the probability you expected? Why do you think there might be a difference?

Use the DATA at the right to solve.

19. What is the size of the sample space if each style comes in each color?

20. What is the probability of choosing a blue sweater at random?

21. What is the probability of choosing a sweater vest at random?

22. **WRITE** Suppose you have a bag containing an equal number of nickels, dimes, and quarters. Suppose you reach into the bag and choose a coin. Is it equally likely that you will pick a dime or a quarter? Explain.

Sweaters	
Color	*Style*
Blue	Cardigan
Pink	Pullover
Red	Vest
Brown	
Black	

OBJECTIVE:
To explore probabilities using Pascal's triangle.

MATERIALS

- Coins

- Math journal to record work

Exploring Pascal's Triangle

■ In probability problems where the underlying experiment has two equally likely outcomes, you can often find solutions using Pascal's triangle.

Problem If three fair coins are tossed, what is the probability of obtaining exactly two heads?

Plan You need to list all possible outcomes and count them to find the denominator. You need to identify the successful outcomes and count them to find the numerator. Then put these numbers into a fraction to write the probability.

$$P = \frac{\text{number of successful outcomes}}{\text{total number of outcomes}}$$

■ Suppose you have a penny, a nickel, and a dime. How can you list all possible outcomes?

1. List the set of all possible outcomes as ordered triples (a, b, c) where a is the outcome of the penny, b the nickel, and c the dime.

   (H,H,H), (H,H,T), (H,T,H), (H,T,T), (T,H,H), (T,H,T), (T,T,H), (T,T,T)

   There are eight possible outcomes.

2. Make a tree diagram in which you consider the outcomes one coin at a time.

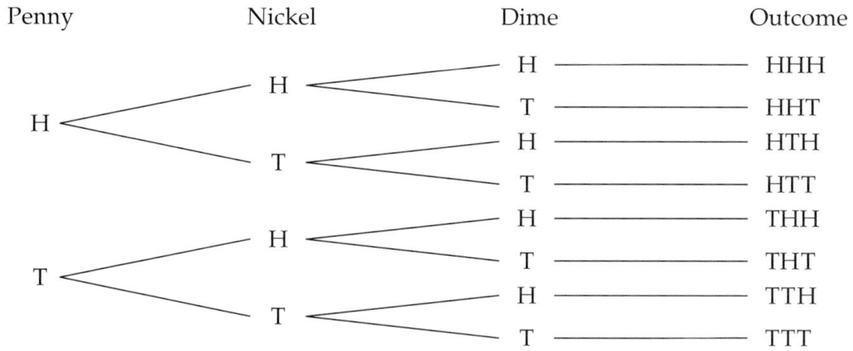

Penny	Nickel	Dime	Outcome
H	H	H	HHH
		T	HHT
	T	H	HTH
		T	HTT
T	H	H	THH
		T	THT
	T	H	TTH
		T	TTT

3. Identify the successful outcomes: HHT, HTH, THH.

4. Write the probability: $P(\text{two heads}) = \frac{3}{8}$.

5. Compare Row 3 in Pascal's triangle with the results of the coin tossing problem.

Row 0					1			
Row 1				1		1		
Row 2			1		2		1	
Row 3		1		3		3		1
Row 4	1		4		6		4		1

6. Find the sum of the numbers in Row 3.

7. How does the sum compare with the total number of outcomes in the coin-tossing problem?

8. Look back at the list of outcomes for tossing three coins. In how many outcomes were there exactly zero heads? Notice that the first number in Row 3 is 1.

9. Look at the list of outcomes for tossing three coins. In how many outcomes were there exactly 1 head? Notice that the second number in Row 3 is 3. We know that there were 3 outcomes with exactly 2 heads. The third number in Row 3 is 3.

10. In how many outcomes were there exactly 3 heads? The fourth number in Row 3 is 1.

■ The numbers in Row 3 of Pascal's triangle tell how many of the possible outcomes in tossing three coins represent exactly 0, 1, 2, or 3 heads.

Use Row 4 of Pascal's triangle to answer each question. Check your results by listing the possible outcomes of the experiment.

11. How many possible outcomes are there for the experiment consisting of tossing four different coins?

12. In how many ways can you obtain exactly 0, 1, 2, 3, or 4 heads?

13. What is the probability of obtaining exactly 2 heads when tossing four coins?

14. What is the probability of obtaining exactly 3 heads when tossing four coins?

15. What is the probability of obtaining exactly 3 tails when tossing four coins?

16. In a family of four children, what is the probability that all four children are girls? *Hint:* There are two equally likely outcomes at the birth of each child, so the situation has the same mathematical structure as flipping a coin.

17. In a family of five children, what is the probability that exactly two of the children are boys?

18. **Write** a similar problem. Trade with a classmate and solve each other's problem.

PROBLEM SOLVING HINT
Extend Pascal's triangle to Row 5.

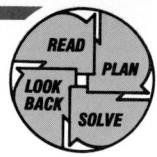

12-7 Simulate the Problem

Dr. Grace Yang is
a statistics professor
at the University of
Maryland. She
received her Ph.D.
degree in 1966
from the University
of California at Berkeley.
Dr. Yang believes it is
important for girls to do
well in mathematics. "If
young women don't
continue taking math
courses in high school, by
the time they enter college
their choice of fields will be
very much restricted."

■ You can solve many probability problems using a *Monte Carlo simulation*. Monte Carlo methods make it possible to model a situation for which a test is impractical and probability formulas are cumbersome. Use the steps below to develop a model.

1. Assign success to one outcome and failure to another.
2. Choose a random device, such as number cubes or a spinner.
3. Determine the probability of the outcome of one trial.
4. Decide the definition of a trial.
5. Perform a sufficient number of trials.
6. Compute the simulated probability $\dfrac{\text{number of successful trials}}{\text{number of trials}}$.

PROBLEM

You have been given a quiz written in ancient Sanskrit. You are expected to match five words with their definitions. What is the probability that you will get 1 out of 5 answers correct?

SOLUTION

READ ▷ What do you want to find? — the probability that you will get 1 out of 5 answers correct

PLAN ▷ Decide on a strategy. — Use a Monte Carlo simulation.

What random device can you use to simulate the problem? — Use a set of cards with the letters a, b, c, d, and e to represent the words. Use a second set of cards with A, B, C, D, and E to represent the definitions.

What is a *successful* outcome? — obtaining two or more correct answers by matching upper and lowercase letters

What is the probability of a match on each draw? — Each probability is $\frac{1}{5}$.

What will represent one *trial*? — drawing five pairs of cards, one card from each pile

SOLVE ▷ How many trials are sufficient? — at least 100 trials

Tally the results. — One student completed 19 successes out of 100 trials.

Give the expected probability. — $\dfrac{19}{100} = \dfrac{\text{number of successes}}{\text{number of trials}}$

LOOK BACK ▷ Did you solve the problem? — The probability is estimated to be $\frac{19}{100}$.

CLASS EXERCISES

1. Perform the experiment.

   a. Compare your results with those in the example.

   b. Why do you think the results of your experiment might differ from those of the student in the example?

2. Repeat the experiment to find the probability of getting two correct answers for each of these matching quizzes in Sanskrit.

   a. a 4-word quiz   **b.** a 6-word quiz

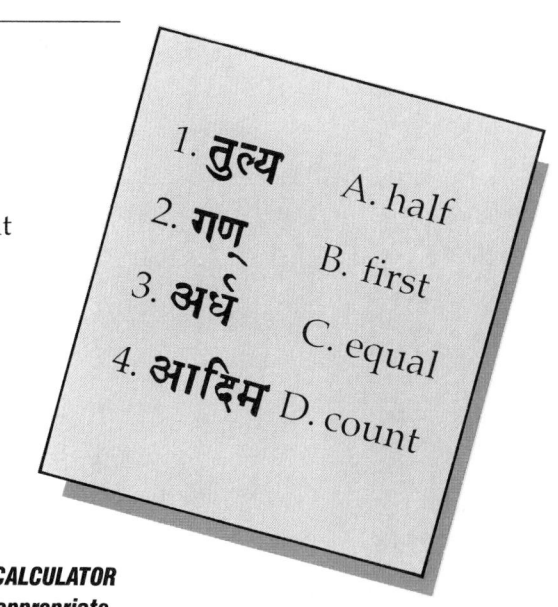

1. तुल्य   A. half
2. गण्   B. first
3. अर्ध   C. equal
4. आदिम   D. count

WRITTEN EXERCISES

 **Use a CALCULATOR where appropriate.**

Solve by simulating the problem.

1. Suppose you take a true-false test. You don't know the answers to any of the ten questions. What is the probability you will get 7 out of 10 correct?

   a. Model the situation using a coin. Let heads represent a true statement and tails represent a false statement.

   b. Let another student prepare an *answer key* by tossing the coin ten times and recording each *correct answer*.

   c. A trial occurs when you toss the coin ten times to represent the ten questions on the quiz. A successful trial occurs when you get seven or more answers that match the *answer key*.

   d. You need to try about 100 trials.

   e. Write the probability: $\frac{\text{number of successful trials}}{\text{number of trials}}$.

2. Suppose you take a ten-question multiple-choice test. Each question has four choices. You don't know any of the answers.

   a. What is the probability you will get 7 out of 10 correct? Model the situation using a spinner with four equal sections.

   b. Compare your answer with Exercise 1. Explain why it is different.

   c. What is the probability you will get 4 out of 10 correct?

Solve using any strategy.

3. What is the probability that exactly three children in a family of five children will be boys?

4. What is the probability that exactly two children in a family of six children will be girls?

5. Thirteen of 25 students are going on a field trip. Six students are traveling in a van. What is the probability that a student chosen at random is *not* traveling in a van?

6. What is the probability that a student will draw a card at random showing A or B from these cards?

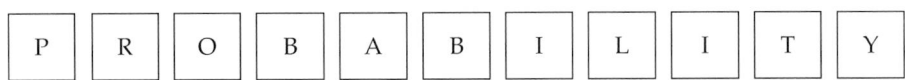

| P | R | O | B | A | B | I | L | I | T | Y |

7. A student is going to choose a date from the month of January at random. What is the probability that the student will choose January 1?

8. Suppose you toss three coins. What is the probability that all the coins will land heads up?

9. A student has a mean of 92 for two quizzes. What grade does the student need on the next quiz to have a mean of 94?

10. A student tells you that she receives an average salary of $3.50/h. Her manager tells you he pays an average of $4/h. The chain they work for says the pay averages $4.75/h. Explain how they could all be telling the truth.

11. A store advertises a jacket for $72. During a sale the store reduces the jacket price by 25%. After the sale, the store raises the jacket price by 25%. What is the price of the jacket after the sale?

12. The sum of five consecutive numbers is 380. What are the numbers?

13. Double a number minus half the number is five minus the number. What is the number?

14. A student uses 24 yd of fencing to make a rectangular pen. The pen is 6 yd longer than it is wide. What are the dimensions of the pen?

15. The circumference of the peg below is 3 in. Will the peg go through the hole? Explain.

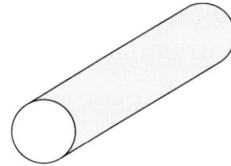
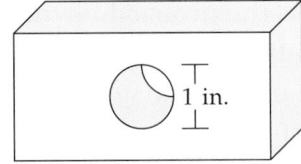

1 in.

16. The average American generates 3.5 lb of waste per day. Of all waste, about 6.5% is plastic. About how much plastic waste does the average American generate each day? each year?

17. In a recent year, the number of major trash composting projects in the United States rose from 42 to 75. Find the percent of change.

Practice

Find the mean, median, mode, and range for each set of data.

1. 6, 7, 8, 7, 6, 15, 24, 36, 28, 26, 18, 11
2. 1, 2, 5, 6, 7, 3, 8, 9, 1, 1, 2, 9, 8, 7, 6
3. 2, 5, 6, 5, 4, 2, 1, 4, 4, 7, 2, 4, 3, 7

Draw a line plot and make a frequency table for each set of data. Find the mean, the median, and the mode.

4. 11, 12, 13, 15, 11, 12, 14, 10, 28
5. 6, 5, 6, 5, 6, 2, 8, 0, 0, 0, 1, 6
6. 20, 30, 40, 50, 20, 30, 20, 50, 60, 10, 20

Make a back-to-back stem and leaf plot for each set of data. Find the median and the mode.

7. Set A: 23, 24, 25, 26, 23, 22   Set B: 19, 22, 25, 26, 17, 23, 21
8. Set C: 45, 46, 50, 51, 48, 49   Set D: 52, 53, 52, 54, 50, 51, 52

Make a box and whisker plot for each set of data. Use a single number line. Then compare.

9. Set A: 2, 4, 6, 1, 2, 3, 4, 12, 15, 10, 10, 8
   Set B: 8, 9, 10, 7, 10, 8, 8, 7, 10, 9, 11, 11
10. Set C: 30, 40, 50, 20, 30, 70, 80, 100, 60, 50, 50, 60
    Set D: 15, 25, 75, 75, 15, 35, 45, 65, 75, 25, 25, 45

Write each expression as a factorial.

11. $4 \cdot 3 \cdot 2 \cdot 1$ 12. $9 \cdot 8 \cdot 7 \cdot 6$
13. $25 \cdot 24 \cdot 23$ 14. $100 \cdot 99 \cdot 98 \cdot 97$

Evaluate.

15. $\frac{10!}{7!}$ 16. $\frac{7!}{4!}$ 17. $\frac{50!}{48!}$

Use the counting principle to solve.

18. A student has 3 clean shirts, 4 clean pairs of socks, and 2 clean pairs of pants. How many different outfits can he wear?

Find the probability of each event when a letter is chosen at random from the word BEEKEEPER.

19. selecting the letter K   20. selecting the letter E
21. selecting a consonant   22. selecting a vowel
23. selecting a letter of the English alphabet
24. selecting a number.

12-8 Independent and Dependent Events

OBJECTIVE:
To calculate probabilities of independent and dependent events.

▼ Some events are a combination of two or more single events. A trip from New York to Seattle via Chicago is actually a combination of two trips: one from New York to Chicago and one from Chicago to Seattle. We call this a *compound event*.

Compound Event	A compound event is a combination of two or more events.

▼ A compound event can be a combination of *independent events*.

Independent Events	Independent events are events in which the outcome of one has no effect on the outcome of the other. For two independent events A and B, $$P(A \text{ and } B) = P(A) \cdot P(B).$$

FLASHBACK

You can use a tree diagram to find a sample space.

Example 1   A student can walk, take the bus, or ride to school with a friend. After school, he can walk or ride with a friend to the library. The student is equally likely to make any of these choices. What is the probability that he will walk to school and then ride with a friend to the library after school?

Solution   *Method 1.* Find the probability of two independent events using the counting principle.

Ways to School   Ways to Library   Possible Outcomes
          3   ×   2   =   6

Favorable outcome, write the probability as:

$$\frac{\text{favorable outcome}}{\text{possible outcomes}} = \frac{1}{6}.$$

Method 2. Find the probability of two independent events using the formula.

$$P(\text{Walk}) = \frac{1}{3} \qquad P(\text{Car}) = \frac{1}{2}$$

$$P(\text{Walk, Car}) = \frac{1}{3} \times \frac{1}{2}$$

$$= \frac{1}{6}$$

The probability of walking to school and then riding to the library with a friend after school is $\frac{1}{6}$.

▼ A compound event can be a combination of *dependent events*.

Dependent Events	Dependent events are events in which the outcome of one depends on the outcome of the other.
	For two dependent events A and B, where B is dependent on A,
	$$P(A \text{ and } B) = P(A) \cdot P(B, \text{ given } A).$$

THINK How are dependent events different from independent events?

Example 2 Three girls and two boys are running for class president and vice president. Slips of paper with the five names are put into a bag. The first name drawn from the bag will be president. The second will be vice president. What is the probability that both officers will be girls?

Solution $P(\text{Girl}) = \frac{3}{5}$ First draw.

$P(\text{Girl}) = \frac{2}{4} = \frac{1}{2}$ Second draw. Assume a girl has been chosen on the first draw. There are 4 names left, so 4 is the number of possible outcomes.

$\frac{3}{5} \times \frac{1}{2} = \frac{3}{10}$ Multiply the probabilities.

The probability that both officers will be girls is $\frac{3}{10}$.

CLASS EXERCISES

Are the events independent or dependent? Explain.

1. You select a card. Without putting the card back, you select a second card.

2. You select a card. After putting it back, you select a second card.

3. You roll a number cube. You roll it again.

4. Cards numbered 5, 5, 3, 7, and 4 are placed face down on a table.

    a. What is the probability that you select a 5 at random?

    b. You do not replace the 5. What is the probability that your next selection is a 4?

    c. You put the cards back on the table before making a second selection. What is the probability of selecting a 5, then a 4?

5. A student has 5 blue socks and 4 orange socks. Find the probability that she will randomly select these items.

    a. a blue sock, then an orange sock   **b.** two blue socks

    c. an orange sock, then a blue sock   **d.** two orange socks

THINK AND DISCUSS

1. Explain why you can multiply probabilities for two independent or two dependent events.

2. When computing the probability of dependent events, how does the probability of the second event show that the events are dependent?

12-8 Independent and Dependent Events

6. A caterer is serving sandwiches from a tray containing 3 chicken, 2 cheese, and 2 peanut butter sandwiches. What is the probability that she will randomly serve the following sandwiches?

  a. 2 chicken sandwiches

  b. a cheese sandwich, then a peanut butter sandwich

  c. a chicken sandwich, a cheese sandwich, then another chicken sandwich

WRITTEN EXERCISES

Are the events independent or dependent? Explain.

1. Two number cubes are thrown. The result on one is 3 and on the other is 5.

2. It has rained for the last three Saturdays. Rain is forecast for next Saturday.

3. You exercise daily. You make the tennis team.

4. You choose a white marble from a bag and do not put it back. You choose again and get another white marble.

For each exercise, assume that events A and B are independent. Then find P(A and B).

5. $P(A) = \frac{1}{2}$, and $P(B) = \frac{1}{5}$.

6. $P(A) = \frac{1}{3}$, and $P(B) = \frac{2}{7}$.

7. $P(A) = \frac{2}{9}$, and $P(B) = \frac{3}{8}$.

8. $P(A) = \frac{7}{16}$, and $P(B) = \frac{8}{35}$.

Tell whether each problem involves dependent or independent events. Then find the probability.

9. A refrigerator contains 12 orange drinks, 4 grape drinks, and 25 apple drinks. Ann is first in line. Mark is second. What is the probability that Ann gets an apple drink and Mark a grape drink if they choose their drinks at random?

10. Suppose you roll a number cube twice. What is the probability that you will roll each of the following pairs of numbers?

  a. 6, then 5   **b.** 6, then 6   **c.** 4, then 3, then 1

11. A student's wallet contains three one-dollar bills, two five-dollar bills, and three ten-dollar bills. The student selects two bills from her wallet at random. What is the probability that the student selects these bills?

  a. a one-dollar bill, then a ten-dollar bill

  b. a ten-dollar bill, then a five-dollar bill

MIXED REVIEW

Find each answer.

1. $\frac{1}{2}$ of 390

2. $\frac{3}{4}$ of 176

Find the probability for each outcome.

3. a coin landing face up

4. rolling a 6 on a number cube

Write an expression.

5. 48 times a number

6. 29 times a number less 5

Solve.

7. A student's age is three times that of her brother. In 15 years, her brother's age will be $\frac{2}{3}$ her age. How old is each now?

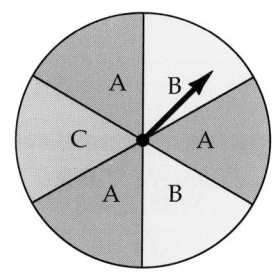

12. Suppose you spin a spinner like the one at the right. What is the probability that you get each outcome?

a. C, then A

b. B, then C, then A

Use the *DATA* at the right.

13. How many students were in the survey? Would a sample be an appropriate way to measure preference in this case? Why or why not?

14. What is the probability that a student selected at random from the class prefers pizza?

15. What is the probability that a boy prefers pizza?

16. What is the probability that a girl does not prefer pizza?

Votes for Class Party

	Barbecue	Pizza	Total
Boys	6	4	10
Girls	9	5	14

17. *PROJECT* Choose a topic from the list below or one of your own and conduct an opinion poll. Survey at least 30 people.

- quality of cafeteria food
- curfew times for 9th graders
- study habits

a. Record the frequency of each response in a table.

b. Find the probability for each response (outcome).

c. *WRITE* three problems based on your poll. Trade with a friend. Solve each other's problem.

TEST YOURSELF

Make a stem and leaf plot for the data. Find the mean, median, and mode.

1. 33, 35, 32, 28, 28, 21, 27, 35, 39, 40, 22, 24

Solve.

2. From Compt there are 4 ways to get to Murch. From Murch there are 5 ways to get to Toll. How many ways are there from Compt to Toll through Murch?

3. You roll a number cube. What is the probability of rolling a 4 and then rolling another 4?

4. You have 12 socks in a drawer and choose 2 at random. Five socks are blue, three brown, and four black. What is the probability that you choose a black sock and then choose a brown one?

Problem Solving Practice

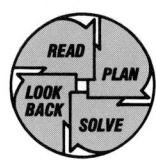

PROBLEM SOLVING STRATEGIES

Look for a Pattern
Guess and Test
Simplify the Problem
Account for All Possibilities
Make an Organized List
Work Backwards
Make a Table
Write an Equation
Solve by Graphing
Draw a Diagram
Make a Model
Simulate the Problem

Solve. Use an appropriate strategy or combination of strategies.

1. A slope of $\frac{1}{10}$ is suitable for a ramp to allow wheelchair access to a building. How far from a doorway will a ramp extend if the doorway is $10\frac{1}{2}$ ft above the ground?

2. The sales tax on an item costing $23.50 is $1.88. What is the sales tax on an item costing $47?

3. A student has a coordinated wardrobe consisting of four blouses, two sweaters, and three skirts. How many three-piece outfits can she make?

4. In a collection of dimes and nickels, there are 9 more nickels than dimes. The collection is worth $1.65. How many nickels and dimes are there?

5. A classroom is 15 ft high. Its floor has an area of 642 ft². Each student needs 300 ft³ of air. How many students can be assigned to the room?

6. The number of calls to a weather information number for fifteen consecutive days was 79, 75, 84, 103, 129, 95, 89, 114, 128, 112, 115, 105, 120, 127, and 101.

   a. Find the median number of calls.

   b. Draw a stem and leaf plot.

   c. What must the number of calls be for the next day to change the median to 107?

7. The sum of two numbers is 11. Twice the greater subtracted from 3 times the lesser equals 3. What are the numbers?

8. A couple pays a babysitter $4.75/h plus $5 taxi fare and expenses. What is the greatest whole number of hours the babysitter can work and still receive less than $25?

9. The mean score of four bowlers is 140. Three scores are the same. The third is twice that of the fourth. Find the scores.

10. Two salespeople drove a distance of 600 mi in one day. The first salesperson drove at least 40 mi more than twice the distance driven by the second. What is the greatest distance that the second salesperson might have driven?

11. A band director wished to arrange the band members in pairs for a marching pattern. He found that he was one person short. He tried to arrange by fives and sevens and was still one person short. What is the least number of people in the marching band?

OBJECTIVE:
To apply capture/ recapture methods to wildlife management.

12-9 *Making Predictions*

Many species of wildlife in the United States have become extinct, including the North Carolina parakeet, the passenger pigeon, and the California grizzly bear. The increased number of wildlife in danger of becoming extinct is a concern for environmentalists.

Capture/recapture is a method for estimating a total population from a sample. Researchers capture, tag, and set free animals of a certain type. At a later time, animals in the same species are recaptured. You can use the following formula to estimate the number of animals in the total population.

$$\frac{\text{tagged animals}}{\text{total population}} = \frac{\text{tagged animals recaptured}}{\text{total animals recaptured}}$$

Example National park rangers wish to know the number of coyotes in a certain section of the Yellowstone National Park. Park rangers capture, tag, and set free 24 coyotes. Two weeks later, rangers capture 38 coyotes. Eight of the coyotes have tags. Estimate the number of coyotes in the section of the park surveyed.

Solution $\dfrac{\text{tagged animals}}{\text{total population}} = \dfrac{\text{tagged animals recaptured}}{\text{total animals recaptured}}$

$\dfrac{24}{n} = \dfrac{8}{38}$ Substitute values in the formula.

$8n = 912$ Write cross products.
$n = 114$

The estimated number of coyotes is 114.

CLASS EXERCISES

Solve.

1. A naturalist and his assistants capture, tag, and set free 32 spotted deer. A week later the scientists capture 45 deer. Twelve have tags.

   a. What is the ratio of tagged animals originally captured to the number of animals in the total population (*n*)?

   b. What is the ratio of tagged animals recaptured to the total number of animals recaptured?

   c. Estimate the total population of spotted deer.

WRITTEN EXERCISES

Solve.

1. In a study of catfish in Beaver Lake, workers for the state extension service caught, tagged, and set free 124 catfish. A few weeks later the workers caught 140 catfish. Thirty-five had tags. Estimate the number of catfish in the lake.

2. There are an unknown number of marbles in a bag. You take 10 marbles out and mark them. You put the marked marbles back into the bag and mix the contents well. You take out 25 marbles. Five of them are marked. Estimate the number of marbles in the bag.

3. You are in a large city. You wish to estimate the number of yellow cabs. You count 75 yellow cabs and you keep track of their license numbers. The next day you count 84 cabs, 20 of which are repeats. Estimate the number of yellow cabs.

4. The ecology class is helping the local conservation society to determine the number of raccoons in a nearby forest. In early October, the students and society members captured, tagged, and set free 68 raccoons. Three weeks later, 84 raccoons were captured, and 16 had tags. Estimate the number of raccoons in the forest.

■■■■■■■ Decision Making ■ **DECISION MAKING** ■ Decision Making ■ Decision Making ■ Decision Making ■

MAKING PREDICTIONS

■ **COLLECT DATA**

The school bookstore plans to stock sweatshirts, hats, and jackets. It is important not to overstock. The store manager asks you to determine the number, color, and size of each item to order.

1. Write a survey questionnaire to find out student interest. Design the questionnaire so that you can estimate the sales by color and size of each item.

2. Who will you survey? Will a random survey suit your purposes or will selecting survey groups from each grade level be a more accurate method of determining your market?

3. Where will you conduct the survey? Will verbal responses be as helpful as written responses?

4. Conduct the survey.

Use the *DATA* below and at the right to solve.

5. The ecology class designed a T-shirt to sell to students as a fund-raiser. The profits are to go to the local conservation society. To determine the number of shirts to order, the class conducted a marketing survey. The results are on the chart at the right. The formula the class used to determine the expected sales is

$$\frac{\text{expected sales}}{\text{total in target group}} = \frac{\text{number of yes responses}}{\text{number of students surveyed}}.$$

One hundred fifty students were surveyed. The target group was the entire school population of 2,000 students.

Yes Responses to Marketing Survey for T-shirts	
small	18
medium	30
large	45

a. What are the expected sales for the small T-shirt?

b. What are the expected sales for the medium T-shirt?

c. What are the expected sales for the large T-shirt?

d. The class did not want to order more T-shirts than they could actually sell. The group decided to order only 80% of the expected sales found in the survey. How many T-shirts in each size did the ecology class order?

e. The amount of money the club makes on each shirt is $1.25. How much money will the ecology club give to the conservation society if the club sells all of the T-shirts ordered?

■ *Decision Making* ■ *Decision Making* ■ *Decision Making* ■ *Decision Making* ■ *Decision Making* ■ *Decision Making* ■

■ **ANALYZE DATA**

5. Calculate the number of expected sales for each item by color and size.

6. In collecting data, was interest expressed in items not on your list? Do you need to expand your choices and do another survey?

■ **MAKE DECISIONS**

7. Decide if you will order exactly the number of items you have found to be your expected sales. Should you order more? less? Explain your decision.

8. Contact a supplier to find the wholesale cost of each item. Determine what price you will set for each item.

9. Present your results to the school bookstore or to some other group for a fund-raising project.

Chapter 12 Review

Write _true_ or _false_. If false, change the underlined word(s) to make the statement true.

1. The <u>median</u> is the number that occurs most often in a set of data.

2. A <u>box and whisker plot</u> is useful in showing the distribution of data by quartiles.

3. A <u>line plot</u> shows data on a number line.

4. <u>Dependent</u> events are events in which the outcome of one has no effect on the outcome of the other.

5. A <u>multiple</u>, written as $n!$, is the product of all whole numbers from n to 1.

Finding Mean, Median, and Mode   12-1

In a set of data,

The _mode_ is the number that occurs most often.

The _mean_ is the sum of n numbers divided by n.

The _median_ is the middle value.

To find the _range_, subtract the least value from the greatest value.

Find the mean, median, mode, and range of each of the following.

6. 5, 7, 9, 6, 7, 8, 6, 8, 9, 7, 8, 9, 8

7. 128, 111, 102, 107, 115, 125, 98, 135, 119

Making Line Plots and Frequency Tables   12-2

To make a line plot, use a number line.

To make a frequency distribution, make a table.

Data: 1, 0, 3, 3, 2, 1, 4, 4, 5, 7, 2, 3

```
              X
      X X X X
    X X X X X X      X
    ←─────────────────────→
    0 1 2 3 4 5 6 7
         Line plot
```

n	0	1	2	3	4	5	6	7
f	1	2	2	3	2	1	0	1

Frequency distribution

Draw a line plot and a frequency distribution for the following.

8. 8, 4, 5, 1, 8, 4, 7, 9, 10, 5, 0, 5, 3, 4, 2

Making a Stem and Leaf Plot and a Box and Whisker Plot

To make a stem and leaf plot, arrange the data along a stem using any reasonable choice of place value.

To make a box and whisker plot, separate the data into four groups by finding the median and the medians of the upper and lower sections of data. Draw a box to extend from the first to the third quartiles. Draw whiskers from the box to the highest and lowest scores.

Data: 70, 65, 72, 83, 85, 78, 85, 78, 82, 74, 68, 76

6	5 8
7	0 2 4 6 8 8
8	2 3 5 5

Stem and Leaf Plot

65   70   75   80   85

Box and Whisker Plot

Make a stem and leaf plot and a box and whisker plot for the following.

9. 75, 70, 80, 85, 85, 55, 60, 60, 65, 85, 75, 95, 50, 55, 75, 80, 65, 75

Using the Counting Principle

Use the counting principle to find the number of outcomes for two or more events. Find the product of the outcomes for each event.

Use factorials when the number of outcomes must be in an ordered arrangement.

$$\text{five factorial} \rightarrow 5! = 5 \cdot 4 \cdot 3 \cdot 2 \cdot 1$$

Find the value of each factorial.

10. $3!$ **11.** $7!$ **12.** $\frac{4!}{2!}$ **13.** $\frac{8!}{4!}$

Solve.

14. Jan has 5 pairs of pants and 7 shirts. How many different pant/shirt combinations are there for him to wear?

Using Probability and Finding the Probability of Independent and Dependent Events

To determine probability, divide the number of favorable outcomes by the total number of possible outcomes.

To find the probability of independent and dependent events, multiply the probability of each event. For dependent events, the probability of the second event is affected by the first event.

Find the probability of each event if a card is drawn at random.

H	A	P	P	Y

15. selecting an H   **16.** selecting a P   **17.** selecting an A   **18.** not selecting an H

19. selecting a Y, replacing it, and then selecting a P

20. selecting a Y, not replacing it, and then selecting a P

Chapter 12   *Test*

Find the mean, median, mode, and range of the following.

1. 15, 18, 23, 22, 19, 15, 17, 22, 29, 20

2. 42, 40, 39, 45, 41, 43

Draw a line plot for the following frequency distributions.

3.

x	1	2	3	4	5	6
f	0	4	2	1	3	2

4.

x	12	13	14	15	16	17
f	4	7	3	1	2	5

Arrange the set of data into a frequency table.

5. the weight of school children   98, 101, 105, 95, 108, 92, 95, 100, 101, 98, 97, 105, 92, 92, 100

Make a stem and leaf plot for the following.

6. 17, 25, 32, 18, 22, 31, 27, 16, 19, 22, 35, 28, 25, 24

7. Make a back-to-back stem and leaf plot for the data below.

200-Meter Dash Time (in seconds)	Year	1960	1964	1968	1972	1976	1980	1984	1988
	Men	20.5	20.3	19.83	20.00	20.23	20.19	19.80	19.75
	Women	24.0	23.0	22.5	22.4	22.37	22.03	21.81	21.34

Make a box and whisker plot for the following.

8. 12, 8, 5, 9, 7, 12, 6, 8, 7, 9, 10, 12

9. 58, 63, 45, 82, 55, 79, 59, 77, 54, 83, 58

Find the value of each factorial.

10. 4!

11. 5!

12. $\frac{9!}{3!}$

13. $\frac{7!}{2!}$

Solve.

14. At the school picnic the children had a choice of a hot dog or a hamburger. They had a choice of one of three toppings. How many choices did they have in all?

15. You and three friends want to have your picture made together. If you line up shoulder to shoulder, in how many ways can the picture be made?

You pick one marble at random from a bag with 4 red marbles, 3 green marbles, and 5 blue marbles. Find each probability.

16. selecting a red marble

17. selecting a yellow marble

18. selecting a green marble

19. selecting a red marble, replacing it, and then selecting another red marble

20. selecting a red marble, not replacing it, and then selecting another red marble

Chapters 1–12   Cumulative Review

Choose the correct answer. Write A, B, C, or D.

1. Name the opposite of $|-3 + (-2)^3|$.
- **A.** 11
- **B.** −11
- **C.** 5
- **D.** not given

2. The square root of a number cubed is 8. What is the number?
- **A.** 8
- **B.** 2
- **C.** 4
- **D.** not given

3. Find a decimal between $(-0.1)^2$ and 0.05.
- **A.** 0.03
- **B.** 0.2
- **C.** 0.3
- **D.** not given

4. Simplify $\frac{x^3y^4}{(x^2y^3)^2}$.
- **A.** xy^2
- **B.** $\frac{x}{y^2}$
- **C.** $x^{-1}y^{-2}$
- **D.** not given

5. Find the median.

```
1 | 6
2 | 5 7
3 | 4 4 4 6 6
4 | 1 2 8 9
5 | 4
```
- **A.** 36.6
- **B.** 36
- **C.** 34
- **D.** not given

6. Find the mean.

250, 280, 240, 230, 270,
240, 270, 240, 230, 250
- **A.** 250
- **B.** 245
- **C.** 240
- **D.** not given

7. Evaluate $\frac{a^5b^3c}{a^6b^2}$ for $a = 2$, $b = -3$, and $c = -4$.
- **A.** 12
- **B.** 6
- **C.** −6
- **D.** not given

8. Find the slope for $2x - 3y = 15$.
- **A.** 2
- **B.** −2
- **C.** −3
- **D.** not given

9. In $\triangle ABC$, $\angle A = 55°$, $\angle C = 15°$. Name the triangle by angles.
- **A.** acute
- **B.** obtuse
- **C.** right
- **D.** not given

10. 25% of r is 200. What is r?
- **A.** 25
- **B.** 50
- **C.** 800
- **D.** not given

11. $3\frac{1}{5} \cdot 1\frac{1}{4} \div 2\frac{2}{3}$
- **A.** $1\frac{1}{2}$
- **B.** 4
- **C.** $4\frac{4}{5}$
- **D.** not given

12. Find the area of $\triangle CDE$.

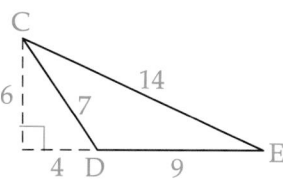
- **A.** 27
- **B.** 36
- **C.** 12
- **D.** not given

13. You have 10 red cards, 5 yellow cards, and 3 green cards. What is the probability of picking a yellow card?
- **A.** $\frac{5}{18}$
- **B.** $\frac{3}{18}$
- **C.** $\frac{5}{10}$
- **D.** not given

14. Write an inequality for *the number t is at least 35*.
- **A.** $t > 35$
- **B.** $t < 35$
- **C.** $t \geq 35$
- **D.** not given

Energy Sources

Energy Sources pie chart:
- Other 22%
- Oil 33%
- Coal 27%
- Natural Gas 18%

COAL, OIL, AND NATURAL GAS are *fossil fuels*. They are formed from plants and animals that lived millions of years ago. *Carbon avoidance* is the comparative cost of a coal-fired electrical plant. The fuel and operating costs of a coal plant are about $.02/kW·h. Pollution costs are about $.015/kW·h. Thus, anything greater than $.035/kW·h is a carbon avoidance cost.

Fossil Fuel Alternative	Carbon Reduction	Carbon Avoidance Cost (per ton)
Improving Energy Efficiency	100 %	$0–19
Wind Power	100 %	$107
Geothermal Energy	99 %	$123
Wood Power	100 %	$141
Steam-injected Gas Turbine	61 %	$109–200
Solar with Gas	7.9 %	$216
Nuclear	86 %	$535

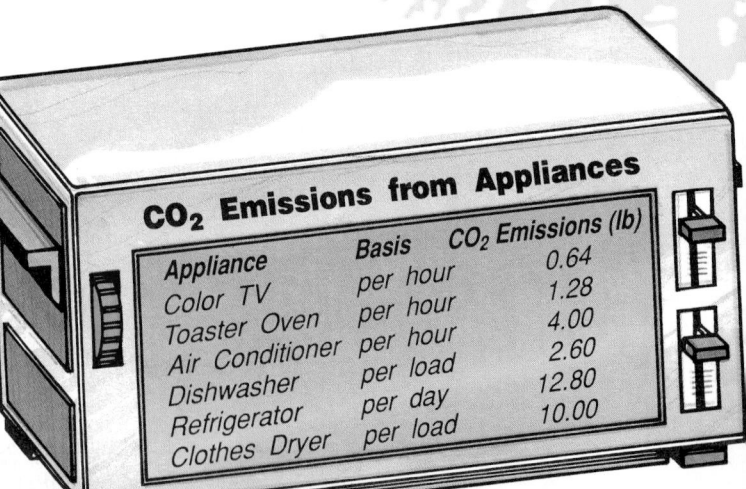

CO_2 Emissions from Appliances

Appliance	Basis	CO_2 Emissions (lb)
Color TV	per hour	0.64
Toaster Oven	per hour	1.28
Air Conditioner	per hour	4.00
Dishwasher	per load	2.60
Refrigerator	per day	12.80
Clothes Dryer	per load	10.00

Polynomials

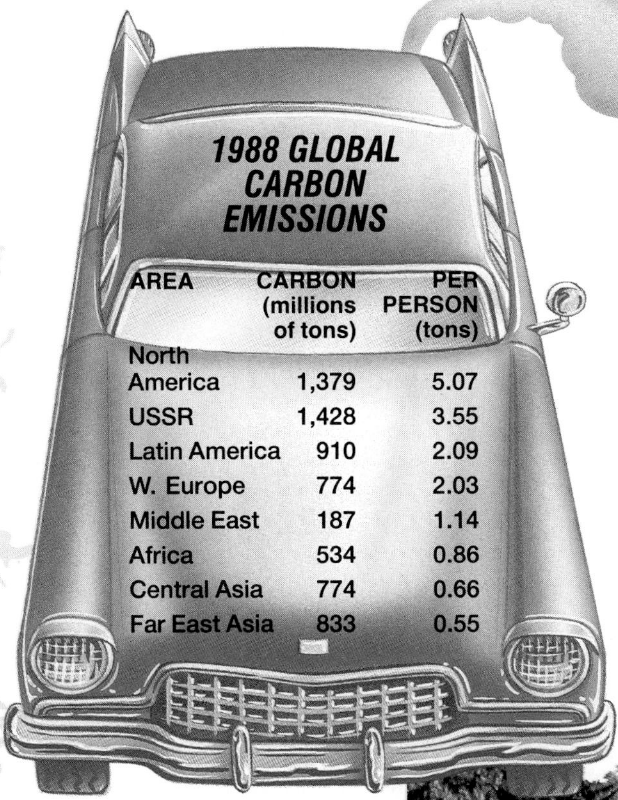

1988 GLOBAL CARBON EMISSIONS

AREA	CARBON (millions of tons)	PER PERSON (tons)
North America	1,379	5.07
USSR	1,428	3.55
Latin America	910	2.09
W. Europe	774	2.03
Middle East	187	1.14
Africa	534	0.86
Central Asia	774	0.66
Far East Asia	833	0.55

GLOBAL WARMING ■ Burning fossil fuels created 5.66 billion t of carbon waste in 1988, more than one ton for every person on the planet. Burning 1 t of carbon releases 3.7 t of carbon dioxide (CO_2). Carbon dioxide is a chief contributor to global warming. Some scientists believe that Earth's average temperature could rise 3°F to 9°F by the year 2050. This could result in the oceans rising, in coastal flooding, and the loss of farm land due to too much salt water.

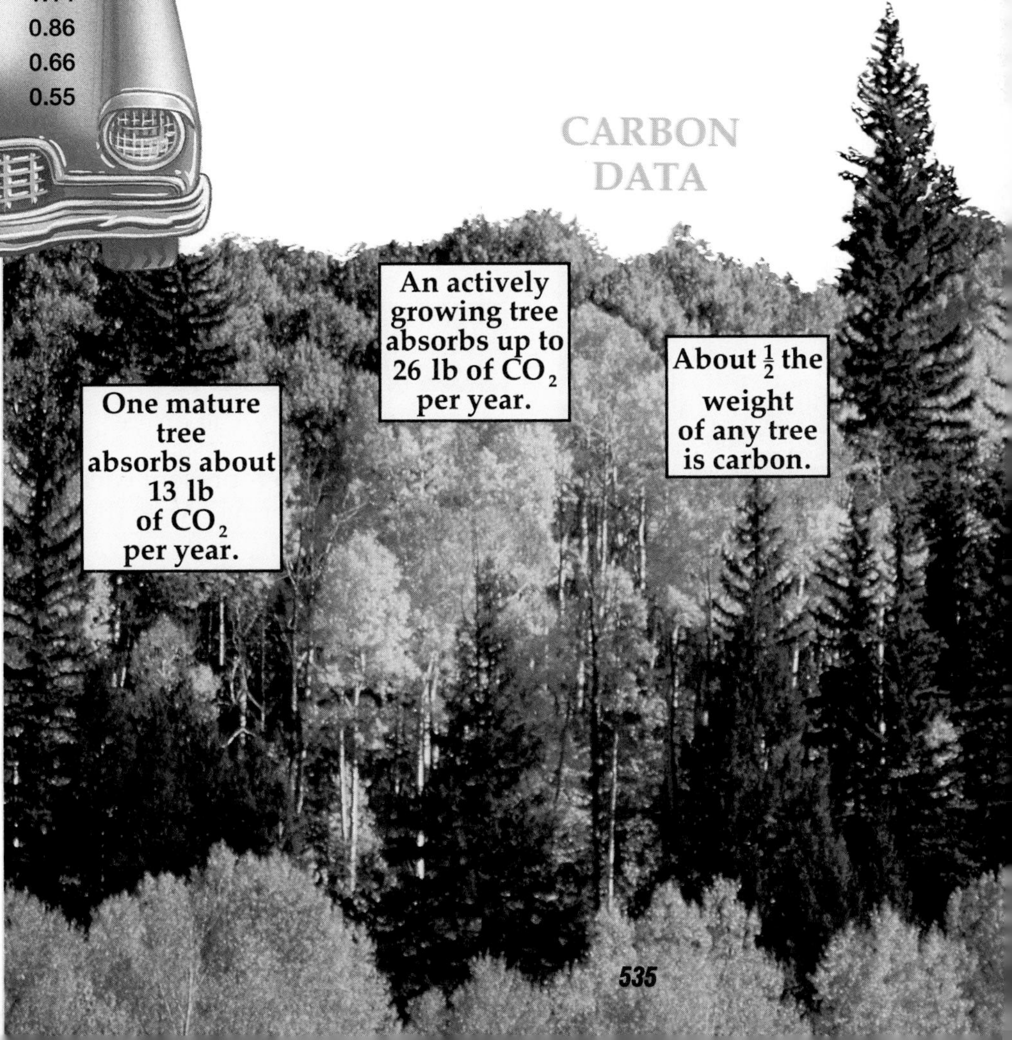

CARBON
DATA

An actively growing tree absorbs up to 26 lb of CO_2 per year.

One mature tree absorbs about 13 lb of CO_2 per year.

About $\frac{1}{2}$ the weight of any tree is carbon.

▼

Think about it...

Look at the Global Carbon Emissions data. Why do you think North America has greater carbon emissions per person than any other part of the world?

OBJECTIVE:
To explore polynomials using models.

MATERIALS

---

* Algebra tiles or colored paper to represent integers, variables, and a variable squared

* Math journal to record work

Exploring Polynomials

▼ You know you can use algebra tiles to represent algebraic expressions such as $4x$, $x + 3$, and $2x + 1$. You can also use algebra tiles to represent expressions such as $x^2 + 2$ and $2x^2 + 3x$.

1. ***Compare*** the models.

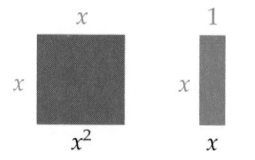

a. ***Describe*** the area of each model.

b. ***Discuss*** how the area describes the value of each model.

2. ***Write*** the expression represented by each model.

a.    b.

c.    d.

3. ***Model*** each expression.

   a. $3x^2 + 2$ b. $2x + 3$ c. $4x^2 + 3x$

   d. $x^2 + x + 4$ e. $3x^2 + x + 2$ f. $5x^2 + 4x$

Jaime Escalante proved to his students that with dedication and hard work, "there are no limits. You can become whatever you want to be." In the first year of his calculus class, all 18 students passed the Advanced Placement exam in college calculus.

▼ You can use models to help you combine like terms.

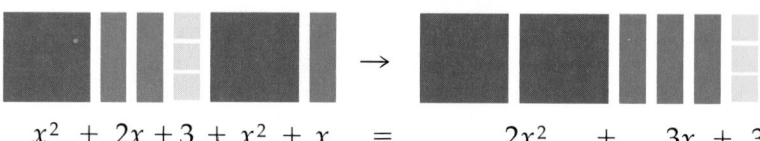

$$x^2 + 2x + 3 + x^2 + x \quad = \quad 2x^2 + 3x + 3$$

4. Use a model to represent each expression. Then use the model to combine like terms. Write the resulting expression.

   a. $2x^2 + 5 + 3x + x^2$

   b. $4x + 3x^2 + 5 + x^2$

   c. $7 + 3x^2 + 4x + 3 + 2x$

   d. $5x + x^2 + 2x + 6$

   e. $3x^2 + 2 + 2x + x^2 + 5$

   f. $12 + 3x^2 + 5x + 2 + x^2 + 4x$

   g. $7 + 2x^2 + 4x + 2 + 2x^2 + 3x$

---

5. ***Describe*** how you can use what you know about pairing like terms to find $(2x^2 + 3x + 4) + (x^2 + x + 3)$.

6. Use models to find each sum.
   a. $(3x^2 + 2x - 7) + (2x^2 + 4x + 2)$
   b. $(2x^2 + 3x) + (5x^2 + 8x + 12)$
   c. $(x^2 + 2) + (3x^2 + x)$
   d. $(x^2 + 3x + 2) + (2x^2 + x + 3)$

7. ***Summarize*** Write a rule for finding the sum of two algebraic expressions.

▼ You can use algebra tiles to help you find the difference of two algebraic expressions.

8. ***Explore*** what happens when you subtract $x^2 + x + 3$ from $3x^2 + 2x + 5$.
   a. Model $3x^2 + 2x + 5$.

   b. Remove tiles that represent $x^2 + x + 3$.
   c. The remaining tiles represent the difference which is $2x^2 + x + 2$.

9. ***Write*** the subtraction expression for each model.

   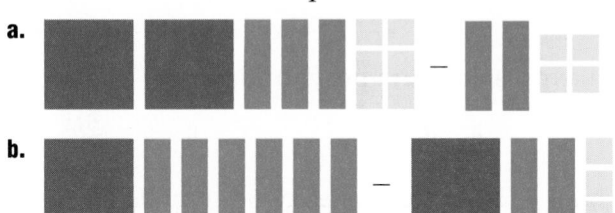

10. ***Model*** each difference. Write the resulting expression.
    a. $(4x^2 + 3x + 5) - (2x^2 + x + 3)$
    b. $(5x^2 + 2x + 1) - (4x^2 + 2x + 1)$
    c. $(3x^2 + 6x + 8) - (x^2 + 2x + 6)$
    d. $(6x^2 + 4x + 7) - (6x^2 + 3x + 7)$
    e. $(4x^2 + 2x + 7) - (x^2 + 2x + 3)$
    f. $(x^2 + 3x + 2) - (x^2 + 2x + 1)$
    g. $(5x^2 + 5x + 5) - (4x^2 + 4x + 4)$

13-1 Polynomials

▼ Mathematicians use algebraic expressions to represent real world situations. The expression $4.8s^2$ represents the distance in meters that an object falls in s seconds. The expression $4.8s^2$ is a *monomial*.

Monomial	A monomial is a real number, a variable, or the product of a real number and one or more variables.

A monomial cannot contain any operation other than multiplication and cannot have a variable as an exponent.

Example 1 Tell which expressions are monomials.

a. $3x^2y$ b. 8 c. $8 + a$ d. $\frac{a}{7y}$

Solution a. monomial; It is the product of a real number (3) and one or more variables (x, x, y).

b. monomial; It is a real number.

c. not a monomial; It is the sum of a real number and a variable.

d. not a monomial; The denominator cannot contain a variable.

▼ Some algebraic expressions that include monomials are *polynomials*.

Polynomial	A polynomial is a monomial or a sum or difference of monomials.

Example 2 Tell which expressions are polynomials.

a. $x + 3y$ b. $\frac{7}{8}a^2 - 2b^2$ c. $\frac{7}{a^2} - 2b^2$

Solution a. polynomial; It is the sum of two monomials.

b. polynomial; It is the difference of two monomials.

c. not a polynomial; The expression $\frac{7}{a^2}$ is *not* a monomial because the denominator contains a variable.

▼ We call the monomials that make up a polynomial its *terms*.

Example 3 How many terms does each polynomial have?

a. $3x^2y$ b. $2x - 4y$ c. $4a^2 + 2ab - 5b^2$

Solution a. one   b. two   c. three

▼ Some polynomials have special names that identify the number of terms in the polynomial.

Polynomial	Terms	Examples
monomial	one	$0.08x$, mn
binomial	two	$a - 3b$, $x^2y + 4$
trinomial	three	$2a - 4 + 6b$, $xy^3 - 0.2xy + 1.55y^4$

Example 4 Identify each expression as a monomial, binomial, or trinomial.

       a. $3x - 2y$ **b.** $8x^3yz$ **c.** $7x^5y + 8y + 18$ **d.** $12 - n$

Solution   **a.** binomial **b.** monomial **c.** trinomial   **d.** binomial

▼ You can write a polynomial for a model.

Example 5 Write the polynomial represented by the model.

  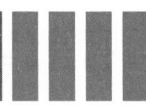

Solution $2x^2$ + $4x$ +   3

▼ You can model a given polynomial.

Example 6 Show a model for $3x^2 + x + 2$.

Solution

▼ You can evaluate any polynomial when given values of the variables.

Example 7 Evaluate each polynomial for $m = 8$ and $p = \text{-}3$.

      a. $3m - 2p$ **b.** $m^2 + 3m - 6$ **c.** $3p^2 - 4m + 15$

Solution   **a.** $3m - 2p = 3(8) - 2(\text{-}3)$

$$= 24 - (\text{-}6)$$
$$= 24 + 6$$
$$= 30$$

       b. $m^2 + 3m - 6 = 8^2 + 3(8) - 6$

$$= 64 + 24 - 6$$
$$= 82$$

       c. $3p^2 - 4m + 15 = 3(\text{-}3)^2 - 4(8) + 15$

$$= 3(9) - 4(8) + 15$$
$$= 27 - 32 + 15$$
$$= 10$$

If you can jump 3 ft on Earth, you can jump 10 ft on Mercury.
Let j = height to which you can jump on Earth. What polynomial would express the height to which you could jump on Mercury?

THINK AND DISCUSS

1. Find the meaning of the prefixes used for the expressions: monomial, binomial, trinomial, and polynomial. Do the prefixes reflect the expressions they represent? What would you call a polynomial with four terms?

2. Is $y^2 + 3y + \frac{7}{y}$ a trinomial? Explain.

CLASS EXERCISES

Which of the following are monomials?

1. $2 + x$ 　　**2.** $18ab^2$ 　　**3.** $\frac{4}{b}$ 　　　　　**4.** 1

Identify each expression as a monomial, binomial, or trinomial.

5. $3xy + 4y^3$ 　**6.** $0.8x$ 　　**7.** $1.7y^2 + 2.4y - 9$ 　**8.** 658

Write the polynomial represented by each model.

9.  　　　　**10.**

Model each polynomial.

11. $3x^2 + 2x + 4$ 　　　　**12.** $5x^2 + 3^2$ 　　　　**13.** $2a^2 + a + 7$

Evaluate each polynomial for $a = 2$ and $b = 4$.

14. $5a + 7b$ 　　　　**15.** $2a^2 - b + 4$ 　　　　**16.** $ab^2 + 5$

WRITTEN EXERCISES

Which of the following are monomials?

1. $2x$ 　　　**2.** $-0.3y + 9.35$ 　　**3.** $\frac{a}{3}$ 　　　**4.** 8

How many terms are in each expression?

5. $-x^2 + 3x$ 　　　　**6.** 5 　　　　　**7.** $27 + x - 4xy$

8. $16 - 3xy + c + x^2$ 　**9.** x 　　　　**10.** $x^2yz - 1$

Identify each expression as a monomial, binomial, or trinomial.

11. $3x^2 + 2x$ 　**12.** 21 　　　**13.** $7p^2$ 　　　**14.** $1 + 4x - xy$

15. $5x$ 　　　**16.** $56 - x$ 　　**17.** $4.5 + 3.7a$ 　**18.** $x^2 + 7x + 4$

Model each polynomial.

19. $2x^2 + x + 4$ 　　**20.** $x^2 + 3x + 1$ 　　**21.** $4x^2 + 2x$

22. $3x^2 + 5$ 　　　**23.** $2x + 6$ 　　　**24.** $4x^2 + 3x$

Write the polynomial represented by each model.

25.  　　　　**26.**

27.

28.

29. WRITE at least five words that begin with mono-, bi-, tri-, or poly-. Give the meaning of each word.

MENTAL MATH Evaluate each polynomial for $a = 1$, $b = 2$, and $c = -1$.

30. $4a + b$

31. $a^2 + 2a + 3$

32. $b^2 + 6$

33. $3c + b$

34. $c^2 + c - 1$

35. $a^2 + c$

CALCULATOR Evaluate each polynomial for $d = 12$, $e = -11$, and $m = 15$.

36. $2d^2 + d$

37. $d^2 + 3d + 7$

38. $3d + 4e$

39. $m^2 - 2m$

40. $e^2 + 4e - 6$

41. $8d + 7m$

EXPLORING CONCLUSIONS

For each Given, tell whether or not the Conclusions are possible.

1. Given: $x - 7 < 0$
$x + 3 > 0$

Conclusions:

a. $x = 0$

b. $x = -1$

c. $x < 7$ and $x > -3$

d. $x > 7$

e. $x < -7$

2. Given: $3y < 100$
$\frac{y}{2} > 5$

Conclusions:

a. $y = 5$

b. $y = -5$

c. $y < 0$

d. $y \geq 0$

e. $y > 10$ and $y < 33\frac{1}{3}$

3. Given: $a^2 > 90$
$a + 3 < 20$

Conclusions:

a. $a < 20$

b. $a > -10$

c. $a = 7$

d. $a = 12$

e. $a < -10$

4. Given: $n^2 + 6 > 30$
$n + 6 > 5$

Conclusions:

a. $n > 0$

b. $n < 0$

c. $n = 0$

d. $n > 5$

e. $n < 5$

MIXED REVIEW

Simplify.

1. $x^2 x^3$ **2.** $(4m^2)^3$

Are the events dependent or independent?

3. $P(A) = \frac{3}{7}$ $P(B) = \frac{1}{3}$
$P(A \text{ and } B) = \frac{1}{7}$

4. $P(A) = \frac{5}{6}$ $P(B) = \frac{2}{5}$
$P(A \text{ and } B) = \frac{5}{24}$

Simplify.

5. $2x^2 + 3x^2 + x^2$

6. $3(x + 3) - 2x - x$

Solve.

7. Four class officers and their advisor want to stand side-by-side for a photograph. How many poses are possible?

13-2 Adding and Subtracting Polynomials

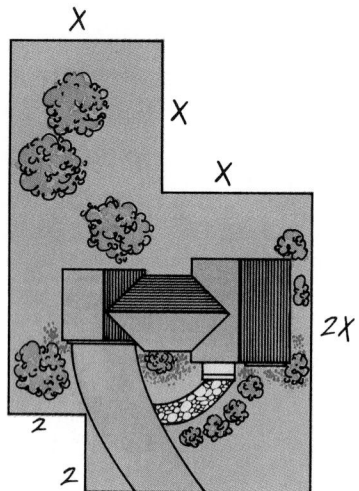

▼ The figure at the left represents a lawn. You can express the area of the lawn by the polynomial $4x^2 - 4 + x^2$ or simplify it as $5x^2 - 4$.

▼ You can model addition of polynomials.

Example 1 Use models to find $(2x^2 + 3x + 7) + (x^2 + x + 3)$.

Solution $2x^2 + 3x + 7$

$x^2 + x + 3$

The sum is $3x^2$ + $4x$ +   10.

▼ You can add polynomials using number properties to combine like terms.

Example 2   Find $(5y^2 + 3y + 9) + (2y^2 + 5y - 7)$.

Solution $(5y^2 + 2y^2) + (3y + 5y) + (9 - 7)$ Group like terms.
                 $(5 + 2)y^2 + (3 + 5)y + (9 - 7)$ Use the distributive
                                                        property.
                 $7y^2$ + $8y$ +   2

THINK How would you use
the associative and
commutative properties to
group like terms?

▼ You can add polynomials in a column by aligning like terms and then combining them.

Example 3   Find the sum of $2z^2 + 5xz - x^2$ and $4z^2 - 3xz + x^2$.

Solution $2z^2 + 5xz - x^2$ Align like terms.
               $+ \; 4z^2 - 3xz + x^2$ Add the terms in each column.
               $\overline{6z^2 + 2xz + 0} = 6z^2 + 2xz$

▼ You can model subtraction of polynomials.

Example 4   Use models to find $(4x^2 + 5x) - (2x^2 + 4x)$.

Solution   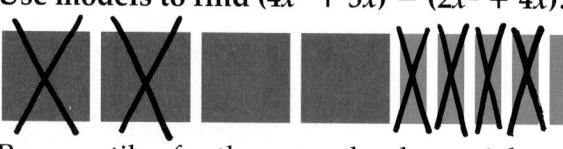 $4x^2 + 5x$

Remove tiles for the second polynomial.
Count the remaining tiles.

The difference is $2x^2 + x$.

▼ You can subtract polynomials by adding the opposite of each term in the second polynomial.

Example 5 Find $(5x - 9 + y) - (2x + 4 - 3y)$.

Solution
$5x - 9 + y + (-2x) + (-4) + 3y$ Add the opposite of the second polynomial.

$5x + (-2x) - 9 + (-4) + y + 3y$ Group like terms.
$(5 - 2)x \quad - \quad 9 - 4 \quad + (1 + 3)y$ Use the distributive property.

$\quad 3x \qquad - \qquad 13 \quad + \quad 4y$

THINK Why is subtracting a polynomial the same as adding its opposite?

▼ You can use these methods to add and subtract polynomials when solving equations.

Example 6 **a.** Write a polynomial for the perimeter of the polygon. Simplify.

b. If $P = 26$ and $b = 3$, find a.

Solution **a.** $4a + b + b + a + a + b + a + b$
$\quad 7a + 4b$ Combine like terms.

b. $\quad 7a + 4b = 26$ Write an equation.
$\quad 7a + 4(3) = 26$ Substitute values.
$\quad 7a + 12 = 26$
$\quad\quad\quad 7a = 14$
$\quad\quad\quad\quad a = 2$

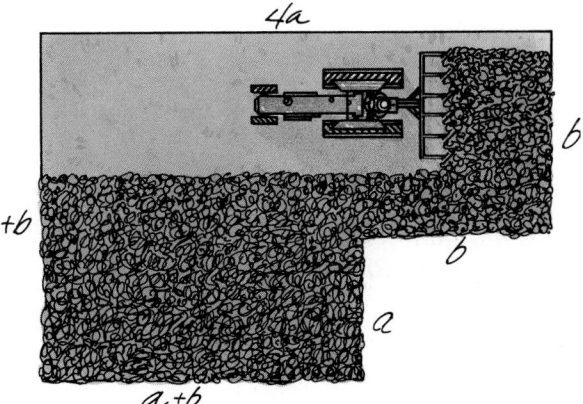

CLASS EXERCISES

Use a model to find each sum.

1. $(x^2 + 3x + 1) + (x^2 + x + 6)$

2. $(x^2 + 5x + 2) + (3x^2 + x + 1)$

Find each sum.

3. $(3x - 2y) + (5x + 4y)$

4. $(x^2 + 3x - 7) + (x^2 - 6x - 9)$

5. $\quad\;\; 5a + 7b$
$\underline{+ \; -3a + 2b}$

6. $x^4 + 3x^3 - x^2 + \;\; x - 2$
$\underline{+ \quad\;\; 7x^3 + x^2 - 5x - 9}$

Use a model to find each difference.

7. $(2x^2 + 3x) - (x^2 + 2x)$

8. $(x^2 + 3x + 5) - (x^2 + x + 2)$

Find each difference by adding opposites.

9. $(8j - 3k + 6m) - (-2j + 3m)$

10. $(-11a^2 + 2a - 1) - (7a^2 + 4a - 1)$

11. $(9x^2 - 4y + 5z) - (-4x^2 - 15z)$

THINK AND DISCUSS

1. Describe the three methods you could use to add polynomials. Which do you prefer? Explain.

2. Explain how you could use a column format to subtract polynomials.

3. What is true about the sum of a polynomial and its opposite?

4. Compare and contrast the methods for adding whole numbers with those for adding polynomials. Then repeat for the subtraction methods.

12. Three numbers are consecutive multiples of 4.

   a. Write an expression for their sum. Use polynomials for each term. Then simplify the expression.

   b. Find the numbers if the sum is 108.

 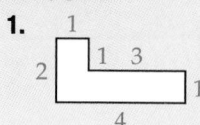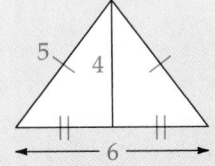

WRITTEN EXERCISES

Use a model to find each sum.

1. $(x^2 + 3x - 2) + (3x^2 + 2x + 4)$

2. $(x^2 + 2x + 1) + (x^2 + 3x + 4)$

Find each sum by combining like terms.

3. $3x + 2 + (-4x + 3)$ **4.** $5x^2 + 3x + 7 + (7x - 2)$

5. $-4x^2 + 2x - 1 + (x^2 - x + 8)$

6. $7x^3 + 4x^2 + 3x - 1 + (8x^3 - 10x + 18)$

7. $x^2 + 4x - 2$ **8.** $xy + 5x - 2y + 4$
$+ \ 8x^2 - 3x + 7$ $+ \ 2xy - 3x - 3y - 8$

9. $x^3 + 5x^2 + 3x - 2$ **10.** $4x^2 - 5xy \qquad + 7$
$+ \ x^3 \qquad\quad - 2x + 6$ $+ \ 8x^2 + 3xy - 3y - 4$

Use a model to find each difference.

11. $(5x + 9) - (2x + 1)$ **12.** $(3x^2 + x + 7) - (2x^2 + x + 2)$

Subtract each by adding the opposite of the second polynomial.

13. $(6y - 8) - (2y + 7)$ **14.** $(x^2 - 3x - 9) - (5x - 4)$

15. $(mn^2 + 4m - n^2) - (-3mn^2 + 2m + n^2)$

16. $(6a^2b + 5ab^2 - 8) - (2a^2b - 3ab^2 + 1)$

17. $(4a^2 + 3ab + b) - (2a^2 - 2ab - b)$

18. $(7p^2q^2 + 5pq - 8) - (4pq - 5)$

Add or subtract.

19. $(3m - 8) - (2m + 1)$ **20.** $(8j^2 + 2j) - (6j^2 - j)$

21. $(ab - 4) + (3ab - 6)$ **22.** $(13d^2q - 3dq^2) + (2d^2q + 5dq^2)$

23. $(w^2 + 5w) + (2w - 6)$ **24.** $(11t^2 + 2) - (3t^2 + 2)$

25. $(x^2 - 5x - 9) + (-4x^2 - 3x + 17)$

26. $(ab + b - 4a) + (-2ab + 6b + 2a)$

27. $(y - 3x + 1) - (5x - 9 + y)$

28. $(-3x^4y^3 - 5xy + 2) + (x^4y^3 + x^2 + xy + 1)$

29. $(9a^7 - 7a^4 + a^2 - 8) + (8a^7 + 15a^4 + 12)$

30. $(m^3n - 3m^2n^2 + 8mn - 6) - (m^3n - 3m^2n^2 + 8mn - 6)$

31. $(4a^3b^2 - 9a^2b + 2ab + 11) + (7a^3b^2 - 6a^2b - 4ab + 12)$

32. *WRITE* a paragraph explaining how you can use the commutative, associative, and distributive properties in the addition and subtraction of polynomials.

Write an expression for each phrase. Use the same variable in each term of the expression.

33. the sum of three consecutive multiples of 2
   a. Simplify the expression.
   b. Find the numbers if their sum is 36.

34. the sum of four consecutive even numbers
   a. Simplify the expression.
   b. Find the numbers if their sum is 84.

35. the sum of five consecutive multiples of 5
   a. Simplify the expression.
   b. Find the numbers if their sum is 375.

Write the perimeter of each figure as a polynomial. Simplify.

36.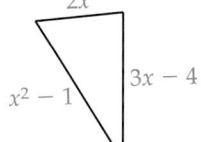

37.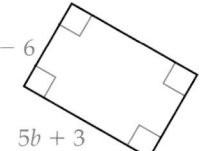

38. $2a^2 - 1$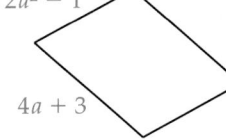

39. The sum of the interior angles of a convex polygon with n sides is $180(n - 2)$. Find the sum of the interior angles for each polygon.
   a. square   **b.** pentagon   **c.** hexagon   **d.** decagon

40. Use the article at the right.
   a. Write a polynomial to represent the amount of fuel the space shuttle burns in m minutes.
   b. Write the speed of the space shuttle in miles per hour. Round to the nearest whole mile. *Hint:* 5,280 ft = 1 mi.
   c. The air distance from New York to Paris is 3,624 mi. Suppose you could fly from New York to Paris on the space shuttle. How long would the trip take? Round to the nearest tenth of an hour. What is the percent of change from Lindbergh's flight? Round to the nearest percent.

Exploring Takes Energy

Charles Lindbergh's historic flight from New York to Paris in 1927 took 33.5 h. Lindbergh's plane, the *Spirit of St. Louis*, had no front window. An extra tank of gas carrying 450 gal of gas weighing 4,000 lb took the window's place. Today's space shuttle uses about 8,000 lb of fuel per minute at liftoff alone. In flight, the space shuttle flies at a speed of 3,700 ft/s at an altitude 100 mi above Earth.

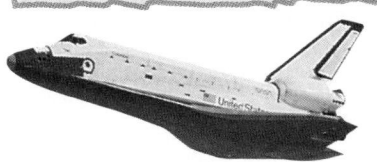

13-3 *Multiplying a Polynomial by a Monomial*

▼ You can write a polynomial to describe the area of the rectangle at the left. You can use a model to illustrate both the area and a way to simplify the resulting expression.

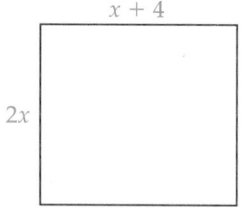

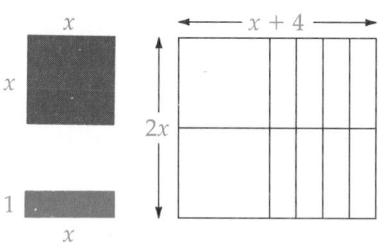

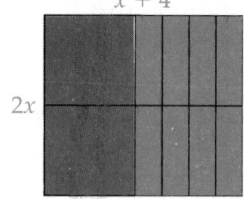

$$2x(x + 4) = 2x^2 + 8x$$

▼ You can use the distributive property to find the product of a monomial and a binomial.

Example 1   **Simplify $3x(x - 4)$.**

Solution $3x(x) + 3x(-4)$ Use the distributive property.
                $3x^2 - 12x$ Simplify.

▼ You can also use the distributive property to find the product of a monomial and a polynomial with more than two terms.

Example 2   **Simplify $-2x(z^2 - 3x + y - 7)$.**

Solution $-2x(z^2) - 2x(-3x) - 2x(y) - 2x(-7)$
                $-2xz^2 + 6x^2 - 2xy + 14x$

▼ You can use the rules of exponents to simplify the product of a monomial and a polynomial.

Example 3   **Simplify $3x^2(8x^2 - 5xy + 2y^3)$.**

Solution $3x^2(8x^2) + 3x^2(-5xy) + 3x^2(2y^3)$
                $3(8)x^2x^2 + 3(-5)x^2xy + 3(2)x^2y^3$
                $24x^4 - 15x^3y + 6x^2y^3$

FLASHBACK

When multiplying powers with the same base, add exponents.

The expression $-2(8t^2 - 70t)$, where t equals time in seconds, represents the height in feet at which a fireworks burst will explode. At what height would a burst explode after 7s?

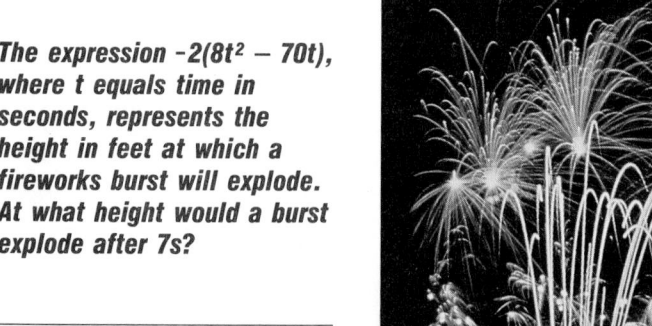

CLASS EXERCISES

Use a model to find each product.

1. $2x(x + 4)$ **2.** $x(2x + 3)$ **3.** $3x(x + 1)$

4. $x(x + 5)$ **5.** $2x(x + 3)$ **6.** $2x(3x + 1)$

Use the distributive property to find each product.

7. $3x(x + 5)$ **8.** $-4xy(2x - 3y)$

9. $5x(-3x^2 + 2x)$ **10.** $4x(7x^6 - 3x^5 + 2x^2 + 1)$

11. $xy(x^2 + 2xy + y^2)$ **12.** $3x^2y(2x^2 - xy + y^2)$

Use the distributive property to find each product. Then evaluate the polynomial for $x = 5$ and $y = 7$.

13. $x^2(y + 7)$ **14.** $-2x(3x + xy - y^2)$

15. $2x^2(y + 3)$ **16.** $2y(x + y)$

Write an expression for the area of each shaded region.

17.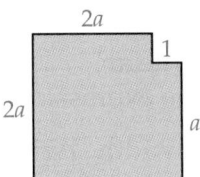

18.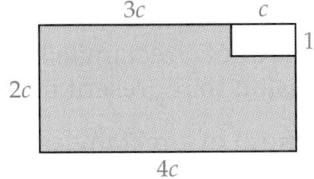

WRITTEN EXERCISES

Use a model to find each product.

1. $2x(x + 6)$ **2.** $x(2x + 6)$ **3.** $2x(3x - 1)$

4. $3x(2x + 4)$ **5.** $x(5x + 3)$ **6.** $2x(4x + 7)$

7. MENTAL MATH Complete each exercise using two different methods. First substitute the value for the variable, then multiply. Next, multiply the polynomial first, then substitute the value for the variable. Evaluate each of the following for $x = 1$, $y = -1$, and $z = 2$.

    a. $3x(-6y + z)$ **b.** $y^2(x - y)$ **c.** $5z(3x + y^2)$ **d.** $2x^2(z^2 - y^2)$

    e. WRITE a paragraph telling which method of solving the expressions above you found to be the easiest. Explain.

CALCULATOR Find each product. Then evaluate the expression for $x = 12$ and $y = -15$.

8. $2x^2(x^2 + y^2)$ **9.** $-4xy(xy - x^2)$ **10.** $x^2(5x + y^2 - y)$

13-3 Multiplying a Polynomial by a Monomial   **547**

Use the distributive property to find each product.

11. $2x(4x - 1)$ **12.** $x(x^2 + 3x)$ **13.** $x^2(2x - 5)$

14. $x^2(x^2 - 9)$ **15.** $y^2(y + 2y^2 - 3)$ **16.** $-3(2x^2 - 3x - 1)$

17. $5xy(x + 5 - y)$ **18.** $5a^2bc^2(abc - a^2b^2c^2 + 6a^2bc)$

19. $-3xy(2x^2y + xy + y^2 - 3)$ **20.** $4z(2z^6 - 3z^5 - 12z^2 + 8)$

21. $8xyz(12x^2y^2 + 3x^3z^5)$ **22.** $-2x^2b^2(-4xb^3 + 3x^3b^2)$

23. $12x^2(x + y^2 + z)$ **24.** $-4x^2y(25x^5y^2z + 8x^3y)$

25. $\frac{1}{2}y(x + xy^2 + 5)$ **26.** $3y\left(x^2 - xy - \frac{1}{3}x\right)$

27. $7x^2(2x^2 + y^2 - xy)$ **28.** $4x^2(x^2 + xy - y^2)$

29. $3x(x^2 + 5) + 2x(x - 3)$ **30.** $2y(-y + 4) + 3(y - 5)$

Solve. Use only one variable for each expression.

31. Assume e is an even integer. Write an expression to represent the product of e and the next consecutive even integer. Simplify.

32. Assume m is a multiple of 6. Write an expression to represent the product of m and the next consecutive integer that is a multiple of 6. Simplify.

33. The width of a rectangle is $\frac{1}{2}$ the length plus 7. Write an expression to represent its area. Then simplify the expression.

34. The length of a rectangle is 5 less than 4 times its width. Write an expression to represent its area. Simplify.

35. The base length of a triangle is $8x$. The triangle's height is twice that plus 5. Write an expression for the area of the triangle. Simplify.

36. The height of an isosceles triangle is $\frac{1}{3}$ its base less 3. Write an expression to represent its area. Simplify.

37. Express the number 792 in expanded form. Let $x = 10$. Write a polynomial to represent the number. Then write a polynomial in x to represent 40. Find the product of the two polynomials. Simplify it and substitute 10 for x. Is your answer equal to 40(792)?

Write an expression for the area of the shaded region.

38.
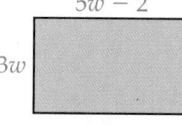
$5w - 2$
$3w$

39.
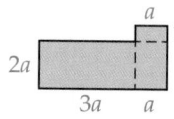
a
$2a$
$3a$ a
1

40.
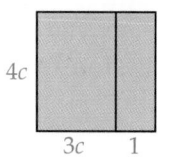
$4c$
$3c$ 1

41.
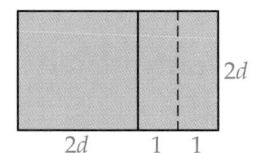
$2d$
$2d$ 1   1

OBJECTIVE:
To explore algebraic expressions.

MATERIALS

• Algebra tiles or colored paper

• Math journal to record work

Exploring Mind-reading Tricks

■   You have probably heard of mind-reading tricks. Most such tricks are simple applications of algebraic expressions.

1. Think of a number. Add 4. Multiply by 2. Subtract 6. Divide by 2. Subtract your original number. What is your final result?

   a. **Model** each step of the process with algebra tiles. The number you think of is the variable. Use the rectangle to represent this number. Use positive tiles to represent the units.

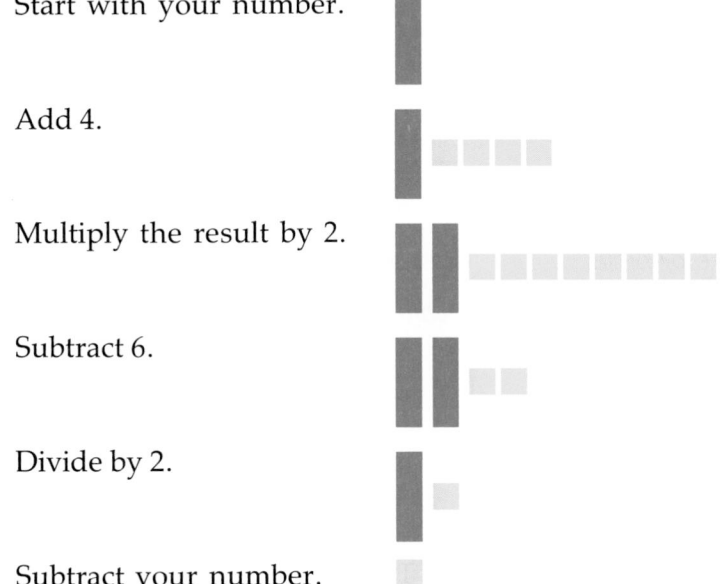

   Start with your number.

   Add 4.

   Multiply the result by 2.

   Subtract 6.

   Divide by 2.

   Subtract your number.
   The result is always 1.

   b. Use a variable to replace the tiles.

Start with your number.	n
Add 4.	$n + 4$
Multiply the result by 2.	$2(n + 4) = 2n + 8$
Subtract 6.	$2n + 8 - 6 = 2n + 2$
Divide by 2.	$\frac{2n + 2}{2} = n + 1$
Subtract your number.	$n + 1 - n = 1$
The result is always 1.	

2. **Explore** Use algebra tiles and then variables to find the result of another trick.

   Think of a number. Triple it. Add 14. Subtract 5. Divide by 3. Subtract your original number. What do you get?

   a. **Write** an equation to summarize your exploration of the trick.

   b. Make up a mind-reading trick of your own and try it on a classmate. Then explain how the trick works.

Isaac Newton (1642–1727) invented the binomial theorem, a formula for finding the product of the expression $(x + y)^2$. By the age of 23, Newton also had made discoveries about the nature of light, had invented calculus, and had established the theory of universal gravitation. When hailed for his achievements, Newton modestly replied, "If I have seen a little farther than others, it is because I have stood on the shoulders of giants."

DISCUSS the meaning of Newton's famous quote.

13-4 Multiplying Binomials

▼ Suppose a is an even integer. You can represent the product of the next two consecutive odd integers, $a + 1$ and $a + 3$, by the expression $(a + 1)(a + 3)$.

You can use a model to help find the product.

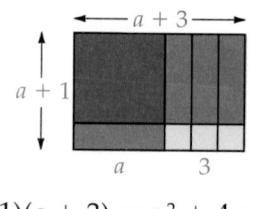

$$(a + 1)(a + 3) = a^2 + 4a + 3$$

▼ If you think of one binomial as a single expression, you can use the distributive property twice to multiply two binomials.

Example 1 Multiply $(x - 3)(x + 4)$.

Solution

$(x - 3)x + (x - 3)4$	Multiply the first binomial by each term in the second.
$x(x) - 3(x) + x(4) - 3(4)$	Multiply each binomial and monomial.
$x^2 - 3x + 4x - 12$	Combine like terms.
$x^2 + x - 12$	Simplify.

▼ The FOIL method is another way to find the product of two binomials.

1. Multiply the **F**irst terms in each binomial.
2. Multiply the **O**utside terms in each binomial.
3. Multiply the **I**nside terms in each binomial.
4. Multiply the **L**ast terms in each binomial.
5. Add the products.

Example 2 Multiply $(x + 2)(x + 6)$.

Solution

Outside
First
$(x + 2)$ $(x + 6)$
Inside
Last

First	Outside	Inside	Last
$x(x)$ +	$x(6)$ +	$2(x)$ +	$2(6)$

$x^2 + 6x + 2x + 12$	Combine like terms.
$x^2 + 8x + 12$	Simplify.

▼ When you use FOIL to multiply the sum and difference of the same terms, or to square a binomial, the product has interesting characteristics.

Example 3   Multiply $(a + 5)(a - 5)$.

Solution $(a + 5)(a - 5) = a^2 - 5a + 5a - 25$
$$= a^2 - 25$$

Example 4   Multiply.

    a. $(a + 7)^2$ **b.** $(a - 3)^2$

Solution   **a.** $(a + 7)(a + 7) = a^2 + 14a + 49$

    b. $(a - 3)(a - 3) = a^2 - 6a + 9$

> **FLASHBACK**
>
> The square of a number is the product of the number and itself.

The examples lead to the following rules for finding special products.

Product of $(a + b)(a - b)$	To find the product of the sum and difference of two terms, square the first term and subtract the square of the second term. $$(a + b)(a - b) = a^2 - b^2$$
Squaring Binomials	To square a binomial, square the first term then add or subtract twice the product of the two terms and add the square of the second term. $$(a + b)^2 = a^2 + 2ab + b^2$$ $$(a - b)^2 = a^2 - 2ab + b^2$$

CLASS EXERCISES

Find each product using models.

1. $(x + 2)(x + 1)$ **2.** $(x + 1)(x + 4)$

3. $(x + 2)(x + 2)$ **4.** $(x + 2)(x + 3)$

Find each product using the distributive property.

5. $(x + 3)(x - 2)$ **6.** $(x + 7)(x + 9)$ **7.** $(y - 2)(y - 4)$

Find each product using the FOIL method.

8. $(a - 9)(a + 1)$ **9.** $(x + 3)(x - 4)$ **10.** $(x - 7)(x + 5)$

Find each product.

11. $(x + 5)^2$ **12.** $(x - 2)(x + 2)$ **13.** $(x - 5)^2$

> **THINK AND DISCUSS**
>
> **1.** How is using FOIL similar to using the distributive property? Which method do you prefer?
>
> **2.** Does the product of two binomials always have three terms? Could it have two? four? more than four? Explain.

WRITTEN EXERCISES

Find each product using models.

1. $(x + 1)(x + 6)$ **2.** $(x + 2)(x + 4)$ **3.** $(a + 1)(a + 7)$

Find each product using the distributive property.

4. $(a - 1)(a + 6)$ **5.** $(a + 3)(a - 2)$ **6.** $(y - 16)(y + 20)$

7. $(a + 3)(a + 8)$ **8.** $(x + 4)(2x + 1)$ **9.** $(x + a)(y + b)$

Find each product using FOIL.

10. $(y + 2)(y + 8)$ **11.** $(x + 1)(x + 12)$ **12.** $(x - 8)(x - 3)$

13. $(3 + x)(5 - x)$ **14.** $(3x + 1)(2x - 4)$ **15.** $(2a + b)(4c - 2d)$

Find each product.

16. $(y + 5)^2$ **17.** $(x - 3)(x + 3)$ **18.** $(a - 8)(a + 8)$

19. $(b - 7)^2$ **20.** $(y - 10)^2$ **21.** $(2a + 5)(2a - 5)$

22. $(a + 7)(a - 8)$ **23.** $(2a + 1)^2$ **24.** $(a - 15)(a + 15)$

25. $(x - 21)(x + 36)$ **26.** $(x - 5)(x - 8)$ **27.** $(3a + 4)(a - 2)$

28. $(x - 2)(x + 11)$ **29.** $(x + 1.3)(x - 4.8)$ **30.** $(3x + y)(x^2 + 2)$

31. $(b - 1)^3$ **32.** $(x + 1)(x^2 + 2x - 3)$ **33.** $-4(2a + 1)(a - 3)$

MENTAL MATH **Find each product mentally.**

34. $(x - 1)^2$ **35.** $(x + 1)^2$ **36.** $(x + 3)^2$

37. $(x - y)(x + y)$ **38.** $(x + 1)(x - 1)$ **39.** $(x + 2)(x + 2)$

Write an expression for the area of each rectangle. Simplify the expression.

40.
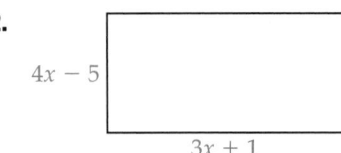
$x + 3$
$2x + 1$

41.
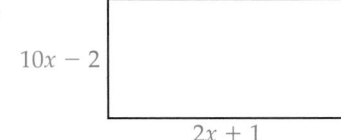
$2x + 4$
$5x + 3$

42.
$4x - 5$
$3x + 1$

43.
$10x - 2$
$2x + 1$

Solve. Write an expression to represent each problem. Use one variable in each expression. Then simplify each expression.

44. Assume e is an even integer. Find the product of the next two consecutive even integers.

45. Assume w is an integer that is a multiple of 3. Find the product of the previous two consecutive integers.

46. The base of a parallelogram is $w + 5$ centimeters. The height is 2 cm less. Find the area of the parallelogram.

47. The side of a square is $(t - 6)$ meters. Find the area.

48. Two right triangles are joined to form a rectangle. The base of the triangle is m units. The height of the triangle is $m + 2$ units. Find the area of the rectangle.

Solve each equation.

49. $3(x + 5) - 2(x + 6) = 5$

50. $4(a - 3) + 5(a + 7) = 14$

51. $-(w + 7) - 6(w + 6) = -43$

52. $5(b - 6) + 4(6 - b) = -8$

53. *DATA FILE 8 (pp. 312–313)* By about how many miles does the center of population move each year?

54. *DATA FILE 10 (pp. 404–405)* The area of Rhode Island is about 1,055 mi². About how long does it take to destroy an area of rain forests equal to the area of Rhode Island?

> **FLASHBACK**
> 27,878,400 ft² = 1 mi²
> 1 acre = 43,560 ft²

TEST YOURSELF

Is each a monomial, binomial, trinomial, or not a polynomial?

1. $4x$

2. $5y + 6$

3. $\dfrac{7}{w}$

4. $m^2 + 3m - 7$

5. $186.5p$

6. $3g + g^2$

7. $14v7v$

8. $\dfrac{a}{3}$

Evaluate each polynomial for $x = 7$, $y = 10$, and $z = -5$.

9. $x^2 + 5x - 3$

10. $y^2 + z$

11. $z^2 + 5z - x$

12. $x^2 - y^2$

13. $y^2 - z + x$

14. $z^2 + x^2 - y^2$

Add or subtract.

15. $(7a + 3) + (4a - 3)$

16. $(p + 7) + (p^2 + 5)$

17. $(3ab^2 + 9) + (2a + b)$

18. $(rs - 6) - (r^2s^2 + 10)$

19. Write an expression for the area of square that has sides of length $a^2 + b$. Simplify the expression.

20. *WRITE* a sentence explaining how to use the FOIL method to find the product of two polynomials.

Practice

Tell how many terms are in each of the following expressions. Then identify each as a monomial, binomial or trinomial.

1. $3x^2 + x$

2. xy

3. $5x + 3$

4. $7x^2 + x + 4$

5. 72

6. $2xy + x + y$

Add or subtract.

7. $(2r^2 - 5) + (4r^2 + 2)$

8. $(5ab - 2) - (ab + 6)$

9. $(-8d + 2) - (-4d + 3)$

10. $(6c^2 - 3a) + (-5c^2 - 2a)$

11. $(-7x^2y - 2xy + 7) - (5x^2 + 4xy - 6)$

12. $(3mn^2 - mn + 6) + (4mn^2 + mn - 2)$

13. $(5rt^2 + 4r^2t - 2t) - (3rt^2 - 2r^2t - 4t)$

14. $(2jk^2 + 5jk + j - 4) + (jk^2 + 3jk - j - 1)$

Use the distributive property to find each product.

15. $3x(7y + 2)$

16. $-6xy(4x^2 - 2y^2)$

17. $5xy(4x + 3y)$

18. $7ab^2(a - b + 4)$

19. $2a^2b^2(5a^2 - 5b^2)$

20. $6x^2y(7x^2 + 3y^2 + 2xy - 5)$

21. $4cd(2c + 3d - 6)$

22. $3x^2yz(4x + 5y + 6z - 2)$

Find each product.

23. $(x + 5)^2$

24. $(x - 7)(2x + 9)$

25. $(x - 1.5)(x - 3)$

26. $(2x + 3)^2$

27. $(x + 5)(x - 5)$

28. $(2x - 4)(2x + 4)$

29. $(x - 5)^2$

30. $(4x - 10)(x - 8)$

31. $(x^2 - 2)(x - 5)$

32. $(x + 1)(x + 1)$

33. $(6x + 2)(2x + 6)$

34. $(x^2 - x)(x^2 - 8)$

35. $(-5x + 2)^2$

36. $9(x + 4)(x - 2)$

37. $(10x^2 - 2)(3x^2 + x)$

38. $9(x + 4)^2$

39. $3(x + 6)(x^2 - 4x)$

40. $\left(\frac{1}{2}x - 67\right)\left(\frac{1}{3}x + 12\right)$

Evaluate each polynomial for $x = 3$, $y = -2$, and $z = 1$.

41. $x^2 + 4$

42. $3x^2 - 2y + z$

43. $4x^2y^2 - 4x + 8$

44. $7xy - 3z$

45. $-3z^2y + 2xy$

46. $-x^2 + 2y - z + 8$

47. $30x^5 - 10z^{10}$

48. $-22xyz^3$

49. $2x^2 + y - 50$

50. $25x^3 + 5y^2 + 10z - 1$

51. $z^5 + x^2 - y$

52. $5x^2 - 2y^2$

53. $y^2 + xyz$

54. $3x + z^2$

55. $y^2 - z + x^2$

56. $(x + y)^2$

OBJECTIVE:
To solve systems of equations using matrices.

13-5 *Using Matrices*

■ You can use a *matrix* to solve a system of linear equations.

Matrix	A matrix is an array of numbers written in brackets.

■ The matrix of a system of two linear equations in two variables is square and is made up of the coefficients from each equation.

Example 1 **Determine the matrix of coefficients for the system of linear equations.**

$$3x + 5y = 13$$
$$2x + 3y = 8$$

Solution $\begin{bmatrix} 3 & 5 \\ 2 & 3 \end{bmatrix}$ Write the coefficients for *x* in one column and the coefficients for *y* in the other column.

■ A *determinant* is real number value associated with a square matrix.

THINK How is evaluating a determinant similar to cross multiplication?

Determinant	We define the determinant (D) of a square matrix as $D = \begin{vmatrix} a_1 & b_1 \\ a_2 & b_2 \end{vmatrix} = a_1 b_2 - a_2 b_1.$

THINK How do you know whether a matrix or a determinant is being shown?

Example 2 **Find the determinant of the matrix below.**

$$\begin{bmatrix} 8 & 3 \\ 4 & 5 \end{bmatrix}$$

Solution $D = \begin{vmatrix} 8 & 3 \\ 4 & 5 \end{vmatrix} = 8(5) - 4(3) = 28$

■ You can use *Cramer's rule* and determinants to find the solution of a system of equations.

Cramer's Rule	Cramer's rule uses the following determinants. $D = \begin{vmatrix} a_1 & b_1 \\ a_2 & b_2 \end{vmatrix} \quad D_x = \begin{vmatrix} c_1 & b_1 \\ c_2 & b_2 \end{vmatrix} \quad D_y = \begin{vmatrix} a_1 & c_1 \\ a_2 & c_2 \end{vmatrix}$ The *x* value of the solution is $\frac{D_x}{D}$ and the *y* value is $\frac{D_y}{D}$. The letter *c* in each matrix represents the constant term in each equation.

Example 3   Solve the system of equations using Cramer's rule.

$$3x + y = 5$$
$$2x + 3y = 8$$

Solution   **1.** Solve for D.

$$D = \begin{vmatrix} 3 & 1 \\ 2 & 3 \end{vmatrix} = 3(3) - 2(1) = 7$$

2. Solve for D_x.

$$D_x = \begin{vmatrix} 5 & 1 \\ 8 & 3 \end{vmatrix} = 5(3) - 8(1) = 7$$

3. Solve for D_y.

$$D_y = \begin{vmatrix} 3 & 5 \\ 2 & 8 \end{vmatrix} = 3(8) - 2(5) = 14$$

4. Solve for x and y.

$$x = \frac{D_x}{D} = \frac{7}{7} = 1 \qquad y = \frac{D_y}{D} = \frac{14}{7} = 2$$

The solution of the system of equations is (1,2).

▼
THINK How could you check to make sure that (1,2) is the solution?

CLASS EXERCISES

Determine the matrix of coefficients for each system of equations. Evaluate the determinant of each matrix.

1. $2x + 6y = 22$
$4x + 3y = 17$

2. $x + 2y = 3$
$3y - x = 2$

3. $-4y + 6x = 16$
$-2x + 3y = -2$

4. What will be the value of the determinant if all elements in one column are zero?

■■■■■■ Decision Making ■ **DECISION MAKING** ■ Decision Making ■ Decision Making ■ Decision Making ■

USING MATRICES

■   You can solve real life problems using matrices.

■   **COLLECT DATA**

1. a. Visit a travel agent and find the prices of a round-trip coach ticket to Paris and to Mexico City. Record the data in a chart like the one below.

City	Travel Cost	Hotel Cost
Paris		
Mexico City		

b. Your travel agent will be able to recommend a hotel in the area. Record the price of the hotel in your chart.

2. Look in the newspaper and find the exchange rate from dollars to francs and from dollars to pesos.

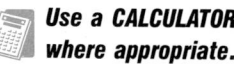
WRITTEN EXERCISES

Write the matrix of coefficients for each system of linear equations.

1. $x + 2y = 16$
$2x + 3y = 26$

2. $y = 2x$
$-x + y = 1$

3. $y = -3x + 17$
$2y + 6 = 2x$

Evaluate each determinant.

4. $\begin{vmatrix} 3 & 4 \\ 2 & 9 \end{vmatrix}$

5. $\begin{vmatrix} 8 & 4 \\ -6 & -2 \end{vmatrix}$

6. $\begin{vmatrix} -7 & -2 \\ 0 & 11 \end{vmatrix}$

Solve each system of linear equations using Cramer's rule.

7. $2x + 4y = 12$
$3x + 5y = 14$

8. $-4x + 7y = 1$
$25 = 2x + 5y$

9. $x + 2y = 3$
$3y - x = 2$

Write a system of linear equations for each situation. Solve using Cramer's rule.

10. At the grocery store, one box of laundry detergent and two bottles of fabric softener cost $7.75. Two boxes of laundry detergent and one bottle of fabric softener cost $8.75. Find the cost of each product.

11. A manufacturer sells packages of pens and pencils. A package of 3 pens and 5 pencils costs $1.65. A package of 5 pens and 10 pencils costs $3.00. Find the price of one pen and two pencils.

■ *Decision Making* ■ *Decision Making* ■ *Decision Making* ■ *Decision Making* ■

■ **ANALYZE DATA**

3. Which city is less expensive to visit? Why might this be true?

4. How much would a meal cost in United States dollars if it costs $16 in Mexico City?

5. Write a system of linear equations using the collected data.

■ **MAKE DECISIONS**

6. A travel agency offers a package deal to Freeport, Bahamas. The four day-three night package is $590 per person. The seven day-six night package is $815 per person. Each price includes the cost of airfare and hotel.

  a. Write a system of linear equations for the situation.

  b. Solve the system using Cramer's rule.

  c. Find the cost of each airfare per person.

  d. Find the cost of the hotel per night.

$590 PER PERSON
4 DAYS 3 NIGHTS

$815 PER PERSON
7 DAYS 6 NIGHTS

THE BAHAMAS

HOTEL AND AIR INCLUDED

13-6 *Using Multiple Strategies*

OBJECTIVE:
To solve problems using one or more strategies.

■ Sometimes you may need to use more than one strategy to solve a problem.

PROBLEM

A rancher bought 104 ft of fencing to make a rectangular corral. The rancher wants the corral to have the greatest possible area. What dimensions should the rancher use?

SOLUTION

READE▶ What do you want to find?

the base and height of a rectangle with $P = 104$ ft and the greatest possible area

What do you know?

$A = bh$
$P = 2b + 2h$
$\quad = 104$ ft

PLAN▶ Decide on strategies.

1. Draw a diagram to represent the information.
2. Use guess and test.
3. Make a table.

SOLVE▶ Draw a diagram.

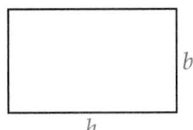

Choose some possible dimensions. Make a table to organize your data.

b	h	P(ft)	A(ft²)
10	42	104	420
11	41	104	451
12	40	104	480

Look for a pattern. Guess some higher numbers and see how long the area continues to increase.

20	32	104	640
22	30	104	660
24	28	104	672
26	26	104	676
28	24	104	672

The corral with the greatest area is a square that is 26 ft on a side.

LOOK BACK▶ Describe the pattern.

As the dimensions of the rectangle get closer to those of a square, the area approaches the greatest possible area.

CLASS EXERCISES

Solve.

1. A gardener wants to fence in the greatest possible area using 200 ft of fencing. What should be the base length and height of the garden?

2. **CALCULATOR** A circle and a square both have an area of 144 square units. Use 3.14 for π.

   a. What is the circumference of the circle? Round to the nearest tenth.

   b. What is the perimeter of the square?

   c. Which figure is the most economical if purchasing fencing materials to surround the figure?

   d. Fencing material is $6.80/unit. How much is saved by choosing the most economical figure?

WRITTEN EXERCISES

 Use a CALCULATOR where appropriate.

Solve.

1. A student playing a computer chess game gets 5 points every time he wins the game. The computer gets 3 points every time it wins the game. They play 128 games and end with a tie score. How many games did the computer win?

2. Two people on bicycles leave home at 10 A.M. and ride towards each other. Their homes are 56 mi apart. The first cyclist pedals at 16 mi/h. The second pedals at 12 mi/h. At what time will they meet?

3. A painter places an 8.5-ft ladder against a wall. The bottom of the ladder is 4 ft from the base of the wall. How high up on the wall does the ladder reach?

4. There are 27 white cubes assembled to form a large cube. The outside surface of the large cube is then painted red. The large cube is then separated into a set of smaller cubes. How many of the small cubes will have exactly two red faces?

5. A student weighs his hamsters two at a time. Together, Sandy and White Ears weigh 209 g. White Ears and Sport weigh 223 g together. Sandy and Sport weigh 216 g together. How much does each hamster weigh?

6. A grocer is arranging cans in a pyramid. She uses 9 cans on each side of the base of the pyramid. How many cans will be in the pyramid?

7. A room has an area of 1,025 ft² and a 10-ft ceiling. Occupancy guidelines recommend at least 200 ft³ per person. What should be the maximum number of people allowed in the room?

8. A man who won the lottery gave his daughter half of the money. He gave his brother half as much as he gave his daughter and kept $3.8 million for himself. How much did the man win?

9. A student has $8 to spend on a phone call to a friend. The cost of a call is $.34 for the first minute and $.24 for each additional minute. How long can she talk to her friend?

10. A student decided to purchase a new telephone. He could choose from 8 different models, 2 different cord lengths, and 4 different colors. How many possible choices did he have if he can choose only one of each model, cord length, and color.

11. How many different angles can you find in the figure?

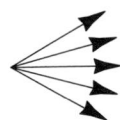

12. A clerk starts working at a beginning salary of $10,400 with an annual increase of $400. The clerk hires an assistant at a starting salary of $9,600 per year with an annual increase of $600. At this rate, in how many years will the assistant be earning more money than the clerk?

13. A lot measures 50 ft by 100 ft. The house on the lot measures 25 ft by 50 ft. What is the area of the lawn?

14. A bus left Freetown at noon traveling 40 mi/h. A car left Freetown at 1:30 P.M. traveling 60 mi/h.

   a. At what time did the car catch up with the bus?

   b. How many miles from Freetown were the car and the bus when they met?

15. A student spends $\frac{1}{3}$ of her money on a movie and $\frac{1}{6}$ of the remaining amount on a snack after the movie. She now has $16. How much money did she originally have?

16. A boy jogs in the park every other day. His sister jogs every third day. They both jogged together on April 2. How many more days in April can they jog together if they maintain this schedule?

17. In how many different ways can you give change from a $100 bill for a $78 purchase if the customer will accept no more than seven singles?

18. *DATA FILE 12 (pp. 486–487)* A base runner tried to steal a base 73 times during the baseball season. Approximately how many times was the base runner out?

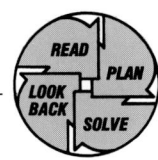
PROBLEM SOLVING STRATEGIES

Draw a Diagram
Make a Table
Look for a Pattern
Guess and Test
Write an Equation
Simplify the Problem
Work Backwards
Account for All Possibilities
Make an Organized List
Solve by Graphing
Make a Model
Simulate the Problem

Solve. Use an appropriate strategy or combination of strategies.

1. There are 7 roads from Mayville to Scottsburg and 4 roads from Scottsburg to Dunlap. How many possible routes can you take from Mayville to Dunlap if you go through Scottsburg?

2. A singles tennis court is 75% as wide as a doubles tennis court. The singles court is 27 ft wide. How wide is the doubles court?

3. A student's average grade for six math quizzes is 85. He received these grades on five math quizzes: 82, 88, 94, 72, 88. What grade did he receive on the other quiz?

4. There are 48 students in the band. Of these students, 24 have blonde hair, and 18 have blue eyes. There are 16 students who do *not* have blonde hair or blue eyes.

    a. How many students have both blonde hair and blue eyes?

    b. How many students do *not* have blond hair?

    c. How many students do *not* have blue eyes?

5. An astronaut's spacesuit weighs 10.02 lb on the moon. This is 16.7% of its weight on Earth. How much does the spacesuit weigh on Earth?

6. A student weighs 10 lb more than his sister. Together they weigh 260 lb. How much does each weigh?

7. The area of rectangle *A* exceeds the area of square *B* by 24 yd². Find the dimensions of each figure.

    w | A | | w | B
    $w + 8$ | | | w

8. A student has 4 one-dollar bills, 2 five-dollar bills, and 5 ten-dollar bills. What is the probability that he will select the following bills at random?

    a. a one-dollar bill, then a ten-dollar bill

    b. a ten-dollar bill, then a five-dollar bill

    c. two ten-dollar bills

9. One hot chocolate for each of the 29 students on a field trip would cost $21.75. The bill for hot chocolate was $27.75. How many students had two hot chocolates?

10. *DATA FILE 13 (pp. 534–535)* About how much carbon is released per year by the 17 million people of Texas? Express your answer in pounds using scientific notation.

Chapter 13 Review

Write an explanation for each of the following.

1. Explain the term monomial and write two examples.

2. Explain the term polynomial and write two examples.

3. Explain how to use the distributive property to find $x(2x - 1)$.

4. Explain how you use FOIL to find the product of $(x + 3)(2x + 1)$.

5. Explain how to find the product of $(a + b)(a - b)$.

6. Explain the phrase *square a binomial* and write an example.

Polynomials

13-1

To name a polynomial, count the number of terms.

Write the polynomial for each model. Then write the name of each polynomial.

7.

8.

9.

Evaluate each polynomial for $a = 1$ and $b = -2$.

10. $3b^2 - ab + 1$

11. $a^2b + 3b - a$

12. $b^3 + ab^2 + 3b$

Adding and Subtracting Polynomials

13-2

To add or subtract polynomials, use models, number properties, or align like terms in columns.

To add polynomials, combine like terms.

To subtract polynomials, add the opposite of each term in the second polynomial.

Use a model to find each sum or difference.

13. $(5x^2 + 3x) + (2x^2 + x)$

14. $(3x^2 + 2x + 4) - (x^2 - x + 3)$

Add or subtract.

15. $(3x + 2y) + (5x + 3y)$

16. $(5m - 3n) - (2m - n)$

17. $(4a^2 + 6b) + (2a^2 - 3b)$

18. $(-r^2 + 2s) - (2r^2 - 3s)$

19. $(3c^2 + 5c - 2) - (-c^2 + 3c - 1)$

20. $(a^2b + b^2 - a) + (a^2b - 2b^2 + 3a)$

Multiplying a Polynomial by a Monomial

To multiply a polynomial by a monomial, you can use models, or you can use the distributive property. Use the rules of exponents to simplify the product.

Use a model to find each product.

21. $2x(x + 5)$

22. $3x(2x + 1)$

Use the distributive property to find each product.

23. $x(x - 5)$

24. $3x(x + 2)$

25. $2x(x - 2)$

26. $4x(x^2 + 3x)$

27. $-5x(-2x^2 + 2x - 3)$

28. $-2xy(x^2 - xy + y^2)$

Multiplying a Polynomial by a Binomial

To multiply a polynomial by a binomial, you can use a model, you can use the distributive property twice, or you can use the FOIL method. FOIL means: multiply the First terms, Outside terms, Inside terms, and Last terms. Then add the products.

Write a multiplication expression for the model. Simplify.

29.

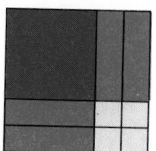

30.

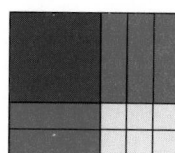

Find each product.

31. $(x - 1)^2$

32. $(a + 3)^2$

33. $(y - 2)(y + 2)$

34. $(b + 3)(b - 2)$

35. $(m + 5)(m - 3)$

36. $(2n - 4)(n + 5)$

Problem Solving

To solve a problem, use an appropriate strategy or combination of strategies.

37. The number of bacteria doubles each minute. A bottle is completely filled after 5 minutes. After how many minutes was the bottle half full?

38. Fourteen boxes contain 152 classic and rock CDs. There are 10 classic CDs in a box and 12 rock CDs in a box. How many boxes contain each kind of CD?

39. The number 72 can be divided into three numbers in the ratio 1 to 2 to 3. Find these three numbers.

40. A gardener plans to use 196 ft of fencing to enclose a garden. What is the largest possible area of the garden?

Chapter 13   Test

Use a model to represent each polynomial.

1. $3x + 2x^2 + 3$

2. $3x^2 + 2x + 1$

Write the polynomial represented by each model.

3.

4.

Identify each expression as a monomial, binomial, or trinomial.

5. $7x - 5$

6. $-3x^2 + 3x + 1$

7. $x^2 + 9$

8. x^2

Evaluate each polynomial for $a = 2$ and $b = -3$.

9. $7a + 3b$

10. $a^2 - b^2 + 1$

11. $(b - 1)^2$

12. $a^2 + 2b - 5$

Find each sum.

13.
$$2x^3 - 3x^2 + x - 1$$
$$+ \quad x^3 + 2x^2 - 3x + 2$$

14.
$$5x^3 + 2x^2 - 3x + 5$$
$$+ \quad 2x^3 - 5x^2 + 6x - 9$$

Add or subtract.

15. $(5x^2 - 2x) - (3x^2 + x)$

16. $(3x^2 + 5x - 3) + (x^2 - 2x + 1)$

17. $(7x^2 + 5x + 3) - (4x^2 + 7x)$

18. $(9x^2 - 4x - 8) + (3x^2 + 6x + 3)$

19. $(-x^2 + 3x + 4) + (2x^2 - 5x + 1)$

20. $(2x^2 - 3x + 4) - (x^2 - 2x - 1)$

Find each product.

21. $(x + 3)^2$

22. $(x - 2)^2$

23. $x(3x^2 - 2x + 5)$

24. $2x(x^2 + 3x - 2)$

25. $3x^2(x + 2y - 1)$

26. $xy(x^2 - 2y + y^2)$

27. $(x - 2)(x + 3)$

28. $(x + 2)(x - 5)$

29. $(2x - 3)(x + 4)$

Solve.

30. The width of a rectangle is $\frac{1}{3}$ the length plus 5. The perimeter is 34. Find the length and the width.

31. A pair of jeans are on sale for 35% off the original price. The sale price is $19.50. What is the original price?

32. The sum of three consecutive multiples of 4 is 60. What is the product of the three multiples?

33. Two students are chosen at random to do a project together. There are 15 girls and 10 boys in the class. What is the probability that both students chosen for the project are boys?

Chapters 1–13 Cumulative Review

Choose the correct answer. Write A, B, C, or D.

1. Add $(3x^2 + 2x - 5) + (2x^2 - 3x + 1)$.
  A. $5x^2 + 5x + 6$ **B.** $5x^2 - x - 4$
  C. $x^2 + 5x - 6$ **D.** not given

2. Find the volume of a cone, $r = 4$, $h = 12$.
  A. 16π **B.** 192π
  C. 64π **D.** not given

3. Multiply $(x - 2)(x - 3)$.
  A. $x^2 - 5x + 6$ **B.** $x^2 - 5x - 6$
  C. $x^2 - 5x - 5$ **D.** not given

4. Find the mode of the following data:
31, 29, 31, 23, 35, 34, 19, 35, 23, 29, 35.
  A. 23   **B.** 29
  C. 35   **D.** not given

5. Find a solution of $x - 2y = 3$ and $3x + y = 2$.
  A. $(1,-1)$ **B.** $(-1,1)$
  C. $(3,2)$ **D.** not given

6. Find the circumference of a circle with $r = 3$.
  A. 3π **B.** 6π
  C. 9π **D.** not given

7. Write the fraction for $37\frac{1}{2}\%$.
  A. $\frac{1}{2}$ **B.** $\frac{75}{2}$
  C. $\frac{3}{8}$ **D.** not given

8. A set of (d) dimes and (n) nickels is worth $3.20. There are 52 coins. How many of each coin are there?
  A. 12 n, 40 d **B.** 40 n, 12 d
  C. 26 n, 26 d **D.** not given

9. Solve $-3x + 1 < 25$.
  A. $x < -8$ **B.** $x > -8$
  C. $x > 8$ **D.** not given

10. 32% of b = 10,000. Find b.
  A. 3,200   **B.** 31,250
  C. 3,125   **D.** not given

11. Multiply $(a - b)^2$.
  A. $a^2 - 2ab + b^2$ **B.** $a^2 + 2ab + b^2$
  C. $a^2 + 2ab - b^2$ **D.** not given

12. Find the distance Joe traveled if he traveled 50 mi/h for $2\frac{1}{2}$ h.
  A. 150 mi   **B.** 100 mi
  C. 250 mi   **D.** not given

13. What is the probability of tossing heads twice with a fair coin?
  A. $\frac{1}{2}$ **B.** 1
  C. $\frac{1}{4}$ **D.** not given

14. Find the next number. 0, -1, $\sqrt{1}$, -2, $\sqrt{4}$, -3, . . .
  A. $\sqrt{5}$ **B.** $\sqrt{9}$
  B. $\sqrt{7}$ **D.** not given

15. Write 568,000,000 in scientific notation.
  A. 5.68×10^6 **B.** 56.8×10^7
  C. 5.68×10^8 **D.** not given

16. Write the expression for the model.

  A. $2(x^2 + 2x) + 3$ **B.** $2x^2 + 2x + 3$
  C. $x^2 + 2x + 3$ **D.** not given

Chapter 1   Extra Practice

Write an integer.

1. opposite of 4

2. opposite of -8

3. $|10|$

4. $|-6|$

Compare. Use <, >, or =.

5. 5 ▓ -1

6. -7 ▓ -3

7. -2 ▓ -2

8. -9 ▓ 0

Find each answer.

9. $-11 + 1$

10. $-4 - (-9)$

11. $-3(-3)$

12. $44 \div (-4)$

13. $28 \cdot (-4)$

14. $-64 \div (-8)$

15. $98 - (-12)$

16. $-52 + (-11)$

17. $-2 + (-7) + 15$

18. $-2 \cdot 10 \cdot (-4)(-1)$

19. $120 \div (-4) \div 10 \div (-1)$

20. $9 \cdot 7 \div (4 - 1)$

21. $5 + 7 \cdot 3 + 1$

22. $3(12 + 6) - 9 \cdot 6$

23. $|12 - (-5)|3$

24. $1 + (-4) \cdot (-7) + 10 - 2$

25. $30 - 7 \cdot 2(22 - 12) \div 5$

Write an expression for each word phrase.

26. a number increased by eight

27. the product of negative seven and x

28. twelve less than the absolute value of negative three

29. the opposite of the quantity seven less than y

30. three times the sum of negative eight and twelve

31. the absolute value of the difference of negative three and ten

32. the quotient of twenty-five and negative five, minus two

33. ten times the quantity seventeen minus negative eleven

Evaluate each expression for the given values of the variables.

34. $4a + 7$, for $a = {}^-2$

35. $8m + 13 + 6n$, for $m = 5$, $n = 3$

36. $7|x - y| + y$, for $x = 3$, $y = 11$

37. $-14 - 2(a - b)$, for $a = 6$, $b = 4$

Solve.

38. A group of children line up in a row. The first child takes 1 step forward. The second child takes 2 steps forward. The third child takes 5 steps, the fourth takes 14, and so on. Following this pattern, how many steps will the next two children take?

39. Concert tickets cost $20 and concert T-shirts cost $12.

   a. Write an expression for the cost of x tickets and y shirts.

   b. Find the cost of 4 tickets and 6 shirts.

   c. How many tickets can you buy for $60? how many T-shirts?

40. *DATA FILE 1 (pp. 2–3)* The air temperature is 5°F. What is the maximum wind speed, in miles per hour, before there is an increased danger of frostbite?

41. After being kicked forward 20 m, a ball is pushed backward 7 m. Describe the position of the ball using an integer.

Chapter 2   Extra Practice

Replace each variable with the given value. State whether the equation is true or false.

1. $17 - a = 7, a = 8$

2. $4 + m = 2m + 8, m = -4$

3. $8 - 2q = 3q + 1, q = 0$

4. $-x + 3 = 2x, x = 1$

5. $4x + y = 20, x = -4, y = 5$

6. $3a = 2b - 9c, a = -3, b = 0, c = 1$

Which of the numbers -1, 0, 1, 3, 5 is a solution?

7. $0 = 121y$

8. $-8 = 2m - 18$

9. $4n = 3n - (-3)$

10. $x(3 - 8) = 5(-x)$

Evaluate.

11. $26 + 8 + 10$

12. $33 \cdot 2 \cdot 5 + 7$

13. $5(8 - 3)$

14. $6[8 - 2 - (-7)]$

15. $5[(-8) + 17 - (2)3]$

16. $510 \div (-5) \cdot 2$

17. $5(8 \div 8) - 33 \cdot 2$

18. $18 + 7 \cdot 4 - 3 \div (-1)$

19. $4(3 + 7) \div 2$

Simplify each expression.

20. $-3(2c)$

21. $41 - 2(m + 1) - m$

22. $3(a + b + 2c)$

23. $3q + 2(q + 1)$

24. $(8 \div 4)r - 3r$

25. $8 + (3s + 2)(-2)$

Solve each equation.

26. $x - 33 = 0$

27. $j + (-22) = 4$

28. $14 = z - 9$

29. $z(3 - 1) = 40$

30. $5q = 26 - 1$

31. $2|n| = 10$

Write an equation for each word sentence.

32. Twice the sum of a number and one is twenty-two.

33. Negative three divided by negative one is three.

34. The sum of three and four times a number x is equal to $6x$.

35. The product of two numbers is the absolute value of negative twenty-four.

Solve.

36. Terry's age is half Bobby's age. The sum of their ages is 36. How old are Terry and Bobby?

37. *DATA FILE 2 (pp. 52–53)* A lightning flash is seen 7 s before the thunder is heard. How far away is the lightning?

38. There are 10 children on a school bus. At the next stop, 5 get on and 1 gets off. Then x get on and none get off. This leaves a total of $3x$ children on the bus. Solve for x. How many children are on the bus?

39. There are twice as many golf balls as ping-pong balls. If 9 golf balls are taken away, there will be the same amount of golf balls and ping-pong balls. How many golf balls and ping-pong balls are there altogether?

Chapter 3   *Extra Practice*

Order from greatest to least.

1. 2.012, 2.12, 2.011   **2.** -0.03, -0.33, -3   **3.** 0.00004, 1.00009, 0.000045   **4.** 278, 2.78, 27.8

Round each decimal to the indicated place.

5. 0.38, nearest tenth   **6.** -3.089, nearest hundredth   **7.** 238.079, nearest whole number

Estimate using the technique which seems best.

8. $-42.039 \div 10.99$ **9.** \$3.74 + \$12.12 + \$3.00   **10.** $-97.3 + (-33.9776) + (-28.0549)$

11. $83.6 + 7.98 + (-2.09)$ **12.** $397 \div 1.9$ **13.** \$238.01 + \$449.99 + \$302.55

Use estimation to place the decimal point in each answer.

14. $4.003 \cdot 0.64 = 256192$ **15.** $4.32 \div 0.02 = 216$ **16.** $12.38 + 8.02 + 10.99 = 3139$

17. $-28 \div 0.24 = -116667$ **18.** $23.05 \cdot 0.07 = 16135$ **19.** $525.1324 \div 5.2 = 100987$

Evaluate each expression for $a = 3.02$ and $b = -12.3$.

20. $a + b$ **21.** $a - b$ **22.** $2a - b$ **23.** $\dfrac{a - b}{2}$

24. $\dfrac{2(a + b)}{4}$ **25.** $\dfrac{-a - b}{5 \div (-1)}$ **26.** $5b - 2a$ **27.** $|a| + |b|$

Solve each equation using any method.

28. $a + 0.03 = 3.75$ **29.** $48.9 + y = 50$ **30.** $q - 4.099 = 2.33$

31. $m - (-1.2) = 3.09$ **32.** $5m = -95$ **33.** $0.5 = \dfrac{x}{33}$

34. $y \div 0.3 = -15$ **35.** $98.53 = 0.9853n$ **36.** $3.3x = 13.2$

Write an equation for each problem.

37. Three hundredths times a number is equal to the opposite of three and one hundredth.

38. x is equal to four hundred ninety-five and seventy-three hundredths.

39. The absolute value of negative nine tenths is equal to two times a number.

40. Five divided by two and five hundredths is equal to q.

Solve.

41. A student is assigned pages 38–130. The student reads a page every 20 s. How long will it take the student to finish the assignment?

42. A painter can paint one window in 17 min. There are 7 windows to paint. How long will it take? Round to the nearest hour.

43. A pound of peanuts costs \$2.87. How many whole pounds can be bought with \$20?

44. *DATA FILE 3 (pp. 96–97)* A collector spent \$7.24 on proof sets in 1936. How much profit would the collector make if he sold them all in 1965?

Evaluate.

1. 4^5

2. $(-2)^4$

3. -2^4

4. -12^0

5. $5x^2 \cdot 3x$

6. $-(2mn)^3$

7. $(4y^4)^3$

8. $(x^2)(x^3)(-x^1)$

9. $[5 + (-7)]^4$

10. $-2(-3 + 4)^5$

11. y^3 for $y = 2$

12. x^4 for $x = -1$

13. $-q^5$ for $q = 1$

14. $(2y)^2$ for $y = -2$

15. $-(a^0bc)$ for $a = 2$, $b = 3$, $c = 4$

16. $(r + 2s + t)^2$ for $r = 3$, $s = -1$, $t = 5$

17. $x^2 + 3x + y^2$ for $x = 7$, $y = -8$

Find the value of a.

18. $4^a = 64$

19. $a^5 = 1$

20. $11^a = 1$

21. $6^a = 36$

22. $a^4 = 625$

23. $3^3 = a$

Write each answer in scientific and standard notation.

24. $(4 \times 10^3)(3 \times 10^2)$

25. $1.32 \times 40{,}000$

26. $(1.4 \times 10^5)2.32$

27. $7(2.6 \times 10^6)$

State which of the numbers 2, 3, 4, 5, or 9 are divisors.

28. 25

29. 72

30. 18

31. 135

32. 24,270

Find the GCF of each set of numbers.

33. 58, 34

34. 21, 63

35. 18, 36, 38

36. $35x^3y^2$, $70x^6y^4$

37. $27a^2b^2$, $9ab^2$

Find the LCM of each set of numbers.

38. 60, 12

39. 55, 100

40. 16, 20, 36

41. $12a^5b$, $6ab$

42. x^4y^3, $200x^2y^4$

Solve.

43. ***DATA FILE 4 (pp. 138–139)*** How many babies are born in 10 s? How many people die in 10 s? Round to the nearest integer.

44. A professional basketball player runs 8 mi in an average game. About how many miles does a player run during games in a season of 82 games?

45. A popcorn popper pops 2 kernels/s for 10 s. After 10 s it pops 4 kernels/s for 20 s. After 20 s it pops 6 kernels/s for 30 s, and so on. At the end of 2 min and 30 s, how many kernels have popped?

46. There are 5 children who want to play a game. Only 2 can play the game at a time. In how many different ways can the children be paired?

47. Find one pair of numbers that satisfies both conditions.

   a. their product is 80

   b. their LCM is 20

48. Find one pair of numbers that satisfies both conditions.

   a. their sum is 40

   b. their GCF is 5

Chapter 5   Extra Practice

Write in lowest terms.

1. $\frac{7}{14}$ 2. $\frac{xyz}{2xz}$ 3. $\frac{4mn}{20mn}$ 4. $\frac{25x}{75y}$ 5. $\frac{3xy}{9xy}$ 6. $\frac{12abc}{144ab}$

Write each decimal as a fraction or mixed number in lowest terms.

7. 0.2   8. 4.1   9. 20.08   10. 0.17   11. 0.005   12. 1.125

Write as a decimal.

13. $\frac{4}{10}$ 14. $\frac{11}{20}$ 15. $\frac{3}{5}$ 16. $\frac{5}{8}$ 17. $\frac{3}{4}$ 18. $\frac{1}{3}$

Order from least to greatest.

19. $\frac{8}{4}, \frac{1}{2}, -\frac{3}{4}$ 20. $-\frac{15}{20}, -\frac{3}{10}, -\frac{4}{5}$ 21. $\frac{2^2}{5}, 2\frac{3}{10}, \frac{9}{10}$ 22. $\frac{a}{3}, \frac{a}{6}, \frac{3a}{2}$ for $a > 0$ 23. $\frac{xy}{15}, \frac{-xy}{5}, \frac{3xy}{10}$ for $xy > 0$

Find each answer. Write in lowest terms.

24. $\frac{5}{6} + \frac{3}{8}$ 25. $\frac{2}{3} - 1\frac{1}{2}$ 26. $\frac{x}{4} - \frac{x}{10}$ 27. $\frac{8}{9}x + \left(\frac{-3}{6}x\right)$

28. $-5 + \left(-\frac{5}{10}\right)$ 29. $8 - \frac{2}{4}$ 30. $\frac{1}{4} \cdot \frac{5}{9}$ 31. $\frac{8}{11} \div \frac{7}{9}$

32. $2\frac{3}{4} \cdot \frac{3}{7}$ 33. $\frac{3x}{5} \cdot \frac{7x}{9}$ 34. $5\frac{4}{7} \div \left(\frac{-3}{14}\right)$ 35. $\frac{4}{5} + 1\frac{2}{15}$

36. $\frac{7}{8}q - \frac{5}{5}q$ 37. $\left(\frac{3}{8}\right)\left(-2\frac{3}{4}\right) - \frac{1}{2}$ 38. $\frac{9}{11} \div \frac{3}{4} \div \frac{2}{7}$ 39. $\frac{-1}{3} \div (-3)$

Simplify.

40. $\frac{15y^7}{33y^3}$ 41. $\frac{a^3 b^2 c^0}{abc}$ 42. $\frac{9m^7 n^2}{3m^3 n}$ 43. $\frac{-y^3 z^5}{y^4 z^5}$ 44. $\frac{16q^2 m^3}{12q^4 m}$

Solve each equation. Write in lowest terms.

45. $h + 3\frac{1}{3} = 4\frac{7}{9}$ 46. $x - |-3.1| = 8\frac{1}{4}$ 47. $c + \left(\frac{-3}{8}\right) = -\frac{7}{10}$ 48. $d + \frac{3}{7} = -2\frac{3}{14}$

49. $\frac{3}{10}c = \frac{3}{4}$ 50. $-\frac{7}{6}z = -4$ 51. $\frac{-9}{10}q = 4$ 52. $\frac{-5}{9}y = -\frac{3}{6}$

Solve.

53. **DATA FILE 4 (pp. 138–139)** How many millions of people speak Chinese, Spanish, German, or Arabic?

54. You have \$20.50 in quarters, dimes, nickels, and pennies. You have an equal number of each coin. How many of each coin do you have?

55. Four children are told to line up and hold hands as they cross the street. How many different ways can they line up?

56. A ball is pushed down a flight of 50 stairs. The ball rolls down four stairs per second. How long will it take the ball to roll down $\frac{4}{5}$ of the stairs?

Chapter 6   *Extra Practice*

Write each ratio as a fraction in lowest terms.

1. $2:6$ **2.** $9:3$ **3.** $7:28$ **4.** $25:45$

5. 3 people out of 27 are wearing hats.   **6.** 18 dogs out of 81 have fleas.

7. 6 out of the 30 TVs are on sale.   **8.** 7 out of the 31 athletes made the team.

Write a proportion to describe each situation. Then solve.

9. An athlete swims 20 laps in 30 min; x laps in 2 hours.

10. 38 lb of soil cost $3.20; 95 lb cost y dollars.

11. 20 stamps cost 95¢; z stamps cost 19¢.

12. A car can travel 282 mi on 14 gal of gas; m miles on 42 gal of gas.

Write a ratio and percent for each.

13. 17 questions right out of 20   **14.** 12 questions right out of 18

15. 40 questions wrong out of 120   **16.** 2 questions wrong out of 20

Solve.

17. What percent of 80 is 36?   **18.** Find 39% of 66.   **19.** 33% of q is 109. What is q?

20. What percent of 33 is 99?   **21.** Find 23% of 28.   **22.** 75% of k is 15. What is k?

Find each percent of change. Round to the nearest tenth.

23. from 18 to 12   **24.** from 88 to 125   **25.** from 15.5 to 25.5   **26.** from 100 to 88

27. from 2.4 to 8.6   **28.** from 11 to 17   **29.** from 92 to 98   **30.** from 34 to 49

Solve.

31. An athlete must swim 18 laps. The athlete swims $\frac{1}{2}$ of the laps and then swims $\frac{1}{3}$ of those remaining. How many laps are left?

32. A florist cuts a wire into three pieces. The first piece is 20% of the second. The third piece is 110% of the second. The wire is 23 cm long. Find the length of each piece.

33. There are 10 girls and 15 boys. What percent of the group is boys?

34. *DATA FILE 6 (pp. 230–231)* What percent of teens study an average of more than 2 h a day?

35. In a town with 12,000 residents, 2 out of 10 voted in the last election. How many residents voted?

36. In a sample of 2,500 ballpoint pens, 15 were found to be defective. How many pens would you expect to be defective in a shipment of 10,000 pens?

37. *DATA* Use the data on page 130. Find the percent of change in the price of a loaf of bread and a half gallon of milk from 1890 to 1980.

38. A salesperson earns $800 per week plus 5% commission on sales over $10,000. How much would the salesperson earn in a week when sales were $25,000?

Solve each equation. Check.

1. $3x + (-12) = x$

2. $2m + -3m - 8 = 26$

3. $4(-y + 2) = -1$

4. $-0.2 - q = 9q$

5. $\frac{3}{4}x - \frac{1}{2}x = 5$

6. $32 = 4(a - 2) + 10$

7. $4(b - 2.1) = b + 0.6$

8. $\frac{1}{4}(x - 8) = \frac{3}{4}x$

9. $48 = \frac{1}{2}(8x - 14) + 15$

Graph each inequality on a number line. Write each inequality as a word sentence.

10. $y < 9$

11. $-3 > q$

12. $0.009 \geq p$

13. $a \geq -2$

14. $c > 99$

15. $c < -99$

16. $n < 7.3$

17. $h \geq -1.2$

18. $-11 \leq b$

Solve each inequality.

19. $y + 3 \geq 9$

20. $y - 3 > -7$

21. $\frac{y}{4} \leq -9$

22. $3q > 0$

23. $-9x \leq -5$

24. $\frac{x}{7} \geq -3$

25. $19 - 3x > -2$

26. $-314 \leq x + 1$

27. $\frac{1}{2}(x - 6) \leq 22$

28. $-5(a - 3) \leq 45$

29. $-\frac{x}{3} + 3 \geq -27$

30. $\frac{2}{3}(4a + 12) \geq \frac{1}{3}(6a - 10)$

Write an inequality to describe the situation. Solve.

31. When a is divided by 8, the result is at most 13. Find a.

32. Four less than n is greater than negative six. Find n.

33. Five less than seven times p is at least twenty-three. Find p.

34. Three times q plus negative twenty-two is less than q. Find q.

Solve.

35. Each month Gil saves $22.27. How long does it take him to save $267.24?

36. Four times a number is fifty-two minus forty. Find the number.

37. A student buys three movie tickets for $6.60 each. The student pays with $20. What is the change?

38. You open a book. The product of the two page numbers is 9,702. What are the page numbers?

39. Nita has test scores of 92, 84, and 87. She needs a 90 average to get an A. What is the lowest score she can get on her next test and still have an A average?

40. *DATA FILE 7 (pp. 272–273)* Estimate which is greater using the figures from 1987: the total of passengers boarding at Chicago/O'Hare, Atlanta, and Miami or the total boarding in Denver, Los Angeles, and San Francisco.

In which quadrant or on which axis does each point fall?

1. $(-3, 18)$ **2.** $(0, 44)$ **3.** $(22, 3)$ **4.** $(-18, -5)$ **5.** $(-0.33, -5)$

Solve for y in terms of x. Find four solutions of each equation.

6. $5y - 10x = 15$ **7.** $4 - y = \frac{1}{2}x$ **8.** $2x + 2y = -4$

9. $\frac{1}{2}y - x = 12$ **10.** $-4x - 0.5y = 4$ **11.** $\frac{1}{3}y - x = 1$

Graph each equation. Name the slope, x-intercept, and y-intercept.

12. $y = -8$ **13.** $y = 2x - 5$ **14.** $x = y$

15. $x + y = 5$ **16.** $-y + 3x = \frac{1}{2}$ **17.** $\frac{1}{4}x + y = -3$

Solve each system by graphing. Check your solutions.

18. $y = x + 4$
$\quad\; y = x - 2$

19. $2x + y = 3$
$\quad\;\; -2y = 14 - x$

20. $y = -3$
$\quad\; 2x + 3y = 6$

Solve each inequality for y in terms of x. Write three ordered pairs that are solutions of the inequality.

21. $3x - y < 5$ **22.** $-x + 4y + 12 \geq 0$

23. $x - 5 + 3y < 44 + 2y + 3x$ **24.** $-x > 2y - 5(x + y)$

Graph each inequality.

25. $y > 7$ **26.** $x + 3y < 2$ **27.** $4x + 4y > 10$

28. $x - \frac{1}{3}y \leq \frac{1}{3}$ **29.** $\frac{3}{4}x - \frac{1}{4}y \leq \frac{1}{4}$ **30.** $3x + 6y > 15$

Solve.

31. At a party 20 guests consume 5 bags of popcorn and 10 gal of juice. At this rate, how much popcorn and juice will 28 guests consume?

32. A line has a slope of $\frac{2}{5}$ and passes through the point $(-10, 7)$. Find the equation of the line. State the quadrants which the line will pass through.

33. Find two consecutive numbers such that the greater number times 3 is 9 less than 5 times the lesser number.

34. *DATA FILE 5 (pp. 180–181)* Write a ratio in lowest terms to compare the number of violas to the number of second violins.

35. A train that is 500 m long is traveling at a speed of 125 km/h. How long will it take the train to entirely pass through a tunnel that is 2 km long?

36. Shoes are $10 off. A customer buys three pairs of shoes for $110. What percent did the customer save on the total purchase? Round to the nearest whole number.

Tell whether each angle is acute, right, obtuse, or straight.

1. 2°   **2.** 75°   **3.** 99°   **4.** 90°   **5.** 180°   **6.** 77°

Find the measure of a complement and a supplement of each angle, if possible.

7. 90°   **8.** 1°   **9.** 45°   **10.** 33°   **11.** 140°   **12.** 101°

Draw a figure to fit each description.

13. a concave octagon   **14.** an obtuse triangle   **15.** a quadrilateral   **16.** a convex rhombus

Find the measure of the third angle of a triangle that has two angles with the given measures.

17. 30°, 60°   **18.** $x°, x°$ **19.** 40°, 60°   **20.** 60°, 60°   **21.** 39°, 57°   **22.** $(x + 2)°, (x - 4)°$

Find each radius or diameter.

23. $r = 29.3$ cm   **24.** $d = 40$ yd   **25.** $d = 78$ in.   **26.** $r = 10$ km   **27.** $r = 228.5$ m

$ABCDE \cong MNOPQ$. Tell whether each statement is true or false.

28. $\angle A \cong \angle P$ **29.** $\overline{AB} \cong \overline{MN}$ **30.** $\angle D \cong \angle P$ **31.** $\overline{CE} \cong \overline{OP}$ **32.** $\angle B \cong \angle N$ **33.** $\angle A \cong \angle M$

Find the circumference. Use 3.14 for π.

34.
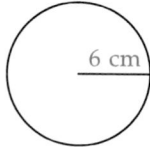
6 cm

35.
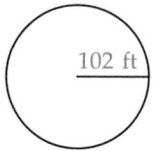
102 ft

36.

0.35 in.

Find the perimeter of each figure.

37. a regular hexagon with side 2.8 in.   **38.** a parallelogram with sides 4 ft and 7 ft

39. an equilateral triangle with side 9 m   **40.** a figure with sides 4 cm, 8 cm, 12 cm, and 12 cm

Solve.

41. Sol and Julia run a race. Sol runs 7.3 mi/h. Julia runs 6.8 mi/h. After 2 h, how far apart will they be?

42. A coat is on sale for 75% off the regular price. If the sale price is $60, what was the original price?

43. Carlos wants to trim a circular carpet in his house. The carpet has a diameter of 20 yd. How much trim does he need? Use 3.14 for π.

44. *DATA FILE 9 (pp. 360–361)* At St. Andrew's golf club a golfer takes a break after the 13th hole. If the golfer has a score of 57, what must the golfer average on the remaining holes to receive a score of par?

Chapter 10   *Extra Practice*

Find the area of each parallelogram with the given base and height. Round to the nearest tenth.

1. $b = 6.3$ cm, $h = 2.9$ cm

2. $b = 13$ ft, $h = 19$ ft

3. $b = 0.8$ m, $h = 1.1$ m

4. $b = 55$ in., $h = 22$ in.

5. $b = 17x$, $h = 33x$

6. $b = x$, $h = 2x$

Find the area of each circle with the given diameter or radius. Round to the nearest tenth. Use 3.14 for π.

7. $r = 8.1$ cm

8. $d = 0.39$ in.

9. $r = 13.2$ m

10. $r = 0.75$ in.

11. $r = 5.6$ m

12. $d = 16z$

13. $r = 14.5$ cm

14. $d = 5.5x$

Find each surface area. Use 3.14 for π.

15. a rectangular prism with base edges 7 in. and 9 in., and height 5 in.

16. a cylinder with radius 7 cm and height 12 cm

17. a square pyramid with edge 59 m and slant height 66 m

18. a cone with radius 9 cm and slant height 15 cm

19. a sphere with radius 12 in.

20. a hemisphere with radius 5 cm

Find each volume. Use 3.14 for π.

21. a triangular prism with base 4 ft, height 7 ft, and a prism height of 10 ft

22. a rectangular prism with length 3 in., width 8 in., and height 9 in.

23. a cylinder with $r = 11$ cm and $h = 6$ cm

24. a cone with radius 9 m and height 13 m

25. a square pyramid with side 5 cm and height 12 cm

26. a sphere with radius 10 in.

Solve.

27. A dress is on sale for 20% off the original price of $89. Another dress not on sale costs $61. Which dress costs less?

28. Ten players line up to shoot baskets. Each player makes at least 60% of her shots. Altogether, there were 300 attempts. What's the smallest number of baskets made?

29. A juice can has radius 1.1 in. and height 4.2 in. What is the volume of the can? Round to the nearest unit. Use 3.14 for π.

30. *DATA FILE 10 (pp. 404–405)* What is the area in square meters of the black bear's home range? Use 3.14 for π.

Find each square root. If necessary, use your calculator. Round decimal answers to the nearest thousandth.

1. $\sqrt{51}$ **2.** $\sqrt{36}$ **3.** $\sqrt{144}$ **4.** $\sqrt{\frac{16}{36}}$

5. $\sqrt{49x^2}$ **6.** $\sqrt{101.101}$ **7.** $\sqrt{(a+b)^2}$ **8.** $\sqrt{a^4b^{12}c^8}$

Determine whether each is a Pythagorean triple.

9. 3, 4, 5   **10.** 9, 7, 12   **11.** $2\sqrt{12}$, 5, $\sqrt{37}$

12. 6, 7, 8   **13.** 5, 12, 13   **14.** $3x^2$, $4x^2$, $5x^2$

Find the missing length.

15. 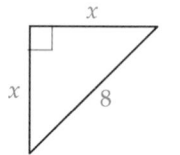   **16.** 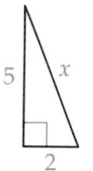   **17.**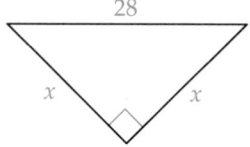

18. 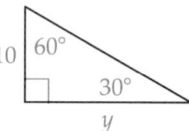   **19.** 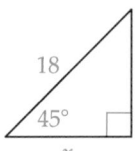   **20.**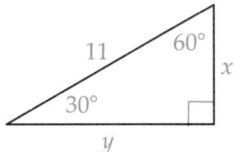

State the trigonometric ratio using the given values.

21. $\tan k°$ **22.** $\sin x°$ **23.** $\cos a°$

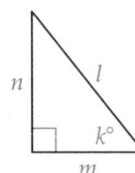   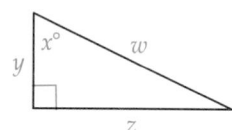   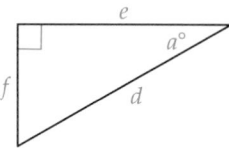

Solve.

24. The diameter of a circular ring is 18 yd. What is the circumference of the ring? What is the area? Use 3.14 for π.

25. At takeoff, an airplane forms a 44° angle with the runway. How many miles will the airplane fly before reaching an altitude of 28,000 ft? Round to the nearest mile.

26. It takes Jonathan 1 min 20 s to walk around the track. Twelve laps equal 1 mile. How long will it take Jonathan to walk 1 mile?

27. **DATA FILE 7 (pp. 272–273)** It is 12 A.M. in Fairbanks, Alaska. What time is it in Chicago, Illinois?

Find the mean, median, mode, and range of each of the following. Round to the nearest tenth.

1. 13, 12, 15, 13, 9, 6, 5   **2.** 28, 1, 5, 6, 9, 1, 3, 10, 1   **3.** 100, 100, 100, 100, 100, 0, 50

4.

x	f
8	5
9	2
10	3
11	1

5. Make a line plot for the table in Exercise 4.

Make a stem and leaf plot for each set of data. Then find the median and the mode for each set of data.

6. 30, 15, 19, 35, 20, 20   **7.** 10, 16, 22, 13, 25, 13, 13, 10

8. 11, 55, 30, 32, 55, 12, 13, 55   **9.** 33, 99, 82, 66, 72, 66

Make a box and whisker plot for each set of data.

10. 40, 43, 48, 48, 50, 66, 60, 61, 70, 69, 45, 46   **11.** 40, 11, 30, 12, 28, 17, 29, 19

Find the value of each factorial.

12. 8!   **13.** $\frac{5!}{4!}$ **14.** 5!   **15.** $6! - 3!$

Suppose you have a deck of 52 cards. Find the probability of selecting each of the following. Cards will always be replaced. An ace is not considered to be a face card.

16. a red card   **17.** a heart   **18.** a king   **19.** a face card

20. a face card first and then an ace   **21.** the jack of hearts first and a king second

Solve.

22. *DATA FILE 5 (pp. 180–181)* If you choose one musician at random from a symphony orchestra, what is the probability that he or she will play the cello?

23. A ball was thrown up a hill 22 ft. It then rolled back 28 ft. Represent this as an integer.

24. Find the probability of rolling one number cube and getting a multiple of 2 first and a 3 second.

25. Find the volume of a sphere with radius 7.5 cm.

26. A right triangle has side lengths 5, $5\sqrt{3}$, and 10. What are the angle measures?

27. The hypotenuse of a 45°-45°-90° triangle has length 12. What is the length of each leg?

28. The sum of three consecutive even integers is 30. Their mean is 10. Find the integers.

29. The sum of the squares of two consecutive positive integers is 85. Find the integers.

EXTRA PRACTICE

1. $(x^2 - 9x + 4) + (2x^2 + x + 1)$

2. $(3x^2 + x + 5) + (x^2 + 2x + 1)$

3. $(mn^2 + 3n - 8) - (3mn^2 - m + n - 5)$

4. $18p^2q^2 + 19 - 18p$

5. $(a^3n^2 - 3a^2n + 5a - 9) - (4a^3n^2 + a^2n - a - 9)$

6. $(-3w^4y^5 - 18w^3y^4 + 2w^2y^3 - 3wy^2) + (3w^4y^5 + 18w^3y^4 - 2w^2y^3 + 3wy^2)$

Simplify.

7. $18x(4x^2 - 2x + 9)$

8. $-m^4(m^2 - 14m + 5)$

9. $\frac{1}{2}a(5a^5 - a^3 - 33)$

10. $4abc(a^4b + 10abc - 8)$

11. $(x + 1)(x + 3)$

12. $(x - 2)(x + 5)$

13. $(x - 9)(x + 9)$

14. $(x - 5)^2$

15. $(x + 2)(2x^2 + x + 1)$

16. $-5(x + 9)(x - 1)$

Write an expression using one variable to represent each product. Then simplify.

17. If m is an even integer, find the product of the next three consecutive even integers.

18. If w is a multiple of 5, find the product of the next two consecutive multiples of 5.

19. If z is a multiple of 4, find the product of the previous two consecutive multiples of 4.

20. If m is an integer, find the product of the next three consecutive integers.

Solve.

21. A ball has a diameter of 12 cm. Find the volume. Use 3.14 for π.

22. A car traveled 192 mi in 3 h. What was the car's average speed?

23. Ron has a choice of 3 sweaters, 2 pairs of pants, and 4 pairs of shoes. How many different outfits can Ron choose?

24. *DATA FILE 9 (pp. 360–361)* What is the average distance that a ball will go if hit with a club having a loft of 31°?

25. Three consecutive integers have a sum of 291. What is the sum of the largest and smallest of these integers?

26. Janet is four years older than Frank. The sum of their ages is 76. How old was Janet eight years ago?

27. A sock drawer contains 4 red socks, 3 green socks, 8 blue socks, and 10 black socks. What is the probability that a blue sock is chosen first and another blue sock second?

28. An average honeybee hive produces 350 oz of honey. How many honeybee hives would be needed to produce 2,275 oz of honey?

Table 1:   Squares and Square Roots

N	N^2	$\sqrt{N}$	N	N^2	$\sqrt{N}$
1	1	1	51	2,601	7.141
2	4	1.414	52	2,704	7.211
3	9	1.732	53	2,809	7.280
4	16	2	54	2,916	7.348
5	25	2.236	55	3,025	7.416
6	36	2.449	56	3,136	7.483
7	49	2.646	57	3,249	7.550
8	64	2.828	58	3,364	7.616
9	81	3	59	3,481	7.681
10	100	3.162	60	3,600	7.746
11	121	3.317	61	3,721	7.810
12	144	3.464	62	3,844	7.874
13	169	3.606	63	3,969	7.937
14	196	3.742	64	4,096	8
15	225	3.873	65	4,225	8.062
16	256	4	66	4,356	8.124
17	289	4.123	67	4,489	8.185
18	324	4.243	68	4,624	8.246
19	361	4.359	69	4,761	8.307
20	400	4.472	70	4,900	8.367
21	441	4.583	71	5,041	8.426
22	484	4.690	72	5,184	8.485
23	529	4.796	73	5,329	8.544
24	576	4.899	74	5,476	8.602
25	625	5	75	5,625	8.660
26	676	5.099	76	5,776	8.718
27	729	5.196	77	5,929	8.775
28	784	5.292	78	6,084	8.832
29	841	5.385	79	6,241	8.888
30	900	5.477	80	6,400	8.944
31	961	5.568	81	6,561	9
32	1,024	5.657	82	6,724	9.055
33	1,089	5.745	83	6,889	9.110
34	1,156	5.831	84	7,056	9.165
35	1,225	5.916	85	7,225	9.220
36	1,296	6	86	7,396	9.274
37	1,369	6.083	87	7,569	9.327
38	1,444	6.164	88	7,744	9.381
39	1,521	6.245	89	7,921	9.434
40	1,600	6.325	90	8,100	9.487
41	1,681	6.403	91	8,281	9.539
42	1,764	6.481	92	8,464	9.592
43	1,849	6.557	93	8,649	9.644
44	1,936	6.633	94	8,836	9.695
45	2,025	6.708	95	9,025	9.747
46	2,116	6.782	96	9,216	9.798
47	2,209	6.856	97	9,409	9.849
48	2,304	6.928	98	9,604	9.899
49	2,401	7	99	9,801	9.950
50	2,500	7.071	100	10,000	10

TABLES

Table 2: Table of Trigonometric Ratios

Angle	Sine	Cosine	Tangent	Angle	Sine	Cosine	Tangent
1°	0.0175	0.9998	0.0175	46°	0.7193	0.6947	1.0355
2°	0.0349	0.9994	0.0349	47°	0.7314	0.6820	1.0724
3°	0.0523	0.9986	0.0524	48°	0.7431	0.6691	1.1106
4°	0.0698	0.9976	0.0699	49°	0.7547	0.6561	1.1504
5°	0.0872	0.9962	0.0875	50°	0.7660	0.6428	1.1918
6°	0.1045	0.9945	0.1051	51°	0.7771	0.6293	1.2349
7°	0.1219	0.9925	0.1228	52°	0.7880	0.6157	1.2799
8°	0.1392	0.9903	0.1405	53°	0.7986	0.6018	1.3270
9°	0.1564	0.9877	0.1584	54°	0.8090	0.5878	1.3764
10°	0.1736	0.9848	0.1763	55°	0.8192	0.5736	1.4281
11°	0.1908	0.9816	0.1944	56°	0.8290	0.5592	1.4826
12°	0.2079	0.9781	0.2126	57°	0.8387	0.5446	1.5399
13°	0.2250	0.9744	0.2309	58°	0.8480	0.5299	1.6003
14°	0.2419	0.9703	0.2493	59°	0.8572	0.5150	1.6643
15°	0.2588	0.9659	0.2679	60°	0.8660	0.5000	1.7321
16°	0.2756	0.9613	0.2867	61°	0.8746	0.4848	1.8040
17°	0.2924	0.9563	0.3057	62°	0.8829	0.4695	1.8807
18°	0.3090	0.9511	0.3249	63°	0.8910	0.4540	1.9626
19°	0.3256	0.9455	0.3443	64°	0.8988	0.4384	2.0503
20°	0.3420	0.9397	0.3640	65°	0.9063	0.4226	2.1445
21°	0.3584	0.9336	0.3839	66°	0.9135	0.4067	2.2460
22°	0.3746	0.9272	0.4040	67°	0.9205	0.3907	2.3559
23°	0.3907	0.9205	0.4245	68°	0.9272	0.3746	2.4751
24°	0.4067	0.9135	0.4452	69°	0.9336	0.3584	2.6051
25°	0.4226	0.9063	0.4663	70°	0.9397	0.3420	2.7475
26°	0.4384	0.8988	0.4877	71°	0.9455	0.3256	2.9042
27°	0.4540	0.8910	0.5095	72°	0.9511	0.3090	3.0777
28°	0.4695	0.8829	0.5317	73°	0.9563	0.2924	3.2709
29°	0.4848	0.8746	0.5543	74°	0.9613	0.2756	3.4874
30°	0.5000	0.8660	0.5774	75°	0.9659	0.2588	3.7321
31°	0.5150	0.8572	0.6009	76°	0.9703	0.2419	4.0108
32°	0.5299	0.8480	0.6249	77°	0.9744	0.2250	4.3315
33°	0.5446	0.8387	0.6494	78°	0.9781	0.2079	4.7046
34°	0.5592	0.8290	0.6745	79°	0.9816	0.1908	5.1446
35°	0.5736	0.8192	0.7002	80°	0.9848	0.1736	5.6713
36°	0.5878	0.8090	0.7265	81°	0.9877	0.1564	6.3138
37°	0.6018	0.7986	0.7536	82°	0.9903	0.1392	7.1154
38°	0.6157	0.7880	0.7813	83°	0.9925	0.1219	8.1443
39°	0.6293	0.7771	0.8098	84°	0.9945	0.1045	9.5144
40°	0.6428	0.7660	0.8391	85°	0.9962	0.0872	11.4301
41°	0.6561	0.7547	0.8693	86°	0.9976	0.0698	14.3007
42°	0.6691	0.7431	0.9004	87°	0.9986	0.0523	19.0811
43°	0.6820	0.7314	0.9325	88°	0.9994	0.0349	28.6363
44°	0.6947	0.7193	0.9657	89°	0.9998	0.0175	57.2900
45°	0.7071	0.7071	1.0000				

Glossary

A

absolute value (p. 5)   The absolute value of an integer is its distance from zero on a number line.

acute angle (p. 365)   An acute angle has measure less than 90°.

acute triangle (p. 374)   An acute triangle is one in which all angles have measure less than 90°.

adding two integers with different signs (p. 10)   To add two integers with different signs, find the *difference* of the absolute values of the addends. The sum has the sign of the integer with the greater absolute value.

adding two integers with the same sign (p. 10)   To add two integers with the same sign, add the absolute values of the integers. The sum has the same sign as the addends.

addition properties for inequalities (p. 296)

1. If $a > b$, then $a + c > b + c$.
2. If $a < b$, then $a + c < b + c$.

addition property of equality (p. 73)   You can add the same value to both sides of an equation.

If $a = b$, then $a + c = b + c$.

additive identity (p. 59)   The additive identity is zero. $a + 0 = a$

adjacent angles (p. 366)   Two angles that have the same vertex and have a common side but no interior points in common form adjacent angles.

altitude (p. 407)   An altitude is a segment from one vertex of a polygon perpendicular to the line containing the opposite side, called the base.

angle (p. 365)   Two rays with a common endpoint form an angle.

area (p. 406)   Area is the amount of surface inside a region. We measure area in square units.

area of a circle (p. 414)   The area of a circle equals the product of π and the square of the radius (r).
$A = \pi r^2$

area of a parallelogram (p. 407)   The area of a parallelogram equals the product of its base length (b) and its height (h). $A = bh$

area of a rectangle (p. 406)   The area of a rectangle equals the product of its base length (b) and its height (h). $A = bh$

area of a trapezoid (p. 411)   The area of a trapezoid equals half the product of the height (h) and the sum of the bases (b_1 and b_2). $A = \frac{1}{2}h(b_1 + b_2)$

area of a triangle (p. 410)   The area of a triangle equals half the product of the base length (b) and the height (h). $A = \frac{1}{2}bh$

associative property of addition (p. 58)   You can change the grouping and then add without changing the sum. $(a + b) + c = a + (b + c)$

associative property of multiplication (p. 59)   You can change the grouping and then multiply without changing the product. $(ab)c = a(bc)$

B

base (p. 141)   A base is a number used as a factor. For a^n, a is the base.

box and whisker plot (p. 502)   A box and whisker plot is an organization of data. It is especially useful to show the distribution of each 25% of data.

C

central angle (p. 377)   A central angle is an angle with the vertex at the center of a circle.

chord (p. 377)   A chord is a segment with endpoints on a circle.

circle (p. 377)   A circle ($\odot$) is the set of all points the same distance from a given point called the center.

circumference (p. 390)   The circumference (C) is the distance around a circle. Use the formula $C = \pi d$ to compute circumference.

common factor (p. 167)   The factors that are the same for a given set of numbers are the common factors. A common factor of 12 and 18 is 6.

common multiples (p. 168)   The multiples that are the same for a given set of whole numbers are the common multiples. A common multiple of 6 and 8 is 24.

commutative property of addition (p. 58)   You can add in any order without changing the sum.
$a + b = b + a$

commutative property of multiplication (p. 58)   You can multiply in any order without changing the product. $a \cdot b = b \cdot a$

compatible numbers (p. 105)   Compatible numbers are two numbers that are easy to compute mentally.

complementary angles (p. 366)   Two angles are complementary angles if the sum of their measures is 90°.

composite number (p. 163)   A composite number is a whole number greater than one with more than two factors.

compound event (p. 522)   A compound event is a combination of two or more events.

cone (p. 421)   A cone is a space figure with one circular base and one vertex.

congruent polygons (p. 380)   Two polygons are congruent if there is a correspondence between their vertices such that the corresponding sides and corresponding angles are congruent.

converse of Pythagorean theorem (p. 462)   If $a^2 + b^2 = c^2$, then the triangle with sides a, b, and c is a right triangle.

convex and concave polygons (p. 370)   A polygon is convex if all points on the diagonals are inside the polygon. Otherwise, the polygon is concave.

coordinate plane (p. 316)   A coordinate plane is the plane which results when two perpendicular number lines intersect at their zero points. The number lines form a grid on the plane.

cosine ratio (p. 473)   In a right triangle, the cosine of $\angle A = \frac{\text{length of side adjacent to } \angle A}{\text{hypotenuse}}$.

counting principle (p. 508)   The counting principle states that the number of outcomes for an event with two or more stages equals the product of the number of outcomes at each stage.

cross products (p. 185)   Finding cross products is a method of checking equivalence of fractions or ratios.
$\frac{a}{b} = \frac{c}{d}$, if $a \cdot d = b \cdot c$

cylinder (p. 421)   A cylinder is a space figure with two circular, parallel, and congruent bases.

D

data base (p. 122)   A data base is a collection of information.

dependent events (p. 523)   Dependent events are events in which the outcome of one depends on the outcome of the other.

For two dependent events A and B, where B is dependent on A,

$P(A \text{ and } B) = P(A) \cdot P(B, \text{ given } A)$.

diagonal (p. 370)   A diagonal is a segment that joins two nonconsecutive vertices of a polygon.

diameter (p. 377)   A diameter is a chord that passes through the center of a circle. The diameter (d) is the length of such a segment.

direct variation (p. 353)   Direct variation means that as one factor increases the other factor also increases. We represent direct variation by an equation in the form $y = kx$, where k is not zero. k is the constant of variation.

distributive property of multiplication over addition (p. 62)   You can distribute a factor to each term inside a set of parentheses.
$a(b + c) = ab + ac \qquad (b + c)a = ba + ca$

distributive property of multiplication over subtraction (p. 62)   You can distribute a factor to each term inside a set of parentheses.
$a(b - c) = ab - ac \qquad (b - c)a = ba - ca$

dividing integers (p. 26)   To divide two integers, find the quotient of the absolute values of the integers. Then use these rules.

1. The quotient of two integers with the same sign is positive.
$(+) \div (+) = + \qquad (-) \div (-) = +$
2. The quotient of two integers with different signs is negative.
$(+) \div (-) = - \qquad (-) \div (+) = -$

dividing two rational numbers (p. 207)   For any two rational numbers $\frac{a}{b}$ and $\frac{c}{d}$,
$\frac{a}{b} \div \frac{c}{d} = \frac{a}{b} \cdot \frac{d}{c} \qquad b \neq 0, c \neq 0, d \neq 0$.

divisible (p. 159)   A number is divisible by a second number if the second number divides the first with no remainder.

divisible by 3 (p. 160)   A number is divisible by 3 if the sum of its digits is divisible by 3.

divisible by 9 (p. 160)   A number is divisible by 9 if the sum of its digits is divisible by 9.

division properties for inequalities (p. 297)

1. If c is positive and $a < b$, then $\frac{a}{c} < \frac{b}{c}$.
2. If c is positive and $a > b$, then $\frac{a}{c} > \frac{b}{c}$.
3. If c is negative and $a < b$, then $\frac{a}{c} > \frac{b}{c}$.
4. If c is negative and $a > b$, then $\frac{a}{c} < \frac{b}{c}$.

division property of equality (p. 76)   You can divide both sides of an equation by the same nonzero value.

If $a = b$, then $a \div c = b \div c$, $\dfrac{a}{c} = \dfrac{b}{c}$, $c \neq 0$.

E

equation (p. 54)   An equation is a mathematical sentence with an equal sign.

equiangular triangle (p. 374)   An equiangular triangle is a triangle in which all angles have equal measure.

equilateral triangle (p. 374)   An equilateral triangle is a triangle in which all sides have equal measure.

equivalent fractions (p. 184)   You can form equivalent fractions by multiplying or dividing the numerator and denominator by the same nonzero factor.

evaluate an expression (p. 44)   To evaluate an expression, replace each variable with a number. Then compute, following order of operations.

exponent (p. 141)   An exponent shows the number of times a base is used as a factor. For a^n, n is the exponent.

F

factor (p. 159)   One number is a factor of another if it divides that number with no remainder.

factorial (p. 509)   A factorial is the product of all whole numbers from n to 1. We write this as $n!$.

FOIL method (p. 550)   Use the FOIL method to find the product of two binomials.

1. Multiply the **F**irst terms in each binomial.
2. Multiply the **O**utside terms in each binomial.
3. Multiply the **I**nside terms in each binomial.
4. Multiply the **L**ast terms in each binomial.
5. Add the products.

formula (p. 128)   A formula is an equation that shows the relationship between two or more variables.

frequency distribution (p. 492)   A frequency distribution is a listing of data that pairs each data item with the number of times it occurs.

front-end estimation (p. 105)   To use front-end estimation:

1. Add the front-end digits.
2. Adjust by estimating the sum of the remaining digits.
3. Add the two values.

G

greatest common factor (GCF) (p. 167)   The greatest common factor of a set of numbers is the greatest number that is a factor of the given numbers.

grouping symbols (p. 40)   Grouping symbols include parentheses, ( ), brackets, [ ], absolute value symbols, and a division bar. These are used to group expressions.

H

height (p. 407)   The height of a figure is the length of its altitude.

hypotenuse (p. 460)   The hypotenuse is the side of a right triangle opposite the right angle.

I

improper fraction (p. 188)   A fraction that has a numerator equal to or greater than the denominator is an improper fraction.

independent events (p. 522)   Independent events are events in which the outcome of one has no affect on the outcome of the other.

For two independent events A and B,
$P(\text{A and B}) = P(\text{A}) \cdot P(\text{B})$.

indirect variation (p. 353)   In indirect variation, one factor increases as the other factor decreases. The equation $xy = k$ represents an indirect variation. k is the constant of variation.

inequality (p. 292)   An inequality is a statement that two expressions are not equal.

integers (p. 4)   The whole numbers and their opposites form the set of integers.

$$\ldots, -4, -3, -2, -1, 0, 1, 2, 3, 4, \ldots$$
negative   zero   positive

inverse operations (p. 72)   Inverse operations are operations that undo each other. Addition and subtraction are inverse operations. Multiplication and division are inverse operations.

GLOSSARY

irrational numbers (p. 455)   Irrational numbers are numbers which we cannot express as either terminating or repeating decimals.

isosceles triangle (p. 374)   An isosceles triangle has at least two sides with equal measure.

L

lateral area of a cone (p. 430)   The lateral area (LA) of a cone equals half the product of the circumference (C) and slant height (l).
$$LA = \frac{1}{2} Cl$$

lateral area of a cylinder (p. 428)   The lateral area (LA) of a cylinder is the product of the circumference of the base (C) and the height of the cylinder (h).
$$A = Ch$$

lateral area of a prism (p. 427)   The lateral area (LA) of a prism is the product of the perimeter of the base (P) and the height of the prism (h).
$$A = Ph$$

least common denominator (LCD) (p. 196)   The least common denominator of two or more fractions is the LCM of the denominators.

least common multiple (LCM) (p. 168)   The least common multiple is the least number that is a common multiple of two or more given numbers.

legs of a right triangle (p. 460)   The legs of a right triangle are the two sides that form the right angle.

like terms (p. 66)   Like terms have the same variable(s).

line (p. 362)   A line continues without end in opposite directions. We denote line AB by $\overleftrightarrow{AB}$.

line plot (p. 492)   A line plot shows data on a number line. You place an $\times$ for each response above the category of the response.

line symmetry (p. 381)   A figure is said to have line symmetry if a line can be drawn through the figure so that one side is a mirror image of the other.

linear equation (p. 324)   A linear equation is an equation for which the graph is a line. The standard form of a linear equation is $Ax + By = C$, where A, B, and C are real numbers and A and B are not both equal to zero.

locating a point on the coordinate plane (p. 316)
To locate $P(x, y)$ on the coordinate plane:
1. Begin at origin.
2. Locate x on the x-axis.
3. Move up or down the absolute value of y units.

lowest terms (p. 185)   When a fraction is in lowest terms, the only common factor of the numerator and denominator is 1.

M

mean (p. 27)   The mean is the sum of a set of numbers divided by the number of items in the set.

measures of central tendency (p. 488)   The measures of central tendency are statistics used to describe data characteristics. These measures are mean, median, and mode.

median (p. 488)   The median is the middle value in a set of data.

mixed number (p. 188)   A mixed number is a number that includes an integer and a fraction.

mode (p. 488)   The mode is the data item that occurs most often.

monomial (p. 538)   A monomial is a real number, a variable, or the product of a real number and one or more variables.

multiple (p. 159)   A multiple of a number is the product of that number and any other whole number.

multiplication properties for inequalities (p. 297)
1. If c is positive and $a < b$, then $ac < bc$.
2. If c is positive and $a > b$, then $ac > bc$.
3. If c is negative and $a < b$, then $ac > bc$.
4. If c is negative and $a > b$, then $ac < bc$.

multiplication property of equality (p. 77)   You can multiply both sides of an equation by the same value. If $a = b$, then $ac = bc$.

multiplicative identity (p. 59)   The multiplicative identity is one. $a \cdot 1 = a$

multiplying integers (p. 22)   To multiply two integers, find the product of the absolute values of the integers. Then use these rules.
1. The product of two integers with the same sign is positive.
   $(+)(+) = +$ $(-)(-) = +$
2. The product of two integers with different signs is negative.
   $(+)(-) = -$ $(-)(+) = -$

N

negative exponents (p. 212)   For any nonzero integers a and n: $a^{-n} = \frac{1}{a^n}$.

numerical coefficient (p. 66)   A numerical coefficient is a number that is multiplied by a variable.

numerical expression (p. 34)   A numerical expression names a number. A numerical expression does not contain variables.

O

obtuse angle (p. 365)   An obtuse angle is an angle with measure between 90° and 180°.

obtuse triangle (p. 374)   An obtuse triangle has one obtuse angle.

open equation (p. 54)   An open equation is an equation that contains one or more variables.

opposites (p. 4)   Opposites are two integers the same distance from zero on a number line, but in opposite directions.

order of operations (p. 40)
1. Do all operations within grouping symbols.
2. Evaluate powers.
3. Multiply and divide from left to right.
4. Add and subtract from left to right.

ordered pair (p. 316)   An ordered pair is a pair of numbers (x,y) assigned to a point on a coordinate plane.

origin (p. 316)   The origin is the intersection point of the x- and y-axes in a coordinate plane. The coordinates of the origin are (0,0).

P

parallel lines (p. 363)   Two lines are parallel if they lie in the same plane and do not intersect.

parallel planes (p. 363)   Two planes are parallel if they do not intersect.

parallelogram (p. 371)   A parallelogram is a quadrilateral with two pairs of opposite parallel sides.

percent (p. 245)   A percent is a ratio that compares a number to 100.

percent equation (p. 256)   Use a triangle to solve percent problems.

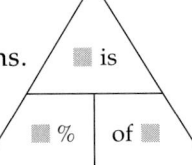

percent of change (p. 260)   Use the following formula to find percent of change.

percent of change = $\frac{\text{amount of change}}{\text{original amount}}$

perimeter (p. 390)   Perimeter is the distance around a figure.

pi (π) (p. 389)   Pi is the ratio of the circumference of a circle to its diameter.

plane (p. 362)   A plane is a flat surface with no thickness that continues without end in all directions.

point (p. 362)   A point represents a position in space.

polygon (p. 370)   A polygon is a closed plane figure such that no two segments with a common endpoint are collinear and segments intersect only at the endpoints.

polyhedron (p. 420)   A polyhedron is a space figure in which all faces are polygons.

polynomial (p. 538)   A polynomial is a monomial or a sum or difference of monomials.

prime factorization (p. 164)   Prime factorization is an expression showing a composite number as a product of its prime factors.

prime number (p. 163)   A prime number is a whole number greater than 1 with exactly two factors, 1 and the number itself.

principal square root (p. 454)   The principal square root of a number is its positive square root. The principal square root is denoted by the symbol $\sqrt{\ }$.

prism (p. 420)   A prism is a polyhedron with two parallel bases that are congruent polygons and sides that are parallelograms.

probability (p. 512)   Probability is the likelihood that a certain event, or set of outcomes, will occur.

$P(E) = \frac{\text{number of favorable outcomes}}{\text{total number of possible outcomes}}$

product of $(a + b)(a - b)$ (p. 551)   To find the product of the sum and difference of two terms, square the first term and subtract the square of the second term.

$(a + b)(a - b) = a^2 - b^2$

product of two rational numbers (p. 206)   For any two rational numbers $\frac{a}{b}$ and $\frac{c}{d}$,

$\frac{a}{b} \cdot \frac{c}{d} = \frac{a \cdot c}{b \cdot d}$, $b \neq 0, d \neq 0$.

proportion (p. 233)   A proportion is a statement that two ratios are equal. If two ratios are equal, their cross products are equal.

a is to b as c is to d

$a : b : : c : d, \frac{a}{b} = \frac{c}{d}, b \neq 0, d \neq 0$

proportions and percents (p. 252)   To find the ratio of a number to 100, use the following formula.

$\frac{\text{part}}{\text{whole}} = \frac{n}{100}$

pyramid (p. 420)   A pyramid is a polyhedron with triangular sides that meet at a vertex. The base of a pyramid is a polygon.

Pythagorean theorem (p. 461)   In any right triangle with legs a and b, and hypotenuse c,

$a^2 + b^2 = c^2$.

Q

quadrant (p. 316)   A quadrant is one of four sections into which the x- and y-axes divide the coordinate plane.

quadrilateral (p. 371)   A quadrilateral is a polygon with four sides.

R

radius (p. 377)   A radius is a segment that has endpoints at the center of a circle and on the circle. The radius (r) is the length of such a segment.

range (p. 489)   The range of a set of data is the difference between the greatest and least values in the set.

rate (p. 234)   A rate is a ratio that compares quantities in different units. A unit rate compares a quantity to one.

ratio (p. 233)   A ratio is a comparison of two quantities by division.

a to b; $a : b$; $\frac{a}{b}$; $b \neq 0$

rational number (p. 192)   A rational number is a number you write in the form $\frac{a}{b}$, where a is any integer, and b is a nonzero integer.

ray (p. 362)   A ray is part of a line with only one endpoint that continues without end in one direction. We denote ray AB as $\overrightarrow{AB}$.

rectangle (p. 371)   A rectangle is a parallelogram with four right angles.

regular polygon (p. 371)   A polygon is regular if the measures of all sides and all angles are equal.

rhombus (p. 371)   A rhombus is a parallelogram with all sides equal.

right angle (p. 365)   A right angle is an angle that measures 90°.

right triangle (p. 374)   A right triangle is a triangle with one right angle.

rule of a power raised to a power (p. 145)   To raise a power to a power, multiply the exponents.

$(a^m)^n = a^{m \cdot n}$

rule of a product raised to a power (p. 146)   To raise a product to a power, raise each factor to the power and then use the rule of exponents for multiplication. $(ab)^m = a^m b^m$

rule of exponents for division (p. 211)   To divide numbers or variables with the *same* base, subtract exponents.

$\frac{a^m}{a^n} = a^{m-n}, a \neq 0$

rule of exponents for multiplication (p. 145)   To multiply numbers or variables with the *same* base, add exponents. $a^m \cdot a^n = a^{m+n}$

S

sample space (p. 512)   The set of possible outcomes is the sample space.

scalene triangle (p. 374)   A scalene triangle is a triangle that has no sides equal.

scientific notation (p. 149)   A number is in scientific notation when it is written as the product of a number greater than or equal to 1 and less than 10, and a power of 10.

segment (p. 362)   A segment is part of a line with two endpoints. We denote segment AB by $\overline{AB}$.

similar figures (p. 384)   Two figures are similar ($\sim$) if corresponding angles are congruent and corresponding sides are in proportion.

similar triangles (p. 385)   Two triangles are similar if two angles of one are congruent to two angles of another.

simplify an expression (p. 67)   To simplify an expression, replace it with an equivalent expression that contains no like terms or parentheses.

sine ratio (p. 473)   In a right triangle, the

sine of $\angle A = \frac{\text{length of side opposite } \angle A}{\text{hypotenuse}}$.

skew lines (p. 363)   Skew lines are lines that do not lie in the same plane and do not intersect.

slant height (p. 430)   A slant height of a cone or a pyramid is the height of a face.

slope (p. 330)   The slope of a line is the ratio of the vertical change in y to the corresponding horizontal change in x. Use the following formula to calculate slope.

$$\text{slope} = \frac{\text{difference in } y \text{ coordinates}}{\text{difference in } x \text{ coordinates}}$$

slope-intercept form (p. 331)   A linear equation in the form $y = mx + b$ is in slope-intercept form. The slope is m and the y-intercept is b.

solution (p. 55)   A solution is a number that replaces a variable to make an open equation true.

solution of a system of linear equations (p. 340)   A solution of a system of linear equations is any ordered pair of numbers that satisfies all equations in the system.

solving a multi-step equation (p. 279)   To solve a multi-step equation:

1. Remove parentheses using the distributive property.
2. Combine like terms.
3. Undo addition or subtraction.
4. Undo multiplication or division.

solving a simple two-step equation (p. 275)   To solve a simple two-step equation:

1. Undo addition or subtraction.
2. Undo multiplication or division.

solving proportions (p. 237)   To solve a proportion:

1. Write the cross products.
2. Solve the equation.

sphere (p. 421)   A sphere is the set of all points in space that are the same distance from a given point called the center.

square (p. 371)   A square is a parallelogram that is both a rectangle and a rhombus.

square root (p. 454)   The square root of a number, n, is a if $a^2 = n$.

squaring binomials (p. 551)   To square a binomial, square the first term. Then add or subtract twice the product of the two terms and add the square of the second term.

$$(a + b)^2 = a^2 + 2ab + b^2$$
$$(a - b)^2 = a^2 - 2ab + b^2$$

stem and leaf plot (p. 498)   A stem and leaf plot is an organization of data that groups data into categories based on place values.

subtracting integers (p. 15)   To subtract an integer, add its opposite.

subtraction properties for inequalities (p. 296)

1. If $a > b$, then $a - c > b - c$.
2. If $a < b$, then $a - c < b - c$.

subtraction property of equality (p. 72)   You can subtract the same value from both sides of an equation.

If $a = b$, then $a - c = b - c$.

supplementary angles (p. 366)   Two angles are supplementary angles if the sum of their measures is 180°.

surface area (p. 427)   Surface area (SA) is the sum of the areas of the base(s) and the side(s). Surface area is measured in square units.

surface area of a sphere (p. 431)   The surface area of a sphere equals the product of 4π and the square of the radius (r).

$$A = 4\pi r^2$$

system of linear equations (p. 340)   A system of linear equations is two or more linear equations using the same variables.

system of linear inequalities (p. 349)   A system of linear inequalities is two or more linear inequalities using the same variables.

T

tangent ratio (p. 473)   In a right triangle, the tangent of $\angle A = \frac{\text{length of side opposite } \angle A}{\text{length of side adjacent to } \angle A}$.

term (p. 66)   A term is a part of an expression. Terms are separated by addition and subtraction symbols.

tessellation (p. 397)   A tessellation is a design that covers a plane with no gaps and no overlaps.

trapezoid (p. 371)   A trapezoid is a quadrilateral with exactly one pair of parallel sides.

triangle (p. 371)   A triangle is a polygon that has three sides.

triangle, 30°-60°-90° (p. 470)   In a 30°-60°-90° triangle, the lengths of the sides have the following relationships.

hypotenuse = 2(shorter leg)

longer leg = shorter leg ($\sqrt{3}$)

shorter leg = $\frac{\text{longer leg}}{\sqrt{3}}$

triangle, 45°-45°-90° (p. 469)   In a 45°-45°-90° right triangle, the lengths of the sides have the following relationships.

hypotenuse = $\sqrt{2} \cdot$ leg

leg = $\dfrac{\text{hypotenuse} \cdot \sqrt{2}}{2}$

trigonometric ratio (p. 473)   A trigonometric ratio is a ratio of the measures of two sides of a right triangle.

V

variable (p. 34)   A variable is a symbol (usually a letter) that stands for a number.

variable expression (p. 34)   A variable expression is an expression that contains at least one variable.

vertex (p. 365)   The vertex of an angle is the common endpoint of the two rays forming the angle.

vertical angles (p. 366)   Two intersecting lines form two pairs of vertical angles. The measures of vertical angles are equal.

volume (p. 437)   Volume is the measure of the space inside a space figure. We measure volume in cubic units.

volume of a cone and a pyramid (p. 440)   The formula for the volume of the cone and pyramid is base area (B) times one-third the height (h).

$V = \dfrac{1}{3} Bh$

volume of a cylinder or a prism (p. 437)   The volume (V) of a prism or a cylinder is base area (B) times the height (h).

$V = Bh$

volume of a sphere (p. 441)   The volume (V) of a sphere with radius r is $V = \frac{4}{3} \pi r^3$.

X

x-axis (p. 316)   The x-axis is the horizontal number line on a coordinate plane.

x-intercept (p. 325)   The x-intercept is the x-coordinate of a point where a graph crosses the x-axis.

Y

y-axis (p. 316)   The y-axis is the vertical number line on a coordinate plane.

y-intercept (p. 325)   The y-intercept is the y-coordinate of a point where a graph crosses the y-axis.

Z

zero as an exponent (p. 211)   Any nonzero number with zero as an exponent equals 1.

$a^0 = 1$ for all $a \neq 0$.

Selected Answers

CHAPTER 1

Integers and Expressions

1-1 pages 6–7
Written Exercises **1.** 110 **3.** -300 **5.** -8 **13.** -6 **15.** 3
17. 4 **19.** -9 **21.** -12,500; -15,617; 0 **23.** -2 **25.** -8
27. 8 **33.** > **35.** < **37.** < **39.** = **41.** zero
43. negative **53. a.** -27°; **b.** -20°; -71°
Mixed Review **1.** 907 **2.** 814 **3.** 1,088 **4.** 42
5. 7,872 **6.** 13

1-2 pages 12–13
Written Exercises **1.** -20 + 18 = -2; still owe $2
3. -10 + (-2) + 8 + (-5) + (-13) + 1 = -21; temp. is 21°
below. **5.** -9 **7.** 4 **9.** 9 **11.** -8 **13.** -40 **15.** -847
17. -5 **19.** 0 **21.** 3 **23.** -13 **25.** 15 **27.** -13 **29.** 4
31. -6 **33.** 9 **35.** -6 < 2 **37.** -2 + (-7) = -9
39. 3 + (-8) = -5 **41.** < **43.** < ; < **45.** 10-yd loss
Mixed Review **1.** -8 **2.** 12 **3.** 10 **4.** 16 **5.** < **6.** >
7. 12 **8.** -13
Critical Thinking **1.** -7, 525, -47 **2.** -19, -50, -198
3. -7, -78, -47 **4.** all neg. **5.** -47, -19, -7; -5, -25, -40

1-3 pages 15–17
Written Exercises **1.** 3 − (-2) = 5 **3.** 3 − 5 = -2
5. 3,000 − 600 **7.** -5 **9.** -16 **11.** -60 **13.** 150 **15.** 66
17. -196 **19.** 178 **21.** 913 **23.** -31 **25.** 25 **27.** -175
29. -422 **31.** 15 **33.** 191 **35.** -101 **37.** 56 **39.** 356
41. 38 **43.** 16; 20; 24; 28; 28 **45.** -7, -6, -1, -3, -8; -15
47. a. The temperature decreases.; **b.** 24°; **c.** decrease;
d. 21,000 m **49.** -15 **57.** 180 **59.** -70 **61.** 2,400
63. -3,600
Mixed Review **1.** -29 **2.** 65 **3.** 7 **4.** -6
5. -6, -7, -8, or -9 **6.** -6 **7.** -925 ft

1-4 pages 20–21
Written Exercises **1.** 78 students
3. 4, 3, 1, 16, 15, 1; 9, 8, 1, 25, 24, 1; **a.** 11 · 11; 1
b. subtract 1; 2,208; **c.** add 1; 4,225
5. 1810 and 1820; 467,174 people **7. a.** $59; $21; **b.** 10
Critical Thinking **1.** 107 **2.** 234 **3.** 37

1-5 pages 24–25
Written Exercises **1.** -60 **3.** -30 **5.** 21 **7.** 20 **9.** A
11. B **13.** 4,661 **15.** 46,354 **17.** 15 **19.** -96
21. -220 **23.** 12,288 **25.** -200 **27.** -56 **29.** -7 **31.** 0
33. -26 **35.** -81 **37.** -19 **39.** 8(-5) = -40
41. 6(-9) = -54 **43.** > **45.** = **47. a.** -$36; **b.** $40
49. -3 and -4 **51.** 5 and -1 **53. a.** 5,000 ft at 40°; **b.** no
Mixed Review **1.** < **2.** > **3.** < **4.** -11 **5.** 3,003
6. |-20| **7.** 6 **8.** 180°

1-6 pages 27–29
Written Exercises **1.** -9(10) = -90 **3.** 8(7) = 56 **5.** -7
7. -5 **9.** -9 **11.** 126 **13.** 56 **15.** 4 **17.** 19 **19.** -1
21. -15 **23.** -384 **25.** -59 **27.** -225 **29.** -80 **31.** -35
33. 64 **35.** 3,375 **37.** -9 **39.** -42(3); -126
41. -25 − 200; -225 **43.** $3 **45.** 0 **47.** < **49.** <
55. -15 **57.** 2 ft/s
Mixed Review **1.** -45 **2.** 24 **3.** -48 **4.** 30
5. 13, 18, 23 **6.** 25, 36, 49
Test Yourself **1.** > **2.** < **3.** = **4.** 8 **5.** -85 **6.** -12
7. -8 **8.** 20 **9.** -45 **10.** 8 **11.** 3 **12.** 44

Practice page 30
1. 55 **3.** -23 **5.** -19 **7.** 133 **9.** -334 **11.** 141
13. -100 **15.** 63 **17.** -89 **19.** -62 **21.** -238 **23.** -224
25. -705 **27.** 63 **29.** -84 **31.** -162 **33.** 375 **35.** -896
37. 288 **39.** -496,000 **41.** -9 **43.** -6 **45.** -5 **47.** 37
49. -37 **51.** 153 **53.** 8 **55.** 142 **57.** -20 **59.** -3
61. 0 **63.** 55 **65.** 10 **67.** -1

1-7 page 33
Written Exercises **1.** 90 C **3.** 230 C **5.** 120 C
7. -580 C **9.** 660 C; about 5 h **11.** 900 C; 18,000 C

1-8 pages 36–37
Written Exercises **1.** $3x − 3$ **3.** $3z + (-2)$ **9.** $23(-9)$
11. $-6 − 8$ **13.** $19 + m$ **15.** $12x$ **17.** $n \div (-1)$
19. $g \cdot 4r$ **21.** $10a$ **23.** $t + 200$ **33. a.** 7 · 1; **b.** 7 · 4;
c. $7w$ **35. a.** 15 − 3; **b.** $15 − p$; **c.** 15 + 10; **d.** $15 + f$
37. $d − 20$ **41. a.** (2 · 25) + (4 · 12); **b.** $25j + 12t$ **43.** b
45. d
Mixed Review **1.** -5 **2.** 20 **3.** 0 **4.** -23 **5.** 100 **6.** 8
7. $2.95

1-9 pages 41–43
Written Exercises **1.** addition **3.** subtraction inside
absolute value symbols **5.** -1 **7.** 3 **9.** 4 **11.** -20
13. -30 **15.** -13 **17.** 243 **19.** 4 **21.** -394 **23.** -8
25. -2[(7 + 8) ÷ 5 + 5] = -16 **27.** >
29. (7 + 4) · 6 = 66 **31.** 3 · (8 − 2 + 5 − 12) = -3
33. no **35.** yes **37.** 25 h **39.** Alice 103; Ray 118
41. A possible answer is [-6 + (-8)](6 + 4) − 2
45. 5 + (4)(9); 41 **47.** 17 − (25 ÷ 5); 12
49. 130 + (116 − 8); 238 **55.** 74 + 5*9 + -7 = 112
57. 70 + 8*-9 = -2 **59.** 2,087*37 − 1,951 = 75,268
61. Yes, computers follow order of operations.
Mixed Review **1.** $6n$ **2.** $x − 6$ **3.** $a + |-7|$ **4.** <
5. < **6.** < **7.** 36

1-10 pages 45–46
Written Exercises **1.** -24 **3.** -5 **5.** -12 **7.** 11 **9.** 21
11. 7 **13.** 20 **15.** -35 **17.** 21 **19.** 1 **21.** 425 **23.** 18
25. 117 **27.** A possible answer is 2. **29.** 8, -8 **31.** -6
33. 0 **35.** 3 **37. a.** $265m$; **b.** 1,590; **c.** 381,600
39. a. $14m$; **b.** 350 C **41.** $400 **43.** 6, 12, -12, 36, 4
45. 55 **47. a.** 13; **b.** 24

Mixed Review   1. -54   **2.** -48   **3.** -5   **4.** -24
5. the sum of 6 and a number
6. twice the quantity of a number minus 2
7. the opposite of 12 times a number   **8.** 83

Problem Solving Practice page 47
1. a. Each month the interest increases by a penny more than the previous month.; **b.** May $1.04, $105.10; June $1.05, $106.15; July $1.06, $107.21; August $1.07, $108.28   **3.** thermosphere, mesosphere, stratosphere, troposphere   **5.** -39°F

Chapter 1 Review pages 48–49
1. grouping symbols; order of operations   **2.** opposite
3. integers   **4.** absolute value
5. variable expression; variable   **6.** mean   **7.** >   **8.** >
9. =   **10.** <   **11.** <   **12.** >   **13.** -7   **14.** 12   **15.** -9
16. 14   **17.** -12   **18.** -16   **19.** -27   **20.** -15   **21.** -1
22. -42   **23.** -5   **24.** 72   **25.** 7   **26.** -3   **27.** -165
28. $x - 25$ **29.** $3rn$ **30.** $y + 2$ **31.** 36   **32.** 33   **33.** 25
34. 24   **35.** 3   **36.** 4   **37.** 19   **38.** 6   **39.** 16   **40.** 14
41. -450   **42.** 16   **43.** $112   **44.** She will gain weight.

Chapter 1 Cumulative Review page 51
1. A   **3.** C   **5.** D   **7.** B   **9.** B   **11.** B   **13.** A   **15.** D

CHAPTER 2

Solving Equations

2-1 pages 56–57
Written Exercises   1. yes   **3.** yes   **5.** open   **7.** false
9. false   **11.** true   **13.** true   **15.** true   **17.** false
19. true   **21.** yes   **23.** yes   **25.** yes   **27.** no   **29.** yes
31. 0   **33.** -2   **35.** 4   **37.** >   **39.** <   **41.** >   **43.** 30; 48
45. 15; 28   **47.** $0 \cdot (-7) = -7$; false
49. $15 + n = 50$; open   **51.** $(-7) + 12 = -5$; false
53. $3 \cdot 32 = 96$; true   **57.** $13b = f$
Mixed Review   1. -1   **2.** 10   **3.** -3   **4.** 13
5. 13, 21, 34 or 12, 17, 23   **6.** 15, 8, 3   **7.** 12h

2-2 pages 60–61
Written Exercises   1. c   **3.** d   **5.** f   **7.** d   **9.** c
11. $z \cdot 25$ **13.** $5(a + b)$ **15.** $3 \cdot (25 \cdot 4)$ **17.** $4(ab)$
19. 47,000   **21.** 2,800   **23.** 100   **25.** 3; 7   **27.** 730; 270
29. 58   **31.** 60   **33.** 60,000   **35. a.** No, it would change the order of operations. **b.** Yes, it does not matter in what order you multiply 6, 5, and -4.
Mixed Review   1. true   **2.** open   **3.** no   **4.** yes   **5.** no
6. yes   **7.** $3 \cdot (4 - 7) + 6 = -3$ **8.** 4 and 9

2-3 pages 64–65
Written Exercises   1. $4(w + 7)$ **3.** $7(x + y + 5)$ **5.** -4
7. c **9.** $-w$ **11.** $-9; -9(x + y)$ **13.** $e; (b - c - d)e$
15. $-1; -1(a + b)$ **17.** w, y **19.** -2, -4   **21.** 5, -2
23. 1,120   **25.** 5,075   **27.** -12   **29.** -30   **31.** 7   **33.** 285
35. 16   **37.** 3,098 mi
Mixed Review   1. C   **2.** AI   **3.** A   **4.** MI   **5.** <
6. =   **7.** <   **8.** 605

Critical Thinking   1. a. 3; **b.** 0; **c.** 1   **2. a.** =; **b.** yes
3. yes   **4.** yes; zero   **5.** It is an operation which is associative and commutative. It has an identity of zero.

2-4 pages 68–69
Written Exercises   1. 2; 5, 8; 5a, 8a; none
3. 2; 2; none; -7   **5.** 2; -7; none; 3
7. 4; 6, 4, 1; 6ab, 4ba, ab; 8   **9.** 9a   **11.** 5b   **13.** A
15. D   **17.** A   **19.** 5a   **21.** 6; 4; 10   **23.** 1m   **25.** 6a
27. $54k + 5$ **29.** $5g + 15$ **31.** $8x - 32w$ **33.** -83x
35. $44a - 59b + 19c$ **37.** -12y; 60   **39.** $3y + 2z - 16$; -17
41. $6x + 7x + 14$; $13x + 14$
43. $3x + 2x + 189$; $5x + 189$
Mixed Review   1. 7   **2.** 3   **3.** 5   **4.** 3   **5.** -4   **6.** 86
7. 46
Test Yourself   1. yes   **2.** no   **3.** no   **4.** C   **5.** A
6. MI   **7.** C   **8.** C   **9.** D   **10.** 50b   **11.** 173   **12.** 18y
13. 9a   **14.** -2   **15.** $16w - 6$

2-5 pages 74–75
Written Exercises   1. $x = 2$ **3.** $w = -2$ **5.** $-2 = x - 3$; 1
7. -5   **9.** -54   **11.** 626   **13.** 82   **15.** -13   **17.** 10,221
19. 41   **21.** 39   **23.** -11   **25.** -300   **27.** 0   **29.** 308
31. 1,364,615   **33.** 77,098   **35.** 500   **37.** 65   **39.** -20
41. 1,598   **43.** 25   **45.** $b - a$ **47.** $d + 5 = 17$; $d = 12$
49. $20 + d = 150$; $d = 130$
51. $5,200 = 2,680 + h$; $h = 2,520$
53. $700 = 119 + p$; $p = 581$ million
Mixed Review   1. 3   **2.** 3   **3.** $4x + 4$ **4.** $2q + 6$ **5.** 3
6. 12   **7.** 512 min

2-6 pages 77–79
Written Exercises   1. $g = 4$ **3.** $h = -3$ **5.** yes   **7.** no
9. $8 = 4x$; 2   **11.** -15   **13.** 6   **15.** -4   **17.** 5   **19.** 52
21. -16   **23.** 300   **25.** -24   **27.** 42   **29.** -15,000
31. 382,300   **33.** -42,336   **35.** -1,586   **37.** -768   **39.** -8
41. 504   **43.** 15   **45.** 31   **47.** 11   **49.** 0   **51.** 875,000
53. 12d   **55.** -6, 6   **57.** $\frac{b}{a}$ **59.** $b + a$
Mixed Review   1. -11   **2.** 17   **3.** -19   **4.** $a - 3 + b$
5. $7(9 - w)$ **6.** $|-8 + q|$ **7.** 60 s or 1 min
Critical Thinking   1. they get thinner   **2.** where all of the lines meet   **3.** All of the dot is on the missing piece.
4. 2   **5.** 3

2-7 pages 81–82
Written Exercises   1. c   **3.** $n - 24 = -9$ **5.** $15c = 30$
9. $x + 46 + 54 = 150$; 50 mm
Mixed Review   1. 515   **2.** 540   **3.** Divide each side by 5.
4. Subtract 5 from each side.   **5.** Add 5 to each side.
6. Multiply each side by 5.   **7.** 1,028 ft
Test Yourself   1. 20   **2.** -68   **3.** -34   **4.** 32   **5.** -23
6. -13   **7.** $n + 12 = 20$; 8   **8.** $(c - 6) - 3 = -10$; -1

2-8 page 86
Written Exercises   1. 12, 84 and 8, 56   **3.** 11, 12
5. -2, -3, -4   **7.** 12:40 P.M.   **9.** -10
11. 30 ft, 40 ft, 50 ft

Written Exercises **1.** $2,860,000,000
3. a. about 2 billion lb; **b.** about 16 billion kW · h
5. $325,000

Practice page 90
1. open **3.** true **5.** open **7.** no **9.** yes **11.** no
13. A **15.** C **17.** MI **19.** -476 **21.** 216 **23.** -22
25. 26 **27.** -16 **29.** -15k **31.** 5g + 8
33. 4x + 4y − 4z **35.** -3w + 4 **37.** 27 **39.** 12 **41.** 9
43. -39 **45.** 3,072 **47.** n + 5 = -123; -128

Problem Solving Practice page 91
1. a. 4; **b.** 8; **c.** yes; 16; 2 **3. a.** total wages for each
employee; **b.** = SUM(B2:B4); =SUM(D2:D4); place in
B5 and D5, respectively **5. a.** $260; **b.** $1\frac{1}{2}$ h

Chapter 2 Review pages 92–93
1. f **2.** a **3.** e **4.** i **5.** k **6.** j **7.** b **8.** c **9.** d
10. g **11.** h **12.** 547 **13.** 80 **14.** 700 **15.** 6,500
16. 115 **17.** 192 **18.** 80 **19.** 0 **20.** 8x + 5y
21. 9a + 16 **22.** x = -1 **23.** x = 3 **24.** a = 35
25. x = 11 **26.** y = 480 **27.** n = 20 **28.** x = -1
29. x = 2 **30.** m = -72 **31.** b = 12 **32.** c = 288
33. k = 18 **34.** 2x + 28 = 54 **35.** x − 17 = 12
38. 5 pkgs of 15 plates; 4 pkgs of 20 plates **39.** 80
billion lb

Chapters 1–2 Cumulative Review page 95
1. B **2.** C **3.** C **4.** D **5.** A **6.** A **7.** A **8.** C
9. C **10.** B **11.** B **12.** D **13.** C **14.** C **15.** B
16. B

CHAPTER 3

Decimals and Equations

3-1 pages 102–103
Written Exercises **5.** 512.73 km/h **11.** > **13.** =
15. > **17.** > **19.** 4.5, 4.05, 4.049
21. 3.003, 0.3002, 0.30, 0.030008, 0.03 **29.** 0.8 **31.** 0.36
33. 365,987 **37. a.** lesser; **b.** greater; **c.** when the digit to
the right is greater than the digit to the left **39.** If the
absolute value of a negative number is less than the
absolute value of another negative number, the first
number is greater than the second number.
Mixed Review **1.** -5 **2.** 3 **3.** -9 **4.** -45 **5.** 3 and 7
6. d − 40 = 182; $222

3-2 pages 106–107
Written Exercises **1.** 0.25 **3.** 60 **5.** 40 **7.** -18,000
9. 300 **11.** 8 **13.** 27 **15.** 3 **17.** 4 **19.** 0.02
21. $2,000 **23.** 0.23 **25.** 200 **27.** -20 **29.** 22.4256
31. 213.76 **33.** 109.571 **35.** 67.3436 **37.** yes
39. food **41.** $2 **43.** $3,200 **45.** about 3,500 yd
Mixed Review **1.** -0.88 **2.** 4.13 **3.** 24 **4.** -2 **5.** -108
6. 11 **7.** 36

3-3 pages 109–110
Written Exercises **1.** 11.5 h **3.** 14.375 h **5.** -7.8
7. 15.1 **9.** 6.14 **11.** -20.62 **13.** -25.48 **15.** -14.965
17. -3.07 **19.** -25 **21.** -20.44 **23.** 3.001 **25.** 7.69
27. -40.416w **29.** -0.8m **31.** 7.6x
33. 17.247a − 24.228 **35.** -1.8102x **37.** -90 **39.** 3
41. a. 12.3a − 1.08; **b.** 102.2523 **43.** $21.67
Mixed Review **1.** $200 **2.** 20,000 **3.** -5 **4.** 0.1 **5.** 4
6. 35 **7.** $.22
Critical Thinking **1.** 0.125 ÷ 0.625 = 0.2; 0.2 ÷ 0.125 =
1.6; 1.6 ÷ 0.2 = 8 **2.** 2.5 and 2; 2 ÷ 2.5 = 0.8; 0.8 ÷ 2 =
0.4; 0.4 ÷ 0.8 = 0.5; 0.5 ÷ 0.4 = 1.25; 1.25 ÷ 0.5 = 2.5;
2.5 ÷ 1.25 = 2; 2 ÷ 2.5 = 0.8; By following the pattern,
you arrive at the numbers you began with; no.
3. 2 and -0.2; -0.2 ÷ 2 = -0.1; -0.1 ÷ (-0.2) = 0.5; 0.5 ÷
(-0.1) = -5; -5 ÷ 0.5 = -10; -10 ÷ (-5) = 2; 2 ÷ (-10) =
-0.2; -0.2 ÷ 2 = -0.1; By following the
pattern, you arrive at the numbers you began with;
no. **4.** By following this pattern, you arrive at the
numbers you began with. It does not matter whether
you use decimals, whole numbers, positive numbers,
or negative numbers.

3-4 pages 112–114
Written Exercises **1.** -13.391 **3.** 1.63 **5.** -0.3698
7. -0.0233 **9.** 12.58 **11.** 1.032 **13.** 13.31 **15.** -23.12
17. 4.66 **19.** 2 **21.** 60,392.0034 **23.** 7.131 **25.** 3.9
27. 0 **29.** -5.4 **31.** 2.9 **33.** 0.4 **35.** -59.9
37. a. apple, grapefruit, orange, grape; **b.** blue
39. b − c = a **41.** x = 0.08 and y = -0.05
43. n − 0.058 = 0.58; 0.638
45. 1.0099 = n + 2; n = -0.9901
47. 3 + n = 8.16; n = 5.16
Mixed Review **1.** 7.629 **2.** -1.6642 **3.** -2.46 **4.** 4.754
5. -39.56x **6.** -0.28y **7.** $1.82
Test Yourself **1.** < **2.** = **3.** > **4.** -9.7 **5.** 4.3
6. 18.0 **7.** 0.3 **8.** 24 **9.** 250 **10.** -13.34 **11.** 3.8
12. -1.2 **13.** x − 0.09 **14.** -12.56y **15.** -6.71
16. 0.111

3-5 pages 116–118
Written Exercises **1.** -2.44 **3.** 0.044 **5.** 1.2 **7.** 42.6
9. 0.374 **11.** -14.85 **13.** -5.4 **15.** 86.7 **17.** 3.0772
19. -708 **21.** 0.048308 **23.** 194.0 **25.** -42.1 **27.** 9.50
29. 236.03 **31.** 36.9 **33.** -0.2 **35.** -6 **37.** x = zy
39. x = yz **41.** 0.004n = 0.88; 220
43. $\frac{n}{-2.35}$ = 400.9; -942.115 **47. a.** $2,537.50; **b.** 205;
c. yes
Mixed Review **1.** 1.446 **2.** 84.72 **3.** 0 **4.** 0.111
5. -1,056 **6.** -360 **7.** 14
Critical Thinking **1.** The outside shape becomes shaded
inside; the shaded shape inside becomes the outside
shape. **2.** c and d

Practice page 119
1. sixty-seven hundredths

3. six hundred thirty-seven and four ten-thousandths
5. 215.74 **7.** 42.07 **9.** > **11.** < **13.** > **15.** =
17. = **19.** 20 **21.** 1 **23.** \$56 **25.** 6.62 **27.** -94
29. -41.706 **31.** -1 **33.** $x = 7.75$ **35.** $a = 0$
37. $z = 30$ **39.** $t = -1.2$ **41.** $y = 42.71$ **43.** $j = -4.036$
45. $x = -1.94$ **47.** $r = -18.57$ **49.** $m = np$ **51.** $m = \frac{n}{p}$
53. $m = \frac{p}{n}$

Problem Solving Practice page 124
1. Christine, Lisa, Nicole, JoAnn **3.** 8.2 mi
5. 276.8 m **7.** on; off **9.** 1.2 h

3-6 pages 126–128
Written Exercises 1. 66.8 g **3.** water:ethyl alcohol,
gasoline; mercury:copper, gasoline, ethyl alcohol,
rubber, and iron **5.** 110 g **7.** 0.917 g/cm³ **9.** 1,050 g

3-7 pages 129–131
Written Exercises 1. 87°F **3.** 52°F **5.** 465.85 mi
7. 1,704 cm **9.** 6,700 mi; high **11.** 0.347 **13.** 0.366
15. 0.345 **17.** Cobb, Hornsby, Jackson, Browning,
Delahanty, Keeler **19.** \$536.25 **21.** \$683.98
23. -128.2°F **25.** \$.43 **27. a.** 7.875; 64.05;
b. \$.32 and \$2.56; **c.** \$116.48 **31.** $V = IR$; $R = \frac{V}{I}$
Mixed Review 1. -30.67 **2.** -2.236 **3.** 34 **4.** -33.8
5. 4.03 **6.** \$2,600
Test Yourself 1. 2.68 **2.** -0.186875 **3.** 20.24372
4. 77.26952 **5.** 40 **6.** 3.03 **7.** $a = \frac{c}{b}$ **8.** $a = b - c$
9. $a = cb$ **10. a.** 168; **b.** 11; **c.** 9.7 h

3-8 page 133
Written Exercises 1. 87 **3.** 23,471.4 **5.** 23
7. 8 airplanes; 16 spaceships **9.** 717

Chapter 3 Review pages 134–135
1. F, hundredths **2.** F, estimating **3.** T **4.** T
5. F, variables **6.** < **7.** = **8.** > **9.** < **10.** <
11. 0.25 **12.** 0.5 **13.** 0.25 **14.** 53 **15.** 0.75 **16.** \$24
17. 0.2 **18.** 12,905 **19.** \$79 **20.** -1.1 **21.** 0.4
22. 4.1 **23.** 11 **24.** 4.5a + 3.1 **25.** $\frac{x}{2}$ **26.** 8a + 13ab
27. -5 **28.** 0.55 **29.** 7.35 **30.** 11 **31.** 10 **32.** 7.3
33. 3 **34.** 3.8 **35.** 192.5 mi **36.** 36 ft **37.** 9.125 h
38. 1,400 children **39.** 10.5 g/cm³

Chapters 1–3 Cumulative Review page 137
1. B **2.** C **3.** A **4.** B **5.** C **6.** D **7.** A **8.** C
9. A **10.** A **11.** A **12.** B **13.** C **14.** B

CHAPTER 4

Number Theory

4-1 pages 142–144
Written Exercises 1. 8^3 **3.** $2r^4s^2$ **5.** x^2y^2z **7.** n^{30}
9. a^a **11.** $(a + 1)^3$ **13. a.** 1; **b.** 1,000,000 **15. a.** -16;
b. 1 **17.** 36 **19.** -4 **21.** 1 **23.** 7 **25.** 9 **27.** >
29. = **31.** < **33.** > **35.** d
37. (-1) raised to an even power is positive; 1

39. The power tells you the number of zeros in the
product. $10^6 = 1,000,000$; $10^{10} = 10,000,000,000$
41. a. 0, 1, 0; 4, 4, 1; 8, 16, 16; 12, 64, 81; 16, 256, 256
b. $n = 2, 4$; $n = 3$; $n = 0, 1$, $n > 4$ **43.** $n = 0$ **45.** $x =$
any pos. value **47.** $x = 3$ **49. a.** It is half as tall.; yes;
b. Each bar is twice as tall as the previous bar.
Mixed Review 1. 19.5 **2.** -19 **3.** 123.75 mi **4.** 280 km
5. 285.75 mi **6.** 4x − 2y **7.** -3w − 7 **8.** 83
Critical Thinking 2. 8; 27; 64 **3.** 1; 8; 27; 64 **4.** 1,000

4-2 pages 146–148
Written Exercises 1. -8 **3.** 8 **5.** x^9 **7.** $10x^9$ **9.** 72
11. $-x^8$ **13.** $16a^6$ **15.** $1,296y^{12}$ **17.** $-27y^{12}$ **19.** -8
21. 531,441 **23.** 9 **25.** 17 **27.** -216
29. F; add exponents; $x^5 \cdot x^3 = x^8$ **31.** T; $1 = 1$
33. T; $(r^2)^3$ is positive, so the opposite is less than 0.
35. no **37.** no **39.** no **41.** yes **43.** < **45.** <
47. < **49.** 3^{50}; $2^{75} = (2^3)^{25}$ and $3^{50} = (3^2)^{25}$ **51.** $x = 2$
53. a. 1,024; **b.** 10^3; **c.** 2^3; **d.** $2^{10} \cdot 2^{10}$; **e.** $2^{20} \cdot 2^3$
Mixed Review 1. 4 **2.** 360 **3.** $-5a^3b^2$ **4.** $-14c^2d^3$
5. -12 **6.** 6 **7.** -1 **8.** 8
Critical Thinking 1. the two numbers diagonally above
it in the preceding row **2.** 1, 6, 15, 20, 15, 6, 1 **3.** 8
4. 1,048,576

4-3 pages 150–152
Written Exercises 1. Ex: 6.25×10^8; 62.5×10^7;
625×10^6 **3.** 6×10^{13} **5.** 6.382×10^7 **7.** 100,000
9. 7,654 **11.** 600.32 **13.** 4,060 **15.** 1.5×10^5; 150,000
17. 9.9×10^{12}; 9,900,000,000,000
19. 4.7×10^6; 4,700,000 **21.** 3 **23.** 8.45 **25.** 0.000845
27. 2.49×10^{21} **29.** 7.89×10^{20} **31.** 3.22×10^{30}
33. 7×10^8 **37.** 5.79×10^7, 1.082×10^8, 1.496×10^8,
2.279×10^8, 7.783×10^8, 1.427×10^9, 2.869×10^9,
4.497×10^9, 5.9×10^9 **39.** 4.06×10^{13} km **43.** 7.6×10^8
Mixed Review 1. multiplicative identity
2. commutative prop. for addition **3.** additive identity
4. distributive property **5.** $3m^7$ **6.** n^6 **7.** $25y^3$
8. 2^5 or 32
Test Yourself 1. a^2b^3 **2.** $4x^3y$ **3.** 64 **4.** 144 **5.** -243
6. 1 **7.** -625 **8.** 512 **9.** 1×10^4 **10.** 1×10^5
11. 1×10^7 **12.** 7.5×10^4 **13.** 8.54×10^5
14. 1.645123×10^6

4-4 pages 154–155
Written Exercises 1. 1.3125×10^{10}
3. a. 2.8×10^8; **b.** about 1,393 da
5. 7.3×10^8 **7.** 7.498×10^6

Practice page 158
1. $3^2 \cdot 5^3$ **3.** $(-3a)^5$ **5.** 512 **7.** -243 **9.** 64 **11.** 16
13. 40,353,607 **15.** 256 **17.** -147 **19.** 6,561
21. 8,388,608 **23.** b^3 **25.** k^{13} **27.** c^{11} **29.** y^6
31. $243r^{15}$ **33.** $405m^{10}$ **35.** 104 **37.** 200 **39.** -81
41. -16,384 **43.** 240,000,000 **45.** 10,000,000
47. 98,367.5 **49.** 3.392×10^6 km **51.** 5.88×10^{21}
53. 1×10^{19} m

4-5 pages 161–162
Written Exercises **1.** yes **3.** yes **5.** yes **7.** no
9. yes **11.** yes **13.** 1, 2, 3, 5, 6, 10, 15, 30 **15.** 1, 5, 11, 55 **17.** 1, 29 **19.** 12, 24, 36, 48, 60 **21.** 25, 50, 75, 100, 125 **23.** 2, 3, 5, 9 **25.** 2, 3 **27.** 5 **29.** 3
31. a. 78, no, no, 96, yes, yes; **b.** If the last two digits are divisible by 4, the number is divisible by 4. **33.** 7 **35.** odd **37.** yes
Mixed Review **1.** $n - 5 = -24$ **2.** $3n - 10 = 57$ **3.** -23 **4.** 36 **5.** -19 **6.** 3.48×10^6 **7.** 2.5×10^2 **8.** 95°F
Test Yourself **1.** 9,604 **2.** 12,300 **3.** 28,560,000,000,000,000 **4.** 9.65×10^6 **5.** 5.48×10^2 **6.** 3×10^6 **7.** 1, 3, 9, 27 **8.** 1, 3, 5, 9, 15, 45 **9.** 1, 2, 3, 4, 5, 6, 10, 12, 15, 20, 30, 60 **10.** 3, 5, 9 **11.** 2, 3, 5 **12.** 3, 9 **13.** 4^4 **14.** 17^3 **15.** z^4 **16.** 20 **17.** 50 **18.** 29 **19.** -9

4-6 pages 165–166
Written Exercises **1.** composite **3.** prime **5.** composite **7.** $5^2 \cdot 17$ **9.** $2 \cdot 3 \cdot 31$ **11.** $3^2 \cdot 5^2 \cdot 7$ **13.** 1,056 **15.** 9,274,720 **17.** $3^3 \cdot 23$ **19.** $11 \cdot 23$ **21.** even **23.** 6, 14, 21, 42 **25.** 841; 960
27. a. China; **b.** Brazil
29. a. 3, 5; 5, 7; 11, 13; 17, 19; 29, 31; 41, 43; 59, 61; **b.** They are all odd.; **c.** yes
Mixed Review **1.** 1, 2, 4, 8 **2.** 8, 16, 24, 32 **3.** 1, 2, 3, 4, 6, 9, 12, 18, 36 **4.** -9 **5.** 45 **6.** 4 **7.** -57 to -59°F
Critical Thinking **1.** They are all located in columns 2, 4, and 6.
2. They are all located in columns 3 and 6.
3. They are in diagonal lines going from right to left, starting with 5, 30, 60, and 90. **4.** 7
5. The multiples of 11 are multiples of 2, 3, 5, or 7.
6. They are all primes. All other numbers are crossed out because they are multiples of 2, 3, 5, and 7.
7. 2, 3, 5, 7, 11, 13, 17, 19, 23, 29, 31, 37, 41, 43, 47, 53, 59, 61, 67, 71, 73, 79, 83, 89, 97, 101, 103, 107, 109, 113, 127, 131, 137, 139, 149, 151, 157, 163, 167, 173, 179, 181, 191, 193, 197, 199; Stop at 13 on the sieve.

4-7 pages 169–170
Written Exercises **1.** 7 **3.** 13 **5.** x^2y **7.** 30a **9.** 3 **11.** 60 **13.** 1,260 **15.** $24a^3b^2$ **17.** 180 **19.** 4; 96 **21.** 5; 37,800 **23.** If a is the LCM of 8 and x, then a is divisible by both 8 and x. Since $8 = 2^3$, a is divisible by 2^3. **25.** 2 times per minute **27.** 2 tables that seated 5 people; 7 tables that seated 8 people **29.** 21 ft. **31.** 59
Mixed Review **1.** $2^2 \cdot 3$ **2.** $3 \cdot 41$ **3.** 1, 2, 3, 4, 6, 12 **4.** 12, 24, 36, 48 **5.** 4 **6.** -11.4 **7.** -16 **8.** 8, 3

4-8 pages 173–174
Written Exercises **1.** 9 **3.** 17 **5.** 24 **7.** 4; the last digits of the powers of 8 form this pattern: 8, 4, 2, 6 **9.** 63 tickets **11.** They are all prime numbers. **13.** $5

Problem Solving Practice page 175
1. every 21,000 mi **5.** 16 (including a plain pizza) **9. a.** 1950 **b.** 1700–1749

Chapter 4 Review pages 176–177
1. b **2.** d **3.** h **4.** f **5.** a **6.** c **7.** e **8.** g **9.** 8 **10.** 1 **11.** 27 **12.** 25 **13.** 16 **14.** a^5 **15.** $8a^6$ **16.** $ab^3 + ab^2$ **17.** a^4b^2 **18.** a^3b^7 **19.** 4.65×10^8 **20.** 1.36×10^7 **21.** 1.28×10^3 **22.** 5.09×10^6 **23.** 210,000 **24.** 61,300,000 **25.** 1,050 **26.** 835 **27.** T **28.** T **29.** T **30.** F **31.** F **32.** T **33.** $3 \cdot 5^2$ **34.** $2^2 \cdot 3 \cdot 5 \cdot 7$ **35.** $2^2 \cdot 3^3$ **36.** $3^2 \cdot 5 \cdot 17$ **37.** $2^2 \cdot 3 \cdot 19$ **38.** $5 \cdot 7 \cdot 17$ **39.** 4 **40.** 8 **41.** 9 **42.** $3x^2$ **43.** 36 **44.** 56 **45.** 105 **46.** $60x^2y^3$ **47.** $198ab^3c^2$ **48.** 45

Chapters 1–4 Cumulative Review page 179
1. C **2.** B **3.** B **4.** A **5.** C **6.** D **7.** C **8.** B **9.** C **10.** A **11.** C **12.** D **13.** B **14.** C **15.** C **16.** A

CHAPTER 5

Rational Numbers and Expressions

5-1 pages 186–187
Written Exercises **1.** $\frac{3}{13}$ **3.** $\frac{1}{2}$; one-fourth; five-sevenths; $\frac{5}{7}$ **5.** $\frac{6}{10}$ or $\frac{3}{5}$ **17.** 2 **19.** 6 **21.** 1 **23.** 4 **25.** $\frac{1}{5}$ **27.** $\frac{2}{3}$ **29.** $\frac{1}{3}$ **31.** $\frac{c}{3}$ **33.** $\frac{1}{2t}$ **37.** $\frac{3}{4}$ **39.** $\frac{3a^2}{5}$ **41.** $\frac{2pq}{3}$ **43.** $\neq$ **45.** $=$ **47.** $\frac{2}{5}$
Mixed Review **1.** 1, 2, 4, 8, 16, 32 **2.** 1, 3, 9, 27 **3.** 2, 3; $2^2 \cdot 3^2$ **4.** 2, 3; $2 \cdot 3^3$ **5.** 200 **6.** 70 **7.** GCF 6; LCM 36 **8.** -54°F

5-2 pages 190–191
Written Exercises **1. a.** $\frac{11}{4}$; **b.** $2\frac{3}{4}$ **5.** $\frac{13}{8}$ **7.** $\frac{47}{8}$ **9.** $\frac{20}{3}$ **11.** $\frac{31}{11}$ **13.** $5\frac{2}{3}$ **15.** $4\frac{3}{5}$ **17.** $1\frac{8}{11}$ **19.** $3\frac{1}{3}$ **21.** $\frac{4}{5}$ **23.** $5\frac{3}{20}$ **25.** $2\frac{1}{2}$ **27.** $6\frac{1}{20}$ **29.** 0.28 **31.** 0.625 **33.** $0.\overline{5}$ **35.** 5.375 **37.** 0.18, $\frac{18}{100}$; 5.73, five and seventy-three hundredths; 0.9, $\frac{9}{10}$ **39. a.** $\frac{15}{104}$; **b.** $\frac{7}{52}$; **c.** $\frac{7}{104}$; **d.** $\frac{33}{52}$ **41.** yes **43.** yes
Mixed Review **1.** > **2.** < **3.** $\frac{2}{3}$ **4.** $\frac{3}{a}$ **5.** 0.6 **6.** 1.5 **7.** 3.485×10^{10}

5-3 pages 194–195
Written Exercises **1.** $\frac{9}{4}$ **3.** $-1\frac{1}{5}$ **5.** $\frac{3}{5}$ **11.** $\frac{4}{9}, \frac{4}{9}$ **13.** $-1\frac{2}{3}, 1\frac{2}{3}$ **15.** a; c **17.** $\frac{4}{5}$ **19.** -4 **21.** $\frac{a}{2b}$ **23.** $\frac{a}{4b}$ **25.** always **27.** sometimes **29.** negative **31.** negative **33.** yes **35.** yes, yes, yes, yes; yes, no, no, no; yes, no, no, no; yes, yes, yes, yes; yes, yes, yes, no
Mixed Review **1.** 0 **2.** -6 **3.** -5 **4.** $-\frac{3}{8}$ **5.** $\frac{2a^2}{5}$ **6.** 0.8 **7.** -3.25 **8.** $\frac{1}{2}, \frac{1}{2}, \frac{3}{8}, \frac{1}{4}$
Test Yourself **1.** $\frac{4}{5}$ **2.** $\frac{3}{4}$ **3.** $\frac{3}{10}$ **4.** $\frac{a^2}{3}$ **5.** $\frac{35n^3}{4}$ **11.** $-\frac{2}{3}, \frac{2}{3}$ **12.** $2\frac{5}{6}, 2\frac{5}{6}$ **13.** $-1\frac{7}{16}, 1\frac{7}{16}$ **14.** $2\frac{3}{4}, 2\frac{3}{4}$

5-4 page 198
Written Exercises **1.** < **3.** < **5.** < **7.** < **9.** < **11.** < **13.** = **15.** < **17.** < **19.** < **21.** <

23. $-\frac{5}{12}$, $-\frac{3}{8}$, $-\frac{1}{4}$ 25. $-\frac{11}{15}$, $-\frac{7}{10}$, $-\frac{13}{20}$, $-\frac{7}{12}$
27. $-2\frac{7}{8}$, $-2\frac{9}{16}$, $2\frac{3}{50}$, $2\frac{19}{25}$ 33. $x < 2.5$ 35. $\frac{1}{14}$
Mixed Review 1. 7 2. 10.58 3. $7\frac{1}{3}$ 4. $1\frac{2}{5}$ 5. $2\frac{7}{9}$
6. -14 7. -2.375 8. 192.5 mi

5-5 pages 201–202
Written Exercises 5. $\frac{1}{3} + \frac{1}{2} = \frac{5}{6}$ 7. $1\frac{7}{24}$ 9. $-\frac{4}{9}$ 11. $2\frac{1}{2}$
13. $9\frac{2}{9}$ 15. $\frac{7}{18}y$ 17. $-4\frac{5}{8}$ 19. 16 21. 150
23. 75 25. $29\frac{2}{3}$ 27. yes 29. no 31. C 33. >
35. > 37. < 39. 42 ft 41. $\frac{1}{4}$, $\frac{5}{8}$ 43. $\frac{1}{12}$, $\frac{7}{12}$, $\frac{1}{4}$, $\frac{3}{4}$
Mixed Review 1. $-3\frac{1}{5}$, $3\frac{1}{5}$ 2. $-5\frac{8}{11}$ 3. $-\frac{7}{10}$, $\frac{7}{-10}$
4. -20 5. < 6. when $y > 4$ 7. 60 8. $150

5-6 page 204
Written Exercises 1. 7 3. $15\frac{3}{16}$ ft 5. 12 y 7. a. $0.\overline{1}$;
b. $0.\overline{2}$; c. $0.\overline{3}$; d. $0.\overline{4}$; e. $0.\overline{5}$; f. $0.\overline{6}$
9. $3\frac{2}{3}$, $4\frac{5}{12}$, $5\frac{1}{6}$

Practice page 205
1. $\frac{1}{5}$ 3. $\frac{2}{3}$ 5. $\frac{3}{5}$ 7. $\frac{3y}{7}$ 9. $\frac{1}{3}$ 11. $\frac{2}{3m}$ 13. $\frac{13}{5}$
15. $\frac{14}{3}$ 17. $\frac{33}{4}$ 19. $\frac{247}{12}$ 21. $2\frac{2}{5}$ 23. $6\frac{1}{4}$ 25. $6\frac{5}{8}$
27. $8\frac{1}{7}$ 29. $-2\frac{3}{8}$, $2\frac{3}{8}$ 31. $18\frac{2}{3}$, $18\frac{2}{3}$ 33. $13\frac{5}{9}$, $13\frac{5}{9}$
35. $\frac{11}{15}$, $\frac{11}{15}$ 37. < 39. > 41. > 43. 1 45. $1\frac{1}{9}$
47. $-\frac{3}{8}$ 49. $-6\frac{1}{4}$ 51. $1\frac{11}{24}$ 53. $6\frac{23}{30}$ 55. $6\frac{3}{7}$ 57. -11
59. $30\frac{5}{16}$

5-7 page 208
Written Exercises 1. $\frac{1}{3}$ 3. 8 5. $\frac{2}{11}$ 7. $\frac{15}{16}$ 9. $-\frac{a}{10}$
11. $5\frac{5}{6}$ 13. 1 15. $\frac{3}{4}$ 17. 39 19. -8 21. -60 23. $1\frac{1}{2}$
25. 130 27. > 29. < 31. = 33. $-1\frac{8}{15}$ 35. $-\frac{9}{10}$
37. a. 200; b. 500; c. 12
Mixed Review 1. 1.4 2. 9.9 3. $\frac{1}{2}$ 4. $\neq$ 5. 0.325
6. 6 7. 5 8. Paul

5-8 pages 213–214
Written Exercises 1. $\frac{1}{36}$ 3. 1 5. $\frac{3}{8}$ 7. $\frac{1}{25}$ 9. a^{-3}
11. $\frac{1}{2}x^7$ 13. x^2y^{-10} 15. $5b^4c^5$ 17. $5m^2$ 19. $\frac{3y^2}{x^3}$
21. a. -25 b. 25 c. $\frac{1}{25}$ d. $\frac{1}{25}$ 23. $\frac{1}{25a^2}$ 25. $a^{10}b^{-15}$ or $\frac{a^{10}}{b^{15}}$
27. $9a^4b$ 29. a. The numbers decrease by 1.; b. The
numbers decrease by a power of 3. 1, $\frac{1}{3}$, $\frac{1}{9}$; c. They are
values of the powers of 3.; d. They are the values of the
powers of 2. 31. T 33. F 35. T 37. T
39. 1,580,000,000,000,000,000 41. $\frac{13}{20}$
Mixed Review 1. $\frac{7}{10}$ 2. $\frac{3}{8}$ 3. $-1\frac{1}{8}$ 4. $6\frac{1}{6}$ 5. 5 6. -12
7. -5.2 8. 34
Critical Thinking 1. If n is the exponent, the decimal
point moves to the left $|n|$ places. 2. 1.2, 0.12, 0.012,
$1.2 \times 10^{-3} = 0.0012$ 3. 0.00037 4. 23 5. Writing long
strings of zeros takes too much space and can be
confusing to read.

5-9 pages 216–217
Written Exercises 1. $x + \frac{3}{5} = \frac{7}{10}$; $\frac{1}{10}$ 3. $-\frac{1}{2}$ 5. $5\frac{3}{8}$ 7. $\frac{13}{24}$
9. $-1\frac{7}{40}$ 11. $\frac{23}{24}$ 13. $2\frac{19}{20}$ 15. 6.1 17. 5 19. 6 21. $\frac{1}{5}$
23. $-8\frac{1}{8}$ 25. $-1\frac{5}{12}$ 27. x must be less than zero
because the sum will be less than zero. 29. yes
31. $b + 3\frac{3}{16} = 5\frac{11}{16}$, $2\frac{1}{2}$ lb 33. $h + 1\frac{5}{8} = 68\frac{1}{2}$, $66\frac{7}{8}$ in.
Mixed Review 1. T 2. $3\frac{8}{13}$ 3. < 4. > 5. $\frac{31}{150}$
6. a^{-4} 7. $x^{-2}y^5$ 8. $3\frac{1}{8}$

5-10 pages 219–221
Written Exercises 1. $1\frac{5}{16}$ 3. $\frac{81}{10}$ or $8\frac{1}{10}$ 5. -12 7. $\frac{1}{2}$
9. 4 11. -0.8 13. neg $\cdot$ neg = pos
15. pos $\cdot$ neg = neg 17. $\frac{25}{9}$, $-\frac{25}{9}$ 19. no solution
21. no solution 23. $\frac{5}{8}d = 12$; $d = 19.2$ 25. $a = \frac{5}{6}$, $b = 1\frac{1}{3}$,
$a < b$ 27. 350 29. $\frac{1}{15}$ 33. whole 35. multiplication
37. $\frac{7}{8}$ 39. 64 41. $2\frac{5}{7}$ 43. $\frac{7}{11}$ 45. $\frac{7}{20}$ 47. No; the
chart does not tell the number of cans recycled in any
year. 49. $\frac{9}{10}$
Mixed Review 1. $-9\frac{1}{3}$ 2. $1\frac{1}{8}$ 3. $11\frac{1}{9}$ 4. 6.1 5. $\frac{29}{36}$
6. 2.2 7. < 8. 126
Test Yourself 1. $\frac{23}{24}$ 2. $10\frac{1}{4}$ 3. $-\frac{7}{8}$ 4. $2\frac{7}{16}$ 5. $-1\frac{5}{9}$
6. $-\frac{27}{32}$ 7. $16\frac{7}{8}$ 8. no solution 9. no solution 10. $\frac{1}{9}$
11. 1 12. 27 13. $\frac{8}{5}$ 14. $5n$ 15. $\frac{3}{a^3}$ 16. $\frac{8x^2}{y^3}$ 17. $\frac{b^6}{a^5}$

5-11 page 224
Written Exercises 1. 62.625 3. 77.125 5. 88.875
7. $3.625 9. a. DQ $2,805.00, MCJ $5,036.25, EDL
$5,992.50, JMB $23,778.75, BBH $27,030.00; b. DQ $510,
MCJ $630, EDL $450, JMB $340, BBH $1,380
11. The commission is figured on different amounts.

Problem Solving Practice page 225
1. 27th 3. 1,223 or 2,486 5. Lena 7. $5.26 11. $\frac{3}{4}$ lb

Chapter 5 Review pages 226–227
1. equivalent fractions 2. lowest terms
3. rational number 4. least common denominator
5. exponents 6. 6 7. 6 8. 8 9. 4 10. 25
11. $3\frac{3}{4}$; 3.75 12. $1\frac{1}{2}$; 1.5 13. $2\frac{2}{5}$; 2.4 14. $2\frac{5}{6}$; $2.8\overline{3}$
15. $2\frac{5}{8}$; 2.625 16. $\frac{3}{5}$ 17. $2\frac{3}{5}$ 18. $5\frac{1}{4}$ 19. $\frac{7}{10}$ 20. $\frac{7}{20}$
21. < 22. > 23. = 24. > 25. $3\frac{1}{12}$ 26. $7\frac{2}{15}$
27. $15\frac{5}{12}$ 28. $6\frac{11}{24}$ 29. 6 A.M. 30. $19,937.50
31. $\frac{9}{10}$ 32. 9 33. 6 34. $\frac{1}{2}$ 35. $\frac{1}{x^5}$ 36. $\frac{6}{a}$ 37. $2m^4$
38. $\frac{2}{b}$ 39. $\frac{3y^3}{x^2}$ 40. $1\frac{2}{15}$ 41. $3\frac{1}{3}$ 42. $-3\frac{1}{8}$ 43. $1\frac{1}{3}$

Chapters 1–5 Cumulative Review page 229
1. C 2. C 3. B 4. B 5. D 6. C 7. B 8. D 9. C
10. A 11. D 12. A 13. C 14. C 15. D 16. B

Ratios, Proportions, and Percent

6-1 pages 235–236
Written Exercises 1. $\frac{3}{8}$ 3. $\frac{8}{11}$ 5. $\frac{3}{5}$ 7. $\frac{5}{2}$ 9. $\frac{1}{5}$ 11. $\frac{1}{6}$
13. $\frac{1}{4}$ 15. $\frac{1}{7}$ 17. 3 to 2; 2 to 3; 2 to 5 25. $\neq$
27. =; prop. 29. $\neq$ 31. $\neq$ 33. $\neq$ 35. =; prop.
37. 6 gal/min 39. 0.18 hits/time at bat
41. 4.375 mi/h 43. 0.3 hits/time at bat
45. 50 to 2; 2 to 50; 2 to 48 47. $\frac{4}{24} \stackrel{?}{=} \frac{6}{30}$; no
49. $\frac{2}{1.69} \stackrel{?}{=} \frac{5}{3.98}$; no, 2 for $1.69 is $.85 each;
5 for $3.98 is $.80 each. 51. **a.** 300 to 70; 300 : 70; $\frac{300}{70}$;
b. $9.00/pt **c.** $22/gal
Mixed Review 1. $\frac{7}{13}$ 2. $\frac{13}{19} > \frac{19}{28}$ 3. $x = -14$ 4. $x = -2\frac{1}{4}$
5. yes 6. no 7. 1,239 mi

6-2 pages 238–240
Written Exercises 1. $a = 20$ 3. $c = 20$ 5. $e = 19.2$
7. $g = 133.\overline{3}$ 9. $j = 17.5$ 11. $m = 16.9$ 13. $x = 1$
15. $\frac{4}{1.85} = \frac{24}{t}$; $11.10 17. $\frac{5}{18.6} = \frac{8}{v}$; $v = 29.76$ min
19. $\frac{6}{2.25} = \frac{y}{\$10}$; $y = 26.67$ lb 21. $\frac{3}{1} = \frac{x}{4}$; $x = 12$ bags
23. $\frac{3}{\$9.60} = \frac{15}{p}$; $p = \$48$ 25. $\frac{3}{750} = \frac{x}{10,000}$; $x = 40$ defects
29. $\frac{7}{3}$ 31. $-\frac{2}{7}$ 33. no 35. no 37. $\frac{30}{100}$ 39. $\frac{12}{1}$
41. 15; 1 43. 32; 8; 32; 16 45. 15 s 47. 360 times
49. 42,048,000 times
Mixed Review 1. F 2. T 3. $\frac{6}{11}$ 4. $\frac{25}{14}$ 5. yes 6. yes
7. $67.97
Critical Thinking 1. even numbers 2. prime numbers
3. odd numbers 4. the even primes
5. the odd primes 6. yes; yes
7. No; Two is the only even prime.

6-3 pages 242–243
Written Exercises 1. 1 in. : 10 ft 3. 20 ft
5. Yes; the scale of the dance floor is 10 : 8.$\overline{3}$. 7. N
9. 4.5 in. 11. 14.4 ft

6-4 pages 246–248
Written Exercises 1. 75% 3. 62.5% 5. 58.3%
7. 140% 9. 33% 11. 6% 13. 4.5% 15. 188%
17. 79% 19. 30% 21. 68% 23. 111% 25. 22.2%
27. 43.8% 29. 80% 31. 25% 33. $\frac{1}{10}$; 10%
35. 0.75; 75% 37. $\frac{1}{4}$; 0.25 39. 112% 41. 60%
43. 47.2% 45. 25% 47. < 49. < 51. < 53. >
55. yes 57. No; 100% is a perfect grade. 59. 100
61. 10 63. week 65. $\frac{5}{12}$ 67. $\frac{3}{4}$
Mixed Review 1. $x = 47$ 2. $x = -0.175$ 3. $x = 68.75$
4. $x = 1,820$ 5. $\frac{1}{4} = 25\%$ 6. $\frac{11}{14} = 78.6\%$ 7. 93

Practice page 249
1. $\frac{2}{5}$ 3. $\frac{2}{5}$ 5. $\frac{3}{7}$ 7. $\neq$ 9. =; prop. 11. =; prop.
13. =; prop. 15. $a = 2$ 17. $c = 12$ 19. $e = 2.25$
21. $g = 2$ 23. 180% 25. 37.5% 27. 76.7% 29. 55%
31. 6.7% 33. 85% 35. 62.5% 37. 12.5% 39. 0.225
41. 0.736 43. $\frac{1}{3}$; 0.$\overline{3}$; 33.3% 45. $\frac{1}{3}$, 0.$\overline{3}$, 33.3%

47. $\frac{2}{3}$, 0.$\overline{6}$, 66.7% 49. $\frac{16}{27}$, 0.$\overline{592}$, 59.3% 51. >
53. = 55. > 57. = 59. >

6-5 pages 253–255
Written Exercises 1. 52% 3. 107.8 5. 33.3% 7. 9
9. 31.5 11. 35% 13. 20 15. 175% 17. = 19. >
21. < 23. = 25. > 27. 20% 29. 25% 31. 24
33. 12 35. 18.5% 37. 44.5 39. 84.2 41. 132 43. 42
45. 8% 47. $1,200 49. You can't tell who got the
better deal without knowing the original price.
51. It makes sense. 53. 15% tip: $30.00; 20% tip: $22.50
Mixed Review 1. 52 2. 39 3. $258\frac{1}{3}\%$ 4. 452.3%
5. 8% 6. 4,560% 7. 38%
Test Yourself 1. $\frac{1}{3}$ 2. $\frac{1}{20}$ 3. $5.78 4. $1.75 5. 75%
6. 89% 7. 87.5% 8. 3% 9. 0.7% 10. 5.4
11. $n = 100$

6-6 pages 257–259
Written Exercises 1. $15\% = \frac{x}{115}$; $0.15 \cdot 115 = x$;
$17.25 = x$ 3. 55% 5. $46\frac{2}{3}$ 7. 60 9. 225%
11. 21.6 13. 2.4 15. 64% 17. 22.5 19. 81
21. 50% 23. 100 25. 22 27. 20% 29. 100 31. 12.5
33. $33\frac{1}{3}\%$ 35. 46.2% 37. 13.3 39. 100 41. $39.38
43. no 45. $25; $18.75 47. $240,000,000
49. 1,442,100
Mixed Review 1. 52 2. 150 3. 12.5% 4. 21
5. 0.62 6. 0.899 7. $15.00
Critical Thinking 1. a and c

6-7 pages 261–263
Written Exercises 1. 32% 3. 137.5% 5. 16.7%
7. 20.8% 9. 150% 11. 166.7% 13. 20% increase
15. 10% decrease 17. 86 19. 58.3 21. 24.1%; I
23. 83.1%; D 25. 69.3%; D 27. 27.7% 29. 29.6%
31. +13.6% 33. +393.8% 35. 1936: 1,175%; 1937:
2,087.5%; 1940: 2,300%; 1955: 445.5%; 1961: 566.7%
37. **a.** +44%, +27%, +90%, -28%, -28% **b.** no
Mixed Review 1. 8 2. 3,600 3. < 4. > 5. 20.25
6. 98.5%
Test Yourself 1. 39.6 2. 52.5 3. 20% 4. 65
5. $66\frac{2}{3}\%$ 6. 150 7. 32% 8. 38.9%

6-8 pages 265–266
Written Exercises 1. $\frac{1}{4}$ 3. 34 in. 5. 54 post holes
7. 5 cm 9. 1 11. $1\frac{7}{8}$ mi 13. 47 students
15. **a.** 28; **b.** 46 ft × 46 ft

Problem Solving Practice page 267
1. 4 3. 1 5. $700 7. **a.** 2.3% **b.** no

Chapter 6 Review pages 268–269
1. false; ratio 2. true 3. true 4. false; percent
5. true 6. =; prop. 7. $\neq$ 8. =; prop. 9. $\neq$ 10. $\neq$
11. 50 mi/h 12. 23 mi/gal 13. 90 words/min
14. $1.89/lb 15. $n = 35$ 16. $x = 12$ 17. $a = 49$
18. $y = 3$ 19. $m = 126$ 20. 187.5 km 21. 0.5 cm
22. 5% 23. 98% 24. 145% 25. 75% 26. 62.5%

27. 12% **28.** 6 **29.** $x = 150$ **30.** $33\frac{1}{3}\%$ **31.** $a = 200$
32. 204 **33.** 5% **34.** 18.2% **35.** 2.7 **36.** $y = 80$
37. $33\frac{1}{3}\%$ **38.** 25% **39.** 75% **40.** 20% **41.** 75%
42. 50% **43.** 21.4%

Chapters 1–6 Cumulative Review page 271
1. C **2.** A **3.** C **4.** B **5.** D **6.** A **7.** D **8.** B
9. B **10.** A **11.** C **12.** C

CHAPTER 7

Equations and Inequalities

7-1 pages 277–278
Written Exercises 1. 6 **3.** 47 **5.** -324 **7.** 12 **9.** 54
11. -70 **13.** -3 **15.** -2 **17.** -7 **19.** 85 **21.** 10 **23.** 60
25. 30 **27.** 5 **29.** 167,645.1$\overline{6}$ **31.** -43.375 **35.** C; 4
39. $3n - 7 = 19$ **41.** $2 = 12n - 4; \frac{1}{2}$ **43.** $8d + 36 = 78$;
5.25 **45.** $30 = 3n - 9$; 13 **47.** $x = \frac{c - b}{a}$ **49.** $8.50
Mixed Review 1. 20 **2.** 4 **3.** 18 **4.** $6.30 **5.** 96
6. $3m + 5$ **7.** $15 - 5x$ **8.** 96°

7-2 pages 281–282
Written Exercises 1. $2\frac{3}{4}$ **3.** $-2\frac{1}{2}$ **5.** 31 **7.** 12 **9.** 5
11. $-3\frac{5}{18}$ **13.** -12 **15.** $4\frac{2}{3}$ **17.** $\frac{5}{7}$ **19.** $3\frac{1}{3}$ **21.** 3 **23.** 6
25. 74.2 **27.** 40.4 **29.** $1.\overline{3}$ **33.** a; $70
35. $p + p + 13 = 171$; 79 **37.** $p - 0.2p = 53$; $66.25
39. $3(n - 8) = 36$; 20 **41.** Step 2 should be
$3x - 3 - 5 = 14$; $x = 7\frac{1}{3}$.
Mixed Review 1. 24 **2.** 30 **3.** $-17\frac{1}{3}$ **4.** 64 **5.** $\frac{1}{4}n - 10$
6. $12n - 5n$ **7.** $27.15
Test Yourself 1. -2 **2.** 162 **3.** 6 **4.** -3 **5.** -1
6. $185 - 11x + 40 = 93$; $12

Problem Solving Practice page 283
1. 28 **3.** 30 **5.** 120 cm **7.** 4 **9.** 1,295 m and 1,575 m
11. 74 and 75 **13.** 15 min

7-3 pages 285–286
Written Exercises 1. $8n - \frac{1}{2}n = 16$
3. $n + (n - 5) = 114.90$, where n = price of boots;
$59.95
5. $c + c + 0.45 = 0.95$; $.25 **7.** $8.75 + 1.25t = 12.50$; 3
9. $x - 0.75x = 175$; 700 **11.** $15x = 240$; 16
13. $\frac{2}{3}s - \frac{2}{5} = \frac{11}{45}; \frac{29}{30}$ **15.** 8 **17.** increased danger
19. 18 bu
Critical Thinking 1. 10:00 **2.** 11:00 **3.** 7 h
4. a. clocktime − (5)(groups of 5 in clocktime); **b.** 1:00;
c. 2:00

7-4 pages 289–290
Written Exercises 1. $4m + 5 = 21$; 4 **3.** 3 **5.** 1 **7.** 4
9. -4 **11.** 6 **13.** -10 **15.** 4 **17.** $-4\frac{2}{3}$ **19.** 4 **21.** $2\frac{2}{3}$
23. 3 **25.** yes **27.** yes **29.** $2.\overline{69}$
31. $x + x + 1 + x + 2 = 165$; 54, 55, and 56
33. $\frac{1}{2}n + 1 = \frac{2}{3}n - 1$; 12 **35.** $2n - 8 = 3n - 16$; 8
37. $2(35) - x = 47$; $x = 23$
Mixed Review 1. $2(n + 4)$ **2.** $c + 14$ **3.** $3n - 6 = 12$; 6
4. $56 = 6x + 8$; 8 **5.** = **6.** = **7.** $93

7-5 pages 294–295
Written Exercises 1. true **3.** true **5.** false **7.** true
9. false **17.** $x \leq 2$ **31.** $3 < 10$ **33.** $p > 0$ **35.** $p \leq 30$
37. $3x < 15,000$ **39.** $x < -10$; $x \geq -5$ **41.** < **43.** <
45. = **47.** > **49.** > **51.** $m > 5$ **53.** $b \geq 15$
55. $s \leq 50$ **57. a.** $5,140; $6,500; $4,400; $2,925; $7,700;
$2,550; **b.** Yes, if the program was input
correctly.; **c.** They determine how the IF command
decides what tax rate to use.
Mixed Review 1. $x = 17$ **2.** $x = -5.\overline{6}$ or $-5\frac{2}{3}$ **3.** $2n - 4$
4. $14 - x$ **5.** 0 **6.** $3n + 6$ **7.** 2 cups

7-6 pages 298–299
Written Exercises 1. same **3.** reversed
5. Divide by -3. **7.** Mult. by 3. **9.** yes **11.** no
13. $8 \leq x$ **15.** $x > 0$ **17.** $x > 4$ **19.** $x < -8$
21. $x > -12$ **23.** $21 \leq g$ **25.** hydroelectric and oil
27. 28
Mixed Review 1. 5 **2.** 1 **5.** $1\frac{4}{5}$ **6.** $-\frac{8}{9}$ **7.** 76 and 88
Test Yourself 1. 5 **2.** 7 **3.** -4 **4.** 8 **5.** $y > -4$
6. $y < 4$ **7.** $s < 42$ **8.** $h > \frac{1}{21}$ **9.** $-8 \geq k$ **10.** $y > -12$
11. $n - 7 > -2$; $n > 5$ **12.** $\frac{n}{-4} \geq 30$; $n \leq -120$
13. $-8 \geq \frac{n}{-3}$; $n \geq 24$

7-7 pages 301–303
Written Exercises 1. Sub. 8. **3.** Sub. 7. **5.** $x > 3$
7. $x \geq 6$ **9.** $x > 5$ **11.** $x \leq 1\frac{2}{5}$ **13.** $x > 4\frac{4}{5}$ **15.** $x \leq -5$
17. $x > 3$ **19.** $x \geq -72$ **21.** $x > -7$ **23.** $x < 3$
25. $x > 2$ **27.** $x < 60$ **29.** $x < 4$ **31.** b; $n \geq -18$
33. $2n - 5 \geq 13$; $n \geq 9$
35. $\frac{x + 88 + 91 + 85}{4} \geq 90$; $x \geq 96$ **37.** 3
41. a. 24,000 acres; **b.** 39.1
Mixed Review 1. $2n = n + 5$; 5 **2.** $2n - 5 = 121$; 63
3. $x \leq -3$ **4.** $x \leq 32$ **5.** $x = 18$ **6.** $x = 5$
7. $7\frac{1}{2}$ m, $12\frac{1}{2}$ m
Critical Thinking 2. D **3.** A **4.** D **5.** C **6.** B

Practice page 304
1. 6 **3.** 4 **5.** 243 **7.** 19 **9.** 3 **11.** 12 **13.** $6\frac{6}{7}$ **15.** 13
17. 10 **19.** -3 **21.** 26 **23.** 6 **25.** 8 **33.** $x > -4$
35. $x > -18$ **37.** $x \leq 3$ **39.** $x \geq 4$ **41.** $x > 2$
43. $x \leq 14$ **45.** $x \geq 15$ **47.** $22x + 47 = 201$; 7
49. $x + x + 1 + x + 2 + x + 3 = -490$; -121, -122, -123,
and -124

7-8 page 307
1. $520.50 **3.** $999.24 **5.** 9 **7.** 11.75 **9.** 47.08
11. a. $630; **b.** $266.39

Chapter 7 Review pages 308–309
1. operations **2.** distributive **3.** combine
4. not equal **5.** negative **6.** equation **7.** $x = 1$
8. $x = 2$ **9.** $a = 5$ **10.** $x = 12$ **11.** $n = 3$ **12.** $b = 18$
13. $x = 7$ **14.** $x = -10$ **15.** $x = \frac{1}{3}$ **16.** $x = -1$
17. $x = 14$ **18.** $x = -\frac{2}{3}$ **19.** $3n - 2(n + 5) = 3$; $n = 13$
20. $2(x + 12) + 3x = 144$; $x = 24$ **21.** $x = -2$ **22.** $x = 4$
23. $n = -10$ **24.** c **25.** a **26.** b **27.** d **28.** $x < -5$

29. $x \geq -3$ **30.** $x < -4$ **31.** $x \leq -8$ **32.** $x \leq 5$
33. $y > 4$ **34.** $b < -9$ **35.** $a < 12$

Chapters 1–7 Cumulative Review page 311
1. B **2.** C **3.** A **4.** C **5.** A **6.** C **7.** C **8.** B
9. D **10.** C **11.** C **12.** A **13.** B **14.** D

CHAPTER 8

Graphing in the Coordinate Plane

8-1 pages 318–319
Written Exercises **1.** Q **3.** M **5.** (2,-3) **7.** (-5,0)
17. (3,0)(0,3)(-3,0)(0,-3) **19.** IV **21.** II **23.** I
25. y-axis **27.** III **29.** parallelogram **31.** triangle
33. (0,-5)
Mixed Review **1.** 2 **2.** 8 **3.** $x < -7$ **4.** $x \leq 9$ **5.** 3
6. -35 **7.** 12 in., 19 in.
Critical Thinking **3. a.** (2,1)(2,3)(-1,3)(-1,1);
b. (-2,-1)(-2,-3)(1,-3)(1,-1); **c.** (2,-1)(2,-3)(-1,-3)(-1,-1);
d. (-4,2)(-4,6)(2,6)(2,2) **4.** When the x-coordinate is
multiplied by -1, the figure slides to the right 1 unit.
When the y-coordinate is multiplied by -1, the figure
is reflected over the x-axis. When each coordinate is
multiplied by -1, the figure slides to the right 1 unit and
is reflected over the x-axis. When each coordinate is
multiplied by 2, the figure moves up 1 unit and each side
is twice the length of the original figure.

8-2 pages 322–323
Written Exercises **1.** no **3.** yes **5.** yes **7.** yes **9.** no
11. -1 **13.** 2 **15.** 11.5 **17.** $y = 3x + 5$ **19.** $y = \frac{3}{2}x - 5$
21. $y = -\frac{1}{6}x$ **23.** $y = -\frac{1}{2}x - \frac{5}{2}$ **25.** $y = \frac{2}{3}x - 4$
27. $y = -\frac{1}{4}x + 4$ **29. b.** 1,092.6 kg/cm² **c.** 2,838.4 kg/cm²
Mixed Review **1.** -16 **2.** -8 **4.** neg., neg. **6.** (0,8)
7. 7:17 A.M.
Test Yourself **1.** F **2.** G **3.** H **4.** E **5.** (-1,3)
6. (3,3) **7.** (4,-2) **8.** (-4,-4) **9.** $y = -\frac{3}{2}x + 2$
10. $y = -\frac{1}{2}x - 3$ **11.** $y = -\frac{1}{3}x + \frac{7}{3}$

8-3 pages 326–327
Written Exercises **1.** $\frac{1}{2}x + y = -3$ **3.** -6 and -3 **5.** $-1\frac{1}{3}$; 4
7. 0; 0 **9.** $y = -x + 2$ **11.** $y = -5$ **21.** $x = -1$ **23.** $y = -6$ **25.** $x - y = 3$; 3 and 0 **27.** $x + y = 6$; 2 oranges and
4 apples **29.** $2x = y$; 4 and 8 **31.** $2x + 2y = 12$; width is
1 and length is 5.
Mixed Review **1.** 4 **2.** 4 **3.** $y = -\frac{2}{5}x + \frac{11}{5}$
4. $y = -\frac{3}{2}x - 6$ **7.** 34 and 35

8-4 pages 332–333
Written Exercises **1.** $\frac{2}{3}$; -2 **3.** $\frac{4}{3}$; -4 **5.** $\frac{1}{3}$; 4 **7.** 0
9. $\frac{10}{3}$ **11.** -2 **19.** $y = 2x + 1$; 2; 1
21. $y = -2x - 3$; -2; -3 **23.** $y = \frac{3}{4}x + \frac{1}{4}$; $\frac{3}{4}$; $\frac{1}{4}$
31. b. The lines are parallel. **c.** They are the same.
d. When two lines have the same slope and different
y-intercepts, they are parallel.
33. $0x + 1y = 6$ **35.** $1x + 0y = -3$

Mixed Review **1.** 80 **2.** 252 **3.** yes **4.** yes **5.** no
6. yes **7.** yes **8.** no **9.** 20%

8-5 pages 335–336
Written Exercises **1. b.** 50°F; **c.** 20°C **3.** 64°F **5.** 3
7. $2.11 **9.** 35 ft **11. a.** $27; **b.** $150
13. 18 quarters and 14 dimes **15.** 20 mi

Problem Solving Practice page 337
1. 12 quarters and 5 dimes **3.** 48 **5.** 36, 37, 38
7. 65 in. or 5 ft 5 in. **9.** 4 ft × 4 ft and 16 ft × 16 ft
11. $27.26 **13.** $1.18

8-6 pages 342–343
Written Exercises **1.** yes **3.** no **5.** (1,5) **7.** (2,1)
9. (2,2) **11.** (3,1) **13.** no solution **15.** (3,4)
17. $x + y = 55$; $x - y = 15$; 20 and 35
19. $x + y = 144$; $x = 3y$; 108 m and 36 m
21. $x + y = 16$; $5x + 10y = 100$; 12 five-point questions
and 4 ten-point questions **23.** parallel **25.** 1850
Mixed Review **1.** $3x^2$ **2.** $\frac{5xy^3}{2}$ **3.** 1; 0 **4.** $-\frac{2}{3}$; 4
5. $x < 3$ **6.** $x \geq -3$ **7.** $75
Test Yourself **1.** 10; 4 **2.** $-\frac{2}{3}$; 2 **3.** -2; 10 **4.** no slope
5. $-\frac{1}{2}$ **6.** $\frac{2}{11}$ **7.** $y = -2x + 7$; -2; 7 **8.** $y = -\frac{2}{3}x$; 0; $-\frac{2}{3}$
9. $y = -\frac{1}{3}x + \frac{2}{3}$; $-\frac{1}{3}$; $\frac{2}{3}$ **10.** (-2,8) **11.** infinite
12. (3,-2)

8-7 pages 346–347
Written Exercises **1.** no **3.** no **5.** no **7.** no
9. $y > \frac{5}{2}x - 5$ **11.** $y < -\frac{1}{3}$ **13.** $y \leq |x| - 4$
15. $y \leq -x + 5$ **19. a.** infinite; **b.** no solution
Mixed Review **1.** 0.075; 7.5% **2.** $0.\overline{2}$; $22.\overline{2}$% **3.** (1,1)
4. (6,2) **6.** below **7.** 12%
Critical Thinking **1.** A and D **2.** C **3.** A **4.** A and C

8-8 pages 350–351
Written Exercises **1.** $2x + y = 3$; solid **3.** $y = -2$; solid
5. $x - 4y = 1$; dotted **7.** $5x - 3y = 2$; dotted
9. $x = 9$; solid **11.** $3x + y = 2$; dotted **13.** no
15. yes **17.** no **19.** yes **21.** no **37.** $x - y > 3$
39. $0.05x + 0.10y < 1$ **47.** $x + y \leq 10$; $y > 2x$
Mixed Review **1.** infinite **2.** no solution **3.** one
6. a. 8; **b.** 5; **c.** (shirts,sweaters); (1,4)(1,3)(1,2)(1,1)(2,3)
(2,2)(2,1)(3,3)(3,2)(3,1)(4,2)(4,1)(5,1)(6,1)

Practice page 352
1. I **3.** IV **5.** (-4,-3) **7.** $y = -3x - 10$ **9.** $y = -2x + 4$
11. 0; 0 **19.** -1 **21.** $\frac{6}{5}$ **23.** $x = 6$ **25.** $y = \frac{1}{4}x - 3$; $\frac{1}{4}$; -3
27. (2,4) **29.** (1,2) **31.** $y > -\frac{4}{5}x - \frac{6}{5}$

8-9 pages 353–355
Written Exercises **1.** direct; 30 **3.** direct; 8.5 **5.** 27.5 lb
7. 1,156 cycles/s **9.** 3 h

Chapter 8 Review pages 356–357
1. false; an ordered pair **2.** true **3.** false; x-axis
4. false; m; b **5.** false; is not part of **6.** (1,-3)
7. (-2,1) **8.** (-3,-3) **9.** (2,2) **10.** (1,2) **11.** (2,-2)

12. (3,3) **13.** yes **14.** no **15.** yes **16.** yes **17.** 2
18. $\frac{3}{2}$ **19.** -1 **20.** 0 **21.** $y = 2x + 3$; 2; 3
22. $y = -\frac{1}{2}x - 2$; $-\frac{1}{2}$; -2 **23.** $y = -x + 5$; -1; 5
24. $y = -5x + \frac{5}{2}$; -5; $\frac{5}{2}$ **25.** 22 liters **26.** yes **27.** no
28. yes

Chapters 1–8 Cumulative Review page 359
1. B **2.** C **3.** A **4.** C **5.** D **6.** A **7.** A **8.** B
9. D **10.** C **11.** B **12.** B **13.** B **14.** A **15.** A
16. B

CHAPTER 9

Algebra in Geometry and Measurement

9-1 page 364
Written Exercises **1.** $\overline{BZ}$, $\overline{BT}$, $\overline{BM}$, $\overline{MT}$, $\overline{ZM}$, $\overline{ZT}$
3. $\overrightarrow{DC}$, $\overrightarrow{DB}$, $\overrightarrow{DA}$ **5.** an infinite number; one
7. a. The intersection of two planes is a line.;
b. the intersection of a floor and wall
9. $2x + 3 = 8x$; 4 **11.** true **13.** true
Mixed Review **2.** $6\frac{1}{2}$ **3.** 34% **4.** 92¢ **5.** $x = 2$
6. a = 64 **7.** 4

9-2 pages 367–368
Written Exercises **1.** obtuse **3.** straight **5.** acute
7. if the sum of their measures is 180°
9. $\angle SRB$ and $\angle WRQ$; $\angle WRA$ and $\angle TRB$
11. 45°; 135° **13.** 70° **15.** 120° **17.** 73° **19.** 22°
21. acute **23.** right **25.** obtuse **27.** acute **29.** none;
90° **31.** none; 65° **33.** 47°; 137° **35.** $(110 - y)°$;
$(200 - y)°$
Mixed Review **1.** $y = \frac{1}{4}x + 2$ **2.** $y = -x + 12$
3. $\overline{AB}$ and $\overline{RM}$ **4.** intersecting **5.** $24.74

9-3 page 372
Written Exercises **1.** F **3.** F **5.** F **7.** T
9. rectangle ABCD; polygon ABCD
11. quad. QRTS; polygon QRTS
13. convex; triangle **19.** 3, 4
Mixed Review **1.** 6.25 **2.** 1.024 **3.** 60° **4.** 47° **5.** B
6. $a > \frac{11}{3}$ **7.** $y = 17$ **8.** Joe 13; Ellen 6

9-4 pages 375–376
Written Exercises **1.** acute **3.** right **5.** isosceles **7.** T
9. T **11.** T **13.** F **19.** 90° **21.** 50° **23.** 90° **25.** 90°
27. 60° **29.** $(80 - x)°$ **31.** obtuse
Mixed Review **1.** $6^2 + (18 + 9) \cdot -2 = -18$
2. $(150 + 17) \cdot 10 = 1,670$ **5.** 0.235 **6.** 0.059
7. 100 for $121.50
Critical Thinking **1. b.** 4 **2.** T **3.** F **4.** T
5. You can make an inductive conclusion after trying
numerous examples, but you cannot prove the
conclusion true. If you have proved the statement to be
false, you are done once you find a counterexample.

9-5 pages 378–379
Written Exercises **1.** F **3.** T **5.** T **7.** 85 in. **9.** 35 cm
11. 250x ft **13.** 31.5 in. **15.** 0.29 cm **17.** 45,044.5 mi
19. a. no; **b.** no; C and D are not on the circle.
Mixed Review **1.** 9 **2.** 15 **3.** 149 **4.** 49,990
5. $m\angle 1 = 100°$; $m\angle 2 = 60°$ **6.** 672,000 km

9-6 pages 381–382
Written Exercises **1.** B **3.** $\overline{EF} \cong \overline{LM}$; $\overline{FG} \cong \overline{MN}$;
$\overline{HG} \cong \overline{ON}$; $\overline{EH} \cong \overline{LO}$; $\angle F \cong \angle M$; $\angle G \cong \angle N$; $\angle H \cong \angle O$;
$\angle E \cong \angle L$; $EFGH \cong LMNO$ **5.** 40° **7.** 3.5 **9.** 4.5 **11.** T
13. T **15.** F **17.** $m\angle 3 = 80°$; $m\angle 4 = 80°$ **23.** yes
Mixed Review **1.** 32.34 **3.** 27 mm **4.** $1\frac{3}{4}$ in. **5.** 5
6. 3 **7.** acute **8.** 25
Test Yourself
1. Answers may vary. $\overleftrightarrow{WY}$, $\overleftrightarrow{VU}$, $\overleftrightarrow{ZX}$; $\overrightarrow{MZ}$, $\overrightarrow{MX}$, $\overrightarrow{MY}$;
$\overline{WM}$, $\overline{UM}$, $\overline{ZX}$; $\angle XMY$, $\angle VMX$, $\angle ZMU$
2. parallelogram **3.** acute **4.** $\overline{AB} \cong \overline{CD}$; $\overline{BD} \cong \overline{BD}$;
$\overline{BC} \cong \overline{AD}$; $\angle BAD \cong \angle DCB$; $\angle ABD \cong \angle CDB$;
$\angle CBD \cong \angle ADB$ **5.** 52 ft **6.** 30 in. **7.** 31 m
8. 11.1 cm

9-7 pages 386–387
Written Exercises **3.** $\frac{MO}{RT} = \frac{OR}{RY} = \frac{ER}{YS} = \frac{ME}{TS}$ **5.** $x = 5$
7. $z = 5.8\overline{3}$ **9.** yes; $\overline{PQ} \leftrightarrow \overline{QS}$; $\overline{PR} \leftrightarrow \overline{ST}$; $\overline{RQ} \leftrightarrow \overline{TQ}$
13. 53.4 cm **15.** A possible answer is 24.5 in. × 21 in.
Mixed Review **1.** 0.375 **2.** 0.41$\overline{6}$ **3.** $\overline{AB} \cong \overline{XY}$;
$\overline{BC} \cong \overline{YZ}$; $\overline{AC} \cong \overline{XZ}$; $\angle A \cong \angle X$; $\angle B \cong \angle Y$; $\angle C \cong \angle Z$
4. 9 **5.** 36 **6.** 1.44 **7.** 10
Critical Thinking card 1 is a triangle; card 2 is a circle;
card 3 is a square

Practice page 388
1. 55° **3.** 75° **5.** 33°, 123° **7.** 47°, 137° **9.** 74°, 164°
11. none; 1° **13.** 90° **15.** 72° **17.** 45° **19.** 44°
21. 113.6 m **23.** 0.19 km **25.** 134,770 mi **27.** chords:
$\overline{LK}$, $\overline{JI}$; $\overline{GJ}$, $\overline{KH}$ diameters: $\overline{GJ}$, $\overline{KH}$; radii: $\overline{OH}$, $\overline{OJ}$, $\overline{OK}$, $\overline{OG}$;
central angles: $\angle GOH$, $\angle HOJ$, $\angle JOK$, $\angle KOG$
29. $\overline{YX} \cong \overline{TS}$, $\overline{XZ} \cong \overline{SU}$, $\overline{ZY} \cong \overline{UT}$, $\angle Y \cong \angle T$, $\angle X \cong \angle S$,
$\angle Z \cong \angle U$

9-8 pages 392–393
Written Exercises **1.** 36 ft **3.** 7 yd 1 ft **5.** 240 **7.** 19
9. 56.52 ft **11.** 8.4 mi **13.** 5a yd, 2.5a yd
15. $\approx 0.8x$ units, $\approx 0.4x$ units **17.** 22.0 **19.** 2.0
21. $1\frac{5}{7}$ **23.** $568\frac{6}{7}$ **25.** 27 **27.** 6 **29.** $2a + 2b = P$
Mixed Review **1.** 20 **2.** 93% **3.** 2.5
4. $\frac{AB}{HI} = \frac{BC}{IJ} = \frac{CD}{JK} = \frac{DA}{KH}$ **5.** 26.62 **6.** 169 **7.** 27
Test Yourself **1.** 6 **2.** 33.4 **3.** 94.2

9-9 page 395
Written Exercises **1.** about 8 **3.** 13
5. a. sun = 324 in.; moon = 0.825 in.
b. sun = 34,875 in.; moon = 90 in.

Problem Solving Practice page 396
1. positive **3.** 13 games **5.** 309 mi
7. 13 **9.** 13,455.33 yen; 52.42 pounds; 516.8 francs
11. $17,340.00 **13.** $90; $60

9-10 pages 399–400
Written Exercises **1.** yes **3.** no **7.** yes

Chapter 9 Review page 400
2. $\overrightarrow{AB} \parallel \overleftrightarrow{CD}$ **3.** Answers may vary. $\overleftrightarrow{AB}, \overleftrightarrow{CD}, \overleftrightarrow{EF}$
4. Answers may vary. $\overline{AE}; \overline{EB}; \overline{EF}; \overline{FD}; \overline{CF}$ **5.** Answers
may vary. $\overrightarrow{EF}, \overrightarrow{CD}, \overrightarrow{BA}, \overrightarrow{AB}, \overrightarrow{EB}, \overrightarrow{FD}, \overrightarrow{FC}, \overrightarrow{EA}, \overrightarrow{FE}$
6. acute **7.** supplementary **8.** $\cong$ **9.** 120° **10.** 125°
11. F **12.** T **13.** F **14.** T **15.** T **16.** T **17.** right
18. obtuse **19.** acute **20.** 60° **21.** 50 cm **22.** 20 cm
23. 7 in. **24.** 8.4 cm **25.** 15 ft **26.** 4.5 ft **27.** $\overline{AB} \cong$
$\overline{WX}; \overline{BC} \cong \overline{XY}; \overline{CD} \cong \overline{YZ}; \overline{AD} \cong \overline{WZ}; \angle A \cong \angle W; \angle B \cong$
$\angle X; \angle C \cong \angle Y; \angle D \cong \angle Z$ **28.** $x = 9$ **29.** $y = 5.4$
30. 84 in. **31.** 471 cm

Chapters 1–9 Cumulative Review page 403
1. C **2.** B **3.** C **4.** B **5.** A **6.** B **7.** A **8.** A **9.** C
10. C **11.** B **12.** B **13.** B **14.** D **15.** C **16.** B

CHAPTER 10

Area and Volume Formulas

10-1 pages 408–409
Written Exercises **7.** 7.02 cm² **9.** 237.16 in.²
11. 154.8 cm² **13.** 5.5 cm **15.** $15x$ **17.** 540 ft²
19. 58.79 km² **21.** 577.5 cm² **23.** $42x^2$ sq. units
25. 32 ft **27.** 49 cm² **29.** 96 ft **31.** 9 ft² **33.** $5\frac{1}{3}$ ft
Mixed Review **1.** 1.474×10^3 **2.** $\frac{4}{81}$ **3.** $>$ **4.** 6 and 7
5. 50.24 **6.** 180° **7.** 22.5 ft

10-2 pages 412–413
Written Exercises **1.** 39.36 m² **3.** 441 in.²
5. 161.7 cm² **7.** 750 cm² **9.** 1,394.64 ft²
11. 119.7 cm² **13.** 1.4 cm² **15.** 3.2 cm²
17. $81x^2$ sq. units **19.** 1.5 ft **21.** T **23.** F **25.** T
Mixed Review **1.** 180 cm² **2.** 764 mm² **3.** 121.7%
4. 1.4352×10^{10} **5.** $18.84x$ **6.** -5 **7.** $\frac{15}{16}$ **8.** 10

10-3 pages 415–416
Written Exercises **1.** 121π mi²; 379.94 mi²
3. 0.36π in.²; 1.13 in.² **5.** 2.56π ft²; 8.04 ft²
7. $25\pi x^2$ sq. units; $78.5x^2$ sq. units **9.** $4.41\pi x^2$ sq. units;
$13.85x^2$ sq. units **11.** e **13.** c **15.** b **17.** 1 circle of
radius 4 is larger. Area is 50.24. Area of 4 circles is
12.56. **19.** 50.24 cm² **21. b.** approximately 6 units
23. 16 in. **25.** 32.7 cm and 84.9 cm² **27.** 116.8 m and
1,086.3 m² **29.** 54.6 m and 237.7 m² **31.** 9.14 sq. units
33. 20π sq. units or 62.8 sq. units **35. a.** 6,280 ft²;
b. 9 ft²; **c.** 698 yd² **37. a.** The circumference is doubled,
tripled.; **b.** No. The area is multiplied by 4.

Mixed Review **1.** 60° **2.** 11 **3.** 8 **4.** 144 **5.** 60 **6.** 70
7. 67.5 **8.** 280 ft²
Test Yourself **1.** πr^2 **2.** $\frac{1}{2}bh$ **3.** bh **4.** $\frac{1}{2}h(b_1 + b_2)$
5. bh **6.** 35.75 cm² **7.** 286 ft² **8.** 910 in.²
9. 961.625 mm² **10.** 10.92 ft² **11.** 1,808.64 ft²

10-4 pages 422–423
Written Exercises **1.** pentagonal prism
3. triangular prism **5.** triangular pyramid **9.** T
11. F **13.** F **15.** rectangles, octagons **17.** 4
19. pentagonal prism, pentagons **21.** rectangular prism
23. sphere **27.** square pyramid
Mixed Review **1.** $9a^2\pi$ square units **2.** $8x$ square units
3. 25π in.² **4.** 35 cm² **5.** -13 **6.** -7 **7.** $1\frac{2}{5}$ **8.** 5:00 A.M.
9. 20°; acute
Critical Thinking **2.** Pattern A: triangle, circle, square,
square; Pattern B: circle, square, square, triangle;
Pattern C: square, square, triangle, circle.
3. Pattern D: square, triangle, circle, square. **4.** C

10-5 page 426
Written Exercises **1.** Use 2 strings of different lengths
with equal weights on the end. Test the time of swings.
3. 200 **5.** 7,042.6 m **7.** 7 **9.** $\frac{2}{15}$ **11.** 65

10-6 page 429
Written Exercises **1.** 1,078 sq. units **3.** 602.88 sq. units
5. 1,056 mm² **7.** 475.2 cm² **9. a.** 6 sq. units, 24 sq.
units, 54 sq. units; **b.** quadrupled; nine times larger
11. 16 gal
Mixed Review **1.** $6x^3$ **2.** $4a^2 + 7a$ **3.** $1\frac{1}{9}$ **4.** 12 **5.** 256
6. 144π or 452.16 **7.** 112 **8.** 1,500 bels **9.** 219.8 cm

10-7 page 432
Written Exercises **1.** 5,600 ft² **3.** 1,040 m²
5. 1,714.44 m² **7.** 2,826 in.² **9.** 4,578.12 m²
11. radii $\frac{2}{5}$; areas $\frac{4}{25}$; Ratio of areas is the square of the
ratio of the radii. **13.** 28.26 m²
Mixed Review **1.** 22 **2.** -8 **3.** $2.99 **4.** $3\frac{1}{5}$ **5.** 79.2 cm
6. 25.8 in. **7.** 1.024×10^9 **8.** Both figures have a
hexagon for a base. The sides of the prism are
rectangles. The sides of the pyramid are triangles.

10-8 pages 434–435
Written Exercises **1. b.** 125.25 ft²; yes; **c.** $626.25;
$1,252.50

Practice page 436
1. 29.2 m² **3.** 30.6 ft² **5.** 44.2 yd² **7.** 126 m² or
1,260,000 cm² **9.** 4,750 mm² **11.** 11,040 in.²
13. triangular pyramid **15.** 52 ft² **17.** 848 cm²
19. 1,256 m² **21.** 1,865.16 m² **23.** 5,024 mm²

10-9 pages 439–440
Written Exercises **1.** 637 in.³ **3.** $27a^3$ **5.** 720 mm³
7. 6,782.4 ft³ **9.** 5,803.72 cm³ **11.** 8,138.88 in.³
13. 128 ft³ **15.** $\frac{1}{2}$; doubles the volume
17. 5,878.08 mm³ **19.** πx^3 **21.** 320 ft³

Mixed Review 1. $(180 - 3x)°$ 2. $\frac{2}{5}$ 3. 94.2 cm 4. 3
5. 3.136×10^{13} square units 6. 391.2 in.^{2} 7. 263.76 ft^2
8. 22
Test Yourself 1. 680 mm^2 2. 477.28 m^2 3. 1,400 cm^2
4. 19,292.16 ft^3 5. 36,000 cm^3 6. 1,200 in.^{3}
7. $6x^3$ cu. units 8. $12.56x^3$ cu. units 9. $50x^3$ cu. units

10-10 pages 443–444
Written Exercises 1. 904.32 cm^3 3. 847.8 ft^3 5. 300 ft^3
7. The box from theater A holds 3 times more. 9. 4 m
11. 5 ft 13. ≈ 12.27 in.^{3} 15. a. 480.42 in. or 40.035 ft;
b. 73,504.3 in.^{2} or 510.45 ft^2;
c. $\approx 1,874,000$ in.^{3} or $\approx 1,085$ ft^3 17. $88,565,333\frac{1}{3}$ ft^3
Mixed Review 1. 61,544 mm^3 2. 43.332 in.
3. 533.8 in.^{2} 4. 1.2×10^5 5. -1 6. 8 7. $\frac{43}{72}$
8. 2,167.5 cm^3
Critical Thinking 3. a. $\frac{2}{3}$; b. $\frac{2}{3}$; c. $\frac{2}{3}$; d. $\frac{4}{9}$ 5. $\frac{5}{8}$, $\frac{25}{64}$

Problem Solving Practice page 445
1. 704 in.^{3} 3. 21 5. 27
7. Juan picked 15 bushels. Kimo picked 5 bushels.
9. Teresa, Fran, Vivian, Clara, Marie, Cindy
11. 12 ft × 20 ft

Chapter 10 Review pages 446–447
1. area 2. polygons 3. triangles 4. prism
5. cylinder 6. cone, vertex 7. sphere, center 8. faces
9. slant height 10. volume 11. 49 cm^2 12. 27 in.^{2}
13. 30 ft^2 14. 15 cm^2 15. 78.5 m^2 16. 200.96 mm^2
17. 56.52 m^2 18. 37.68 in.^{2} 19. square pyramid
20. triangular prism 21. cylinder 22. 13 in. × $24\frac{1}{2}$ in.
23. 164 cm^2 24. 62.8 in.^{2} 25. 84 cm^2 26. 216 m^2
27. 310.86 in.^{3} 28. 384 cm^3 29. 18 ft^3 30. 904.32 cm^3

Chapters 1–10 Cumulative Review page 449
1. B 2. A 3. C 4. A 5. D 6. C 7. C 8. A
9. B 10. C 11. B 12. B 13. A 14. A

CHAPTER 11

Right Triangles in Algebra

11-1 pages 456–457
Written Exercises 1. false 3. false 5. true 7. true
9. 256 11. $\frac{4}{9}$ 13. $25x^6$ 15. 81 17. 100 19. 8 21. 7
23. $\frac{4}{5}$ 25. 7.035 27. $4y^5$ 29. 16 31. 4.472 33. (7), 8
35. (2), 3 37. (-2), -3 39. (4), 5 41. rational
43. irrational 45. rational 47. rational 49. 7.071
51. 9.950 53. 6.557 55. 7.348
Mixed Review 1. 403.44 cm^2 2. 0.00254 m^3 3. $n \leq \frac{7}{8}$
4. $x \geq -13\frac{1}{2}$ 5. $-\frac{4}{7}$ 6. $x = 16\frac{1}{3}$ 7. 1,502% 8. $12
Critical Thinking 1. You keep getting 6.85 and 6.86. Go
halfway between the numbers to get 6.855. 2. 4.359
3. Calculators and computers can calculate square roots
instantly.

11-2 page 459
Written Exercises 1. lost $8 3. 4 h; 12 mi; 6 mi 5. -3
7. 3:02 P.M.

11-3 pages 463–464
Written Exercises 1. 5 3. $\frac{9}{25}$ 5. 7.937 7. 5.657
9. $\overline{AC}$ and $\overline{CB}$; $\overline{AB}$ 11. 10 13. 9
15. $50^2 + 120^2 = x^2$; $x = 130$
17. $x^2 + (6\sqrt{5})^2 = 18^2$; $x = 12$
19. $11^2 + x^2 = \sqrt{202}^2$; $x = 9$
21. $3^2 + 7^2 = h^2$; $x = 4.62$ 23. yes 25. no 27. no
29. yes for $p > 0$ 31. $\sqrt{2}$, $\sqrt{3}$, 2, $\sqrt{5}$, $\sqrt{6}$, $\sqrt{7}$
33. 106 ft 35. 21.21 in. 37. 14.1 ft 39. a. 21.63 in.;
b. 461.44 in.^{3}
Mixed Review 1. $25ab^2$ 2. xy 3. yes 4. 33°; 123°
5. 58°; 148° 6. 4 7. 256 8. 36°F

11-4 pages 467–468
Written Exercises 1. 27 3. 3 5. $x = 8.602$
7. $x = 9.487$ 9. $x = 10.5$ 11. $x = 12$; $y = 15$
13. $x = 36$; $y = 69.97$ 15. 43.75 ft
17. a. 611.45 ft; b. 570,025 ft^2
Mixed Review 1. yes 2. no 3. 8.96×10^{12} 4. 6
5. 38 6. $\frac{4}{2x} = \frac{1}{8} \cdot 12$; $x = 1\frac{1}{3}$ 7. $\frac{6x}{2} = x + 4$; $x = 2$
8. $0.02 \times 50 = x$; 1
Test Yourself 1. $x = 8$ 2. $x = 8.5$ 3. $x = 14.7$
4. 8.062 cm 5. 7.5 ft

11-5 pages 471–472
Written Exercises 1. 9; $9\sqrt{2}$ 3. 4; 4 5. $2\sqrt{3}$; 4
7. $7\sqrt{3}$; 14 9. $x = \frac{27}{\sqrt{2}}$ 11. $x = \frac{14}{\sqrt{3}}$; $y = \frac{28}{\sqrt{3}}$
13. a. 8.5 in.; b. 433.5 in^2 15. $26\sqrt{3}$ in. 17. 55.04 cm^2
19. 51 in.
Mixed Review 1. -12 2. 10 3. $x = 4.75$ 4. $-16x^6$
5. 6 6. pentagon 7. 27% 8. $33.32
Critical Thinking Lisa–bedroom; Nicole–bathroom;
Robert–living room; Eric–family room; JoAnn–kitchen

11-6 pages 475–476
Written Exercises 1. 0.1736 3. 0.2679 5. 0.9781
7. 84° 9. 63° 11. $\sqrt{3}$ 13. $\tan z° = \frac{f}{e}$ 15. $\sin y° = \frac{d}{c}$
17. $x \approx 54$; $y \approx 36$; $z = 1.27$
19. $x = 68$; $y = 9.90$; $z = 10.68$ 21. $x \approx 28$; $y \approx 62$
23. 13.3 mi 25. 41 ft
Mixed Review 1. 3.4 ft 2. 11.56 ft^2 3. 8 in.; $8\sqrt{3}$ in.
4. 0 5. acute 6. 5 m 7. -13, -14, -15
Test Yourself 1. 30°-60°-90° 2. 45°-45°-90° 3. neither
4. $x = 11$ 5. $x = 3$; $y = 6$; $z = 60$ 6. $x = 56$; $y = 8.09$;
$z = 14.48$

11-7 page 479
Written Exercises 11. a. $m\angle A \approx 23°$; $m\angle B \approx 67°$

Practice page 480
1. 13 3. $\frac{9}{2}$ 5. $\frac{x}{y}$ 7. $20x^3$ 9. $11c^2$ 11. 1 13. 3
15. 10 17. rational 19. rational 21. no 23. no
25. no 27. yes 29. 45°-45°-90° 31. neither
33. $x = 24$ 35. $y = 10$ 37. $y = 15$ 39. $a = 5$

Problem Solving Practice page 481
1. 42 3. 35°, 58°, and 87° 5. 1.36 min 7. 12
9. 657 cm^3 11. 8, 18, and 22

Chapter 11 Review pages 482–483

1. g **2.** d **3.** f **4.** b **5.** a **6.** h **7.** c **8.** i **9.** e
10. 14 **11.** $8p$ **12.** 1.732 **13.** $x - 2$ **14.** 25 **15.** 6
16. 18 **17.** 5 **18.** 15 **19.** 25 **20.** 6.708 **21.** 39 **22.** 9
23. 25 **24.** 32 **25.** 18 **26.** $8\sqrt{3}$ **27.** 20 **28.** $x = 25$;
$y = 45.315$; $z = 21.13$ **29.** $x = 70$; $y = 26.312$; $z = 9.576$
30. $x = 68$; $y = 24.752$; $z = 26.695$ **31.** $x = 50$;
$y = 51.424$; $z = 61.28$ **32.** 13.610 ft **33.** 2°

Chapters 1–11 Cumulative Review page 485

1. A **2.** B **3.** D **4.** B **5.** B **6.** C **7.** A **8.** C
9. B **10.** A **11.** A **12.** B

CHAPTER 12

Statistics and Probability

12-1 pages 490–491

Written Exercises 1. 4.8, 5, 5, 4
3. 21.5, 22.5, no mode, 10.3 **5.** 2, 2, 2, 4
7. 4.5, 4.5, 2, 6 **9.** 84.2, 84, 84, 16
11. 101, 101, 101, 8 **13. a.** 10; 8; 3 **b.** The median.
It is not influenced by the extreme of 30 points.
25. a. The mean, because it is the highest average.;
b. 87 **c.** 90
Mixed Review 1. 33.2 in.^{2} **2.** 360 ft^2 **3.** $\frac{4}{5}$ **4.** $\frac{3}{4}$
5. 3rd and 4th **6.** 1st and 2nd **7.** $7.16

12-2 pages 494–495

Written Exercises 1. 4; 4 **3.** 3.5; 1 and 6 **5.** 3.5, 2
7. 7.3, 7, 6 **9.** 25.8, 25, 25 **11.** 4, 4
13. 17.5, 15 and 20 **15. c.** 4.1, 3, 2 **17. b.** 2.7, 2, 0
21. a. men 40–44, women 30–34; **b.** Total number
entered. Divide by 2 to find middle number. Add
numbers entered one group at a time. Start at the top
until the middle number is reached or surpassed. Find
corresponding age. Men: 35–39. Women 35–39.
Mixed Review 1. -5.5 **2.** 62.5%, 0.625
3. 15.7, 16, 16 and 18 **4.** 14.4, 15, no mode **5.** 5
6. $-\frac{7}{8}$ **7.** 156

12-3 pages 500–501

Written Exercises 1. 774, 768 and 785 **3.** 82, 74
5. 11.65, 11.8 **7.** Set A: 62.5, 63; Set B: 57, no mode
9. Set E: 5.85, no mode; Set F: 6.45, no mode
11. a. 0; **c.** 10, 12, and 15; **d.** 13 **13.** 6, 7, 8, 9
15. Class A: 79.5, 74, 79 and 96; Class B: 84, 99
Mixed Review 1. 6,-6 **2.** 37.5 in.^{2} **3.** 2 **4.** 2
5. 18, 9, 27 **6.** 46, 23, 69 **7.** 852.375; 803.5; 774
Critical Thinking 1. A change in the groupings of the
horizontal scale changes heights on the vertical scale.
2. The shape of the graph is changed, giving a
different impact.

12-4 pages 504–505

Written Exercises 5. $220, $50 **7.** 75% **9.** no
17. 7.76, 7.7, 7.4, mean

Mixed Review 1. 118 **2.** 37.5% **3.** 79, 25 **4.** 79.4
5. 79 **7.** 120
Test Yourself 1. 65.3, 66, 45, 42

12-5 pages 510–511

Written Exercises 1. 120 **3.** 3,628,800 **5.** 60
7. 30,240 **9.** 479,001,600 **11.** 360,360 **13.** 6 **15.** 90
17. T **19.** F **21.** 12 **23.** 80 **25.** 440 **27. a.** 7; **b.** 6;
c. 5; **d.** 210 **29.** 36 **31.** 18
Mixed Review 1. 1×10^{11} **2.** 1×10^{-4} **3.** 19 **5.** $\frac{1}{3}$
6. $\frac{5}{11}$ **7.** $28.50
Critical Thinking 1. 2 **2.** red

12-6 pages 514–515

Written Exercises 1. $\frac{1}{2}$ **3.** $\frac{7}{11}$ **5.** $\frac{6}{11}$ **7.** $\frac{4}{25}$ **9.** $\frac{3}{7}$
11. a. $\frac{6}{13}$; **b.** $\frac{13}{25}$; **c.** $\frac{24}{49}$; **d.** Yes. The sample space is
different for each question. **13. a.** $\frac{4}{25}$; **b.** $\frac{21}{25}$; **c.** Any
prime number has 1 or more digits. **15. a.** $\frac{1}{7}$; **b.** $\frac{2}{7}$;
c. $\frac{5}{14}$; **d.** $\frac{1}{7}$; **e.** $\frac{1}{14}$; **f.** 1 **17. a.** $\frac{1}{5}$; **b.** $\frac{1}{5}$; **c.** $\frac{1}{10}$; **d.** $\frac{1}{5}$; **e.** $\frac{1}{5}$;
f. The event of having the digit 0 as the last digit is not
included. **19.** 15 **21.** $\frac{1}{3}$
Mixed Review 1. 9 **2.** $\frac{2}{5}$ **3.** 720 **4.** 840 **5.** 7.25
7. $5x = 850$; 170 tickets

12-7 pages 519–520

Written Exercises 3. $\frac{5}{16}$ **5.** $\frac{19}{25}$ **7.** $\frac{1}{31}$ **9.** 98 **11.** $67.50
13. 2 **15.** Yes. The circumference of the hole is 3.14 in.
17. 78.6%

Practice page 521

1. 16, 13, 6 and 7, 30 **3.** 4, 4, 4, 6 **5.** 3.75, 5, 6
7. Set A: 23.5, 23 Set B: 22, no mode **9.** The data for
Set A is spread out. Set B data is consistent, staying close
to the median, which is 9. **11.** 4! **13.** $\frac{25!}{22!}$ **15.** 720
17. 2,450 **19.** $\frac{1}{9}$ **21.** $\frac{4}{9}$ **23.** 1

12-8 pages 524–525

Written Exercises 1. independent **3.** dependent **5.** $\frac{1}{10}$
7. $\frac{1}{12}$ **9.** Dependent $\frac{5}{82}$ **11.** dependent **a.** $\frac{9}{56}$; **b.** $\frac{3}{28}$
13. 24; No. The class is small enough to ask each
person for his/her preference. **15.** $\frac{2}{5}$
Mixed Review 1. 195 **2.** 132 **3.** $\frac{1}{2}$ **4.** $\frac{1}{6}$ **5.** $48n$
6. $29n - 5$ **7.** 5 y, 15 y
Test Yourself 1. 30.3, 30, 28 and 35 **2.** 20 **3.** $\frac{1}{36}$
4. $\frac{1}{11}$

Problem Solving Practice page 526

1. 105 ft **3.** 24 **5.** 32 students **7.** 5 and 6
9. 160, 160, 160, 80 or 112, 112, 224, 112 **11.** 69

12-9 pages 528–529

Written Exercises 1. 496 **3.** 315 **5. a.** 240; **b.** 400;
c. 600; **d.** 192, 320, 480; **e.** $1,240

Chapter 12 Review pages 530–531

1. false, mode **2.** true **3.** true **4.** false, independent
5. false, factorial **6.** 7.46, 8, 8, 4
7. 115.56, 115, no mode, 37 **10.** 6 **11.** 5,040

12. 12   13. 1,680   14. 35   15. $\frac{1}{5}$ 16. $\frac{2}{5}$ 17. $\frac{1}{5}$ 18. $\frac{4}{5}$
19. $\frac{2}{25}$ 20. $\frac{1}{10}$

Chapters 1–12 Cumulative Review page 533
1. B   2. C   3. A   4. C   5. B   6. A   7. B   8. D
9. B   10. C   11. A   12. A   13. A   14. C

CHAPTER 13

Polynomials

13-1 pages 540–541
Written Exercises   1. monomial   **3.** monomial   **5.** 2
7. 3   **9.** 1   **11.** binomial   **13.** monomial
15. monomial   **17.** binomial   **25.** $x^2 + 3$
27. $x^2 + 2x + 3$ **31.** 6   **33.** -1   **35.** 0   **37.** 187
39. 195   **41.** 201
Mixed Review   1. x^5 **2.** $64m^6$ **3.** independent
4. dependent   **5.** $6x^2$ **6.** 9   **7.** 120 poses
Critical Thinking   1. a. yes; **b.** yes; **c.** yes; **d.** no; **e.** no
2. a. no; **b.** no; **c.** no; **d.** no; **e.** yes   **3. a.** no; **b.** no;
c. no; **d.** yes; **e.** yes   **4. a.** no; **b.** no; **c.** no; **d.** yes;
e. no

13-2 pages 544–545
Written Exercises   1. $4x^2 + 5x + 2$ **3.** $-x + 5$
5. $-3x^2 + x + 7$ **7.** $9x^2 + x + 5$ **9.** $2x^3 + 5x^2 + x + 4$
11. $3x + 8$ **13.** $4y - 15$ **15.** $4mn^2 + 2m - 2n^2$
17. $2a^2 + 5ab + 2b$ **19.** $m - 9$ **21.** $4ab - 10$
23. $w^2 + 7w - 6$ **25.** $-3x^2 - 8x + 8$ **27.** $-8x + 10$
29. $17a^7 + 8a^4 + a^2 + 4$ **31.** $11a^3b^2 - 15a^2b - 2ab + 23$
33. $2a + (2a + 2) + (2a + 4)$; **a.** $6a + 6$; **b.** 10, 12, 14
35. $5a + (5a + 5) + (5a + 10) + (5a + 15) + (5a + 20)$;
a. $25a + 50$; **b.** 65, 70, 75, 80, 85   **37.** $8b^2 + 10b - 6$
39. a. 360; **b.** 540; **c.** 720; **d.** 1,440
Mixed Review   1. 5 sq. units   **2.** 12 sq. units   **3.** 2   **4.** 3
5. $17x - 6$ **6.** $24x + 6 - 20y$ **7.** 7.125 mi

13-3 pages 547–548
Written Exercises   1. $2x^2 + 12x$ **3.** $6x^2 - 2x$ **5.** $5x^2 + 3x$
7. a. 24; **b.** 2; **c.** 40; **d.** 6   **9.** $-4x^2y^2 + 4x^3y$; -233,280
11. $8x^2 - 2x$ **13.** $2x^3 - 5x^2$ **15.** $2y^4 + y^3 - 3y^2$
17. $5x^2y + 25xy - 5xy^2$ **19.** $-6x^3y^2 - 3x^2y^2 - 3xy^3 + 9xy$
21. $96x^3y^3z + 24x^4yz^6$ **23.** $12x^3 + 12x^2y^2 + 12x^2z$
25. $\frac{1}{2}xy + \frac{1}{2}xy^3 + \frac{5}{2}y$ **27.** $14x^4 + 7x^2y^2 - 7x^3y$
29. $3x^3 + 2x^2 + 9x$ **31.** $e(e + 2)$; $e^2 + 2e$
33. $l\left(\frac{1}{2}l + 7\right)$; $\frac{1}{2}l^2 + 7l$ **35.** $\frac{1}{2}(8x)(16x + 5)$; $64x^2 + 20x$
37. $7 \times 10^2 + 9 \times 10 + 2$; $7x^2 + 9x + 2$; $4x$;
$(7x^2 + 9x + 2)4x = 28x^3 + 36x^2 + 8x$;
$28(10)^3 + 36(10)^2 + 8(10) = 31,680 = 40(792)$; yes
39. $8a^2 + a$ **41.** $4d^2 + 4d$
Mixed Review   1. 2.75   **2.** 27.52 m²   **3.** $3x^2 + 7x + 6$
4. $-9x^2 - 5x + 13$ **5.** x^4 **6.** x^{10} **7.** $449

13-4 pages 552–553
Written Exercises   1. $x^2 + 7x + 6$ **3.** $a^2 + 8a + 7$
5. $a^2 + a - 6$ **7.** $a^2 + 11a + 24$ **9.** $xy + xb + ay + ab$

11. $x^2 + 13x + 12$ **13.** $15 + 2x - x^2$
15. $8ac - 4ad + 4bc - 2bd$ **17.** $x^2 - 9$
19. $b^2 - 14b + 49$ **21.** $4a^2 - 25$ **23.** $4a^2 + 4a + 1$
25. $x^2 + 15x - 756$ **27.** $3a^2 - 2a - 8$
29. $x^2 - 3.5x - 6.24$ **31.** $b^3 - 3b^2 + 3b - 1$
33. $-8a^2 + 20a + 12$ **35.** $x^2 + 2x + 1$ **37.** $x^2 - y^2$
39. $x^2 + 4x + 4$ **41.** $10x^2 + 26x + 12$ **43.** $20x^2 + 6x - 2$
45. $(w - 1)(w - 2) = w^2 - 3w + 2$
47. $(t - 6)^2 = t^2 - 12t + 36$ **49.** $x = 2$ **51.** $w = 0$
53. about 50 mi
Mixed Review   1. 2   **2.** 13.5   **3.** $6x^2 + 2x$
4. $-5x^3 + 10x^2$ **5.** 20   **6.** 6   **7.** 72 ft by 72 ft
Test Yourself   1. monomial   **2.** binomial   **3.** not a
polynomial   **4.** trinomial   **5.** monomial   **6.** binomial
7. monomial   **8.** monomial   **9.** 81   **10.** 95   **11.** -7
12. -51   **13.** 112   **14.** -26   **15.** $11a$
16. $p^2 + p + 12$ **17.** $3ab^2 + 2a + b + 9$
18. $-r^2s^2 + rs - 16$ **19.** $(a^2 + b)(a^2 + b) = a^4 + 2a^2b + b^2$

Practice page 554
1. 2; binomial   3. 2; binomial   5. 1; monomial
7. $6r^2 - 3$ 9. $-4d - 1$ 11. $-7x^2y - 6xy - 5x^2 + 13$
13. $2rt^2 + 6r^2t + 2t$ 15. $21xy + 6x$ 17. $20x^2y + 15xy^2$
19. $10a^4b^2 - 10a^2b^4$ 21. $8c^2d + 12cd^2 - 24cd$
23. $x^2 + 10x + 25$ 25. $x^2 - 4.5x + 4.5$ 27. $x^2 - 25$
29. $x^2 - 10x + 25$ 31. $x^3 - 5x^2 - 2x + 10$
33. $12x^2 + 40x + 12$ 35. $25x^2 - 20x + 4$
37. $30x^4 + 10x^3 - 6x^2 - 2x$ 39. $3x^3 + 6x^2 - 72x$ 41. 13
43. 140   45. -6   47. 7,280   49. -34   51. 12   53. -2
55. 12

13-5 page 557
Written Exercises   1. $\begin{bmatrix} 1 & 2 \\ 2 & 3 \end{bmatrix}$ **3.** $\begin{bmatrix} 3 & 1 \\ -2 & 2 \end{bmatrix}$
5. 8   **7.** (-2,4)   **9.** (1,1)   **11.** One pen and two pencils
cost $.60.

13-6 pages 559–560
Written Exercises   1. 80 games   **3.** 7.5 ft
5. Sandy = 101 g; White Ears = 108 g; Sport = 115 g
7. 51 people   **9.** 32.9 min   **11.** 10 angles   **13.** 3,750 ft²
15. $28.80   **17.** 6 ways

Problem Solving Practice page 561
1. 28 possible routes   3. 86   5. 60 lb
7. A is 3 yd by 11 yd; B is 3 yd by 3 yd
9. 8 students

Chapter 13 Review pages 562–563
1. A monomial is a real number, variable, or the
product of a real number and one or more variables.
Examples: $6x^2$; $3x$.   2. A polynomial is a monomial or a
sum or difference of monomials. Examples: $5x - 2$;
$12x^2 - 6x - 5$.   3. Multiply x by each term within the
parentheses. $x(2x - 1) = x \cdot 2x - x \cdot 1 = 2x^2 - x$
4. Multiply the first terms, $x \cdot 2x$, the outer terms, $x \cdot 1$,
the inner terms, $3 \cdot 2x$, and the last terms, $3 \cdot 1$.
Then add the products. $2x^2 + x + 6x + 3 = 2x^2 + 7x + 3$
5. Square the first term and subtract the square of the

second term. $(a + b)(a - b) = a^2 - b^2$ **6.** To square a binomial like $(a + b)^2$ or $(a - b)^2$, square the first term. Add or subtract twice the product of the two terms and add the square of the last term. $(a + b)^2 = a^2 + 2ab + b^2$; $(a - b)^2 = a^2 - 2ab + b^2$
7. $2x^2 + 3x$; binomial   **8.** $x^2 + 2x + 4$; trinomial
9. $3x^2$; monomial   **10.** 15   **11.** -9   **12.** -10
13. $7x^2 + 4x$ **14.** $2x^2 + 3x + 1$ **15.** $8x + 5y$
16. $3m - 2n$ **17.** $6a^2 + 3b$ **18.** $-3r^2 + 5s$
19. $4c^2 + 2c - 1$ **20.** $2a^2b - b^2 + 2a$ **21.** $2x^2 + 10x$
22. $6x^2 + 3x$ **23.** $x^2 - 5x$ **24.** $3x^2 + 6x$ **25.** $2x^2 - 4x$
26. $4x^3 + 12x^2$ **27.** $10x^3 - 10x^2 + 15x$
28. $-2x^3y + 2x^2y^2 - 2xy^3$
29. $(x + 2)(x + 2) = x^2 + 4x + 4$
30. $(x + 2)(x + 3) = x^2 + 5x + 6$ **31.** $x^2 - 2x + 1$
32. $a^2 + 6a + 9$ **33.** $y^2 - 4$ **34.** $b^2 + b - 6$
35. $m^2 + 2m - 15$ **36.** $2n^2 + 6n - 20$ **37.** 4 min
38. 8 classic; 6 rock   **39.** 12, 24, 36   **40.** 2,401 ft^2

Chapters 1–13 Cumulative Review page 565

1. B   **2.** C   **3.** A   **4.** C   **5.** A   **6.** B   **7.** C   **8.** B
9. B   **10.** B   **11.** A   **12.** D   **13.** C   **14.** B   **15.** C
16. B

CHAPTER 1

Extra Practice

page 566
1. -4   **3.** 10   **5.** >   **7.** =   **9.** -10   **11.** 9   **13.** -112
15. 110   **17.** 6   **19.** 3   **21.** 27   **23.** 51   **25.** 2   **27.** $-7x$
29. $-(y - 7)$ **31.** $|-3 - 10|$ **33.** $10[17 - (-11)]$
35. 71   **37.** -18   **39. a.** $20x + 12y$; **b.** $152; **c.** 3; 5
41. +13

CHAPTER 2

Extra Practice

page 567
1. false   **3.** false   **5.** false   **7.** 0   **9.** 3   **11.** 44   **13.** 25
15. 15   **17.** -61   **19.** 20   **21.** $-3m + 39$ **23.** $5q + 2$
25. $-6s + 4$ **27.** $j = 26$ **29.** $z = 20$ **31.** $n = 5$ or $n = -5$
33. $-3 \div (-1) = 3$ **35.** $xy = |-24|$ **37.** 2,422 m   **39.** 27

CHAPTER 3

Extra Practice

page 568
1. 2.12, 2.012, 2.011   **3.** 1.00009, 0.000045, 0.00004
5. 0.4   **7.** 238   **9.** $19   **11.** 90   **13.** $1,000   **15.** 216
17. -116.667   **19.** 100.987   **21.** 15.32   **23.** 7.66
25. -1.856   **27.** 15.32   **29.** $y = 1.1$ **31.** $m = 1.89$
33. $x = 16.5$ **35.** $n = 100$ **37.** $0.03x = -3.01$
39. $|-0.9| = 2x$ **41.** 31 min   **43.** 6

CHAPTER 4

Extra Practice

page 569
1. 1,024   **3.** -16   **5.** $15x^3$ **7.** $64y^{12}$ **9.** 16   **11.** 8
13. -1   **15.** -12   **17.** 134   **19.** 1   **21.** 2   **23.** 27
25. 5.28×10^4; 52,800   **27.** 1.82×10^7; 18,200,000
29. 2,3,4,9   **31.** 3,5,9   **33.** 2   **35.** 2   **37.** $9ab^2$
39. 1,100   **41.** $12a^5b$ **43.** 45; 15   **45.** 1,100
47. 20 and 4

CHAPTER 5

Extra Practice

page 570
1. $\frac{1}{2}$ **3.** $\frac{1}{5}$ **5.** $\frac{1}{3}$ **7.** $\frac{1}{5}$ **9.** $20\frac{2}{25}$ **11.** $\frac{1}{200}$ **13.** 0.4
15. 0.6   **17.** 0.75   **19.** $-\frac{3}{4}, \frac{1}{2}, \frac{8}{4}$ **21.** $\frac{2^2}{5}, \frac{9}{10}, 2\frac{3}{10}$
23. $\frac{-xy}{5}, \frac{xy}{15}, \frac{3xy}{10}$ **25.** $-\frac{5}{6}$ **27.** $\frac{7}{18}x$ **29.** $7\frac{1}{2}$ **31.** $\frac{72}{77}$
33. $\frac{7x^2}{15}$ **35.** $1\frac{14}{15}$ **37.** $-1\frac{17}{32}$ **39.** $\frac{1}{9}$ **41.** $\frac{a^2b}{c}$ **43.** $\frac{-1}{y}$
45. $1\frac{4}{9}$ **47.** $\frac{-13}{40}$ **49.** $2\frac{1}{2}$ **51.** $-4\frac{4}{9}$
53. 1,205 million people   **55.** 24

CHAPTER 6

Extra Practice

page 571
1. $\frac{1}{3}$ **3.** $\frac{1}{4}$ **5.** $\frac{1}{9}$ **7.** $\frac{1}{5}$ **9.** $\frac{20}{30} = \frac{x}{120}$; $x = 80$
11. $\frac{20}{95} = \frac{z}{19}$; $z = 4$ **13.** $\frac{17}{20}$; 85%   **15.** $\frac{40}{120}$; $33\frac{1}{3}\%$
17. 45%   **19.** $330.\overline{30}$ **21.** 6.44   **23.** -33.3%
25. +64.5%   **27.** +258.3%   **29.** +6.5%   **31.** 6   **33.** 60%
35. 2,400   **37.** bread: +4,533%; milk: +679%

CHAPTER 7

Extra Practice

page 572
1. $x = 6$ **3.** $y = 2\frac{1}{4}$ **5.** $x = 20$ **7.** $b = 3$ **9.** $x = 10$
19. $y \geq 6$ **21.** $y \leq -36$ **23.** $x \geq \frac{5}{9}$ **25.** $x < 7$
27. $x \leq 50$ **29.** $x \leq 90$ **31.** $\frac{a}{8} \leq 13$; $a \leq 104$
33. $7p - 5 \geq 23$; $p \geq 4$
35. 12 months   **37.** $.20
39. 97

CHAPTER 8

Extra Practice

page 573
1. II   **3.** I   **5.** III   **7.** $y = -\frac{1}{2}x + 4$ **9.** $y = 2x + 24$

11. $y = 3x + 3$ **13.** 2; $2\frac{1}{2}$; -5 **15.** -1; 5; 5
17. $-\frac{1}{4}$; -12; -3 **19.** (4,-5) **21.** $y > 3x - 5$
23. $y < 2x + 49$
31. 7 bags of popcorn and 14 gal of juice
33. 6 and 7 **35.** 1 min 12 s

CHAPTER 9

Extra Practice

page 574
1. acute **3.** obtuse **5.** straight **7.** not possible; 90
9. 45; 135 **11.** not possible; 40 **17.** 90 **19.** 80 **21.** 84
23. $d = 58.6$ cm **25.** $r = 39$ in. **27.** $d = 457$ m
29. true **31.** false **33.** true **35.** 640.56 ft
37. 16.8 in. **39.** 27 m **41.** 1 mi **43.** 62.8 yd

CHAPTER 10

Extra Practice

page 575
1. 18.3 cm² **3.** 0.9 m² **5.** $561x^2$ **7.** 206 cm²
9. 547.1 m² **11.** 98.5 m² **13.** 660.2 cm² **15.** 286 in.²
17. 11,269 m² **19.** 1,808.64 in.² **21.** 140 ft³
23. 2,279.64 cm³ **25.** 100 cm³ **27.** the $61 dress
29. 16 in.³

CHAPTER 11

Extra Practice

page 576
1. 7.141 **3.** 12 **5.** $7x$ **7.** $a + b$ **9.** yes **11.** no
13. yes **15.** $x = 4\sqrt{2}$ **17.** $x = 14\sqrt{2}$ **19.** $x = 9\sqrt{2}$
21. $\frac{n}{m}$ **23.** $\frac{e}{d}$ **25.** 8 mi **27.** 3 A.M.

CHAPTER 12

Extra Practice

page 577
1. 10.4; 12; 13; 10 **3.** 78.6; 100; 100; 100 **7.** 13; 13
9. 69; 66 **13.** 5 **15.** 714 **17.** $\frac{1}{4}$ **19.** $\frac{3}{13}$ **21.** $\frac{1}{676}$
23. -6 **25.** 1,766.25 cm³ **27.** $6\sqrt{2}$ **29.** 6 and 7

CHAPTER 13

Extra Practice

page 578
1. $3x^2 + 4x + 5$ **3.** $-2mn^2 + m + 2n - 3$
5. $-3a^3n^2 - 4a^2n + 6a$ **7.** $72x^3 - 36x^2 + 162x$
9. $\frac{5}{2}a^6 - \frac{1}{2}a^4 - \frac{33}{2}a$ **11.** $x^2 + 4x + 3$ **13.** $x^2 - 81$
15. $2x^3 + 5x^2 + 3x + 2$
17. $(m + 2)(m + 4)(m + 6)$; $m^3 + 12m^2 + 44m + 48$
19. $(z - 4)(z - 8)$; $z^2 - 12z + 32$ **21.** 904.32 cm³ **23.** 24
25. 194 **27.** $\frac{7}{75}$

Index

INDEX

Hypotenuse, 460, 461, 469, 470
Hypothesis, exploring a, 444

I

Identities
  additive, 59
  multiplicative, 59
Improper fractions, 188, 218
Independent events, 522–525
Indirect variation, 353
Inductive reasoning, exploring, 376
Inequalities, 291, 303
  and addition and subtraction
    properties for, 296
  and multiplication and division
    properties for, 297
  exploring, 291
  graphing, 291, 292–295, 348–351
  linear, 344–351
  one-step, 296–299
  solving, 296–299, 300–303, 344–347
  two-step, 300–303
Infinity, exploring, 209–210
Integers, 4–33
  absolute value, 5
  addition, 8–9, 10–13
  and number line, 4–5
  classification, 13
  comparing, 5
  consecutive, 86
  division, 26–29
  exploring, 8–9
  models of, 8
  multiplying, 22–25
  opposite, 4–5, 8–9
  positive and negative, 4, 8
  set of, 4
  subtraction, 14–17
Intersection
  perpendicular lines, 316
  points of, 363
  segments, rays, or lines, 367
  Venn diagram, 21
Inverse operations, 26, 72
Irrational numbers, 455
Isosceles right triangle, 469

L

Lateral area, 427. *See also* Surface
  area
LCD, 196. *See* Least common
  denominator (LCD)
LCM, 168–170. *See* Least common
  multiple

Least common denominator (LCD),
  196
Least common multiple (LCM), 168–
  170
Legs, triangle, 460, 461, 470
Light year, 152
Like terms, 66, 80
  combining, 279, 288
Line plots, 492–495
Line symmetry, 381
Linear equations
  graphing, 324–327, 340–343
  slope-intercept form, 331
  solving systems of, 340–343
  system of, 340
Linear inequalities
  graphing, 348–351
  solving, 344–347, 349
  system of, 349
Linear programming, 351
Lines
  coordinate plane, 316
  graphing, 331
  graphs of linear equation, 324
  parallel, 363
  perpendicular, 316
  properties, 362
  skew, 363
  slope, 329, 330
  symbol, 362
Logic, exploring, 472
Logical thinking, exploring, 65
LOGO, exploring with, 373
Lowest terms, 185

M

Maps, 241, 316
Matrices, 555
Mean, 27, 488–491, 493
Median, 488–491, 493
Mental math, 12, 16, 24, 28, 42, 45,
  56, 60, 61, 64, 75, 77, 78, 109, 113,
  117, 143, 187, 198, 201, 202, 208,
  217, 254, 258, 262, 277, 281, 289,
  303, 318, 319, 322, 327, 332, 378,
  438, 456, 463, 467, 471, 475, 490,
  510, 541, 547, 552
Metric system, 125–127
Mind-reading tricks, exploring, 549
Mixed number, 188, 200, 206, 218
Mode, 488–491, 492, 493
Models
  decimals, 98, 99, 101, 244
  equations, 70–71, 215, 274, 287
  fractions, 182, 184
  integers, 8

Models (cont.)
  number sentences, 8
  percents, 244
  polynomials, 539, 542
  problem solving with, 425–426
  Pythagorean theorem, 461
  rational numbers, 199, 206, 215
  simulations, 338, 339
  variable expressions, 34
  zero, 8
Monomials, 538
  multiplying by polynomials, 546–
    548
Monte Carlo simulations, 518
Multiples, 156–157, 159–162
  common, 168
  exploring, 156–157
  factors and, 156–157, 159–162
  least common (LCM), 168–170,
    196
Multiplication
  associative property, 58–59, 108
  binomials, 550–553
  commutative property, 58–59
  equations, 115–118, 218–221
  exponents, 145
  FOIL method, 550
  in monomials, 538
  integers, 22–25
  polynomials, 546–548
  properties for inequalities, 297
  property of equality, 77
  rational numbers, 206–208
  sum and difference of two terms,
    551
Multiplicative identity, 59

N

Naming
  circles, 377
  polygons, 371
Natural numbers, 195
Nautical mile, 343
Net, 421, 427, 430
Notes & quotes, 10, 16, 20, 28, 35,
  56, 67, 85, 102, 142, 161, 165, 166,
  196, 215, 246, 248, 281, 296, 317,
  353, 362, 378, 391, 393, 397, 428,
  455, 461, 492, 512, 550
Number line
  comparing integers, 5
  fractions, 197
  inequalities, 291, 292
  integers on, 4, 10
  line plots, 492–495
  opposite integers, 4
  rational numbers, 193

INDEX

INDEX

Acknowledgments

PHOTO CREDITS

KEY TO PHOTO SOURCE ABBREVIATIONS
Bruce Coleman, Inc.= BC; Freelance Photographers Guild = FPG; Ken Karp = KK; Russ Lappa = RL; Larry Lawfer = LL; Picture Cube = PC; PhotoEdit = PE; Photo Researchers, Inc. = PR; Tom Stack & Associates = TSA; Stock Market = SM; Tony Stone Worldwide = TSW; Woodfin Camp & Associates = WC.

KEY TO PHOTO POSITION ON TEXT PAGE
T=Top; **M**=Middle; **B**=Bottom; **L**=Left; **R**=Right.

Back Cover: Top, James H. Carmichael/BC; Center, PR; Bottom, Hank Morgan/PR.

Front Matter: i T, Photo by Mark Richards; **i B,** Hank Morgan/PR; **vi TR,** Patrick Aventurier/Gamma-Liaison; **vi BL,** Rolf Sorensen/TSW; **vii TMR,** Nancy Sheehan; **vii TR,** Chris Hackett/The Image Bank; **viii TL,** Tony Freeman/PE; **ix TL,** David Ball/SM; **ix BR,** TSW; **x MR,** J. J. Raynal/PR; **xi TM,** Brownie Harris/SM; **xi BL,** European Space Agency/PR.

CHAPTER ONE 2, Annie Griffiths/BC; **2-3,** PR; **3,** Rolf Sorensen/TSW; **4,** Keith Lanpher; **9,** Richard Haynes; **13,** David Madison/BC; **17,** David Austen/TSW; **23,** Greg Vaughn/TSA; **30,** Thomas Braise/SM; **33,** FPG; **40,** Bob Daemmrich/TSW; **42,** Photo by Mark Richards; **47,** Jack Finch/PR.

CHAPTER TWO 52 M, Armando Jenik/The Image Bank; **52 B,** Carl Roessler/Animals Animals; **52 MR,** Carl Roessler/FPG; **52-53,** John L. Pontier/Animals Animals; **53,**FPG; **61 T,** Clyde H. Smith/FPG; **61 (inset),** Lee Foster/FPG; **67,** The Granger Collection; **69,** Peter Menzel; **71, LL; 76,** Michael Melford/The Image Bank; **80,** LL/PC; **89,** Arnold John Kaplan/PC; **90,** Brownie Harris/SM.

CHAPTER THREE 96, Patrick Aventurier/Gamma-Liaison; **96-97,** Nancy Sheehan; **97 T, B,** Nancy Sheehan; **98, LL; 99,** Meral Dabcovich; **100,** Jack Dermid/BC; **102,** The Granger Collection; **111,** FPG; **115,** Steve Ogden/TS; **119,** Pete Saloutos/SM; **120,** Peter Steiner/SM; **124,** TSW; **127 T,** Bob and Clara Calhoun/BC; **127 B,** Meral Dabcovich; **129,** UPI/Bettmann Newsphotos; **133,** Doug Armand/TSW.

CHAPTER FOUR 139 T, Peter Miller/The Image Bank; **139 BR,** Chris Hackett/The Image Bank; **139 (inset),** Nancy Sheehan; **141,** Robert Knauft/PR; **144,** M. Richards/PE; **150,** FPG; **152,** NASA; **155,** KK; **156,** Michal Heron/WC; **167, 168,** KK.

CHAPTER FIVE 180, Milton Feinberg/PC; **180-181,** Dave Schaefer/PC; **181, LL; 181 T,** Richard Anders/FPG; **181 B,** Phil Degginger/BC; **183,** Richard Haynes; **187, LL; 189,** KK; **192,** Kim Taylor/BC; **195,** Sarah Putnam/PC; **196,** Mackson/FPG; **198,** Photo by Mark Richards; **199,** Franz Lazi/FPG; **205,** Michael Keller/FPG; **206,** TSW; **211,** Chris Bjornberg/PR; **213,** Photo by Mark Richards; **214,** Thomas Kitchin/TS; **218,** Meral Dabcovich; **223,** Alan Klehr/TSW; **228,** Ken Karp.

CHAPTER SIX 230, Tony Freeman/PE; **231,** David Young-Wolff/PE; **232,** KK; **236,** Kindra Clineff PC; **237,** Zur Veroffentlichung/FPG; **240,** Robert Huntzinger/SM; **243 T,** LL; **243 B,** Nancy Sheehan; **245,** Michal Heron/WC; **248,** Brian Seed/TSW; **249,** Steve Liss/Gamma-Liaison; **250-251,** Richard Hutchings/ InfoEdit; **252,** Martin Rogers/TSW; **259,** LL; **260,** Richard Laird/FPG; **265,** Nancy Sheehan; **266,** Joe Baraban/SM.

CHAPTER SEVEN 272, John Blaustein/WC; **272-273,** Joe Tower/SM; **273,** Chris Sorenson/SM; **274,** Richard Haynes; **276,** J. H. Robinson/PR; **279,** Tom Campbell/FPG; **282,** T. J. Florian/Rainbow; **284,** Scott Deitrich/TSW; **292,** Gary Buss/FPG; **295,** Frank Siteman/PC; **296,** Novosti/Science Photo Library/PR; **300,** Jon Feingersh/TSA; **303,** Alan Carey/PR; **304,** Dick Luria/FPG; **307,** Charles West/SM.

CHAPTER EIGHT 312, Tom Bean/SM; **312-313,** The Granger Collection; **313,** Jeffry Myers/FPG; **314 (all),** RL; **315,** Richard Haynes; **318,** Keith Olson/TSW; **320,** TSW; **323,** Charles Seaborn/WC; **329,** Cathlyn Melloan/TSW; **333,** Wesley Bocxe/PR; **335,** Peter Gridley/FPG; **336,** David Young-Wolff/PE; **337,** David Young-Wolff/PE; **338, 339 L,** Lily Yamamoto; **339 R,** European Space Agency/Science Photo Library/PR; **344,** Tony Freeman/PE; **346,** All photos by Mark Richards; **352,** Richard Hutchings/PR; **354,** J. Mejuto/FPG; **355,** KK.

CHAPTER NINE 361, Henley and Savage/TSW; **360-361,** Nancy Sheehan; **360,** David Ball/SM; **362,** D. Wilder/TSA; **367,** S.L. Craig/BC; **369 (all),** RL; **370,** John Lamb/TSW; **374,** David Ball/PC; **377 T,** Stanley Rowin/PC; **377 B,** Dr. Jeremy Burgess/Science Photo Library/PR; **380,** Tony Freeman/PE; **383 L,** Ray Coleman/PR; **383 M,** Brian Parker/TSA; **383 R,** Michael Keller/SM; **384,** Dan McCoy/Rainbow; **388,** Paulette Brunner/TSA; **389,** FPG; **394,** Vandystadt/PR; **395,** Michael Dunn/SM; **397,** Art Resource; **399,** Aga Khan Program Archives, M.I.T., Photo by George J. Kostaras, 1983.

CHAPTER TEN 404, FPG; **404-405,** FPG; **405,** TSW; **406,** RL; **411,** Tom Tracy/FPG; **414,** David Ball/PC; **415,** Meral Dabcovich; **417,** Photo by Mark Richards; **418, 419 (all),** RL; **421,** Richard Haynes; **430,** Hugh Sitton/TSW; **431 L,** Frank Cezus/FPG; **431 R,** Bob Brudd/TSW; **432,** Alan Smith/TSW; **434,** R. B. Sanchez/SM; **435 T,** Joe Sohn/SM; **436,** Dan McCoy/Rainbow; **439,** Photo by Mark Richards; **440,** The Granger Collection; **441,** Tom Tracy/FPG; **443,** RL; **445,** José Carrillo/TSW.

CHAPTER ELEVEN 450, Tom Sanders/SM; **450-451,** J. J. Raynal/PR; **451,** Richard Burda/FPG; **455,** RL; **457,** Bill Sanderson/Science Photo Library/PR; **458,** John Terence Turner/FPG; **459,** Henley and Savage/TSW; **461,** Photoworld/FPG; **468,** K&G Photo/FPG; **477,** David Jeffrey/The Image Bank; **479,** Stock Imagery; **480,** Bill Losh/FPG; **482,** J. J. Raynal/PR.

CHAPTER TWELVE 486 T, Tim Davis/Duomo; **486 B, 487,** David Madison/Duomo; **491,** Morris Lane/SM; **492,** David Conklin/PE; **503,** Mitchell Layton/Duomo; **504,** David Weintraub/PR; **507 T, B,** Richard Haynes; **508,** David Madison/Duomo; **513,** KK; **514,** Bob Peterson/FPG; **521,** Tom Tracy/FPG; **527,** Bonnie L. Lange/Stock Imagery; **528,** Alan Carey/PR; **529,** KK.

CHAPTER THIRTEEN 534, FPG; **535,** Stock Imagery; **537,** Richard Haynes; **545 T,** The Bettmann Archive; **545 B,** Robert P. Morrison/FPG; **546 T, B,** John Gillmoure/SM; **550,** The Granger Collection; **554,** Ed Lettau/FPG; **560,** KK; **561,** NASA/SB/FPG.

ILLUSTRATION CREDITS

Technical art by York Graphic Services, Inc., Synergy 2000 Series.

Bob Barner: 42, 86, 148, 198, 213, 281, 346, 417, 439

Eliot Bergman: 12, 25, 31, 53, 84, 103, 113, 128, 138, 139, 154, 181, 191, 221, 255, 259, 267, 299, 378, 396

Boston Graphics, Inc.: 17, 18, 27, 79, 150, 230, 231, 242, 264, 316, 360, 413, 423, 451, 465, 476, 486, 496, 500, 534, 545

John W. Cataldo: 450

Donald Doyle: 246

Function Thru Form, Inc., Guilbert Gates and Kathleen Katims: 241, 272, 312, 313, 404

Andrea Grassi: Decision Making logo, 458: figure icons, 313: Statue of Liberty icon

Mark Herman: 44, 110, 173, 217, 275, 319, 334, 363, 425, 433, 442, 469, 489, 557

Fran Jarvis: 507: spinner, 460: grid designs, 487: 511: 534

Barbara Maslen: 21, 32, 63, 104, 117, 151, 184, 219, 278, 343, 390, 506, 515, 524

Eve Melnechuk: Problem Solving logo

Terry Presnall: Calculator logo, computer logo, 2, 6, 10, 11, 19, 20, 29, 34, 52, 66, 88, 96, 101, 107, 111, 130, 131, 145, 153, 163, 172, 180, 204, 215, 230, 231, 232, 233, 239, 246, 247, 263, 273, 290, 312, 317, 361, 383, 385, 387, 416, 460, 487, 495, 499, 502, 519, 522, 534, 542, 543

Susan Spellman: 121, 287, 345, 517, 539, 559

Gary Torrisi: 2, 14, 46, 58, 72, 156, 157, 158, 210, 225, 330, 364, 404, 405, 420, 428, 438, 464, 497, 510, 535, 552

C. A. Trachok: 43, 75, 82, 100, 108, 123, 170, 174, 286, 351, 487, 511, 520

Cameron Wasson: 37, 54, 114, 203, 220, 235, 250, 251, 264, 285, 347, 426, 444, 453, 472, 509, 523, 538, 557

Any photo or illustration acknowledgment inadvertently omitted will be amended upon notification.

ACKNOWLEDGMENTS

Inflation Rate
(GDP Deflator)

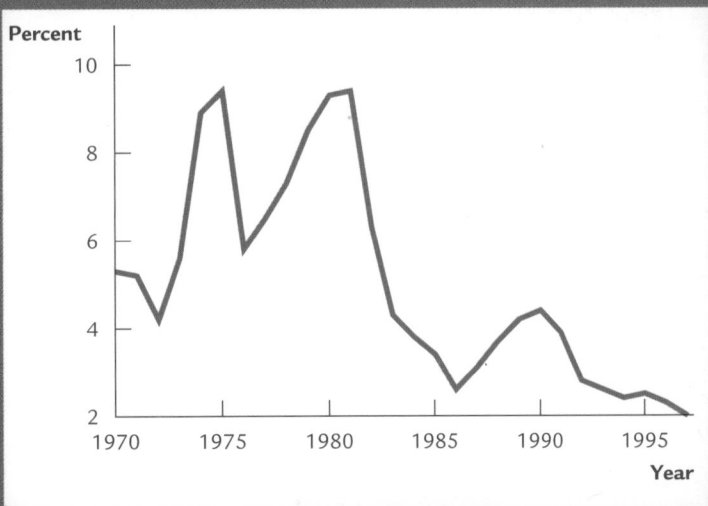

Nominal Interest Rate
(Three-Month Treasury Bills)

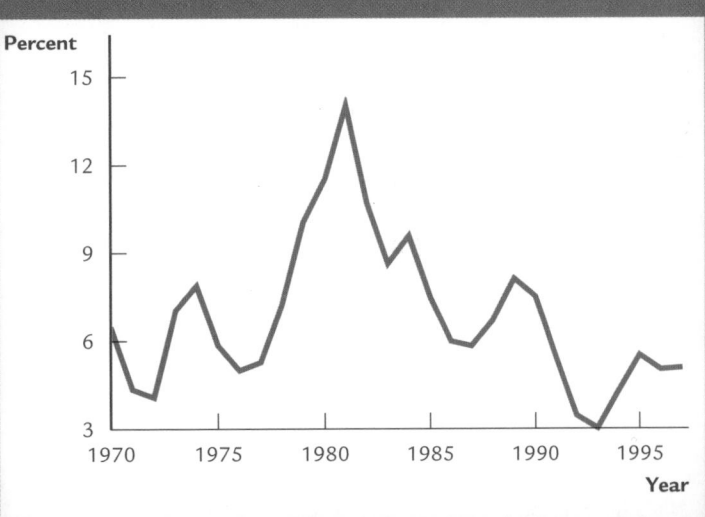

macro economics

N. GREGORY MANKIW

Harvard University

Worth Publishers

Macroeconomics, Fourth Edition

Copyright © 2000, 1997, 1994, 1992 by Worth Publishers
All rights reserved
Manufactured in the United States of America

ISBN: 1-57259-644-9
Printing: 4 5 03 02 01

Project Director: Scott Hitchcock
Development Editor: Jane Tufts
Design Director: Barbara Rusin
Designer: Lissi Sigillo
Production Editor: Margaret Comaskey
Production Manager: Barbara Anne Seixas
Composition and Separations: Progressive Information Technologies
Printing and Binding: R. R. Donnelley & Sons
Photo Credit: p. v. © Ingrid Kannel, Wellesley, MA
Cover: Lissi Sigillo

Library of Congress Cataloging-in-Publication Data
Mankiw, N. Gregory.
   Macroeconomics / by N. Gregory Mankiw. — 4th ed.
      p.   cm.
   Multimedia teaching aids are available for this edition, including an
   Internet website.
   Includes index.
   ISBN 1-57259-644-9
   1. Macroeconomics.   I. Title.
   HB172.5.M357   1999
   339 — dc21   99-22254
                                                        CIP

Worth Publishers
41 Madison Avenue
New York, NY 10010
http://www.worthpublishers.com

about the author

N. Gregory Mankiw is Professor of Economics at Harvard University. He began his study of economics at Princeton University, where he received an A.B. *summa cum laude* in 1980. After earning a Ph.D. in economics from MIT, he began teaching at Harvard in 1985 and was promoted to full professor in 1987. Today, he regularly teaches both undergraduate and graduate courses in macroeconomics.

Professor Mankiw is a prolific writer and a regular participant in academic and policy debates. His research ranges across many fields within economics and includes work on price adjustment, consumer behavior, financial markets, monetary and fiscal policy, and economic growth. In addition to his duties at Harvard, he has served as Director of the Monetary Economics Program of the National Bureau of Economic Research, as an adviser to the Federal Reserve Bank of Boston and the Congressional Budget Office, and as a columnist for *Fortune* magazine. He is also author of the popular introductory textbook, *Principles of Economics*.

Professor Mankiw lives in Wellesley, Massachusetts, with his wife Deborah and their children, Catherine, Nicholas, and Peter.

To Deborah

Those branches of politics, or of the laws of social life, on which there exists a collection of facts sufficiently sifted and methodized to form the beginning of a science should be taught *ex professo*. Among the chief of these is Political Economy, the sources and conditions of wealth and material prosperity for aggregate bodies of human beings. . . .

The same persons who cry down Logic will generally warn you against Political Economy. It is unfeeling, they will tell you. It recognises unpleasant facts. For my part, the most unfeeling thing I know of is the law of gravitation: it breaks the neck of the best and most amiable person without scruple, if he forgets for a single moment to give heed to it. The winds and waves too are very unfeeling. Would you advise those who go to sea to deny the winds and waves—or to make use of them, and find the means of guarding against their dangers? My advice to you is to study the great writers on Political Economy, and hold firmly by whatever in them you find true; and depend upon it that if you are not selfish or hard-hearted already, Political Economy will not make you so.

—John Stuart Mill
1867

brief contents

contents

part TWO
The Economy in the Long Run — **41**

part THREE
The Economy in the Short Run   235

part FOUR
Macroeconomic Policy Debates   381

part FIVE

More on the Microeconomics Behind Macroeconomics 433

An economist must be "mathematician, historian, statesman, philosopher, in some degree. . . . as aloof and incorruptible as an artist, yet sometimes as near the earth as a politician." So remarked John Maynard Keynes, the great British economist who, as much as anyone, could be called the father of macroeconomics. No single statement summarizes better what it means to be an economist.

As Keynes's assessment suggests, students who aim to learn economics need to draw on many disparate talents. The job of helping students find and develop these talents falls to instructors and textbook authors. When writing this textbook for intermediate-level courses in macroeconomics, my goal was to make macroeconomics understandable, relevant, and (believe it or not) fun. Those of us who have chosen to be professional macroeconomists have done so because we are fascinated by the field. More important, we believe that the study of macroeconomics can illuminate much about the world and that the lessons learned, if properly applied, can make the world a better place. I hope this book conveys not only our profession's accumulated wisdom but also its enthusiasm and sense of purpose.

This Book's Approach

Although macroeconomists share a common body of knowledge, they do not all have the same perspective on how that knowledge is best taught. Let me begin this new edition by recapping four of my objectives, which together define this book's approach to the field.

First, I try to offer a balance between short-run and long-run issues in macroeconomics. All economists agree that public policies and other events influence the economy over different time horizons. We live in our own short run, but we also live in the long run that our parents bequeathed us. As a result, courses in macroeconomics need to cover both short-run topics, such as the business cycle and stabilization policy, and long-run topics, such as economic growth, the natural rate of unemployment, persistent inflation, and the effects of government debt. Neither time horizon trumps the other.

Second, I integrate the insights of Keynesian and classical theories. Although Keynes's *General Theory* provides the foundation for much of our current understanding of economic fluctuations, it is important to remember that classical economics provides the right answers to many fundamental questions. In this book I incorporate many of the contributions of the classical economists before Keynes and the new classical economists of the past two decades. Substantial coverage is given, for example, to the loanable-funds theory of the interest rate, the quantity theory of money, and the problem of time inconsistency. At the same time, however, I recognize that many of the ideas of Keynes and the new Keynesians are necessary for understanding economic fluctuations. Substantial coverage is given also to the $IS-LM$ model of aggregate demand, the short-run tradeoff between inflation and unemployment, and modern theories of wage and price rigidity.

Third, I present macroeconomics using a variety of simple models. Instead of pretending that there is one model that is complete enough to explain all facets of the economy, I encourage students to learn how to use and compare a set of prominent models. This approach has the pedagogical value that each model can be kept relatively simple and presented within one or two chapters. More important, this approach asks students to think like economists, who always keep various models in mind when analyzing economic events or public policies.

Fourth, I emphasize that macroeconomics is an empirical discipline, motivated and guided by a wide array of experience. This book contains numerous case studies that use macroeconomic theory to shed light on real-world data or events. To highlight the broad applicability of the basic theory, I have drawn the case studies both from current issues facing the world's economies and from dramatic historical episodes. The case studies analyze the policies of Alan Greenspan, George Bush, Henry Ford, and Alexander Hamilton. They teach the reader how to apply economic principles to issues from fourteenth-century Europe, the island of Yap, the land of Oz, and today's newspaper.

What's New in the Fourth Edition?

I have improved this book in its fourth edition in several ways. Most obviously, the book has been updated to incorporate new events, data, and ideas. Since the third edition was written, the Treasury Department introduced inflation-indexed bonds, Japan experienced a deep recession, Europe adopted a common currency, and capital flight forced several Asian currencies to collapse. As always, new research has refined our understanding of economic growth and fluctuations. Although the basics of macroeconomic theory are much the same as they were three years ago, enough has changed in the details and practice of macroeconomics to warrant publishing a new edition.

In addition, the book's coverage, pedagogy, and organization have been further refined. The analysis of economic growth, now in Chapters 4 and 5, includes a more extensive discussion of the new theories of endogenous growth. The chapter on government debt and budget deficits, Chapter 15, has been expanded to examine more fully the debates over this important policy issue. The chapter on recent developments in the theory of economic fluctuations, Chapter 19, which discusses real business cycle theory and new Keynesian economics, has been moved to the end of the book, although instructors who wish to cover this material earlier can continue to do so. Throughout the book, new case studies have been added, and some old ones have been omitted or revised. Together with various editors and students, I have scrutinized each sentence of the book to see whether it can be made clearer.

Finally, all the changes that I made, and the many others that I considered, were evaluated keeping in mind the benefits of brevity. From my own experience as a student, I know that long books are less likely to be read. My goal in this book is to offer the clearest, most up-to-date, most accessible course in macroeconomics in the fewest words possible.

The Arrangement of Topics

This new edition maintains the strategy of first examining the long run when prices are flexible and then examining the short run when prices are sticky. That is, it begins with classical models of the economy and explains fully the long-run equilibrium before discussing deviations from that equilibrium. This strategy has several advantages:

➤ Because the classical dichotomy permits the separation of real and monetary issues, the long-run material is easier for students to understand.

➤ When students begin studying short-run fluctuations, they understand fully the long-run equilibrium around which the economy is fluctuating.

➤ Beginning with market-clearing models makes clearer the link between macroeconomics and microeconomics.

➤ Students learn first the material that is less controversial among macro-economists.

When I proposed this organizational strategy in the first edition, some instructors greeted it with skepticism. But this skepticism has faded with time and experience. Many instructors have reported to me that this organization greatly simplifies the teaching of macroeconomics.

I move now from strategy to tactics. What follows is a whirlwind tour of the book.

Part One: Introduction

The introductory material in Part One is brief so that students can get to the core topics quickly. Chapter 1 discusses the broad questions that macro-economists address and the economist's approach of building models to explain the world. Chapter 2 introduces the key data of macroeconomics, emphasizing gross domestic product, the consumer price index, and the unemployment rate.

Part Two: The Economy in the Long Run

Part Two examines the long run over which prices are flexible. Chapter 3 presents the basic classical model of national income. In this model, the factors of production and the production technology determine the level of income, and the marginal products of the factors determine its distribution to households. In addition, the model shows how fiscal policy influences the allocation of the economy's resources among consumption, investment, and government purchases, and it highlights how the real interest rate equilibrates the supply and demand for goods and services.

Chapters 4 and 5 make the classical analysis of the economy dynamic by using the Solow growth model to examine the evolution of the economy over time. The Solow model provides the basis for discussing why the standard of living varies so widely across countries and how public policies influence the level and growth of the standard of living. Chapter 5 also introduces the student to the modern theories of endogenous growth.

Chapter 6 relaxes the assumption of full employment by discussing the dynamics of the labor market and the natural rate of unemployment. It examines various causes of unemployment, including job search, minimum-wage laws, union power, and efficiency wages. It also presents some important facts about patterns of unemployment.

Money and the price level are introduced in Chapter 7. Because prices are assumed to be fully flexible, the chapter presents the prominent ideas of classical monetary theory: the quantity theory of money, the inflation tax, the Fisher effect, the social costs of inflation, and the causes and costs of hyperinflation.

The study of open-economy macroeconomics begins in Chapter 8. Maintaining the assumption of full employment, this chapter presents models to explain the trade balance and the exchange rate. Various policy issues are addressed: the relationship between the budget deficit and the trade deficit, the macroeconomic impact of protectionist trade policies, and the effect of monetary policy on the value of a currency in the market for foreign exchange.

Part Three: The Economy in the Short Run

Part Three examines the short run when prices are sticky. It begins in Chapter 9 by introducing the model of aggregate supply and aggregate demand as well as the role of stabilization policy. Subsequent chapters refine the ideas introduced here.

Chapters 10 and 11 look more closely at aggregate demand. Chapter 10 presents the Keynesian cross and the theory of liquidity preference and uses these models as building blocks for developing the $IS-LM$ model. Chapter 11 uses the $IS-LM$ model to explain economic fluctuations and the aggregate demand curve. It concludes with an extended case study of the Great Depression.

The study of short-run fluctuations continues in Chapter 12, which focuses on aggregate demand in an open economy. This chapter presents the Mundell–Fleming model and shows how monetary and fiscal policies affect the economy under floating and fixed exchange-rate systems. It also discusses the debate over whether exchange rates should be floating or fixed.

Chapter 13 looks more closely at aggregate supply. It examines various approaches to explaining the short-run aggregate supply curve and discusses the short-run tradeoff between inflation and unemployment.

Part Four: Macroeconomic Policy Debates

Once the student has command of standard long-run and short-run models of the economy, the book uses these models as the foundation for discussing some of the key debates over economic policy. Chapter 14 considers the debate over how policymakers should respond to short-run economic fluctuations. It emphasizes two broad questions. Should monetary and fiscal policy be active or passive? Should policy be conducted by rule or by discretion? The chapter presents arguments on both sides of these questions.

Chapter 15 focuses on the various debates over government debt and budget deficits. It gives some sense of the magnitude of government indebtedness, discusses why measuring budget deficits is not always straightforward, recaps the traditional view of the effects of government debt, presents Ricardian equivalence as an alternative view, and discusses various other perspectives on government debt. As in the previous chapter, students are not handed conclusions but are given the tools to evaluate the alternative viewpoints on their own.

Part Five: More on the Microeconomics Behind Macroeconomics

After developing theories to explain the economy in the long run and in the short run and then applying those theories to macroeconomic policy debates, the book turns to several topics that refine our understanding of the economy. The last four chapters analyze more fully the microeconomics behind macroeconomics. These chapters can be presented at the end of a course, or they can be covered earlier, depending on an instructor's preferences.

Chapter 16 presents the various theories of consumer behavior, including the Keynesian consumption function, Fisher's model of intertemporal choice, Modigliani's life-cycle hypothesis, and Friedman's permanent-income hypothesis. Chapter 17 examines the theory behind the investment function. Chapter 18 provides additional material on the money market, including the role of the banking system in determining the money supply and the Baumol-Tobin model of money demand. Chapter 19 discusses advances in the theory of economic fluctuations, including the theory of real business cycles and new Keynesian theories of sticky prices; these recent theories apply microeconomic analysis in an attempt to better understand short-run economic fluctuations.

Epilogue

The book ends with a brief epilogue that reviews the broad lessons about which most macroeconomists agree and discusses some of the most important open questions. Regardless of which chapters an instructor chooses to cover, this capstone chapter can be used to remind students how the many models and themes of macroeconomics relate to one another. Here and throughout the book I emphasize that, despite the disagreements among macroeconomists, there is much that we know about how the economy works.

Alternative Syllabus

Instructors differ in the emphasis they place on various topics and in the sequence of topics they prefer. I have, therefore, tried to make this book as flexible as possible. Many of the chapters are self-contained. Instructors can change the emphases of their courses by rearranging chapters or by omitting some chapters entirely.

One example of an alternative syllabus is presented here. This syllabus maintains the strategy of first examining the economy in the long run when prices are flexible, but it introduces sticky prices and short-run fluctuations earlier in the course. It does this by deferring all open-economy macroeconomics until after the study of fluctuations and deferring the study of economic growth until the end of the course. It omits altogether the chapters on microfoundations and, therefore, allows the instructor to spend more time on the other topics.

Introduction
1. The Science of Macroeconomics
2. The Data of Macroeconomics

Income, Unemployment, and Inflation in the Long Run
3. National Income: Where It Comes From and Where It Goes
6. Unemployment
7. Money and Inflation

Short-Run Economic Fluctuations
9. Introduction to Economic Fluctuations
10. Aggregate Demand I
11. Aggregate Demand II
13. Aggregate Supply

Macroeconomic Policy
14. Stabilization Policy
15. Government Debt and Budget Deficits

Open-Economy Macroeconomics
8. The Open Economy
12. Aggregate Demand in the Open Economy

Economic Growth
4. Economic Growth I
5. Economic Growth II

Epilogue

Learning Tools

I am pleased that students have found the previous editions of this book user-friendly. I have tried to make this fourth edition even more so.

Case Studies

Economics comes to life when it is applied to understanding actual events. Therefore, the numerous case studies (many new or revised in this edition) are an important learning tool. The frequency with which these case studies occur ensures that a student does not have to grapple with an overdose of theory before seeing the theory applied. Students report that the case studies are their favorite part of the book.

FYI Boxes

These boxes present ancillary material "for your information." I use these boxes to clarify difficult concepts, to provide additional information about the tools of economics, and to show how economics relates to our daily lives. Several are new or revised in this edition.

Graphs

Understanding graphical analysis is a key part of learning macroeconomics, and I have worked hard to make the figures easy to follow. I often use comment boxes within figures that describe briefly and draw attention to the important points that the figures illustrate. They should help students both learn and review the material.

Mathematical Notes

I use occasional mathematical footnotes to keep more difficult material out of the body of the text. These notes make an argument more rigorous or present a proof of a mathematical result. They can easily be skipped by those students who have not been introduced to the necessary mathematical tools.

Chapter Summaries

Every chapter ends with a brief, nontechnical summary of its major lessons. Students can use the summaries to place the material in perspective and to review for exams.

Key Concepts

Learning the language of a field is a major part of any course. Within the chapter, each key concept is in **boldface** when it is introduced. At the end of the chapter, the key concepts are listed for review.

Questions for Review

After studying a chapter, students can immediately test their understanding of its basic lessons by answering the Questions for Review.

Problems and Applications

Every chapter includes Problems and Applications designed for homework assignments. Some of these are numerical applications of the theory in the chapter. Others encourage the student to go beyond the material in the chapter by addressing new issues that are closely related to the chapter topics.

Chapter Appendixes

Several chapters include appendixes that offer additional material, sometimes at a higher level of mathematical sophistication. These are designed so that professors can cover certain topics in greater depth if they wish. The appendixes can be skipped altogether without loss of continuity.

Glossary

To help students become familiar with the language of macroeconomics, a glossary of more than 250 terms is provided at the back of the book.

Supplements for Students

Worth Publishers and I have been delighted at the positive feedback we have received on the supplements that accompany the book. There are two supplements for students that instructors can use in their courses.

Student Guide and Workbook

Roger Kaufman (Smith College) has revised his superb study guide for students. This guide offers various ways for students to learn the material in the text and assess their understanding.

> *Fill-In Questions* give students the opportunity to review and check their knowledge of the key terms and concepts in the chapter.
> *Multiple-Choice Questions* allow students to test themselves on the chapter material.
> *Exercises* guide students step by step through the various models using graphs and numerical examples.
> *Problems* ask students to apply the models on their own.
> *Questions to Think About* require critical thinking as well as economic analysis.
> *Data Questions* ask students to obtain and learn about readily available economic data.

Macroeconomics 4e Companion Website, Featuring MacroBytes

David Weil (Brown University) has updated his innovative software package for students, and Worth Publishers has made it available over the Internet. *MacroBytes* provides a range of activities to aid and motivate the student throughout the course.

> *Data Plotter.* Students can explore macroeconomic data with time-series graphs and scatterplots.
> *Macro Models.* These modules provide simulations of the models presented in the book. Students can change the exogenous variables and see the outcomes in terms of shifting curves and recalculated numerical

values of the endogenous variables. Each module contains exercises that instructors can assign as homework.

➤ *2001: A Game for Macroeconomists.* The game allows students to become President of the United States in the year 2001 and to make macroeconomic policy decisions based on news events, economic statistics, and approval ratings. It gives students a sense of the complex interconnections that influence the economy. It is also fun to play.

In addition to *MacroBytes,* the *Macroeconomics 4e Companion Website* also offers a wealth of resources, including interactive flash cards, online quizzing (with results stored for the instructor), "Economics in the News" essays, example test questions with outlined answers, and links to some of my other writings.

The *Macroeconomics 4e* Website and *MacroBytes* can be found on the Internet at http://www.worthpublishers.com/mankiw

Supplements for Instructors

Additional supplements are available from Worth Publishers to help instructors enhance their courses.

Instructor's Resources

Patricia Pollard (Federal Reserve Bank of St. Louis) and Andrew John (University of Virginia) have revised their impressive resource manual for instructors. For each chapter of this book, the manual contains notes to the instructor, a detailed lecture outline, additional case studies, and coverage of advanced topics. Instructors can use the manual to prepare their lectures, and they can reproduce whatever pages they choose as handouts for students.

Solutions Manual

John Fernald (Federal Reserve Board) has updated the *Solutions Manual* for all of the Questions for Review and Problems and Applications. The manual also contains the answers to selected questions from the *Student Guide and Workbook.*

Test Bank

Nancy Jianakoplos (Colorado State University) has updated the *Test Bank* so that it now includes over 1000 multiple-choice questions to accompany the text. Several short numerical problems are also provided for each chapter. The *Test Bank* is available both as a printed book and on disks. The disks include a test-generation program and are available in both Windows and Macintosh formats.

PowerPoint Presentation Slides

All of the text figures will be available in editable PowerPoint™ Presentation format and accessible via the Internet at http://www.worthpublishers.com/mankiw

Transparencies

Overhead transparencies are available for key figures and tables in the book, including all those that present data. In addition, instructors can obtain enlarged transparency master copies of all the figures in the text to prepare their own overhead transparencies for use in class.

Translations

The English-language version of this book has been used in dozens of countries. To make the book more accessible for students around the world, editions are now (or will soon be) available in 14 other languages: Armenian, Chinese (simplified), French, German, Greek, Hungarian, Italian, Japanese, Korean, Mandarin, Portuguese, Romanian, Russian, and Spanish. Instructors who would like information about these translations should contact Worth Publishers.

Acknowledgments

When writing and revising this book, I benefitted from the input of many reviewers and colleagues in the economics profession. I would like to thank each of those who, for this or previous editions, gave up their scarce time to help me improve the economics or pedagogy of this text:

Francis Ahking
University of Connecticut

Steven Allen
North Carolina State University

Laurence Ball
Johns Hopkins University

Robert Barry
College of William and Mary

Robert Barsky
University of Michigan

Susanto Basu
University of Michigan

Charles Bischoff
Binghamton University

Dwight M. Blood
Brigham Young University

Ronald Bodkin
University of Ottawa

Kathleen Brook
New Mexico State University

Alison Butler
Florida International University

John Campbell
Harvard University

Niko Canner
McKinsey and Company

Christopher D. Carroll
Johns Hopkins University

Christopher Cornell
Ohio State University

Vanessa Craft
Bentley College

Ron Cronovich
University of Nevada, Las Vegas

David DeJong
University of Pittsburgh

Charles DeLorme, Jr.
University of Georgia

Paula DeMasi
International Monetary Fund

William Dickens
University of California at Berkeley

John Driscoll
Brown University

Donald Dutkowsky
Syracuse University

Mark Dwyer
University of California, Los Angeles

Karen Dynan
Federal Reserve Board

Douglas Elmendorf
Federal Reserve Board

Gerald Epstein
University of Massachusetts

Mark Evans
California State University at Bakersfield

Liang-Shing Fan
Colorado State University

Antonio Fatas
INSEAD

John Fernald
Federal Reserve Board

Chris Foote
Harvard University

Peter Frevert
University of Kansas

Rachel Friedberg
Brown University

Michelle R. Garfinkel
University of California at Irvine

Edward Gramlich
University of Michigan

Lisa Grobar
California State University, Long Beach

Richard Grossman
Wesleyan University

Chris Hanes
University of Pennsylvania

Daniel Himarios
University of Texas at Arlington

Steven Holland
University of Kentucky

Dennis Jansen
Texas A&M University

Nancy Jianakoplos
Colorado State University

Andrew John
University of Virginia

Klaus Dieter John
Chemnitz University of Technology

David Johnson
Harvard University

Richard Johnson
Harvard University

Roger Kaufman
Smith College

Manfried Keil
Northeastern University

Robert W. Kilpatrick
Office of Management and Budget

David C. Klingaman
Ohio University

Kenneth Koelln
University of North Texas

John Laitner
University of Michigan

John Lapp
North Carolina State University

Emily C. Lawrance
Denison University

John Leahy
Boston University

Daniel Levy
Emory University

Bill Maloney
University of Illinois at Urbana-Champaign

Deborah Mankiw
NBER

W. Douglas McMillin
Louisiana State University

Starr McMullen
Oregon State University

David Meinster
Formerly Temple University

Andrew Metrick
Harvard University

Jeffrey Miron
Boston University

Bruce Mizrach
Rutgers University

Olivier Morand
University of Connecticut

Egon Neuberger
State University of New York at Stony Brook

Neil Niman
University of New Hampshire

Lee Ohanian
Federal Reserve Bank of Minneapolis

Michael Oldfather
Kansas State University

Stefan Oppers
International Monetary Fund

David Parsley
Vanderbilt University

Parag Pathak
Harvard University

Thomas Pogue
University of Iowa

Uri M. Possen
Cornell University

Michael Rashes
Harvard University

Salim Rashid
University of Illinois at Urbana-Champaign

David Rearden
University of Kansas

Kevin Reffett
University of Arizona

Karen Reid
University of Tennessee, Knoxville

Changyong Rhee
Seoul National University

Joseph Ritter
St. Louis Federal Reserve

David Romer
University of California at Berkeley

Marjorie Rose
Dartmouth College

Bennett Rushkoff
Federal Trade Commission

Amy Salsbury
Harvard University

Laurence S. Seidman
University of Delaware

Matthew Shapiro
University of Michigan

Brian Silverstone
University of Waikato

Boris Simkovich
Harvard University

David Spencer
Brigham Young University

Edward Steinberg
New York University

David Tabak
NERA

Lowell Taylor
Carnegie-Mellon University

Richard Trethewey
Kenyon College

Brian M. Trinque
University of Texas

John Veitch
University of San Francisco

Anne Villamil
University of Illinois at Urbana-Champaign

Ping Wang
Pennsylvania State University

David Weil
Brown University

Charles Whiteman
The University of Iowa

Justin Wolfers
Harvard University

Jeffrey Zax
University of Colorado at Boulder

The people at Worth Publishers have continued to be congenial and dedicated. I am grateful to Stephen Dietrich (Editor), Julie Kerr (Project Director),

Scott Hitchcock (Project Director), Margaret Comaskey (Project Editor), Barbara Seixas (Production Manager), Conrad Nava (Editorial Assistant), Stacey Alexander (Supplements Manager), and Lissi Sigillo (Designer).

Many other people in publishing made valuable contributions as well. Most important, Jane Tufts, freelance developmental editor, worked her magic on this book for the first time in this edition, and her improvements show on almost every page. Alexandra Nickerson once again did a great job preparing the index. I must also thank Paul Shensa, whose contributions to the first three editions are still very evident in this one.

I am also grateful to Yvonne Zinfon, my secretary at Harvard, for her reliability, patience, and good cheer, as she once again helped me proofread the entire book.

Finally, I would like to thank my seven-year-old daughter, Catherine, four-year-old son, Nicholas, and newborn son, Peter. They helped immensely with this revision—both by providing a pleasant distraction and by reminding me that textbooks are written for the next generation.

N. Gregory Mankiw

Cambridge, Massachusetts
May 1999

macro.economics

part ONE

Introduction

Part One introduces you to the study of macroeconomics. Chapter 1 discusses why macroeconomics is an exciting and important subject, explains the tools that economists use to analyze the economy, and outlines the plan of this book. Chapter 2 discusses the types of data that economists and policymakers use to keep track of what's happening in the economy.

chapter 1

The Science of Macroeconomics

The whole of science is nothing more than the refinement of everyday thinking.

—*Albert Einstein*

1-1 | What Macroeconomists Study

Why have some countries experienced rapid growth in incomes over the past century while others stay mired in poverty? Why do some countries have high rates of inflation while others maintain stable prices? Why do all countries experience recessions and depressions—recurrent periods of falling incomes and rising unemployment—and how can government policy reduce the frequency and severity of these episodes? **Macroeconomics,** the study of the economy as a whole, attempts to answer these and many related questions.

To appreciate the importance of macroeconomics, you need only read the newspaper or listen to the news. Every day you can see headlines such as IN-COME GROWTH SLOWS, FED MOVES TO COMBAT INFLATION, or STOCKS FALL AMID RECESSION FEARS. Although these macroeconomic events may seem abstract, they touch all of our lives. Business executives forecasting the demand for their products must guess how fast consumers' incomes will grow. Senior citizens living on fixed incomes wonder how fast prices will rise. Recent college graduates looking for jobs hope that the economy will boom and that firms will be hiring.

Because the state of the economy affects everyone, macroeconomic issues play a central role in political debate. Voters are keenly aware of how the economy is doing, and they know that government policy can affect the economy in powerful ways. As a result, the popularity of the incumbent president rises when the economy is doing well and falls when it is doing poorly. During the election of 1992, Clinton's chief strategist wanted to keep the campaign focused on the key issue, so he kept a sign in his office that read, "The economy, stupid."

Macroeconomic issues are also at the center of world politics. In recent years, Europe has moved toward a common currency, many Asian countries have experienced financial turmoil and capital flight, and the United States has financed large trade deficits by borrowing heavily from abroad. When world leaders meet, these topics are often high on their agenda.

Although the job of making economic policy falls to world leaders, the job of explaining how the economy as a whole works falls to macroeconomists. Toward this end, macroeconomists collect data on incomes, prices, unemployment, and many other variables from different time periods and different countries. They then attempt to formulate general theories that help to explain these data. Like astronomers studying the evolution of stars or biologists studying the evolution of species, macroeconomists cannot conduct controlled experiments. Instead, they must make use of the data that history gives them. Macroeconomists observe that economies differ from one another and that they change over time. These observations provide both the motivation for developing macroeconomic theories and the data for testing them.

To be sure, macroeconomics is a young and imperfect science. The macroeconomist's ability to predict the future course of economic events is no better than the meteorologist's ability to predict next month's weather. But, as you will see, macroeconomists do know quite a lot about how the economy works. This knowledge is useful both for explaining economic events and for formulating economic policy.

Every era has its own economic problems. In the 1970s, Presidents Richard Nixon, Gerald Ford, and Jimmy Carter all wrestled in vain with a rising rate of inflation. In the 1980s, inflation subsided, but Presidents Ronald Reagan and George Bush presided over large federal budget deficits. In the 1990s, as President Bill Clinton occupied the Oval Office, the budget deficit shrank and even turned into a small budget surplus, but federal taxes as a share of national income reached a historic high. Although the basic principles of macroeconomics do not change from decade to decade, the macroeconomist must apply these principles with flexibility and creativity to meet changing circumstances.

CASE STUDY

The Historical Performance of the U.S. Economy

Economists use many types of data to measure the performance of an economy. Three macroeconomic variables are particularly important: real gross domestic product (GDP), the inflation rate, and the unemployment rate. **Real GDP** measures the total income of everyone in the economy (adjusted for the level of prices). The **inflation rate** measures how quickly prices are rising. The **unemployment rate** measures the fraction of the labor force that is out of work. Macroeconomists study how these variables are determined, why they change over time, and how they interact with one another.

Figure 1-1 shows real GDP per person in the United States. Two aspects of this figure are noteworthy. First, real GDP grows over time. Real GDP per person is today about five times its level in 1900. This growth in average

figure 1-1

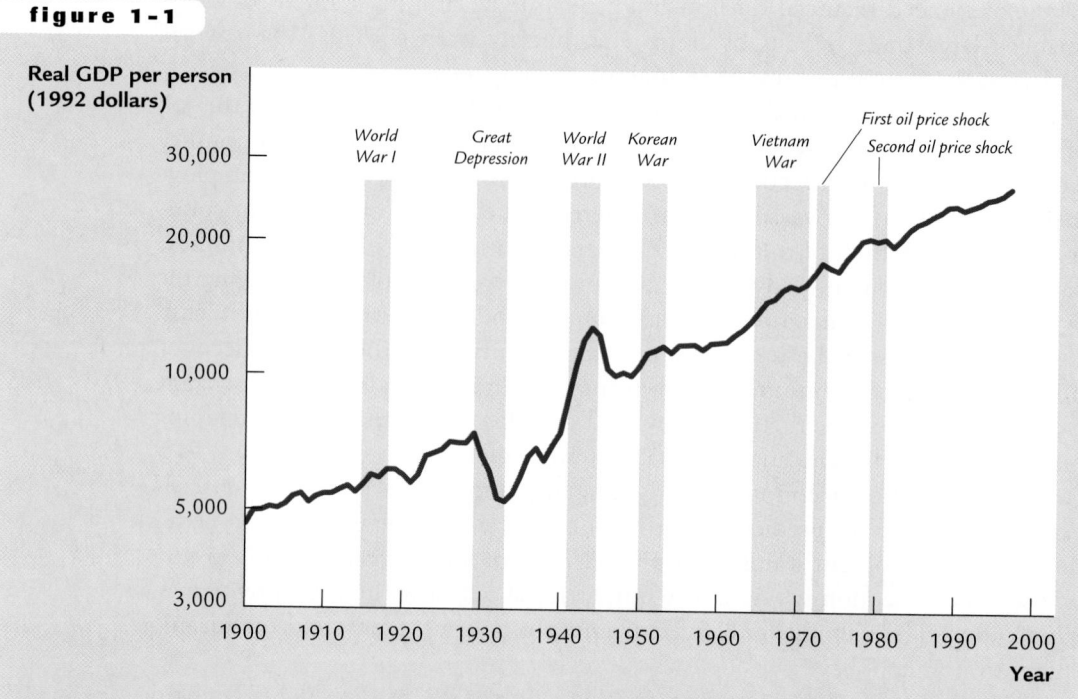

Real GDP per person (1992 dollars)

World War I · Great Depression · World War II · Korean War · Vietnam War · First oil price shock · Second oil price shock

Real GDP per Person in the U.S. Economy Real GDP measures the total income of everyone in the economy, and real GDP per person measures the income of the average person in the economy. This figure shows that real GDP per person tends to grow over time and that this normal growth is sometimes interrupted by periods of declining income, called recessions or depressions.

Note: Real GDP is plotted here on a logarithmic scale. On such a scale, equal distances on the vertical axis represent equal *percentage* changes. Thus, the distance between $5,000 and $10,000 (a 100 percent change) is the same as the distance between $10,000 and $20,000 (a 100 percent change).

Source: U.S. Bureau of the Census (*Historical Statistics of the United States: Colonial Times to 1970*) and U.S. Department of Commerce.

income allows us to enjoy a higher standard of living than our great-grandparents did. Second, although real GDP rises in most years, this growth is not completely reliable. There are repeated periods during which real GDP falls, the most dramatic instance being the early 1930s. Such periods are called **recessions** if they are mild and **depressions** if they are more severe. Not surprisingly, periods of declining income are associated with substantial economic hardship.

Figure 1-2 shows the U.S. inflation rate. You can see that inflation varies substantially. In the first half of the twentieth century, the inflation rate averaged only slightly above zero. Periods of falling prices, called **deflation,** were almost as common as periods of rising prices. In the past half century, inflation has been the norm. The inflation problem became most severe during the late 1970s, when prices rose persistently at a rate of almost 10 percent per year. In

figure 1-2

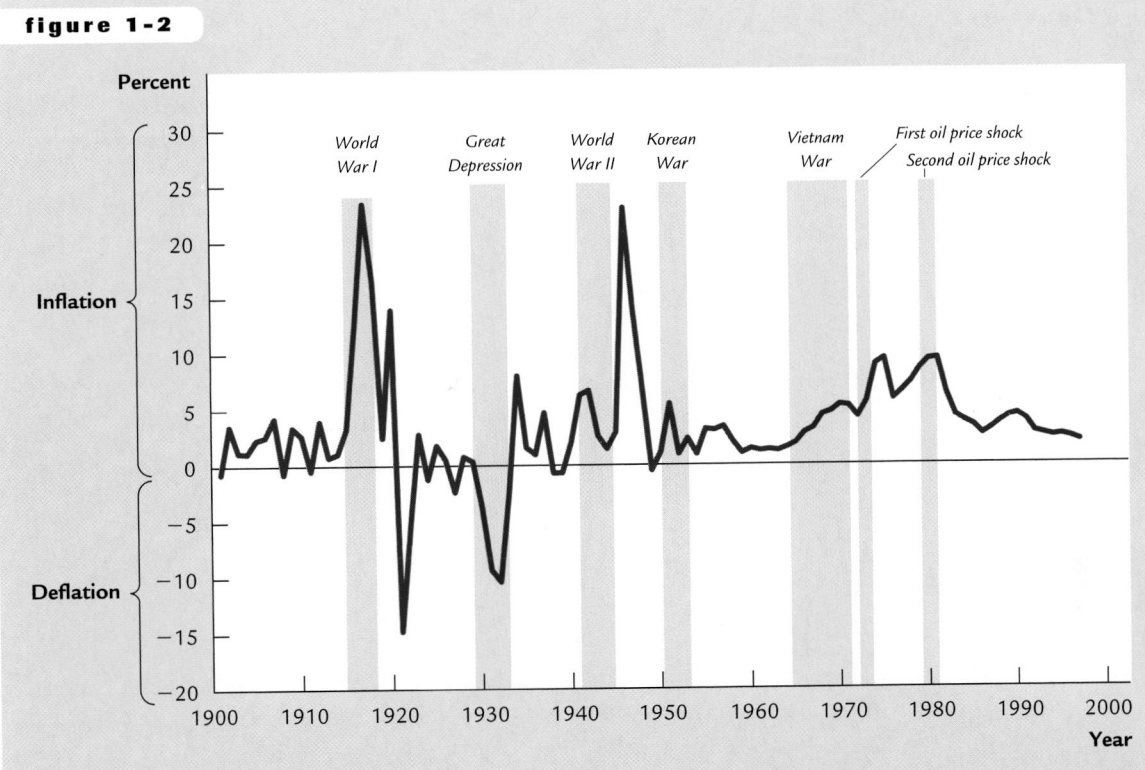

The Inflation Rate in the U.S. Economy The inflation rate measures the percentage change in the average level of prices from the year before. When the inflation rate is above zero, prices are rising. When it is below zero, prices are falling. If the inflation rate declines but remains positive, prices are rising but at a slower rate.

Note: The inflation rate is measured here using the GDP deflator.

Source: U.S. Bureau of the Census (*Historical Statistics of the United States: Colonial Times to 1970*) and U.S. Department of Commerce.

recent years, the inflation rate has been about 2 or 3 percent per year, indicating that prices have been fairly stable.

Figure 1–3 shows the U.S. unemployment rate. Notice that there is always some unemployment in our economy. In addition, although there is no long-term trend, the amount of unemployment varies substantially from year to year. Recessions and depressions are associated with unusually high unemployment. The highest rates of unemployment were reached during the Great Depression of the 1930s.

These three figures offer a glimpse at the history of the U.S. economy. In the chapters that follow, we first discuss how these variables are measured and then develop theories to explain how they behave.

figure 1-3

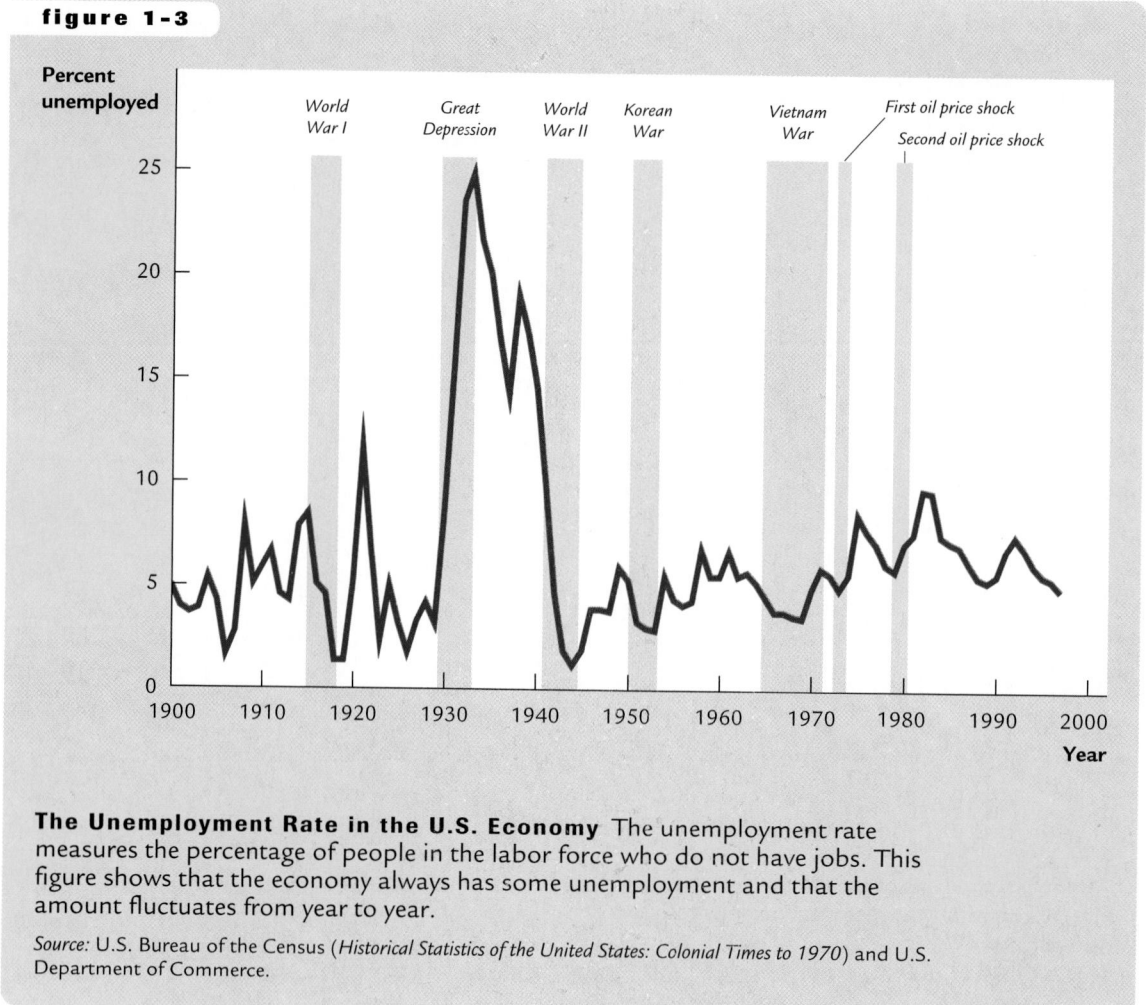

The Unemployment Rate in the U.S. Economy The unemployment rate measures the percentage of people in the labor force who do not have jobs. This figure shows that the economy always has some unemployment and that the amount fluctuates from year to year.

Source: U.S. Bureau of the Census (*Historical Statistics of the United States: Colonial Times to 1970*) and U.S. Department of Commerce.

1-2 | How Economists Think

Although economists often study politically charged issues, they try to address these issues with a scientist's objectivity. Like any science, economics has its own set of tools—terminology, data, and a way of thinking—that can seem foreign and arcane to the layman. The best way to become familiar with these tools is to practice using them, and this book will afford you ample opportunity to do so. To make these tools less forbidding, however, let's discuss a few of them here.

Theory as Model Building

Young children learn much about the world around them by playing with toy versions of real objects. Often they put together models of, for instance, cars, trains, or planes. These models are far from realistic, but the model-builder learns a lot from them nonetheless. The model illustrates the essence of the real object it is designed to resemble.

Economists also use **models** to understand the world, but an economist's model is more likely to be made of symbols and equations than plastic and glue. Economists build their "toy economies" to help explain economic variables, such as GDP, inflation, and unemployment. Economic models illustrate, often in mathematical terms, the relationships among the variables. They are useful because they help us to dispense with irrelevant details and to focus on important connections more clearly.

Models have two kinds of variables: endogenous variables and exogenous variables. **Endogenous variables** are those variables that a model tries to explain. **Exogenous variables** are those variables that a model takes as given. The purpose of a model is to show how the exogenous variables affect the endogenous variables. In other words, as Figure 1-4 illustrates, exogenous variables come from outside the model and serve as the model's input, whereas endogenous variables are determined inside the model and are the model's output.

To make these ideas more concrete, let's review the most celebrated of all economic models—the model of supply and demand. Imagine that an economist was interested in figuring out what influences the price of pizza and the quantity of pizza sold. He or she would proceed by developing a model that described the behavior of pizza buyers, the behavior of pizza sellers, and their interaction in the market for pizza. For example, the economist supposes that the quantity of pizza demanded by consumers Q^d depends on the price of pizza P and on aggregate income Y. This relationship is expressed in the equation

$$Q^d = D(P, Y),$$

where $D(\ )$ represents the demand function. Similarly, the economist supposes that the quantity of pizza supplied by pizzerias Q^s depends on the price of pizza P and on the price of materials P_m, such as cheese, tomatoes, flour, and anchovies. This relationship is expressed as

$$Q^s = S(P, P_m),$$

figure 1-4

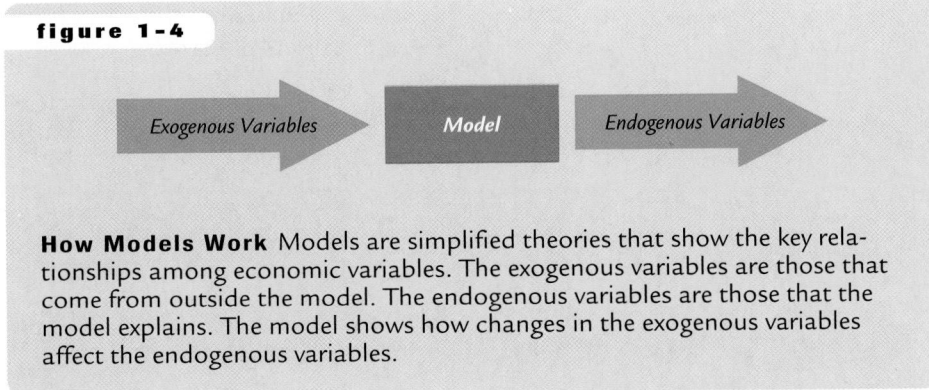

How Models Work Models are simplified theories that show the key relationships among economic variables. The exogenous variables are those that come from outside the model. The endogenous variables are those that the model explains. The model shows how changes in the exogenous variables affect the endogenous variables.

where $S(\ )$ represents the supply function. Finally, the economist assumes that the price of pizza adjusts to bring the quantity supplied and quantity demanded into balance:

$$Q^s = Q^d.$$

These three equations compose a model of the market for pizza.

The economist illustrates the model with a supply-and-demand diagram, as in Figure 1-5. The demand curve shows the relationship between the quantity of pizza demanded and the price of pizza, while holding aggregate income constant. The demand curve slopes downward because a higher price of pizza encourages consumers to switch to other foods and buy less pizza. The supply curve shows the relationship between the quantity of pizza supplied and the price of pizza, while holding the price of materials constant. The supply curve slopes upward because a higher price of pizza makes selling pizza more profitable, which encourages pizzerias to produce more of it. The equilibrium for the market is the price and quantity at which the supply and demand curves intersect. At the equilibrium price, consumers choose to buy exactly the amount of pizza that pizzerias choose to produce.

This model of the pizza market has two exogenous variables and two endogenous variables. The exogenous variables are aggregate income and the price of materials. The model does not attempt to explain them but takes them as given (perhaps to be explained by another model). The endogenous variables are the price of pizza and the quantity of pizza exchanged. These are the variables that the model attempts to explain.

figure 1-5

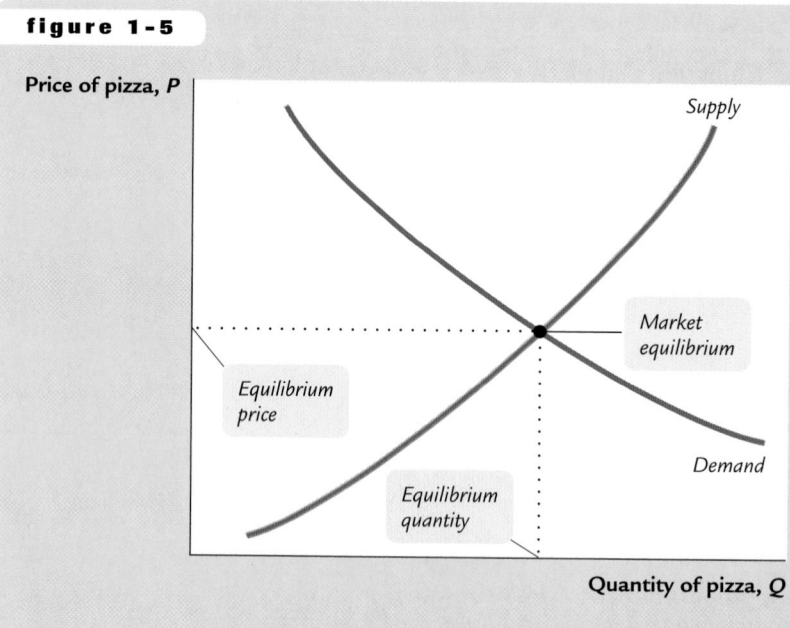

The Model of Supply and Demand The most famous economic model is that of supply and demand for a good or service—in this case, pizza. The demand curve is a downward-sloping curve relating the price of pizza to the quantity of pizza that consumers demand. The supply curve is an upward-sloping curve relating the price of pizza to the quantity of pizza that pizzerias supply. The price of pizza adjusts until the quantity supplied equals the quantity demanded. The point where the two curves cross is the market equilibrium, which shows the equilibrium price of pizza and the equilibrium quantity of pizza.

figure 1-6

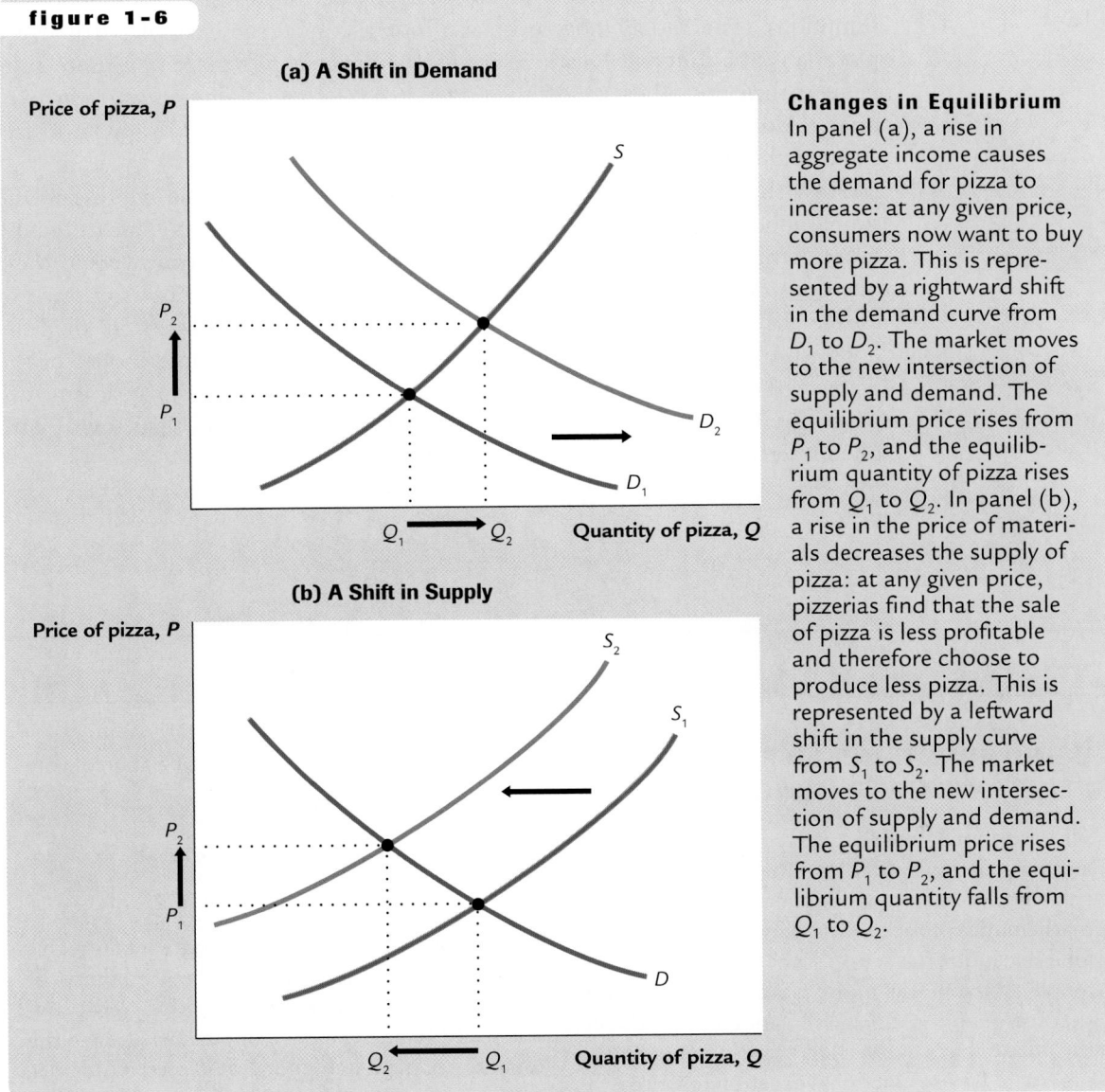

(a) A Shift in Demand

Price of pizza, *P*

S

P_2

P_1

D_2

D_1

Q_1 Q_2 Quantity of pizza, *Q*

(b) A Shift in Supply

Price of pizza, *P*

S_2

S_1

P_2

P_1

D

Q_2 Q_1 Quantity of pizza, *Q*

Changes in Equilibrium
In panel (a), a rise in aggregate income causes the demand for pizza to increase: at any given price, consumers now want to buy more pizza. This is represented by a rightward shift in the demand curve from D_1 to D_2. The market moves to the new intersection of supply and demand. The equilibrium price rises from P_1 to P_2, and the equilibrium quantity of pizza rises from Q_1 to Q_2. In panel (b), a rise in the price of materials decreases the supply of pizza: at any given price, pizzerias find that the sale of pizza is less profitable and therefore choose to produce less pizza. This is represented by a leftward shift in the supply curve from S_1 to S_2. The market moves to the new intersection of supply and demand. The equilibrium price rises from P_1 to P_2, and the equilibrium quantity falls from Q_1 to Q_2.

The model shows how a change in one of the exogenous variables affects both endogenous variables. For example, if aggregate income increases, then the demand for pizza increases, as in panel (a) of Figure 1-6. The model shows that both the equilibrium price and the equilibrium quantity of pizza rise. Similarly, if the price of materials increases, then the supply of pizza decreases, as in panel (b) of Figure 1-6. The model shows that in this case the equilibrium price of pizza rises and the equilibrium quantity of pizza falls. Thus, the model shows how changes in aggregate income or in the price of materials affect price and quantity in the market for pizza.

Like all models, this model of the pizza market makes many simplifying assumptions. The model does not take into account, for example, that every pizzeria is in a different location. For each customer, one pizzeria is more convenient than the others, and thus pizzerias have some ability to set their own prices. Although the model assumes that there is a single price for pizza, in fact there could be a different price at every pizzeria.

How should we react to the model's lack of realism? Should we discard the simple model of pizza supply and pizza demand? Should we attempt to build a more complex model that allows for diverse pizza prices? The answers to these questions depend on our purpose. If our goal is to explain how the price of cheese affects the average price of pizza and the amount of pizza sold, then the diversity of pizza prices is probably not important. The simple model of the pizza market does a good job of addressing that issue. Yet if our goal is to explain why towns with three pizzerias have lower pizza prices than towns with one pizzeria, the simple model is less useful.

---

f y i

USING FUNCTIONS TO EXPRESS RELATIONSHIPS AMONG VARIABLES

All economic models express relationships among economic variables. Often, these relationships are expressed as functions. A *function* is a mathematical concept that shows how one variable depends on a set of other variables. For example, in the model of the pizza market, we said that the quantity of pizza demanded depends on the price of pizza and on aggregate income. To express this, we use functional notation to write

$$Q^d = D(P, Y).$$

This equation says that the quantity of pizza demanded Q^d is a function of the price of pizza P and aggregate income Y. In functional notation, the variable preceding the parentheses denotes the function. In this case, $D( )$ is the function expressing how the variables in parentheses determine the quantity of pizza demanded.

If we knew more about the pizza market, we could give a numerical formula for the quantity of pizza demanded. We might be able to write

$$Q^d = 60 - 10P + 2Y.$$

In this case, the demand function is

$$D(P, Y) = 60 - 10P + 2Y.$$

For any price of pizza and aggregate income, this function gives the corresponding quantity of pizza demanded. For example, if aggregate income is $10 and the price of pizza is $2, then the quantity of pizza demanded is 60 pies; if the price of pizza rises to $3, the quantity of pizza demanded falls to 50 pies.

Functional notation allows us to express a relationship among variables even when the precise numerical relationship is unknown. For example, we might know that the quantity of pizza demanded falls when the price rises from $2 to $3, but we might not know by how much it falls. In this case, functional notation is useful: as long as we know that a relationship among the variables exists, we can remind ourselves of that relationship using functional notation.

The art in economics is in judging when an assumption is clarifying and when it is misleading. Any model constructed to be completely realistic would be too complicated for anyone to understand. Simplification is a necessary part of building a useful model. Yet models lead to incorrect conclusions if they assume away features of the economy that are crucial to the issue at hand. Economic modeling therefore requires care and common sense.

A Multitude of Models

Macroeconomists study many facets of the economy. For example, they examine the influence of national saving on economic growth, the impact of labor unions on the unemployment rate, and the effect of inflation on interest rates. Macroeconomics is as diverse as the economy.

Although economists use models to address all these issues, no single model can answer all questions. Just as carpenters use different tools for different tasks, economists uses different models to explain different economic phenomena. Students of macroeconomics, therefore, must keep in mind that there is no single "correct" model useful for all purposes. Instead, there are many models, each of which is useful for shedding light on a different facet of the economy. The field of macroeconomics is like a Swiss army knife—a set of complementary but distinct tools that can be applied in different ways in different circumstances.

This book therefore presents many different models that address different questions and that make different assumptions. Remember that a model is only as good as its assumptions and that an assumption that is useful for some purposes may be misleading for others. When using a model to address a question, the economist must keep in mind the underlying assumptions and judge whether these are reasonable for the matter at hand.

Prices: Flexible Versus Sticky

Throughout this book, one group of assumptions will prove especially important—those concerning the speed with which wages and prices adjust. Economists normally presume that the price of a good or a service moves quickly to bring quantity supplied and quantity demanded into balance. In other words, they assume that a market goes to the equilibrium of supply and demand. This assumption is called **market clearing** and is central to the model of the pizza market discussed earlier. For answering most questions, economists use market-clearing models.

Yet the assumption of *continuous* market clearing is not entirely realistic. For markets to clear continuously, prices must adjust instantly to changes in supply and demand. In fact, however, many wages and prices adjust slowly. Labor contracts often set wages for up to three years. Many firms leave their product prices the same for long periods of time—for example, magazine publishers typically change their newsstand prices only every three or four years. Although market-clearing models assume that all wages and prices are **flexible,** in the real world some wages and prices are **sticky.**

The apparent stickiness of prices does not necessarily make market-clearing models useless. After all, prices are not stuck forever; eventually, they do adjust to changes in supply and demand. Market-clearing models might not describe the economy at every instant, but they do describe the equilibrium toward which the economy slowly gravitates. Therefore, most macroeconomists believe that price flexibility is a good assumption for studying long-run issues, such as the growth in real GDP that we observe from decade to decade.

For studying short-run issues, such as year-to-year fluctuations in real GDP and unemployment, the assumption of price flexibility is less plausible. Over short periods, many prices are fixed at predetermined levels. Therefore, most macroeconomists believe that price stickiness is a better assumption for studying the behavior of the economy in the short run.

Microeconomic Thinking and Macroeconomic Models

Microeconomics is the study of how households and firms make decisions and how these decisionmakers interact in the marketplace. A central principle of microeconomics is that households and firms *optimize*—they do the best they can for themselves given their objectives and the constraints they face. In microeconomic models, households choose their purchases to maximize their level of satisfaction, which economists call *utility,* and firms make production decisions to maximize their profits.

Because economy-wide events arise from the interaction of many households and many firms, macroeconomics and microeconomics are inextricably linked. When we study the economy as a whole, we must consider the decisions of individual economic actors. For example, to understand what determines total consumer spending, we must think about a family deciding how much to spend today and how much to save for the future. To understand what determines total investment spending, we must think about a firm deciding whether to build a new factory. Because aggregate variables are simply the sum of the variables describing many individual decisions, macroeconomic theory inevitably rests on a microeconomic foundation.

Although microeconomic decisions always underlie economic models, in many models the optimizing behavior of households and firms is implicit rather than explicit. The model of the pizza market we discussed earlier is an example. Households' decisions about how much pizza to buy underlie the demand for pizza, and pizzerias' decisions about how much pizza to produce underlie the supply of pizza. Presumably, households make their decisions to maximize utility, and pizzerias make their decisions to maximize profit. Yet the model did not focus on these microeconomic decisions; it left them in the background. Similarly, in much of macroeconomics, the optimizing behavior of households and firms is left implicit.

1-3 | How This Book Proceeds

This book has five parts. This chapter and the next make up Part One, the Introduction. Chapter 2 discusses how economists measure economic variables, such as aggregate income, the inflation rate, and the unemployment rate.

Part Two, The Economy in the Long Run, presents the classical model of the economy. The key assumption of the classical model is that prices are flexible. That is, with only a few exceptions, the classical model assumes market clearing. For the reasons we have discussed, this assumption is best viewed as describing the economy in the long run.

Part Three, The Economy in the Short Run, examines the behavior of the economy when prices are sticky. The non-market-clearing model developed here is designed to analyze short-run issues, such as the reasons for economic fluctuations and the influence of government policy on those fluctuations.

Part Four, Macroeconomic Policy Debates, builds on the previous analysis to consider what role the government should take in the economy. It considers how, if at all, the government should respond to short-run fluctuations in real GDP and unemployment. It also examines the various views on the effects of government debt.

Part Five, More on the Microeconomics Behind Macroeconomics, presents some of the microeconomic models that are useful for analyzing macroeconomic issues. For example, it examines the household's decisions regarding how much to consume and how much money to hold and the firm's decision regarding how much to invest. These individual decisions together form the larger macroeconomic picture. The goal of studying these microeconomic decisions in detail is to refine our understanding of the aggregate economy.

Summary

1. Macroeconomics is the study of the economy as a whole—including growth in incomes, changes in prices, and the rate of unemployment. Macroeconomists attempt both to explain economic events and to devise policies to improve economic performance.

2. To understand the economy, economists use models—theories that simplify reality in order to reveal how exogenous variables influence endogenous variables. The art in the science of economics is in judging whether a model usefully captures the important economic relationships for the matter at hand. Because no single model can answer all questions, macroeconomists use different models to look at different issues.

3. A key feature of a macroeconomic model is whether it assumes that prices are flexible or sticky. According to most macroeconomists, models with flexible prices describe the economy in the long run, whereas models with sticky prices offer a better description of the economy in the short run.

4. Microeconomics is the study of how firms and individuals make decisions and how these decisionmakers interact. Because macroeconomic events arise from many microeconomic interactions, macroeconomists use many of the tools of microeconomics.

KEY CONCEPTS

Macroeconomics	Recession	Exogenous variables
Real GDP	Depression	Market clearing
Inflation and deflation	Models	Flexible and sticky prices
Unemployment	Endogenous variables	Microeconomics

QUESTIONS FOR REVIEW

1. Explain the difference between macroeconomics and microeconomics. How are these two fields related?

2. Why do economists build models?

3. What is a market-clearing model? When is the assumption of market clearing appropriate?

PROBLEMS AND APPLICATIONS

1. What macroeconomic issues have been in the news lately?

2. What do you think are the defining characteristics of a science? Does the study of the economy have these characteristics? Do you think macroeconomics should be called a science? Why or why not?

3. Use the model of supply and demand to explain how a fall in the price of frozen yogurt would affect the price of ice cream and the quantity of ice cream sold. In your explanation, identify the exogenous and endogenous variables.

4. How often does the price you pay for a haircut change? What does your answer imply about the usefulness of market-clearing models for analyzing the market for haircuts?

chapter 2

The Data of Macroeconomics

It is a capital mistake to theorize before one has data. Insensibly one be-
gins to twist facts to suit theories, instead of theories to fit facts.

— *Sherlock Holmes*

Scientists, economists, and detectives have much in common: they all want to figure out what's going on in the world around them. To do this, they rely on a combination of theory and observation. They build theories in an attempt to make sense of what they see happening. Having developed these theories, they turn to more systematic observation to evaluate the theories' validity. Only when theory and data come into line do they feel they understand the situation.

This chapter discusses the types of data used to create and test macroeconomic theories. The most obvious source of information about the economy is casual observation. When you go shopping, you see how fast prices are rising. When you look for a job, you learn whether firms are hiring. Because we are all participants in the economy, we get some sense of economic conditions as we go about our lives. These casual observations provide the first clues about how the economy works.

Economic statistics are a more systematic and objective source of information. The government regularly surveys households and firms to learn about their economic activity—how much they are earning, what they are buying, what prices they are charging, and so on. From these surveys, various statistics are computed that summarize the state of the economy. These statistics are used by economists to study the economy and by policymakers to monitor economic developments and formulate appropriate policies.

This chapter focuses on the three economic statistics that economists and policymakers use most often. **Gross domestic product,** or **GDP,** tells us the nation's total income and the total expenditure on its output of goods and services. The **consumer price index,** or **CPI,** measures the level of prices. The **unemployment rate** tells us the fraction of workers who are unemployed. In the following pages, we see how these statistics are computed and what they tell us about the economy.

2-1 | Measuring the Value of Economic Activity: Gross Domestic Product

Gross domestic product is often considered the best measure of how well the economy is performing. This statistic is computed every three months by the Bureau of Economic Analysis (a part of the U.S. Department of Commerce) from a large number of primary data sources. The goal of GDP is to summarize in a single number the dollar value of economic activity in a given period of time.

There are two ways to view this statistic. One way to view GDP is as *the total income of everyone in the economy*. Another way to view GDP is as *the total expenditure on the economy's output of goods and services*. From either viewpoint, it is clear why GDP is a gauge of economic performance. GDP measures something people care about—their incomes. Similarly, an economy with a large output of goods and services can better satisfy the demands of households, firms, and the government.

How can GDP measure both the economy's income and the expenditure on its output? The reason is that these two quantities are really the same: for the economy as a whole, income must equal expenditure. That fact, in turn, follows from an even more fundamental one: because every transaction has both a buyer and a seller, every dollar of expenditure by a buyer must become a dollar of income to a seller. When Joe paints Jane's house for $1,000, that $1,000 is income to Joe and expenditure by Jane. The transaction contributes $1,000 to GDP, regardless of whether we are adding up all income or adding up all expenditure.

To understand the meaning of GDP more fully, we turn to **national income accounting,** the accounting system used to measure GDP and many related statistics.

Income, Expenditure, and the Circular Flow

Imagine an economy that produces a single good, bread, from a single input, labor. Figure 2-1 illustrates all the economic transactions that occur between households and firms in this economy.

The inner loop in Figure 2-1 represents the flows of bread and labor. The households sell their labor to the firms. The firms use the labor of their workers to produce bread, which the firms in turn sell to the households. Hence, labor flows from households to firms, and bread flows from firms to households.

The outer loop in Figure 2-1 represents the corresponding flow of dollars. The households buy bread from the firms. The firms use some of the revenue from these sales to pay the wages of their workers, and the remainder is the profit belonging to the owners of the firms (who themselves are part of the household sector). Hence, expenditure on bread flows from households to firms, and income in the form of wages and profit flows from firms to households.

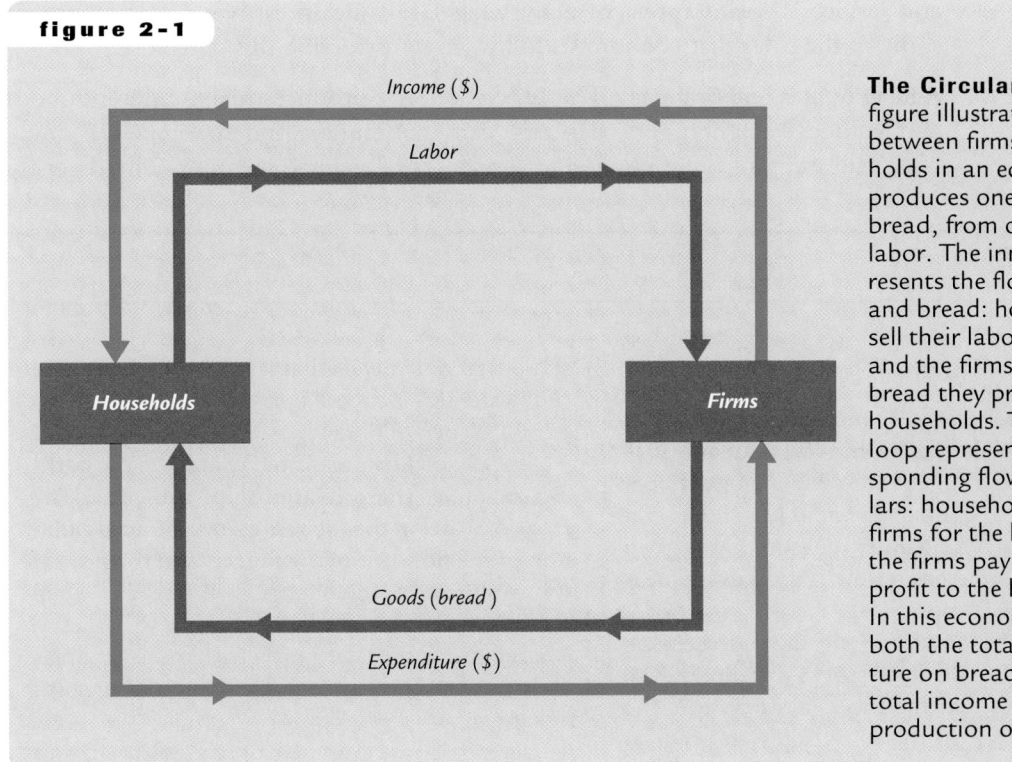

figure 2-1

Income ($)

Labor

Households

Firms

Goods (bread)

Expenditure ($)

The Circular Flow This figure illustrates the flows between firms and households in an economy that produces one good, bread, from one input, labor. The inner loop represents the flows of labor and bread: households sell their labor to firms, and the firms sell the bread they produce to households. The outer loop represents the corresponding flows of dollars: households pay the firms for the bread, and the firms pay wages and profit to the households. In this economy, GDP is both the total expenditure on bread and the total income from the production of bread.

GDP measures the flow of dollars in this economy. We can compute it in two ways. GDP is the total income from the production of bread, which equals the sum of wages and profit—the top half of the circular flow of dollars. GDP is also the total expenditure on purchases of bread—the bottom half of the circular flow of dollars. To compute GDP, we can look at either the flow of dollars from firms to households or the flow of dollars from households to firms.

These two ways of computing GDP must be equal because the expenditure of buyers on products is, by the rules of accounting, income to the sellers of those products. Every transaction that affects expenditure must affect income, and every transaction that affects income must affect expenditure. For example, suppose that a firm produces and sells one more loaf of bread to a household. Clearly this transaction raises total expenditure on bread, but it also has an equal effect on total income. If the firm produces the extra loaf without hiring any more labor (such as by making the production process more efficient), then profit increases. If the firm produces the extra loaf by hiring more labor, then wages increase. In both cases, expenditure and income increase equally.

Some Rules for Computing GDP

In the hypothetical economy that produces only bread, we can compute GDP simply by adding up the total expenditure on bread. A nation's economy, however, includes the production and sale of a vast number of diverse goods and services. To interpret correctly what GDP measures, we must understand some of the rules that economists follow in constructing this statistic.

Adding Apples and Oranges The U.S. economy produces many different goods and services—hamburgers, haircuts, cars, computers, and so on. GDP combines the value of these goods and services into a single measure. The diversity

---

f y i

STOCKS AND FLOWS

Many economic variables measure a quantity of something—a quantity of money, a quantity of goods, and so on. Economists distinguish between two types of quantity variables: stocks and flows. A **stock** is a quantity measured at a given point in time, whereas a **flow** is a quantity measured per unit of time.

The bathtub, shown in Figure 2-2, is the classic example used to illustrate stocks and flows. The amount of water in the tub is a stock: it is the quantity of water in the tub at a given point in time. The amount of water coming out of the faucet is a flow: it is the quantity of water being added to the tub per unit of time. Note that we measure stocks and flows in different units. We say that the bathtub contains 50 *gallons* of water, but that water is coming out of the faucet at 5 *gallons per minute.*

GDP is probably the most important flow variable in economics: it tells us how many dollars are flowing around the economy's circular flow per unit of time. When you hear someone say that the U.S. GDP is $8 trillion, you should under-

stand that this means that it is $8 trillion *per year.* (Equivalently, we could say that U.S. GDP is $250,000 per second.)

Stocks and flows are often related. In the bathtub example, these relationships are clear. The stock of water in the tub represents the accumulation of the flow out of the faucet, and the flow of water represents the change in the stock. When building theories to explain economic variables, it is often useful to determine whether the variables are stocks or flows and whether any relationships link them.

Here are some examples of related stocks and flows that we study in future chapters:

➤ A person's wealth is a stock; his income and expenditure are flows.

➤ The number of unemployed people is a stock; the number of people losing their jobs is a flow.

➤ The amount of capital in the economy is a stock; the amount of investment is a flow.

➤ The government debt is a stock; the government budget deficit is a flow.

figure 2-2

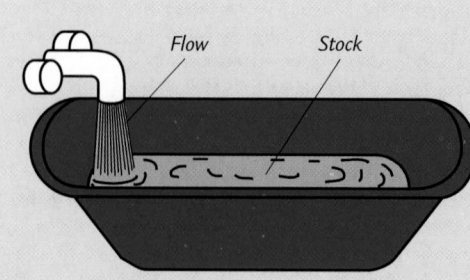
Flow   *Stock*

Stocks and Flows The amount of water in a bathtub is a stock: it is a quantity measured at a given moment in time. The amount of water coming out of the faucet is a flow: it is a quantity measured per unit of time.

of products in the economy complicates the calculation of GDP because different products have different values.

Suppose, for example, that the economy produces four apples and three oranges. How do we compute GDP? We could simply add apples and oranges and conclude that GDP equals seven pieces of fruit. But this makes sense only if we thought apples and oranges had equal value, which is generally not true. (This would be even clearer if the economy had produced four watermelons and three grapes.)

To compute the total value of different goods and services, the national income accounts use market prices because these prices reflect how much people are willing to pay for a good or service. Thus, if apples cost $0.50 each and oranges cost $1.00 each, GDP would be

$$
\begin{aligned}
\text{GDP} &= (\text{Price of Apples} \times \text{Quantity of Apples}) \\
&\quad + (\text{Price of Oranges} \times \text{Quantity of Oranges}) \\
&= (\$0.50 \times 4) + (\$1.00 \times 3) \\
&= \$5.00.
\end{aligned}
$$

GDP equals $5.00—the value of all the apples, $2.00, plus the value of all the oranges, $3.00.

Used Goods   When the Topps Company makes a package of baseball cards and sells it for 50 cents, that 50 cents is added to the nation's GDP. But what about when a collector sells a rare Mickey Mantle card to another collector for $500? That $500 is not part of GDP. GDP measures the value of currently produced goods and services. The sale of the Mickey Mantle card reflects the transfer of an asset, not an addition to the economy's income. Thus, the sale of used goods is not included as part of GDP.

The Treatment of Inventories   Imagine that a bakery hires workers to produce more bread, pays their wages, and then fails to sell the additional bread. How does this transaction affect GDP?

The answer depends on what happens to the unsold bread. Let's first suppose that the bread spoils. In this case, the firm has paid more in wages but has not received any additional revenue, so the firm's profit is reduced by the amount that wages are increased. Total expenditure in the economy hasn't changed because no one buys the bread. Total income hasn't changed either—although more is distributed as wages and less as profit. Because the transaction affects neither expenditure nor income, it does not alter GDP.

Now suppose, instead, that the bread is put into inventory to be sold later. In this case, the transaction is treated differently. The owners of the firm are assumed to have "purchased" the bread for the firm's inventory, and the firm's profit is not reduced by the additional wages it has paid. Because the higher wages raise total income, and greater spending on inventory raises total expenditure, the economy's GDP rises.

What happens later when the firm sells the bread out of inventory? This case is much like the sale of a used good. There is spending by bread consumers, but there is inventory disinvestment by the firm. This negative spending by the firm offsets the positive spending by consumers, so the sale out of inventory does not affect GDP.

The general rule is that when a firm increases its inventory of goods, this investment in inventory is counted as expenditure by the firm owners. Thus, production for inventory increases GDP just as much as production for final sale. A sale out of inventory, however, is a combination of positive spending (the purchase) and negative spending (inventory disinvestment), so it does not influence GDP. This treatment of inventories ensures that GDP reflects the economy's current production of goods and services.

Intermediate Goods and Value Added Many goods are produced in stages: raw materials are processed into intermediate goods by one firm and then sold to another firm for final processing. How should we treat such products when computing GDP? For example, suppose a cattle rancher sells one-quarter pound of meat to McDonald's for $0.50, and then McDonald's sells you a hamburger for $1.50. Should GDP include both the meat and the hamburger (a total of $2.00), or just the hamburger ($1.50)?

The answer is that GDP includes only the value of final goods. Thus, the hamburger is included in GDP but the meat is not: GDP increases by $1.50, not by $2.00. The reason is that the value of intermediate goods is already included as part of the market price of the final goods in which they are used. To add the intermediate goods to the final goods would be double counting—that is, the meat would be counted twice. Hence, GDP is the total value of final goods and services produced.

One way to compute the value of all final goods and services is to sum the value added at each stage of production. The **value added** of a firm equals the value of the firm's output less the value of the intermediate goods that the firm purchases. In the case of the hamburger, the value added of the rancher is $0.50 (assuming that the rancher bought no intermediate goods), and the value added of McDonald's is $1.50 − $0.50, or $1.00. Total value added is $0.50 + $1.00, which equals $1.50. For the economy as a whole, the sum of all value added must equal the value of all final goods and services. Hence, GDP is also the total value added of all firms in the economy.

Housing Services and Other Imputations Although most goods and services are valued at their market prices when computing GDP, some are not sold in the marketplace and therefore do not have market prices. If GDP is to include the value of these goods and services, we must use an estimate of their value. Such an estimate is called an **imputed value.**

Imputations are especially important for determining the value of housing. A person who rents a house is buying housing services and providing income for the landlord; the rent is part of GDP, both as expenditure by the renter and as income for the landlord. Many people, however, live in their own homes. Although they do not pay rent to a landlord, they are enjoying housing services similar to those that renters purchase. To take account of the housing services enjoyed by homeowners, GDP includes the "rent" that these homeowners "pay" to themselves. Of course, homeowners do not in fact pay themselves this rent. The Department of Commerce estimates what the market rent for a house would be if it were rented and includes that imputed rent as part of GDP. This imputed rent is included both in the homeowner's expenditure and in the homeowner's income.

Imputations also arise in valuing government services. For example, police officers, fire fighters, and senators provide services to the public. Giving a value to these services is difficult because they are not sold in a marketplace and therefore do not have a market price. The national income accounts include these services in GDP by valuing them at their cost. That is, the wages of these public servants are used as a measure of the value of their output.

In many cases, an imputation is called for in principle but, to keep things simple, is not made in practice. Because GDP includes the imputed rent on owner-occupied houses, one might expect it also to include the imputed rent on cars, lawn mowers, jewelry, and other durable goods owned by households. Yet the value of these rental services is left out of GDP. In addition, some of the output of the economy is produced and consumed at home and never enters the marketplace. For example, meals cooked at home are similar to meals cooked at a restaurant, yet the value added in meals at home is left out of GDP.

Finally, no imputation is made for the value of goods and services sold in the *underground economy*. The underground economy is the part of the economy that people hide from the government either because they wish to evade taxation or because the activity is illegal. Domestic workers paid "off the books" is one example. The illegal drug trade is another.

Because the imputations necessary for computing GDP are only approximate, and because the value of many goods and services is left out altogether, GDP is an imperfect measure of economic activity. These imperfections are most problematic when comparing standards of living across countries. The size of the underground economy, for instance, varies from country to country. Yet as long as the magnitude of these imperfections remains fairly constant over time, GDP is useful for comparing economic activity from year to year.

Real GDP Versus Nominal GDP

Economists use the rules just described to compute GDP, which values the economy's total output of goods and services. But is GDP a good measure of economic well-being? Consider once again the economy that produces only apples and oranges. In this economy GDP is the sum of the value of all the apples produced and the value of all the oranges produced. That is,

$$\text{GDP} = (\text{Price of Apples} \times \text{Quantity of Apples})$$
$$+ (\text{Price of Oranges} \times \text{Quantity of Oranges}).$$

Notice that GDP can increase either because prices rise or because quantities rise.

It is easy to see that GDP computed this way is not a good gauge of economic well-being. That is, this measure does not accurately reflect how well the economy can satisfy the demands of households, firms, and the government. If all prices doubled without any change in quantities, GDP would double. Yet it would be misleading to say that the economy's ability to satisfy demands has doubled, because the quantity of every good produced remains the same. Economists call the value of goods and services measured at current prices **nominal GDP.**

A better measure of economic well-being would tally the economy's output of goods and services and would not be influenced by changes in prices. For this purpose, economists use **real GDP,** which is the value of goods and services measured using a constant set of prices. That is, real GDP shows what would have happened to expenditure on output if quantities had changed but prices had not.

To see how real GDP is computed, imagine we wanted to compare output in 1998 and output in 1999 in our apple-and-orange economy. We could begin by choosing a set of prices, called *base-year prices,* such as the prices that prevailed in 1998. Goods and services are then added up using these base-year prices to value the different goods in both years. Real GDP for 1998 would be

Real GDP = (1998 Price of Apples × 1998 Quantity of Apples)
+ (1998 Price of Oranges × 1998 Quantity of Oranges).

Similarly, real GDP in 1999 would be

Real GDP = (1998 Price of Apples × 1999 Quantity of Apples)
+ (1998 Price of Oranges × 1999 Quantity of Oranges).

And real GDP in 2000 would be

Real GDP = (1998 Price of Apples × 2000 Quantity of Apples)
+ (1998 Price of Oranges × 2000 Quantity of Oranges).

Notice that 1998 prices are used to compute real GDP for all three years. Because the prices are held constant, real GDP varies from year to year only if the quantities produced vary. Because a society's ability to provide economic satisfaction for its members ultimately depends on the quantities of goods and services produced, real GDP provides a better measure of economic well-being than nominal GDP.

The GDP Deflator

From nominal GDP and real GDP we can compute a third statistic: the GDP deflator. The **GDP deflator,** also called the implicit price deflator for GDP, is defined as the ratio of nominal GDP to real GDP:

$$\text{GDP Deflator} = \frac{\text{Nominal GDP}}{\text{Real GDP}}.$$

The GDP deflator reflects what's happening to the overall level of prices in the economy.

To better understand this, consider again an economy with only one good, bread. If P is the price of bread and Q is the quantity sold, then nominal GDP is the total number of dollars spent on bread in that year, $P \times Q$. Real GDP is the number of loaves of bread produced in that year times the price of bread in some base year, $P_{base} \times Q$. The GDP deflator is the price of bread in that year relative to the price of bread in the base year, P/P_{base}.

The definition of the GDP deflator allows us to separate nominal GDP into two parts: one part measures quantities (real GDP) and the other measures prices (the GDP deflator). That is,

$$\text{Nominal GDP} = \text{Real GDP} \times \text{GDP Deflator}.$$

Nominal GDP measures the current dollar value of the output of the economy. Real GDP measures output valued at constant prices. The GDP deflator measures the price of output relative to its price in the base year.

Chain-Weighted Measures of Real GDP

We have been discussing real GDP as if the prices used to compute this measure never change from their base-year values. If this were truly the case, over time the prices would become more and more dated. For instance, the price of computers has fallen substantially in recent years, while the price of a year at college has risen. When valuing the production of computers and education, it would be misleading to use the prices that prevailed ten or twenty years ago.

To solve this problem, the Bureau of Economic Analysis used to update periodically the prices used to compute real GDP. About every five years, a new base year was chosen. The prices were then held fixed and used to measure year-to-year changes in the production of goods and services until the base year was updated once again.

In 1995, the Bureau announced a new policy for dealing with changes in the base year. In particular, it now emphasizes *chain-weighted* measures of real GDP. With these new measures, the base year changes continuously over time. In essence, average prices in 1995 and 1996 are used to measure real growth from 1995 to 1996; average prices in 1996 and 1997 are used to measure real growth from 1996 to 1997; and so on. These various year-to-year growth rates are then put together to form a "chain" that can be used to compare the output of goods and services between any two dates.

This new chain-weighted measure of real GDP is better than the more traditional measure because it ensures that the prices used to compute real GDP are never far out of date. For most purposes, however, the differences are not important. It turns out that the two measures of real GDP are highly correlated with each other. The reason for this close association is that most relative prices change slowly over time. Thus, both measures of real GDP reflect the same thing: economy-wide changes in the production of goods and services.

The Components of Expenditure

Economists and policymakers care not only about the economy's total output of goods and services but also about the allocation of this output among

---

f y i

TWO ARITHMETIC TRICKS FOR WORKING WITH PERCENTAGE CHANGES

For manipulating many relationships in economics, there is an arithmetic trick that is useful to know: *The percentage change of a product of two variables is approximately the sum of the percentage changes in each of the variables.*

To see how this trick works, consider an example. Let P denote the GDP deflator and Y denote real GDP. Nominal GDP is $P \times Y$. The trick states that

> Percentage Change in ($P \times Y$)
> $\approx$ (Percentage Change in P)
> $+$ (Percentage Change in Y).

For instance, suppose that in one year, real GDP is 100 and the GDP deflator is 2; the next year, real GDP is 103 and the GDP deflator is 2.1. We can calculate that real GDP rose by 3 percent and that the GDP deflator rose by 5 percent. Nominal GDP rose from 200 the first year to 216.3 the sec-

ond year, an increase of 8.15 percent. Notice that the growth in nominal GDP (8.15 percent) is approximately the sum of the growth in the GDP deflator (5 percent) and the growth in real GDP (3 percent).[1]

A second arithmetic trick follows as a corollary to the first: *The percentage change of a ratio is approximately the percentage change in the numerator minus the percentage change in the denominator.* Again, consider an example. Let Y denote GDP and L denote the population, so that Y/L is GDP per person. The second trick states

> Percentage Change in (Y/L)
> $\approx$ (Percentage Change in Y)
> $-$ (Percentage Change in L).

For instance, suppose that in the first year, Y is 100,000 and L is 100, so Y/L is 1,000; in the second year, Y is 110,000 and L is 103, so Y/L is 1,068. Notice that the growth in GDP per person (6.8 percent) is approximately the growth in income (10 percent) minus the growth in population (3 percent).

---

alternative uses. The national income accounts divide GDP into four broad categories of spending:

- ➤ Consumption (C)
- ➤ Investment (I)
- ➤ Government purchases (G)
- ➤ Net exports (NX).

Thus, letting Y stand for GDP,

$$Y = C + I + G + NX.$$

GDP is the sum of consumption, investment, government purchases, and net exports. Each dollar of GDP falls into one of these categories. This equation is an *identity*—an equation that must hold because of the way the variables are defined. It is called the **national income accounts identity.**

---

[1] *Mathematical note:* The proof that this trick works begins with the chain rule from calculus:
$$d(PY) = Y\,dP + P\,dY.$$
Now divide both sides of this equation by PY to obtain:
$$d(PY)/(PY) = dP/P + dY/Y.$$
Notice that all three terms in this equation are percentage changes.

---

f y i

WHAT IS INVESTMENT?

Newcomers to macroeconomics are sometimes confused by how macroeconomists use familiar words in new and specific ways. One example is the term "investment." The confusion arises because what looks like investment for an individual may not be investment for the economy as a whole. The general rule is that the economy's investment does not include purchases that merely reallocate existing assets among different individuals. Investment, as macroeconomists use the term, creates new capital.

Let's consider some examples. Suppose we observe these two events:

➤ Smith buys for himself a 100-year-old Victorian house.

➤ Jones builds for herself a brand-new contemporary house.

What is total investment here? Two houses, one house, or zero?

A macroeconomist seeing these two transactions counts only the Jones house as investment.

Smith's transaction has not created new housing for the economy; it has merely reallocated existing housing. Smith's purchase is investment for Smith, but it is disinvestment for the person selling the house. By contrast, Jones has added new housing to the economy; her new house is counted as investment.

Similarly, consider these two events:

➤ Gates buys $5 million in IBM stock from Buffett on the New York Stock Exchange.

➤ General Motors sells $10 million in stock to the public and uses the proceeds to build a new car factory.

Here, investment is $10 million. In the first transaction, Gates is investing in IBM stock, and Buffett is disinvesting; there is no investment for the economy. By contrast, General Motors is using some of the economy's output of goods and services to add to its stock of capital; hence, its new factory is counted as investment.

Consumption consists of the goods and services bought by households. It is divided into three subcategories: nondurable goods, durable goods, and services. Nondurable goods are goods that last only a short time, such as food and clothing. Durable goods are goods that last a long time, such as cars and TVs. Services include the work done for consumers by individuals and firms, such as haircuts and doctor visits.

Investment consists of goods bought for future use. Investment is also divided into three subcategories: business fixed investment, residential fixed investment, and inventory investment. Business fixed investment is the purchase of new plant and equipment by firms. Residential investment is the purchase of new housing by households and landlords. Inventory investment is the increase in firms' inventories of goods (if inventories are falling, inventory investment is negative).

Government purchases are the goods and services bought by federal, state, and local governments. This category includes such items as military equipment, highways, and the services that government workers provide. It does not include transfer payments to individuals, such as Social Security and welfare. Because transfer payments reallocate existing income and are not made in exchange for goods and services, they are not part of GDP.

The last category, **net exports,** takes into account trade with other countries. Net exports are the value of goods and services exported to other countries minus the value of goods and services that foreigners provide us. Net exports represent the net expenditure from abroad on our goods and services, which provides income for domestic producers.

CASE STUDY

GDP and Its Components

In 1997 the GDP of the United States totaled about $8 trillion. This number is so large that it is almost impossible to comprehend. We can make it easier to understand by dividing it by the 1997 U.S. population of 268 million. In this way, we obtain GDP per person—the amount of expenditure for the average American—which equaled $30,173 in 1997.

How did this GDP get used? Table 2-1 shows that about two-thirds of it, or $20,487 per person, was spent on consumption. Investment was $4,620 per person. Government purchases were $5,427 per person, $1,309 of which was spent by the federal government on national defense.

table 2-1

GDP and the Components of Expenditure: 1997

	Total (billions of dollars)	Per Person (dollars)
Gross Domestic Product	**8,083.4**	**30,173**
Consumption	**5,488.6**	**20,487**
Nondurable goods	1,592.7	5,945
Durable goods	659.4	2,461
Services	3,236.5	12,081
Investment	**1,237.6**	**4,620**
Nonresidential fixed investment	845.4	3,156
Residential fixed investment	327.5	1,222
Inventory investment	64.6	241
Government Purchases	**1,453.9**	**5,427**
Federal	524.8	1,959
Defense	350.8	1,309
Nondefense	174.0	649
State and local	929.1	3,468
Net Exports	**−96.7**	**−361**
Exports	958.8	3,579
Imports	1,055.5	3,940

Source: U.S. Department of Commerce.

The average American bought $3,940 of goods imported from abroad and produced $3,579 of goods that were exported to other countries. Because the average American imported more than he exported, net exports were negative. Furthermore, because the average American earned less from selling to foreigners than he spent on foreign goods, he must have financed the difference by taking out loans from foreigners (or, equivalently, by selling them some of his assets). Thus, the average American borrowed $361 from abroad in 1997.

Other Measures of Income

The national income accounts include other measures of income that differ slightly in definition from GDP. It is important to be aware of the various measures, because economists and the press often refer to them.

To see how the alternative measures of income relate to one another, we start with GDP and add or subtract various quantities. To obtain *gross national product* (*GNP*), we add receipts of factor income (wages, profit, and rent) from the rest of the world and subtract payments of factor income to the rest of the world:

GNP = GDP + Factor Payments From Abroad − Factor Payments to Abroad.

Whereas GDP measures the total income produced *domestically,* GNP measures the total income earned by *nationals* (residents of a nation). For instance, if a Japanese resident owns an apartment building in New York, the rental income he earns is part of U.S. GDP because it is earned in the United States. But because this rental income is a factor payment to abroad, it is not part of U.S. GNP. In the United States, factor payments from abroad and factor payments to abroad are similar in size—each representing about 3 percent of GDP—so GDP and GNP are quite close.

To obtain *net national product* (*NNP*), we subtract the depreciation of capital—the amount of the economy's stock of plants, equipment, and residential structures that wears out during the year:

$$NNP = GNP - Depreciation.$$

In the national income accounts, depreciation is called the *consumption of fixed capital*. It equals about 10 percent of GNP. Because the depreciation of capital is a cost of producing the output of the economy, subtracting depreciation shows the net result of economic activity.

The next adjustment in the national income accounts is for indirect business taxes, such as sales taxes. These taxes, which make up about 10 percent of NNP, place a wedge between the price that consumers pay for a good and the price that firms receive. Because firms never receive this tax wedge, it is not part of their income. Once we subtract indirect business taxes from NNP, we obtain a measure called *national income*:

$$National\ Income = NNP - Indirect\ Business\ Taxes.$$

National income measures how much everyone in the economy has earned.

The national income accounts divide national income into five components, depending on the way the income is earned. The five categories, and the percentage of national income paid in each category, are

➤ *Compensation of employees* (71%). The wages and fringe benefits earned by workers.

➤ *Proprietors' income* (8%). The income of noncorporate businesses, such as small farms, mom-and-pop stores, and law partnerships.

➤ *Rental income* (2%). The income that landlords receive, including the imputed rent that homeowners "pay" to themselves, less expenses, such as depreciation.

➤ *Corporate profits* (12%). The income of corporations after payments to their workers and creditors.

➤ *Net interest* (7%). The interest domestic businesses pay minus the interest they receive, plus interest earned from foreigners.

A series of adjustments takes us from national income to *personal income*, the amount of income that households and noncorporate businesses receive. Three of these adjustments are most important. First, we reduce national income by the amount that corporations earn but do not pay out, either because the corporations are retaining earnings or because they are paying taxes to the government. This adjustment is made by subtracting corporate profits (which equals the sum of corporate taxes, dividends, and retained earnings) and adding back dividends. Second, we increase national income by the net amount the government pays out in transfer payments. This adjustment equals government transfers to individuals minus social insurance contributions paid to the government. Third, we adjust national income to include the interest that households earn rather than the interest that businesses pay. This adjustment is made by adding personal interest income and subtracting net interest. (The difference between personal interest and net interest arises in part from the interest on the government debt.) Thus, personal income is

$$
\begin{aligned}
\text{Personal Income} = \ &\text{National Income} \\
&- \text{Corporate Profits} \\
&- \text{Social Insurance Contributions} \\
&- \text{Net Interest} \\
&+ \text{Dividends} \\
&+ \text{Government Transfers to Individuals} \\
&+ \text{Personal Interest Income.}
\end{aligned}
$$

Next, if we subtract personal tax payments and certain nontax payments to the government (such as parking tickets), we obtain *disposable personal income*:

$$
\begin{aligned}
\text{Disposable Personal Income} = \ &\text{Personal Income} \\
&- \text{Personal Tax and Nontax Payments.}
\end{aligned}
$$

We are interested in disposable personal income because it is the amount households and noncorporate businesses have available to spend after satisfying their tax obligations to the government.

CASE STUDY

The Seasonal Cycle and Seasonal Adjustment

Because real GDP and the other measures of income reflect how well the economy is performing, economists are interested in studying the quarter-to-quarter fluctuations in these variables. Yet when we start to do so, one fact leaps out: all these measures of income exhibit a regular seasonal pattern. The output of the economy rises during the year, reaching a peak in the fourth quarter (October, November, and December), and then falling in the first quarter (January, February, and March) of the next year. These regular seasonal changes are substantial. From the fourth quarter to the first quarter, real GDP falls on average about 8 percent.[2]

It is not surprising that real GDP follows a seasonal cycle. Some of these changes are attributable to changes in our ability to produce: for example, building homes is more difficult during the cold weather of winter than during other seasons. In addition, people have seasonal tastes: they have preferred times for such activities as vacations and Christmas shopping.

When economists study fluctuations in real GDP and other economic variables, they often want to eliminate the portion of fluctuations due to predictable seasonal changes. You will find that most of the economic statistics reported in the newspaper are *seasonally adjusted*. This means that the data have been adjusted to remove the regular seasonal fluctuations. (The precise statistical procedures used are too elaborate to bother with here, but in essence they involve subtracting those changes in income that are predictable just from the change in season.) Therefore, when you observe a rise or fall in real GDP or any other data series, you must look beyond the seasonal cycle for the explanation.

2-2 | Measuring the Cost of Living: The Consumer Price Index

A dollar today doesn't buy as much as it did twenty years ago. The cost of almost everything has gone up. This increase in the overall level of prices is called *inflation*, and it is one of the primary concerns of economists and

---

[2] Robert B. Barsky and Jeffrey A. Miron, "The Seasonal Cycle and the Business Cycle," *Journal of Political Economy* 97 (June 1989): 503–534.

policymakers. In later chapters we examine in detail the causes and effects of inflation. Here we discuss how economists measure changes in the cost of living.

The Price of a Basket of Goods

The most commonly used measure of the level of prices is the **consumer price index (CPI).** The Bureau of Labor Statistics, which is part of the U.S. Department of Labor, has the job of computing the CPI. It begins by collecting the prices of thousands of goods and services. Just as GDP turns the quantities of many goods and services into a single number measuring the value of production, the CPI turns the prices of many goods and services into a single index measuring the overall level of prices.

How should economists aggregate the many prices in the economy into a single index that reliably measures the price level? They could simply compute an average of all prices. Yet this approach would treat all goods and services equally. Because people buy more chicken than caviar, the price of chicken should have a greater weight in the CPI than the price of caviar. The Bureau of Labor Statistics weights different items by computing the price of a basket of goods and services purchased by a typical consumer. The CPI is the price of this basket of goods and services relative to the price of the same basket in some base year.

For example, suppose that the typical consumer buys 5 apples and 2 oranges every month. Then the basket of goods consists of 5 apples and 2 oranges, and the CPI is

$$\text{CPI} = \frac{(5 \times \text{Current Price of Apples}) + (2 \times \text{Current Price of Oranges})}{(5 \times 1992 \text{ Price of Apples}) + (2 \times 1992 \text{ Price of Oranges})}.$$

In this CPI, 1992 is the base year. The index tells us how much it costs now to buy 5 apples and 2 oranges relative to how much it cost to buy the same basket of fruit in 1992.

The consumer price index is the most closely watched index of prices, but it is not the only such index. Another is the producer price index, which measures the price of a typical basket of goods bought by firms rather than consumers. In addition to these overall price indices, the Bureau of Labor Statistics computes price indices for specific types of goods, such as food, housing, and energy.

The CPI Versus the GDP Deflator

Earlier in this chapter we saw another measure of prices—the implicit price deflator for GDP, which is the ratio of nominal GDP to real GDP. The GDP deflator and the CPI give somewhat different information about what's happening to the overall level of prices in the economy. There are three key differences between the two measures.

The first difference is that the GDP deflator measures the prices of all goods and services produced, whereas the CPI measures the prices of only the goods and services bought by consumers. Thus, an increase in the price of goods bought by firms or the government will show up in the GDP deflator but not in the CPI.

The second difference is that the GDP deflator includes only those goods produced domestically. Imported goods are not part of GDP and do not show up in the GDP deflator. Hence, an increase in the price of a Toyota made in Japan and sold in this country affects the CPI, because the Toyota is bought by consumers, but it does not affect the GDP deflator.

The third and most subtle difference results from the way the two measures aggregate the many prices in the economy. The CPI assigns fixed weights to the prices of different goods, whereas the GDP deflator assigns changing weights. In other words, the CPI is computed using a fixed basket of goods, whereas the GDP deflator allows the basket of goods to change over time as the composition of GDP changes. The following example shows how these approaches differ. Suppose that major frosts destroy the nation's orange crop. The quantity of oranges produced falls to zero, and the price of the few oranges that remain on grocers' shelves is driven sky-high. Because oranges are no longer part of GDP, the increase in the price of oranges does not show up in the GDP deflator. But because the CPI is computed with a fixed basket of goods that includes oranges, the increase in the price of oranges causes a substantial rise in the CPI.

Economists call a price index with a fixed basket of goods a *Laspeyres index* and a price index with a changing basket a *Paasche index.* Economic theorists have studied the properties of these different types of price indices to determine which is a better measure of the cost of living. The answer, it turns out, is that neither is clearly superior. When prices of different goods are changing by different amounts, a Laspeyres (fixed basket) index tends to overstate the increase in the cost of living because it does not take into account that consumers have the opportunity to substitute less expensive goods for more expensive ones. By contrast, a Paasche (changing basket) index tends to understate the increase in the cost of living. While it accounts for the substitution of alternative goods, it does not reflect the reduction in consumers' welfare that may result from such substitutions.

The example of the destroyed orange crop shows the problems with Laspeyres and Paasche price indices. Because the CPI is a Laspeyres index, it overstates the impact of the increase in orange prices on consumers: by using a fixed basket of goods, it ignores consumers' ability to substitute apples for oranges. By contrast, because the GDP deflator is a Paasche index, it understates the impact on consumers: the GDP deflator shows no rise in prices, yet surely the higher price of oranges makes consumers worse off.

Luckily, the difference between the GDP deflator and the CPI is usually not large in practice. Figure 2-3 shows the percentage change in the GDP deflator and the percentage change in the CPI for each year since 1948. Both measures usually tell the same story about how quickly prices are rising.

figure 2-3

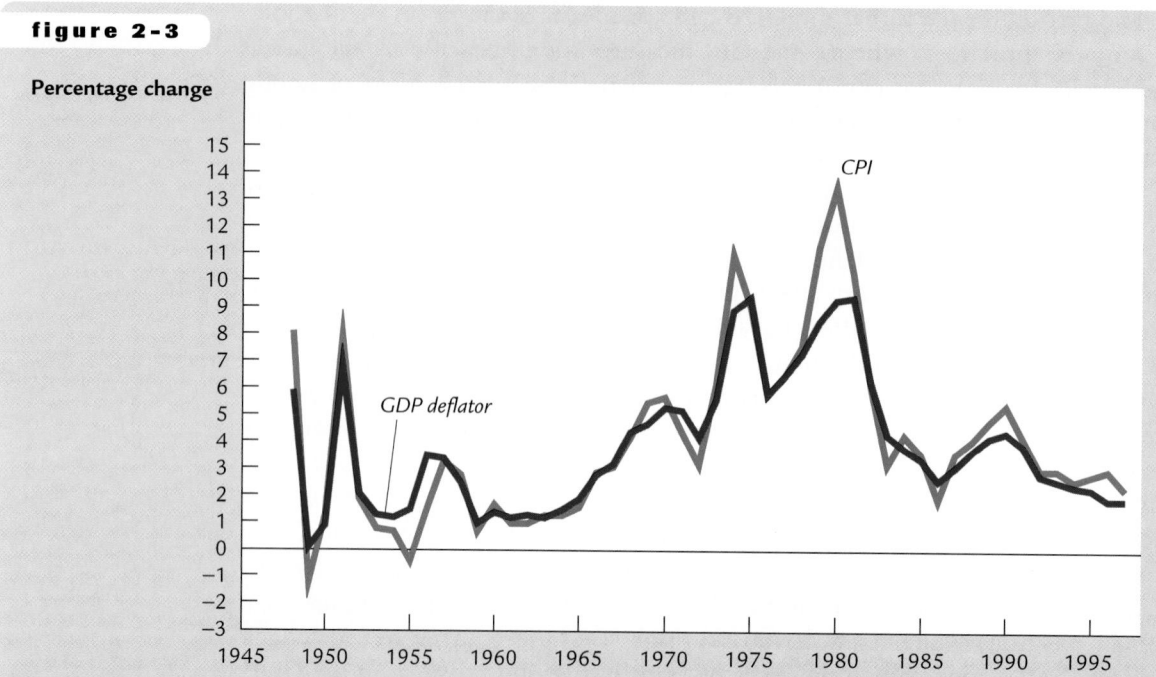

Percentage change

The GDP Deflator and the CPI This figure shows the percentage change in the GDP deflator and in the CPI for every year since 1948. Although these two measures of prices diverge at times, they usually tell the same story about how quickly prices are rising. Both the CPI and the GDP deflator show that prices rose slowly in most of the 1950s and 1960s, that they rose much more quickly in the 1970s, and that they rose slowly again in the 1980s and early 1990s.

Source: U.S. Department of Commerce, U.S. Department of Labor.

CASE STUDY

Does the CPI Overstate Inflation?

The consumer price index is a closely watched measure of inflation. Policy-makers in the Federal Reserve monitor the CPI when choosing monetary policy. In addition, many laws and private contracts have cost-of-living allowances, called *COLAs*, which use the CPI to adjust for changes in the price level. For instance, Social Security benefits are adjusted automatically every year so that inflation will not erode the living standard of the elderly.

Because so much depends on the CPI, it is important to ensure that this measure of the price level is accurate. Many economists believe that, for a number of reasons, the CPI tends to overstate inflation.

One problem is the substitution bias we have already discussed. Because the CPI measures the price of a fixed basket of goods, it does not reflect the ability of consumers to substitute toward goods whose relative prices have fallen. Thus, when relative prices change, the true cost of living rises less rapidly than the CPI.

A second problem is the introduction of new goods. When a new good is introduced into the marketplace, consumers are better off, because they have more products from which to choose. In effect, the introduction of new goods increases the real value of the dollar. Yet this increase in the purchasing power of the dollar is not reflected in a lower CPI.

A third problem is unmeasured changes in quality. When a firm changes the quality of a good it sells, not all of the good's price change reflects a change in the cost of living. The Bureau of Economic Analysis does its best to account for changes in the quality of goods over time. For example, if Ford increases the horsepower of a particular car model from one year to the next, the CPI will reflect the change: the quality-adjusted price of the car will not rise as fast as the unadjusted price. Yet many changes in quality, such as comfort or safety, are hard to measure. If unmeasured quality improvement (rather than unmeasured quality deterioration) is typical, then the measured CPI rises faster than it should.

Because of these measurement problems, some economists have suggested revising laws to reduce the degree of indexation. For example, Social Security benefits could be indexed to CPI inflation minus 1 percent. Such a change would provide a rough way of offsetting these measurement problems. At the same time, it would automatically slow the growth in government spending.

In 1995, the Senate Finance Committee appointed a panel of five noted economists—Michael Boskin, Ellen Dulberger, Robert Gordon, Zvi Griliches, and Dale Jorgenson—to study the magnitude of the measurement error in the CPI. According to the panel's report, the CPI is biased upward by 0.8 to 1.6 percentage points per year, with their "best estimate" being 1.1 percentage points. This finding has important implications for policy. Correcting this measurement error would reduce the federal government's debt by more than $1 trillion over a dozen years. So far, however, the report has not led to major changes either in the way the CPI is computed or in the way the CPI is used in legislation.[3]

2-3 | Measuring Joblessness: The Unemployment Rate

One aspect of economic performance is how well an economy uses its resources. Because an economy's workers are its chief resource, keeping workers employed is a paramount concern of economic policymakers. The unemployment rate is the statistic that measures the percentage of those people wanting to work who do not have jobs.

Every month the U.S. Bureau of Labor Statistics computes the unemployment rate and many other statistics that economists and policymakers use to

[3] For further discussion of these issues, see Matthew Shapiro and David Wilcox, "Mismeasurement in the Consumer Price Index: An Evaluation," *NBER Macroeconomics Annual*, 1996, and the symposium on "Measuring the CPI" in the Winter 1998 issue of *The Journal of Economic Perspectives*.

monitor developments in the labor market. These statistics come from a survey of about 60,000 households. Based on the responses to survey questions, each adult (16 years and older) in each household is placed into one of three categories: employed, unemployed, or not in the labor force. A person is employed if he or she spent most of the previous week working at a paid job, as opposed to keeping house, going to school, or doing something else. A person is un-

"Well, so long, Eddie. The recession's over."

employed if he or she is not employed and is waiting for the start date of a new job, is on temporary layoff, or has been looking for a job. A person who fits into neither of the first two categories, such as a student or retiree, is not in the labor force. A person who wants a job but has given up looking—a *discouraged worker*—is counted as not being in the labor force.

The **labor force** is defined as the sum of the employed and unemployed, and the **unemployment rate** is defined as the percentage of the labor force that is unemployed. That is,

$$\text{Labor Force} = \text{Number of Employed} + \text{Number of Unemployed},$$

and

$$\text{Unemployment Rate} = \frac{\text{Number of Unemployed}}{\text{Labor Force}} \times 100.$$

A related statistic is the **labor-force participation rate,** the percentage of the adult population that is in the labor force:

$$\text{Labor-Force Participation Rate} = \frac{\text{Labor Force}}{\text{Adult Population}} \times 100.$$

The Bureau of Labor Statistics computes these statistics for the overall population and for groups within the population: men and women, whites and blacks, teenagers and prime-age workers.

Figure 2-4 shows the breakdown of the population into the three categories for 1997. The statistics broke down as follows:

$$\text{Labor Force} = 129.6 + 6.7 = 136.3 \text{ million.}$$
$$\text{Unemployment Rate} = (6.7/136.3) \times 100 = 4.9\%.$$
$$\text{Labor-Force Participation Rate} = (136.3/203.1) \times 100 = 67.1\%.$$

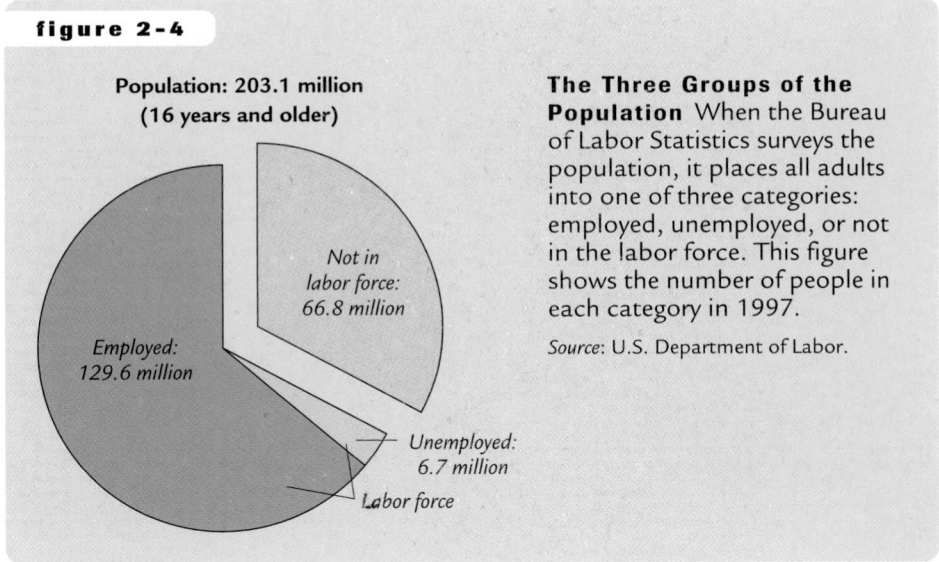

figure 2-4

Population: 203.1 million
(16 years and older)

Not in labor force: 66.8 million

Employed: 129.6 million

Unemployed: 6.7 million

Labor force

The Three Groups of the Population When the Bureau of Labor Statistics surveys the population, it places all adults into one of three categories: employed, unemployed, or not in the labor force. This figure shows the number of people in each category in 1997.

Source: U.S. Department of Labor.

Hence, about two-thirds of the adult population was in the labor force, and about 5 percent of those in the labor force did not have a job.

CASE STUDY

Unemployment, GDP, and Okun's Law

What relationship should we expect to find between unemployment and real GDP? Because employed workers help to produce goods and services and unemployed workers do not, increases in the unemployment rate should be associated with decreases in real GDP. This negative relationship between unemployment and GDP is called **Okun's law,** after Arthur Okun, the economist who first studied it.[4]

Figure 2-5 uses annual data for the United States to illustrate Okun's law. This figure is a scatterplot—a scatter of points where each point represents one observation (in this case, the data for a particular year). The horizontal axis represents the change in the unemployment rate from the previous year, and the vertical axis represents the percentage change in GDP. This figure shows clearly that year-to-year changes in the unemployment rate are closely associated with year-to-year changes in real GDP.

We can be more precise about the magnitude of the Okun's law relationship. The line drawn through the scatter of points (estimated with a statistical

[4] Arthur M. Okun, "Potential GNP: Its Measurement and Significance," in *Proceedings of the Business and Economics Statistics Section, American Statistical Association* (Washington, DC: American Statistical Association, 1962), 98–103; reprinted in Arthur M. Okun, *Economics for Policymaking* (Cambridge, MA: MIT Press, 1983), 145–158.

figure 2-5

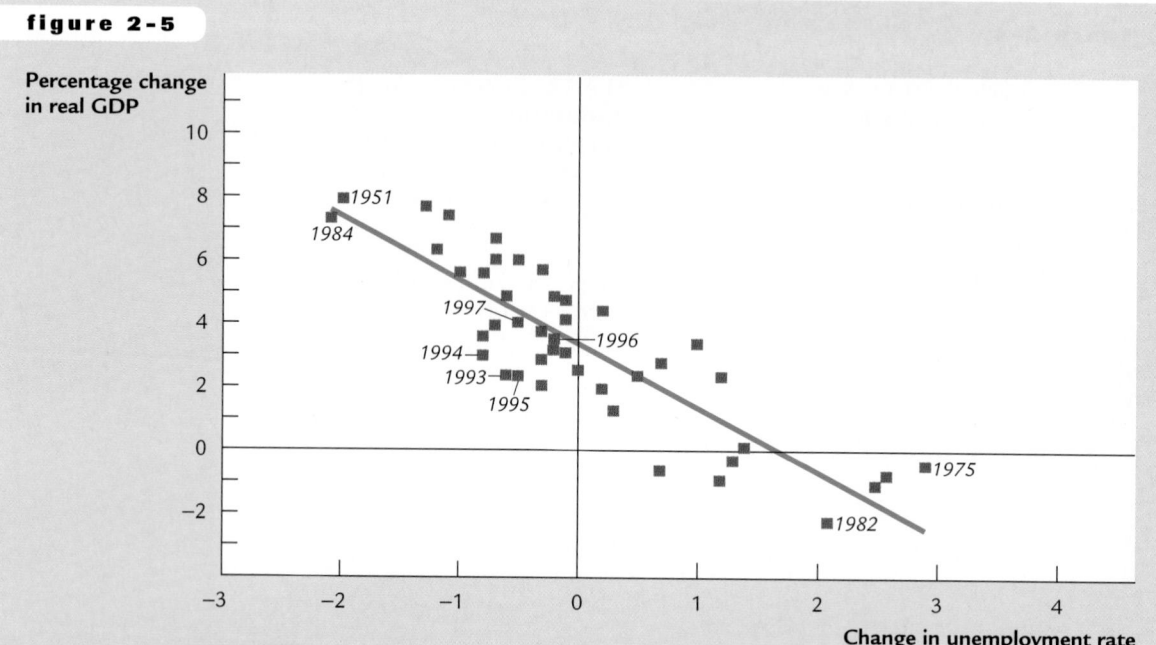

Okun's Law This figure is a scatterplot of the change in the unemployment rate on the horizontal axis and the percentage change in real GDP on the vertical axis, using data on the U.S. economy. Each point represents one year. The negative correlation between these variables shows that increases in unemployment tend to be associated with lower-than-normal growth in real GDP.

Source: U.S. Department of Commerce, U.S. Department of Labor.

procedure called ordinary least squares) tells us that

> Percentage Change in Real GDP
>
> = 3% − 2 × Change in the Unemployment Rate.

If the unemployment rate remains the same, real GDP grows by about 3 percent; this normal growth is due to population growth, capital accumulation, and technological progress. In addition, for every percentage point the unemployment rate rises, real GDP growth typically falls by 2 percent. Hence, if the unemployment rate rises from 6 to 8 percent, then real GDP growth would be

> Percentage Change in Real GDP = 3% − 2 × (8% − 6%)
>
> = −1%.

In this case, Okun's law says that GDP would fall by 1 percent, indicating that the economy is in a recession.

2-4 | Conclusion: From Economic Statistics to Economic Models

The three statistics discussed in this chapter—gross domestic product, the consumer price index, and the unemployment rate—quantify the performance of the economy. Public and private decisionmakers use these statistics to monitor changes in the economy and to formulate appropriate policies. Economists use these statistics to develop and test theories about how the economy works.

In the chapters that follow, we examine some of these theories. That is, we build models that explain how these variables are determined and how economic policy affects them. Chapters 3, 4, and 5 study models of GDP, Chapter 6 studies unemployment, and Chapter 7 studies inflation. Having learned how to measure economic performance, we now learn how to explain it.

Summary

1. Gross domestic product (GDP) measures both the income of everyone in the economy and the total expenditure on the economy's output of goods and services.

2. Nominal GDP values goods and services at current prices. Real GDP values goods and services at constant prices. Real GDP rises only when the amount of goods and services has increased, whereas nominal GDP can rise either because output has increased or because prices have increased.

3. GDP is the sum of four categories of expenditure: consumption, investment, government purchases, and net exports.

4. The consumer price index (CPI) measures the price of a fixed basket of goods and services purchased by a typical consumer. Like the GDP deflator, which is the ratio of nominal GDP to real GDP, the CPI measures the overall level of prices.

5. The unemployment rate shows what fraction of those who would like to work do not have a job. When the unemployment rate rises, real GDP typically grows slower than its normal rate and may even fall.

KEY CONCEPTS |

Gross domestic product (GDP)	GDP deflator	Consumer price index (CPI)
National income accounting	National income accounts identity	Labor force
Stocks and flows	Consumption	Unemployment rate
Value added	Investment	Labor-force participation rate
Imputed value	Government purchases	Okun's law
Nominal versus real GDP	Net exports	

QUESTIONS FOR REVIEW

1. List the two things that GDP measures. How can GDP measure two things at once?

2. What does the consumer price index measure?

3. List the three categories used by the Bureau of Labor Statistics to classify everyone in the economy. How does the Bureau compute the unemployment rate?

4. Explain Okun's law.

PROBLEMS AND APPLICATIONS

1. Look at the newspapers for the past few days. What new economic statistics have been released? How do you interpret these statistics?

2. A farmer grows a bushel of wheat and sells it to a miller for $1.00. The miller turns the wheat into flour and then sells the flour to a baker for $3.00. The baker uses the flour to make bread and sells the bread to an engineer for $6.00. The engineer eats the bread. What is the value added by each person? What is GDP?

3. Suppose that a woman marries her butler. After they are married, her husband continues to wait on her as before, and she continues to support him as before (but as a husband rather than as an employee). How does the marriage affect GDP? How should it affect GDP?

4. Place each of the following transactions in one of the four components of expenditure: consumption, investment, government purchases, and net exports.

   a. Boeing sells an airplane to the Air Force.

   b. Boeing sells an airplane to American Airlines.

   c. Boeing sells an airplane to Air France.

   d. Boeing sells an airplane to Amelia Earhart.

   e. Boeing builds an airplane to be sold next year.

5. Find data on GDP and its components, and compute the percentage of GDP for the following components for 1950, 1970, and 1990.

   a. Personal consumption expenditures

   b. Gross private domestic investment

   c. Government purchases

   d. Net exports

   e. National defense purchases

   f. State and local purchases

   g. Imports

   Do you see any stable relationships in the data? Do you see any trends? (*Hint:* A good place to look for data is the statistical appendices of the *Economic Report of the President*, which is written each year by the Council of Economic Advisers. Alternatively, you can go over the internet to www.bea.doc.gov, which is the website of the Bureau of Economic Analysis.)

6. Consider an economy that produces and consumes bread and automobiles. In the table below are data for two different years.

	Year 2000	Year 2010
Price of an automobile	$50,000	$60,000
Price of a loaf of bread	$10	$20
Number of automobiles produced	100	120
Number of loaves of bread produced	500,000	400,000

   a. Using the year 2000 as the base year, compute the following statistics for each year: nominal GDP, real GDP, the implicit price deflator for GDP, and a fixed-weight price index such as the CPI.

   b. How much have prices risen between year 2000 and year 2010? Compare the answers given by the Laspeyres and Paasche price indices. Explain the difference.

   c. Suppose you are a senator writing a bill to index Social Security and federal pensions.

That is, your bill will adjust these benefits to offset changes in the cost of living. Will you use the GDP deflator or the CPI? Why?

7. Abby consumes only apples. In year 1, red apples cost $1 each, green apples cost $2 each, and Abby buys 10 red apples. In year 2, red apples cost $2, green apples cost $1, and Abby buys 10 green apples.

   a. Compute a consumer price index for apples for each year. Assume that year 1 is the base year in which the consumer basket is fixed. How does your index change from year 1 to year 2?

   b. Compute Abby's nominal spending on apples in each year. How does it change from year 1 to year 2?

   c. Using year 1 as the base year, compute Abby's real spending on apples in each year. How does it change from year 1 to year 2?

   d. Defining the implicit price deflator as nominal spending divided by real spending, compute the deflator for each year. How does the deflator change from year 1 to year 2?

   e. Suppose that Abby is equally happy eating red or green apples. How much has the true cost of living increased for Abby? Compare this answer to your answers to parts (a) and (d). What does this example tell you about Laspeyres and Paasche price indices?

8. Consider how each of the following events is likely to affect real GDP. Do you think the change in real GDP reflects a similar change in economic well-being?

   a. A hurricane in Florida forces Disney World to shut down for a month.

   b. The discovery of a new, easy-to-grow strain of wheat increases farm harvests.

   c. Increased hostility between unions and management sparks a rash of strikes.

   d. Firms throughout the economy experience falling demand, causing them to lay off workers.

   e. Congress passes new environmental laws that prohibit firms from using production methods that emit large quantities of pollution.

   f. More high-school students drop out of school to take jobs mowing lawns.

   g. Fathers around the country reduce their workweeks to spend more time with their children.

9. In a speech that Senator Robert Kennedy gave when he was running for president in 1968, he said the following about GDP:

   [It] does not allow for the health of our children, the quality of their education, or the joy of their play. It does not include the beauty of our poetry or the strength of our marriages, the intelligence of our public debate or the integrity of our public officials. It measures neither our courage, nor our wisdom, nor our devotion to our country. It measures everything, in short, except that which makes life worthwhile, and it can tell us everything about America except why we are proud that we are Americans.

   Was Robert Kennedy right? If so, why do we care about GDP?

part TWO

The Economy in the Long Run

Economists use the variables introduced in Chapter 2 — GDP, inflation, and unemployment — to compare economic performance from year to year and from country to country. Measuring performance, however, is only the first step. The second and more significant step is to explain economic performance and, perhaps, to improve it. To do this, we need models that shed light on the behavior of the economy, the relationships among variables, and the effects of public policy. Developing those models is our primary task in the rest of this book.

In this part of the book we examine classical *models of the economy. The key assumption of classical models is that prices are flexible. Most economists agree that this assumption describes how the economy behaves in the long run.*

Chapter 3 builds the most basic classical model, which provides the foundation for many of the models in later chapters. It discusses how much the economy produces, who gets the income from production, and how the economy's resources are allocated among alternative uses.

Whereas Chapter 3 assumes that capital, labor, and technology are fixed, Chapters 4, 5, and 6 look at these more closely. Chapter 4 develops a model of economic growth with which we can discuss the very long run over which the economy's stock of capital can change. Chapter 5 extends this model to incorporate the effects of technological progress. Chapter 6 examines the labor market to explain what determines the natural rate of unemployment.

The next two chapters expand the analysis. Chapter 7 introduces the classical theory of money and inflation. Chapter 8 extends the classical model to describe open economies, which export, import, and borrow and lend in world financial markets.

National Income: Where It Comes From and Where It Goes

A large income is the best recipe for happiness I ever heard of.

—*Jane Austen*

The most important macroeconomic variable is gross domestic product (GDP). As we have seen, GDP measures both a nation's total output of goods and services and its total income. To appreciate the significance of GDP, one needs only to take a quick look at international data: compared with their poorer counterparts, nations with a high level of GDP per person have everything from better childhood nutrition to more televisions per household. A large GDP does not ensure that all of a nation's citizens are happy, but it is surely the best recipe for happiness that macroeconomists have to offer.

This chapter addresses four groups of questions about the sources and uses of a nation's GDP:

> ➤ How much do the firms in the economy produce? What determines a nation's total income?

> ➤ Who gets the income from production? How much goes to compensate workers and how much goes to compensate owners of capital?

> ➤ Who buys the output of the economy? How much do households purchase for consumption, how much do households and firms purchase for investment, and how much does the government buy for public purposes?

> ➤ What equilibrates the demand for and supply of goods and services? What ensures that desired spending on consumption, investment, and government purchases equals the level of production?

To answer these questions, we must examine how the various parts of the economy interact.

A good place to start is the circular flow diagram. In Chapter 2 we traced the circular flow of dollars in a hypothetical economy that produced one product, bread, from labor services. Figure 3-1 more accurately reflects how real economies function. It shows the linkages among the economic actors—

figure 3-1

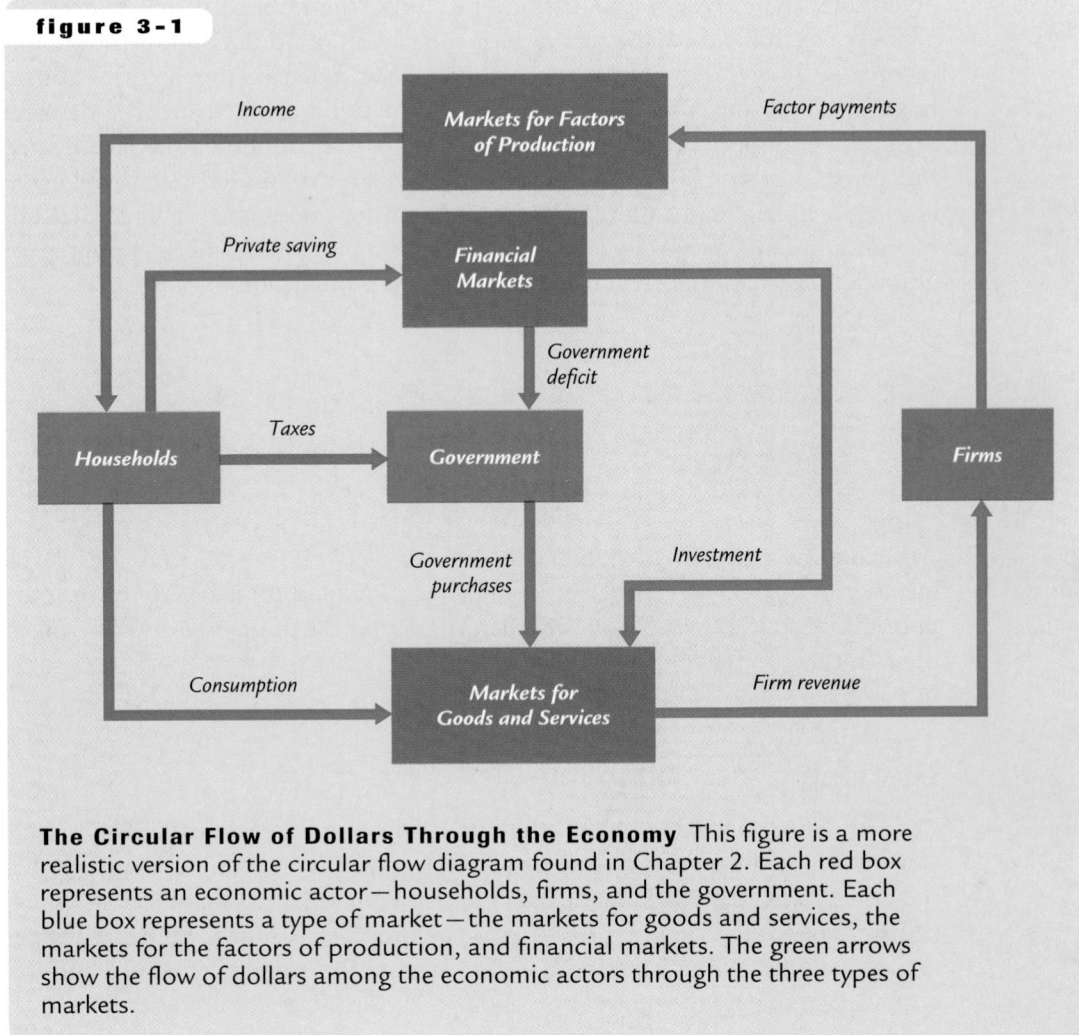

The Circular Flow of Dollars Through the Economy This figure is a more realistic version of the circular flow diagram found in Chapter 2. Each red box represents an economic actor—households, firms, and the government. Each blue box represents a type of market—the markets for goods and services, the markets for the factors of production, and financial markets. The green arrows show the flow of dollars among the economic actors through the three types of markets.

households, firms, and the government—and how dollars flow among them through the various markets in the economy.

Let's look at the flow of dollars from the viewpoints of these economic actors. Households receive income and use it to pay taxes to the government, to consume goods and services, and to save through the financial markets. Firms receive revenue from the sale of goods and services and use it to pay for the factors of production. Both households and firms borrow in financial markets to buy investment goods, such as housing, plant, and equipment. The government receives revenue from taxes, uses it to pay for government purchases, and, if it spends more than it receives, borrows in the financial markets to cover the deficit.

In this chapter we develop a basic classical model to explain the economic interactions depicted in Figure 3-1. We begin with firms and look at what determines their level of production (and, thus, the level of national income). Then we examine how the markets for the factors of production distribute this income to households. Next, we consider how much of this income households consume and how much they save. In addition to discussing the demand for goods and services arising from the consumption of households, we discuss the demand arising from investment and government purchases. Finally, we come full circle and examine how the demand for goods and services (the sum of consumption, investment, and government purchases) and the supply of goods and services (the level of production) are brought into balance.

3-1 | What Determines the Total Production of Goods and Services?

An economy's output of goods and services—its GDP—depends on (1) its quantity of inputs, called the factors of production, and (2) its ability to turn inputs into output, as represented by the production function. We discuss each of these in turn.

The Factors of Production

Factors of production are the inputs used to produce goods and services. The two most important factors of production are capital and labor. Capital is the set of tools that workers use: the construction worker's crane, the accountant's calculator, and this author's personal computer. Labor is the time people spend working. We use the symbol K to denote the amount of capital and the symbol L to denote the amount of labor.

In this chapter we take the economy's factors of production as given. In other words, we assume that the economy has a fixed amount of capital and a fixed amount of labor. We write

$$K = \overline{K}.$$
$$L = \overline{L}.$$

The overbar means that each variable is fixed at some level. In Chapter 4 we examine what happens when the factors of production change over time, as they do in the real world. For now, to keep our analysis simple, we assume fixed amounts of capital and labor.

We also assume here that the factors of production are fully utilized—that is, that no resources are wasted. Again, in the real world, part of the labor force is unemployed, and some capital lies idle. In Chapter 6 we examine the reasons for unemployment, but for now we assume that capital and labor are fully employed.

The Production Function

The available production technology determines how much output is produced from given amounts of capital and labor. Economists express the available technology using a **production function.** Letting Y denote the amount of output, we write the production function as

$$Y = F(K, L).$$

This equation states that output is a function of the amount of capital and the amount of labor.

The production function reflects the available technology for turning capital and labor into output. If someone invents a better way to produce a good, the result is more output from the same amounts of capital and labor. Thus, technological change alters the production function.

Many production functions have a property called **constant returns to scale.** A production function has constant returns to scale if an increase of an equal percentage in all factors of production causes an increase in output of the same percentage. If the production function has constant returns to scale, then we get 10 percent more output when we increase both capital and labor by 10 percent. Mathematically, a production function has constant returns to scale if

$$zY = F(zK, zL)$$

for any positive number z. This equation says that if we multiply both the amount of capital and the amount of labor by some number z, output is also multiplied by z. In the next section we see that the assumption of constant returns to scale has an important implication for how the income from production is distributed.

As an example of a production function, consider production at a bakery. The kitchen and its equipment are the bakery's capital, the workers hired to make the bread are its labor, and the loaves of bread are its output. The bakery's production function shows that the number of loaves produced depends on the amount of equipment and the number of workers. If the production function has constant returns to scale, then doubling the amount of equipment and the number of workers doubles the amount of bread produced.

The Supply of Goods and Services

We can now see that the factors of production and the production function together determine the quantity of goods and services supplied, which in turn equals the economy's output. To express this mathematically, we write

$$Y = F(\overline{K}, \overline{L})$$
$$= \overline{Y}.$$

In this chapter, because we assume that the supplies of capital and labor and the technology are fixed, output is also fixed (at a level denoted here as $\overline{Y}$). When we discuss economic growth in Chapters 4 and 5, we will examine how increases in capital and labor and improvements in the production technology lead to growth in the economy's output.

3-2 | How Is National Income Distributed to the Factors of Production?

As we discussed in Chapter 2, the total output of an economy equals its total income. Because the factors of production and the production function together determine the total output of goods and services, they also determine national income. The circular flow diagram in Figure 3-1 shows that this national income flows from firms to households through the markets for the factors of production.

In this section we continue developing our model of the economy by discussing how these factor markets work. Economists have long studied factor markets to understand the distribution of income. (For example, Karl Marx, the noted nineteenth-century economist, spent much time trying to explain the incomes of capital and labor. The political philosophy of communism was in part based on Marx's now-discredited theory.) Here we examine the modern theory of how national income is divided among the factors of production. This theory, called the *neoclassical theory of distribution*, is accepted by most economists today.

Factor Prices

The distribution of national income is determined by factor prices. **Factor prices** are the amounts paid to the factors of production—the wage workers earn and the rent the owners of capital collect. As Figure 3-2 illustrates, the price each factor of production receives for its services is in turn determined by the supply and demand for that factor. Because we have assumed that the economy's factors of production are fixed, the factor supply curve in Figure 3-2 is vertical. The intersection of the downward-sloping factor demand curve and the vertical supply curve determines the equilibrium factor price.

To understand factor prices and the distribution of income, we must examine the demand for the factors of production. Because factor demand arises from the thousands of firms that use capital and labor, we now look at the decisions faced by a typical firm about how much of these factors to employ.

The Decisions Facing the Competitive Firm

The simplest assumption to make about a typical firm is that it is **competitive.** A competitive firm is small relative to the markets in which it trades, so it has little influence on market prices. For example, our firm produces a good and

figure 3-2

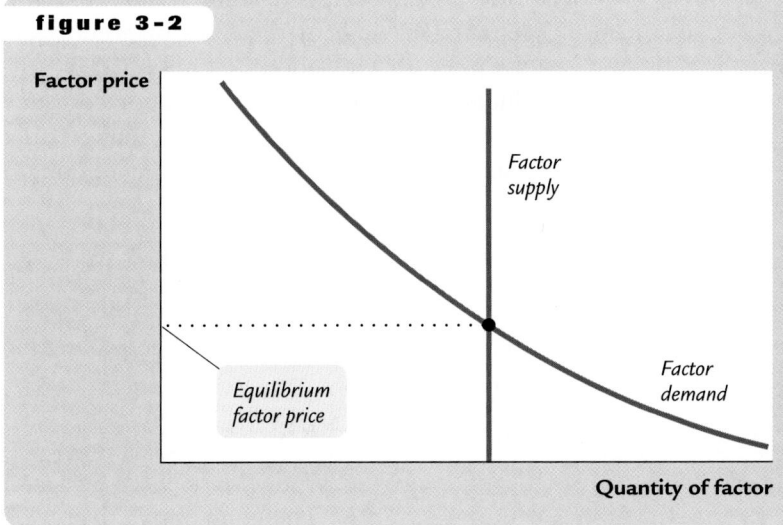

Factor price

Factor supply

Equilibrium factor price

Factor demand

Quantity of factor

How a Factor of Production Is Compensated The price paid to any factor of production depends on the supply and demand for that factor's services. Because we have assumed that supply is fixed, the supply curve is vertical. The demand curve is downward sloping. The intersection of supply and demand determines the equilibrium factor price.

sells it at the market price. Because many firms produce this good, our firm can sell as much as it wants without causing the price of the good to fall, or it can stop selling altogether without causing the price of the good to rise. Similarly, our firm cannot influence the wages of the workers it employs because many other local firms also employ workers. The firm has no reason to pay more than the market wage, and if it tried to pay less, its workers would take jobs elsewhere. Therefore, the competitive firm takes the prices of its output and its inputs as given.

To make its product, the firm needs two factors of production, capital and labor. As we did for the aggregate economy, we represent the firm's production technology by the production function

$$Y = F(K, L),$$

where Y is the number of units produced (the firm's output), K the number of machines used (the amount of capital), and L the number of hours worked by the firm's employees (the amount of labor). The firm produces more output if it has more machines or if its employees work more hours.

The firm sells its output at a price P, hires workers at a wage W, and rents capital at a rate R. Notice that when we speak of firms renting capital, we are assuming that households own the economy's stock of capital. In this analysis, households rent out their capital, just as they sell their labor. The firm obtains both factors of production from the households that own them.[1]

---

[1] This is a simplification. In the real world, the ownership of capital is indirect because firms own capital and households own the firms. That is, real firms have two functions: owning capital and producing output. To help us understand how the factors of production are compensated, however, we assume that firms only produce output and that households own capital directly.

The goal of the firm is to maximize profit. *Profit* is revenue minus costs—it is what the owners of the firm keep after paying for the costs of production. Revenue equals $P \times Y$, the selling price of the good P multiplied by the amount of the good the firm produces Y. Costs include both labor costs and capital costs. Labor costs equal $W \times L$, the wage W times the amount of labor L. Capital costs equal $R \times K$, the rental price of capital R times the amount of capital K. We can write

$$\text{Profit} = \text{Revenue} - \text{Labor Costs} - \text{Capital Costs}$$
$$= PY - WL - RK.$$

To see how profit depends on the factors of production, we use the production function $Y = F(K, L)$ to substitute for Y to obtain

$$\text{Profit} = PF(K, L) - WL - RK.$$

This equation shows that profit depends on the product price P, the factor prices W and R, and the factor quantities L and K. The competitive firm takes the product price and the factor prices as given and chooses the amounts of labor and capital that maximize profit.

The Firm's Demand for Factors

We now know that our firm will hire labor and rent capital in the quantities that maximize profit. But how does it figure out what those profit-maximizing quantities are? To answer this question, we first consider the quantity of labor and then the quantity of capital.

The Marginal Product of Labor The more labor the firm employs, the more output it produces. The **marginal product of labor (MPL)** is the extra amount of output the firm gets from one extra unit of labor, holding the amount of capital fixed. We can express this using the production function:

$$MPL = F(K, L + 1) - F(K, L).$$

The first term on the right-hand side is the amount of output produced with K units of capital and $L + 1$ units of labor; the second term is the amount of output produced with K units of capital and L units of labor. This equation states that the marginal product of labor is the difference between the amount of output produced with $L + 1$ units of labor and the amount produced with only L units of labor.

Most production functions have the property of **diminishing marginal product:** holding the amount of capital fixed, the marginal product of labor decreases as the amount of labor increases. For example, consider again the production of bread at a bakery. As a bakery hires more labor, it produces more bread. The *MPL* is the amount of extra bread produced when an extra unit of labor is hired. As more labor is added to a fixed amount of capital, however, the *MPL* falls. Fewer additional loaves are produced because workers are less productive when the kitchen is more crowded. In other words, holding the size of the kitchen fixed, each additional worker adds fewer loaves of bread to the bakery's output.

Figure 3-3 graphs the production function. It illustrates what happens to the amount of output when we hold the amount of capital constant and vary the amount of labor. This figure shows that the marginal product of labor is the slope of the production function. As the amount of labor increases, the production function becomes flatter, indicating diminishing marginal product.

From the Marginal Product of Labor to Labor Demand When the competitive, profit-maximizing firm is deciding whether to hire an additional unit of labor, it considers how that decision would affect profits. It therefore compares the extra revenue from the increased production that results from the added labor to the extra cost of higher spending on wages. The increase in revenue from

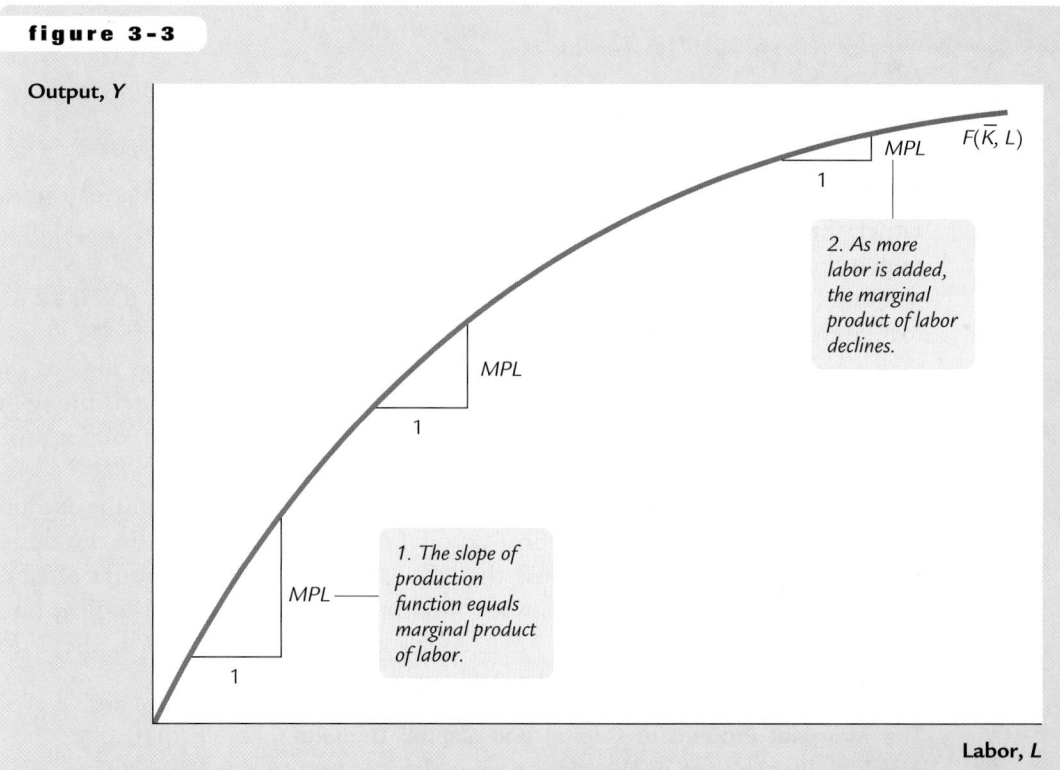

figure 3-3

Output, *Y*

MPL

$F(\overline{K}, L)$

1

2. As more labor is added, the marginal product of labor declines.

MPL

1

1. The slope of production function equals marginal product of labor.

MPL

1

Labor, *L*

The Production Function This curve shows how output depends on labor input, holding the amount of capital constant. The marginal product of labor *MPL* is the change in output when the labor input is increased by 1 unit. As the amount of labor increases, the production function becomes flatter, indicating diminishing marginal product.

an additional unit of labor depends on two variables: the marginal product of labor and the price of the output. Because an extra unit of labor produces *MPL* units of output and each unit of output sells for *P* dollars, the extra revenue is $P \times MPL$. The extra cost of hiring one more unit of labor is the wage *W*. Thus, the change in profit from hiring an additional unit of labor is

$$\Delta\text{Profit} = \Delta\text{Revenue} - \Delta\text{Cost}$$
$$= (P \times MPL) - W.$$

The symbol Δ (called *delta*) denotes the change in a variable.

We can now answer the question we asked at the beginning of this section: How much labor does the firm hire? The firm's manager knows that if the extra revenue $P \times MPL$ exceeds the wage *W*, an extra unit of labor increases profit. Therefore, the manager continues to hire labor until the next unit would no longer be profitable—that is, until the *MPL* falls to the point where the extra revenue equals the wage. The firm's demand for labor is determined by

$$P \times MPL = W.$$

We can also write this as

$$MPL = W/P.$$

W/P is the **real wage**—the payment to labor measured in units of output rather than in dollars. To maximize profit, the firm hires up to the point at which the marginal product of labor equals the real wage.

For example, again consider a bakery. Suppose the price of bread *P* is $2 per loaf, and a worker earns a wage *W* of $20 per hour. The real wage W/P is 10 loaves per hour. In this example, the firm keeps hiring workers as long as the additional worker would produce at least 10 loaves per hour. When the *MPL* falls to 10 loaves per hour or less, hiring additional workers is no longer profitable.

Figure 3-4 shows how the marginal product of labor depends on the amount of labor employed (holding the firm's capital stock constant). That is, this figure graphs the *MPL* schedule. Because the *MPL* diminishes as the amount of labor increases, this curve slopes downward. For any given real wage, the firm hires up to the point at which the *MPL* equals the real wage. Hence, the *MPL* schedule is also the firm's labor demand curve.

The Marginal Product of Capital and Capital Demand The firm decides how much capital to rent in the same way it decides how much labor to hire. The **marginal product of capital (MPK)** is the amount of extra output the firm gets from an extra unit of capital, holding the amount of labor constant:

$$MPK = F(K + 1, L) - F(K, L).$$

Thus, the marginal product of capital is the difference between the amount of output produced with $K + 1$ units of capital and that produced with only K units of capital. Like labor, capital is subject to diminishing marginal product.

figure 3-4

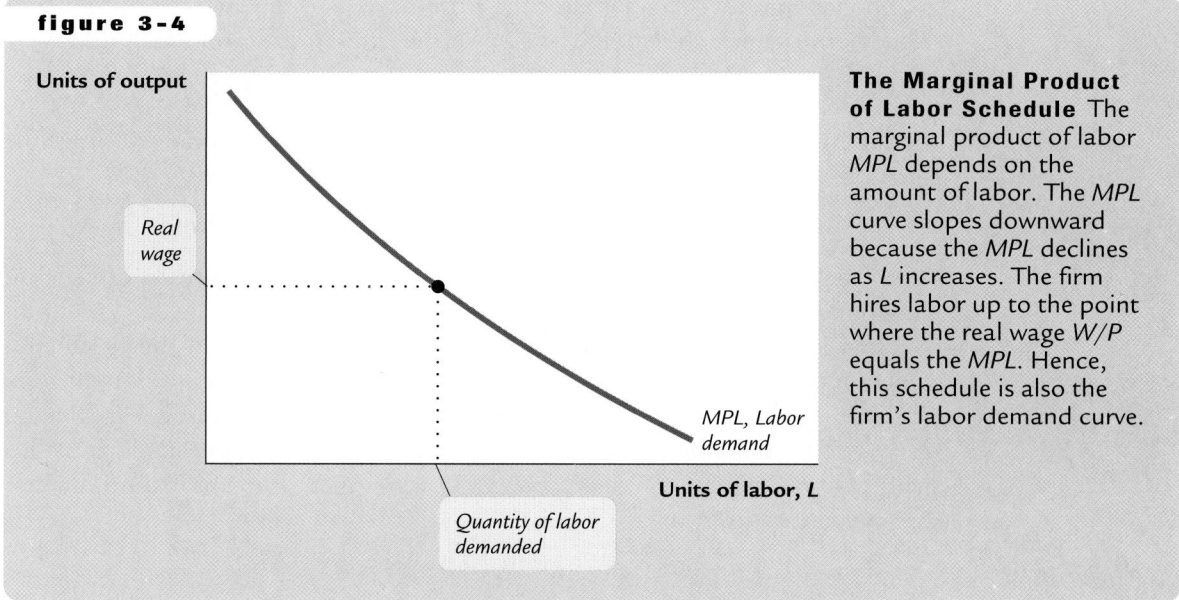

Units of output

Real wage

MPL, Labor demand

Units of labor, L

Quantity of labor demanded

The Marginal Product of Labor Schedule The marginal product of labor *MPL* depends on the amount of labor. The *MPL* curve slopes downward because the *MPL* declines as *L* increases. The firm hires labor up to the point where the real wage *W/P* equals the *MPL*. Hence, this schedule is also the firm's labor demand curve.

The increase in profit from renting an additional machine is the extra revenue from selling the output of that machine minus the machine's rental price:

$$\Delta \text{Profit} = \Delta \text{Revenue} - \Delta \text{Cost}$$
$$= (P \times MPK) - R.$$

To maximize profit, the firm continues to rent more capital until the *MPK* falls to equal the real rental price:

$$MPK = R/P.$$

The **real rental price of capital** is the rental price measured in units of goods rather than in dollars.

To sum up, the competitive, profit-maximizing firm follows a simple rule about how much labor to hire and how much capital to rent. *The firm demands each factor of production until that factor's marginal product falls to equal its real factor price.*

The Division of National Income

Having analyzed how a firm decides how much of each factor to employ, we can now explain how the markets for the factors of production distribute the economy's total income. If all firms in the economy are competitive and profit-maximizing, then each factor of production is paid its marginal contribution to the production process. The real wage paid to each worker equals the *MPL*, and the real rental price paid to each owner of capital equals the *MPK*. The total real wages paid to labor are therefore *MPL* × *L*, and the total real return paid to capital owners is *MPK* × *K*.

The income that remains after the firms have paid the factors of production is the **economic profit** of the owners of the firms. Real economic profit is

$$\text{Economic Profit} = Y - (MPL \times L) - (MPK \times K).$$

Because we want to examine the distribution of national income, we rearrange the terms as follows:

$$Y = (MPL \times L) + (MPK \times K) + \text{Economic Profit}.$$

Total income is divided among the return to labor, the return to capital, and economic profit.

How large is economic profit? The answer is surprising: if the production function has the property of constant returns to scale, as is often thought to be the case, then economic profit must be zero. That is, nothing is left after the factors of production are paid. This conclusion follows from a famous mathematical result called *Euler's theorem*,[2] which states that if the production function has constant returns to scale, then

$$F(K, L) = (MPK \times K) + (MPL \times L).$$

If each factor of production is paid its marginal product, then the sum of these factor payments equals total output. In other words, constant returns to scale, profit maximization, and competition together imply that economic profit is zero.

If economic profit is zero, how can we explain the existence of "profit" in the economy? The answer is that the term "profit" as normally used is different from economic profit. We have been assuming that there are three types of agents: workers, owners of capital, and owners of firms. Total income is divided among wages, return to capital, and economic profit. In the real world, however, most firms own rather than rent the capital they use. Because firm owners and capital owners are the same people, economic profit and the return to capital are often lumped together. If we call this alternative definition **accounting profit,** we can say that

$$\text{Accounting Profit} = \text{Economic Profit} + (MPK \times K).$$

Under our assumptions—constant returns to scale, profit maximization, and competition—economic profit is zero. If these assumptions approximately describe the world, then the "profit" in the national income accounts must be mostly the return to capital.

We can now answer the question posed at the beginning of this chapter about how the income of the economy is distributed from firms to households. Each factor of production is paid its marginal product, and these factor payments exhaust total output. *Total output is divided between the payments to capital and the payments to labor, depending on their marginal productivities.*

---

[2] *Mathematical note:* To prove Euler's theorem, begin with the definition of constant returns to scale: $zY = F(zK, zL)$. Now differentiate with respect to z and then evaluate at $z = 1$.

CASE STUDY

The Black Death and Factor Prices

As we have just learned, in the neoclassical theory of distribution, factor prices equal the marginal products of the factors of production. Because the marginal products depend on the quantities of the factors, a change in the quantity of any one factor alters the marginal products of all the factors. Therefore, a change in the supply of a factor alters equilibrium factor prices.

Fourteenth-century Europe provides a vivid example of how factor quantities affect factor prices. The outbreak of the bubonic plague—the Black Death—in 1348 reduced the population of Europe by about one-third within a few years. Because the marginal product of labor increases as the amount of labor falls, this massive reduction in the labor force raised the marginal product of labor. (The economy moved to the left along the curves in Figures 3-3 and 3-4.) Real wages did increase substantially during the plague years—doubling, by some estimates. The peasants who were fortunate enough to survive the plague enjoyed economic prosperity.

The reduction in the labor force caused by the plague also affected the return to land, the other major factor of production in medieval Europe. With fewer workers available to farm the land, an additional unit of land produced less additional output. This fall in the marginal product of land led to a decline in real rents of 50 percent or more. Thus, while the peasant classes prospered, the landed classes suffered reduced incomes.[3]

3-3 | What Determines the Demand for Goods and Services?

We have seen what determines the level of production and how the income from production is distributed to workers and owners of capital. We now continue our tour of the circular flow diagram, Figure 3-1, and examine how the output from production is used.

In Chapter 2 we identified the four components of GDP:

➤ Consumption (*C*)

➤ Investment (*I*)

➤ Government purchases (*G*)

➤ Net exports (*NX*).

---

[3] Carlo M. Cipolla, *Before the Industrial Revolution: European Society and Economy, 1000–1700,* 2d ed. (New York: Norton, 1980), 200–202.

The circular flow diagram contains only the first three components. For now, to simplify the analysis, we assume a *closed economy*—a country that does not trade with other countries. Thus, net exports are always zero. (We examine the macroeconomics of *open economies* in Chapter 8.)

A closed economy has three uses for the goods and services it produces. These three components of GDP are expressed in the national income accounts identity:

$$Y = C + I + G.$$

Households consume some of the economy's output; firms and households use some of the output for investment; and the government buys some of the output for public purposes. We want to see how GDP is allocated among these three uses.

Consumption

When we eat food, wear clothing, or go to a movie, we are consuming some of the output of the economy. All forms of consumption together make up two-thirds of GDP. Because consumption is so large, macroeconomists have devoted much energy to studying how households decide how much to consume. Chapter 16 examines this work in detail. Here we consider the simplest story of consumer behavior.

Households receive income from their labor and their ownership of capital, pay taxes to the government, and then decide how much of their after-tax income to consume and how much to save. As we discussed in Section 3-2, the income that households receive equals the output of the economy Y. The government then taxes households an amount T. (Although the government imposes many kinds of taxes, such as personal and corporate income taxes and sales taxes, for our purposes we can lump all these taxes together.) We define income after the payment of all taxes, $Y - T$, as **disposable income.** Households divide their disposable income between consumption and saving.

We assume that the level of consumption depends directly on the level of disposable income. The higher is disposable income, the greater is consumption. Thus,

$$C = C(Y - T).$$

This equation states that consumption is a function of disposable income. The relationship between consumption and disposable income is called the **consumption function.**

The **marginal propensity to consume (MPC)** is the amount by which consumption changes when disposable income increases by one dollar. The MPC is between zero and one: an extra dollar of income increases consumption, but by less than one dollar. Thus, if households obtain an extra dollar of income, they save a portion of it. For example, if the MPC is 0.7, then households spend 70 cents of each additional dollar of disposable income on consumer goods and services and save 30 cents.

figure 3-5

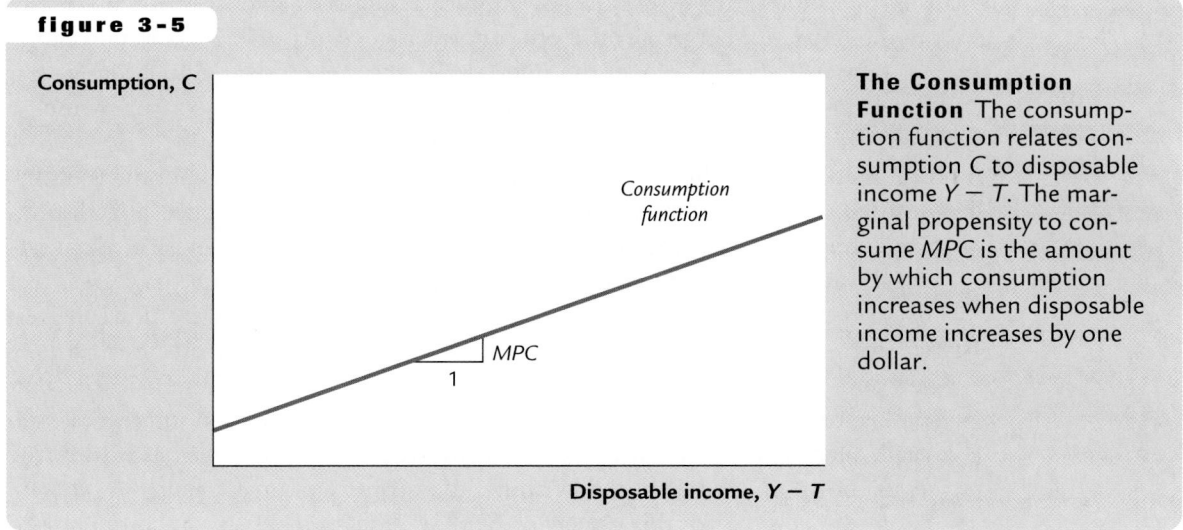

The Consumption Function The consumption function relates consumption C to disposable income $Y - T$. The marginal propensity to consume MPC is the amount by which consumption increases when disposable income increases by one dollar.

Figure 3-5 illustrates the consumption function. The slope of the consumption function tells us how much consumption increases when disposable income increases by one dollar. That is, the slope of the consumption function is the *MPC*.

Investment

Both firms and households purchase investment goods. Firms buy investment goods to add to their stock of capital and to replace existing capital as it wears out. Households buy new houses, which are also part of investment. Total investment in the United States averages about 15 percent of GDP.

The quantity of investment goods demanded depends on the interest rate, which measures the cost of the funds used to finance investment. For an investment project to be profitable, its return (the revenue from increased future production of goods and services) must exceed its cost (the payments for borrowed funds). If the interest rate rises, fewer investment projects are profitable, and the quantity of investment goods demanded falls.

For example, suppose that a firm is considering whether it should build a $1 million factory that would yield a return of $100,000 per year, or 10 percent. The firm compares this return to the cost of borrowing the $1 million. If the interest rate is below 10 percent, the firm borrows the money in financial markets and makes the investment. If the interest rate is above 10 percent, the firm forgoes the investment opportunity and does not build the factory.

The firm makes the same investment decision even if it does not have to borrow the $1 million but rather uses its own funds. The firm can always deposit this money in a bank or a money market fund and earn interest on it. Building the factory is more profitable than the deposit if and only if the interest rate is less than the 10 percent return on the factory.

A person wanting to buy a new house faces a similar decision. The higher the interest rate, the greater the cost of carrying a mortgage. A $100,000 mortgage costs $8,000 per year if the interest rate is 8 percent and $10,000 per year if the interest rate is 10 percent. As the interest rate rises, the cost of owning a home rises, and the demand for new homes falls.

When studying the role of interest rates in the economy, economists distinguish between the nominal interest rate and the real interest rate. This distinction is relevant when the overall level of prices is changing. The **nominal interest rate** is the interest rate as usually reported: it is the rate of interest that investors pay to borrow money. The **real interest rate** is the nominal interest rate corrected for the effects of inflation. If the nominal interest rate is 8 percent and the inflation rate is 3 percent, then the real interest rate is 5 percent. In Chapter 7 we discuss the relation between nominal and real interest rates in detail. Here it is sufficient to note that the real interest rate measures the true cost of borrowing and, thus, determines the quantity of investment.

We can summarize this discussion with an equation relating investment I to the real interest rate r:

$$I = I(r).$$

Figure 3-6 shows this investment function. It slopes downward, because as the interest rate rises, the quantity of investment demanded falls.

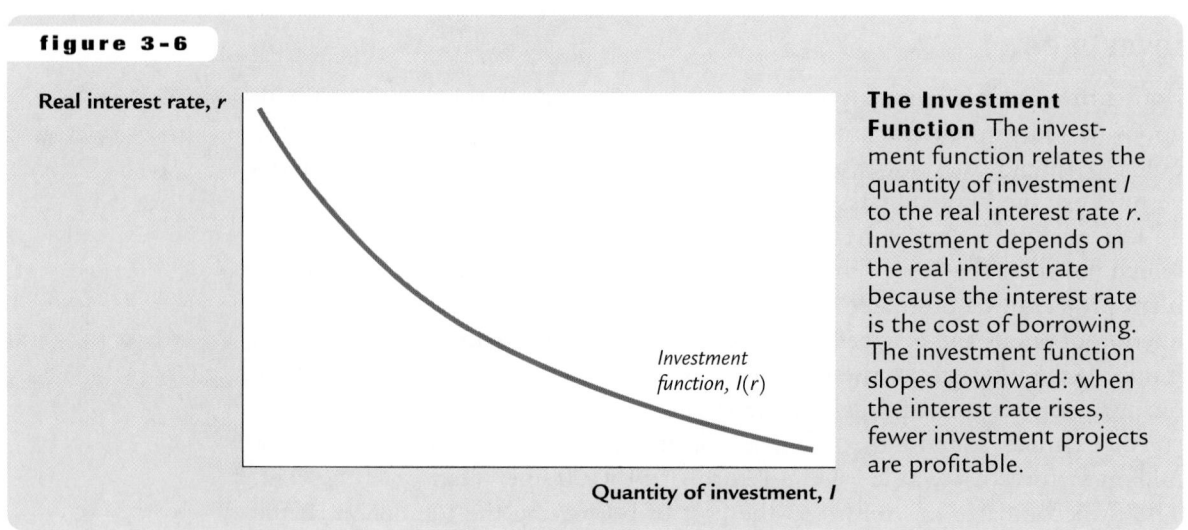

figure 3-6

Real interest rate, r

Investment function, $I(r)$

Quantity of investment, I

The Investment Function The investment function relates the quantity of investment I to the real interest rate r. Investment depends on the real interest rate because the interest rate is the cost of borrowing. The investment function slopes downward: when the interest rate rises, fewer investment projects are profitable.

Government Purchases

Government purchases are the third component of the demand for goods and services. The federal government buys guns, missiles, and the services of government employees. Local governments buy library books, build schools, and

f y i

THE MANY DIFFERENT INTEREST RATES

If you look in the business section of a newspaper, you will find many different interest rates reported. By contrast, throughout this book, we will talk about "the" interest rate, as if there were only one interest rate in the economy. The only distinction we will make is between the nominal interest rate (which is not corrected for inflation) and the real interest rate (which is corrected for inflation). Almost all of the interest rates reported in the newspaper are nominal.

Why does the newspaper report so many interest rates? The various interest rates differ in three ways:

> *Term.* Some loans in the economy are for short periods of time, even as short as overnight. Other loans are for thirty years or even longer. The interest rate on a loan depends on its term. Long-term interest rates are usually, but not always, higher than short-term interest rates.

> *Credit risk.* In deciding whether to make a loan, a lender must take into account the probability that the borrower will repay. The law allows borrowers to default on their loans by declar-

ing bankruptcy. The higher the perceived probability of default, the higher the interest rate. The safest credit risk is the government, and so government bonds tend to pay a low interest rate. At the other extreme, financially shaky corporations can raise funds only by issuing *junk bonds*, which pay a high interest rate to compensate for the high risk of default.

> *Tax treatment.* The interest on different types of bonds is taxed differently. Most important, when state and local governments issue bonds, called *municipal bonds*, the holders of the bonds do not pay federal income tax on the interest income. Because of this tax advantage, municipal bonds pay a lower interest rate.

When you see two different interest rates in the newspaper, you can almost always explain the difference by considering the term, the credit risk, and the tax treatment of the loan.

Although there are many different interest rates in the economy, macroeconomists can usually ignore these distinctions. The various interest rates tend to move up and down together. The assumption that there is only one interest rate is, for our purposes, a useful simplification.

---

hire teachers. Governments at all levels build roads and other public works. All these transactions make up government purchases of goods and services, which account for about 20 percent of GDP in the United States.

These purchases are only one type of government spending. The other type is transfer payments to households, such as welfare for the poor and Social Security payments for the elderly. Unlike government purchases, transfer payments are not made in exchange for some of the economy's output of goods and services. Therefore, they are not included in the variable G.

Transfer payments do affect the demand for goods and services indirectly. Transfer payments are the opposite of taxes: they increase households' disposable income, just as taxes reduce disposable income. Thus, an increase in transfer payments financed by an increase in taxes leaves disposable income unchanged. We can now revise our definition of T to equal taxes minus transfer payments. Disposable income, $Y - T$, includes both the negative impact of taxes and the positive impact of transfer payments.

If government purchases equal taxes minus transfers, then $G = T$, and the government has a *balanced budget*. If G exceeds T, the government runs a *budget deficit*, which it funds by issuing government debt—that is, by borrowing in the financial markets. If G is less than T, the government runs a *budget surplus*, which it can use to repay some of its outstanding debt.

Here we do not try to explain the political process that leads to a particular fiscal policy—that is, to the level of government purchases and taxes. Instead, we take government purchases and taxes as exogenous variables. To denote that these variables are fixed outside of our model of national income, we write

$$G = \overline{G}.$$
$$T = \overline{T}.$$

We do, however, want to examine the impact of fiscal policy on the variables determined within the model, the endogenous variables. The endogenous variables here are consumption, investment, and the interest rate.

To see how the exogenous variables affect the endogenous variables, we must complete the model. This is the subject of the next section.

3-4 | What Brings the Supply and Demand for Goods and Services Into Equilibrium?

We have now come full circle in the circular flow diagram, Figure 3-1. We began by examining the supply of goods and services, and we have just discussed the demand for them. How can we be certain that all these flows balance? In other words, what ensures that the sum of consumption, investment, and government purchases equals the amount of output produced? We will see that in this classical model, the interest rate has the crucial role of equilibrating supply and demand.

There are two ways to think about the role of the interest rate in the economy. We can consider how the interest rate affects the supply and demand for goods or services. Or we can consider how the interest rate affects the supply and demand for loanable funds. As we will see, these two approaches are two sides of the same coin.

Equilibrium in the Market for Goods and Services: The Supply and Demand for the Economy's Output

The following equations summarize the discussion of the demand for goods and services in Section 3-3:

$$Y = C + I + G.$$
$$C = C(Y - T).$$
$$I = \underline{I(r)}.$$
$$G = \overline{G}.$$
$$T = \overline{T}.$$

The demand for the economy's output comes from consumption, investment, and government purchases. Consumption depends on disposable income; investment depends on the real interest rate; and government purchases and taxes are the exogenous variables set by fiscal policymakers.

To this analysis, let's add what we learned about the supply of goods and services in Section 3-1. There we saw that the factors of production and the production function determine the quantity of output supplied to the economy:

$$Y = F(\overline{K}, \overline{L})$$
$$= \overline{Y}.$$

Now let's combine these equations describing the supply and demand for output. If we substitute the consumption function and the investment function into the national income accounts identity, we obtain

$$Y = C(Y - T) + I(r) + G.$$

Because the variables G and T are fixed by policy, and the level of output Y is fixed by the factors of production and the production function, we can write

$$\overline{Y} = C(\overline{Y} - \overline{T}) + I(r) + \overline{G}.$$

This equation states that the supply of output equals its demand, which is the sum of consumption, investment, and government purchases.

Notice that the interest rate r is the only variable not already determined in the last equation. This is because the interest rate still has a key role to play: it must adjust to ensure that the demand for goods equals the supply. The greater the interest rate, the lower the level of investment, and thus the lower the demand for goods and services, $C + I + G$. If the interest rate is too high, investment is too low, and the demand for output falls short of the supply. If the interest rate is too low, investment is too high, and the demand exceeds the supply. *At the equilibrium interest rate, the demand for goods and services equals the supply.*

This conclusion may seem somewhat mysterious. One might wonder how the interest rate gets to the level that balances the supply and demand for goods and services. The best way to answer this question is to consider how financial markets fit into the story.

Equilibrium in the Financial Markets: The Supply and Demand for Loanable Funds

Because the interest rate is the cost of borrowing and the return to lending in financial markets, we can better understand the role of the interest rate in the economy by thinking about the financial markets. To do this, rewrite the national income accounts identity as

$$Y - C - G = I.$$

The term $Y - C - G$ is the output that remains after the demands of consumers and the government have been satisfied; it is called **national saving** or simply **saving (S).** In this form, the national income accounts identity shows that saving equals investment.

To understand this identity more fully, we can split national saving into two parts—one part representing the saving of the private sector and the other representing the saving of the government:

$$(Y - T - C) + (T - G) = I.$$

The term $(Y - T - C)$ is disposable income minus consumption, which is **private saving.** The term $(T - G)$ is government revenue minus government spending, which is **public saving.** (If government spending exceeds government revenue, the government runs a budget deficit, and public saving is negative.) National saving is the sum of private and public saving. The circular flow diagram in Figure 3-1 reveals an interpretation of this equation: this equation states that the flows into the financial markets (private and public saving) must balance the flows out of the financial markets (investment).

To see how the interest rate brings financial markets into equilibrium, substitute the consumption function and the investment function into the national income accounts identity:

$$Y - C(Y - T) - G = I(r).$$

Next, note that G and T are fixed by policy and Y is fixed by the factors of production and the production function:

$$\overline{Y} - C(\overline{Y} - \overline{T}) - \overline{G} = I(r).$$
$$\overline{S} = I(r).$$

The left-hand side of this equation shows that national saving depends on income Y and the fiscal policy variables G and T. For fixed values of Y, G, and T, national saving S is also fixed. The right-hand side of the equation shows that investment depends on the interest rate.

Figure 3-7 graphs saving and investment as a function of the interest rate. The saving function is a vertical line because in this model saving does not depend on the interest rate (although we relax this assumption later). The investment function slopes downward: the higher the interest rate, the fewer investment projects are profitable.

From a quick glance at Figure 3-7, one might think it was a supply and demand diagram for a particular good. In fact, saving and investment can be interpreted in terms of supply and demand. In this case, the "good" is **loanable funds,** and its "price" is the interest rate. Saving is the supply of loanable funds—households lend their saving to investors or deposit their saving in a bank that then loans the funds out. Investment is the demand for loanable funds—investors borrow from the public directly by selling bonds or indirectly

figure 3-7

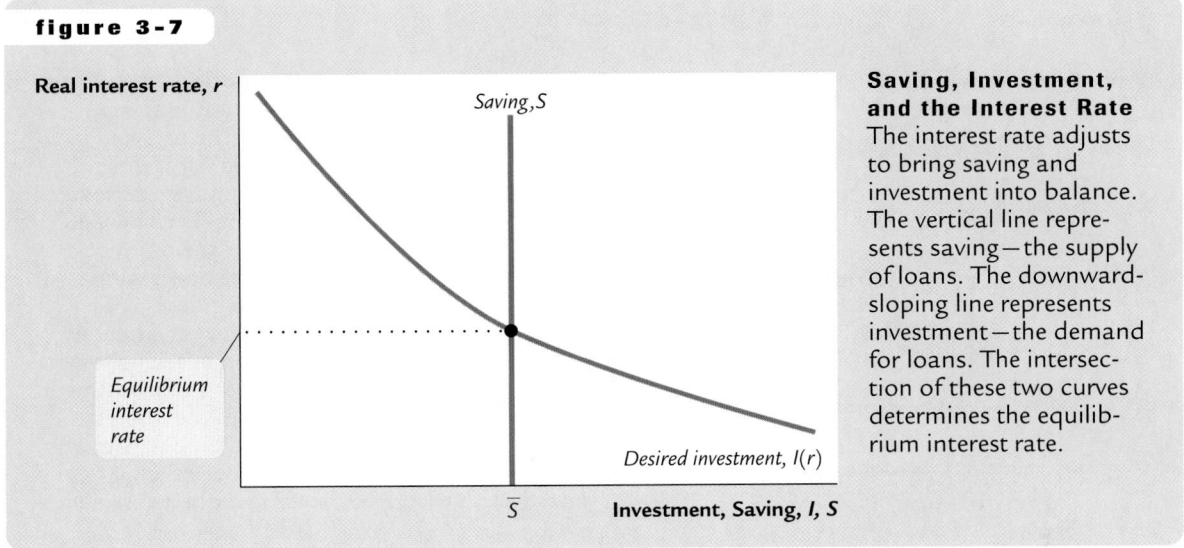

Saving, Investment, and the Interest Rate The interest rate adjusts to bring saving and investment into balance. The vertical line represents saving—the supply of loans. The downward-sloping line represents investment—the demand for loans. The intersection of these two curves determines the equilibrium interest rate.

by borrowing from banks. Because investment depends on the interest rate, the quantity of loanable funds demanded also depends on the interest rate.

The interest rate adjusts until the amount that firms want to invest equals the amount that households want to save. If the interest rate is too low, investors want more of the economy's output than households want to save. Equivalently, the quantity of loans demanded exceeds the quantity supplied. When this happens, the interest rate rises. Conversely, if the interest rate is too high, households want to save more than firms want to invest; because the quantity of loans supplied is greater than the quantity demanded, the interest rate falls. The equilibrium interest rate is found where the two curves cross. *At the equilibrium interest rate, households' desire to save balances firms' desire to invest, and the quantity of loans supplied equals the quantity demanded.*

Changes in Saving: The Effects of Fiscal Policy

We can use our model to show how fiscal policy affects the economy. When the government changes its spending or the level of taxes, it affects the demand for the economy's output of goods and services and alters national saving, investment, and the equilibrium interest rate.

An Increase in Government Purchases Consider first the effects of an increase in government purchases of an amount ΔG. The immediate impact is to increase the demand for goods and services by ΔG. But since total output is fixed by the factors of production, the increase in government purchases must be met by a decrease in some other category of demand. Since disposable income $Y - T$ is unchanged, consumption C is unchanged. The increase in government purchases must be met by an equal decrease in investment.

figure 3-8

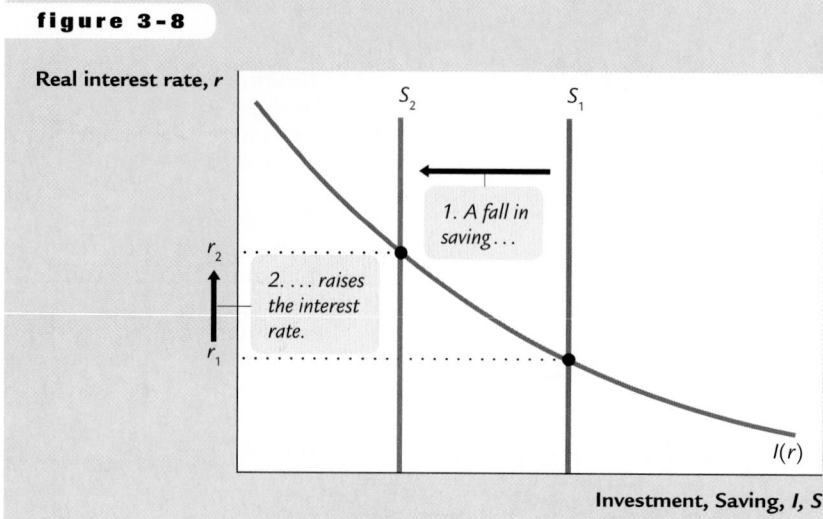

Real interest rate, r

1. A fall in saving...

2. ... raises the interest rate.

r_2

r_1

S_2 S_1

$I(r)$

Investment, Saving, I, S

A Reduction in Saving A reduction in saving, possibly the result of a change in fiscal policy, shifts the saving schedule to the left. The new equilibrium is the point at which the new saving schedule crosses the investment schedule. A reduction in saving lowers the amount of investment and raises the interest rate. Fiscal-policy actions that reduce saving are said to crowd out investment.

To induce investment to fall, the interest rate must rise. Hence, the increase in government purchases causes the interest rate to increase and investment to decrease. Government purchases are said to **crowd out** investment.

To grasp the effects of an increase in government purchases, consider the impact on the market for loanable funds. Since the increase in government purchases is not accompanied by an increase in taxes, the government finances the additional spending by borrowing—that is, by reducing public saving. Since private saving is unchanged, this government borrowing reduces national saving. As Figure 3-8 shows, a reduction in national saving is represented by a leftward shift in the supply of loanable funds available for investment. At the initial interest rate, the demand for loans exceeds the supply. The equilibrium interest rate rises to the point where the investment schedule crosses the new saving schedule. Thus, an increase in government purchases causes the interest rate to rise from r_1 to r_2.

CASE STUDY

Wars and Interest Rates in the United Kingdom, 1730–1920

Wars are traumatic—both for those who fight them and for a nation's economy. Because the economic changes accompanying them are often large, wars provide a natural experiment with which economists can test their theories. We can learn about the economy by seeing how in wartime the endogenous variables respond to the major changes in the exogenous variables.

One exogenous variable that changes substantially in wartime is the level of government purchases. Figure 3-9 shows military spending as a percentage of GDP for the United Kingdom from 1730 to 1919. This graph shows, as one would expect, that government purchases rose suddenly and dramatically during the eight wars of this period.

figure 3-9

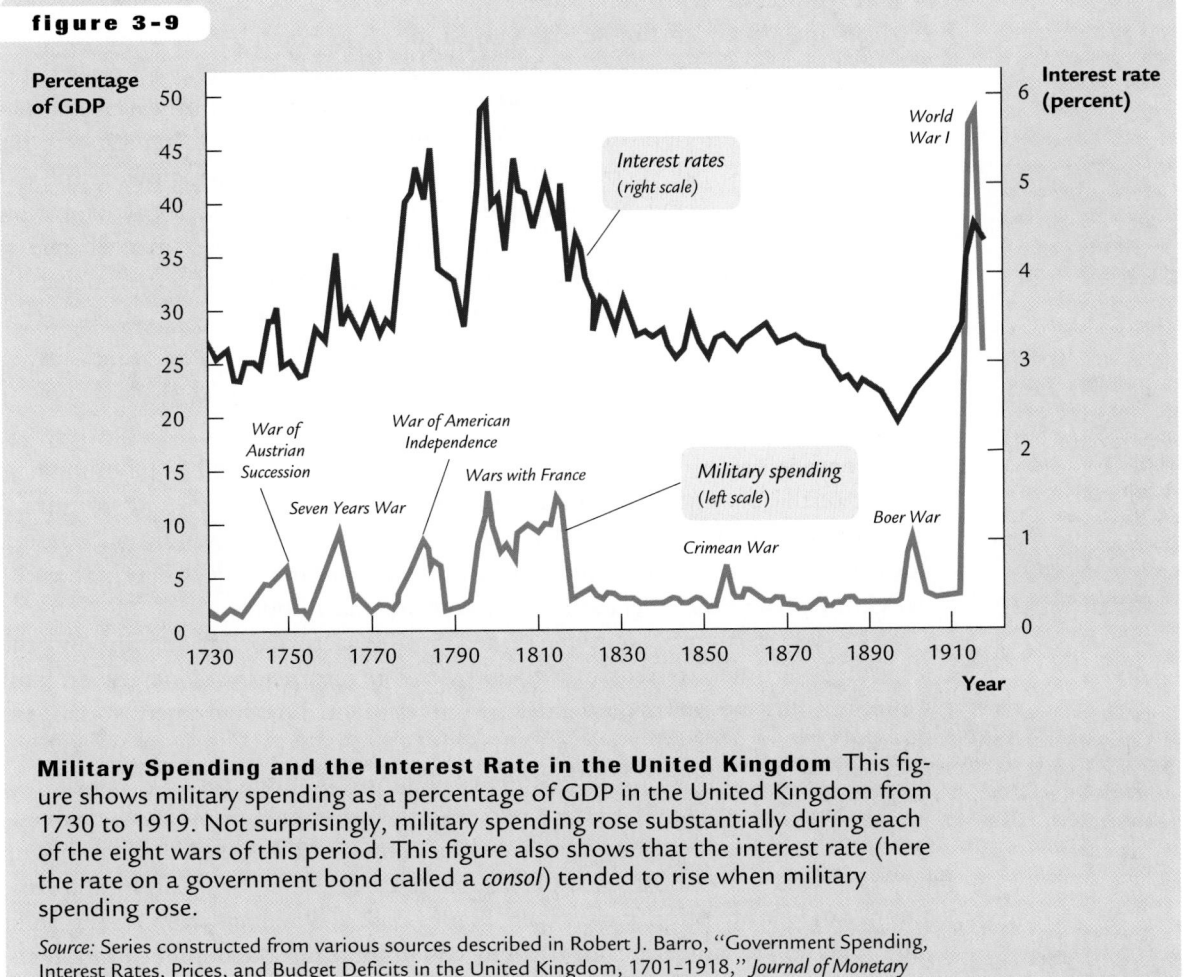

Military Spending and the Interest Rate in the United Kingdom This figure shows military spending as a percentage of GDP in the United Kingdom from 1730 to 1919. Not surprisingly, military spending rose substantially during each of the eight wars of this period. This figure also shows that the interest rate (here the rate on a government bond called a *consol*) tended to rise when military spending rose.

Source: Series constructed from various sources described in Robert J. Barro, "Government Spending, Interest Rates, Prices, and Budget Deficits in the United Kingdom, 1701–1918," *Journal of Monetary Economics* 20 (September 1987): 221–248.

Our model predicts that this wartime increase in government purchases—and the increase in government borrowing to finance the wars—should have raised the demand for goods and services, reduced the supply of loanable funds, and raised the interest rate. To test this prediction, Figure 3-9 also shows the interest rate on long-term government bonds, called *consols* in the United Kingdom. A positive association between military purchases and interest rates is apparent in this figure. These data support the model's prediction: interest rates do tend to rise when government purchases increase.[4]

---

[4] Daniel K. Benjamin and Levis A. Kochin, "War, Prices, and Interest Rates: A Martial Solution to Gibson's Paradox," in M. D. Bordo and A. J. Schwartz, eds., *A Retrospective on the Classical Gold Standard, 1821–1931* (Chicago: University of Chicago Press, 1984), 587-612; Robert J. Barro, "Government Spending, Interest Rates, Prices, and Budget Deficits in the United Kingdom, 1701–1918," *Journal of Monetary Economics* 20 (September 1987): 221–248.

One problem with using wars to test theories is that many economic changes may be occurring at the same time. For example, in World War II, while government purchases increased dramatically, rationing also restricted consumption of many goods. In addition, the risk of defeat in the war and default by the government on its debt presumably increases the interest rate the government must pay. Economic models predict what happens when one exogenous variable changes and all the other exogenous variables remain constant. In the real world, however, many exogenous variables may change at once. Unlike controlled laboratory experiments, the natural experiments on which economists must rely are not always easy to interpret.

A Decrease in Taxes Now consider a reduction in taxes of ΔT. The immediate impact of the tax cut is to raise disposable income and thus to raise consumption. Disposable income rises by ΔT, and consumption rises by an amount equal to ΔT times the marginal propensity to consume *MPC*. The higher the *MPC*, the greater the impact of the tax cut on consumption.

Since the economy's output is fixed by the factors of production and the level of government purchases is fixed by the government, the increase in consumption must be met by a decrease in investment. For investment to fall, the interest rate must rise. Hence, a reduction in taxes, like an increase in government purchases, crowds out investment and raises the interest rate.

We can also analyze the effect of a tax cut by looking at saving and investment. Since the tax cut raises disposable income by ΔT, consumption goes up by $MPC \times \Delta T$. National saving S, which equals $Y - C - G$, falls by the same amount as consumption rises. As in Figure 3-8, the reduction in saving shifts the supply of loanable funds to the left, which increases the equilibrium interest rate and crowds out investment.

CASE STUDY

Fiscal Policy in the 1980s

One of the most dramatic economic events in recent history was the large change in U.S. fiscal policy in 1981. In 1980 Ronald Reagan was elected president on a platform that promised increases in military spending and reduced taxes. The result of this combination of policies was, not surprisingly, a large imbalance between government spending and revenue. The federal budget deficit skyrocketed in the 1980s, and the government borrowed at a rate unprecedented in peacetime.

As our model predicts, this change in fiscal policy led to higher interest rates and lower national saving. The real interest rate (as measured by the yield on government bonds minus the inflation rate) rose from 0.4 percent in the 1970s to 5.7 percent in the 1980s. Gross national saving as a percentage of GDP fell from 16.7 percent in the 1970s to 14.1 percent in the 1980s. The change in fiscal policy in the 1980s had the effects that our simple model of the economy would predict.

Changes in Investment Demand

So far, we have discussed how fiscal policy can change national saving. We can also use our model to examine the other side of the market—the demand for investment. In this section we look at the causes and effects of changes in investment demand.

One reason investment demand might increase is technological innovation. Suppose, for example, that someone invents a new technology, such as the railroad or the computer. Before a firm or household can take advantage of the innovation, it must buy investment goods. The invention of the railroad had no value until railroad cars were produced and tracks were laid. The idea of the computer was not productive until computers were manufactured. Thus, technological innovation leads to an increase in investment demand.

Investment demand may also change because the government encourages or discourages investment through the tax laws. For example, suppose that the government increases personal income taxes and uses the extra revenue to provide tax cuts for those who invest in new capital. Such a change in the tax laws makes more investment projects profitable and, like a technological innovation, increases the demand for investment goods.

Figure 3-10 shows the effects of an increase in investment demand. At any given interest rate, the demand for investment goods (and also for loans) is

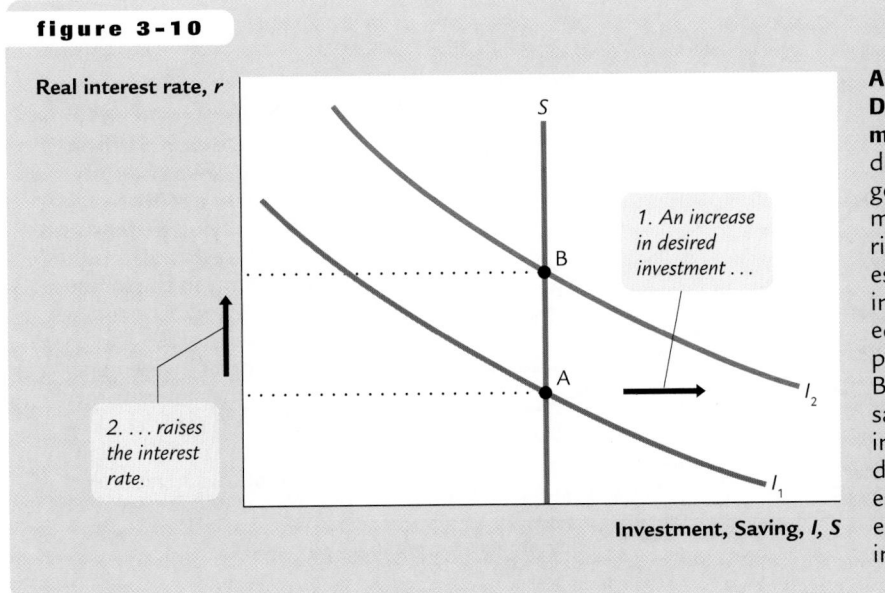

figure 3-10

Real interest rate, *r*

1. An increase in desired investment . . .

2. . . . raises the interest rate.

Investment, Saving, *I, S*

An Increase in the Demand for Investment An increase in the demand for investment goods shifts the investment schedule to the right. At any given interest rate, the amount of investment is greater. The equilibrium moves from point A to point B. Because the amount of saving is fixed, the increase in investment demand raises the interest rate while leaving the equilibrium amount of investment unchanged.

figure 3-11

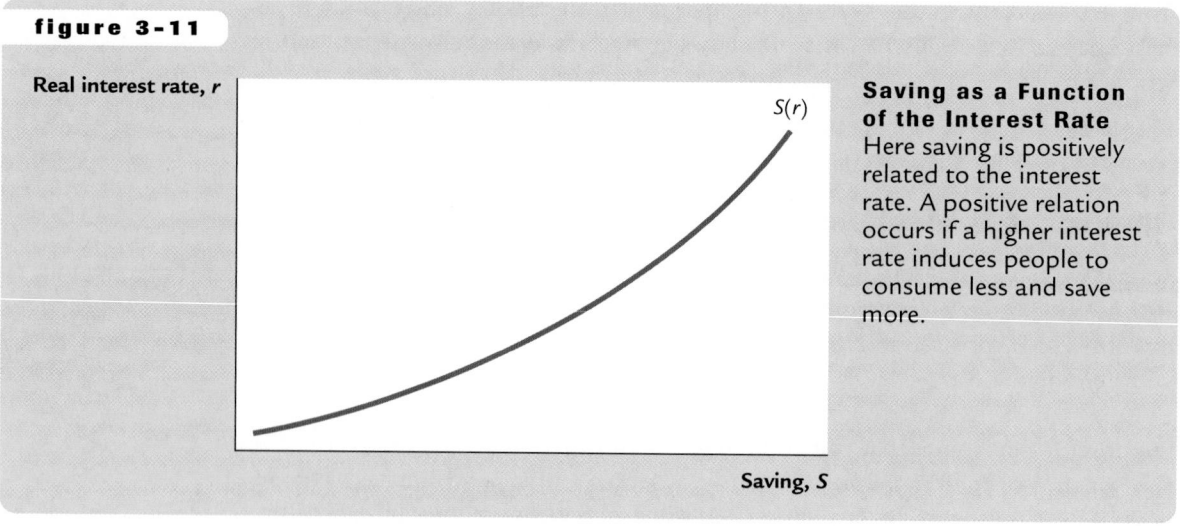

Saving as a Function of the Interest Rate Here saving is positively related to the interest rate. A positive relation occurs if a higher interest rate induces people to consume less and save more.

higher. This increase in demand is represented by a shift in the investment schedule to the right. The economy moves from the old equilibrium, point A, to the new equilibrium, point B.

The surprising implication of Figure 3-10 is that the equilibrium amount of investment is unchanged. Under our assumptions, the fixed level of saving determines the amount of investment; in other words, there is a fixed supply of loans. An increase in investment demand merely raises the equilibrium interest rate.

figure 3-12

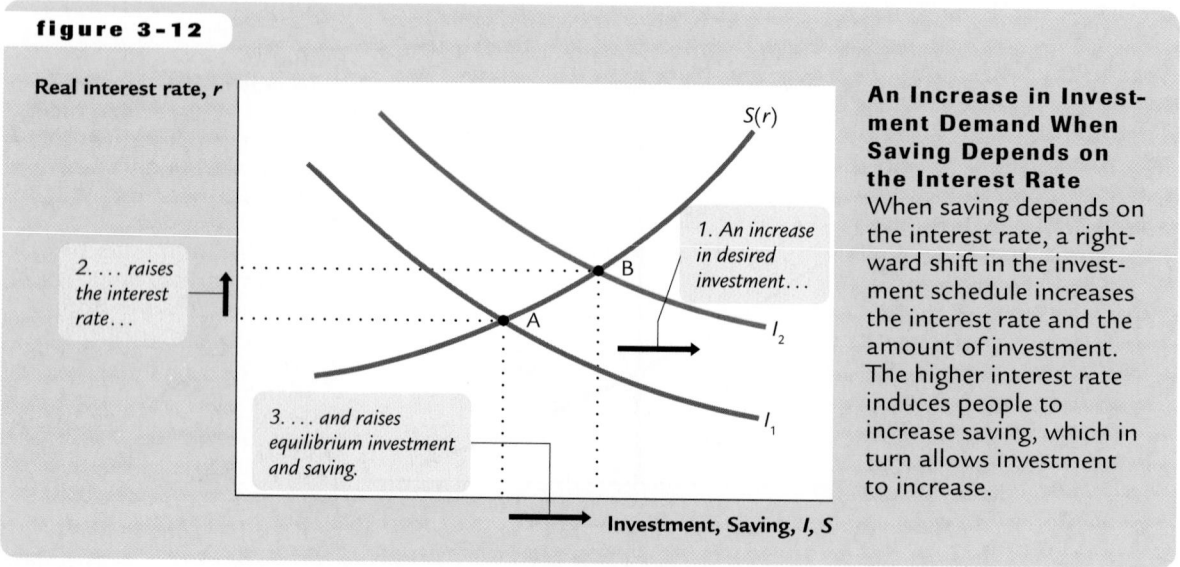

An Increase in Investment Demand When Saving Depends on the Interest Rate When saving depends on the interest rate, a rightward shift in the investment schedule increases the interest rate and the amount of investment. The higher interest rate induces people to increase saving, which in turn allows investment to increase.

We would reach a different conclusion, however, if we modified our simple consumption function and allowed consumption (and its flip side, saving) to depend on the interest rate. Because the interest rate is the return to saving (as well as the cost of borrowing), a higher interest rate might reduce consumption and increase saving. If so, the saving schedule would be upward sloping, as it is in Figure 3-11, rather than vertical.

With an upward-sloping saving schedule, an increase in investment demand would raise both the equilibrium interest rate and the equilibrium quantity of investment. Figure 3-12 shows such a change. The increase in the interest rate causes households to consume less and save more. The decrease in consumption frees resources for investment.

3-5 | Conclusion

In this chapter we have developed a model that explains the production, distribution, and allocation of the economy's output of goods and services. Because the model incorporates all the interactions illustrated in the circular flow diagram in Figure 3-1, it is sometimes called a *general equilibrium model*. The model emphasizes how prices adjust to equilibrate supply and demand. Factor prices equilibrate factor markets. The interest rate equilibrates the supply and demand for goods and services (or, equivalently, the supply and demand for loanable funds).

Throughout the chapter, we have discussed various applications of the model. The model can explain how income is divided among the factors of production and how factor prices depend on factor supplies. We have also used the model to discuss how fiscal policy alters the allocation of output among its alternative uses — consumption, investment, and government purchases — and how it affects the equilibrium interest rate.

At this point it is useful to review some of the simplifying assumptions we have made in this chapter. In the following chapters we relax some of these assumptions in order to address a greater range of questions.

➤ We have assumed that the capital stock, the labor force, and the production technology are fixed. In Chapters 4 and 5 we see how changes over time in each of these lead to growth in the economy's output of goods and services.

➤ We have assumed that the labor force is fully employed. In Chapter 6 we examine the reasons for unemployment and see how public policy influences the level of unemployment.

➤ We have ignored the role of money, the asset with which goods and services are bought and sold. In Chapter 7 we discuss how money affects the economy and the influence of monetary policy.

➤ We have assumed that there is no trade with other countries. In Chapter 8 we consider how international interactions affect our conclusions.

f y i

THE IDENTIFICATION PROBLEM

In our model, investment depends on the interest rate. The higher the interest rate, the fewer investment projects are profitable. The investment schedule therefore slopes downward.

Economists who look at macroeconomic data, however, usually fail to find an obvious association between investment and interest rates. In years when interest rates are high, investment is not always low. In years when interest rates are low, investment is not always high.

How do we interpret this finding? Does it mean that investment does not depend on the interest rate? Does it suggest that our model of saving, investment, and the interest rate is inconsistent with how the economy actually functions?

Luckily, we do not have to discard our model. The inability to find an empirical relationship between investment and interest rates is an example of the *identification problem*. The identification problem arises when variables are related in more than one way. When we look at data, we are observing a combination of these different relationships, and it is difficult to "identify" any one of them.

To understand this problem more concretely, consider the relationships among saving, investment, and the interest rate. Suppose, on the one hand, that all changes in the interest rate resulted from changes in saving—that is, from shifts in the saving schedule. Then, as shown in the left-hand side of panel (a) in Figure 3-13, all changes would represent movement along a fixed investment schedule. As the right-hand side of panel (a) shows, the data would trace out this investment schedule. Thus, we would observe a negative relationship between investment and interest rates.

Suppose, on the other hand, that all changes in the interest rate resulted from technological innovations—that is, from shifts in the investment schedule. Then, as shown in panel (b), all changes would represent movements in the investment schedule along a fixed saving schedule. As the right-hand side of panel (b) shows, the data would reflect this saving schedule. Thus, we would observe a positive relationship between investment and interest rates.

In the real world, interest rates change sometimes because of shifts in the saving schedule and sometimes because of shifts in the investment schedule. In this mixed case, as shown in panel (c), a plot of the data would reveal no recognizable relation between interest rates and the quantity of investment, just as economists observe in actual data. The moral of the story is simple and is applicable to many other situations: The empirical relationship we expect to observe depends crucially on which exogenous variables we think are changing.

> ➤ We have ignored the role of short-run sticky prices. In Chapters 9 through 13, we develop a model of short-run fluctuations that includes sticky prices. We then discuss how the model of short-run fluctuations relates to the model of national income developed in this chapter.

Before going on to these chapters, go back to the beginning of this one and make sure you can answer the four groups of questions about national income that begin the chapter.

figure 3-13

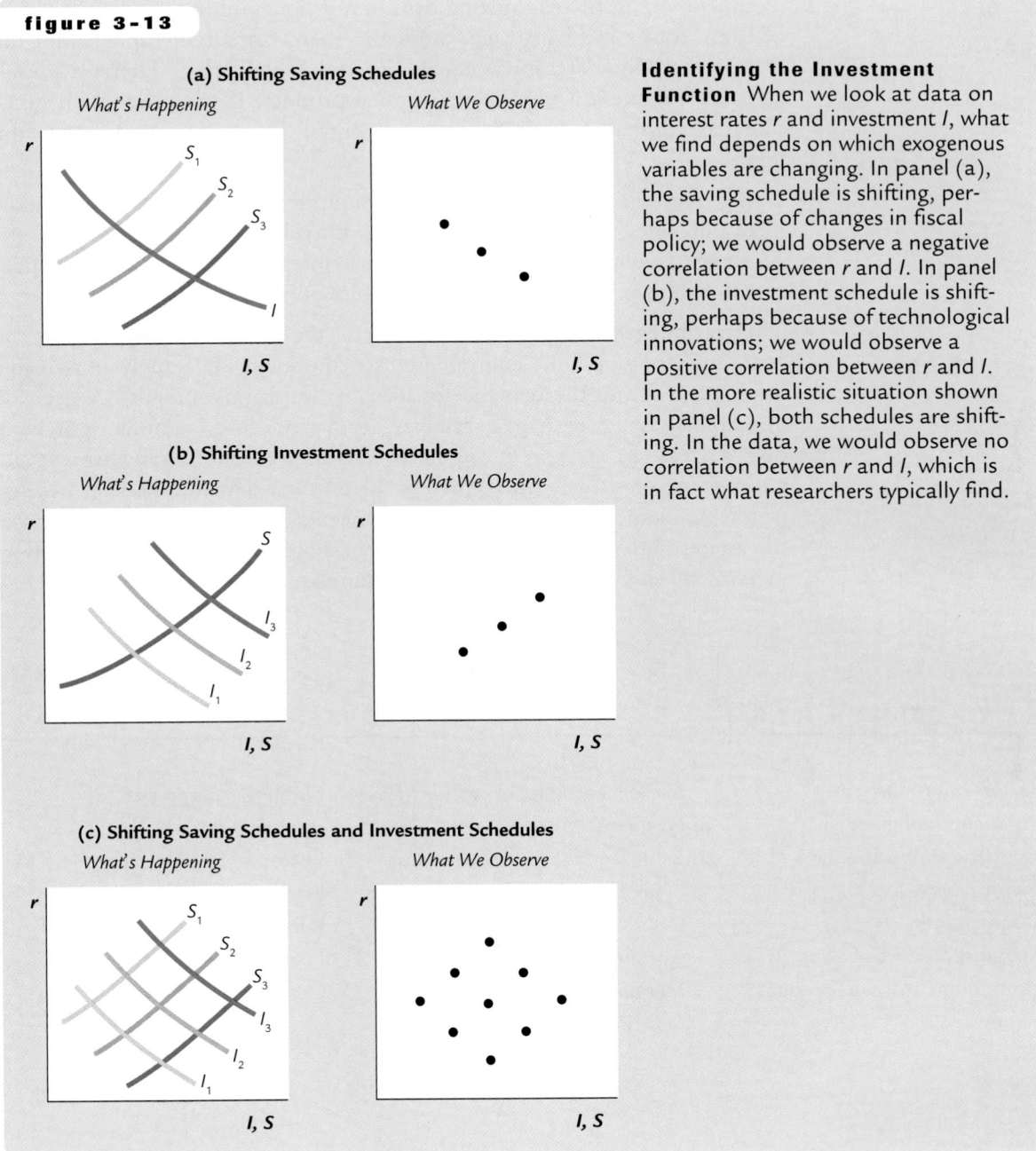

(a) Shifting Saving Schedules

What's Happening   What We Observe

(b) Shifting Investment Schedules

What's Happening   What We Observe

(c) Shifting Saving Schedules and Investment Schedules

What's Happening   What We Observe

Identifying the Investment Function When we look at data on interest rates r and investment I, what we find depends on which exogenous variables are changing. In panel (a), the saving schedule is shifting, perhaps because of changes in fiscal policy; we would observe a negative correlation between r and I. In panel (b), the investment schedule is shifting, perhaps because of technological innovations; we would observe a positive correlation between r and I. In the more realistic situation shown in panel (c), both schedules are shifting. In the data, we would observe no correlation between r and I, which is in fact what researchers typically find.

Summary

1. The factors of production and the production technology determine the economy's output of goods and services. An increase in one of the factors of production or a technological advance raises output.

2. Competitive, profit-maximizing firms hire labor until the marginal product of labor equals the real wage. Similarly, these firms rent capital until the marginal product of capital equals the real rental price. Therefore, each factor of production is paid its marginal product. If the production function has constant returns to scale, all output is used to compensate the inputs.

3. The economy's output is used for consumption, investment, and government purchases. Consumption depends positively on disposable income. Investment depends negatively on the real interest rate. Government purchases and taxes are the exogenous variables of fiscal policy.

4. The real interest rate adjusts to equilibrate the supply and demand for the economy's output—or, equivalently, to equilibrate the supply of loanable funds (saving) and the demand for loanable funds (investment). A decrease in national saving, perhaps because of an increase in government purchases or a decrease in taxes, reduces the equilibrium amount of investment and raises the interest rate. An increase in investment demand, perhaps because of a technological innovation or a tax incentive for investment, also raises the interest rate. An increase in investment demand increases the quantity of investment only if higher interest rates stimulate additional saving.

KEY CONCEPTS

Factors of production

Production function

Constant returns to scale

Factor prices

Competition

Marginal product of labor (*MPL*)

Diminishing marginal product

Real wage

Marginal product of capital (*MPK*)

Real rental price of capital

Economic profit versus accounting profit

Disposable income

Consumption function

Marginal propensity to consume (*MPC*)

Nominal interest rate

Real interest rate

National saving (saving) (*S*)

Private saving

Public saving

Loanable funds

Crowding out

QUESTIONS FOR REVIEW

1. What determines the amount of output an economy produces?

2. Explain how a competitive, profit-maximizing firm decides how much of each factor of production to demand.

3. What is the role of constant returns to scale in the distribution of income?

4. What determines consumption and investment?

5. Explain the difference between government pur-

chases and transfer payments. Give two examples of each.

6. What makes the demand for the economy's output of goods and services equal the supply?

7. Explain what happens to consumption, investment, and the interest rate when the government increases taxes.

PROBLEMS AND APPLICATIONS

1. Use the neoclassical theory of distribution to predict the impact on the real wage and the real rental price of capital of each of the following events:

   a. A wave of immigration increases the labor force.

   b. An earthquake destroys some of the capital stock.

   c. A technological advance improves the production function.

2. If a 10-percent increase in both capital and labor causes output to increase by less than 10 percent, the production function is said to exhibit *decreasing returns to scale*. If it causes output to increase by more than 10 percent, the production function is said to exhibit *increasing returns to scale*. Why might a production function exhibit decreasing or increasing returns to scale?

3. According to the neoclassical theory of distribution, the real wage earned by any worker equals that worker's marginal productivity. Let's use this insight to examine the incomes of two groups of workers: farmers and barbers.

   a. Over the past century, the productivity of farmers has risen substantially because of technological progress. According to the neoclassical theory, what should have happened to their real wage?

   b. In what units is the real wage discussed in part (a) measured?

   c. Over the same period, the productivity of barbers has remained constant. What should have happened to their real wage?

   d. In what units is the real wage in part (c) measured?

   e. Suppose workers can move freely between being farmers and being barbers. What does this mobility imply for the wages of farmers and barbers?

   f. What do your previous answers imply for the price of haircuts relative to the price of food?

   g. Who benefits from technological progress in farming—farmers or barbers?

4. The government raises taxes by $100 billion. If the marginal propensity to consume is 0.6, what happens to the following? Do they rise or fall? By what amounts?

   a. Public saving.

   b. Private saving.

   c. National saving.

   d. Investment.

5. Suppose that an increase in consumer confidence raises consumers' expectations of future income and thus the amount they want to consume today. This might be interpreted as an upward shift in the consumption function. How does this shift affect investment and the interest rate?

6. Consider an economy described by the following equations:

$$Y = C + I + G,$$
$$Y = 5,000,$$
$$G = 1,000,$$
$$T = 1,000,$$
$$C = 250 + 0.75(Y-T),$$
$$I = 1,000 - 50r.$$

   a. In this economy, compute private saving, public saving, and national saving.

   b. Find the equilibrium interest rate.

c. Now suppose that G rises to 1,250. Compute private saving, public saving, and national saving.

d. Find the new equilibrium interest rate.

7. Suppose that the government increases taxes and government purchases by equal amounts. What happens to the interest rate and investment in response to this balanced budget change? Does your answer depend on the marginal propensity to consume?

8. When the government subsidizes investment, such as with an investment tax credit, the subsidy often applies to only some types of investment. This question asks you to consider the effect of such a change. Suppose there are two types of investment in the economy: business investment and residential investment. And suppose that the government institutes an investment tax credit only for business investment.

a. How does this policy affect the demand curve for business investment? The demand curve for residential investment?

b. Draw the economy's supply and demand for loanable funds. How does this policy affect the supply and demand for loans? What happens to the equilibrium interest rate?

c. Compare the old and the new equilibrium. How does this policy affect the total quantity of investment? The quantity of business investment? The quantity of residential investment?

9. If consumption depended on the interest rate, how would that affect the conclusions reached in this chapter about the effects of fiscal policy?

appendix

The Cobb–Douglas Production Function

What production function describes how actual economies turn capital and labor into GDP? The answer to this question came from a historic collaboration between a U.S. senator and a mathematician.

Paul Douglas was a U.S. senator from Illinois from 1949 to 1966. In 1927, however, when he was still a professor of economics, he noticed a surprising fact: The division of national income between capital and labor had been roughly constant over a long period. In other words, as the economy grew more prosperous over time, the total income of workers and the total income of capital owners grew at almost exactly the same rate. This observation caused Douglas to wonder what conditions lead to constant factor shares.

Douglas asked Charles Cobb, a mathematician, what production function, if any, would produce constant factor shares if factors always earned their marginal products. The production function would need to have the property that

$$\text{Capital Income} = MPK \times K = \alpha Y$$

and

$$\text{Labor Income} = MPL \times L = (1 - \alpha)\, Y,$$

where α is a constant between zero and one that measures capital's share of income. That is, α determines what share of income goes to capital and what share goes to labor. Cobb showed that the function with this property is

$$Y = F(K, L) = AK^{\alpha}L^{1-\alpha},$$

where A is a parameter greater than zero that measures the productivity of the available technology. This function became known as the *Cobb–Douglas production function.*

Let's take a closer look at some of the properties of this production function. First, the Cobb–Douglas production function has constant returns to scale. That is, if capital and labor are increased by the same proportion, then output increases by that proportion as well.[5]

---

[5] *Mathematical note:* To prove that the Cobb–Douglas production function has constant returns to scale, examine what happens when we multiply capital and labor by a constant z:

$$F(zK, zL) = A(zK)^{\alpha}(zL)^{1-\alpha}.$$

Expanding terms on the right,

$$F(zK, zL) = Az^{\alpha}K^{\alpha}z^{1-\alpha}L^{1-\alpha}.$$

(footnote continues)

Next, consider the marginal products for the Cobb–Douglas production function. The marginal product of labor is[6]

$$MPL = (1 - \alpha)AK^\alpha L^{-\alpha},$$

and the marginal product of capital is

$$MPK = \alpha AK^{\alpha-1}L^{1-\alpha}.$$

From these equations, recalling that α is between zero and one, we can see what causes the marginal products of the two factors to change. An increase in the amount of capital raises the MPL and reduces the MPK. Similarly, an increase in the amount of labor reduces the MPL and raises the MPK. A technological advance that increases the parameter A raises the marginal product of both factors proportionately.

The marginal products for the Cobb–Douglas production function can also be written as[7]

$$MPL = (1 - \alpha)Y/L.$$

$$MPK = \alpha Y/K.$$

The MPL is proportional to output per worker, and the MPK is proportional to output per unit of capital. Y/L is called *average labor productivity*, and Y/K is called *average capital productivity*. If the production function is Cobb–Douglas, then the marginal productivity of a factor is proportional to its average productivity.

We can now verify that if factors earn their marginal products, then the parameter α indeed tells us how much income goes to labor and how much goes to capital. The total wage bill, which we have seen is $MPL \times L$, is simply

---

Rearranging to bring like terms together, we get

$$F(zK, zL) = z^\alpha z^{1-\alpha} AK^\alpha L^{1-\alpha}.$$

Since $z^\alpha z^{1-\alpha} = z$, our function becomes

$$F(zK, zL) = zAK^\alpha L^{1-\alpha}.$$

But $AK^\alpha L^{1-\alpha} = F(K, L)$. Thus,

$$F(zK, zL) = zF(K, L) = zY.$$

Hence, the amount of output Y increases by the same factor z, which implies that this production function has constant returns to scale.

[6] *Mathematical note:* Obtaining the formulas for the marginal products from the production function requires a bit of calculus. To find the MPL, differentiate the production function with respect to L. This is done by multiplying by the exponent $(1 - \alpha)$, and then subtracting 1 from the old exponent to obtain the new exponent, $-\alpha$. Similarly, to obtain the MPK, differentiate the production function with respect to K.

[7] *Mathematical note:* To check these expressions for the marginal products, substitute in the production function for Y to show that these expressions are equivalent to the earlier formulas for the marginal products.

$(1 - \alpha)Y$. Therefore, $(1 - \alpha)$ is labor's share of output. Similarly, the total return to capital, $MPK \times K$, is αY, and α is capital's share of output. The ratio of labor income to capital income is a constant, $(1 - \alpha)/\alpha$, just as Douglas observed. The factor shares depend only on the parameter α, not on the amounts of capital or labor or on the state of technology as measured by the parameter A.

More recent U.S. data are also consistent with the Cobb–Douglas production function. Figure 3-14 shows the ratio of labor income to total income in the United States from 1960 to 1996. Despite the many changes in the economy over the past four decades, this ratio has remained about 0.7. This division of income is easily explained by a Cobb–Douglas production function in which the parameter α is about 0.3.

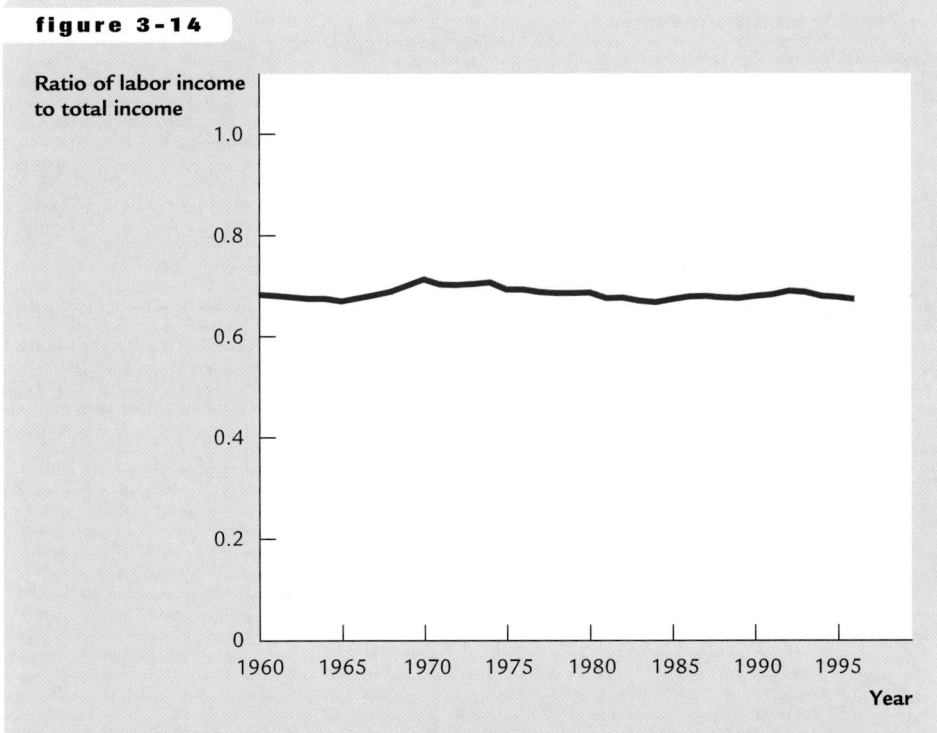

figure 3-14

The Ratio of Labor Income to Total Income Labor income has remained about 0.7 of total income over a long period of time. This approximate constancy of factor shares is evidence for the Cobb-Douglas production function. (This figure is produced from U.S. national income accounts data. Labor income is compensation of employees. Total income is the sum of labor income, corporate profits, net interest, rental income, and depreciation. Proprietors' income is excluded from these calculations, because it is a combination of labor income and capital income.)

Source: U.S. Department of Commerce.

MORE PROBLEMS AND APPLICATIONS

1. Suppose that the production function is Cobb–Douglas with parameter $\alpha = 0.3$.

   a. What fractions of income do capital and labor receive?

   b. Suppose that immigration raises the labor force by 10 percent. What happens to total output (in percent)? The rental price of capital? The real wage?

   c. Suppose that a gift of capital from abroad raises the capital stock by 10 percent. What happens to total output (in percent)? The rental price of capital? The real wage?

   d. Suppose that a technological advance raises the value of the parameter A by 10 percent. What happens to total output (in percent)? The rental price of capital? The real wage?

2. (This problem requires the use of calculus.) Consider a Cobb–Douglas production function with three inputs. K is capital (the number of machines), L is labor (the number of workers), and H is human capital (the number of college degrees among the workers). The production function is

   $$Y = K^{1/3}L^{1/3}H^{1/3}.$$

   a. Derive an expression for the marginal product of labor. How does an increase in the amount of human capital affect the marginal product of labor?

   b. Derive an expression for the marginal product of human capital. How does an increase in the amount of human capital affect the marginal product of human capital?

   c. What is the income share paid to labor? What is the income share paid to human capital? In the national income accounts of this economy, what share of total income do you think workers would appear to receive? (*Hint:* Consider where the return to human capital shows up.)

   d. An unskilled worker earns the marginal product of labor, whereas a skilled worker earns the marginal product of labor plus the marginal product of human capital. Using your answers to (a) and (b), find the ratio of the skilled wage to the unskilled wage. How does an increase in the amount of human capital affect this ratio? Explain.

   e. Some people advocate government funding of college scholarships as a way of creating a more egalitarian society. Others argue that scholarships help only those who are able to go to college. Do your answers to the above questions shed light on this debate?

Economic Growth I

The question of growth is nothing new but a new disguise for an age-old issue, one which has always intrigued and preoccupied economics: the present versus the future.

— *James Tobin*

If you have ever spoken with your grandparents about what their lives were like when they were young, most likely you learned an important lesson about economics: material standards of living have improved substantially over time for most families in most countries. This advance comes from rising incomes, which have allowed people to consume greater quantities of goods and services.

To measure economic growth, economists use data on gross domestic product, which measures the total income of everyone in the economy. The real GDP of the United States today is more than three times its 1950 level, and real GDP per person is more than twice its 1950 level. In any given year, we can also observe large differences in the standard of living among countries. Table 4-1 shows income per person in 1997 of the world's 12 most populous countries. The United States tops the list with an income of $28,740 per person. Nigeria has an income per person of only $880—about 3 percent of the figure for the United States.

Our goal in this and the next chapter is to understand what causes these differences in income over time and across countries. In Chapter 3 we identified the factors of production—capital and labor—and the production technology as the sources of the economy's output and, thus, of its total income. Differences in income, then, must come from differences in capital, labor, and technology.

Our primary task is to develop a theory of economic growth called the **Solow growth model.** Our analysis in Chapter 3 enabled us to describe how the economy produces and uses its output at one point in time. The analysis was static—a snapshot of the economy. To explain why our national income grows, and why some economies grow faster than others, we must broaden our analysis so that it describes changes in the economy over time. By developing such a model, we make our analysis dynamic—more like a movie than a photograph. The Solow growth model shows how saving,

table 4-1

International Differences in the Standard of Living, 1997

Country	Income per Person (in U.S. dollars)
United States	$28,740
Japan	23,400
Germany	21,300
Mexico	8,120
Brazil	6,240
Russian Federation	4,190
China	3,570
Indonesia	3,450
India	1,650
Pakistan	1,590
Bangladesh	1,050
Nigeria	880

Source: World Bank.

population growth, and technological progress affect the level of an economy's output and its growth over time. In this chapter we analyze the roles of saving and population growth. In the next chapter we introduce technological progress.[1]

4-1 | The Accumulation of Capital

The Solow growth model is designed to show how growth in the capital stock, growth in the labor force, and advances in technology interact in an economy, and how they affect a nation's total output of goods and services. We build this model in steps. Our first step is to examine how the supply and demand for goods determine the accumulation of capital. In this first step, we assume that the labor force and technology are fixed. We then relax these assumptions, by introducing changes in the labor force later in this chapter and by introducing changes in technology in the next.

---

[1] The Solow growth model is named after economist Robert Solow and was developed in the 1950s and 1960s. In 1987 Solow won the Nobel Prize in economics for his work in economic growth. The model was introduced in Robert M. Solow, "A Contribution to the Theory of Economic Growth," *Quarterly Journal of Economics* (February 1956): 65–94.

The Supply and Demand for Goods

The supply and demand for goods played a central role in our static model of the economy in Chapter 3. The same is true for the Solow model. By considering the supply and demand for goods, we can see what determines how much output is produced at any given time and how this output is allocated among alternative uses.

The Supply of Goods and the Production Function   The supply of goods in the Solow model is based on the now-familiar production function, which states that output depends on the capital stock and the labor force:

$$Y = F(K, L).$$

The Solow growth model assumes that the production function has constant returns to scale. This assumption is often considered realistic, and as we will see shortly, it helps simplify the analysis. Recall that a production function has constant returns to scale if

$$zY = F(zK, zL)$$

for any positive number z. That is, if we multiply both capital and labor by z, we also multiply the amount of output by z.

Production functions with constant returns to scale allow us to analyze all quantities in the economy relative to the size of the labor force. To see that this is true, set $z = 1/L$ in the equation above to obtain

$$Y/L = F(K/L, 1).$$

This equation shows that the amount of output per worker Y/L is a function of the amount of capital per worker K/L. (The number "1" is, of course, constant and thus can be ignored.) The assumption of constant returns to scale implies that the size of the economy—as measured by the number of workers—does not affect the relationship between output per worker and capital per worker.

Because the size of the economy does not matter, it will prove convenient to denote all quantities in per-worker terms. We designate these with lower-case letters, so $y = Y/L$ is output per worker, and $k = K/L$ is capital per worker. We can then write the production function as

$$y = f(k),$$

where we define $f(k) = F(k,1)$. Figure 4-1 illustrates this production function.

The slope of this production function shows how much extra output a worker produces when given an extra unit of capital. This amount is the marginal product of capital MPK. Mathematically, we write

$$MPK = f(k + 1) - f(k).$$

Note that in Figure 4-1, as the amount of capital increases, the production function becomes flatter, indicating that the production function exhibits

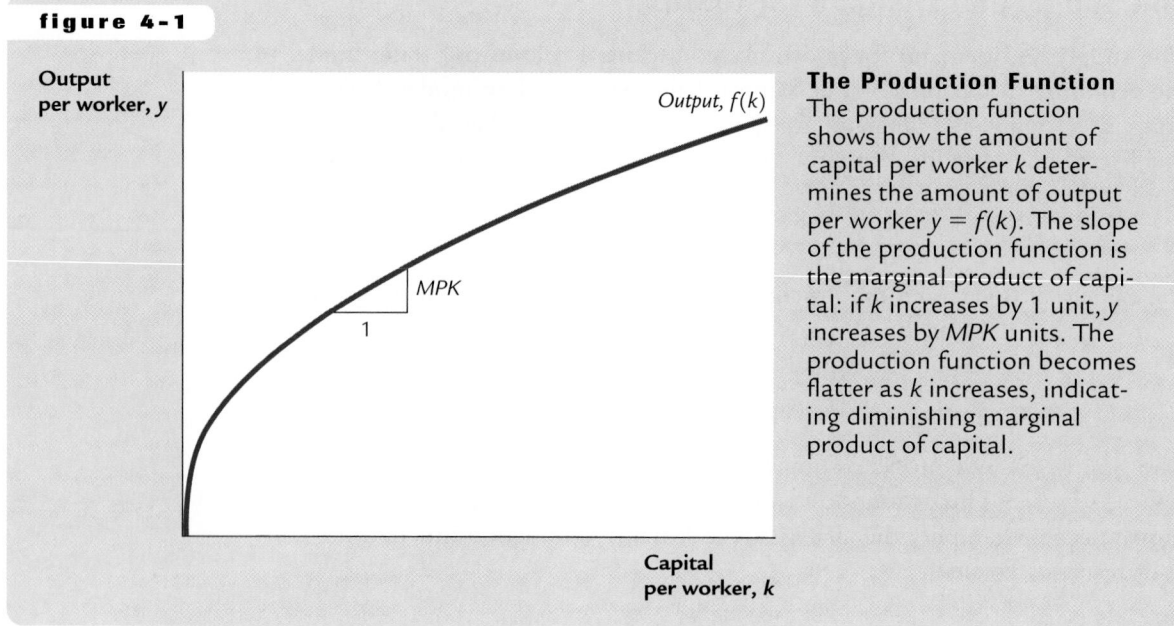

figure 4-1

The Production Function
The production function shows how the amount of capital per worker k determines the amount of output per worker $y = f(k)$. The slope of the production function is the marginal product of capital: if k increases by 1 unit, y increases by MPK units. The production function becomes flatter as k increases, indicating diminishing marginal product of capital.

diminishing marginal product of capital. When k is low, the average worker has only a little capital to work with, so an extra unit of capital is very useful and produces a lot of additional output. When k is high, the average worker has a lot of capital, so an extra unit increases production only slightly.

The Demand for Goods and the Consumption Function   The demand for goods in the Solow model comes from consumption and investment. In other words, output per worker y is divided between consumption per worker c and investment per worker i:

$$y = c + i.$$

This equation is the per-worker version of the national income accounts identity for the economy. Notice that it omits government purchases (which for present purposes we can ignore) and net exports (because we are assuming a closed economy).

The Solow model assumes that each year people save a fraction s of their income and consume a fraction $(1 - s)$. We can express this idea with a consumption function with the simple form

$$c = (1 - s)y,$$

where s, the saving rate, is a number between zero and one. Keep in mind that various government policies can potentially influence a nation's saving rate, so one of our goals is to find what saving rate is desirable. For now, however, we just take the saving rate s as given.

To see what this consumption function implies for investment, substitute $(1 - s)y$ for c in the national income accounts identity:

$$y = (1 - s)y + i.$$

Rearrange the terms to obtain

$$i = sy.$$

This equation shows that investment equals saving, as we first saw in Chapter 3. Thus, the rate of saving s is also the fraction of output devoted to investment.

We have now introduced the two main ingredients of the Solow model—the production function and the consumption function—which describe the economy at any moment in time. For any given capital stock k, the production function $y = f(k)$ determines how much output the economy produces, and the saving rate s determines the allocation of that output between consumption and investment.

Growth in the Capital Stock and the Steady State

At any moment, the capital stock is a key determinant of the economy's output, but the capital stock can change over time, and those changes can lead to economic growth. In particular, two forces influence the capital stock: investment and depreciation. *Investment* refers to the expenditure on new plant and equipment, and it causes the capital stock to rise. *Depreciation* refers to the wearing out of old capital, and it causes the capital stock to fall. Let's consider each of these in turn.

figure 4-2

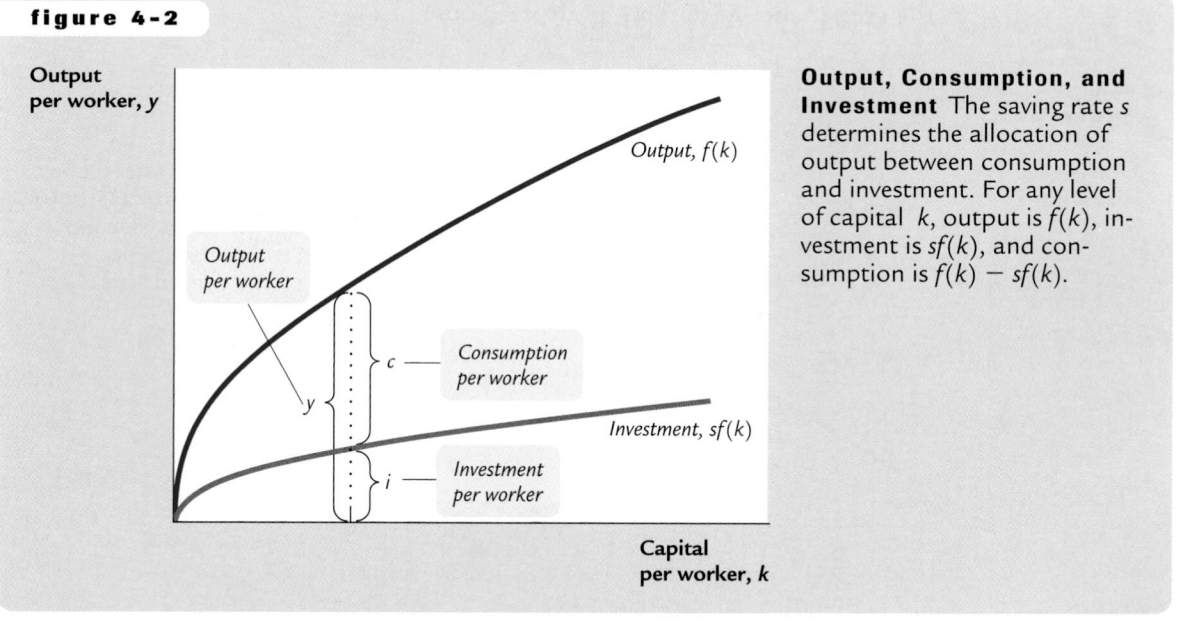

Output, Consumption, and Investment The saving rate s determines the allocation of output between consumption and investment. For any level of capital k, output is $f(k)$, investment is $sf(k)$, and consumption is $f(k) - sf(k)$.

As we have already noted, investment per worker i equals sy. By substituting the production function for y, we can express investment per worker as a function of the capital stock per worker:

$$i = sf(k).$$

This equation relates the existing stock of capital k to the accumulation of new capital i. Figure 4-2 shows this relationship. This figure illustrates how, for any value of k, the amount of output is determined by the production function $f(k)$, and the allocation of that output between consumption and saving is determined by the saving rate s.

To incorporate depreciation into the model, we assume that a certain fraction δ of the capital stock wears out each year. Here δ (the lowercase Greek letter delta) is called the *depreciation rate*. For example, if capital lasts an average of 25 years, then the depreciation rate is 4 percent per year ($\delta = 0.04$). The amount of capital that depreciates each year is δk. Figure 4-3 shows how the amount of depreciation depends on the capital stock.

We can express the impact of investment and depreciation on the capital stock with this equation:

$$\text{Change in Capital Stock} = \text{Investment} - \text{Depreciation}$$
$$\Delta k \quad\quad = \quad i \quad - \quad \delta k,$$

where Δk is the change in the capital stock between one year and the next. Because investment i equals $sf(k)$, we can write this as

$$\Delta k = sf(k) - \delta k.$$

Figure 4-4 graphs the terms of this equation—investment and depreciation—for different levels of the capital stock k. The higher the capital stock, the greater the amounts of output and investment. Yet the higher the capital stock, the greater also the amount of depreciation.

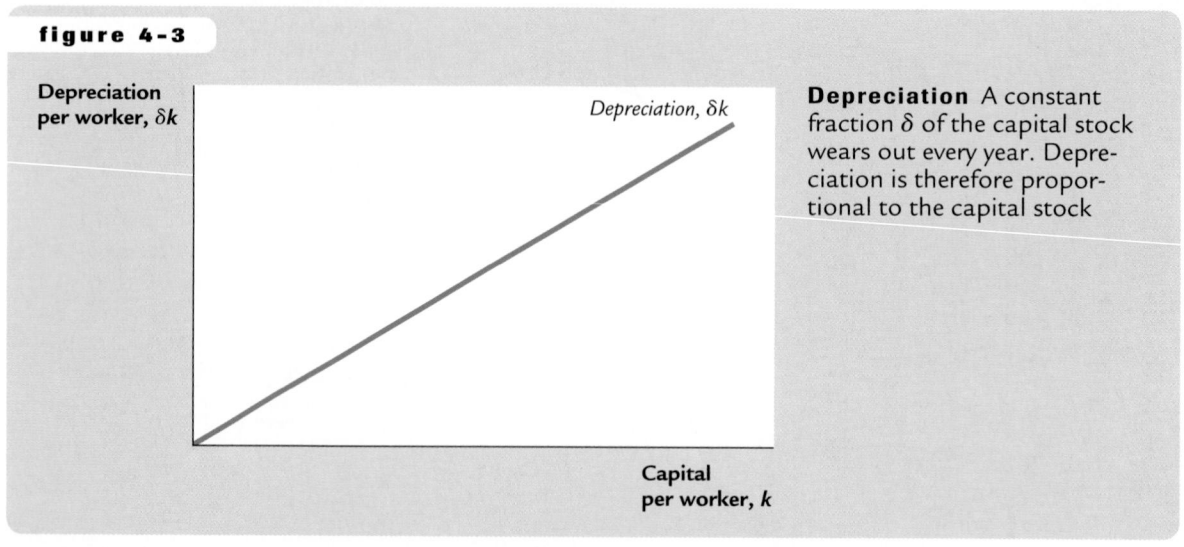

figure 4-3

Depreciation per worker, δk

Depreciation, δk

Capital per worker, k

Depreciation A constant fraction δ of the capital stock wears out every year. Depreciation is therefore proportional to the capital stock

figure 4-4

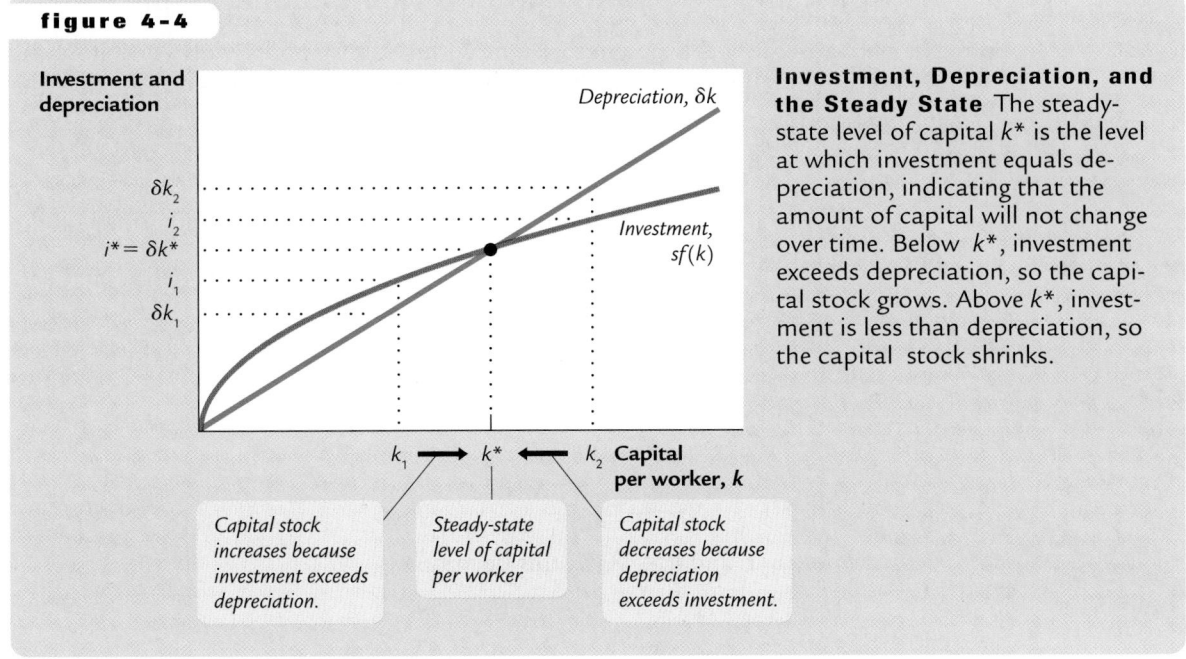

figure 4-4

Investment, Depreciation, and the Steady State The steady-state level of capital k^* is the level at which investment equals depreciation, indicating that the amount of capital will not change over time. Below k^*, investment exceeds depreciation, so the capital stock grows. Above k^*, investment is less than depreciation, so the capital stock shrinks.

As Figure 4-4 shows, there is a single capital stock k^* at which the amount of investment equals the amount of depreciation. If the economy ever finds itself at this level of the capital stock, the capital stock will not change because the two forces acting on it—investment and depreciation—just balance. That is, at k^*, $\Delta k = 0$, so the capital stock k and output $f(k)$ are steady over time (rather than growing or shrinking). We therefore call k^* the **steady-state** level of capital.

The steady state is significant for two reasons. As we have just seen, an economy at the steady state will stay there. In addition, and just as important, an economy not at the steady state will go there. That is, regardless of the level of capital with which the economy begins, it ends up with the steady-state level of capital. In this sense, *the steady state represents the long-run equilibrium of the economy.*

To see why an economy always ends up at the steady state, suppose that the economy starts with less than the steady-state level of capital, such as level k_1 in Figure 4-4. In this case, the level of investment exceeds the amount of depreciation. Over time, the capital stock will rise and will continue to rise—along with output $f(k)$—until it approaches the steady state k^*.

Similarly, suppose that the economy starts with more than the steady-state level of capital, such as level k_2. In this case, investment is less than depreciation: capital is wearing out faster than it is being replaced. The capital stock will fall, again approaching the steady-state level. Once the capital stock reaches the steady state, investment equals depreciation, and there is no pressure for the capital stock to either increase or decrease.

Approaching the Steady State: A Numerical Example

Let's use a numerical example to see how the Solow model works and how the economy approaches the steady state. For this example, we assume that the production function is[2]

$$Y = K^{1/2}L^{1/2}.$$

To derive the per-worker production function $f(k)$, divide both sides of the production function by the labor force L:

$$\frac{Y}{L} = \frac{K^{1/2}L^{1/2}}{L}.$$

Rearrange to obtain

$$\frac{Y}{L} = \left(\frac{K}{L}\right)^{1/2}.$$

Because $y = Y/L$ and $k = K/L$, this becomes

$$y = k^{1/2}.$$

This equation can also be written as

$$y = \sqrt{k}.$$

This form of the production function states that output per worker is equal to the square root of the amount of capital per worker.

To complete the example, let's assume that 30 percent of output is saved ($s = 0.3$), that 10 percent of the capital stock depreciates every year ($\delta = 0.1$), and that the economy starts off with 4 units of capital per worker ($k = 4$). Given these numbers, we can now examine what happens to this economy over time.

We begin by looking at the production and allocation of output in the first year. According to the production function, the 4 units of capital per worker produce 2 units of output per worker. Because 30 percent of output is saved and invested and 70 percent is consumed, $i = 0.6$ and $c = 1.4$. Also, because 10 percent of the capital stock depreciates, $\delta k = 0.4$. With investment of 0.6 and depreciation of 0.4, the change in the capital stock is $\Delta k = 0.2$. The second year begins with 4.2 units of capital per worker.

Table 4-2 shows how the economy progresses year by year. Every year, new capital is added and output grows. Over many years, the economy approaches a steady state with 9 units of capital per worker. In this steady state, investment of 0.9 exactly offsets depreciation of 0.9, so that the capital stock and output are no longer growing.

---

[2] If you read the appendix to Chapter 3, you will recognize this as the Cobb–Douglas production function with the parameter α equal to $1/2$.

table 4-2

Approaching the Steady State: A Numerical Example

Assumptions: $y = \sqrt{k}$; $s = 0.3$; $\delta = 0.1$;   initial $k = 4.0$

Year	k	y	c	i	δk	Δk
1	4.000	2.000	1.400	0.600	0.400	0.200
2	4.200	2.049	1.435	0.615	0.420	0.195
3	4.395	2.096	1.467	0.629	0.440	0.189
4	4.584	2.141	1.499	0.642	0.458	0.184
5	4.768	2.184	1.529	0.655	0.477	0.178
⋮						
10	5.602	2.367	1.657	0.710	0.560	0.150
⋮						
25	7.321	2.706	1.894	0.812	0.732	0.080
⋮						
100	8.962	2.994	2.096	0.898	0.896	0.002
⋮						
∞	9.000	3.000	2.100	0.900	0.900	0.000

Following the progress of the economy for many years is one way to find the steady-state capital stock, but there is another way that requires fewer calculations. Recall that

$$\Delta k = sf(k) - \delta k.$$

This equation shows how k evolves over time. Because the steady state is (by definition) the value of k at which $\Delta k = 0$, we know that

$$0 = sf(k^*) - \delta k^*,$$

or, equivalently,

$$\frac{k^*}{f(k^*)} = \frac{s}{\delta}.$$

This equation provides a way of finding the steady-state level of capital per worker, k^*. Substituting in the numbers and production function from our example, we obtain

$$\frac{k^*}{\sqrt{k^*}} = \frac{0.3}{0.1}.$$

Now square both sides of this equation to find

$$k^* = 9.$$

The steady-state capital stock is 9 units per worker. This result confirms the calculation of the steady state in Table 4-2.

CASE STUDY

The Miracle of Japanese and German Growth

Japan and Germany are two success stories of economic growth. Although today they are economic superpowers, in 1945 the economies of both countries were in shambles. World War II had destroyed much of their capital stocks. In the decades after the war, however, these two countries experienced some of the most rapid growth rates on record. Between 1948 and 1972, output per person grew at 8.2 percent per year in Japan and 5.7 percent per year in Germany, compared to only 2.2 percent per year in the United States.

Are the postwar experiences of Japan and Germany so surprising from the standpoint of the Solow growth model? Consider an economy in steady state. Now suppose that a war destroys some of the capital stock. (That is, suppose the capital stock drops from k^* to k_1 in Figure 4-4.) Not surprisingly, the level of output immediately falls. But if the saving rate—the fraction of output devoted to saving and investment—is unchanged, the economy will then experience a period of high growth. Output grows because, at the lower capital stock, more capital is added by investment than is removed by depreciation. This high growth continues until the economy approaches its former steady state. Hence, although destroying part of the capital stock immediately reduces output, it is followed by higher than normal growth. The "miracle" of rapid growth in Japan and Germany, as it is often described in the business press, is what the Solow model predicts for countries in which war has greatly reduced the capital stock.

How Saving Affects Growth

The explanation of Japanese and German growth after World War II is not quite as simple as suggested in the preceding case study. Another relevant fact is that both Japan and Germany save and invest a higher fraction of their output than does the United States. To understand more fully the international differences in economic performance, we must consider the effects of different saving rates.

Consider what happens to an economy when its saving rate increases. Figure 4-5 shows such a change. The economy is assumed to begin in a steady state with saving rate s_1 and capital stock k_1^*. When the saving rate increases from s_1 to s_2, the $sf(k)$ curve shifts upward. At the initial saving rate s_1 and the initial capital stock k_1^*, the amount of investment just offsets the amount of depreciation. Immediately after the saving rate rises, investment is higher, but the capital stock and depreciation are unchanged. Therefore, investment exceeds depreciation. The capital stock will gradually rise until the economy reaches the

figure 4-5

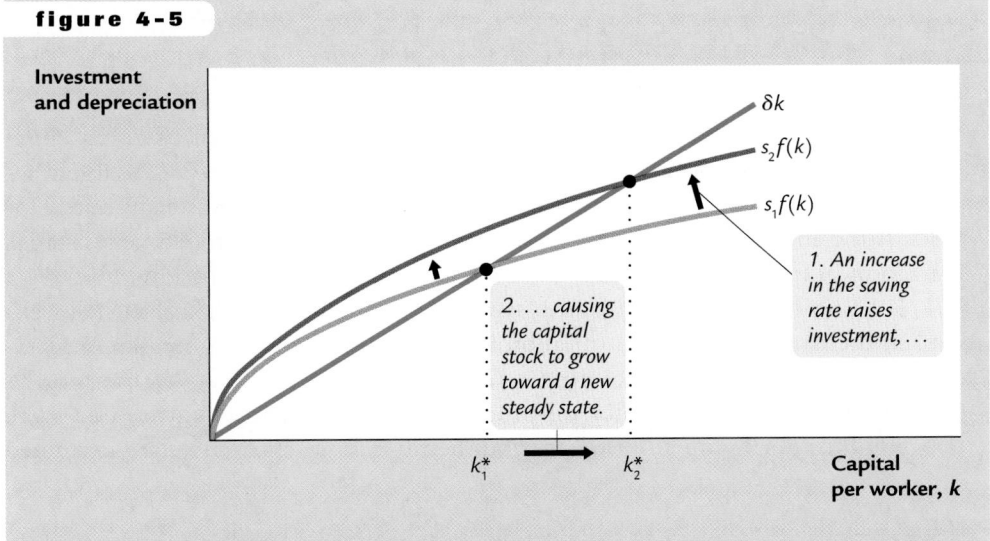

An Increase in the Saving Rate An increase in the saving rate *s* implies that the amount of investment for any given capital stock is higher. It therefore shifts the saving function upward. At the initial steady state k_1^*, investment now exceeds depreciation. The capital stock rises until the economy reaches a new steady state k_2^*, with more capital and output.

new steady state k_2^*, which has a higher capital stock and a higher level of output than the old steady state.

The Solow model shows that the saving rate is a key determinant of the steady-state capital stock. *If the saving rate is high, the economy will have a large capital stock and a high level of output. If the saving rate is low, the economy will have a small capital stock and a low level of output.* This conclusion sheds light on many discussions of fiscal policy. As we saw in Chapter 3, a government budget deficit can reduce national saving and crowd out investment. Now we can see that the long-run consequences of a reduced saving rate are a lower capital stock and lower national income. This is why many economists are critical of persistent budget deficits.

What does the Solow model say about the relationship between saving and economic growth? Higher saving leads to faster growth in the Solow model, but only temporarily. An increase in the rate of saving raises growth until the economy reaches the new steady state. If the economy maintains a high saving rate, it will also maintain a large capital stock and a high level of output, but it will not maintain a high rate of growth forever.

Now that we understand how saving affects growth, we can more fully explain the impressive economic performance of Germany and Japan after World War II. Not only were their initial capital stocks low because of the war, but their steady-state capital stocks were high because of their high saving rates. Both of these facts help explain the rapid growth of these two countries in the 1950s and 1960s.

CASE STUDY

Saving and Investment Around the World

We started this chapter with an important question: Why are some countries so rich while others are mired in poverty? Our analysis has taken us a step closer to the answer. According to the Solow model, if a nation devotes a large fraction of its income to saving and investment, it will have a high steady-state capital stock and a high level of income. If a nation saves and invests only a small fraction of its income, its steady-state capital and income will be low.

Let's now look at some data to see if this theoretical result in fact helps explain the large international variation in standards of living. Figure 4-6 is a scatterplot of data from 84 countries. (The figure includes most of the world's economies. It excludes major oil-producing countries and countries that were communist during much of this period, because their experiences are explained

figure 4-6

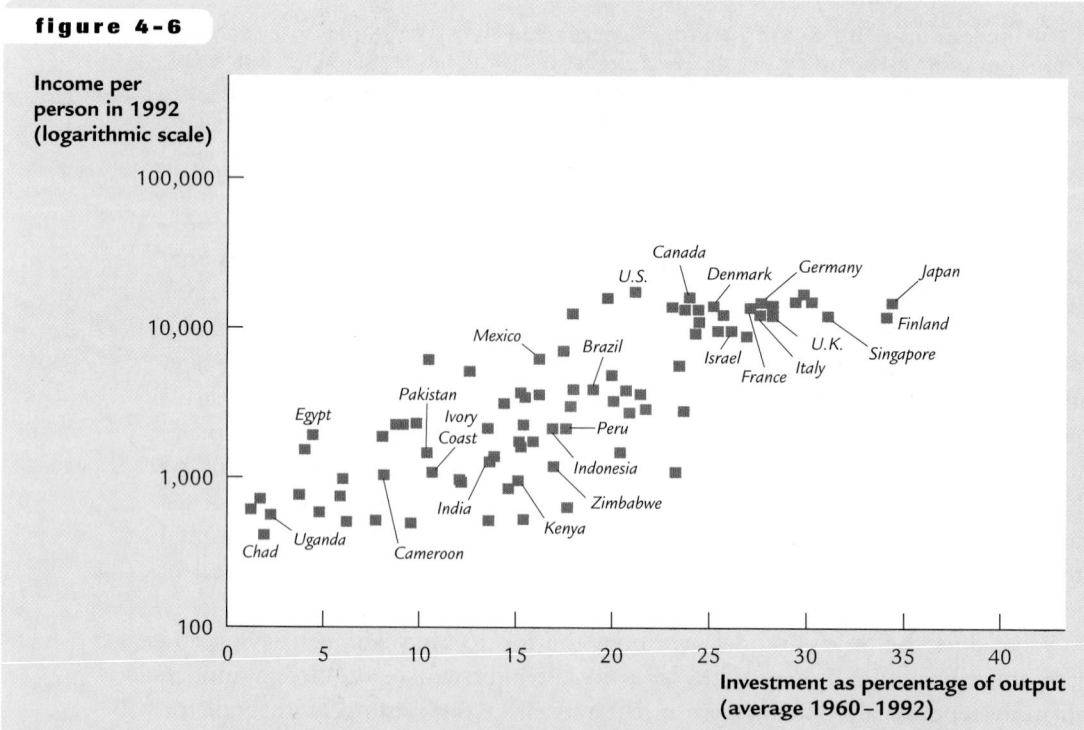

International Evidence on Investment Rates and Income per Person This scatterplot shows the experience of 84 countries, each represented by a single point. The horizontal axis shows the country's rate of investment, and the vertical axis shows the country's income per person. High investment is associated with high income per person, as the Solow model predicts.

Source: Robert Summers and Alan Heston, Supplement (Mark 5.6) to "The Penn World Table (Mark 5): An Expanded Set of International Comparisons 1950–1988," *Quarterly Journal of Economics* (May 1991): 327–368.

by their special circumstances.) The data show a positive relationship between the fraction of output devoted to investment and the level of income per person. That is, countries with high rates of investment, such as the United States and Japan, usually have high incomes, whereas countries with low rates of investment, such as Uganda and Chad, have low incomes. Thus, the data are consistent with the Solow model's prediction that the investment rate is a key determinant of whether a country is rich or poor.

The strong correlation shown in this figure is an important fact, but it raises as many questions as it resolves. One might naturally ask, why do rates of saving and investment vary so much from country to country? There are many potential answers, such as tax policy, retirement patterns, the development of financial markets, and cultural differences. In addition, political stability may play a role: not surprisingly, rates of saving and investment tend to be low in countries with frequent wars, revolutions, and coups. Saving and investment also tend to be low in countries with poor political institutions, as measured by estimates of official corruption. A final interpretation of the evidence in Figure 4-6 is reverse causation: perhaps high levels of income somehow foster high rates of saving and investment. Unfortunately, there is no consensus among economists about which of the many possible explanations is most important.

The association between investment rates and income per person is strong, and it is an important clue as to why some countries are rich and others poor, but it is not the whole story. The correlation between these two variables is far from perfect. Mexico and Zimbabwe, for instance, have had similar investment rates, but income per person is more than three times higher in Mexico. There must be other determinants of living standards beyond saving and investment. We therefore return to the international differences later in the chapter to see what other variables enter the picture.

4-2 | The Golden Rule Level of Capital

So far, we have used the Solow model to examine how an economy's rate of saving and investment determines its steady-state levels of capital and income. This analysis might lead you to think that higher saving is always a good thing, for it always leads to greater income. Yet suppose a nation had a saving rate of 100 percent. That would lead to the largest possible capital stock and the largest possible income. But if all of this income is saved and none is ever consumed, what good is it?

This section uses the Solow model to discuss what amount of capital accumulation is optimal from the standpoint of economic well-being. In the next chapter, we discuss how government policies influence a nation's saving rate. But first, in this section, we present the theory behind these policy decisions.

Comparing Steady States

To keep our analysis simple, let's assume that a policymaker can set the economy's saving rate at any level. By setting the saving rate, the policymaker determines the economy's steady state. What steady state should the policymaker choose?

When choosing a steady state, the policymaker's goal is to maximize the well-being of the individuals who make up the society. Individuals themselves do not care about the amount of capital in the economy, or even the amount of output. They care about the amount of goods and services they can consume. Thus, a benevolent policymaker would want to choose the steady state with the highest level of consumption. The steady-state value of k that maximizes consumption is called the **Golden Rule level of capital** and is denoted k^*_{gold}.[3]

How can we tell whether an economy is at the Golden Rule level? To answer this question, we must first determine steady-state consumption per worker. Then we can see which steady state provides the most consumption.

To find steady-state consumption per worker, we begin with the national income accounts identity

$$y = c + i$$

and rearrange it as

$$c = y - i.$$

Consumption is simply output minus investment. Because we want to find steady-state consumption, we substitute steady-state values for output and investment. Steady-state output per worker is $f(k^*)$, where k^* is the steady-state capital stock per worker. Furthermore, because the capital stock is not changing in the steady state, investment is equal to depreciation δk^*. Substituting $f(k^*)$ for y and δk^* for i, we can write steady-state consumption per worker as

$$c^* = f(k^*) - \delta k^*.$$

According to this equation, steady-state consumption is what's left of steady-state output after paying for steady-state depreciation. This equation shows that an increase in steady-state capital has two opposing effects on steady-state consumption. On the one hand, more capital means more output. On the other hand, more capital also means that more output must be used to replace capital that is wearing out.

Figure 4-7 graphs steady-state output and steady-state depreciation as a function of the steady-state capital stock. Steady-state consumption is the gap between output and depreciation. This figure shows that there is one level of the capital stock—the Golden Rule level k^*_{gold}—that maximizes consumption.

When comparing steady states, we must keep in mind that higher levels of capital affect both output and depreciation. If the capital stock is below the

[3] Edmund Phelps, "The Golden Rule of Accumulation: A Fable for Growthmen," *American Economic Review* 51 (September 1961): 638–643.

figure 4-7

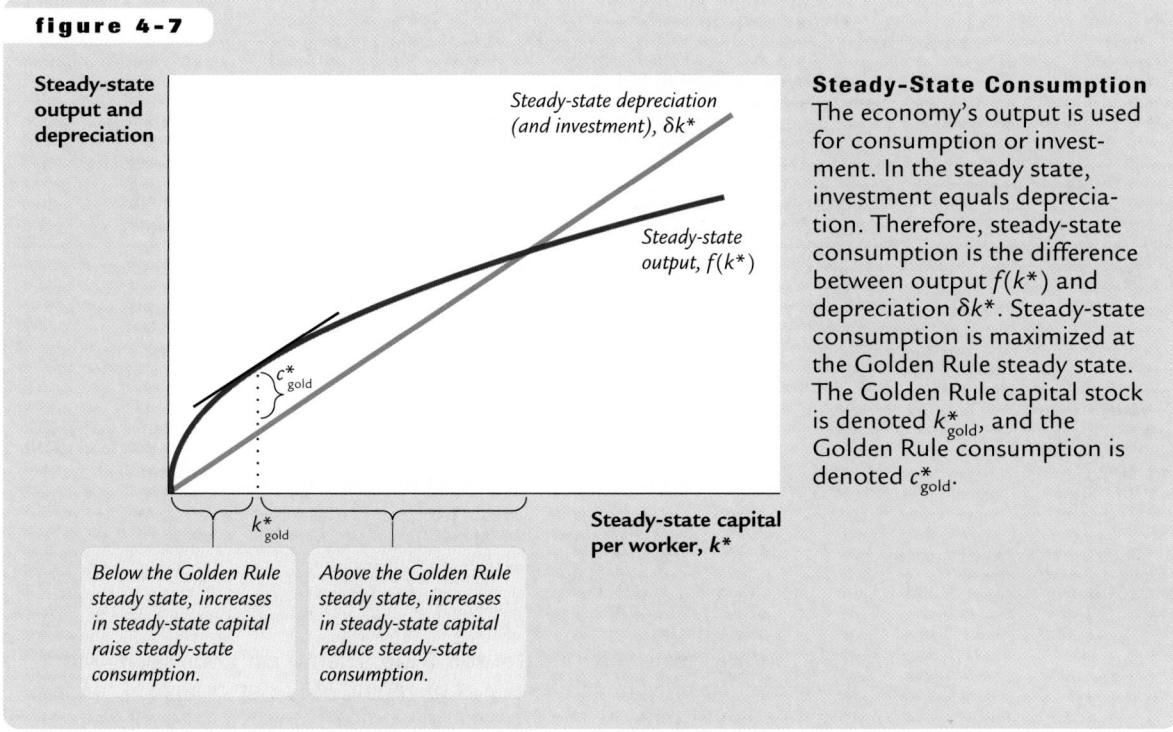

Steady-state output and depreciation

Steady-state depreciation (and investment), δk^*

Steady-state output, $f(k^*)$

c^*_{gold}

k^*_{gold}

Steady-state capital per worker, k^*

Below the Golden Rule steady state, increases in steady-state capital raise steady-state consumption.

Above the Golden Rule steady state, increases in steady-state capital reduce steady-state consumption.

Steady-State Consumption
The economy's output is used for consumption or investment. In the steady state, investment equals depreciation. Therefore, steady-state consumption is the difference between output $f(k^*)$ and depreciation δk^*. Steady-state consumption is maximized at the Golden Rule steady state. The Golden Rule capital stock is denoted k^*_{gold}, and the Golden Rule consumption is denoted c^*_{gold}.

Golden Rule level, an increase in the capital stock raises output more than depreciation, so that consumption rises. In this case, the production function is steeper than the δk^* line, so the gap between these two curves—which equals consumption—grows as k^* rises. By contrast, if the capital stock is above the Golden Rule level, an increase in the capital stock reduces consumption, since the increase in output is smaller than the increase in depreciation. In this case, the production function is flatter than the δk^* line, so the gap between the curves—consumption—shrinks as k^* rises. At the Golden Rule level of capital, the production function and the δk^* line have the same slope, and consumption is at its greatest level.

We can now derive a simple condition that characterizes the Golden Rule level of capital. Recall that the slope of the production function is the marginal product of capital MPK. The slope of the δk^* line is δ. Because these two slopes are equal at k^*_{gold}, the Golden Rule is described by the equation

$$MPK = \delta.$$

At the Golden Rule level of capital, the marginal product of capital equals the depreciation rate.

To make the point somewhat differently, suppose that the economy starts at some steady-state capital stock k^* and that the policymaker is considering increasing the capital stock to $k^* + 1$. The amount of extra output from this increase in capital would be $f(k^* + 1) - f(k^*)$, which is the marginal product of capital MPK. The amount of extra depreciation from having 1 more unit

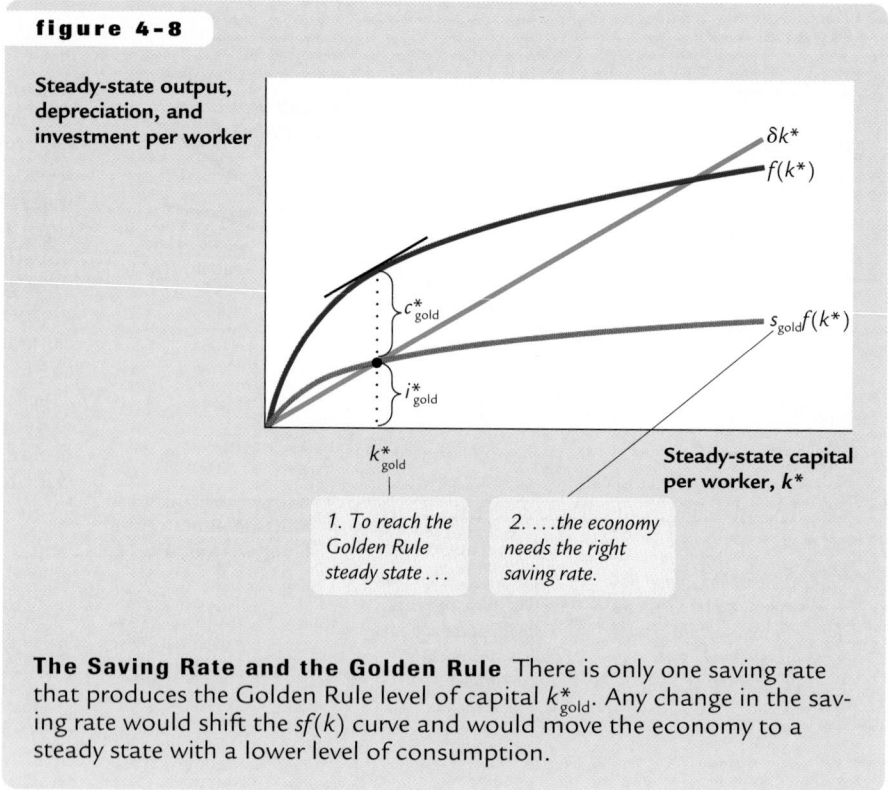

figure 4-8

Steady-state output, depreciation, and investment per worker

δk^*

$f(k^*)$

c^*_{gold}

$s_{gold}f(k^*)$

i^*_{gold}

k^*_{gold}

Steady-state capital per worker, k^*

1. To reach the Golden Rule steady state . . .

2. . . .the economy needs the right saving rate.

The Saving Rate and the Golden Rule There is only one saving rate that produces the Golden Rule level of capital k^*_{gold}. Any change in the saving rate would shift the $sf(k)$ curve and would move the economy to a steady state with a lower level of consumption.

of capital is the depreciation rate δ. Thus, the net effect of this extra unit of capital on consumption is then $MPK - \delta$. If $MPK - \delta > 0$, then increases in capital increase consumption, so k^* must be below the Golden Rule level. If $MPK - \delta < 0$, then increases in capital decrease consumption, so k^* must be above the Golden Rule level. Therefore, the following condition describes the Golden Rule:

$$MPK - \delta = 0.$$

At the Golden Rule level of capital, the marginal product of capital net of depreciation ($MPK - \delta$) equals zero. As we will see, a policymaker can use this condition for figuring out the Golden Rule capital stock for any given economy.[4]

Keep in mind that the economy does not automatically gravitate toward the Golden Rule steady state. If we want any particular steady-state capital stock, such as the Golden Rule, we need a particular saving rate to support it. Figure 4-8 shows the steady state if the saving rate is set to produce the Golden Rule level of capital. If the saving rate is higher than the one used in

---

[4] *Mathematical note:* Another way to derive the condition for the Golden Rule uses a bit of calculus. Recall that $c^* = f(k^*) - \delta k^*$. To find the k^* that maximizes c^*, differentiate to find $dc^*/dk^* = f'(k^*) - \delta$ and set this derivative equal to zero. Noting that $f'(k^*)$ is the marginal product of capital, we obtain the Golden Rule condition in the text.

this figure, the steady-state capital stock will be too high. If the saving rate is lower, the steady-state capital stock will be too low. In either case, steady-state consumption will be lower than it is at the Golden Rule steady state.

Finding the Golden Rule Steady State: A Numerical Example

Consider the decision of a policymaker choosing a steady state in the following economy. The production function is the same as in our earlier example:

$$y = \sqrt{k}.$$

Output per worker is the square root of capital per worker. Depreciation δ is again 10 percent of capital. This time, the policymaker chooses the saving rate s and thus the economy's steady state.

To see the outcomes available to the policymaker, recall that the following equation holds in the steady state:

$$\frac{k^*}{f(k^*)} = \frac{s}{\delta}.$$

In this economy, this equation becomes

$$\frac{k^*}{\sqrt{k^*}} = \frac{s}{0.1}.$$

Squaring both sides of this equation yields a solution for the steady-state capital stock. We find

$$k^* = 100s^2.$$

Using this result, we can compute the steady-state capital stock for any saving rate.

Table 4-3 presents calculations showing the steady states that result from various saving rates in this economy. We see that higher saving leads to a higher capital stock, which in turn leads to higher output and higher depreciation. Steady-state consumption, the difference between output and depreciation, first rises with higher saving rates and then declines. Consumption is highest when the saving rate is 0.5. Hence, a saving rate of 0.5 produces the Golden Rule steady state.

Recall that another way to identify the Golden Rule steady state is to find the capital stock at which the net marginal product of capital ($MPK - \delta$) equals zero. For this production function, the marginal product is[5]

$$MPK = \frac{1}{2\sqrt{k}}.$$

---

[5] *Mathematical note:* To derive this formula, note that the marginal product of capital is the derivative of the production function with respect to k.

table 4-3

Finding the Golden Rule Steady State: A Numerical Example

Assumptions: $y = \sqrt{k}$; $\delta = 0.1$

s	k*	y*	δk*	c*	MPK	MPK − δ
0.0	0.0	0.0	0.0	0.0	∞	∞
0.1	1.0	1.0	0.1	0.9	0.500	0.400
0.2	4.0	2.0	0.4	1.6	0.250	0.150
0.3	9.0	3.0	0.9	2.1	0.167	0.067
0.4	16.0	4.0	1.6	2.4	0.125	0.025
0.5	**25.0**	**5.0**	**2.5**	**2.5**	**0.100**	**0.000**
0.6	36.0	6.0	3.6	2.4	0.083	−0.017
0.7	49.0	7.0	4.9	2.1	0.071	−0.029
0.8	64.0	8.0	6.4	1.6	0.062	−0.038
0.9	81.0	9.0	8.1	0.9	0.056	−0.044
1.0	100.0	10.0	10.0	0.0	0.050	−0.050

Using this formula, the last two columns of Table 4-3 present the values of *MPK* and *MPK − δ* in the different steady states. Note that the net marginal product of capital is exactly zero when the saving rate is at its Golden Rule value of 0.5. Because of diminishing marginal product, the net marginal product of capital is greater than zero whenever the economy saves less than this amount, and it is less than zero whenever the economy saves more.

This numerical example confirms that the two ways of finding the Golden Rule steady state—looking at steady-state consumption or looking at the marginal product of capital—give the same answer. If we want to know whether an actual economy is currently at, above, or below its Golden Rule capital stock, the second method is usually more convenient, because estimates of the marginal product of capital are easy to come by. By contrast, evaluating an economy with the first method requires estimates of steady-state consumption at many different saving rates; such information is hard to obtain. Thus, when we apply this kind of analysis to the U.S. economy in the next chapter, we will find it useful to examine estimates of the marginal product of capital.

The Transition to the Golden Rule Steady State

Let's now make our policymaker's problem more realistic. So far, we have been assuming that the policymaker can simply choose the economy's steady state and jump there immediately. In this case, the policymaker would choose the steady state with highest consumption—the Golden Rule steady state. But now suppose that the economy has reached a steady state other than the Golden Rule. What happens to consumption, investment, and capital when the economy makes the transition between steady states? Might the impact of the transition deter the policymaker from trying to achieve the Golden Rule?

We must consider two cases: the economy might begin with more capital than in the Golden Rule steady state, or with less. It turns out that the two cases offer very different problems for policymakers. (As we will see in the next chapter, the second case—too little capital—describes most actual economies, including that of the United States.)

Starting With Too Much Capital   We first consider the case in which the economy begins at a steady state with more capital than it would have in the Golden Rule steady state. In this case, the policymaker should pursue policies aimed at reducing the rate of saving in order to reduce the capital stock. Suppose that these policies succeed and that at some point—call it time t_0—the saving rate falls to the level that will eventually lead to the Golden Rule steady state.

Figure 4-9 shows what happens to output, consumption, and investment when the saving rate falls. The reduction in the saving rate causes an immediate increase in consumption and a decrease in investment. Because investment and depreciation were equal in the initial steady state, investment will now be less than depreciation, which means the economy is no longer in a steady state. Gradually, the capital stock falls, leading to reductions in output, consumption, and investment. These variables continue to fall until the economy reaches the new steady state. Because we are assuming that the new steady state is the Golden Rule steady state, consumption must be higher than it was

figure 4-9

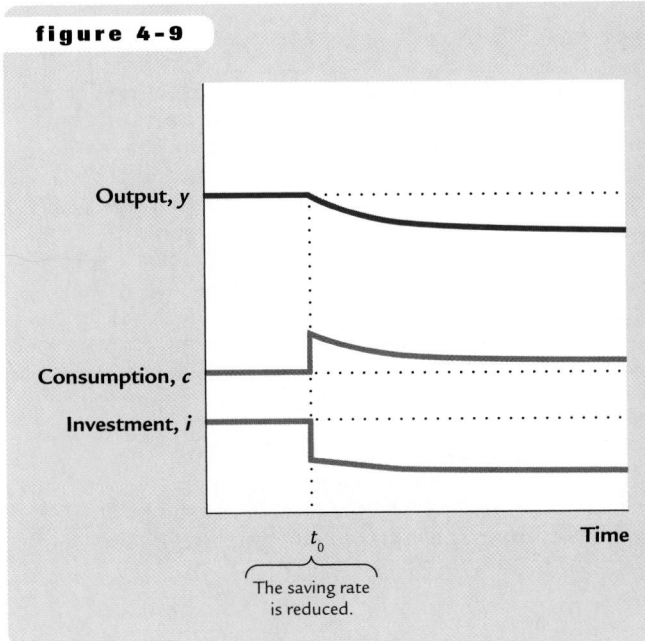

Reducing Saving When Starting With More Capital Than in the Golden Rule Steady State This figure shows what happens over time to output, consumption, and investment when the economy begins with more capital than the Golden Rule level and the saving rate is reduced. The reduction in the saving rate (at time t_0) causes an immediate increase in consumption and an equal decrease in investment. Over time, as the capital stock falls, output, consumption, and investment fall together. Because the economy began with too much capital, the new steady state has a higher level of consumption than the initial steady state.

before the change in the saving rate, even though output and investment are lower.

Note that, compared to the old steady state, consumption is higher not just in the new steady state but also along the entire path to it. When the capital stock exceeds the Golden Rule level, reducing saving is clearly a good policy, for it increases consumption at every point in time.

Starting With Too Little Capital   When the economy begins with less capital than in the Golden Rule steady state, the policymaker must raise the saving rate to reach the Golden Rule. Figure 4-10 shows what happens. The increase in the saving rate at time t_0 causes an immediate fall in consumption and a rise in investment. Over time, higher investment causes the capital stock to rise. As capital accumulates, output, consumption, and investment gradually increase, eventually approaching the new steady-state levels. Because the initial steady state was below the Golden Rule, the increase in saving eventually leads to a higher level of consumption than that which prevailed initially.

Does the increase in saving that leads to the Golden Rule steady state raise economic welfare? Eventually it does, because the steady-state level of consumption is higher. But achieving that new steady state requires an initial period of reduced consumption. Note the contrast to the case in which the economy begins above the Golden Rule. *When the economy begins above the Golden Rule, reaching the Golden Rule produces higher consumption at all points in time. When the economy begins below the Golden Rule, reaching the Golden Rule requires initially reducing consumption to increase consumption in the future.*

When deciding whether to try to reach the Golden Rule steady state, policymakers have to take into account that current consumers and future con-

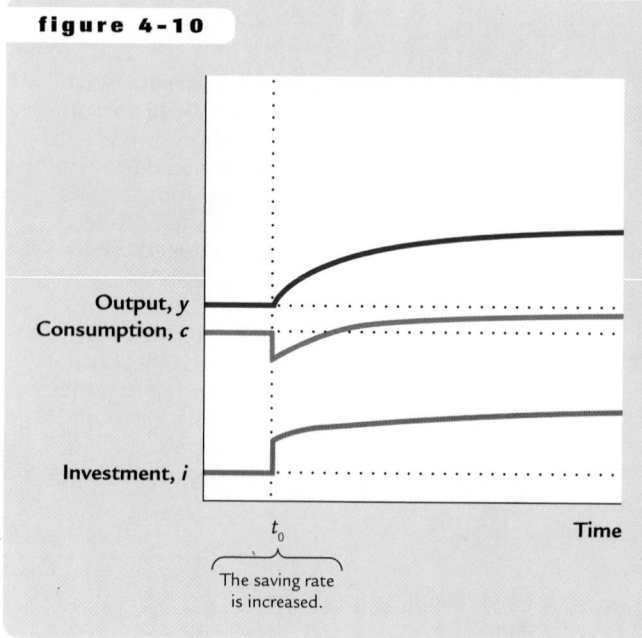

figure 4-10

Increasing Saving When Starting With Less Capital Than in the Golden Rule Steady State This figure shows what happens over time to output, consumption, and investment when the economy begins with less capital than the Golden Rule, and the saving rate is increased. The increase in the saving rate (at time t_0) causes an immediate drop in consumption and an equal jump in investment. Over time, as the capital stock grows, output, consumption, and investment increase together. Because the economy began with less capital than the Golden Rule, the new steady state has a higher level of consumption than the initial steady state.

Output, y
Consumption, c

Investment, i

t_0

Time

The saving rate
is increased.

sumers are not always the same people. Reaching the Golden Rule achieves the highest steady-state level of consumption and thus benefits future generations. But when the economy is initially below the Golden Rule, reaching the Golden Rule requires raising investment and thus lowering the consumption of current generations. Thus, when choosing whether to increase capital accumulation, the policymaker faces a tradeoff among the welfare of different generations. A policymaker who cares more about current generations than about future generations may decide not to pursue policies to reach the Golden Rule steady state. By contrast, a policymaker who cares about all generations equally will choose to reach the Golden Rule. Even though current generations will consume less, an infinite number of future generations will benefit by moving to the Golden Rule.

Thus, optimal capital accumulation depends crucially on how we weigh the interests of current and future generations. The biblical Golden Rule tells us, "do unto others as you would have them do unto you." If we heed this advice, we give all generations equal weight. In this case, it is optimal to reach the Golden Rule level of capital—which is why it is called the "Golden Rule."

4-3 | Population Growth

The basic Solow model shows that capital accumulation, by itself, cannot explain sustained economic growth: high rates of saving lead to high growth temporarily, but the economy eventually approaches a steady state in which capital and output are constant. To explain the sustained economic growth that we observe in most parts of the world, we must expand the Solow model to incorporate the other two sources of economic growth—population growth and technological progress. In this section we add population growth to the model.

Instead of assuming that the population is fixed, as we did in Sections 4-1 and 4-2, we now suppose that the population and the labor force grow at a constant rate n. For example, the U.S. population grows about 1 percent per year, so $n = 0.01$. This means that if 150 million people are working one year, then 151.5 million (1.01 × 150) are working the next year, and 153.015 million (1.01 × 151.5) the year after that, and so on.

The Steady State With Population Growth

How does population growth affect the steady state? To answer this question, we must discuss how population growth, along with investment and depreciation, influences the accumulation of capital per worker. As we noted before, investment raises the capital stock, and depreciation reduces it. But now there is a third force acting to change the amount of capital per worker: the growth in the number of workers causes capital per worker to fall.

We continue to let lowercase letters stand for quantities per worker. Thus, $k = K/L$ is capital per worker, and $y = Y/L$ is output per worker. Keep in mind, however, that the number of workers is growing over time.

The change in the capital stock per worker is

$$\Delta k = i - (\delta + n)k.$$

This equation shows how new investment, depreciation, and population growth influence the per-worker capital stock. New investment increases k, whereas depreciation and population growth decrease k. We have seen this equation earlier in this chapter for the special case of a constant population ($n = 0$).

We can think of the term $(\delta + n)k$ as defining *break-even investment*—the amount of investment necessary to keep the capital stock per worker constant. Break-even investment includes the depreciation of existing capital, which equals δk. It also includes the amount of investment necessary to provide new workers with capital. The amount of investment necessary for this purpose is nk, because there are n new workers for each existing worker, and because k is the amount of capital for each worker. The equation shows that population growth reduces the accumulation of capital per worker much the way depreciation does. Depreciation reduces k by wearing out the capital stock, whereas population growth reduces k by spreading the capital stock more thinly among a larger population of workers.[6]

Our analysis with population growth now proceeds much as it did previously. First, we substitute $sf(k)$ for i. The equation can then be written as

$$\Delta k = sf(k) - (\delta + n)k.$$

To see what determines the steady-state level of capital per worker, we use Figure 4-11, which extends the analysis of Figure 4-4 to include the effects of population growth. An economy is in a steady state if capital per worker k is unchanging. As before, we designate the steady-state value of k as k^*. If k is less than k^*, investment is greater than break-even investment, so k rises. If k is greater than k^*, investment is less than break-even investment, so k falls.

In the steady state, the positive effect of investment on the capital stock per worker just balances the negative effects of depreciation and population growth. That is, at k^*, $\Delta k = 0$ and $i^* = \delta k^* + nk^*$. Once the economy is in the steady state, investment has two purposes. Some of it (δk^*) replaces the depreciated capital, and the rest (nk^*) provides the new workers with the steady-state amount of capital.

---

[6] *Mathematical note:* Formally deriving the equation for the change in k requires a bit of calculus. Note that the change in k per unit of time is $dk/dt = d(K/L)/dt$. After applying the chain rule, we can write this as $dk/dt = (1/L)(dK/dt) - (K/L^2)(dL/dt)$. Now use the following facts to substitute in this equation: $dK/dt = I - \delta K$ and $(dL/dt)/L = n$. After a bit of manipulation, this produces the equation in the text.

figure 4-11

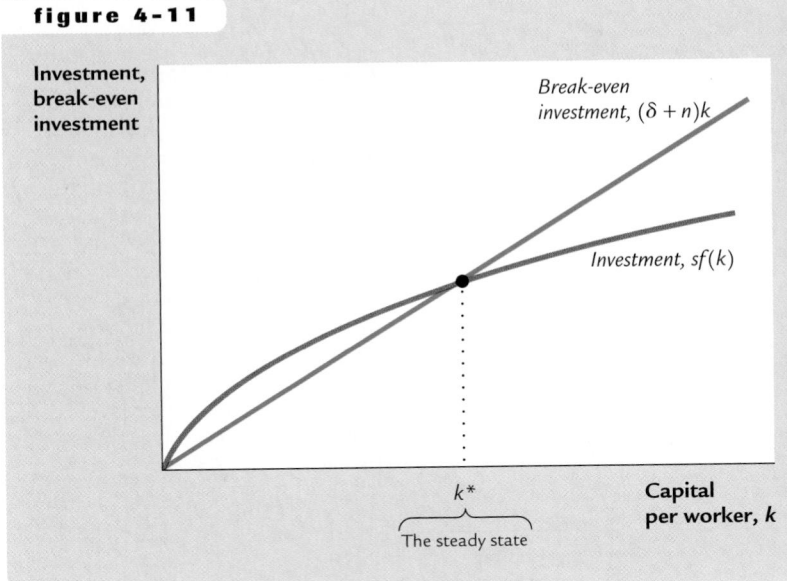

Population Growth in the Solow Model Like depreciation, population growth is one reason why the capital stock per worker shrinks. If n is the rate of population growth and δ is the rate of depreciation, then $(\delta + n)k$ is *break-even investment*—the amount of investment necessary to keep constant the capital stock per worker k. For the economy to be in a steady state, investment $sf(k)$ must offset the effects of depreciation and population growth $(\delta + n)k$. This is represented by the crossing of the two curves.

The Effects of Population Growth

Population growth alters the basic Solow model in three ways. First, it brings us closer to explaining sustained economic growth. In the steady state with population growth, capital per worker and output per worker are constant. Because the number of workers is growing at rate n, however, *total* capital and *total* output must also be growing at rate n. Hence, while population growth cannot explain sustained growth in the standard of living (because output per worker is constant in the steady state), it can help explain sustained growth in total output.

Second, population growth gives us another explanation for why some countries are rich and others are poor. Consider the effects of an increase in population growth. Figure 4-12 shows that an increase in the rate of population growth from n_1 to n_2 reduces the steady-state level of capital per worker from k_1^* to k_2^*. Because k^* is lower, and because $y^* = f(k^*)$, the level of output per worker y^* is also lower. Thus, the Solow model predicts that countries with higher population growth will have lower levels of GDP per person.

Finally, population growth affects our criterion for determining the Golden Rule (consumption-maximizing) level of capital. To see how this criterion changes, note that consumption per worker is

$$c = y - i.$$

Because steady-state output is $f(k^*)$ and steady-state investment is $(\delta + n)k^*$, we can express steady-state consumption as

$$c^* = f(k^*) - (\delta + n)k^*.$$

figure 4-12

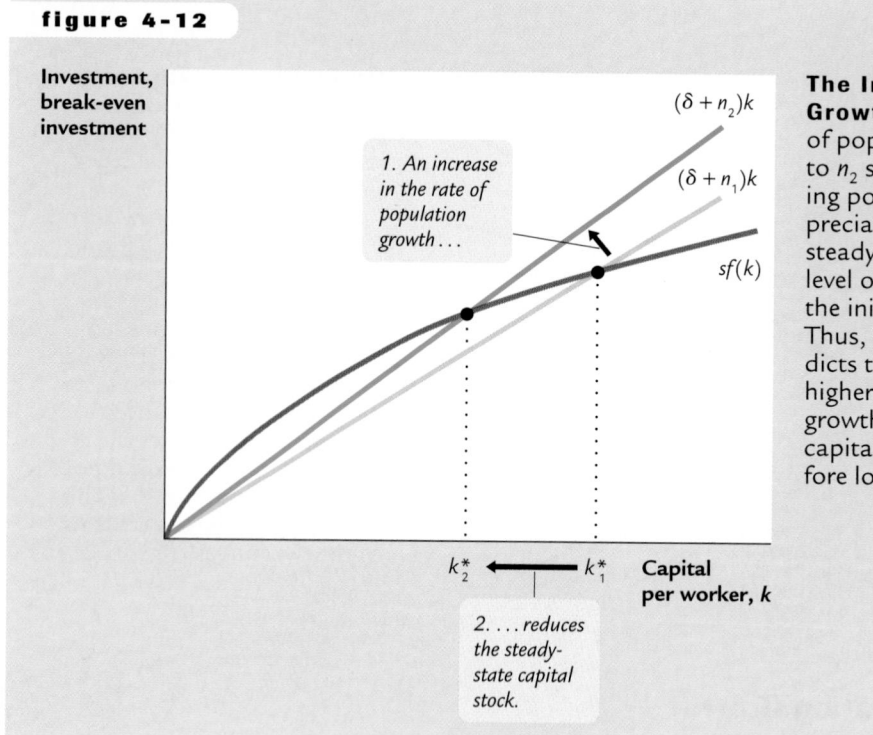

Investment, break-even investment

1. An increase in the rate of population growth . . .

$(\delta + n_2)k$

$(\delta + n_1)k$

$sf(k)$

k_2^* ← k_1^* Capital per worker, k

2. . . . reduces the steady-state capital stock.

The Impact of Population Growth An increase in the rate of population growth from n_1 to n_2 shifts the line representing population growth and depreciation upward. The new steady state k_2^* has a lower level of capital per worker than the initial steady state k_1^*. Thus, the Solow model predicts that economies with higher rates of population growth will have lower levels of capital per worker and therefore lower incomes.

Using an argument largely the same as before, we conclude that the level of k^* that maximizes consumption is the one at which

$$MPK = \delta + n,$$

or equivalently,

$$MPK - \delta = n.$$

In the Golden Rule steady state, the marginal product of capital net of depreciation equals the rate of population growth.

CASE STUDY

Population Growth Around the World

Let's return now to the question of why standards of living vary so much around the world. The analysis we have just completed suggests that population growth may be one of the answers. According to the Solow model, a nation with a high rate of population growth will have a low steady-state capital stock per worker and thus also a low level of income per worker. In other words, high population growth tends to impoverish a country because it is hard to maintain a high level of capital per worker when the number of workers is growing quickly. To see whether the evidence supports this conclusion, we again look at cross-country data.

Figure 4-13 is a scatterplot of data for the same 84 countries examined in the previous case study (and in Figure 4-6). The figure shows that countries with high rates of population growth tend to have low levels of income per person. The international evidence is consistent with our model's prediction that the rate of population growth is one determinant of a country's standard of living.

This conclusion is not lost on policymakers. Those trying to pull the world's poorest nations out of poverty, such as the advisers sent to developing nations by the World Bank, often advocate reducing fertility by increasing education about birth-control methods and expanding women's job opportunities. Toward the same end, China has followed the totalitarian policy of allowing only one child per couple. These policies to reduce population growth should, if the Solow model is right, raise income per person in the long run.

figure 4-13

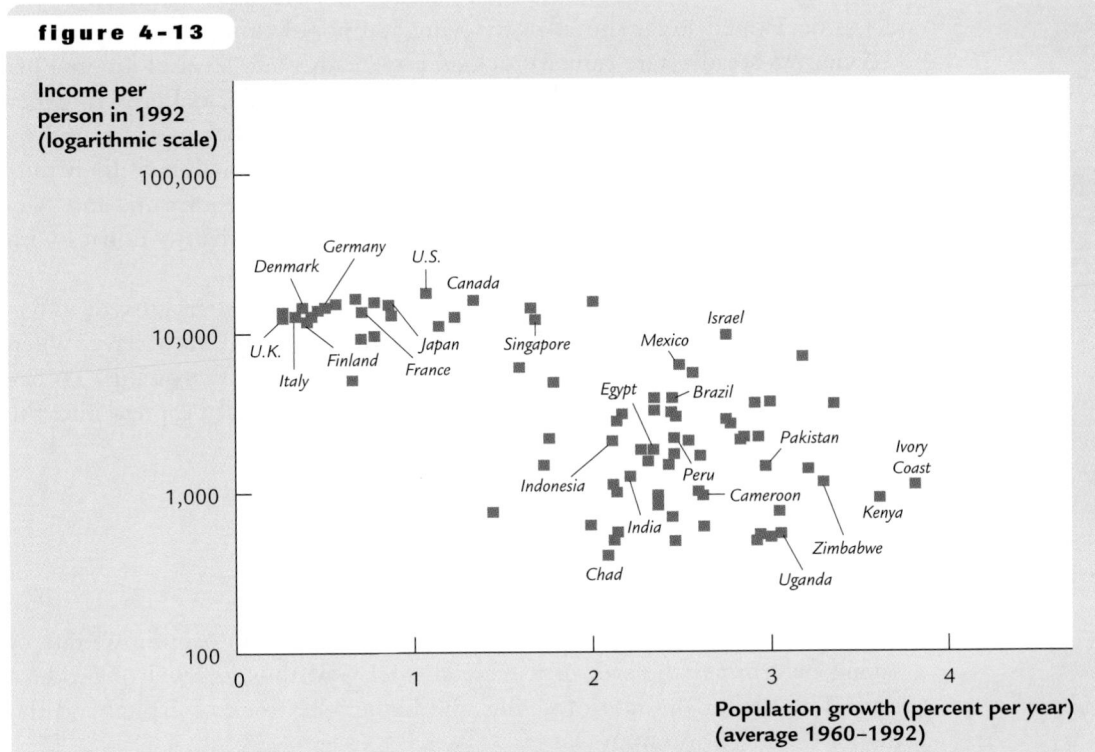

International Evidence on Population Growth and Income per Person This figure is a scatterplot of data from 84 countries. It shows that countries with high rates of population growth tend to have low levels of income per person, as the Solow model predicts.

Source: Robert Summers and Alan Heston, Supplement (Mark 5.6) to "The Penn World Table (Mark 5): An Expanded Set of International Comparisons 1950–1988," *Quarterly Journal of Economics* (May 1991): 327–368.

In interpreting the cross–country data, however, it is important to keep in mind that correlation does not imply causation. The data show that low population growth is typically associated with high levels of income per person, and the Solow model offers one possible explanation for this fact, but other explanations are also possible. It is conceivable that high income encourages low population growth, perhaps because birth-control techniques are more readily available in richer countries. The international data can help us evaluate a theory of growth, such as the Solow model, because they show us whether the theory's predictions are borne out in the world. But often more than one theory can explain the same facts.

4-4 | Conclusion

This chapter has started the process of building the Solow growth model. The model as developed so far shows how saving and population growth determine the economy's steady-state capital stock and its steady-state level of income per person. As we have seen, it sheds light on many features of actual growth experiences—why Germany and Japan grew so rapidly after being devastated by World War II, why countries that save and invest a high fraction of their output are richer than countries that save and invest a smaller fraction, and why countries with high rates of population growth are poorer than countries with low rates of population growth.

What the model cannot do, however, is explain the persistent growth in living standards we observe in most countries. In the model we now have, when the economy reaches its steady state, output per worker stops growing. To explain persistent growth, we need to introduce technological progress into the model. That is our first job in the next chapter.

Summary

1. The Solow growth model shows that in the long run, an economy's rate of saving determines the size of its capital stock and thus its level of production. The higher the rate of saving, the higher the stock of capital and the higher the level of output.

2. In the Solow model, an increase in the rate of saving causes a period of rapid growth, but eventually that growth slows as the new steady state is reached. Thus, although a high saving rate yields a high steady-state level of output, saving by itself cannot generate persistent economic growth.

3. The level of capital that maximizes steady-state consumption is called the Golden Rule level. If an economy has more capital than in the Golden Rule steady state, then reducing saving will increase consumption at all

points in time. By contrast, if the economy has less capital in the Golden Rule steady state, then reaching the Golden Rule requires increased investment and thus lower consumption for current generations.

4. The Solow model shows that an economy's rate of population growth is another long-run determinant of the standard of living. The higher the rate of population growth, the lower the level of output per worker.

KEY CONCEPTS |

Solow growth model
Steady state
Golden Rule level of capital

QUESTIONS FOR REVIEW |

1. In the Solow model, how does the saving rate affect the steady-state level of income? How does it affect the steady-state rate of growth?

2. Why might an economic policymaker choose the Golden Rule level of capital?

3. Might a policymaker choose a steady state with more capital than in the Golden Rule steady

state? With less capital than in the Golden Rule steady state? Explain your answers.

4. In the Solow model, how does the rate of population growth affect the steady-state level of income? How does it affect the steady-state rate of growth?

PROBLEMS AND APPLICATIONS |

1. Country A and country B both have the production function

$$Y = F(K, L) = K^{1/2}L^{1/2}.$$

a. Does this production function have constant returns to scale? Explain.

b. What is the per-worker production function, $y = f(k)$?

c. Assume that neither country experiences population growth or technological progress and that 5 percent of capital depreciates each year. Assume further that country A saves 10 percent of output each year and country B saves

20 percent of output each year. Using your answer from part (b) and the steady-state condition that investment equals depreciation, find the steady-state level of capital per worker for each country. Then find the steady-state levels of income per worker and consumption per worker.

d. Suppose that both countries start off with a capital stock per worker of 2. What are the levels of income per worker and consumption per worker? Remembering that the change in the capital stock is investment less depreciation, use a calculator to show how the capital stock per worker will evolve over time in both countries. For each year, calculate income per worker and consumption per worker. How many years will it be before the consumption in country B is higher than the consumption in country A?

2. In the discussion of German and Japanese postwar growth, the text describes what happens when part of the capital stock is destroyed in a war. By contrast, suppose that a war does not directly affect the capital stock, but that casualties reduce the labor force.

   a. What is the immediate impact on total output and on output per person?

   b. Assuming that the saving rate is unchanged and that the economy was in a steady state before the war, what happens subsequently to output per worker in the postwar economy? Is the growth rate of output per worker after the war smaller or greater than normal?

3. Consider an economy described by the production function: $Y = F(K, L) = K^{0.3}L^{0.7}$.

   a. What is the per-worker production function?

   b. Assuming no population growth or technological progress, find the steady-state capital stock per worker, output per worker, and consumption per worker as a function of the saving rate and the depreciation rate.

   c. Assume that the depreciation rate is 10 percent per year. Make a table showing steady-state capital per worker, output per worker, and consumption per worker for saving rates of 0 percent, 10 percent, 20 percent, 30 percent, and so on. (You will need a calculator with an exponent key for this.) What saving rate maximizes output per worker? What saving rate maximizes consumption per worker?

   d. (Harder) Use calculus to find the marginal product of capital. Add to your table the mar-

ginal product of capital net of depreciation for each of the saving rates. What does your table show?

4. The 1983 *Economic Report of the President* contained the following statement: "Devoting a larger share of national output to investment would help restore rapid productivity growth and rising living standards." Do you agree with this claim? Explain.

5. One view of the consumption function is that workers have high propensities to consume and capitalists have low propensities to consume. To explore the implications of this view, suppose that an economy consumes all wage income and saves all capital income. Show that if the factors of production earn their marginal product, this economy reaches the Golden Rule level of capital. (*Hint:* Begin with the identity that saving equals investment. Then use the steady-state condition that investment is just enough to keep up with depreciation and population growth, and the fact that saving equals capital income in this economy.)

6. Many demographers predict that the United States will have zero population growth in the twenty-first century, in contrast to average population growth of about 1 percent per year in the twentieth century. Use the Solow model to forecast the effect of this slowdown in population growth on the growth of total output and the growth of output per person. Consider the effects both in the steady state and in the transition between steady states.

7. In the Solow model, population growth leads to steady-state growth in total output, but not in output per worker. Do you think this would still be true if the production function exhibited increasing or decreasing returns to scale? Explain. (For the definitions of increasing and decreasing returns to scale, see Chapter 3, "Problems and Applications," Problem 2.)

Economic Growth II

Is there some action a government of India could take that would lead the Indian economy to grow like Indonesia's or Egypt's? If so, what, exactly? If not, what is it about the "nature of India" that makes it so? The consequences for human welfare involved in questions like these are simply staggering: Once one starts to think about them, it is hard to think about anything else.

— *Robert E. Lucas, Jr.*

This chapter continues our analysis of the forces governing long-run economic growth. With the basic version of the Solow growth model as our starting point, we take on three new tasks.

Our first task is to make the Solow model more general and more realistic. In Chapter 3 we saw that capital, labor, and technology are the key determinants of a nation's production of goods and services. In Chapter 4 we developed the Solow model to show how changes in capital (saving and investment) and changes in the labor force (population growth) affect the economy's output. We are now ready to add the third source of growth—changes in technology—into the mix.

Our second task is to examine how a nation's public policies can influence the level and growth of its standard of living. In particular, we address four questions: Should our society save more or save less? How can policy influence the rate of saving? Are there some types of investment that policy should especially encourage? How can policy increase the rate of technological progress? The Solow growth model provides the framework within which we consider each of these issues.

Our third task is to consider what the Solow model leaves out. As we have discussed previously, models help us understand the world by simplifying it. After completing an analysis of a model, therefore, it is important to consider whether we have oversimplified matters. As we will see, although most economists view the Solow model as the natural starting point for understanding economic growth, it is far from the last word on the subject.

5-1 | Technological Progress in the Solow Model

We now incorporate technological progress, the third source of economic growth, into the Solow model. So far, our model has assumed an unchanging relationship between the inputs of capital and labor and the output of goods and services. Yet the model can be modified to allow for exogenous increases in society's ability to produce.

The Efficiency of Labor

To incorporate technological progress, we must return to the production function that relates total capital K and total labor L to total output Y. Thus far, the production function has been

$$Y = F(K, L).$$

We now write the production function as

$$Y = F(K, L \times E),$$

where E is a new (and somewhat abstract) variable called the **efficiency of labor.** The efficiency of labor is meant to reflect society's knowledge about production methods: as the available technology improves, the efficiency of labor rises. For instance, the efficiency of labor rose when assembly-line production transformed manufacturing in early twentieth century, and it rose again when computerization was introduced in the the late twentieth century. The efficiency of labor also rises when there are improvements in the health, education, or skills of the labor force.

The term $L \times E$ measures the number of *effective workers*. It takes into account the number of workers L and the efficiency of each worker E. This new production function states that total output Y depends on the number of units of capital K and on the number of effective workers, $L \times E$. Increases in the efficiency of labor E are, in effect, like increases in the labor force L.

The simplest assumption about technological progress is that it causes the efficiency of labor E to grow at some constant rate g. For example, if $g = 0.02$, then each unit of labor becomes 2 percent more efficient each year: output increases as if the labor force had increased by an additional 2 percent. This form of technological progress is called *labor augmenting,* and g is called the rate of **labor-augmenting technological progress.** Because the labor force L is growing at rate n, and the efficiency of each unit of labor E is growing at rate g, the number of effective workers $L \times E$ is growing at rate $n + g$.

The Steady State With Technological Progress

Expressing technological progress as labor augmenting makes it analogous to population growth. In the last chapter we analyzed the economy in terms of quantities per worker and allowed the number of workers to rise over time. Now we analyze the economy in terms of quantities per effective worker and allow the number of effective workers to rise.

To do this, we need to reconsider our notation. We now let $k = K/(L \times E)$ stand for capital per effective worker, and $y = Y/(L \times E)$ stand for output per effective worker. With these definitions, we can again write $y = f(k)$.

This notation is not really as new as it seems. If we hold the efficiency of labor E constant at the arbitrary value of 1, as we have done implicitly up to now, then these new definitions of k and y reduce to our old ones. When the efficiency of labor is growing, however, we must keep in mind that k and y now refer to quantities per effective worker (not per actual worker).

Our analysis of the economy proceeds just as it did when we examined population growth. The equation showing the evolution of k over time now changes to

$$\Delta k = sf(k) - (\delta + n + g)k.$$

As before, the change in the capital stock Δk equals investment $sf(k)$ minus break-even investment $(\delta + n + g)k$. Now, however, because $k = K/EL$, break-even investment includes three terms: to keep k constant, δk is needed to replace depreciating capital, nk is needed to provide capital for new workers, and gk is needed to provide capital for the new "effective workers" created by technological progress.

As shown in Figure 5-1, the inclusion of technological progress does not substantially alter our analysis of the steady state. There is one level of k, denoted k^*, at which capital per effective worker and output per effective worker are constant. As before, this steady state represents the long-run equilibrium of the economy.

figure 5-1

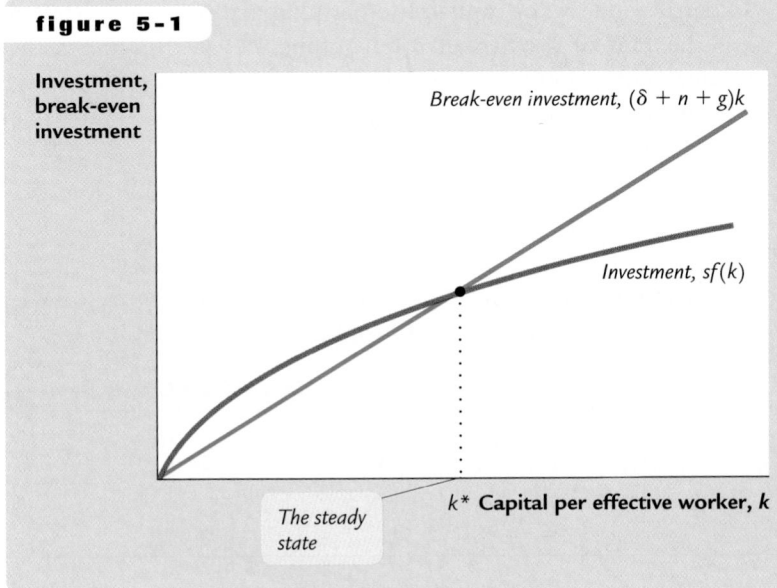

Investment, break-even investment

Break-even investment, $(\delta + n + g)k$

Investment, $sf(k)$

k^* Capital per effective worker, k

The steady state

Technological Progress and the Solow Growth Model Labor-augmenting technological progress at rate g affects the Solow growth model in much the same way as did population growth at rate n. Now that k is defined as the amount of capital per effective worker, increases in the number of effective workers because of technological progress tend to decrease k. In the steady state, investment $sf(k)$ exactly offsets the reductions in k due to depreciation, population growth, and technological progress.

The Effects of Technological Progress

Table 5-1 shows how four key variables behave in the steady state with technological progress. As we have just seen, capital per effective worker k is constant in the steady state. Because $y = f(k)$, output per effective worker is also constant. Remember, though, that the efficiency of each actual worker is growing at rate g. Hence, output per worker $(Y/L = y \times E)$ also grows at rate g. Total output $[Y = y \times (E \times L)]$ grows at rate $n + g$.

With the addition of technological progress, our model can finally explain the sustained increases in standards of living that we observe. That is, we have shown that technological progress can lead to sustained growth in output per worker. By contrast, a high rate of saving leads to a high rate of growth only until the steady state is reached. Once the economy is in steady state, the rate of growth of output per worker depends only on the rate of technological progress. *According to the Solow model, only technological progress can explain persistently rising living standards.*

The introduction of technological progress also modifies the criterion for the Golden Rule. The Golden Rule level of capital is now defined as the steady state that maximizes consumption per effective worker. Following the same arguments that we have used before, we can show that steady-state consumption per effective worker is

$$c^* = f(k^*) - (\delta + n + g)k^*.$$

Steady-state consumption is maximized if

$$MPK = \delta + n + g,$$

or

$$MPK - \delta = n + g.$$

That is, at the Golden Rule level of capital, the net marginal product of capital, $MPK - \delta$, equals the rate of growth of total output, $n + g$. Because actual economies experience both population growth and technological progress, we must use this criterion to evaluate whether they have more or less capital than at the Golden Rule steady state.

table 5-1

Steady-State Growth Rates in the Solow Model With Technological Progress

Variable	Symbol	Steady-State Growth Rate
Capital per effective worker	$k = K/(E \times L)$	0
Output per effective worker	$y = Y/(E \times L) = f(k)$	0
Output per worker	$Y/L = y \times E$	g
Total output	$Y = y \times (E \times L)$	$n + g$

CASE STUDY

Steady-State Growth in the United States

Now that we have introduced technological progress into the Solow model and explained sustained growth in standards of living, we should ask how well our theory fits the facts. According to the Solow model, technological progress will cause the values of many variables to rise together. In the steady state, output per worker and the capital stock per worker both grow at the rate of technological progress. Data for the United States over the past 40 years show that output per worker and the capital stock per worker have in fact grown at approximately the same rate—about 2 percent per year.

Technological progress also affects factor prices. Problem 3(d) at the end of the chapter asks you to show that in the steady state, the real wage grows at the rate of technological progress. The real rental price of capital, however, is constant over time. Again, these predictions hold true for the United States. Over the past 40 years, the real wage has increased about 2 percent per year; it has increased about the same amount as real GDP per worker. Yet the real rental price of capital (measured as real capital income divided by the capital stock) has remained about the same.

The Solow model's prediction about factor prices—and the success of this prediction—is especially noteworthy when contrasted with Karl Marx's theory of the development of capitalist economies. Marx predicted that the return to capital would decline over time and that this would lead to economic and political crisis. Economic history has not supported Marx's prediction, which partly explains why we now study Solow's theory of growth rather than Marx's.

CASE STUDY

Will the World's Economies Converge?

If you travel around the world, you will see tremendous variation in living standards. The world's poor countries have average levels of income per person that are less than one-tenth the average levels in the world's rich countries. These differences in income are reflected in almost every measure of the quality of life—from the number of televisions and telephones per household to the infant mortality rate and life expectancy.

Much research has been devoted to the question of whether economies converge over time to one another. In particular, do economies that start off poor subsequently grow faster than economies that start off rich? If they do, then the world's poor economies will tend to catch up with the world's rich economies. If not, then income disparities will persist.

As a matter of theory, whether economies converge depends on why they differed in the first place. On the one hand, if two economies with the same steady state start off with different capital stocks, then we should expect them to converge. The economy with the smaller capital stock will naturally grow more quickly. (In a case study in Chapter 4, we applied this logic to explain rapid growth in Germany and Japan after World War II.) On the other hand, if two economies have different steady states, perhaps because the economies have different rates of saving, then we should not expect convergence. Instead, each economy will approach its own steady state.

Experience is consistent with this analysis. In samples of economies with similar cultures and policies, studies find that economies converge to one another at a rate of about 2 percent per year. That is, the gap between rich and poor economies closes by about 2 percent each year. An example is the economies of individual American states. For historical reasons, such as the Civil War of the 1860s, income levels varied greatly among states a century ago. Yet these differences have slowly disappeared over time.

In international data, a more complex picture emerges. When researchers examine only data on income per person, they find little evidence of convergence: countries that start off poor do not grow faster on average than countries that start off rich. This finding suggests that different countries have different steady states. If statistical techniques are used to control for some of the determinants of the steady state, such as saving rates, population growth rates, and educational attainment, then once again the data show convergence at a rate of about 2 percent per year. In other words, the economies of the world exhibit *conditional convergence:* they appear to be converging to their own steady states, which in turn are determined by saving, population growth, and education.[1]

5-2 | Policies to Promote Growth

Having used the Solow model to uncover the relationships among the different sources of economic growth, we can now use the theory to help guide our thinking about economic policy.

Evaluating the Rate of Saving

According to the Solow growth model, how much a nation saves and invests is a key determinant of its citizens' standard of living. So let's begin our policy discussion with a natural question: Is the rate of saving in the U.S. economy too low, too high, or about right?

---

[1] Robert Barro and Xavier Sala-i-Martin, "Convergence Across States and Regions," *Brookings Papers on Economic Activity* (1991, no. 1): 107–182; N. Gregory Mankiw, David Romer, and David N. Weil, "A Contribution to the Empirics of Economic Growth," *Quarterly Journal of Economics* (May 1992): 407–437.

As we have seen, the saving rate determines the steady-state levels of capital and output. One particular saving rate produces the Golden Rule steady state, which maximizes consumption per worker and thus economic well-being. The Golden Rule provides the benchmark against which we can compare the U.S. economy.

To decide whether the U.S. economy is at, above, or below the Golden Rule steady state, we need to compare the marginal product of capital net of depreciation ($MPK - \delta$) with the growth rate of total output ($n + g$). As we established earlier, at the Golden Rule steady state, $MPK - \delta = n + g$. If the economy is operating with less capital than in the Golden Rule steady state, then diminishing marginal product tells us that $MPK - \delta > n + g$. In this case, increasing the rate of saving will eventually lead to a steady state with higher consumption. On the other hand, if the economy is operating with too much capital, then $MPK - \delta < n + g$, and the rate of saving should be reduced.

To make this comparison for a real economy, such as the U.S. economy, we need an estimate of the growth rate ($n + g$) and an estimate of the net marginal product of capital ($MPK - \delta$). Real GDP in the United States grows an average of 3 percent per year, so $n + g = 0.03$. We can estimate the net marginal product of capital from the following three facts:

1. The capital stock is about 2.5 times one year's GDP.

2. Depreciation of capital is about 10 percent of GDP.

3. Capital income is about 30 percent of GDP.

Using the notation of our model (and the result from Chapter 3 that capital owners earn income of MPK for each unit of capital), we can write these facts as

1. $k = 2.5y$.

2. $\delta k = 0.1y$.

3. $MPK \times k = 0.3y$

We solve for the rate of depreciation δ by dividing equation 2 by equation 1:

$$\delta k/k = (0.1y)/(2.5y)$$
$$\delta = 0.04.$$

And we solve for the marginal product of capital MPK by dividing equation 3 by equation 1:

$$(MPK \times k)/k = (0.3y)/(2.5y)$$
$$MPK = 0.12.$$

Thus, about 4 percent of the capital stock depreciates each year, and the marginal product of capital is about 12 percent per year. The net marginal product of capital, $MPK - \delta$, is about 8 percent per year.

We can now see that the return to capital ($MPK - \delta = 8$ percent per year) is well in excess of the economy's average growth rate ($n + g = 3$ percent per year). This fact, together with our previous analysis, indicates that the capital stock in the U.S. economy is well below the Golden Rule level. In other words, if the United States saved and invested a higher fraction of its income, it would grow more rapidly and eventually reach a steady state with higher consumption. This finding suggests that policymakers should want to increase the rate of saving and investment. In fact, for many years, increasing capital formation has been a high priority of economic policy.

Changing the Rate of Saving

The preceding calculations show that to move the U.S. economy toward the Golden Rule steady state, policymakers should increase national saving. But how can they do that? We saw in Chapter 3 that, as a matter of sheer accounting, higher national saving means higher public saving, higher private saving, or some combination of the two. Much of the debate over policies to increase growth centers on which of these is likely to be most effective.

The most direct way in which the government affects national saving is through public saving—the difference between what the government receives in tax revenue and what it spends. When the government's spending exceeds its revenue, the government is said to run a *budget deficit,* which represents negative public saving. As we saw in Chapter 3, a budget deficit raises interest rates and crowds out investment; the resulting reduction in the capital stock is part of the burden of the national debt on future generations. Conversely, if the government spends less than it raises in revenue, it is said to run a *budget surplus.* It can then retire some of the national debt and stimulate investment. This influence of government budget policy on capital accumulation explains why President Clinton made reducing the budget deficit an important priority when he moved into the White House in 1993.

The government also affects national saving by influencing private saving—the saving done by households and firms. In particular, how much people decide to save depends on the incentives they face, and these incentives are altered by a variety of public policies. Many economists argue that high tax rates on capital income—including the corporate income tax, the federal income tax, and many state income taxes—discourage private saving by reducing the rate of return that savers earn. On the other hand, tax-exempt retirement accounts, such as IRAs, are designed to encourage private saving by giving preferential treatment to income saved in these accounts.

Many disagreements among economists over public policy are rooted in different views about how much private saving responds to incentives. For example, suppose that the government were to expand the amount that people can put into tax-exempt retirement accounts. Would people respond to the increased incentive to save by saving more? Or would people merely transfer saving done in other forms into these accounts—reducing tax revenue and thus public saving without any stimulus to private saving? Clearly, the desirability of the policy depends on the answers to these questions. Unfortunately, despite much research on this issue, no consensus has emerged.

CASE STUDY

Should the Social Security System Be Reformed?

Although many government policies are designed to encourage saving, such as the preferential tax treatment given to pension plans and other retirement accounts, one important policy is often thought to reduce saving: the Social Security system. Social Security is a transfer system designed to maintain individuals' income in their old age. These transfers to the elderly are financed with a payroll tax on the working-age population. This system is thought to reduce private saving because it reduces individuals' need to provide for their own retirement.

To counteract the reduction in national saving attributed to Social Security, many economists have proposed reforms of the Social Security system. The system is now largely *pay-as-you-go:* most of the current tax receipts are paid out to the current elderly population. One suggestion is that Social Security should be *fully funded.* Under this plan, the government would put aside in a trust fund the payments a generation makes when it is young and working; the government would then pay out the principal and accumulated interest to this same generation when it is older and retired. Under a fully funded Social Security system, an increase in public saving would offset the reduction in private saving.

A closely related proposal is *privatization,* which means turning this government program for the elderly into a system of mandatory private savings accounts, much like private pension plans. In principle, the issues of funding and privatization are distinct. A fully funded system could be either public (in which case the government holds the funds) or private (in which case private financial institutions hold the funds). In practice, however, the issues are often linked. Some economists have argued that a fully funded public system is problematic. They note that such a system would end up holding a large share of the nation's wealth, which would increase the role of the government in allocating capital. In addition, they fear that a large publicly controlled fund would tempt politicians to cut taxes or increase spending, which could deplete the fund and cause the system to revert to pay-as-you-go status. History gives some support to this fear: the initial architects of Social Security wanted the system to accumulate a much larger trust fund than ever materialized.

These issues rose to prominence in the late 1990s, as policymakers became aware that the current Social Security system was not sustainable. That is, the amount of revenue being raised by the payroll tax appeared insufficient to pay all the benefits being promised. According to most projections, this problem was to become acute as the large baby-boom generation retired during the early decades of the twenty-first century. Various solutions were proposed.

One possibility was to maintain the current system with some combination of smaller benefits and higher taxes. Other possibilities included movements toward a fully funded system, perhaps also including private accounts. As this book was going to press, the resolution to the problem was still under debate.[2]

Allocating the Economy's Investment

The Solow model makes the simplifying assumption that there is only one type of capital. In the world, of course, there are many types. Private businesses invest in traditional types of capital, such as bulldozers and steel plants, and newer types of capital, such as computers and robots. The government invests in various forms of public capital, called *infrastructure,* such as roads, bridges, and sewer systems.

In addition, there is *human capital*—the knowledge and skills that workers acquire through education, from early childhood programs such as Head Start to on-the-job training for adults in the labor force. Although the basic Solow model includes only physical capital and does not try to explain the efficiency of labor, in many ways human capital is analogous to physical capital. Like physical capital, human capital raises our ability to produce goods and services. Raising the level of human capital requires investment in the form of teachers, libraries, and student time. Recent research on economic growth has emphasized that human capital is at least as important as physical capital in explaining international differences in standards of living.[3]

Policymakers trying to stimulate economic growth must confront the issue of what kinds of capital the economy needs most. In other words, what kinds of capital yield the highest marginal products? To a large extent, policymakers can rely on the marketplace to allocate the pool of saving to alternative types of investment. Those industries with the highest marginal products of capital will naturally be most willing to borrow at market interest rates to finance new investment. Many economists advocate that the government should merely create a "level playing field" for different types of capital—for example, by ensuring that the tax system treats all forms of capital equally. The government can then rely on the market to allocate capital efficiently.

Other economists have suggested that the government should actively encourage particular forms of capital. Suppose, for instance, that technological advance occurs as a by-product of certain economic activities. This would happen if new and improved production processes are devised during the process of building capital (a phenomenon called *learning by doing*) and if these ideas become part of society's pool of knowledge. Such a by-product is called a *techno-*

[2] To learn more about the debate over Social Security, see Steven A. Sass and Robert K. Triest, eds., *Social Security Reform: Links to Saving, Investment, and Growth,* Conference Series No. 41, Federal Reserve Bank of Boston, June 1997.

[3] N. Gregory Mankiw, David Romer, and David N. Weil, "A Contribution to the Empirics of Economic Growth," *Quarterly Journal of Economics* (May 1992): 407–437.

logical externality (or a *knowledge spillover*). In the presence of such externalities, the social returns to capital exceed the private returns, and the benefits of increased capital accumulation to society are greater than the Solow model suggests.[4] Moreover, some types of capital accumulation may yield greater externalities than others. If, for example, installing robots yields greater technological externalities than building a new steel mill, then perhaps the government should use the tax laws to encourage investment in robots. The success of such an *industrial policy,* as it is sometimes called, requires that the government be able to measure the externalities of different economic activities so it can give the correct incentive to each activity.

Most economists are skeptical about industrial policies, for two reasons. First, measuring the externalities from different sectors is so difficult as to be virtually impossible. If policy is based on poor measurements, its effects might be close to random and, thus, worse than no policy at all. Second, the political process is far from perfect. Once the government gets in the business of rewarding specific industries with subsidies and tax breaks, the rewards are as likely to be based on political clout as the magnitude of externalties.

One type of capital that necessarily involves the government is public capital. Local, state, and federal governments are always deciding whether to borrow to finance new roads, bridges, and transit systems. During his first presidential campaign, Bill Clinton argued that the United States had been investing too little in infrastructure. He claimed that a higher level of infrastructure investment would make the economy substantially more productive. Among economists, this claim had both defenders and critics. Yet all of them agree that measuring the marginal product of public capital is difficult. Private capital generates an easily measured rate of profit for the firm owning the capital, whereas the benefits of public capital are more diffuse.

Encouraging Technological Progress

The Solow model shows that sustained growth in income per worker must come from technological progress. The Solow model, however, takes technological progress as exogenous; it does not explain it. Unfortunately, the determinants of technological progress are not well understood.

Despite this limited understanding, many public policies are designed to stimulate technological progress. Most of these policies encourage the private sector to devote resources to technological innovation. For example, the patent system gives a temporary monopoly to inventors of new products; the tax code offers tax breaks for firms engaging in research and development; and government agencies such as the National Science Foundation directly subsidize basic research in universities. In addition, as discussed above, proponents of industrial policy argue that the government should take a more active role in promoting specific industries that are key for rapid technological progress.

---

[4] Paul Romer, "Crazy Explanations for the Productivity Slowdown," *NBER Macroeconomics Annual* 2 (1987): 163–201.

CASE STUDY

The Worldwide Slowdown in Economic Growth

One of the most perplexing problems that policymakers have faced in recent decades is the worldwide slowdown in economic growth that began in the early 1970s. Table 5-2 presents data on the growth in real GDP per person for the seven major world economies. Growth in the United States fell from 2.2 percent to 1.5 percent. Other countries experienced similar or more severe declines.

Studies have shown that the slowdown in growth is attributable to a slowdown in the rate at which the production function is improving over time. The appendix to this chapter explains how economists measure changes in the production function with a variable called *total factor productivity,* which is closely related to the efficiency of labor in the Solow model. Accumulated over many years, even a small change in the rate of productivity growth has a large effect on economic welfare. Real income in the United States today is more than 20 percent lower than it would have been had productivity growth remained at its previous level.

Many economists have attempted to explain this adverse change. Let's consider some of their explanations.

Measurement Problems One possibility is that the productivity slowdown did not really occur and that it shows up in the data simply because the data are flawed. As you may recall from Chapter 2, one problem in measuring inflation is correcting for changes in the quality of goods and services. The same issue arises when measuring output and productivity. For instance, if technological advance leads to *more* computers being built, then the increase in output and productivity is easy to measure. But if technological advance leads to *faster* computers being built, then output and productivity have in effect increased, but that increase is more subtle and harder to measure. Government statisticians

table 5-2

The Slowdown in Growth Around the World

| Country | GROWTH IN OUTPUT PER PERSON (PERCENT PER YEAR) | |
	1948–1972	1972–1995
Canada	2.9	1.8
France	4.3	1.6
West Germany	5.7	2.0
Italy	4.9	2.3
Japan	8.2	2.6
United Kingdom	2.4	1.8
United States	2.2	1.5

Source: Angus Maddison, *Phases of Capitalist Development* (Oxford: Oxford University Press, 1982); *OECD National Accounts.*

try to correct for changes in quality, but despite their best efforts, the resulting data are far from perfect.

Unmeasured quality improvements mean that our standard of living is rising more rapidly than the official data indicate. This issue should make us suspicious of the data, but by itself it cannot explain the productivity slowdown. To explain a *slowdown* in growth, one must argue that the measurement problems have gotten *worse*. There is some indication that this might be so. Over time, fewer people are working in industries with tangible and easily measured output, such as agriculture, and more people are working in industries with intangible and less easily measured output, such as medical services. Yet few economists believe that measurement problems are the full story.

Oil Prices When the productivity slowdown began around 1973, the obvious hypothesis to explain it was the large increase in oil prices caused by the actions of the OPEC oil cartel. The primary piece of evidence was the timing: productivity growth slowed at almost exactly the same time that oil prices skyrocketed. Over time, however, this explanation has appeared less likely. One reason is that the accumulated shortfall in productivity seems too large to be explained by an increase in oil prices—oil is not that large a fraction of the typical firm's costs. In addition, if this explanation were right, productivity should have sped up when political turmoil in OPEC caused oil prices to plummet in 1986. Unfortunately, that did not happen.

Worker Quality Some economists have suggested that the productivity slowdown might be attributable to changes in the labor force. In the early 1970s, the large baby-boom generation started leaving school and taking jobs. At the same time, changing social norms encouraged many women to leave full-time housework and enter the labor force. Both of these developments lowered the average level of experience among workers, which in turn lowered average productivity.

Other economists point to changes in worker quality due to human capital. Although the educational attainment of the labor force is now as high as it has ever been, educational attainment is not increasing as rapidly as it has in the past. In addition, declining performance on some standardized tests suggests that the quality of education has been declining over time. If so, this could explain slowing productivity growth.

The Depletion of Ideas Still other economists have suggested that the world has started to run out of new ideas about how to produce and, as a result, we have entered an age of slower technological progress. These economists often argue that the anomaly is not the period since 1970 but the two decades before that. In the late 1940s, the economy had a large backlog of ideas that had not been fully implemented because of the Great Depression of the 1930s and World War II in the first half of 1940s. After the economy used up this backlog, the argument goes, a slowdown in productivity growth was inevitable. Indeed, while recent growth rates are disappointing compared to those of the 1950s and 1960s, they are not any lower than average growth rates from 1870 to 1950. Perhaps lower productivity growth is something we just have to get used to.

Which of these suspects is the culprit? All of them are plausible, but it is difficult to prove beyond a reasonable doubt that any one of them is guilty. The worldwide slowdown in economic growth largely remains a mystery.[5]

5-3 | Beyond the Solow Model: Endogenous Growth Theory

A chemist, a physicist, and an economist are all trapped on a desert island, trying to figure out how to open a can of food.

"Let's heat the can over the fire until it explodes," says the chemist.

"No, no," says the physicist, "Let's drop the can onto the rocks from the top of a high tree."

"I have an idea," says the economist. "First, we assume a can opener . . . ."

This old joke takes aim at how economists use assumptions to simplify—and sometimes oversimplify—the problems they face. It is particularly apt when evaluating the theory of economic growth. One goal of growth theory is to explain the persistent rise in living standards that we observe in most parts of the world. The Solow growth model shows that such persistent growth must come from technological progress. But where does technological progress come from? In the Solow model, it is just assumed!

To understand fully the process of economic growth, we need to go beyond the Solow model and develop models that explain technological progress. Models that do this often go by the label **endogenous growth theory** because they reject the Solow model's assumption of exogenous technological change. Although the field of endogenous growth theory is large and sometimes complex, here we get a quick taste of this modern research.[6]

The Basic Model

To illustrate the idea behind endogenous growth theory, let's start with a particularly simple production function:

$$Y = AK,$$

---

[5] For various views on the growth slowdown, see "Symposium: The Slowdown in Productivity Growth," *The Journal of Economic Perspectives* 2 (Fall 1988): 3–98.

[6] This section provides a brief introduction to the large and fascinating literature on endogenous growth theory. Early and important contributions to this literature include Paul M. Romer, "Increasing Returns and Long-Run Growth," *Journal of Political Economy* 94 (October 1986): 1002–1037; and Robert E. Lucas, Jr., "On the Mechanics of Economic Development," *Journal of Monetary Economics* 22 (1988): 3–42. The reader can learn more about this topic in the undergraduate textbook by Charles I. Jones, *Introduction to Economic Growth* (New York: Norton, 1998).

where Y is output, K is the capital stock, and A is a constant measuring the amount of output produced for each unit of capital. Notice that this production function does not exhibit the property of diminishing returns to capital. One extra unit of capital produces A extra units of output, regardless of how much capital there is. This absence of diminishing returns to capital is the key difference between this model and the Solow model.

Now let's see what this production function says about economic growth. As before, we assume a fraction s of income is saved and invested. We therefore describe capital accumulation with an equation similar to those we used previously:

$$\Delta K = sY - \delta K.$$

This equation states that the change in the capital stock (ΔK) equals investment (sY) minus depreciation (δK). Combining this equation with the $Y = AK$ production function, we obtain after a bit of manipulation

$$\Delta Y/Y = \Delta K/K = sA - \delta.$$

This equation shows what determines the growth rate of output $\Delta Y/Y$. Notice that, as long as $sA > \delta$, the economy's income grows forever, even without the assumption of exogenous technological progress.

Thus, a simple change in the production function can alter dramatically the predictions about economic growth. In the Solow model, saving leads to growth temporarily, but diminishing returns to capital eventually force the economy to approach a steady state in which growth depends only on exogenous technological progress. By contrast, in this endogenous growth model, saving and investment can lead to persistent growth.

But is it reasonable to abandon the assumption of diminishing returns to capital? The answer depends on how we interpret the variable K in the production function $Y = AK$. If we take the traditional view that K includes only the economy's stock of plants and equipment, then it is natural to assume diminishing returns. Giving 10 computers to each worker does not make the worker ten times as productive as he or she is with one computer.

Advocates of endogenous growth theory, however, argue that the assumption of constant (rather than diminishing) returns to capital is more palatable if K is interpreted more broadly. Perhaps the best case for the endogenous growth model is to view knowledge as a type of capital. Clearly, knowledge is an important input into the economy's production—both its production of goods and services and its production of new knowledge. Compared to other forms of capital, however, it is less natural to assume that knowledge exhibits the property of diminishing returns. (Indeed, the increasing pace of scientific and technological innovation over the past few centuries has led some economists to argue that there are increasing returns to knowledge.) If we accept the view that knowledge is a type of capital, then this endogenous growth model with its assumption of constant returns to capital becomes a more plausible description of long-run economic growth.

A Two-Sector Model

Although the $Y = AK$ model is the simplest example of endogenous growth, the theory has gone well beyond this. One line of research has tried to develop models with more than one sector of production in order to offer a better description of the forces that govern technological progress. To see what we might learn from such models, let's sketch out an example.

The economy has two sectors, which we can call manufacturing firms and research universities. Firms produce goods and services, which are used for consumption and investment in physical capital. Universities produce a factor of production called "knowledge," which is then freely used in both sectors. The economy is described by the production function for firms, the production function for universities, and the capital-accumulation equation:

$$Y = F[K,(1 - u)EL] \quad \text{(production function in manufacturing firms)},$$
$$\Delta E = g(u)E \quad \text{(production function in research universities)},$$
$$\Delta K = sY - \delta K \quad \text{(capital accumulation)},$$

where u is the fraction of the labor force in universities (and $1 - u$ is the fraction in manufacturing), E is the stock of knowledge (which in turn determines the efficiency of labor), and g is a function that shows how the growth in knowledge depends on the fraction of the labor force in universities. The rest of the notation is standard. As usual, the production function for the manufacturing firms is assumed to have constant returns to scale: if we double both the amount of physical capital (K) and the number of effective workers in manufacturing [$(1 - u)EL$], we double the output of goods and services (Y).

This model is a cousin of the $Y = AK$ model. Most important, this economy exhibits constant (rather than diminishing) returns to capital, as long as capital is broadly defined to include knowledge. In particular, if we double both physical capital K and knowledge E, then we double the output of both sectors in the economy. As a result, like the $Y = AK$ model, this model can generate persistent growth without the assumption of exogenous shifts in the production function. Here persistent growth arises endogenously because the creation of knowledge in universities never slows down.

At the same time, however, this model is also a cousin of the Solow growth model. If u, the fraction of the labor force in universities, is held constant, then the efficiency of labor E grows at the constant rate $g(u)$. This result of constant growth in the efficiency of labor at rate g is precisely the assumption made in the Solow model with technological progress. Moreover, the rest of the model—the manufacturing production function and the capital-accumulation equation—also resembles the rest of the Solow model. As a result, for any given value of u, this endogenous growth model works just like the Solow model.

There are two key decision variables in this model. As in the Solow model, the fraction of output used for saving and investment, s, determines the steady-state stock of physical capital. In addition, the fraction of labor in universities, u, determines the growth in the stock of knowledge. Both s and u affect the level of income, although only u affects the steady-state growth rate of income. Thus, this model of endogenous growth takes a small step in the direction of showing which societal decisions determine the rate of technological change.

The Microeconomics of Research and Development

The two-sector endogenous growth model just presented takes us closer to understanding technological progress, but it still tells only a rudimentary story about the creation of knowledge. If one thinks about the process of research and development for even a moment, three facts become apparent. First, although knowledge is largely a public good (that is, a good freely available to everyone), much research is done in firms that are driven by the profit motive. Second, research is profitable because innovations give firms temporary monopolies, either because of the patent system or because there is an advantage to being the first firm on the market with a new product. Third, when one firm innovates, other firms build on that innovation to produce the next generation of innovations. These (essentially microeconomic) facts are not easily connected with the (essentially macroeconomic) growth models we have discussed so far.

Some endogenous growth models try to incorporate these facts about research and development. Doing this requires modeling the decisions that firms face as they engage in research and modeling the interactions among firms that have some degree of monopoly power over their innovations. Going into more detail about these models is beyond the scope of this book. But it should be clear already that one virtue of these endogenous growth models is that they offer a more complete description of the process of technological innovation.

One question these models are designed to address is whether, from the standpoint of society as a whole, private profit-maximizing firms tend to engage in too little or too much research. In other words, is the social return to research (which is what society cares about) greater or smaller than the private return (which is what motivates individual firms)? It turns out that, as a theoretical matter, there are effects in both directions. On the one hand, when a firm creates a new technology, it makes other firms better off by giving them a base of knowledge on which to build in future research. As Isaac Newton famously remarked, "If I have seen farther than others, it is because I was standing on the shoulder of giants." On the other hand, when one firm invests in research, it can also make other firms worse off by merely being first to discover a technology that another firm would have invented. This duplication of research effort has been called the "stepping on toes" effect. Whether firms left to their own devices do too little or too much research depends on whether the positive "standing on shoulders" externality or the negative "stepping on toes" externality is more prevalent.

Although theory alone is ambiguous about the optimality of research effort, the empirical work in this area is usually less so. Many studies have suggested the "standing on shoulders" externality is important and, as a result, the social return to research is large—often in excess of 40 percent per year. This is an impressive rate of return, especially when compared to the return to physical capital, which we earlier estimated to be about 8 percent per year. In the judgment of some economists, this finding justifies substantial government subsidies to research.[7]

5-4 | Conclusion

Long-run economic growth is the single most important determinant of the economic well-being of a nation's citizens. Everything else that macroeconomists study—unemployment, inflation, trade deficits, and so on—pales in comparison.

Fortunately, economists know quite a lot about the forces that govern economic growth. The Solow growth model and the more recent endogenous growth models show how saving, population growth, and technological progress interact in determining the level of and growth in a nation's standard of living. Although these theories offer no magic pill to ensure an economy achieves rapid growth, they do offer much insight, and they provide the intellectual framework for much of the debate over public policy.

Summary

1. In the steady state of the Solow growth model, the growth rate of income per person is determined solely by the exogenous rate of technological progress.

2. In the Solow model with population growth and technological progress, the Golden Rule (consumption-maximizing) steady state is characterized by equality between the net marginal product of capital ($MPK - \delta$) and the steady-state growth rate ($n + g$). By contrast, in the U.S. economy, the net marginal product of capital is well in excess of the growth rate, indicating that the U.S. economy has much less capital than in the Golden Rule steady state.

3. Policymakers in the United States and other countries often claim that their nations should devote a larger percentage of their output to saving and investment. Increased public saving and tax incentives for private saving are two ways to encourage capital accumulation.

4. In the early 1970s, the rate of growth fell substantially in most industrialized countries. The cause of this slowdown is not well understood.

---

[7] For an overview of the empirical literature on the effects of research, see Zvi Griliches, "The Search for R&D Spillovers," *Scandinavian Journal of Economics* 94 (1991): 29–47.

5. Modern theories of endogenous growth attempt to explain the rate of technological progress, which the Solow model takes as exogenous. These models try to explain the decisions that determine the creation of knowledge through research and development.

KEY CONCEPTS

Efficiency of labor
Labor-augmenting technological
   progress
Endogenous growth theory

QUESTIONS FOR REVIEW

1. In the Solow model, what determines the steady-state rate of growth of income per worker?

2. What data would you need to determine whether an economy has more or less capital than in the Golden Rule steady state?

3. How can policymakers influence a nation's saving rate?

4. What has happened to the rate of productivity growth over the past 40 years? How might you explain this phenomenon?

5. How does endogenous growth theory explain persistent growth without the assumption of exogenous technological progress? How does this differ from the Solow model?

PROBLEMS AND APPLICATIONS

1. An economy described by the Solow growth model has the following production function:

$$y = \sqrt{k}.$$

  a. Solve for the steady-state value of y as a function of s, n, g, and δ.

  b. A developed country has a saving rate of 28 percent and a population growth rate of 1 percent per year. A less-developed country has a saving rate of 10 percent and a population growth rate of 4 percent per year. In both countries, $g = 0.02$ and $\delta = 0.04$. Find the steady-state value of y for each country.

  c. What policies might the less-developed country pursue to raise its level of income?

2. In the United States, the capital share of GDP is about 30 percent; the average growth in output is about 3 percent per year; the depreciation rate is about 4 percent per year; and the capital–output ratio is about 2.5. Suppose that the production function is Cobb–Douglas, so that the capital share in output is constant, and that the United States has been in a steady state. (For a discussion of the Cobb–Douglas production function, see the appendix to Chapter 3.)

  a. What must the saving rate be in the initial steady state? [*Hint:* Use the steady-state relationship, $sy = (\delta + n + g)k.$]

  b. What is the marginal product of capital in the initial steady state?

c. Suppose that public policy raises the saving rate so that the economy reaches the Golden Rule level of capital. What will the marginal product of capital be at the Golden Rule steady state? Compare the marginal product at the Golden Rule steady state to the marginal product in the initial steady state. Explain.

d. What will the capital–output ratio be at the Golden Rule steady state? (*Hint:* For the Cobb–Douglas production function, the capital–output ratio is related to the marginal product of capital.)

e. What must the saving rate be to reach the Golden Rule steady state?

3. Prove each of the following statements about the steady state with population growth and technological progress.

a. The capital–output ratio is constant.

b. Capital and labor each earn a constant share of an economy's income. [*Hint:* Recall the definition $MPK = f(k + 1) - f(k)$.]

c. Total capital income and total labor income both grow at the rate of population growth plus the rate of technological progress, $n + g$.

d. The real rental price of capital is constant, and the real wage grows at the rate of technological progress g. (*Hint:* The real rental price of capital equals total capital income divided by the capital stock, and the real wage equals total labor income divided by the labor force.)

4. The amount of education the typical person receives varies substantially among countries. Suppose you were to compare a country with a highly educated labor force and a country with a less educated labor force. Assume that education affects only the level of the efficiency of labor. Also assume that the countries are otherwise the same: they have the same saving rate, the same depreciation rate, the same population growth rate, and the same rate of technological progress. Both countries are described by the Solow model and are in their steady states. What would you predict for the following variables?

a. The rate of growth of total income.

b. The level of income per worker.

c. The real rental price of capital.

d. The real wage.

5. This question asks you to analyze in more detail the two-sector endogenous growth model presented in the text.

a. Rewrite the production function for manufactured goods in terms of output per effective worker and capital per effective worker.

b. In this economy, what is break-even investment (the amount of investment needed to keep capital per effective worker constant)?

c. Write down the equation of motion for k, which shows Δk as saving minus break-even investment. Use this equation to draw a graph showing the determination of steady-state k. (*Hint:* This graph will look much like those we used to analyze the Solow model.)

d. In this economy, what is the steady-state growth rate of output per worker Y/L? How do the saving rate s and the fraction of the labor force in universities u affect this steady-state growth rate?

e. Using your graph, show the impact of an increase in u. (*Hint:* This change affects both curves.) Describe both the immediate and the steady-state effects.

f. Based on your analysis, is an increase in u an unambiguously good thing for the economy? Explain.

appendix

Accounting for the Sources of Economic Growth

Real GDP in the United States has grown an average of 3 percent per year over the past 40 years. What explains this growth? In Chapter 3 we linked the output of the economy to the factors of production—capital and labor—and to the production technology. Here we develop a technique called *growth accounting* that divides the growth in output into three different sources: increases in capital, increases in labor, and advances in technology. This breakdown provides us with a measure of the rate of technological change.

Increases in the Factors of Production

We first examine how increases in the factors of production contribute to increases in output. To do this, we start by assuming there is no technological change, so the production function relating output Y to capital K and labor L is constant over time:

$$Y = F(K, L).$$

In this case, the amount of output changes only because the amount of capital or labor changes.

Increases in Capital First, consider changes in capital. If the amount of capital increases by ΔK units, by how much does the amount of output increase? To answer this question, we need to recall the definition of the marginal product of capital MPK:

$$MPK = F(K + 1, L) - F(K, L).$$

The marginal product of capital tells us how much output increases when capital increases by 1 unit. Therefore, when capital increases by ΔK units, output increases by approximately $MPK \times \Delta K$.[8]

For example, suppose that the marginal product of capital is 1/5; that is, an additional unit of capital increases the amount of output produced by one-fifth

---

[8] Note the word "approximately" here. This answer is only an approximation because the marginal product of capital varies: it falls as the amount of capital increases. An exact answer would take into account that each unit of capital has a different marginal product. If the change in K is not too large, however, the approximation of a constant marginal product is very accurate.

of a unit. If we increase the amount of capital by 10 units, we can compute the amount of additional output as follows:

$$\Delta Y = MPK \times \Delta K$$
$$= \frac{1}{5} \times \frac{\text{Units of Output}}{\text{Unit of Capital}} \times 10 \text{ Units of Capital}$$
$$= 2 \text{ Units of Output.}$$

By increasing capital by 10 units, we obtain 2 more units of output. Thus, we use the marginal product of capital to convert changes in capital into changes in output.

Increases in Labor   Next, consider changes in labor. If the amount of labor increases by ΔL units, by how much does output increase? We answer this question the same way we answered the question about capital. The marginal product of labor MPL tells us how much output changes when labor increases by 1 unit—that is,

$$MPL = F(K, L + 1) - F(K, L).$$

Therefore, when the amount of labor increases by ΔL units, output increases by approximately $MPL \times \Delta L$.

For example, suppose that the marginal product of labor is 2; that is, an additional unit of labor increases the amount of output produced by 2 units. If we increase the amount of labor by 10 units, we can compute the amount of additional output as follows:

$$\Delta Y = MPL \times \Delta L$$
$$= 2 \frac{\text{Units of Output}}{\text{Unit of Labor}} \times 10 \text{ Units of Labor}$$
$$= 20 \text{ Units of Output.}$$

By increasing labor by 10 units, we obtain 20 more units of output. Thus, we use the marginal product of labor to convert changes in labor into changes in output.

Increases in Capital and Labor   Finally, let's consider the more realistic case in which both factors of production change. Suppose that the amount of capital increases by ΔK and the amount of labor increases by ΔL. The increase in output then comes from two sources: more capital and more labor. We can divide this increase into the two sources using the marginal products of the two inputs:

$$\Delta Y = (MPK \times \Delta K) + (MPL \times \Delta L).$$

The first term in parentheses is the increase in output resulting from the increase in capital, and the second term in parentheses is the increase in output resulting from the increase in labor. This equation shows us how to attribute growth to each factor of production.

We now want to convert this last equation into a form that is easier to interpret and apply to the available data. First, with some algebraic rearrangement, the equation becomes[9]

$$\frac{\Delta Y}{Y} = \left(\frac{MPK \times K}{Y} \right) \frac{\Delta K}{K} + \left(\frac{MPL \times L}{Y} \right) \frac{\Delta L}{L}.$$

This form of the equation relates the growth rate of output, $\Delta Y/Y$, to the growth rate of capital, $\Delta K/K$, and the growth rate of labor, $\Delta L/L$.

Next, we need to find some way to measure the terms in parentheses in the last equation. In Chapter 3 we showed that the marginal product of capital equals its real rental price. Therefore, $MPK \times K$ is the total return to capital, and $(MPK \times K)/Y$ is capital's share of output. Similarly, the marginal product of labor equals the real wage. Therefore, $MPL \times L$ is the total compensation that labor receives, and $(MPL \times L)/Y$ is labor's share of output. Under the assumption that the production function has constant returns to scale, Euler's theorem (which we discussed in Chapter 3) tells us that these two shares sum to 1. In this case, we can write

$$\frac{\Delta Y}{Y} = \alpha \frac{\Delta K}{K} + (1 - \alpha) \frac{\Delta L}{L}.$$

where α is capital's share and $(1 - \alpha)$ is labor's share.

This last equation gives us a simple formula for showing how changes in inputs lead to changes in output. In particular, we must weight the growth rates of the inputs by the factor shares. As we discussed in the appendix to Chapter 3, capital's share in the United States is about 30 percent, that is, $\alpha = 0.30$. Therefore, a 10-percent increase in the amount of capital ($\Delta K/K = 0.10$) leads to a 3-percent increase in the amount of output ($\Delta Y/Y = 0.03$). Similarly, a 10-percent increase in the amount of labor ($\Delta L/L = 0.10$) leads to a 7-percent increase in the amount of output ($\Delta Y/Y = 0.07$).

Technological Progress

So far in our analysis of the sources of growth, we have been assuming that the production function does not change over time. In practice, of course, technological progress improves the production function. For any given amount of inputs, we get more output today than we did in the past. We now extend the analysis to allow for technological progress.

---

[9] *Mathematical note:* To see that this is equivalent to the previous equation, note that we can multiply both sides of this equation by Y and thereby cancel Y from three places in which it appears. We can cancel the K in the top and bottom of the first term on the right-hand side and the L in the top and bottom of the second term on the right-hand side. These algebraic manipulations turn this equation into the previous one.

We include the effects of the changing technology by writing the production function as

$$Y = AF(K, L),$$

where A is a measure of the current level of technology called *total factor productivity*. Output now increases not only because of increases in capital and labor but also because of increases in total factor productivity. If total factor productivity increases by 1 percent and if the inputs are unchanged, then output increases by 1 percent.

Allowing for a changing technology adds another term to our equation accounting for economic growth:

$$\frac{\Delta Y}{Y} = \alpha \frac{\Delta K}{K} + (1 - \alpha) \frac{\Delta L}{L} + \frac{\Delta A}{A}$$

$$\begin{matrix} \text{Growth in} \\ \text{Output} \end{matrix} = \begin{matrix} \text{Contribution} \\ \text{of Capital} \end{matrix} + \begin{matrix} \text{Contribution} \\ \text{of Labor} \end{matrix} + \begin{matrix} \text{Growth in Total} \\ \text{Factor Productivity.} \end{matrix}$$

This is the key equation of growth accounting. It identifies and allows us to measure the three sources of growth: changes in the amount of capital, changes in the amount of labor, and changes in total factor productivity.

Because total factor productivity is not observable directly, it is measured indirectly. We have data on the growth in output, capital, and labor; we also have data on capital's share of output. From these data and the growth-accounting equation, we can compute the growth in total factor productivity to make sure that everything adds up:

$$\frac{\Delta A}{A} = \frac{\Delta Y}{Y} - \alpha \frac{\Delta K}{K} - (1 - \alpha) \frac{\Delta L}{L}.$$

$\Delta A/A$ is the change in output that cannot be explained by changes in inputs. Thus, the growth in total factor productivity is computed as a residual—that is, as the amount of output growth that remains after we have accounted for the determinants of growth that we can measure. Indeed, $\Delta A/A$ is sometimes called the *Solow residual,* after Robert Solow, who first showed how to compute it.[10]

Total factor productivity can change for many reasons. Changes most often arise because of increased knowledge about production methods, and the Solow residual is often used as a measure of technological progress. Yet other factors, such as education and government regulation, can affect total factor

---

[10] Robert M. Solow, "Technical Change and the Aggregate Production Function," *Review of Economics and Statistics* 39 (1957): 312–320. It is natural to ask how growth in labor efficiency E relates to growth in total factor productivity. One can show that $\Delta A/A = (1 - \alpha)\Delta E/E$, where α is capital's share. Thus, technological change as measured by growth in the efficiency of labor is proportional to technological change as measured by the Solow residual.

productivity as well. For example, if higher public spending raises the quality of education, then workers may become more productive and output may rise, which implies higher total factor productivity. As another example, if government regulations require firms to purchase capital to reduce pollution or increase worker safety, then the capital stock may rise without any increase in measured output, which implies lower total factor productivity. *Total factor productivity captures anything that changes the relation between measured inputs and measured output.*

The Sources of Growth in the United States

Having learned how to measure the sources of economic growth, we now look at the data. Table 5-3 uses U.S. data to measure the contributions of the three sources of growth between 1950 and 1996.

This table shows that real GDP has grown an average of 3.2 percent per year since 1950. Of this 3.2 percent, 0.9 percent is attributable to increases in the capital stock, 1.2 percent to increases in the labor input, and 1.1 percent to increases in total factor productivity. These data show that increases in capital, labor, and productivity have contributed almost equally to economic growth in the United States.

Table 5-3 also shows that the growth in total factor productivity slowed substantially around 1970. In a previous case study in this chapter, we discussed some hypotheses to explain this productivity slowdown.

table 5-3

Accounting for Economic Growth in the United States

			SOURCE OF GROWTH			
Years	Output Growth $\Delta Y/Y$	=	Capital $\alpha\Delta K/K$	+	Labor $(1-\alpha)\Delta L/L$ +	Total Factor Productivity $\Delta A/A$
			(average percentage increase per year)			
1950–1960	3.5		1.1		0.8	1.6
1960–1970	4.1		1.2		1.3	1.7
1970–1980	3.1		0.9		1.6	0.5
1980–1990	2.9		0.8		1.3	0.8
1990–1996	2.2		0.6		0.8	0.8
1950–1996	3.2		0.9		1.2	1.1

Source: U.S. Department of Commerce, U.S. Department of Labor, and the author's calculations. The parameter α is set to equal 0.3.

CASE STUDY

Growth in the East Asian Tigers

Perhaps the most spectacular growth experiences in recent history have been those of the "Tigers" of East Asia: Hong Kong, Singapore, South Korea, and Taiwan. From 1966 to 1990, while real income per person was growing about 2 percent per year in the United States, it grew more than 7 percent per year in each of these countries. In the course of a single generation, real income per person increased fivefold, moving the Tigers from among the world's poorest countries to among the richest. (In the late 1990s, a period of pronounced financial turmoil tarnished the reputation of some of these economies. But this short-run problem, which we examine in a case study in Chapter 12, doesn't come close to reversing the spectacular long-run growth performance that the Asian Tigers have experienced.)

What accounts for these growth miracles? Some commentators have argued that the success of these four countries is hard to reconcile with basic growth theory, such as the Solow growth model, which takes technology as growing at a constant, exogenous rate. They have suggested that these countries' rapid growth is due to their ability to imitate foreign technologies. By adopting technology developed abroad, the argument goes, these countries managed to improve their production functions substantially in a relatively short period of time. If this argument is correct, these countries should have experienced unusually rapid growth in total factor productivity.

One recent study shed light on this issue by examining in detail the data from these four countries. The study found that their exceptional growth can be traced to large increases in measured factor inputs: increases in labor-force participation, increases in the capital stock, and increases in educational attainment. In South Korea, for example, the investment–GDP ratio rose from about 5 percent in the 1950s to about 30 percent in the 1980s; the percentage of the working population with at least a high-school education went from 26 percent in 1966 to 75 percent in 1991.

Once we account for growth in labor, capital, and human capital, little of the growth in output is left to explain. None of these four countries experienced unusually rapid growth in total factor productivity. Indeed, the average growth in total factor productivity in the East Asian Tigers was almost exactly the same as in the United States. Thus, although these countries' rapid growth has been truly impressive, it is easy to explain using the tools of basic growth theory.[11]

---

[11] Alwyn Young, "The Tyranny of Numbers: Confronting the Statistical Realities of the East Asian Growth Experience," *Quarterly Journal of Economics* 101 (August 1995): 641–680.

MORE PROBLEMS AND APPLICATIONS

1. In the economy of Solovia, the owners of capital get two-thirds of national income, and the workers receive one-third.

   a. The men of Solovia stay at home performing household chores, while the women work in factories. If some of the men started working outside the home so that the labor force increased by 5 percent, what would happen to the measured output of the economy? Does labor productivity—defined as output per worker—increase, decrease, or stay the same? Does total factor productivity increase, decrease, or stay the same?

   b. In year 1, the capital stock was 6, the labor input was 3, and output was 12. In year 2, the capital stock was 7, the labor input was 4, and output was 14. What happened to total factor productivity between the two years?

2. Labor productivity is defined as Y/L, the amount of output divided by the amount of labor input. Start with the growth-accounting equation and show that the growth in labor productivity depends on growth in total factor productivity and growth in the capital–labor ratio. In particular, show that

$$\frac{\Delta(Y/L)}{Y/L} = \frac{\Delta A}{A} + \alpha \frac{\Delta(K/L)}{K/L}.$$

(*Hint:* You may find the following mathematical trick helpful. If $z = wx$, then the growth rate of z is approximately the growth rate of w plus the growth rate of x. That is,

$$\Delta z/z \approx \Delta w/w + \Delta x/x.)$$

3. Suppose an economy described by the Solow model is in a steady state with population growth n of 1.0 percent per year and technological progress g of 2.0 percent per year. Total output and total capital grow at 3.0 percent per year. Suppose further that the capital share of output is 0.3. If you used the growth-accounting equation to divide output growth into three sources—capital, labor, and total factor productivity—how much would you attribute to each source? Compare your results to the figures we found for the United States in Table 5-3.

chapter 6

Unemployment

A man willing to work, and unable to find work, is perhaps the saddest sight that fortune's inequality exhibits under the sun.

— *Thomas Carlyle*

Unemployment is the macroeconomic problem that affects people most directly and severely. For most people, the loss of a job means a reduced living standard and psychological distress. It is no surprise that unemployment is a frequent topic of political debate and that politicians often claim that their proposed policies would help create jobs.

Economists study unemployment to identify its causes and to help improve the public policies that affect the unemployed. Some of these policies, such as job-training programs, assist people in finding employment. Others, such as unemployment insurance, alleviate some of the hardships that the unemployed face. Still other policies affect the prevalence of unemployment inadvertently. Laws mandating a high minimum wage, for instance, are widely thought to raise unemployment among the least skilled and experienced members of the labor force. By showing the effects of various policies, economists help policymakers evaluate their options.

In our discussions of the labor market in the previous three chapters, we ignored unemployment. Our models of national income (Chapter 3) and economic growth (Chapters 4 and 5) were built with the assumption that the economy was always at full employment. In reality, of course, not everyone in the labor force has a job all the time: all free-market economies experience some unemployment.

Figure 6-1 shows the rate of unemployment—the percentage of the labor force unemployed—in the United States since 1948. Although the rate of unemployment fluctuates from year to year, it never gets even close to zero. The average is between 5 and 6 percent, meaning that about 1 out of every 18 people wanting a job does not have one.

In this chapter we begin our study of unemployment by discussing why there is always some unemployment and what determines its level. We do not study what determines the year-to-year fluctuations in the rate of unemployment until Part Three of this book, where we examine short-run economic fluctuations. Here we examine the determinants of the **natural rate of**

figure 6-1

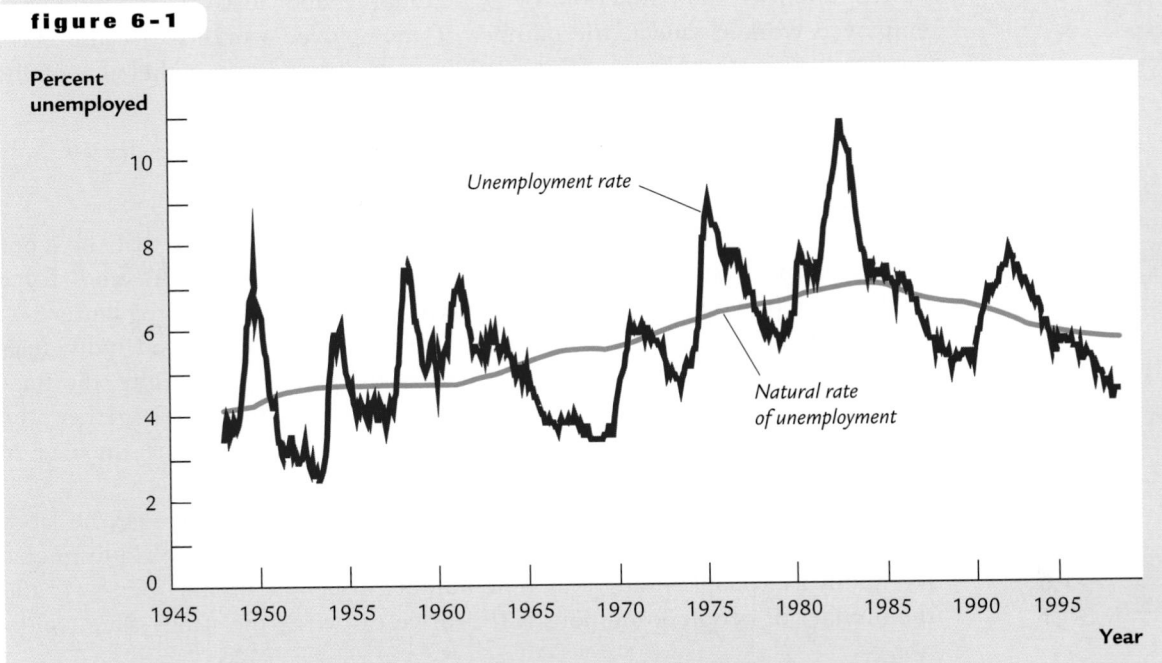

The Unemployment Rate and the Natural Rate of Unemployment in the United States There is always some unemployment. The natural rate of unemployment is the average level around which the unemployment rate fluctuates. (The natural rate of unemployment for any particular year is estimated here by averaging all the unemployment rates from ten years earlier to ten years later. Future unemployment rates are set at 5.5 percent.)

unemployment—the average rate of unemployment around which the economy fluctuates. The natural rate can be viewed as the steady-state rate of unemployment because it is the rate toward which the economy gravitates in the long run.

6-1 | Job Loss, Job Finding, and the Natural Rate of Unemployment

Every day some workers lose or quit their jobs, and some unemployed workers are hired. This perpetual ebb and flow determines the fraction of the labor force that is unemployed. In this section we develop a model of labor-force dynamics that shows what determines the natural rate of unemployment.[1]

---

[1] Robert E. Hall, "A Theory of the Natural Rate of Unemployment and the Duration of Unemployment," *Journal of Monetary Economics* 5 (April 1979): 153–169.

We start with some notation. Let L denote the labor force, E the number of employed workers, and U the number of unemployed workers. Because every worker is either employed or unemployed, the labor force is the sum of the employed and the unemployed:

$$L = E + U.$$

In this notation, the rate of unemployment is U/L.

To see what determines the unemployment rate, we assume that the labor force L is fixed and focus on the transition of individuals in the labor force between employment and unemployment. This is illustrated in Figure 6-2. Let s denote the rate of job separation, the fraction of employed individuals who lose their job each month. Let f denote the rate of job finding, the fraction of unemployed individuals who find a job each month. Together, the rate of job separation s and the rate of job finding f determine the rate of unemployment.

If the unemployment rate is neither rising nor falling—that is, if the labor market is in a steady state—then the number of people finding jobs must equal the number of people losing jobs. The number of people finding jobs is fU and the number of people losing jobs is sE, so we can write the steady-state condition as

$$fU = sE.$$

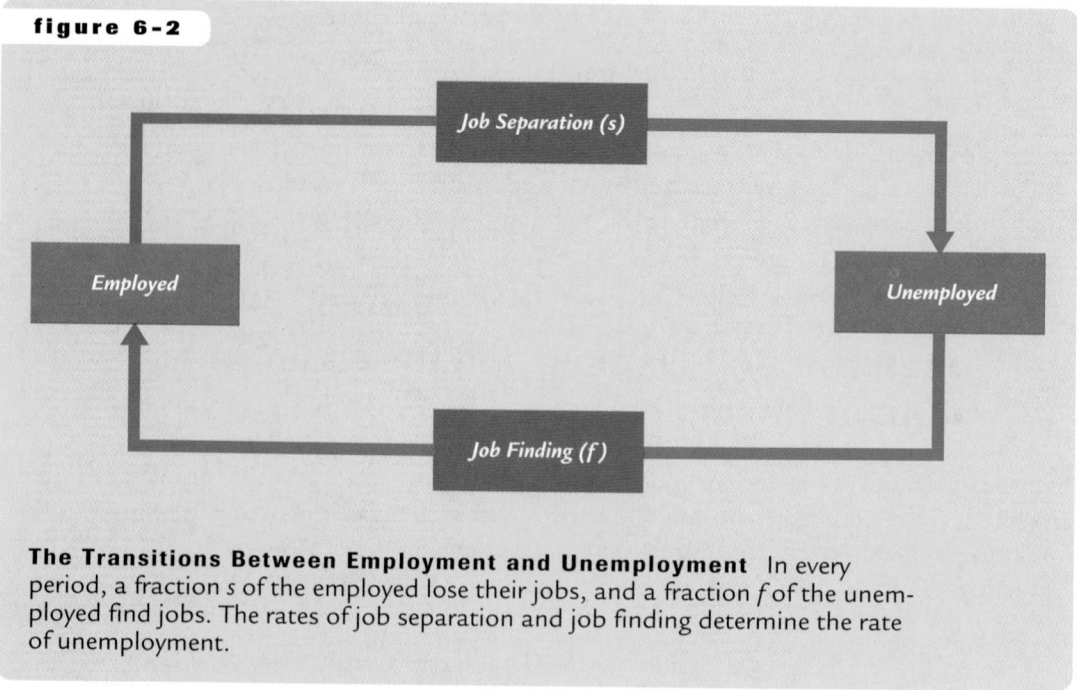

figure 6-2

The Transitions Between Employment and Unemployment In every period, a fraction s of the employed lose their jobs, and a fraction f of the unemployed find jobs. The rates of job separation and job finding determine the rate of unemployment.

We can use this equation to find the steady-state unemployment rate. From an earlier equation, we know that $E = L - U$; that is, the number of employed equals the labor force minus the number of unemployed. If we substitute $(L - U)$ for E in the steady-state condition, we find

$$fU = s(L - U).$$

To get closer to solving for the unemployment rate, divide both sides of this equation by L to obtain

$$f\frac{U}{L} = s\left(1 - \frac{U}{L}\right).$$

Now we can solve for U/L to find

$$\frac{U}{L} = \frac{s}{s + f}.$$

This equation shows that the steady-state rate of unemployment U/L depends on the rates of job separation s and job finding f. The higher the rate of job separation, the higher the unemployment rate. The higher the rate of job finding, the lower the unemployment rate.

Here's a numerical example. Suppose that 1 percent of the employed lose their jobs each month ($s = 0.01$). This means that on average jobs last 100 months, or about 8 years. Suppose further that about 20 percent of the unemployed find a job each month ($f = 0.20$), so that spells of unemployment last 5 months on average. Then the steady-state rate of unemployment is

$$\frac{U}{L} = \frac{0.01}{0.01 + 0.20}$$

$$= 0.0476.$$

The rate of unemployment in this example is about 5 percent.

This model of the natural rate of unemployment has an obvious but important implication for public policy. *Any policy aimed at lowering the natural rate of unemployment must either reduce the rate of job separation or increase the rate of job finding. Similarly, any policy that affects the rate of job separation or job finding also changes the natural rate of unemployment.*

Although this model is useful in relating the unemployment rate to job separation and job finding, it fails to answer a central question: Why is there unemployment in the first place? If a person could always find a job quickly, then the rate of job finding would be very high and the rate of unemployment would be near zero. This model of the unemployment rate assumes that job finding is not instantaneous, but it fails to explain why. In the next two sections, we examine two underlying reasons for unemployment: job search and wage rigidity.

6-2 | Job Search and Frictional Unemployment

One reason for unemployment is that it takes time to match workers and jobs. The equilibrium model of the aggregate labor market discussed in Chapter 3 assumes that all workers and all jobs are identical, and therefore that all workers are equally well suited for all jobs. If this were really true and the labor market were in equilibrium, then a job loss would not cause unemployment: a laid-off worker would immediately find a new job at the market wage.

In fact, workers have different preferences and abilities, and jobs have different attributes. Furthermore, the flow of information about job candidates and job vacancies is imperfect, and the geographic mobility of workers is not instantaneous. For all these reasons, searching for an appropriate job takes time and effort, and this tends to reduce the rate of job finding. Indeed, because different jobs require different skills and pay different wages, unemployed workers may not accept the first job offer they receive. The unemployment caused by the time it takes workers to search for a job is called **frictional unemployment.**

Some frictional unemployment is inevitable in a changing economy. For many reasons, the types of goods that firms and households demand vary over time. As the demand for goods shifts, so does the demand for the labor that produces those goods. The invention of the personal computer, for example, reduced the demand for typewriters and, as a result, for labor by typewriter manufacturers. At the same time, it increased the demand for labor in the electronics industry. Similarly, because different regions produce different goods, the demand for labor may be rising in one part of the country while it is falling in another. A decline in the price of oil may cause the demand for labor to fall in oil-producing states such as Texas, but because cheap oil makes driving less expensive, it increases the demand for labor in auto-producing states such as Michigan. Economists call a change in the composition of demand among industries or regions a **sectoral shift.** Because sectoral shifts are always occurring, and because it takes time for workers to change sectors, there is always frictional unemployment.

Sectoral shifts are not the only cause of job separation and frictional unemployment. In addition, workers find themselves unexpectedly out of work when their firm fails, when their job performance is deemed unacceptable, or when their particular skills are no longer needed. Workers also may quit their jobs to change careers or to move to different parts of the country. As long as the supply and demand for labor among firms is changing, frictional unemployment is unavoidable.

Public Policy and Frictional Unemployment

Many public policies seek to decrease the natural rate of unemployment by reducing frictional unemployment. Government employment agencies disseminate information about job vacancies in order to match jobs and workers more efficiently. Publicly funded retraining programs are designed to ease the transition of workers from declining to growing industries. If these programs succeed at increasing the rate of job finding, they decrease the natural rate of unemployment.

Other government programs inadvertently increase the amount of frictional unemployment. One of these is **unemployment insurance.** Under this program, unemployed workers can collect a fraction of their wages for a certain period after losing their jobs. Although the precise terms of the program differ from year to year and from state to state, a typical worker covered by unemployment insurance in the United States receives 50 percent of his or her former wages for 26 weeks. In many European countries, unemployment-insurance programs are even more generous.

By softening the economic hardship of unemployment, unemployment insurance increases the amount of frictional unemployment and raises the natural rate. The unemployed who receive unemployment-insurance benefits are less pressed to search for new employment and are more likely to turn down unattractive job offers. Both of these changes in behavior reduce the rate of job finding. In addition, because workers know that their incomes are partially protected by unemployment insurance, they are less likely to seek jobs with stable employment prospects and are less likely to bargain for guarantees of job security. These behavioral changes raise the rate of job separation.

That unemployment insurance raises the natural rate of unemployment does not necessarily imply that the policy is ill advised. The program has the benefit of reducing workers' uncertainty about their incomes. Moreover, inducing workers to reject unattractive job offers may lead to a better matching between workers and jobs. Evaluating the costs and benefits of different systems of unemployment insurance is a difficult task that continues to be a topic of much research.

Economists who study unemployment insurance often propose reforms that would reduce the amount of unemployment. One common proposal is to require a firm that lays off a worker to bear the full cost of that worker's unemployment benefits. Such a system is called *100 percent experience rated,* because the rate that each firm pays into the unemployment-insurance system fully reflects the unemployment experience of its own workers. Most current programs are *partially experience rated.* Under this system, when a firm lays off a worker, it is charged for only part of the worker's unemployment benefits; the remainder comes from the program's general revenue. Because a firm pays only a fraction of the cost of the unemployment it causes, it has an incentive to lay off workers when its demand for labor is temporarily low. By reducing that incentive, the proposed reform may reduce the prevalence of temporary layoffs.

CASE STUDY

Unemployment Insurance and the Rate of Job Finding

Many studies have examined the effect of unemployment insurance on job search. The most persuasive studies use data on the experiences of unemployed individuals, rather than economy-wide rates of unemployment. Individual data often yield sharp results that are open to few alternative explanations.

One study followed the experience of individual workers as they used up their eligibility for unemployment-insurance benefits. It found that when unemployed workers become ineligible for benefits, they are more likely to find new jobs. In particular, the probability of a person finding a new job more than doubles when his or her benefits run out. One possible explanation is that an absence of benefits increases the search effort of unemployed workers. Another possibility is that workers without benefits are more likely to accept job offers that would otherwise be declined because of low wages or poor working conditions.[2]

Additional evidence on how economic incentives affect job search comes from an experiment that the state of Illinois ran in 1985. Randomly selected new claimants for unemployment insurance were each offered a $500 bonus if they found employment within 11 weeks. The subsequent experience of this group was compared to that of a control group not offered the incentive. The average duration of unemployment for the group offered the $500 bonus was 17.0 weeks, compared to 18.3 weeks for the control group. Thus, the bonus reduced the average spell of unemployment by 7 percent, suggesting that more effort was devoted to job search. This experiment shows clearly that the incentives provided by the unemployment-insurance system affect the rate of job finding.[3]

6-3 | Real-Wage Rigidity and Wait Unemployment

A second reason for unemployment is **wage rigidity**—the failure of wages to adjust until labor supply equals labor demand. In the equilibrium model of the labor market, as outlined in Chapter 3, the real wage adjusts to equilibrate supply and demand. Yet wages are not always flexible. Sometimes the real wage is stuck above the market-clearing level.

Figure 6-3 shows why wage rigidity leads to unemployment. When the real wage is above the level that equilibrates supply and demand, the quantity of labor supplied exceeds the quantity demanded. Firms must in some way ration the scarce jobs among workers. Real-wage rigidity reduces the rate of job finding and raises the level of unemployment.

---

[2] Lawrence F. Katz and Bruce D. Meyer, "Unemployment Insurance, Recall Expectations, and Unemployment Outcomes," *Quarterly Journal of Economics* 105 (November 1990): 973–1002.

[3] Stephen A. Woodbury and Robert G. Spiegelman, "Bonuses to Workers and Employers to Reduce Unemployment: Randomized Trials in Illinois," *American Economic Review* 77 (September 1987): 513–530.

figure 6-3

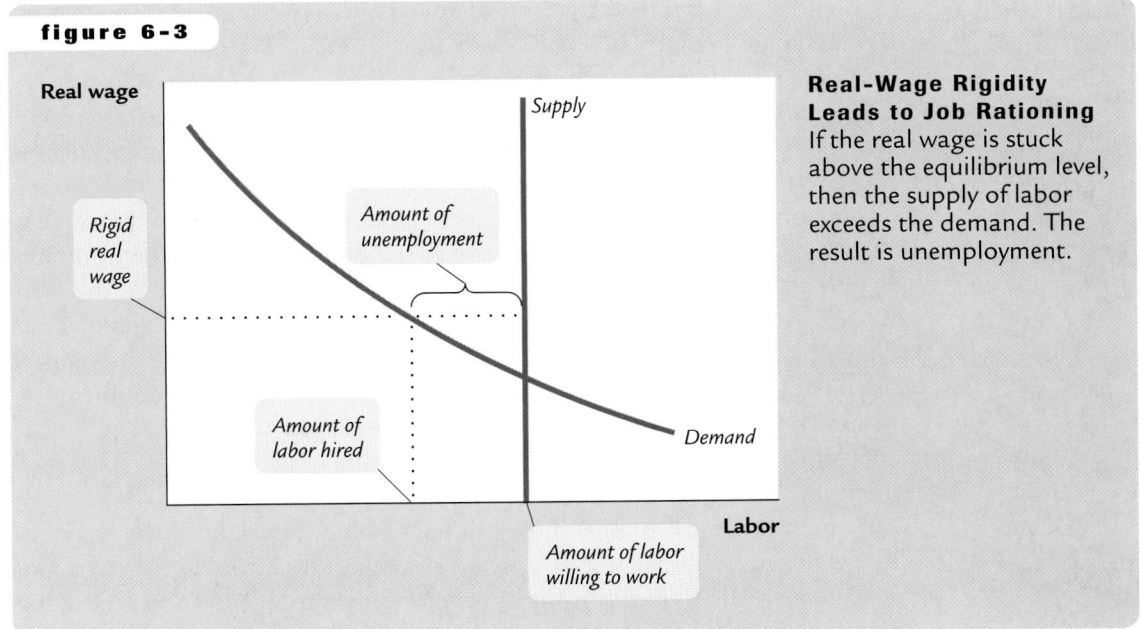

Real-Wage Rigidity Leads to Job Rationing If the real wage is stuck above the equilibrium level, then the supply of labor exceeds the demand. The result is unemployment.

The unemployment resulting from wage rigidity and job rationing is called **wait unemployment.** Workers are unemployed not because they are actively searching for the jobs that best suit their individual skills but because, at the going wage, the supply of labor exceeds the demand. These workers are simply waiting for jobs to become available.

To understand wage rigidity and wait unemployment, we must examine why the labor market does not clear. When the real wage exceeds the equilibrium level and the supply of workers exceeds the demand, we might expect firms to lower the wages they pay. Wait unemployment arises because firms fail to reduce wages despite an excess supply of labor. We now turn to three causes of this wage rigidity: minimum-wage laws, the monopoly power of unions, and efficiency wages.

Minimum-Wage Laws

The government causes wage rigidity when it prevents wages from falling to equilibrium levels. Minimum-wage laws set a legal minimum on the wages that firms pay their employees. Since the passage of the Fair Labor Standards Act of 1938, the U.S. federal government has enforced a minimum wage that usually has been between 30 and 50 percent of the average wage in manufacturing. For most workers, this minimum wage is not binding, because they earn well above the minimum. Yet for some workers, especially the unskilled and inexperienced, the minimum wage raises their wage above its equilibrium level. It therefore reduces the quantity of their labor that firms demand.

Economists believe that the minimum wage has its greatest impact on teenage unemployment. The equilibrium wages of teenagers tend to be low for two reasons. First, because teenagers are among the least skilled and least experienced members of the labor force, they tend to have low marginal productivity. Second, teenagers often take some of their "compensation" in the form of on-the-job training rather than direct pay. An apprenticeship is a classic example of training offered in place of wages. For both these reasons, the wage at which the supply of teenage workers equals the demand is low. The minimum wage is therefore more often binding for teenagers than for others in the labor force.

Many economists have studied the impact of the minimum wage on teenage employment. These researchers compare the variation in the minimum wage over time with the variation in the number of teenagers with jobs. These studies find that a 10-percent increase in the minimum wage reduces teenage employment by 1 to 3 percent.[4]

The minimum wage is a perennial source of political debate. Advocates of a higher minimum wage view it as a means of raising the income of the working poor. Certainly, the minimum wage provides only a meager standard of living: in the United States, two adults working full time at minimum-wage jobs would just exceed the official poverty level for a family of four. While minimum-wage advocates often admit that the policy causes unemployment for some workers, they argue that this cost is worth bearing to raise others out of poverty.

Opponents of a higher minimum wage claim that it is not the best way to help the working poor. They contend not only that the increased labor costs would raise unemployment, but also that the minimum wage is poorly targeted. Many minimum-wage earners are teenagers from middle-class homes working for discretionary spending money. Of the approximately 3 million workers who earn the minimum wage, more than one-third are teenagers.

To mitigate the effects on teenage unemployment, some economists and policymakers have long advocated exempting young workers from the regular minimum wage. This would permit a lower wage for teenagers, thereby reducing their unemployment and enabling them to get training and job experience. Opponents of this exemption argue that it gives firms an incentive to substitute teenagers for unskilled adults, thereby raising unemployment among that group. A limited exemption of this kind was tried from 1991 to 1993. Because of many restrictions on its use, however, it had only a limited effect and, therefore, was not renewed by Congress.

Many economists and policymakers believe that tax credits are a better way to increase the incomes of the working poor. The *earned income tax credit* is an amount that poor working families are allowed to subtract from the taxes they owe. For a family with very low income, the credit exceeds its taxes, and the family receives a payment from the government. Unlike the minimum wage,

[4] Charles Brown, "Minimum Wage Laws: Are They Overrated?" *Journal of Economic Perspectives* 2 (Summer 1988): 133–146.

the earned income tax credit does not raise labor costs to firms and, therefore, does not reduce the quantity of labor that firms demand. It has the disadvantage, however, of reducing the government's tax revenue.

CASE STUDY

A Revisionist View of the Minimum Wage

Although most economists believe that increases in the minimum wage reduce employment among workers with little skill and experience, some recent studies question this conclusion. Three widely respected labor economists—David Card, Lawrence Katz, and Alan Krueger—examined several instances of minimum-wage changes in order to determine the magnitude of the employment response. What they found was startling.

One study examined hiring by fast-food restaurants in New Jersey when New Jersey raised the state minimum wage. Fast-food restaurants are a natural type of firm to examine because they employ many low-wage workers. To control for other effects, such as overall economic conditions, the New Jersey restaurants were compared to similar restaurants across the river in Pennsylvania. Pennsylvania did not raise its minimum wage at the same time. According to standard theory, employment in New Jersey restaurants should have fallen relative to employment in Pennsylvania restaurants. In contrast to this hypothesis, the data showed that employment *rose* in the New Jersey restaurants.

How is this seemingly perverse result possible? One explanation is that firms have some market power in the labor market. As you may have learned in courses in microeconomics, a monopsony firm buys less labor at a lower wage than a competitive firm would. In essence, the firm reduces employment in order to depress the wage it has to pay. A minimum wage prevents the monopsony firm from following this strategy and so (up to a point) can increase employment.

This new view of the minimum wage is controversial. Critics have questioned the reliability of the data used in the New Jersey study. Some studies using other data sources have reached the traditional conclusion that the minimum wage depresses employment. Moreover, most economists are skeptical of the monopsony explanation, since most firms compete with many other firms for workers. Yet this new view has directly affected the policy debate. Lawrence Katz was the first chief economist in the Department of Labor during the Clinton Administration. He was followed in this job by Alan Krueger. It is therefore not surprising that President Clinton has supported increases in the national minimum wage.[5]

---

[5] To read more about this new view of the minimum wage, see David Card and Alan Krueger, *Myth and Measurement: The New Economics of the Minimum Wage* (Princeton, NJ: Princeton University Press, 1995); Lawrence Katz and Alan Krueger, "The Effects of the Minimum Wage on the Fast-Food Industry," *Industrial and Labor Relations Review* 46 (October 1992): 6–21.

Unions and Collective Bargaining

A second cause of wage rigidity is the monopoly power of unions. Table 6-1 shows the importance of unions in 12 major countries. In the United States, only 16 percent of workers belong to unions. In most European countries, unions play a much larger role.

The wages of unionized workers are determined not by the equilibrium of supply and demand but by collective bargaining between union leaders and firm management. Often, the final agreement raises the wage above the equilibrium level and allows the firm to decide how many workers to employ. The result is a reduction in the number of workers hired, a lower rate of job finding, and an increase in wait unemployment.

Unions can also influence the wages paid by firms whose work forces are not unionized because the threat of unionization can keep wages above the equilibrium level. Most firms dislike unions. Unions not only raise wages but also increase the bargaining power of labor on many other issues, such as hours of employment and working conditions. A firm may choose to pay its workers high wages to keep them happy in order to discourage them from forming a union.

The unemployment caused by unions and by the threat of unionization is an instance of conflict between different groups of workers—**insiders** and **outsiders.** Those workers already employed by a firm, the insiders, typically try to keep their firm's wages high. The unemployed, the outsiders, bear part of the cost of higher wages because at a lower wage they might be hired. These two groups inevitably have conflicting interests. The effect of any bargaining process on wages and employment depends crucially on the relative influence of each group.

The conflict between insiders and outsiders is resolved differently in different countries. In some countries, such as the United States, wage bargaining takes place at the level of the firm or plant. In other countries, such as Sweden, wage bargaining takes place at the national level—with the government often playing a key role. Despite a highly unionized labor force, Sweden has not experienced extraordinarily high unemployment throughout its history. One possible explanation is that the centralization of wage bargaining and the role of

table 6-1

Union Membership as a Percentage of Employment

Sweden	84	Germany	33
Denmark	75	Netherlands	28
Italy	47	Switzerland	28
United Kingdom	41	Japan	26
Australia	34	United States	16
Canada	33	France	11

Source: Clara Chang and Constance Sorrentino, "Union Membership Statistics in 12 Countries," *Monthly Labor Review* (December 1991): 46–53.

the government in the bargaining process gives more influence to the outsiders, which keeps wages closer to the equilibrium level.

CASE STUDY

Unionization and Unemployment in the United States and Canada

Throughout the 1960s the United States and Canada had similar labor markets. The rates of unemployment in the two countries were about the same on average, and they fluctuated together. In the mid-1970s, the experiences of the two countries began to diverge. Unemployment became much more prevalent in Canada than in the United States. Over the past decade, the Canadian unemployment rate has been about 2 to 3 percentage points above the U.S. unemployment rate.

The changing roles of unions in the two countries is one possible explanation for this divergence. In the 1960s, about 30 percent of the labor force was unionized in each country. But Canadian labor laws did more to foster unionization than U.S. laws did. Unionization rose in Canada while it fell in the United States.

As one might have predicted, changes in real wages accompanied the change in unionization. The real wage in Canada increased by about 30 percent relative to the real wage in the United States. This evidence suggests that unions in Canada pushed the real wage further above the equilibrium level, leading to more wait unemployment.

The divergence in the two unemployment rates may also be attributable to the increase in the availability of unemployment-insurance benefits in Canada. Not only does unemployment insurance raise search times and the amount of frictional unemployment, but it also interacts with the effects of unionization in two ways. First, unemployment insurance makes unemployed workers more willing to wait for a high-wage job in a unionized firm rather than take a lower-wage job in a nonunion firm. Second, because unemployment insurance partially protects the incomes of unemployed workers, it makes unions more willing to press for high wages at the expense of lower employment.[6]

Efficiency Wages

Efficiency-wage theories propose a third cause of wage rigidity in addition to minimum-wage laws and unionization. These theories hold that high wages make workers more productive. The influence of wages on worker efficiency may explain the failure of firms to cut wages despite an excess supply of labor. Even though a wage reduction would lower a firm's wage bill, it would

---

[6] Herbert G. Grubel, "Drifting Apart: Canadian and U.S. Labor Markets," *Contemporary Policy Issues* 6 (January 1988): 39–55, also in *Journal of Economic and Monetary Affairs* 2 (Winter 1988): 59–75.

also—if these theories are correct—lower worker productivity and the firm's profits.

Economists have proposed various theories to explain how wages affect worker productivity. One efficiency-wage theory, which is applied mostly to poorer countries, holds that wages influence nutrition. Better-paid workers can afford a more nutritious diet, and healthier workers are more productive. A firm may decide to pay a wage above the equilibrium level to maintain a healthy work force. Obviously, this consideration is not important for employers in wealthy countries, such as the United States and most of Europe, since the equilibrium wage is well above the level necessary to maintain good health.

A second efficiency-wage theory, which is more relevant for developed countries, holds that high wages reduce labor turnover. Workers quit jobs for many reasons—to accept better positions at other firms, to change careers, or to move to other parts of the country. The more a firm pays its workers, the greater their incentive to stay with the firm. By paying a high wage, a firm reduces the frequency of quits, thereby decreasing the time spent hiring and training new workers.

A third efficiency-wage theory holds that the average quality of a firm's work force depends on the wage it pays its employees. If a firm reduces its wage, the best employees may take jobs elsewhere, leaving the firm with inferior employees who have fewer alternative opportunities. Economists recognize this unfavorable sorting as an example of *adverse selection*—the tendency of people with more information (in this case, the workers, who know their own outside opportunities) to self-select in a way that disadvantages people with less information (the firm). By paying a wage above the equilibrium level, the firm may reduce adverse selection, improve the average quality of its work force, and thereby increase productivity.

A fourth efficiency-wage theory holds that a high wage improves worker effort. This theory posits that firms cannot perfectly monitor their employees' work effort, and that employees must themselves decide how hard to work. Workers can choose to work hard, or they can choose to shirk and risk getting caught and fired. Economists recognize this possibility as an example of *moral hazard*—the tendency of people to behave inappropriately when their behavior is imperfectly monitored. The firm can reduce the problem of moral hazard by paying a high wage. The higher the wage, the greater the cost to the worker of getting fired. By paying a higher wage, a firm induces more of its employees not to shirk and thus increases their productivity.

Although these four efficiency-wage theories differ in detail, they share a common theme: because a firm operates more efficiently if it pays its workers a high wage, the firm may find it profitable to keep wages above the level that balances supply and demand. The result of this higher-than-equilibrium wage is a lower rate of job finding and greater wait unemployment.[7]

---

[7] For more extended discussions of efficiency wages, see Janet Yellen, "Efficiency Wage Models of Unemployment," *American Economic Review Papers and Proceedings* (May 1984): 200–205; and Lawrence Katz, "Efficiency Wages: A Partial Evaluation," *NBER Macroeconomics Annual* (1986): 235–276.

CASE STUDY

Henry Ford's $5 Workday

In 1914 the Ford Motor Company started paying its workers $5 per day. Since the prevailing wage at the time was between $2 and $3 per day, Ford's wage was well above the equilibrium level. Not surprisingly, long lines of job seekers waited outside the Ford plant gates hoping for a chance to earn this high wage.

What was Ford's motive? Henry Ford later wrote, "We wanted to pay these wages so that the business would be on a lasting foundation. We were building for the future. A low wage business is always insecure . . . . The payment of five dollars a day for an eight hour day was one of the finest cost cutting moves we ever made."

From the standpoint of traditional economic theory, Ford's explanation seems peculiar. He was suggesting that *high* wages imply *low* costs. But perhaps Ford had discovered efficiency-wage theory. Perhaps he was using the high wage to increase worker productivity.

Evidence suggests that paying such a high wage did benefit the company. According to an engineering report written at the time, "The Ford high wage does away with all the inertia and living force resistance. . . . The workingmen are absolutely docile, and it is safe to say that since the last day of 1913, every single day has seen major reductions in Ford shops' labor costs." Absenteeism fell by 75 percent, suggesting a large increase in worker effort. Alan Nevins, a historian who studied the early Ford Motor Company, wrote, "Ford and his associates freely declared on many occasions that the high wage policy had turned out to be good business. By this they meant that it had improved the discipline of the workers, given them a more loyal interest in the institution, and raised their personal efficiency."[8]

6-4 | Patterns of Unemployment

So far we have developed the theory behind the natural rate of unemployment. We began by showing that the economy's steady-state unemployment rate depends on the rates of job separation and job finding. Then we discussed two reasons why job finding is not instantaneous: the process of job search (which leads to frictional unemployment) and wage rigidity (which leads to wait unemployment). Wage rigidity, in turn, arises from minimum-wage laws, unionization, and efficiency wages.

With these theories as background, we now examine some additional facts about unemployment. These facts will help us to evaluate our theories and assess public policies aimed at reducing unemployment.

---

[8] Jeremy I. Bulow and Lawrence H. Summers, "A Theory of Dual Labor Markets With Application to Industrial Policy, Discrimination, and Keynesian Unemployment," *Journal of Labor Economics* 4 (July 1986): 376–414; Daniel M. G. Raff and Lawrence H. Summers, "Did Henry Ford Pay Efficiency Wages?" *Journal of Labor Economics* 5 (October 1987, Part 2): S57–S86.

The Duration of Unemployment

When a person becomes unemployed, is the spell of unemployment likely to be short or long? The answer to this question is important because it indicates the reasons for the unemployment and what policy response is appropriate. On the one hand, if most unemployment is short-term, one might argue that it is frictional and perhaps unavoidable. Unemployed workers may need some time to search for the job that is best suited to their skills and tastes. On the other hand, long-term unemployment cannot easily be attributed to the time it takes to match jobs and workers: we would not expect this matching process to take many months. Long-term unemployment is more likely to be wait unemployment. Thus, data on the duration of unemployment can affect our view about the reasons for unemployment.

The answer to our question turns out to be subtle. The data show that most spells of unemployment are short, but that most weeks of unemployment are attributable to the long-term unemployed. Consider the data for a typical year, 1974, during which the unemployment rate was 5.6 percent. In that year, 60 percent of the spells of unemployment ended within one month, yet 69 percent of the weeks of unemployment occurred in spells that lasted two or more months.[9]

To see how both these facts can be true, consider the following example. Suppose that 10 people are unemployed for part of a given year. Of these 10 people, 8 are unemployed for 1 month and 2 are unemployed for 12 months, totaling 32 months of unemployment. In this example, most spells of unemployment are short: 8 of the 10 unemployment spells, or 80 percent, end in 1 month. Yet most months of unemployment are attributable to the long-term unemployed: 24 of the 32 months of unemployment, or 75 percent, are experienced by the 2 workers who are unemployed for 12 months. Depending on whether we look at spells of unemployment or months of unemployment, most unemployment can appear to be short-term or long-term.

This evidence on the duration of unemployment has an important implication for public policy. If the goal is to lower substantially the natural rate of unemployment, policies must aim at the long-term unemployed, because these individuals account for a large amount of unemployment. Yet policies must be carefully targeted, because the long-term unemployed constitute a small minority of those who become unemployed. Most people who become unemployed find work within a short time.

Variation in the Unemployment Rate Across Demographic Groups

The rate of unemployment varies substantially across different groups within the population. Table 6-2 presents the U.S. unemployment rates for different demographic groups for 1997, when the overall rate was 4.9 percent.

---

[9] Kim B. Clark and Lawrence H. Summers, "Labor Market Dynamics and Unemployment: A Reconsideration," *Brookings Papers on Economic Activity* (1979:1): 13–72.

table 6-2

Unemployment Rate by Demographic Group: 1997

Age	White Male	White Female	Black Male	Black Female
16–19	14.3	12.8	36.5	28.7
20 and over	3.6	3.7	8.5	8.8

Source: U.S. Department of Labor.

This table shows that younger workers have much higher unemployment rates than older ones. To explain this difference, recall our model of the natural rate of unemployment. The model isolates two possible causes for a high rate of unemployment: a low rate of job finding and a high rate of job separation. When economists study data on the transition of individuals between employment and unemployment, they find that those groups with high unemployment tend to have high rates of job separation. They find less variation across groups in the rate of job finding. For example, an employed white male is four times more likely to become unemployed if he is a teenager than if he is middle-aged; once unemployed, his rate of job finding is not closely related to his age.

These findings help explain the higher unemployment rates for younger workers. Younger workers have only recently entered the labor market, and they are often uncertain about their career plans. It may be best for them to try different types of jobs before making a long-term commitment to a specific occupation. If so, we should expect a higher rate of job separation and a higher rate of frictional unemployment for this group.

Another fact that stands out from Table 6-2 is that unemployment rates are much higher for blacks than for whites. This phenomenon is not well understood. Data on transitions between employment and unemployment show that the higher unemployment rates for blacks, and especially for black teenagers, arise because of both higher rates of job separation and lower rates of job finding. Possible reasons for the lower rates of job finding include less access to informal job-finding networks and discrimination by employers.

Trends in U.S. Unemployment

Over the past half century, the natural rate of unemployment in the United States has not been stable. If you look back at Figure 6-1, you will see that unemployment averaged well below 5 percent in the 1950s and 1960s, rose to well over 6 percent in the 1970s and 1980s, and then drifted back below 5 percent in the 1990s. Although economists do not have a conclusive explanation for these changes, they have proposed at least two major hypotheses.

One explanation stresses the changing composition of the U.S. labor force. After World War II, birth rates rose dramatically: the number of births rose from 2.9 million in 1945 to a peak of 4.3 million in 1957, before falling back to 3.1 million in 1973. This rise in births in the 1950s led to a rise in the number of young workers in the 1970s. Younger workers have higher unemployment rates, however, so when the baby-boom generation entered the labor force, they increased the average level of unemployment. Then as the baby-boom workers aged, the average age of the labor force increased, lowering the average unemployment rate in the 1990s.

This demographic change, however, cannot fully explain the trends in unemployment because similar trends are apparent for fixed demographic groups. For example, for men between the ages of 25 and 54, the average unemployment rate rose from 3.0 percent in the 1960s to 6.1 percent in the 1980s. Thus, while demographic changes may be part of the story of rising unemployment over this period, there must be other explanations of the long-term trend as well.

A second explanation is based on changes in the prevalence of sectoral shifts. The greater the amount of sectoral reallocation, the greater the rate of job separation and the higher the level of frictional unemployment. One source of sectoral shifts during the 1970s and early 1980s was the great volatility in oil prices caused by OPEC, the international oil cartel. These large changes in oil prices may have required reallocating labor between more-energy-intensive and less-energy-intensive sectors. If so, oil-price volatility may have increased unemployment during this period. Although this explanation is hard to evaluate, it is consistent with recent developments: the fall in unemployment during the 1990s coincided with increased stability in oil prices.

In the end, the trends in the unemployment rate remain a mystery. The proposed explanations are plausible, but neither seems conclusive on its own. Perhaps there is no single answer. The upward drift in the unemployment rate in the 1970s and 1980s and the downward drift in the 1990s may be the result of several unrelated developments.[10]

Transitions Into and Out of the Labor Force

So far we have been ignoring an important aspect of labor-market dynamics: the movement of individuals into and out of the labor force. Our model of the natural rate of unemployment assumes that the size of the labor force is fixed. In this case, the sole reason for unemployment is job separation, and the sole reason for leaving unemployment is job finding.

In fact, changes in the labor force are important. About one-third of the unemployed have only recently entered the labor force. Some of these entrants are young workers still looking for their first jobs; others have worked before but had temporarily left the labor force. In addition, not all unemployment

---

[10] For work analyzing the role of demographics, see Robert Shimer, "Why Is the U.S. Unemployment Rate So Much Lower?" *NBER Macroeconomics Annual* 13 (1998). For work analyzing the role of sectoral shifts, see David M. Lilien, "Sectoral Shifts and Cyclical Unemployment," *Journal of Political Economy* 90 (August 1982): 777–793.

ends with job finding: almost half of all spells of unemployment end in the unemployed person's withdrawal from the labor market.

Individuals entering and leaving the labor force make unemployment statistics more difficult to interpret. On the one hand, some individuals calling themselves unemployed may not be seriously looking for a job and perhaps should best be viewed as out of the labor force. Their "unemployment" may not represent a social problem. On the other hand, some individuals may want a job but, after an unsuccessful search, have given up looking. These **discouraged workers** are counted as being out of the labor force and do not show up in unemployment statistics. Even though their joblessness is unmeasured, it may nonetheless be a social problem.

The Rise in European Unemployment

Although our discussion has focused largely on the United States, one puzzling question about unemployment concerns recent developments in Europe. Figure 6-4 shows the rate of unemployment in the countries that make up the European Community—Austria, Belgium, Denmark, Finland, France, Germany, Greece, Ireland, Italy, Luxembourg, the Netherlands, Portugal, Spain, Sweden, and the United Kingdom. As you can see, the rate of unemployment

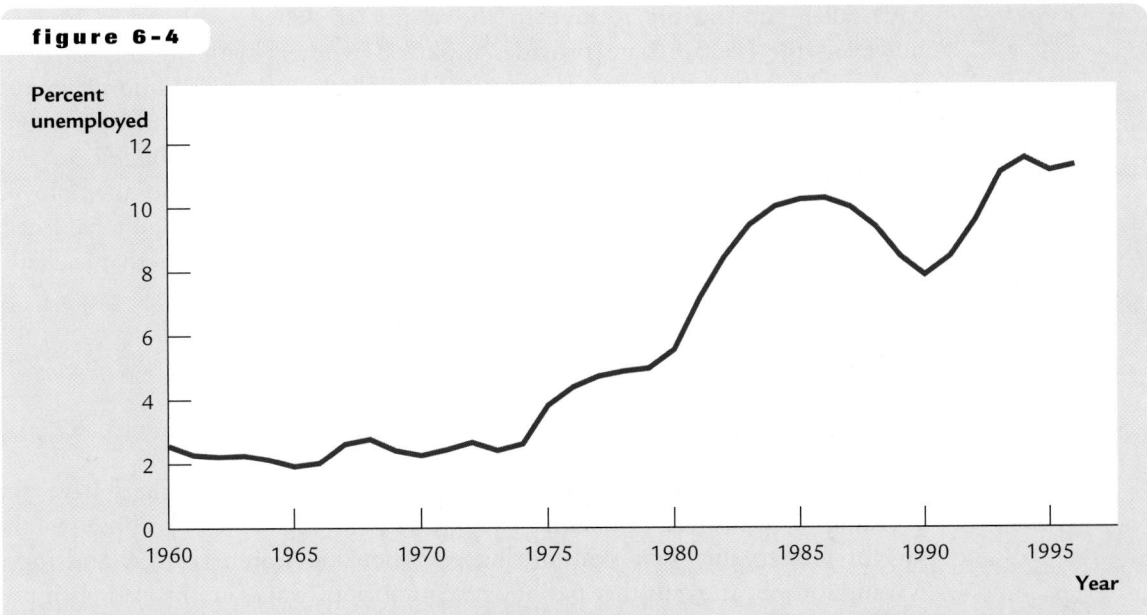

figure 6-4

Unemployment in the European Community This figure shows the unemployment rate in the 15 countries that make up the European Community. The figure shows that the European unemployment rate has risen substantially since 1980.

Source: OECD.

in these countries has risen substantially: it averaged less than 3 percent in the 1960s and more than 10 percent in recent years.

What is the cause of rising European unemployment? No one knows for sure, but there is a leading theory. Many economists believe that the problem can be traced to generous benefits for unemployed workers, coupled with a technologically driven fall in the demand for unskilled workers relative to skilled workers.

There is no question that most European countries have generous programs for those without jobs. These programs go by various names: social insurance, the welfare state, or simply "the dole." Many countries allow the unemployed to collect benefits indefinitely, rather than for only a short period of time as in the United States. Studies have shown that countries with more generous benefits tend to have higher rates of unemployment. In some sense, those living on the dole are really out of the labor force: given the employment opportunities available, taking a job is less attractive than remaining without work. Yet these people are often counted as unemployed in government statistics.

There is also no question that the demand for unskilled workers has fallen relative to the demand for skilled workers. This change in demand is probably due to changes in technology: computers, for example, increase the demand for workers who can use them while reducing the demand for those who cannot. In the United States, this change in demand has been reflected in wages rather than unemployment: over the past two decades, the wages of unskilled workers have fallen substantially relative to the wages of skilled workers. In Europe, however, the welfare state provides unskilled workers with an alternative to working for low wages. As the wages of unskilled workers fall, more workers view the dole as their best available option. The result is higher unemployment.

This diagnosis of high European unemployment does not suggest an easy remedy. Reducing the magnitude of government benefits for the unemployed would encourage workers to get off the dole and accept low-wage jobs. But it would also exacerbate economic inequality—the very problem that welfare-state policies were designed to address.[11]

6-5 | Conclusion

Unemployment represents wasted resources. Unemployed workers have the potential to contribute to national income but are not doing so. Those searching for jobs to suit their skills are happy when the search is over, and those waiting for jobs in firms that pay above-equilibrium wages are happy when positions open up.

---

[11] For more discussion of these issues, see Paul Krugman, "Past and Prospective Causes of High Unemployment," in *Reducing Unemployment: Current Issues and Policy Options,* Federal Reserve Bank of Kansas City, August 1994.

Unfortunately, neither frictional unemployment nor wait unemployment can be easily reduced. The government cannot make job search instantaneous, nor can it easily bring wages closer to equilibrium levels. Zero unemployment is not a plausible goal for free-market economies.

Yet public policy is not powerless in the fight to reduce unemployment. Job-training programs, the unemployment-insurance system, the minimum wage, and the laws governing collective bargaining are often topics of political debate. The policies we choose are likely to have important effects on the economy's natural rate of unemployment.

Summary

1. The natural rate of unemployment is the steady-state rate of unemployment. It depends on the rate of job separation and the rate of job finding.

2. Because it takes time for workers to search for the job that best suits their individual skills and tastes, some frictional unemployment is inevitable. Various government policies, such as unemployment insurance, alter the amount of frictional unemployment.

3. Wait unemployment results when the real wage remains above the level that equilibrates labor supply and labor demand. Minimum-wage legislation is one cause of wage rigidity. Unions and the threat of unionization are another. Finally, efficiency-wage theories suggest that, for various reasons, firms may find it profitable to keep wages high despite an excess supply of labor.

4. Whether we conclude that most unemployment is short-term or long-term depends on how we look at the data. Most spells of unemployment are short. Yet most weeks of unemployment are attributable to the small number of long-term unemployed.

5. The unemployment rates among demographic groups differ substantially. In particular, the unemployment rates for younger workers are much higher than for older workers. This results from a difference in the rate of job separation rather than from a difference in the rate of job finding.

6. The natural rate of unemployment in the United States has exhibited long-term trends. In particular, it rose from the 1950s to the 1970s and then started drifting downward again in the 1990s. Various explanations have been proposed, including the changing demographic composition of the labor force and changes in the prevalence of sectoral shifts.

7. Individuals who have recently entered the labor force, including both new entrants and reentrants, make up about one-third of the unemployed. Transitions into and out of the labor force make unemployment statistics more difficult to interpret.

KEY CONCEPTS

Natural rate of unemployment

Frictional unemployment

Sectoral shift

Unemployment insurance

Wage rigidity

Wait unemployment

Insiders versus outsiders

Efficiency wages

Discouraged workers

QUESTIONS FOR REVIEW

1. What determines the natural rate of unemployment?

2. Describe the difference between frictional unemployment and wait unemployment.

3. Give three explanations why the real wage may remain above the level that equilibrates labor supply and labor demand.

4. Is most unemployment long-term or short-term? Explain your answer.

5. How do economists explain the high natural rate of unemployment in the 1970s and 1980s? How do they explain the fall in the natural rate in the 1990s?

PROBLEMS AND APPLICATIONS

1. Answer the following questions about your own experience in the labor force:

   a. When you or one of your friends is looking for a part-time job, how many weeks does it typically take? After you find a job, how many weeks does it typically last?

   b. From your estimates, calculate (in a rate per week) your rate of job finding f and your rate of job separation s. (*Hint:* If f is the rate of job finding, then the average spell of unemployment is $1/f$.)

   c. What is the natural rate of unemployment for the population you represent?

2. In this chapter we saw that the steady-state rate of unemployment is $U/L = s/(s + f)$. Suppose that the unemployment rate does not begin at this level. Show that unemployment will evolve over time and reach this steady state. (*Hint:* Express the change in the number of unemployed as a function of s, f, and U. Then show that if unemployment is above the natural rate, unemployment falls, and if unemployment is below the natural rate, unemployment rises.)

3. The residents of a certain dormitory have collected the following data: People who live in the dorm can be classified as either involved in a relationship or uninvolved. Among involved people, 10 percent experience a breakup of their relationship every month. Among uninvolved people, 5 percent will enter into a relationship every month. What is the steady-state fraction of residents who are uninvolved?

4. Suppose that Congress passes legislation making it more difficult for firms to fire workers. (An example is a law requiring severance pay for fired workers.) If this legislation reduces the rate of job separation without affecting the rate of job finding, how would the natural rate of unemployment change? Do you think that it is plausible that the legislation would not affect the rate of job finding? Why or why not?

5. Consider an economy with the following Cobb–Douglas production function:

$$Y = K^{1/3}L^{2/3}.$$

The economy has 1,000 units of capital and a labor force of 1,000 workers.

a. Derive the equation describing labor demand in this economy as a function of the real wage and the capital stock. (*Hint:* Review the appendix to Chapter 3.)

b. If the real wage can adjust to equilibrate labor supply and labor demand, what is the real wage? In this equilibrium, what is employment, output, and the total amount earned by workers?

c. Now suppose that Congress, concerned about the welfare of the working class, passes a law requiring firms to pay workers a real wage of 1 unit of output. How does this wage compare to the equilibrium wage?

d. Congress cannot dictate how many workers firms hire at the mandated wage. Given this fact, what are the effects of this law? Specifically, what happens to employment, output, and the total amount earned by workers?

e. Will Congress succeed in its goal of helping the working class? Explain.

f. Do you think that this analysis provides a good way of thinking about a minimum-wage law? Why or why not?

6. Suppose that a country experiences a reduction in productivity—that is, an adverse shock to the production function.

a. What happens to the labor demand curve?

b. How would this change in productivity affect the labor market—that is, employment, unemployment, and real wages—if the labor market were always in equilibrium?

c. How would this change in productivity affect the labor market if unions prevented real wages from falling?

7. In any city at any time, some of the stock of usable office space is vacant. This vacant office space is unemployed capital. How would you explain this phenomenon? Is it a social problem?

8. Consider how unemployment would affect the Solow growth model of Chapter 4. Suppose that output is produced according to the production function $Y = K^{\alpha}[(1 - u^*)L]^{1-\alpha}$, where K is capital, L is the labor force, and u^* is the natural rate of unemployment. The national saving rate is s, the labor force grows at rate n, and capital depreciates at rate δ. There is no technological progress.

a. Express output per worker ($y = Y/L$) as a function of capital per worker ($k = K/L$) and the natural rate of unemployment. Describe the steady state of this economy.

b. Suppose that some change in government policy reduces the natural rate of unemployment. Describe how this change affects output both immediately and over time. Is the steady-state effect on output larger or smaller than the immediate effect? Explain.

Money and Inflation

There is no subtler, no surer means of overturning the existing basis of society than to debauch the currency. The process engages all the hidden forces of economic law on the side of destruction, and does it in a manner which not one man in a million is able to diagnose.

— *John Maynard Keynes*

In 1970 the *New York Times* cost 15 cents, the median price of a single-family home was $23,400, and the average wage in manufacturing was $3.36 per hour. In 1997 the *Times* cost 60 cents, the price of a home was $146,000, and the average wage was $13.16 per hour. This overall increase in prices is called **inflation,** and it is the subject of this chapter.

The rate of inflation—the percentage change in the overall level of prices— varies substantially over time and across countries. In the United States, prices rose an average of 2.4 percent per year in the 1960s, 6.7 percent per year in the 1970s, 5.0 percent per year in the 1980s, and 2.8 percent in the 1990s. When inflation approached double-digit levels, President Gerald Ford declared it "public enemy number one," and President Ronald Reagan called it "the cruelest tax." Although the United States has not had much inflation in recent years, policymakers remain vigilant so it does not return.

Even at its worst, the U.S. experience with inflation during the twentieth century was moderate by international standards. In Russia in 1998, for instance, inflation was running about 50 percent per year. In Germany in 1923, prices rose an average of 500 percent *per month.* Such an episode of extraordinarily high inflation is called a **hyperinflation.**

In this chapter we examine the classical theory of the causes, effects, and social costs of inflation. The theory is "classical" in the sense that it assumes that prices are fully flexible. As we first discussed in Chapter 1, most economists believe this assumption accurately describes the behavior of the economy in the long run. By contrast, many prices are thought to be sticky in the short run, and beginning in Chapter 9, we incorporate this fact into our analysis. Yet, for now, we ignore short-run price stickiness. As we will see, the classical theory of inflation not only provides a good description of the long run, it also provides a useful foundation for the short-run analysis we develop later.

The "hidden forces of economic law" that lead to inflation are not nearly as mysterious as Keynes claims in the quotation that opens this chapter. Inflation is simply an increase in the average level of prices, and a price is the rate at which money is exchanged for a good or a service. To understand inflation, therefore, we must understand money—what it is, what affects its supply and demand, and what influence it has on the economy. Thus, Section 7-1 begins our analysis of inflation by discussing the economist's concept of "money" and how, in most modern economies, the government controls the quantity of money in the hands of the public. Section 7-2 shows that the quantity of money determines the price level and that the rate of growth in the quantity of money determines the rate of inflation.

Inflation in turn has numerous effects of its own on the economy. Section 7-3 discusses the revenue that the government raises by printing money, sometimes called the *inflation tax*. Section 7-4 examines how inflation affects the nominal interest rate. Section 7-5 discusses how the nominal interest rate in turn affects the quantity of money people wish to hold and, thereby, the price level.

After completing our analysis of the causes and effects of inflation, in Section 7-6 we address what is perhaps the most important question about inflation: Is it a major social problem? Does inflation really amount to "overturning the existing basis of society," as the chapter's opening quotation suggests?

Finally, in Section 7-7, we discuss the extreme case of hyperinflation. Hyperinflations are interesting to examine because they show clearly the causes, effects, and costs of inflation. Just as seismologists learn much by studying earthquakes, economists learn much by studying how hyperinflations begin and end.

7-1 | What Is Money?

When we say that a person has a lot of money, we usually mean that he or she is wealthy. By contrast, economists use the term *money* in a more specialized way. To an economist, money does not refer to all wealth but only to one type of it: **money** is the stock of assets that can be readily used to make transactions. Roughly speaking, the dollars in the hands of the public make up the nation's stock of money.

The Functions of Money

Money has three purposes. It is a store of value, a unit of account, and a medium of exchange.

As a **store of value,** money is a way to transfer purchasing power from the present to the future. If I work today and earn $100, I can hold the money and spend it tomorrow, next week, or next month. Of course, money is an imperfect store of value: if prices are rising, the amount you can buy with any given quantity of money is falling. Even so, people hold money because they can trade the money for goods and services at some time in the future.

As a **unit of account,** money provides the terms in which prices are quoted and debts are recorded. Microeconomics teaches us that resources are allocated according to relative prices—the prices of goods relative to other goods—yet stores post their prices in dollars and cents. A car dealer tells you that a car costs $12,000, not 400 shirts (even though it may amount to the same thing). Similarly, most debts require the debtor to deliver a specified number of dollars in the future, not a specified amount of some commodity. Money is the yardstick with which we measure economic transactions.

As a **medium of exchange,** money is what we use to buy goods and services. "This note is legal tender for all debts, public and private" is printed on the U.S. dollar. When we walk into stores, we are confident that the shopkeepers will accept our money in exchange for the items they are selling. The ease with which money is converted into other things—goods and services—is sometimes called money's *liquidity*.

To better understand the functions of money, try to imagine an economy without it: a barter economy. In such a world, trade requires the *double coincidence of wants*—the unlikely happenstance of two people each having a good that the other wants at the right time and place to make an exchange. A barter economy permits only simple transactions.

Money makes more indirect transactions possible. A professor uses her salary to buy books; the book publisher uses its revenue from the sale of books to buy paper; the paper company uses its revenue from the sale of paper to pay the lumberjack; the lumberjack uses his income to send his child to college; and the college uses its tuition receipts to pay the salary of the professor. In a complex, modern economy, trade is usually indirect and requires the use of money.

The Types of Money

Money takes many forms. In the U.S. economy we make transactions with an item whose sole function is to act as money: dollar bills. These pieces of green paper with small portraits of famous Americans would have little value if they were not widely accepted as money. Money that has no intrinsic value is called **fiat money** because it is established as money by government decree, or fiat.

Although fiat money is the norm in most economies today, historically most societies have used for money a commodity with some intrinsic value. Money of this sort is called **commodity money.** The most widespread example of commodity money is gold. When people use gold as money (or use paper money that is redeemable for gold), the economy is said to be on a **gold standard.** Gold is a form of commodity money because it can be used for various purposes—jewelry,

"And how would you like your funny money?"

dental fillings, and so on—as well as for transactions. The gold standard was common throughout the world during the late nineteenth century.

CASE STUDY

Money in a POW Camp

An unusual form of commodity money developed in some Nazi prisoner of war (POW) camps during World War II. The Red Cross supplied the prisoners with various goods—food, clothing, cigarettes, and so on. Yet these rations were allocated without close attention to personal preferences, so naturally the allocations were often inefficient. One prisoner may have preferred chocolate, while another may have preferred cheese, and a third may have wanted a new shirt. The differing tastes and endowments of the prisoners led them to trade with one another.

Barter proved to be an inconvenient way to allocate these resources, however, because it required the double coincidence of wants. In other words, a barter system was not the easiest way to ensure that each prisoner received the goods he valued most. Even the limited economy of the POW camp needed some form of money to facilitate transactions.

Eventually, cigarettes became the established "currency" in which prices were quoted and with which trades were made. A shirt, for example, cost about 80 cigarettes. Services were also quoted in cigarettes: some prisoners offered to do other prisoners' laundry for 2 cigarettes per garment. Even non-smokers were happy to accept cigarettes in exchange, knowing they could trade the cigarettes in the future for some good they did enjoy. Within the POW camp the cigarette became the store of value, the unit of account, and the medium of exchange.[1]

How Fiat Money Evolves

It is not surprising that some form of commodity money arises to facilitate exchange: people are willing to accept a commodity currency such as gold because it has intrinsic value. The development of fiat money, however, is more perplexing. What would make people begin to value something that is intrinsically useless?

To understand how the evolution from commodity money to fiat money takes place, imagine an economy in which people carry around bags of gold. When a purchase is made, the buyer measures out the appropriate amount of gold. If the seller is convinced that the weight and purity of the gold are right, the buyer and seller make the exchange.

---

[1] R.A. Radford, "The Economic Organisation of a P.O.W. Camp," *Economica* (November 1945): 189–201. The use of cigarettes as money is not limited to this example. In the Soviet Union in the late 1980s, packs of Marlboros were preferred to the ruble in the large underground economy.

The government might first get involved in the monetary system to help people reduce transaction costs. Using raw gold as money is costly because it takes time to verify the purity of the gold and to measure the correct quantity. To reduce these costs, the government can mint gold coins of known purity and weight. The coins are easier to use than gold bullion because their values are widely recognized.

The next step is for the government to accept gold from the public in exchange for gold certificates—pieces of paper that can be redeemed for a certain quantity of gold. If people believe the government's promise to redeem the paper bills for gold, the bills are just as valuable as the gold itself. In addition, because the bills are lighter than gold (and gold coins), they are easier to use in transactions. Eventually, no one carries gold around at all, and these gold-backed government bills become the monetary standard.

Finally, the gold backing becomes irrelevant. If no one ever bothers to redeem the bills for gold, no one cares if the option is abandoned. As long as everyone continues to accept the paper bills in exchange, they will have value and serve as money. Thus, the system of commodity money evolves into a system of fiat money. Notice that in the end, the use of money in exchange is largely a social convention, in the sense that everyone values fiat money simply because they expect everyone else to value it.

CASE STUDY

Money and Social Conventions on the Island of Yap

The economy of Yap, a small island in the Pacific, once had a type of money that was something between commodity and fiat money. The traditional medium of exchange in Yap was *fei,* stone wheels up to 12 feet in diameter. These stones had holes in the center so that they could be carried on poles and used for exchange.

Large stone wheels are not a convenient form of money. The stones were heavy, so it took substantial effort for a new owner to take his *fei* home after completing a transaction. Although the monetary system facilitated exchange, it did so at great cost.

Eventually, it became common practice for the new owner of the *fei* not to bother to take physical possession of the stone. Instead, the new owner merely accepted a claim to the *fei* without moving it. In future bargains, he traded this claim for goods that he wanted. Having physical possession of the stone became less important than having legal claim to it.

This practice was put to a test when an extremely valuable stone was lost at sea during a storm. Because the owner lost his money by accident rather than through negligence, it was universally agreed that his claim to the *fei* remained valid. Even generations later, when no one alive had ever seen this stone, the claim to this *fei* was still valued in exchange.[2]

---

[2] Norman Angell, *The Story of Money* (New York: Frederick A. Stokes Company, 1929), 88–89.

How the Quantity of Money Is Controlled

The quantity of money available is called the **money supply.** In an economy that uses commodity money, the money supply is the quantity of that commodity. In an economy that uses fiat money, such as most economies today, the government controls the supply of money: legal restrictions give the government a monopoly on the printing of money. Just as the level of taxation and the level of government purchases are policy instruments of the government, so is the supply of money. The control over the money supply is called **monetary policy**.

In the United States and many other countries, monetary policy is delegated to a partially independent institution called the **central bank.** The central bank of the United States is the **Federal Reserve**—often called *the Fed*. If you look at a U.S. dollar bill, you will see that it is called a *Federal Reserve Note*. Decisions over monetary policy are made by the Federal Open Market Committee. This committee is made up of members of the Federal Reserve Board, who are appointed by the president and confirmed by Congress, together with the presidents of the regional Federal Reserve Banks. The Federal Open Market Committee meets about every six weeks to discuss and set monetary policy.

The primary way in which the Fed controls the supply of money is through **open-market operations**—the purchase and sale of government bonds. When the Fed wants to increase the money supply, it uses some of the dollars it has to buy government bonds from the public. Because these dollars leave the Fed and enter into the hands of the public, the purchase increases the quantity of money in circulation. Conversely, when the Fed wants to decrease the money supply, it sells some government bonds from its own portfolio. This open-market sale of bonds takes some dollars out of the hands of the public and, thus, decreases the quantity of money in circulation.

In Chapter 18 we discuss in detail how the Fed controls the supply of money. For our current discussion, these details are not crucial. It is sufficient to assume that the Fed directly controls the supply of money.

How the Quantity of Money Is Measured

One of the goals of this chapter is to determine how the money supply affects the economy; we turn to that problem in the next section. As a background for that analysis, let's first discuss how economists measure the quantity of money.

Because money is the stock of assets used for transactions, the quantity of money is the quantity of those assets. In simple economies, this quantity is easily measured. In the POW camp, the quantity of money was the quantity of cigarettes in the camp. But how can we measure the quantity of money in more complex economies such as ours? The answer is not obvious, because no single asset is used for all transactions. People can use various assets to make transactions, such as cash or checks, although some assets are more convenient than others. This ambiguity leads to numerous measures of the quantity of money.

The most obvious asset to include in the quantity of money is **currency,** the sum of outstanding paper money and coins. Most day-to-day transactions use currency as the medium of exchange.

A second type of asset used for transactions is **demand deposits,** the funds people hold in their checking accounts. If most sellers accept personal checks, assets in a checking account are almost as convenient as currency. In both cases, the assets are in a form ready to facilitate a transaction. Demand deposits are therefore added to currency when measuring the quantity of money.

Once we admit the logic of including demand deposits in the measured money stock, many other assets become candidates for inclusion. Funds in savings accounts, for example, can be easily transferred into checking accounts; these assets are almost as convenient for transactions. Money market mutual funds allow investors to write checks against their accounts, although restrictions often apply with regard to the size of the check or the number of checks written. Because these assets can be easily used for transactions, they should arguably be included in the quantity of money.

Because it is hard to judge exactly which assets should be included in the money stock, various measures are available. Table 7-1 presents the five measures of the money stock that the Federal Reserve calculates for the U.S. economy, together with a list of which assets are included in each measure. From the smallest to the largest, they are designated *C, M*1, *M*2, *M*3, and *L*. The most commonly used measures for studying the effects of money on the economy are *M*1 and *M*2. There is no consensus, however, about which measure of the money stock is best. Disagreements about monetary policy sometimes arise because different measures of money are moving in different directions.

table 7-1

The Measures of Money

Symbol	Assets Included	Amount in April 1998 (billions of dollars)
C	Currency	434
*M*1	Currency plus demand deposits, traveler's checks, and other checkable deposits	1,081
*M*2	M1 plus retail money market mutual fund balances, saving deposits (including money market deposit accounts), and small time deposits	4,165
*M*3	M2 plus large time deposits, repurchase agreements, Eurodollars, and institution-only money market mutual fund balances	5,574
L	M3 plus other liquid assests such as savings bonds and short-term Treasury securities	6,826

Source: Federal Reserve.

7-2 | The Quantity Theory of Money

Having defined what money is and described how it is controlled and measured, we can now examine how the quantity of money affects the economy. To do this, we must see how the quantity of money is related to other economic variables, such as prices and incomes.

Transactions and the Quantity Equation

People hold money to buy goods and services. The more money they need for such transactions, the more money they hold. Thus, the quantity of money in the economy is closely related to the number of dollars exchanged in transactions.

The link between transactions and money is expressed in the following equation, called the **quantity equation:**

$$\text{Money} \times \text{Velocity} = \text{Price} \times \text{Transactions}$$
$$M \quad \times \quad V \quad = \quad P \quad \times \quad T.$$

Let's examine each of the four variables in this equation.

The right-hand side of the quantity equation tells us about transactions. T represents the total number of transactions during some period of time, say, a year. In other words, T is the number of times in a year that goods or services are exchanged for money. P is the price of a typical transaction — the number of dollars exchanged. The product of the price of a transaction and the number of transactions, PT, equals the number of dollars exchanged in a year.

The left-hand side of the quantity equation tells us about the money used to make the transactions. M is the quantity of money. V is called the **transactions velocity of money** and measures the rate at which money circulates in the economy. In other words, velocity tells us the number of times a dollar bill changes hands in a given period of time.

For example, suppose that 60 loaves of bread are sold in a given year at $0.50 per loaf. Then T equals 60 loaves per year, and P equals $0.50 per loaf. The total number of dollars exchanged is

$$PT = \$0.50/\text{loaf} \times 60 \text{ loaves/year} = \$30/\text{year}.$$

The right-hand side of the quantity equation equals $30 per year, which is the dollar value of all transactions.

Suppose further that the quantity of money in the economy is $10. By rearranging the quantity equation, we can compute velocity as

$$V = PT/M$$
$$= (\$30/\text{year})/(\$10)$$
$$= 3 \text{ times per year.}$$

That is, for $30 of transactions per year to take place with $10 of money, each dollar must change hands 3 times per year.

The quantity equation is an *identity:* the definitions of the four variables make it true. The equation is useful because it shows that if one of the variables changes, one or more of the others must also change to maintain the equality. For example, if the quantity of money increases and the velocity of money stays unchanged, then either the price or the number of transactions must rise.

From Transactions to Income

When studying the role of money in the economy, economists usually use a slightly different version of the quantity equation than the one just introduced. The problem with the first equation is that the number of transactions is difficult to measure. To solve this problem, the number of transactions T is replaced by the total output of the economy Y.

Transactions and output are closely related, because the more the economy produces, the more goods are bought and sold. They are not the same, however. When one person sells a used car to another person, for example, they make a transaction using money, even though the used car is not part of current output. Nonetheless, the dollar value of transactions is roughly proportional to the dollar value of output.

If Y denotes the amount of output and P denotes the price of one unit of output, then the dollar value of output is PY. We encountered measures for these variables when we discussed the national income accounts in Chapter 2: Y is real GDP, P the GDP deflator, and PY nominal GDP. The quantity equation becomes

$$\text{Money} \times \text{Velocity} = \text{Price} \times \text{Output}$$
$$M \quad \times \quad V \quad = \quad P \quad \times \quad Y.$$

Because Y is also total income, V in this version of the quantity equation is called the **income velocity of money.** The income velocity of money tells us the number of times a dollar bill enters someone's income in a given period of time. This version of the quantity equation is the most common, and it is the one we use from now on.

The Money Demand Function and the Quantity Equation

When we analyze how money affects the economy, it is often useful to express the quantity of money in terms of the quantity of goods and services it can buy. This amount, M/P, is called **real money balances.**

Real money balances measure the purchasing power of the stock of money. For example, consider an economy that produces only bread. If the quantity of money is $10, and the price of a loaf is $0.50, then real money balances are 20 loaves of bread. That is, at current prices, the stock of money in the economy is able to buy 20 loaves.

A **money demand function** is an equation that shows what determines the quantity of real money balances people wish to hold. A simple money demand function is

$$(M/P)^d = kY,$$

where k is a constant that tells us how much money people want to hold for every dollar of income. This equation states that the quantity of real money balances demanded is proportional to real income.

The money demand function is like the demand function for a particular good. Here the "good" is the convenience of holding real money balances. Just as owning an automobile makes it easier for a person to travel, holding money makes it easier to make transactions. Therefore, just as higher income leads to a greater demand for automobiles, higher income also leads to a greater demand for real money balances.

This money demand function offers another way to view the quantity equation. To see this, add to the money demand function the condition that the demand for real money balances $(M/P)^d$ must equal the supply M/P. Therefore,

$$(M/P) = kY.$$

A simple rearrangement of terms changes this equation into

$$M(1/k) = PY,$$

which can be written as

$$MV = PY,$$

where $V = 1/k$. This simple mathematics shows the link between the demand for money and the velocity of money. When people want to hold a lot of money for each dollar of income (k is large), money changes hands infrequently (V is small). Conversely, when people want to hold only a little money (k is small), money changes hands frequently (V is large). In other words, the money demand parameter k and the velocity of money V are opposite sides of the same coin.

The Assumption of Constant Velocity

The quantity equation can be viewed as merely a definition: it defines velocity V as the ratio of nominal GDP, PY, to the quantity of money M. Yet if we make the additional assumption that the velocity of money is constant, then the quantity equation becomes a useful theory of the effects of money, called the **quantity theory of money.**

As with many of the assumptions in economics, the assumption of constant velocity is only an approximation to reality. Velocity does change if the money demand function changes. For example, when automatic teller machines were introduced, people could reduce their average money holdings, which meant a fall in the money demand parameter k and an increase in velocity V. Nonetheless, experience shows that the assumption of constant velocity provides a good approximation in many situations. Let's therefore assume that velocity is constant and see what this assumption implies about the effects of the money supply on the economy.

Once we assume that velocity is constant, the quantity equation can be seen as a theory of what determines nominal GDP. The quantity equation says

$$M\bar{V} = PY,$$

where the bar over V means that velocity is fixed. Therefore, a change in the quantity of money (M) must cause a proportionate change in nominal GDP (PY). That is, if velocity is fixed, the quantity of money determines the dollar value of the economy's output.

Money, Prices, and Inflation

We now have a theory to explain what determines the economy's overall level of prices. The theory has three building blocks:

1. The factors of production and the production function determine the level of output Y. We borrow this conclusion from Chapter 3.

2. The money supply determines the nominal value of output, PY. This conclusion follows from the quantity equation and the assumption that the velocity of money is fixed.

3. The price level P is then the ratio of the nominal value of output, PY, to the level of output Y.

In other words, the productive capability of the economy determines real GDP, the quantity of money determines nominal GDP, and the GDP deflator is the ratio of nominal GDP to real GDP.

This theory explains what happens when the Fed changes the supply of money. Because velocity is fixed, any change in the supply of money leads to a proportionate change in nominal GDP. Because the factors of production and the production function have already determined real GDP, the change in nominal GDP must represent a change in the price level. Hence, the quantity theory implies that the price level is proportional to the money supply.

Because the inflation rate is the percentage change in the price level, this theory of the price level is also a theory of the inflation rate. The quantity equation, written in percentage-change form, is

% Change in M + % Change in V = % Change in P + % Change in Y.

Consider each of these four terms. First, the percentage change in the quantity of money M is under the control of the central bank. Second, the percentage change in velocity V reflects shifts in money demand; we have assumed that velocity is constant, so the percentage change in velocity is zero. Third, the percentage change in the price level P is the rate of inflation; this is the variable in the equation that we would like to explain. Fourth, the percentage change in output Y depends on growth in the factors of production and on technological progress, which for our present purposes we can take as given. This analysis tells us that (except for a constant that depends on exogenous growth in output) the growth in the money supply determines the rate of inflation.

Thus, the quantity theory of money states that the central bank, which controls the money supply, has ultimate control over the rate of inflation. If the central bank keeps the money supply stable, the price level will be stable. If the central bank increases the money supply rapidly, the price level will rise rapidly.

CASE STUDY

Inflation and Money Growth

"Inflation is always and everywhere a monetary phenomenon." So wrote Milton Friedman, the great economist who won the Nobel Prize in economics in 1976. The quantity theory of money leads us to agree that the growth in the quantity of money is the primary determinant of the inflation rate. Yet

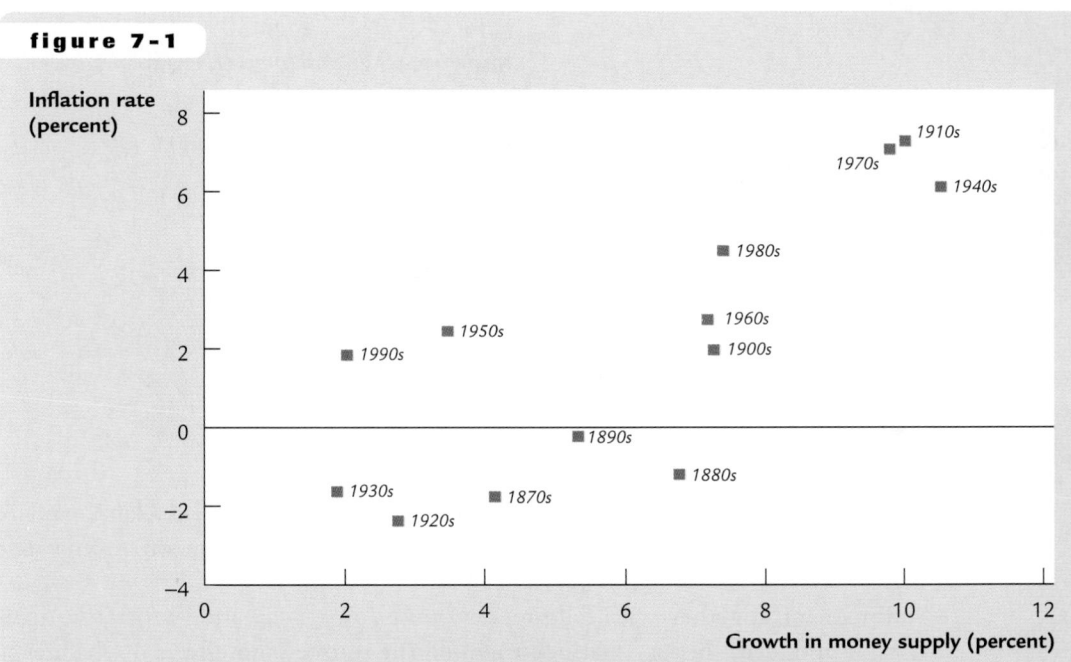

figure 7-1

Historical Data on U.S. Inflation and Money Growth In this scatterplot of money growth and inflation, each point represents a decade. The horizontal axis shows the average growth in the money supply (as measured by *M*2) over the decade, and the vertical axis shows the average rate of inflation (as measured by the GDP deflator). The positive correlation between money growth and inflation is evidence for the quantity theory's prediction that high money growth leads to high inflation.

Source: For the data through the 1960s: Milton Friedman and Anna J. Schwartz, *Monetary Trends in the United States and the United Kingdom: Their Relation to Income, Prices, and Interest Rates 1867–1975* (Chicago: University of Chicago Press, 1982). For recent data: U.S. Department of Commerce, Federal Reserve Board.

figure 7-2

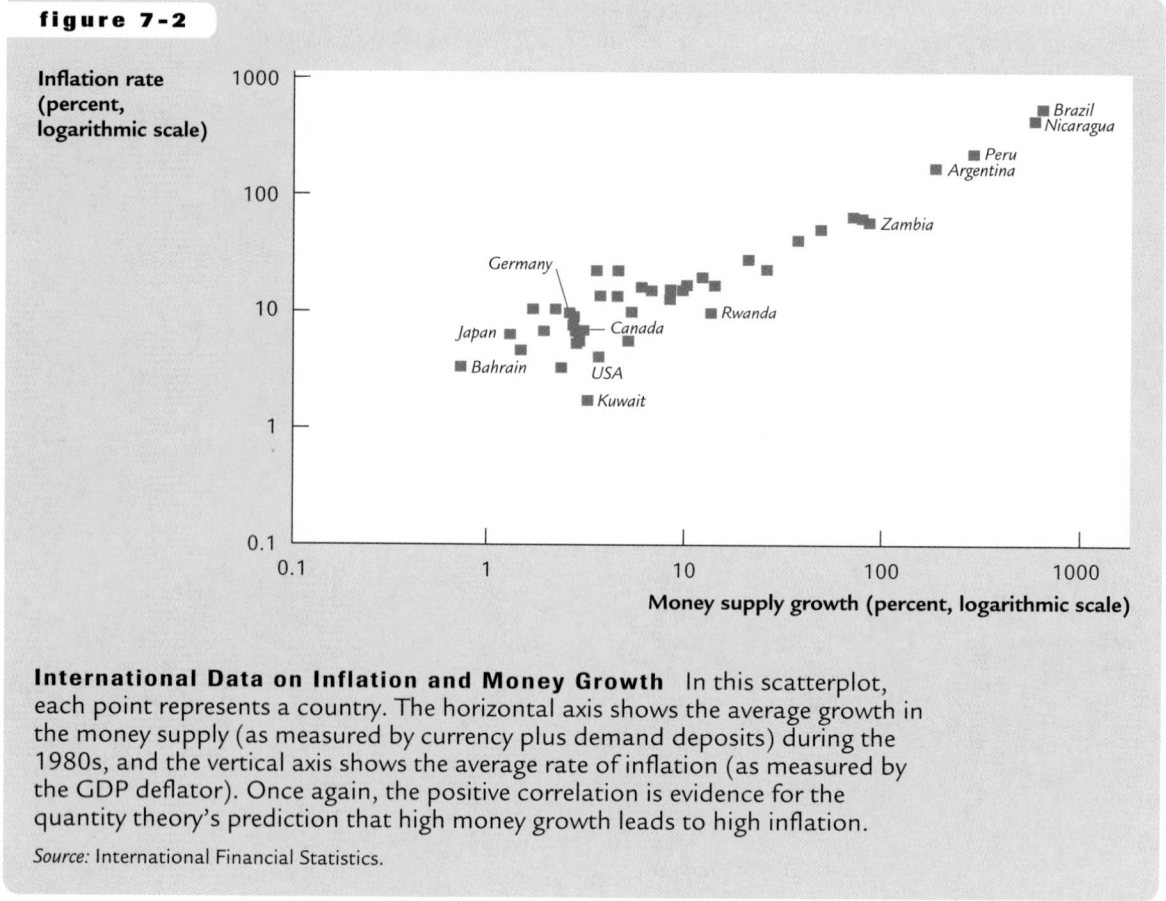

International Data on Inflation and Money Growth In this scatterplot, each point represents a country. The horizontal axis shows the average growth in the money supply (as measured by currency plus demand deposits) during the 1980s, and the vertical axis shows the average rate of inflation (as measured by the GDP deflator). Once again, the positive correlation is evidence for the quantity theory's prediction that high money growth leads to high inflation.

Source: International Financial Statistics.

Friedman's claim is empirical, not theoretical. To evaluate his claim, and to judge the usefulness of our theory, we need to look at data on money and prices.

Friedman, together with fellow economist Anna Schwartz, wrote two treatises on monetary history that documented the sources and effects of changes in the quantity of money over the past century.[3] Figure 7-1 uses some of their data and plots the average rate of money growth and the average rate of inflation in the United States over each decade since the 1870s. The data verify the link between inflation and growth in the quantity of money. Decades with high money growth tend to have high inflation, and decades with low money growth tend to have low inflation.

---

[3] Milton Friedman and Anna J. Schwartz, *A Monetary History of the United States, 1867–1960* (Princeton, NJ: Princeton University Press, 1963); Milton Friedman and Anna J. Schwartz, *Monetary Trends in the United States and the United Kingdom: Their Relation to Income, Prices, and Interest Rates, 1867–1975* (Chicago: University of Chicago Press, 1982).

Figure 7-2 examines the same question with international data. It shows the average rate of inflation and the average rate of money growth in 34 countries during the 1980s. Again, the link between money growth and inflation is clear. Countries with high money growth tend to have high inflation, and countries with low money growth tend to have low inflation.

If we looked at monthly data on money growth and inflation, rather than data for 10-year periods, we would not see as close a connection between these two variables. This theory of inflation works best in the long run, not in the short run. We examine the short-run impact of changes in the quantity of money when we turn to economic fluctuations in Part Three of this book.

7-3 | Seigniorage: The Revenue From Printing Money

So far, we have seen how growth in the money supply causes inflation. But what might ever induce the government to increase the money supply? Here we examine one answer to this question.

Let's start with an indisputable fact: all governments spend money. Some of this spending is to buy goods and services (such as roads and police), and some is to provide transfer payments (for the poor and elderly, for example). A government can finance its spending in three ways. First, it can raise revenue through taxes, such as personal and corporate income taxes. Second, it can borrow from the public by selling government bonds. Third, it can simply print money.

The revenue raised through the printing of money is called **seigniorage.** The term comes from *seigneur,* the French word for "feudal lord." In the Middle Ages, the lord had the exclusive right on his manor to coin money. Today this right belongs to the central government, and it is one source of revenue.

When the government prints money to finance expenditure, it increases the money supply. The increase in the money supply, in turn, causes inflation. Printing money to raise revenue is like imposing an *inflation tax.*

At first it may not be obvious that inflation can be viewed as a tax. After all, no one receives a bill for this tax—the government merely prints the money it needs. Who then pays the inflation tax? The answer is the holders of money. As prices rise, the real value of the money in your wallet falls. When the government prints new money for its use, it makes the old money in the hands of the public less valuable. Thus, inflation is like a tax on holding money.

The amount raised by printing money varies substantially from country to country. In the United States, the amount has been small: seigniorage has usually accounted for less than 3 percent of government revenue. In Italy and

Greece, seigniorage has often been over 10 percent of government revenue.[4] In countries experiencing hyperinflation, seigniorage is often the government's chief source of revenue—indeed, the need to print money to finance expenditure is a primary cause of hyperinflation.

CASE STUDY

Paying for the American Revolution

Although seigniorage has not been a major source of revenue for the U.S. government in recent history, the situation was very different two centuries ago. Beginning in 1775 the Continental Congress needed to find a way to finance the Revolution, but it had limited ability to raise revenue through taxation. It therefore relied heavily on the printing of fiat money to help pay for the war.

The Continental Congress's reliance on seigniorage increased over time. In 1775 new issues of continental currency were approximately $6 million. This amount increased to $19 million in 1776, $13 million in 1777, $63 million in 1778, and $125 million in 1779.

Not surprisingly, this rapid growth in the money supply led to massive inflation. At the end of the war, the price of gold measured in continental dollars was more than 100 times its level of only a few years earlier. The large quantity of the continental currency made the continental dollar nearly worthless. This experience also gave birth to a once popular expression: people used to say something was "not worth a continental" to mean that the item had little real value.

7-4 | Inflation and Interest Rates

As we first discussed in Chapter 3, interest rates are among the most important macroeconomic variables. In essence, they are the prices that link the present and the future. Here we discuss the relationship between inflation and interest rates.

Two Interest Rates: Real and Nominal

Suppose you deposit your savings in a bank account that pays 8 percent interest annually. Next year, you withdraw your savings and the accumulated interest. Are you 8 percent richer than you were when you made the deposit a year earlier?

---

[4] Stanley Fischer, "Seigniorage and the Case for a National Money," *Journal of Political Economy* 90 (April 1982): 295–313.

The answer depends on what "richer" means. Certainly, you have 8 percent more dollars than you had before. But if prices have risen, so that each dollar buys less, then your purchasing power has not risen by 8 percent. If the inflation rate was 5 percent, then the amount of goods you can buy has increased by only 3 percent. And if the inflation rate was 10 percent, then your purchasing power actually fell by 2 percent.

Economists call the interest rate that the bank pays the **nominal interest rate** and the increase in your purchasing power the **real interest rate.** If i denotes the nominal interest rate, r the real interest rate, and π the rate of inflation, then the relationship among these three variables can be written as

$$r = i - \pi.$$

The real interest rate is the difference between the nominal interest rate and the rate of inflation.[5]

The Fisher Effect

Rearranging terms in our equation for the real interest rate, we can show that the nominal interest rate is the sum of the real interest rate and the inflation rate:

$$i = r + \pi.$$

The equation written in this way is called the **Fisher equation,** after economist Irving Fisher (1867–1947). It shows that the nominal interest rate can change for two reasons: because the real interest rate changes or because the inflation rate changes.

Once we separate the nominal interest rate into these two parts, we can use this equation to develop a theory that explains the nominal interest rate. Chapter 3 showed that the real interest rate adjusts to equilibrate saving and investment. The quantity theory of money shows that the rate of money growth determines the rate of inflation. The Fisher equation then tells us to add the real interest rate and the inflation rate together to determine the nominal interest rate.

The quantity theory and the Fisher equation together tell us how money growth affects the nominal interest rate. *According to the quantity theory, an increase in the rate of money growth of 1 percent causes a 1 percent increase in the rate of inflation. According to the Fisher equation, a 1 percent increase in the rate of inflation in turn causes a 1 percent increase in the nominal interest rate.* The one-for-one relation between the inflation rate and the nominal interest rate is called the **Fisher effect.**

---

[5] *Mathematical note:* This equation relating the real interest rate, nominal interest rate, and inflation rate is only an approximation. The exact formula is $(1 + r) = (1 + i)/(1 + \pi)$. The approximation in the text is reasonably accurate as long as r, i, and π are relatively small (say, less than 20 percent per year).

CASE STUDY

Inflation and Nominal Interest Rates

How useful is the Fisher effect in explaining interest rates? To answer this question we look at two types of data on inflation and nominal interest rates.

Figure 7-3 shows the variation over time in the nominal interest rate and the inflation rate in the United States. You can see that the Fisher effect has done a good job of explaining fluctuations in the nominal interest rate over the past forty years. When inflation is high, nominal interest rates are typically high, and when inflation is low, nominal interest rates are typically low as well.

Similar support for the Fisher effect comes from examining the variation across countries at a single point in time. As Figure 7-4 shows, a nation's inflation rate and its nominal interest rate are closely related. Countries with high inflation tend to have high nominal interest rates as well, and countries with low inflation tend to have low nominal interest rates.

The link between inflation and interest rates is well known to Wall Street investment firms. Because bond prices move inversely with interest rates, one can get rich by predicting correctly the direction in which interest rates will move. Many Wall Street firms hire *Fed watchers* to monitor monetary policy and news about inflation in order to anticipate changes in interest rates.

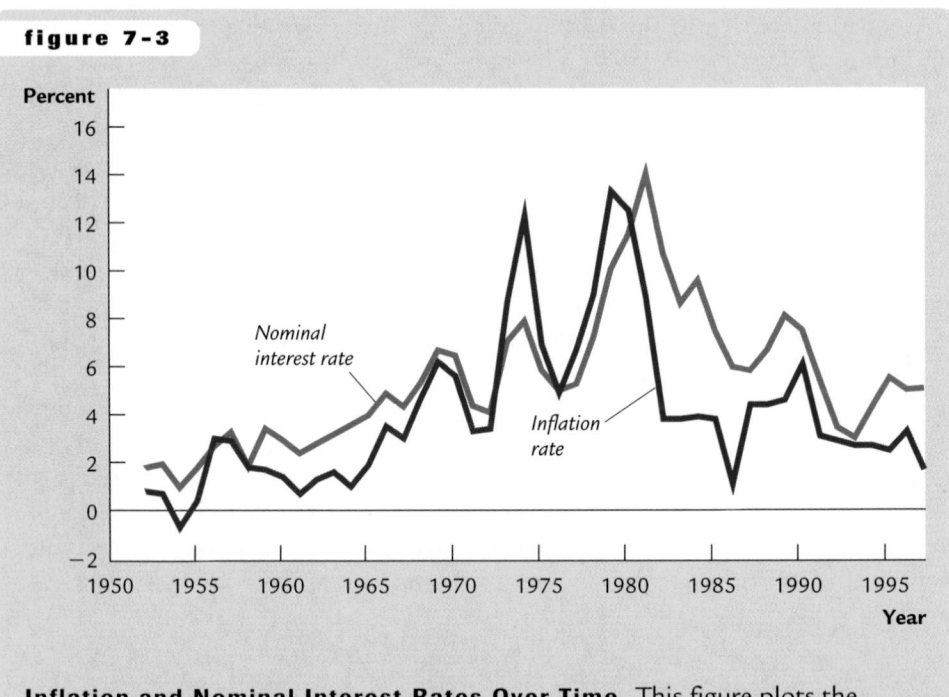

figure 7-3

Inflation and Nominal Interest Rates Over Time This figure plots the nominal interest rate (on three-month Treasury bills) and the inflation rate (as measured by the CPI) in the United States since 1952. It shows the Fisher effect: higher inflation leads to a higher nominal interest rate.

Source: U.S. Department of Treasury and U.S. Department of Labor.

figure 7-4

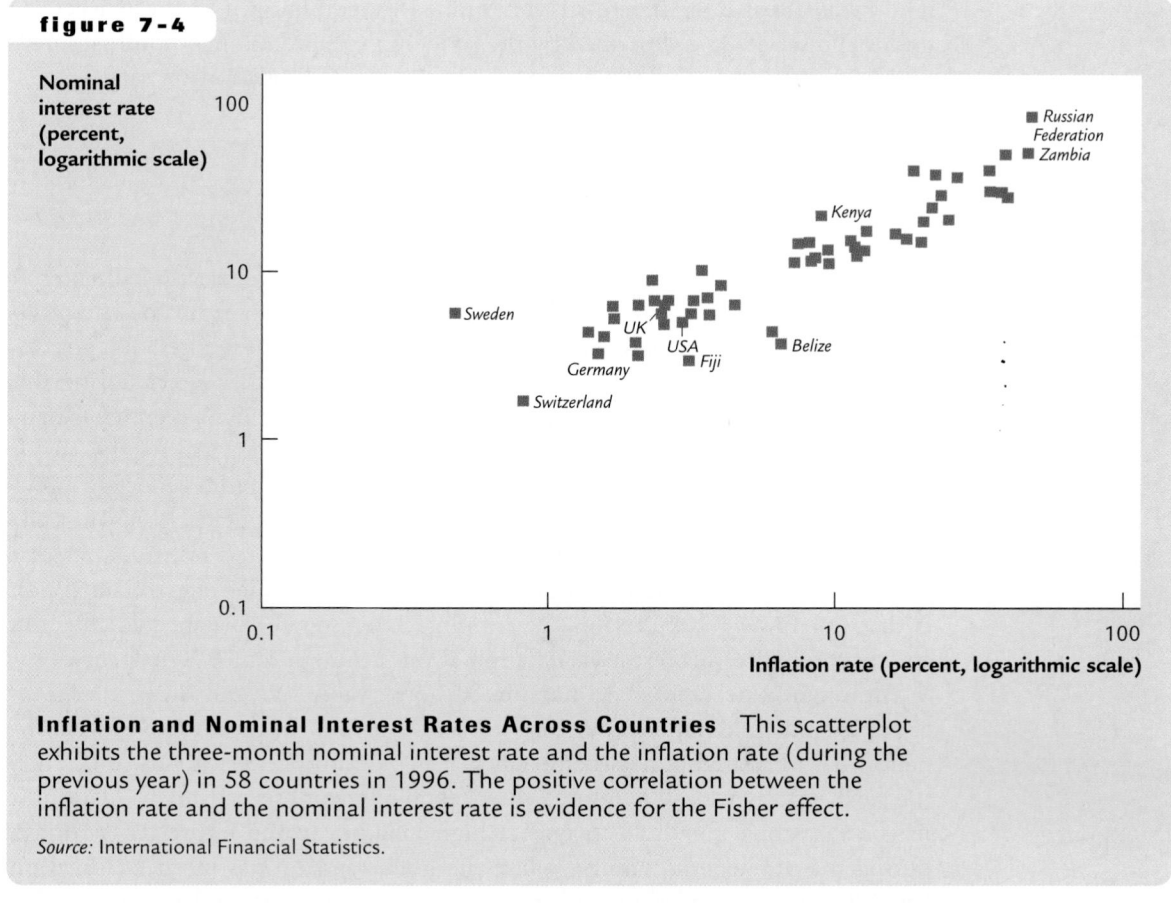

Inflation and Nominal Interest Rates Across Countries   This scatterplot exhibits the three-month nominal interest rate and the inflation rate (during the previous year) in 58 countries in 1996. The positive correlation between the inflation rate and the nominal interest rate is evidence for the Fisher effect.

Source: International Financial Statistics.

Two Real Interest Rates: *Ex Ante* and *Ex Post*

When a borrower and lender agree on a nominal interest rate, they do not know what the inflation rate over the term of the loan will be. Therefore, we must distinguish between two concepts of the real interest rate: the real interest rate the borrower and lender expect when the loan is made, called the ***ex ante real interest rate,*** and the real interest rate actually realized, called the ***ex post real interest rate.***

Although borrowers and lenders cannot predict future inflation with certainty, they do have some expectation of the inflation rate. Let π denote actual future inflation and π^e the expectation of future inflation. The *ex ante* real interest rate is $i - \pi^e$, and the *ex post* real interest rate is $i - \pi$. The two real interest rates differ when actual inflation π differs from expected inflation π^e.

How does this distinction between actual and expected inflation modify the Fisher effect? Clearly, the nominal interest rate cannot adjust to actual inflation, because actual inflation is not known when the nominal interest rate is set. The nominal interest rate can adjust only to expected inflation. The Fisher effect is more precisely written as

$$i = r + \pi^e.$$

The *ex ante* real interest rate *r* is determined by equilibrium in the market for goods and services, as described by the model in Chapter 3. The nominal interest rate *i* moves one-for-one with changes in expected inflation π^e.

CASE STUDY

Nominal Interest Rates in the Nineteenth Century

Although recent data show a positive relationship between nominal interest rates and inflation rates, this finding is not universal. In data from the late nineteenth and early twentieth centuries, high nominal interest rates did not accompany high inflation. The apparent absence of any Fisher effect during this time puzzled Irving Fisher. He suggested that inflation "caught merchants napping."

How should we interpret the absence of an apparent Fisher effect in nineteenth-century data? Does this period of history provide evidence against the adjustment of nominal interest rates to inflation? Recent research suggests that this period has little to tell us about the validity of the Fisher effect. The reason is that the Fisher effect relates the nominal interest rate to expected inflation and, according to this research, inflation at this time was largely unexpected.

Although expectations are not directly observable, we can draw inferences about them by examining the persistence of inflation. In recent experience, inflation has been highly persistent: when it is high one year, it tends to be high the next year as well. Therefore, when people have observed high inflation, it has been rational for them to expect high inflation in the future. By contrast, during the nineteenth century, when the gold standard was in effect, inflation had little persistence. High inflation in one year was just as likely to be followed the next year by low inflation as by high inflation. Therefore, high inflation did not imply high expected inflation and did not lead to high nominal interest rates. So, in a sense, Fisher was right to say that inflation "caught merchants napping."[6]

7-5 | The Nominal Interest Rate and the Demand for Money

The quantity theory is based on a simple money demand function: it assumes that the demand for real money balances is proportional to income. Although the quantity theory is a good place to start when analyzing the effects of money on the economy, it is not the whole story. Here we add another determinant of the quantity of money demanded—the nominal interest rate.

[6] Robert B. Barsky, "The Fisher Effect and the Forecastability and Persistence of Inflation," *Journal of Monetary Economics* 19 (January 1987): 3–24.

The Cost of Holding Money

The money you hold in your wallet does not earn interest. If instead of holding that money you used it to buy government bonds or deposited it in a savings account, you would earn the nominal interest rate. The nominal interest rate is the opportunity cost of holding money: it is what you give up by holding money rather than bonds.

Another way to see that the cost of holding money equals the nominal interest rate is by comparing the real returns on alternative assets. Assets other than money, such as government bonds, earn the real return r. Money earns an expected real return of $-\pi^e$, because its real value declines at the rate of inflation. When you hold money, you give up the difference between these two returns. Thus, the cost of holding money is $r - (-\pi^e)$, which the Fisher equation tells us is the nominal interest rate i.

Just as the quantity of bread demanded depends on the price of bread, the quantity of money demanded depends on the price of holding money. Hence, the demand for real money balances depends both on the level of income and on the nominal interest rate. We write the general money demand function as

$$(M/P)^d = L(i, Y).$$

The letter L is used to denote money demand because money is the economy's most liquid asset (the asset most easily used to make transactions). This equation states that the demand for the liquidity of real money balances is a function of income and the nominal interest rate. The higher the level of income Y, the greater the demand for real money balances. The higher the nominal interest rate i, the lower the demand for real money balances.

Future Money and Current Prices

Money, prices, and interest rates are now related in several ways. Figure 7-5 illustrates the linkages we have discussed. As the quantity theory of money explains, money supply and money demand together determine the equilibrium price level. Changes in the price level are, by definition, the rate of inflation. Inflation, in turn, affects the nominal interest rate through the Fisher effect. But now, because the nominal interest rate is the cost of holding money, the nominal interest rate feeds back to affect the demand for money.

Consider how the introduction of this last link affects our theory of the price level. First, equate the supply of real money balances M/P to the demand $L(i, Y)$:

$$M/P = L(i, Y).$$

Next, use the Fisher equation to write the nominal interest rate as the sum of the real interest rate and expected inflation:

$$M/P = L(r + \pi^e, Y).$$

This equation states that the level of real money balances depends on the expected rate of inflation.

figure 7-5

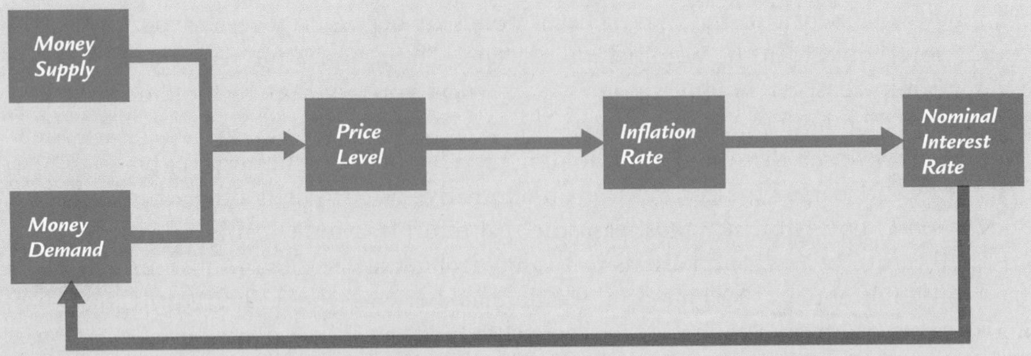

The Linkages Among Money, Prices, and Interest Rates This figure illustrates the relationships among money, prices, and interest rates. Money supply and money demand determine the price level. Changes in the price level determine the inflation rate. The inflation rate influences the nominal interest rate. Because the nominal interest rate is the cost of holding money, it may affect money demand. This last link (shown as a red line) is omitted from the basic quantity theory of money.

The last equation tells a more sophisticated story than the quantity theory about the determination of the price level. The quantity theory of money says that today's money supply determines today's price level. This conclusion remains partly true: if the nominal interest rate and the level of output are held constant, the price level moves proportionately with the money supply. Yet the nominal interest rate is not constant; it depends on expected inflation, which in turn depends on growth in the money supply. The presence of the nominal interest rate in the money demand function yields an additional channel through which money supply affects the price level.

This general money demand equation implies that the price level depends not just on today's money supply but also on the money supply expected in the future. To see why, suppose the Fed announces that it will raise the money supply in the future, but it does not change the money supply today. This announcement causes people to expect higher money growth and higher inflation. Through the Fisher effect, this increase in expected inflation raises the nominal interest rate. The higher nominal interest rate immediately reduces the demand for real money balances. Because the quantity of money has not changed, the reduced demand for real money balances leads to a higher price level. Hence, higher expected money growth in the future leads to a higher price level today.

The effect of money on prices is fairly complex. The appendix to this chapter works out the mathematics relating the price level to current and future money. The conclusion of the analysis is that the price level depends on a weighted average of the current money supply and the money supply expected to prevail in the future.

7-6 | The Social Costs of Inflation

Our discussion of the causes and effects of inflation does not tell us much about the social problems that result from inflation. We turn to those problems now.

The Layman's View and the Classical Response

If you ask the average person why inflation is a social problem, he will probably answer that inflation makes him poorer. "Each year my boss gives me a raise, but prices go up and that takes some of my raise away from me." The implicit assumption in this statement is that if there were no inflation, he would get the same raise and be able to buy more goods.

This complaint about inflation is a common fallacy. From Chapters 3, 4, and 5, we know that increases in the purchasing power of labor come from capital accumulation and technological progress. In particular, the real wage does not depend on how much money the government chooses to print. If the government reduced inflation by slowing the rate of money growth, workers would not see their real wage increasing more rapidly. Instead, when inflation slowed, firms would increase the prices of their products less each year and, as a result, would give their workers smaller raises.

According to the classical theory of money, a change in the overall price level is like a change in the units of measurement. It is as if we switched from measuring distances in feet to measuring them in inches: numbers get larger, but nothing really changes. Imagine that tomorrow morning you wake up and find that, for some reason, all dollar figures in the economy have been multiplied by ten. The price of everything you buy has increased tenfold, but so has your wage and the value of your savings. What difference would this make? All numbers would have an extra zero at the end, but nothing else would change. Your economic well-being depends on relative prices, not the overall price level.

Why, then, is a persistent increase in the price level a social problem? It turns out that the costs of inflation are subtle. Indeed, economists disagree about the size of the social costs. To the surprise of many laymen, some economists argue that the costs of inflation are small—at least for the moderate rates of inflation that most countries have experienced in recent years.[7]

---

[7] See, for example, Chapter 2 of Alan Blinder, *Hard Heads, Soft Hearts: Tough-Minded Economics for a Just Society* (Reading, MA: Addison Wesley, 1987).

CASE STUDY

What Economists and the Public Say About Inflation

As we have been discussing, laymen and economists hold very different views about the costs of inflation. Economist Robert Shiller has documented this difference of opinion in a survey of the two groups. The survey results are striking, for they show how radically the study of economics changes a person's attitudes.

In one question, Shiller asked people whether their "biggest gripe about inflation" was that "inflation hurts my real buying power, it makes me poorer." Of the general public, 77 percent agreed with this statement, compared to only 12 percent of economists. Shiller also asked people whether they agreed with the following statement: "When I see projections about how many times more a college education will cost, or how many times more the cost of living will be in coming decades, I feel a sense of uneasiness; these inflation projections really make me worry that my own income will not rise as much as such costs will." Among the general public, 66 percent said they fully agreed with this statement, while only 5 percent of economists agreed with it.

Survey respondents were asked to judge the seriousness of inflation as a policy problem: "Do you agree that preventing high inflation is an important national priority, as important as preventing drug abuse or preventing deterioration in the quality of our schools?" Fifty-two percent of laymen, but only 18 percent of economists, fully agreed with this view. Apparently, inflation worries the public much more than it does the economics profession.

The public's distaste for inflation may be partly psychological. Shiller asked those surveyed if they agreed with the following statement: "I think that if my pay went up I would feel more satisfaction in my job, more sense of fulfillment, even if prices went up just as much." Of the public, 49 percent fully or partly agreed with this statement, compared to 8 percent of economists.

Do these survey results mean that laymen are wrong and economists are right about the costs of inflation? Not necessarily. But economists do have the advantage of having given the issue more thought. So let's now consider what some of the costs of inflation might be.[8]

The Costs of Expected Inflation

Consider first the case of expected inflation. Suppose that every month the price level rose by 1 percent. What would be the social costs of such a steady and predictable 12 percent annual inflation?

---

[8] Robert J. Shiller, "Why Do People Dislike Inflation?" in Christina D. Romer and David H. Romer, eds., *Reducing Inflation: Motivation and Strategy* (Chicago: University of Chicago Press, 1997).

One cost is the distortion of the inflation tax on the amount of money people hold. As we have already discussed, a higher inflation rate leads to a higher nominal interest rate, which in turn leads to lower real money balances. If people are to hold lower money balances on average, they must make more frequent trips to the bank to withdraw money—for example, they might withdraw $50 twice a week rather than $100 once a week. The inconvenience of reducing money holding is metaphorically called the **shoeleather cost** of inflation, because walking to the bank more often causes one's shoes to wear out more quickly.

A second cost of inflation arises because high inflation induces firms to change their posted prices more often. Changing prices is sometimes costly: for example, it may require printing and distributing a new catalog. These costs are called **menu costs,** because the higher the rate of inflation, the more often restaurants have to print new menus.

A third cost of inflation arises because firms facing menu costs change prices infrequently; therefore, the higher the rate of inflation, the greater the variability in relative prices. For example, suppose a firm issues a new catalog every January. If there is no inflation, then the firm's prices relative to the overall price level are constant over the year. Yet if inflation is 1 percent per month, then from the beginning to the end of the year the firm's relative prices fall by 12 percent. Sales from this catalog will tend to be low early in the year (when its prices are relatively high) and high later in the year (when its prices are relatively low). Hence, when inflation induces variability in relative prices, it leads to microeconomic inefficiencies in the allocation of resources.

A fourth cost of inflation results from the tax laws. Many provisions of the tax code do not take into account the effects of inflation. Inflation can alter individuals' tax liability, often in ways that lawmakers did not intend.

One example of the failure of the tax code to deal with inflation is the tax treatment of capital gains. Suppose you buy some stock today and sell it a year from now at the same real price. It would seem reasonable for the government not to levy a tax, since you have earned no real income from this investment. Indeed, if there is no inflation, a zero tax liability would be the outcome. But suppose the rate of inflation is 12 percent and you initially paid $100 per share for the stock; for the real price to be the same a year later, you must sell the stock for $112 per share. In this case the tax code, which ignores the effects of inflation, says that you have earned $12 per share in income, and the government taxes you on this capital gain. The problem, of course, is that the tax code measures income as the nominal rather than the real capital gain. In this example, and in many others, inflation distorts how taxes are levied.

A fifth cost of inflation is the inconvenience of living in a world with a changing price level. Money is the yardstick with which we measure economic transactions. When there is inflation, that yardstick is changing in length. To continue the analogy, suppose that Congress passed a law specifying that a yard would equal 36 inches in 2001, 35 inches in 2002, 34 inches in 2003, and so on. Although the law would result in no ambiguity, it would be highly inconvenient. When someone measured a distance in yards, it would be necessary to specify whether the measurement was in 2001 yards or 2002 yards; to compare distances measured in different years, one would need to make an "inflation" correction. Similarly, the dollar is a less useful measure when its value is always changing.

For example, a changing price level complicates personal financial planning. One important decision that all households face is how much of their income to consume today and how much to save for retirement. A dollar saved today and invested at a fixed nominal interest rate will yield a fixed dollar amount in the future. Yet the real value of that dollar amount—which will determine the retiree's living standard—depends on the future price level. Deciding how much to save would be much simpler if people could count on the price level in 30 years being similar to its level today.

The Costs of Unexpected Inflation

Unexpected inflation has an effect that is more pernicious than any of the costs of steady, anticipated inflation: it arbitrarily redistributes wealth among individuals. You can see how this works by examining long-term loans. Loan agreements typically specify a nominal interest rate, which is based on the rate of inflation expected at the time of the agreement. If inflation turns out differently from what was expected, the *ex post* real return that the debtor pays to the creditor differs from what both parties anticipated. On the one hand, if inflation turns out to be higher than expected, the debtor wins and the creditor loses because the debtor repays the loan with less valuable dollars. On the other hand, if inflation turns out to be lower than expected, the creditor wins and the debtor loses because the repayment is worth more than the two parties anticipated.

Consider, for example, a person taking out a mortgage in 1960. At the time, a 30-year mortgage had an interest rate of about 6 percent per year. This rate was based on a low rate of expected inflation—inflation over the previous decade had averaged only 2.5 percent. The creditor probably expected to receive a real return of about 3.5 percent, and the debtor expected to pay this real return. In fact, over the life of the mortgage, the inflation rate averaged 5 percent, so the *ex post* real return was only 1 percent. This unanticipated inflation benefited the debtor at the expense of the creditor.

Unanticipated inflation also hurts individuals on fixed pensions. Workers and firms often agree on a fixed nominal pension when the worker retires (or even earlier). Since the pension is deferred earnings, the worker is essentially providing the firm a loan: the worker provides labor services to the firm while young but does not get fully paid until old age. Like any creditor, the worker is hurt when inflation is higher than anticipated. Like any debtor, the firm is hurt when inflation is lower than anticipated.

These situations provide a clear argument against highly variable inflation. The more variable the rate of inflation, the greater the uncertainty that both debtors and creditors face. Since most people are *risk averse*—they dislike uncertainty—the unpredictability caused by highly variable inflation hurts almost everyone.

Given these effects of uncertain inflation, it is puzzling that nominal contracts are so prevalent. One might expect debtors and creditors to protect themselves from this uncertainty by writing contracts in real terms—that is, by indexing to some measure of the price level. In economies with extremely high and variable inflation, indexation is often widespread; sometimes this indexation takes the form of writing contracts using a more stable foreign currency. In economies with moderate inflation, such as the United States, indexation is less common. Yet even in the United States, some long-term obligations are indexed. For example, Social Security benefits for the elderly are adjusted annually in response to changes in the consumer price index. And in 1997, the U.S. federal government issued inflation-indexed bonds for the first time.

Finally, in thinking about the costs of inflation, it is important to note a widely documented but little understood fact: high inflation is variable inflation. That is, countries with high average inflation also tend to have inflation rates that change greatly from year to year. The implication is that if a country decides to pursue a high-inflation monetary policy, it will likely have to accept highly variable inflation as well. As we have just discussed, highly variable inflation increases uncertainty for both creditors and debtors by subjecting them to arbitrary and potentially large redistributions of wealth.

CASE STUDY

The Free Silver Movement, the Election of 1896, and the Wizard of Oz

The redistributions of wealth caused by unexpected changes in the price level are often a source of political turmoil, as evidenced by the Free Silver movement in the late nineteenth century. From 1880 to 1896 the price level in the United States fell 23 percent. This deflation was good for creditors, primarily the bankers of the Northeast, but it was bad for debtors, primarily the farmers of the South and West. One proposed solution to this problem was to replace the gold standard with a bimetallic standard, under which both gold and silver could be minted into coin. The move to a bimetallic standard would increase the money supply and stop the deflation.

The silver issue dominated the presidential election of 1896. William McKinley, the Republican nominee, campaigned on a platform of preserving the gold standard. William Jennings Bryan, the Democratic nominee, supported the bimetallic standard. In a famous speech, Bryan proclaimed, "You shall not press down upon the brow of labor this crown of thorns, you shall not crucify mankind upon a cross of gold." Not surprisingly, McKinley was the candidate of the conservative eastern establishment, while Bryan was the candidate of the southern and western populists.

This debate over silver found its most memorable expression in a children's book, *The Wizard of Oz*. Written by a midwestern journalist, L. Frank Baum, just after the 1896 election, it tells the story of Dorothy, a girl lost in a strange land far from her home in Kansas. Dorothy (representing traditional American values) makes three friends: a scarecrow (the farmer), a tin woodman (the industrial worker), and a lion whose roar exceeds his might (William Jennings Bryan). Together, the four of them make their way along a perilous yellow brick road (the gold standard), hoping to find the Wizard who will help Dorothy return home. Eventually they arrive in Oz (Washington), where everyone sees the world through green glasses (money). The Wizard (William McKinley) tries to be all things to all people but turns out to be a fraud. Dorothy's problem is solved only when she learns about the magical power of her silver slippers.[9]

Although the Republicans won the election of 1896 and the United States stayed on a gold standard, the Free Silver advocates got what they ultimately wanted: inflation. Around the time of the election, gold was discovered in Alaska, Australia, and South Africa. In addition, gold refiners devised the cyanide process, which facilitated the extraction of gold from ore. These developments led to increases in the money supply and in prices. From 1896 to 1910 the price level rose 35 percent.

7-7 | Hyperinflation

Hyperinflation is often defined as inflation that exceeds 50 percent per month, which is just over 1 percent per day. Compounded over many months, this rate of inflation leads to very large increases in the price level. An inflation rate of 50 percent per month implies a more than 100-fold increase in the price level over a year, and a more than 2-million-fold increase over three years. Here we consider the costs and causes of such extreme inflation.

The Costs of Hyperinflation

Although economists debate whether the costs of moderate inflation are large or small, no one doubts that hyperinflation extracts a high toll on society. The costs are qualitatively the same as those we discussed earlier. When inflation reaches extreme levels, however, these costs are more apparent because they are so severe.

The shoeleather costs associated with reduced money holding, for instance, are serious under hyperinflation. Business executives devote much time and energy to cash management when cash loses its value quickly. By diverting this time and energy from more socially valuable activities, such as production and investment decisions, hyperinflation makes the economy run less efficiently.

---

[9] The movie made forty years later hid much of the allegory by changing Dorothy's slippers from silver to ruby. For more on this topic, see Henry M. Littlefield, "The Wizard of Oz: Parable on Populism," *American Quarterly* 16 (Spring 1964): 47–58; and Hugh Rockoff, "The Wizard of Oz as a Monetary Allegory," *Journal of Political Economy* 98 (August 1990): 739–760.

f y i

KEYNES (AND LENIN) ON THE COST OF INFLATION

The great economist John Maynard Keynes was no friend of inflation, as this chapter's opening quotation indicates. Here is the more complete passage from his famous book, *The Economic Consequences of the Peace,* in which Keynes predicted (correctly) that the treaty imposed on Germany after World War I would lead to economic hardship and renewed international tensions:

> Lenin is said to have declared that the best way to destroy the Capitalist System was to debauch the currency. By a continuing process of inflation, governments can confiscate, secretly and unobserved, an important part of the wealth of their citizens. By this method they not only confiscate, but they confiscate *arbitrarily;* and, while the process impoverishes many, it actually enriches some. The sight of this arbitrary rearrangement of riches strikes not only at security, but at confidence in the equity of the existing distribution of wealth. Those to whom the system brings windfalls, beyond their deserts and even beyond their expectations or desires, become "profiteers," who are the object of the hatred of the bourgeoisie, whom the inflationism has impoverished, not less than of the proletariat. As the inflation proceeds and the real value of the currency fluctuates wildly from month to month, all permanent relations between debtors and creditors, which form the ultimate foundation of capitalism, become so utterly disordered as to be almost meaningless; and the process of wealth-getting degenerates into a gamble and a lottery.

> Lenin was certainly right. There is no subtler, no surer means of overturning the existing basis of society than to debauch the currency. The process engages all the hidden forces of economic law on the side of destruction, and does it in a manner which not one man in a million is able to diagnose.*

History has given ample support to this assessment. A recent example occurred in Russia in 1998, where many citizens saw high rates of inflation wipe out their ruble-denominated savings. And, as Lenin would have predicted, this inflation put the country's burgeoning capitalist system in serious jeopardy.

* John Maynard Keynes, *The Economic Consequences of the Peace* (London: Macmillan, 1920): 219–220.

Menu costs also become larger under hyperinflation. Firms have to change prices so often that normal business practices, such as printing and distributing catalogs with fixed prices, become impossible. In one restaurant during the German hyperinflation of the 1920s, a waiter would stand up on a table every 30 minutes to call out the new prices.

Similarly, relative prices do not do a good job of reflecting true scarcity during hyperinflations. When prices change frequently by large amounts, it is hard for customers to shop around for the best price. Highly volatile and rapidly rising prices can alter behavior in many ways. According to one report, when patrons entered a pub during the German hyperinflation, they would often buy two pitchers of beer. Although the second pitcher would lose value by getting warm over time, it would lose value less rapidly than the money left sitting in the patron's wallet.

Tax systems are also distorted by hyperinflation—but in ways that are quite different from those under moderate inflation. In most tax systems there is a delay between the time when a tax is levied and the time when the tax is paid to the government. In the United States, for example, taxpayers are required to make estimated income tax payments every three months. This short delay does not matter much under low inflation. By contrast, during hyperinflation, even a short delay greatly reduces real tax revenue. By the time the government gets the money it is due, the money has fallen in value. As a result, once hyperinflations start, the real tax revenue of the government often falls substantially.

Finally, no one should underestimate the sheer inconvenience of living with hyperinflation. When carrying money to the grocery store is as burdensome as carrying the groceries back home, the monetary system is not doing its best to facilitate exchange. The government tries to overcome this problem by adding more and more zeros to the paper currency, but often it cannot keep up with the exploding price level.

Eventually, these costs of hyperinflation become intolerable. Over time, money loses its role as a store of value, unit of account, and medium of exchange. Barter becomes more common. And more stable unofficial monies—cigarettes or the U.S. dollar—naturally start to replace the official money.

CASE STUDY

Life During the Bolivian Hyperinflation

The following article from the *Wall Street Journal* shows what life was like during the Bolivian hyperinflation of 1985.[10] What costs of inflation does this article emphasize?

Precarious Peso—Amid Wild Inflation, Bolivians Concentrate on Swapping Currency

LA PAZ, Bolivia   When Edgar Miranda gets his monthly teacher's pay of 25 million pesos, he hasn't a moment to lose. Every hour, pesos drop in value. So, while his wife rushes to market to lay in a month's supply of rice and noodles, he is off with the rest of the pesos to change them into black-market dollars.

Mr. Miranda is practicing the First Rule of Survival amid the most out-of-control inflation in the world today. Bolivia is a case study of how runaway inflation undermines a society. Price increases are so huge that the figures build up almost beyond comprehension. In one six-month period, for example, prices soared at an annual rate of 38,000%. By official count, however, last year's inflation reached 2,000%, and this year's is expected to hit 8,000%—though other estimates range many times higher. In any event, Bolivia's rate dwarfs Israel's 370% and Argentina's 1,100%—two other cases of severe inflation.

It is easier to comprehend what happens to the 38-year-old Mr. Miranda's pay if he doesn't quickly change it into dollars. The day he was paid 25 million pesos, a dollar cost 500,000 pesos. So he received $50. Just days later, with the rate at 900,000 pesos, he would have received $27.

"We think only about today and converting every peso into dollars," says Ronald MacLean, the manager of a gold-mining firm. "We have become myopic."

---

[10] Reprinted by permission of the *Wall Street Journal,* © August 13, 1985, page 1, Dow Jones & Company, Inc. All Rights Reserved Worldwide.

And intent on survival. Civil servants won't hand out a form without a bribe. Lawyers, accountants, hairdressers, even prostitutes have almost given up working to become money-changers in the streets. Workers stage repeated strikes and steal from their bosses. The bosses smuggle production abroad, take out phony loans, duck taxes—anything to get dollars for speculation.

The production at the state mines, for example, dropped to 12,000 tons last year from 18,000. The miners pad their wages by smuggling out the richest ore in their lunch pails, and the ore goes by a contraband network into neighboring Peru. Without a major tin mine, Peru now exports some 4,000 metric tons of tin a year.

"We don't produce anything. We are all currency speculators," a heavy-equipment dealer in La Paz says. "People don't know what's good and bad anymore. We have become an amoral society. . . ."

It is an open secret that practically all of the black-market dollars come from the illegal cocaine trade with the U.S. Cocaine traffickers earn an estimated $1 billion a year. . . .

But meanwhile the country is suffering from inflation largely because the government's revenues cover a mere 15% of its expenditures and its deficit has widened to nearly 25% of the country's total annual output. The revenues are hurt by a lag in tax payments, and taxes aren't being collected largely because of widespread theft and bribery.

The Causes of Hyperinflation

Why do hyperinflations start, and how do they end? This question can be answered at different levels.

The most obvious answer is that hyperinflations are due to excessive growth in the supply of money. When the central bank prints money, the price level rises. When it prints money rapidly enough, the result is hyperinflation. To stop the hyperinflation, the central bank must simply reduce the rate of money growth.

This answer is incomplete, however, for it leaves open the question of why central banks in hyperinflating economies choose to print so much money. To address this deeper question, we must turn our attention from monetary to fiscal policy. Most hyperinflations begin when the government has inadequate tax revenue to pay for its spending. Although the government might prefer to finance this budget deficit by issuing debt, it may find itself unable to borrow, perhaps because lenders view the government as a bad credit risk. To cover the deficit, the government turns to the only mechanism at its disposal—the printing press. The result is rapid money growth and hyperinflation.

Once the hyperinflation is under way, the fiscal problems become even more severe. Because of the delay in collecting tax payments, real tax revenue falls as inflation rises. Thus, the government's need to rely on seigniorage is self-reinforcing. Rapid money creation leads to hyperinflation, which leads to a larger budget deficit, which leads to even more rapid money creation.

The ends of hyperinflations almost always coincide with fiscal reforms. Once the magnitude of the problem becomes apparent, the government finally

"I told you the Fed should have tightened."

musters the political will to reduce government spending and increase taxes. These fiscal reforms reduce the need for seigniorage, which allows a reduction in money growth. Hence, even if inflation is always and everywhere a monetary phenomenon, the end of hyperinflation is usually a fiscal phenomenon as well.[11]

CASE STUDY

Hyperinflation in Interwar Germany

After World War I, Germany experienced one of history's most spectacular examples of hyperinflation. At the war's end, the Allies demanded that Germany pay substantial reparations. These payments led to fiscal deficits in Germany, which the German government eventually financed by printing large quantities of money.

Panel (a) of Figure 7-6 shows the quantity of money and the general price level in Germany from January 1922 to December 1924. During this period

---

[11] For more on these issues, see Thomas J. Sargent, "The End of Four Big Inflations," in Robert Hall, ed., *Inflation* (Chicago: University of Chicago Press, 1983), 41–98; and Rudiger Dornbusch and Stanley Fischer, "Stopping Hyperinflations: Past and Present," *Weltwirtschaftliches Archiv* 122 (April 1986): 1–47.

figure 7-6

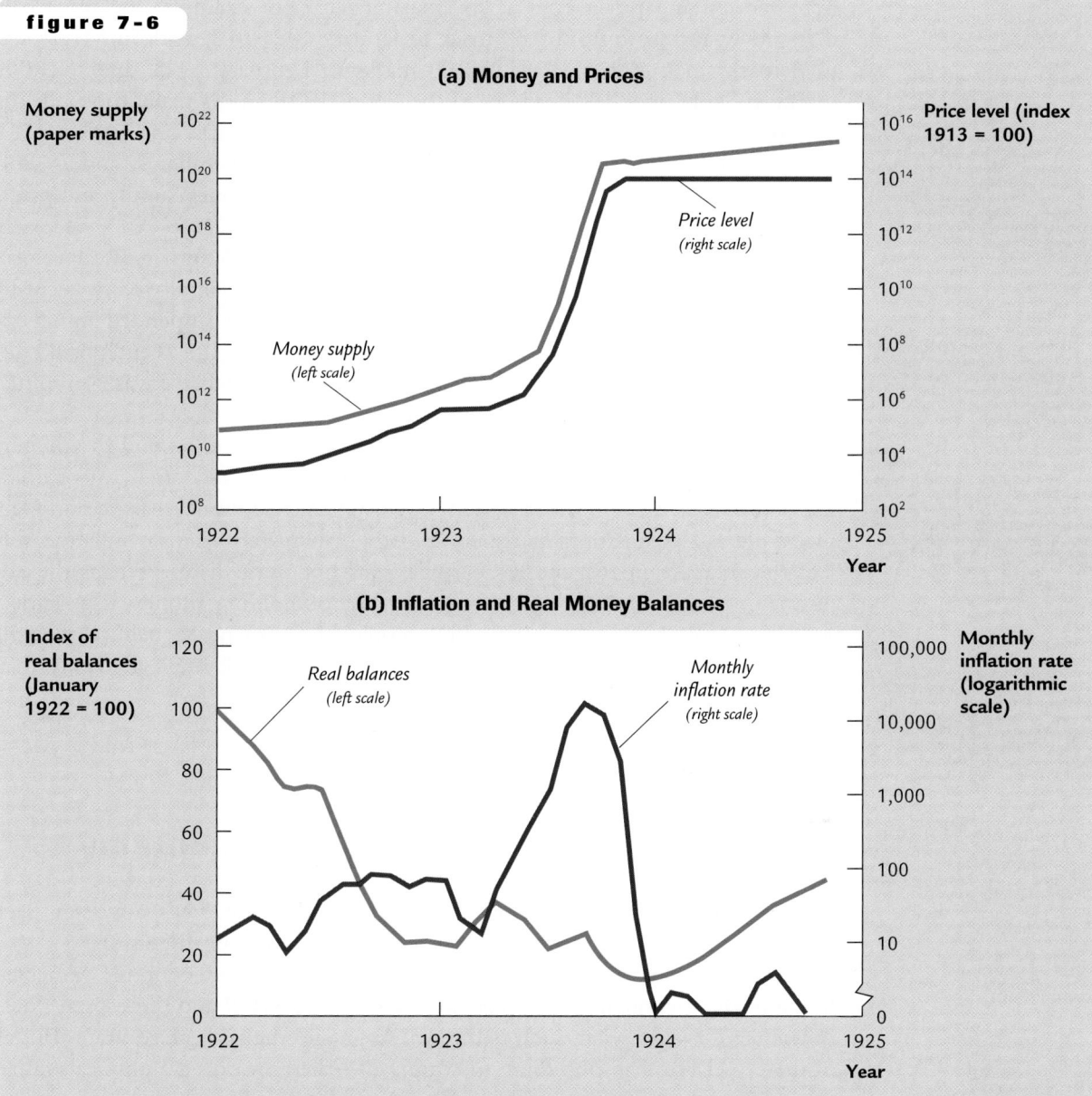

(a) Money and Prices

Money supply (paper marks) / Price level (index 1913 = 100)

Money supply (left scale)

Price level (right scale)

Year

(b) Inflation and Real Money Balances

Index of real balances (January 1922 = 100) / Monthly inflation rate (logarithmic scale)

Real balances (left scale)

Monthly inflation rate (right scale)

Year

Money and Prices in Interwar Germany Panel (a) shows the money supply and the price level in Germany from January 1922 to December 1924. The immense increases in the money supply and the price level provide a dramatic illustration of the effects of printing large amounts of money. Panel (b) shows inflation and real money balances. As inflation rose, real money balances fell. When the inflation ended at the end of 1923, real money balances rose.

Source: Adapted from Thomas J. Sargent, "The End of Four Big Inflations," in Robert Hall, ed., *Inflation* (Chicago: University of Chicago Press, 1983): 41–98.

both money and prices rose at an amazing rate. For example, the price of a daily newspaper rose from 0.30 mark in January 1921 to 1 mark in May 1922, to 8 marks in October 1922, to 100 marks in February 1923, and to 1,000 marks in September 1923. Then, in the fall of 1923, prices really took off: the newspaper sold for 2,000 marks on October 1, 20,000 marks on October 15, 1 million marks on October 29, 15 million marks on November 9, and 70 million marks on November 17. In December 1923 the money supply and prices abruptly stabilized.[12]

Just as fiscal problems caused the German hyperinflation, a fiscal reform ended it. At the end of 1923, the number of government employees was cut by one-third, and the reparations payments were temporarily suspended and eventually reduced. At the same time, a new central bank, the Rentenbank, replaced the old central bank, the Reichsbank. The Rentenbank was committed to not financing the government by printing money.

According to our theoretical analysis of money demand, an end to a hyperinflation should lead to an increase in real money balances as the cost of holding money falls. Panel (b) of Figure 7-6 shows that real money balances in Germany did fall as inflation increased, and then increased again as inflation fell. Yet the increase in real money balances was not immediate. Perhaps the adjustment of real money balances to the cost of holding money is a gradual process. Or perhaps it took time for people in Germany to believe that the inflation had really ended, so that expected inflation fell more gradually than actual inflation.

7-8 | Conclusion: The Classical Dichotomy

We have finished our discussion of money and inflation. Let's now step back and examine a key assumption that has been implicit in our discussion.

In Chapters 3 through 6, we explained many macroeconomic variables. Some of these variables were *quantities,* such as real GDP and the capital stock; others were *relative prices,* such as the real wage and the real interest rate. But all of these variables had one thing in common—they measured a physical (rather than a monetary) quantity. Real GDP is the quantity of goods and services produced in a given year, and the capital stock is the quantity of machines and structures available at a given time. The real wage is the quantity of output a worker earns for each hour of work, and the real interest rate is the quantity of output a person earns in the future by lending one unit of output today. All variables measured in physical units, such as quantities and relative prices, are called **real variables.**

---

[12] The data on newspaper prices are from Michael Mussa, "Sticky Individual Prices and the Dynamics of the General Price Level," *Carnegie-Rochester Conference on Public Policy* 15 (Autumn 1981): 261–296.

In this chapter we examined **nominal variables**—variables expressed in terms of money. The economy has many nominal variables, such as the price level, the inflation rate, and the dollar wage a person earns.

At first it may seem surprising that we were able to explain real variables without introducing nominal variables or the existence of money. In previous chapters we studied the level and allocation of the economy's output without mentioning the price level or the rate of inflation. Our theory of the labor market explained the real wage without explaining the nominal wage.

Economists call this theoretical separation of real and nominal variables the **classical dichotomy.** It is the hallmark of classical macroeconomic theory. The classical dichotomy is an important insight, because it greatly simplifies economic theory. In particular, it allows us to examine real variables, as we have done, while ignoring nominal variables. The classical dichotomy arises because, in classical economic theory, changes in the money supply do not influence real variables. This irrelevance of money for real variables is called **monetary neutrality.** For many purposes—in particular for studying long-run issues—monetary neutrality is approximately correct.

Yet monetary neutrality does not fully describe the world in which we live. Beginning in Chapter 9, we discuss departures from the classical model and monetary neutrality. These departures are crucial for understanding many macroeconomic phenomena, such as short-run economic fluctuations.

Summary

1. Money is the stock of assets used for transactions. It serves as a store of value, a unit of account, and a medium of exchange. Different sorts of assets are used as money: commodity money systems use an asset with intrinsic value, whereas fiat money systems use an asset whose sole function is to serve as money. In modern economies, a central bank such as the Federal Reserve is responsible for controlling the supply of money.

2. The quantity theory of money assumes that the velocity of money is stable and concludes that nominal GDP is proportional to the stock of money. Because the factors of production and the production function determine real GDP, the quantity theory implies that the price level is proportional to the quantity of money. Therefore, the rate of growth in the quantity of money determines the inflation rate.

3. Seigniorage is the revenue that the government raises by printing money. It is a tax on money holding. Although seigniorage is quantitatively small in most economies, it is often a major source of government revenue in economies experiencing hyperinflation.

4. The nominal interest rate is the sum of the real interest rate and the inflation rate. The Fisher effect says that the nominal interest rate moves one-for-one with expected inflation.

5. The nominal interest rate is the opportunity cost of holding money. Thus, one might expect the demand for money to depend on the nominal interest rate. If it does, then the price level depends on both the current quantity of money and the quantities of money expected in the future.

6. The costs of expected inflation include shoeleather costs, menu costs, the cost of relative price variability, tax distortions, and the inconvenience of making inflation corrections. In addition, unexpected inflation causes arbitrary redistributions of wealth between debtors and creditors.

7. During hyperinflations, most of the costs of inflation become severe. Hyperinflations typically begin when governments finance large budget deficits by printing money. They end when fiscal reforms eliminate the need for seigniorage.

8. According to classical economic theory, money is neutral: the money supply does not affect real variables. Therefore, classical theory allows us to study how real variables are determined without any reference to the money supply. The equilibrium in the money market then determines the price level and, as a result, all other nominal variables. This theoretical separation of real and nominal variables is called the classical dichotomy.

KEY CONCEPTS

Inflation	Central bank	Seigniorage
Hyperinflation	Federal Reserve	Nominal and real interest rates
Money	Open-market operations	Fisher equation and Fisher effect
Store of value	Currency	*Ex ante* and *ex post* real interest
Unit of account	Demand deposits	rates
Medium of exchange	Quantity equation	Shoeleather costs
Fiat money	Transactions velocity of money	Menu costs
Commodity money	Income velocity of money	Real and nominal variables
Gold standard	Real money balances	Classical dichotomy
Money supply	Money demand function	Monetary neutrality
Monetary policy	Quantity theory of money	

QUESTIONS FOR REVIEW

1. Describe the functions of money.

2. What is fiat money? What is commodity money?

3. Who controls the money supply and how?

4. Write the quantity equation and explain it.

5. What does the assumption of constant velocity imply?

6. Who pays the inflation tax?

7. If inflation rises from 6 to 8 percent, what hap-

pens to real and nominal interest rates according to the Fisher effect?

8. List all the costs of inflation you can think of, and rank them according to how important you think they are.

9. Explain the roles of monetary and fiscal policy in causing and ending hyperinflations.

10. Define the terms *real variable* and *nominal variable,* and give an example of each.

PROBLEMS AND APPLICATIONS |

1. What are the three functions of money? Which of the functions do the following items satisfy? Which do they not satisfy?

   a. A credit card

   b. A painting by Rembrandt

   c. A subway token

2. In the country of Wiknam, the velocity of money is constant. Real GDP grows by 5 percent per year, the money stock grows by 14 percent per year, and the nominal interest rate is 11 percent. What is the real interest rate?

3. In 1994, a newspaper article written by the Associated Press reported that the U.S. economy was experiencing a low rate of inflation. It said that "low inflation has a downside: 45 million recipients of Social Security and other benefits will see their checks go up by just 2.8 percent next year."

   a. Why does inflation affect the increase in Social Security and other benefits?

   b. Is this effect a cost of inflation, as the article suggests? Why or why not?

4. Suppose you are advising a small country (such as Bermuda) on whether to print its own money or to use the money of its larger neighbor (such as the United States). What are the costs and benefits of a national money? Does the relative political stability of the two countries have any role in this decision?

5. During World War II, both Germany and England had plans for a paper weapon: they each printed the other's currency, with the intention of dropping large quantities by airplane. Why might this have been an effective weapon?

6. Calvin Coolidge once said that "inflation is repudiation." What might he have meant by this? Do you agree? Why or why not? Does it matter whether the inflation is expected or unexpected?

7. Some economic historians have noted that during the period of the gold standard, gold discoveries were most likely to occur after a long deflation. (The discoveries of 1896 are an example.) Why might this be true?

8. Suppose that consumption depends on the level of real money balances (on the grounds that real money balances are part of wealth). Show that if real money balances depend on the nominal interest rate, then an increase in the rate of money growth affects consumption, investment, and the real interest rate. Does the nominal interest rate adjust more than one-for-one or less than one-for-one to expected inflation?

   This deviation from the classical dichotomy and the Fisher effect is called the *Mundell–Tobin effect.* How might you decide whether the Mundell–Tobin effect is important in practice?

The Cagan Model: How Current and Future Money Affect the Price Level

In this chapter we showed that if the quantity of real money balances demanded depends on the cost of holding money, the price level depends on both the current money supply and the future money supply. This appendix develops the *Cagan model* to show more explicitly how this works.[13]

To keep the math as simple as possible, we posit a money demand function that is linear in the natural logarithms of all the variables. The money demand function is

$$m_t - p_t = -\gamma(p_{t+1} - p_t), \tag{A1}$$

where m_t is the log of the quantity of money at time t, p_t is the log of the price level at time t, and γ is a parameter that governs the sensitivity of money demand to the rate of inflation. By the property of logarithms, $m_t - p_t$ is the log of real money balances, and $p_{t+1} - p_t$ is the inflation rate between period t and period $t + 1$. This equation states that if inflation goes up by 1 percentage point, real money balances fall by γ percent.

We have made a number of assumptions in writing the money demand function in this way. First, by excluding the level of output as a determinant of money demand, we are implicitly assuming that it is constant. Second, by including the rate of inflation rather than the nominal interest rate, we are assuming that the real interest rate is constant. Third, by including actual inflation rather than expected inflation, we are assuming perfect foresight. All of these assumptions are to keep the analysis as simple as possible.

We want to solve Equation A1 to express the price level as a function of current and future money. To do this, note that Equation A1 can be rewritten as

$$p_t = \left(\frac{1}{1+\gamma}\right) m_t + \left(\frac{\gamma}{1+\gamma}\right) p_{t+1}. \tag{A2}$$

This equation states that the current price level is a weighted average of the current money supply and the next period's price level. The next period's price level will be determined the same way as this period's price level:

$$p_{t+1} = \left(\frac{1}{1+\gamma}\right) m_{t+1} + \left(\frac{\gamma}{1+\gamma}\right) p_{t+2}. \tag{A3}$$

---

[13] This model is derived from Phillip Cagan, "The Monetary Dynamics of Hyperinflation," in Milton Friedman, ed., *Studies in the Quantity Theory of Money* (Chicago: University of Chicago Press, 1956).

Use Equation A3 to substitute for p_{t+1} in Equation A2 to obtain

$$p_t = \frac{1}{1 + \gamma} m_t + \frac{\gamma}{(1 + \gamma)^2} m_{t+1} + \frac{\gamma^2}{(1 + \gamma)^2} p_{t+2}. \qquad (A4)$$

Equation A4 states that the current price level is a weighted average of the current money supply, the next period's money supply, and the following period's price level. Once again, the price level in $t+2$ is determined as in Equation A2:

$$p_{t+2} = \left(\frac{1}{1 + \gamma} \right) m_{t+2} + \left(\frac{\gamma}{1 + \gamma} \right) p_{t+3}. \qquad (A5)$$

Now use Equation A5 to substitute into Equation A4 to obtain

$$p_t = \frac{1}{1 + \gamma} m_t + \frac{\gamma}{(1 + \gamma)^2} m_{t+1} + \frac{\gamma^2}{(1 + \gamma)^3} m_{t+2} + \frac{\gamma^3}{(1 + \gamma)^3} p_{t+3}. \qquad (A6)$$

By now you see the pattern. We can continue to use Equation A2 to substitute for the future price level. If we do this an infinite number of times, we find

$$p_t = \left(\frac{1}{1 + \gamma} \right) \left[m_t + \left(\frac{\gamma}{1 + \gamma} \right) m_{t+1} \right. $$
$$\left. + \left(\frac{\gamma}{1 + \gamma} \right)^2 m_{t+2} + \left(\frac{\gamma}{1 + \gamma} \right)^3 m_{t+3} + \cdots \right],$$
$$(A7)$$

where "$\cdots$" indicates an infinite number of analogous terms. According to Equation A7, the current price level is a weighted average of the current money supply and all future money supplies.

Note the importance of γ, the parameter governing the sensitivity of real money balances to inflation. The weights on the future money supplies decline geometrically at rate $\gamma/(1 + \gamma)$. If γ is small, then $\gamma/(1 + \gamma)$ is small, and the weights decline quickly. In this case, the current money supply is the primary determinant of the price level. (Indeed, if γ equals zero, then we obtain the quantity theory of money: the price level is proportional to the current money supply, and the future money supplies do not matter at all.) If γ is large, then $\gamma/(1 + \gamma)$ is close to 1, and the weights decline slowly. In this case, the future money supplies play a key role in determining today's price level.

Finally, let's relax the assumption of perfect foresight. If the future is not known with certainty, then we should write the money demand function as

$$m_t - p_t = -\gamma (Ep_{t+1} - p_t), \qquad (A8)$$

where Ep_{t+1} is the expected price level. Equation A8 states that real money balances depend on expected inflation. By following steps similar to those above, we can show that

$$
p_t = \left(\frac{1}{1+\gamma}\right) \left[m_t + \left(\frac{\gamma}{1+\gamma}\right) Em_{t+1} \right.
$$
$$
\left. + \left(\frac{\gamma}{1+\gamma}\right)^2 Em_{t+2} + \left(\frac{\gamma}{1+\gamma}\right)^3 Em_{t+3} + \cdots \right].
$$

(A9)

Equation A9 states that the price level depends on the current money supply and expected future money supplies.

Some economists use this model to argue that *credibility* is important for ending hyperinflation. Because the price level depends on both current and expected future money, inflation depends on both current and expected future money growth. Therefore, to end high inflation, both money growth and expected money growth must fall. Expectations, in turn, depend on credibility—the perception that the central bank is truly committed to a new, more stable policy.

How can a central bank achieve credibility in the midst of hyperinflation? Credibility is often achieved by removing the underlying cause of the hyperinflation—the need for seigniorage. Thus, a credible fiscal reform is often necessary for a credible change in monetary policy. This fiscal reform might take the form of reducing government spending and making the central bank more independent from the government. Reduced spending decreases the need for seigniorage in the present. Increased independence allows the central bank to resist government demands for seigniorage in the future.

MORE PROBLEMS AND APPLICATIONS

1. In the Cagan model, if the money supply is expected to grow at some constant rate μ (so that $Em_{t+s} = m_t + s\mu$), then Equation A9 can be shown to imply that $p_t = m_t + \gamma\mu$.

   a. Intepret this result.

   b. What happens to the price level p_t when the money supply m_t changes, holding the money growth rate μ constant?

   c. What happens to the price level p_t when the money growth rate μ changes, holding the current money supply m_t constant?

   d. If a central bank is about to reduce the rate of money growth μ but wants to hold the price level p_t constant, what should it do with m_t? Can you see any practical problems that might arise in following such a policy?

   e. How do your previous answers change in the special case where money demand does not depend on the expected rate of inflation (so that $\gamma = 0$)?

8

The Open Economy

No nation was ever ruined by trade.

— *Benjamin Franklin*

Even if you never leave your home town, you are an active participant in a global economy. When you go to the grocery store, for instance, you might choose between apples grown locally and grapes grown in Chile. When you make a deposit into your local bank, the bank might lend those funds to your next-door neighbor or to a Japanese company building a factory outside Tokyo. Because our economy is integrated with many others around the world, consumers have more goods and services from which to choose, and savers have more opportunities to invest their wealth.

In previous chapters we simplified our analysis by assuming a closed economy. In actuality, however, most economies are open: they export goods and services abroad, they import goods and services from abroad, and they borrow and lend in world financial markets. Figure 8-1 gives some sense of the importance of these international interactions by showing imports and exports as a percentage of GDP for seven major industrial countries. As the figure shows, imports and exports in the United States are about 13 percent of GDP. Trade is even more important for many other countries—in Canada and the United Kingdom, for instance, imports and exports are over 30 percent of GDP. In these countries, international trade is central to analyzing economic developments and formulating economic policies.

This chapter begins our study of open-economy macroeconomics. We begin in Section 8-1 with questions of measurement. To understand how the open economy works, we must understand the key macroeconomic variables that measure the interactions among countries. Accounting identities reveal a key insight: the flow of goods and services across national borders is always matched by an equivalent flow of funds to finance capital accumulation.

In Section 8-2 we examine the determinants of these international flows. We develop a model of the small open economy that corresponds to our model of the closed economy in Chapter 3. The model shows the factors that determine whether a country is a borrower or a lender in world markets, and how policies at home and abroad affect the flows of capital and goods.

In Section 8-3 we extend the model to discuss the prices at which a country makes exchanges in world markets. We examine what determines the price of

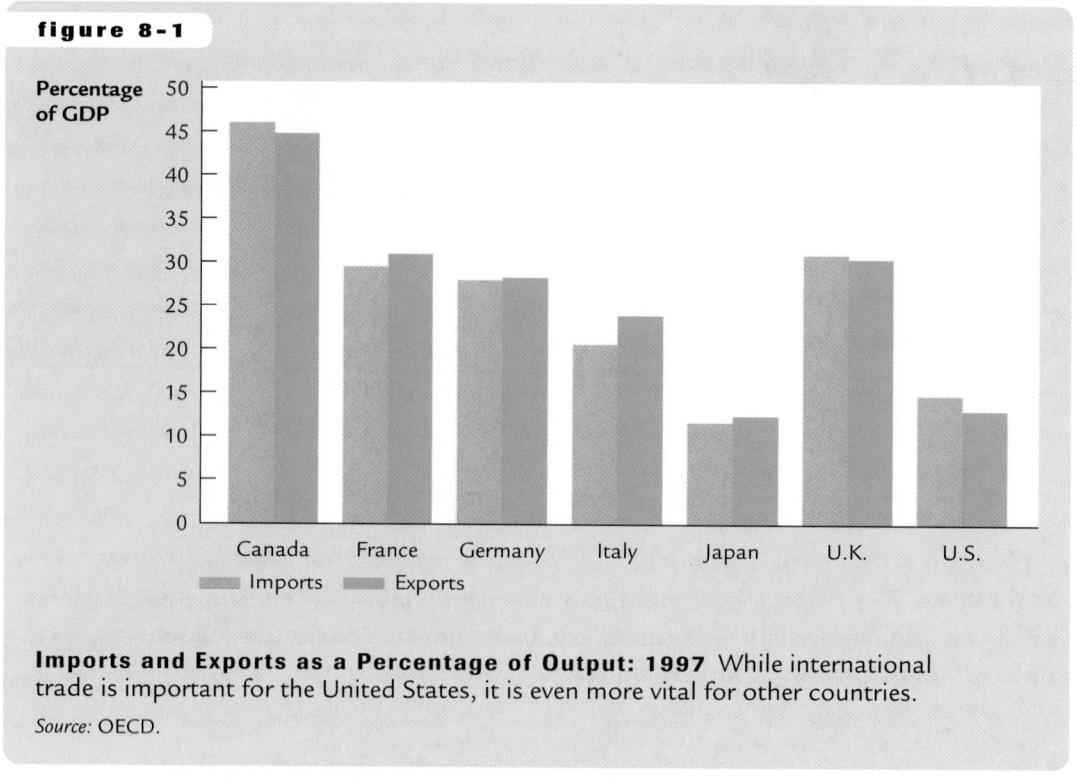

figure 8-1

Imports and Exports as a Percentage of Output: 1997 While international trade is important for the United States, it is even more vital for other countries.
Source: OECD.

domestic goods relative to foreign goods. We also examine what determines the rate at which the domestic currency trades for foreign currencies. Our model shows how protectionist trade policies—policies designed to protect domestic industries from foreign competition—influence the amount of international trade and the exchange rate.

8-1 | The International Flows of Capital and Goods

The key macroeconomic difference between open and closed economies is that, in an open economy, a country's spending in any given year need not equal its output of goods and services. A country can spend more than it produces by borrowing from abroad, or it can spend less than it produces and lend the difference to foreigners. To understand this more fully, let's take another look at national income accounting, which we first discussed in Chapter 2.

The Role of Net Exports

Consider the expenditure on an economy's output of goods and services. In a closed economy, all output is sold domestically, and expenditure is divided into three components: consumption, investment, and government purchases. In an open economy, some output is sold domestically and some is exported to be sold abroad. We can divide expenditure on an open economy's output Y into four components:

➤ C^d, consumption of domestic goods and services,

➤ I^d, investment in domestic goods and services,

➤ G^d, government purchases of domestic goods and services,

➤ EX, exports of domestic goods and services.

The division of expenditure into these components is expressed in the identity

$$Y = C^d + I^d + G^d + EX.$$

The sum of the first three terms, $C^d + I^d + G^d$, is domestic spending on domestic goods and services. The fourth term, EX, is foreign spending on domestic goods and services.

We now want to make this identity more useful. To do this, note that domestic spending on all goods and services is the sum of domestic spending on domestic goods and services and on foreign goods and services. Hence, total consumption C equals consumption of domestic goods and services C^d plus consumption of foreign goods and services C^f; total investment I equals investment in domestic goods and services I^d plus investment in foreign goods and services I^f; and total government purchases G equals government purchases of domestic goods and services G^d plus government purchases of foreign goods and services G^f. Thus,

$$C = C^d + C^f,$$
$$I = I^d + I^f,$$
$$G = G^d + G^f.$$

We substitute these three equations into the identity above:

$$Y = (C - C^f) + (I - I^f) + (G - G^f) + EX.$$

We can rearrange to obtain

$$Y = C + I + G + EX - (C^f + I^f + G^f).$$

The sum of domestic spending on foreign goods and services $(C^f + I^f + G^f)$ is expenditure on imports (IM). We can thus write the national income accounts identity as

$$Y = C + I + G + EX - IM.$$

Because spending on imports is included in domestic spending $(C + I + G)$, and because goods and services imported from abroad are not part of a country's output, this equation subtracts spending on imports. Defining **net exports** to be exports minus imports $(NX = EX - IM)$, the identity becomes

$$Y = C + I + G + NX.$$

This equation states that expenditure on domestic output is the sum of consumption, investment, government purchases, and net exports. This is the most common form of the national income accounts identity; it should be familiar from Chapter 2.

The national income accounts identity shows how domestic output, domestic spending, and net exports are related. In particular,

$$NX \quad = \quad Y \quad - \quad (C + I + G)$$

Net Exports = Output − Domestic Spending.

This equation shows that in an open economy, domestic spending need not equal the output of goods and services. *If output exceeds domestic spending, we export the difference: net exports are positive. If output falls short of domestic spending, we import the difference: net exports are negative.*

Net Foreign Investment and the Trade Balance

In an open economy, as in the closed economy we discussed in Chapter 3, financial markets and goods markets are closely related. To see the relationship, we must rewrite the national income accounts identity in terms of saving and investment. Begin with the identity

$$Y = C + I + G + NX.$$

Subtract C and G from both sides to obtain

$$Y - C - G = I + NX.$$

Recall from Chapter 3 that $Y - C - G$ is national saving S, the sum of private saving, $Y - T - C$, and public saving, $T - G$. Therefore,

$$S = I + NX.$$

Subtracting I from both sides of the equation, we can write the national income accounts identity as

$$S - I = NX.$$

This form of the national income accounts identity shows that an economy's net exports must always equal the difference between its saving and its investment.

Let's look more closely at each part of this identity. The easy part is the right-hand side, NX, which is simply our net export of goods and services. Another name for net exports is the **trade balance,** because it tells us how our trade in goods and services departs from the benchmark of equal imports and exports.

The left-hand side of the identity is the difference between domestic saving and domestic investment, $S - I$, which is called **net foreign investment.** Net foreign investment equals the amount that domestic residents are lending abroad minus the amount that foreigners are lending to us. If net foreign investment is positive, our saving exceeds our investment and we are lending the excess to foreigners. If net foreign investment is negative, our investment exceeds our saving and we are financing this extra investment by borrowing from abroad. Thus, net foreign investment reflects the international flow of funds to finance capital accumulation.

The national income accounts identity shows that net foreign investment always equals the trade balance. That is,

$$\text{Net Foreign Investment} = \text{Trade Balance}$$
$$S - I = NX.$$

If $S - I$ and NX are positive, we have a **trade surplus.** In this case, we are net lenders in world financial markets, and we are exporting more goods than we are importing. If $S - I$ and NX are negative, we have a **trade deficit.** In this case, we are net borrowers in world financial markets, and we are importing more goods than we are exporting. If $S - I$ and NX are exactly zero, we are said to have **balanced trade** because the value of imports equals the value of exports.

The national income accounts identity shows that the international flow of funds to finance capital accumulation and the international flow of goods and services are two sides of the same coin. On the one hand, if our saving exceeds our investment, the saving that is not invested domestically is used to make loans to foreigners. Foreigners require these loans because we are providing them with more goods and services than they are providing us. That is, we are running a trade surplus. On the other hand, if our investment exceeds our saving, the extra investment must be financed by borrowing from abroad. These foreign loans enable us to import more goods and services than we export. That is, we are running a trade deficit.

Note that the international flow of capital can take many forms. It is easiest to assume—as we have done so far—that when we run a trade deficit, foreigners make loans to us. This happens, for example, when the Japanese buy the debt issued by U.S. corporations or by the U.S. government. But, equivalently, the flow of capital can take the form of foreigners buying domestic assets. For example, if a Japanese investor buys an apartment building in New York City, that transaction reduces U.S. net foreign investment. In both the case of foreigners buying domestically issued debt and the case of foreigners buying domestically owned assets, foreigners are obtaining a claim to the future returns to domestic capital. In other words, in both cases, foreigners end up owning some of the domestic capital stock.

8-2 | Saving and Investment in a Small Open Economy

So far in our discussion of the international flows of goods and capital, we have merely rearranged accounting identities. That is, we have defined some of the variables that measure transactions in an open economy, and we have shown the links among these variables that follow from their definitions. Our next step is to develop a model that explains the behavior of these variables. We can then use the model to answer questions such as how the trade balance responds to changes in policy.

Capital Mobility and the World Interest Rate

In a moment we present a model of the international flows of capital and goods. Because net foreign investment equals domestic saving minus domestic investment, our model explains net foreign investment (and thus the trade balance) by explaining what determines these two variables. To develop this model, we use some elements that should be familiar from Chapter 3, but in contrast to the Chapter 3 model, we do not assume that the real interest rate equilibrates saving and investment. Instead, we allow the economy to run a trade deficit and borrow from other countries, or to run a trade surplus and lend to other countries.

If the real interest rate does not adjust to equilibrate saving and investment in this model, what *does* determine the real interest rate? We answer this question here by considering the simple case of a **small open economy** with perfect capital mobility. By "small" we mean that this economy is a small part of the world market and thus, by itself, can have only a negligible effect on the world interest rate. By "perfect capital mobility" we mean that residents of the country have full access to world financial markets. In particular, the government does not impede international borrowing or lending.

Because of this assumption of perfect capital mobility, the interest rate in our small open economy, r, must equal the **world interest rate** r^*, the real interest rate prevailing in world financial markets:

$$r = r^*.$$

Residents of the small open economy need never borrow at any interest rate above r^*, because they can always get a loan at r^* from abroad. Similarly, residents of this economy need never lend at any interest rate below r^* because they can always earn r^* by lending abroad. Thus, the world interest rate determines the interest rate in our small open economy.

Let us discuss for a moment what determines the world real interest rate. In a closed economy, the equilibrium of domestic saving and domestic investment determines the interest rate. Barring interplanetary trade, the world economy is a closed economy. Therefore, the equilibrium of world saving and world investment determines the world interest rate. Our small open economy has a negligible effect on the world real interest rate because, being a small part of the world, it has a negligible effect on world saving and world investment. Hence, our small open economy takes the world interest rate as an exogenously given variable.

The Model

To build the model of the small open economy, we take three assumptions from Chapter 3:

➤ The economy's output Y is fixed by the factors of production and the production function. We write this as

$$Y = \overline{Y} = F(\overline{K}, \overline{L}).$$

➤ Consumption C is positively related to disposable income $Y - T$. We write the consumption function as

$$C = C(Y - T).$$

➤ Investment I is negatively related to the real interest rate r. We write the investment function as

$$I = I(r).$$

These are the three key parts of our model. If you do not understand these relationships, review Chapter 3 before continuing.

We can now return to the accounting identity and write it as

$$NX = (Y - C - G) - I$$
$$NX = S - I.$$

Substituting our three assumptions from Chapter 3 and the condition that the interest rate equals the world interest rate, we obtain

$$NX = \underbrace{[\overline{Y} - C(\overline{Y} - T) - G]}_{S} - I(r^*)$$
$$= \phantom{[\overline{Y} - C(\overline{Y} - T) - G]} - I(r^*).$$

This equation shows what determines saving S and investment I—and thus the trade balance NX. Remember that saving depends on fiscal policy: lower government purchases G or higher taxes T raise national saving. Investment depends on the world real interest rate r^*: high interest rates make some investment projects unprofitable. Therefore, the trade balance depends on these variables as well.

In Chapter 3 we graphed saving and investment as in Figure 8-2. In the closed economy studied in that chapter, the real interest rate adjusts to equilibrate saving and investment—that is, the real interest rate is found where the saving and investment curves cross. In the small open economy, however, the real interest rate equals the world real interest rate. *The trade balance is determined by the difference between saving and investment at the world interest rate.*

At this point, you might wonder about the mechanism that causes the trade balance to equal net foreign investment. The determinants of net foreign investment are easy to understand. When domestic saving falls short of domestic investment, domestic investors borrow from abroad; when saving exceeds investment, the excess is lent to other countries. But what causes those who

figure 8-2

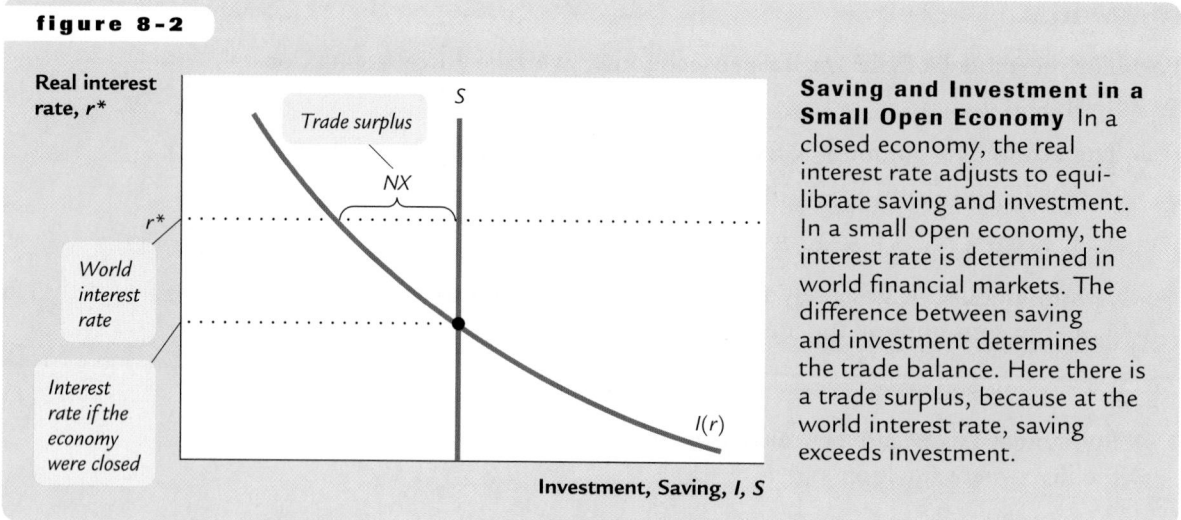

Real interest rate, r^*

Trade surplus

NX

r^*

World interest rate

Interest rate if the economy were closed

S

$I(r)$

Investment, Saving, I, S

Saving and Investment in a Small Open Economy In a closed economy, the real interest rate adjusts to equilibrate saving and investment. In a small open economy, the interest rate is determined in world financial markets. The difference between saving and investment determines the trade balance. Here there is a trade surplus, because at the world interest rate, saving exceeds investment.

import and export to behave in a way that ensures that the international flow of goods exactly balances this international flow of capital? For now we leave this question unanswered, but we return to it in Section 8-3 when we discuss the determination of exchange rates.

How Policies Influence the Trade Balance

Suppose that the economy begins in a position of balanced trade. That is, at the world interest rate, investment I equals saving S, and net exports NX equal zero. Let's use our model to predict the effects of government policies at home and abroad.

Fiscal Policy at Home Consider first what happens to the small open economy if the government expands domestic spending by increasing government purchases. The increase in G reduces national saving, because $S = Y - C - G$. With an unchanged world real interest rate, investment remains the same. Therefore, saving falls below investment, and some investment must now be financed by borrowing from abroad. Since $NX = S - I$, the fall in S implies a fall in NX. The economy now runs a trade deficit.

The same logic applies to a decrease in taxes. A tax cut lowers T, raises disposable income $Y - T$, stimulates consumption, and reduces national saving. (Even though some of the tax cut finds its way into private saving, public saving falls by the full amount of the tax cut; in total, saving falls.) Since $NX = S - I$, the reduction in national saving in turn lowers NX.

Figure 8-3 illustrates these effects. A fiscal policy change that increases private consumption C or public consumption G reduces national saving

figure 8-3

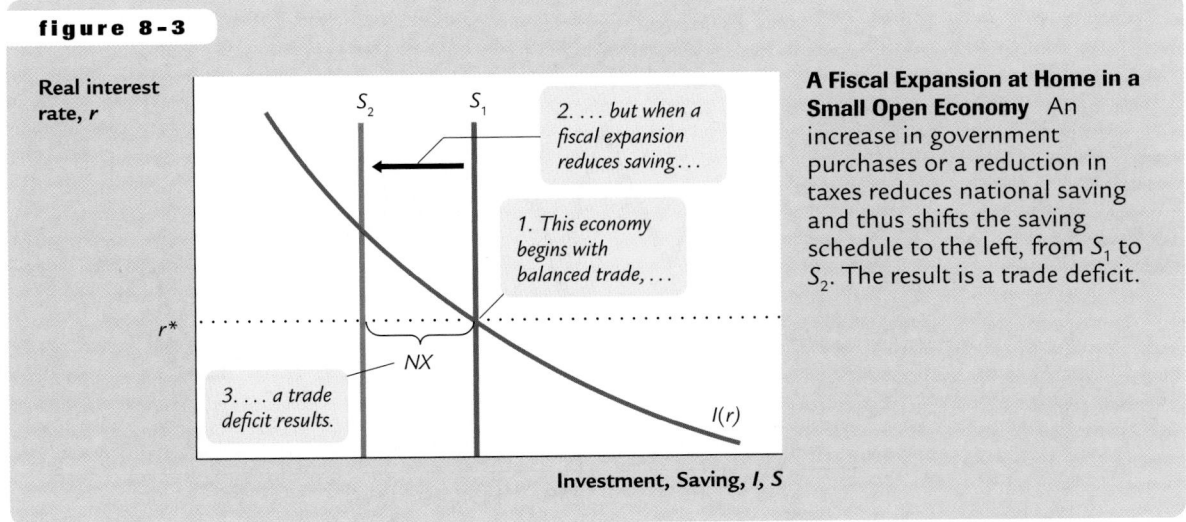

A Fiscal Expansion at Home in a Small Open Economy   An increase in government purchases or a reduction in taxes reduces national saving and thus shifts the saving schedule to the left, from S_1 to S_2. The result is a trade deficit.

$(Y - C - G)$ and, therefore, shifts the vertical line that represents saving from S_1 to S_2. Because NX is the distance between the saving schedule and the investment schedule at the world interest rate, this shift reduces NX. Hence, *starting from balanced trade, a change in fiscal policy that reduces national saving leads to a trade deficit.*

CASE STUDY

The Twin Deficits

The United States experienced an unusual episode of expansionary fiscal policy in the 1980s and 1990s. With the support of President Ronald Reagan, the Congress passed legislation in 1981 that substantially cut personal income taxes over the next three years. Because these tax cuts were not met with equal cuts in government spending, the federal budget went into deficit. These budget deficits were among the largest ever experienced in a period of peace and prosperity, and they continued long after Reagan left office.

According to our model, such a policy should reduce national saving, thereby causing a trade deficit. And, in fact, that is exactly what happened. Figure 8-4 shows national saving, investment, the trade balance, and the federal budget balance as a percentage of GDP since 1960. Before 1980, the federal budget was, on average, roughly in balance. Budget surpluses were common, as the debt used to finance World War II was gradually being paid off. During this time, the trade balance also averaged a small surplus. Americans were saving more than they were investing at home, and the difference was invested abroad.

The situation changed dramatically around 1981. At that time, the federal government started to run a budget deficit of a size unprecedented in peacetime.

figure 8-4

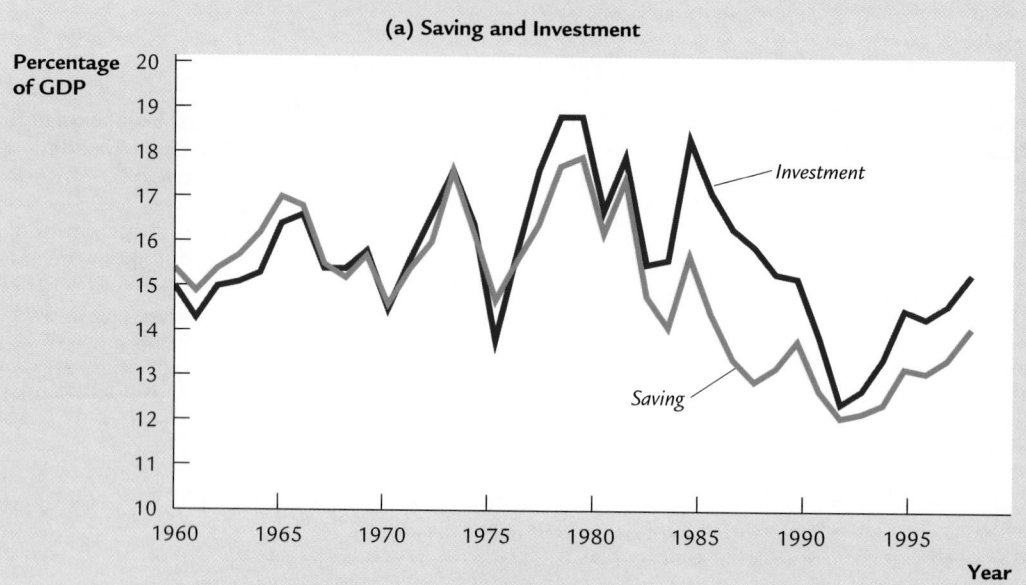

(a) Saving and Investment

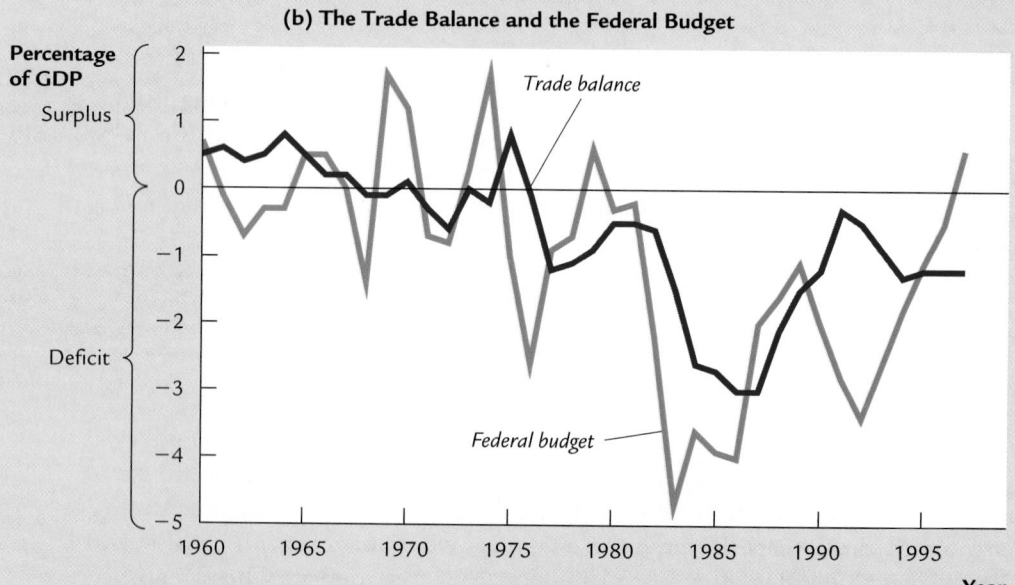

(b) The Trade Balance and the Federal Budget

Saving, Investment, the Trade Balance, and the Budget Deficit: The U.S. Experience Panel (a) shows national saving and investment as a percentage of GDP since 1960. The trade balance equals saving minus investment. Panel (b) shows the trade balance and the federal budget balance as a percentage of GDP. Positive numbers represent a surplus, and negative numbers represent a deficit. Note that in the early 1980s, the federal government began running large budget deficits, which reduced national saving and led to large trade deficits.

Note: The numbers for the budget deficit are corrected for the effects of inflation: only the real interest on the debt is counted as expenditure. For a discussion of this correction, see Chapter 15. The numbers for the trade balance are net exports in current dollars from the national income accounts.

Source: U.S. Department of Commerce.

This policy reduced national saving, leading to a large trade deficit. That is, because U.S. saving was no longer sufficient to finance U.S. investment, other countries started lending to the United States.

This long period of borrowing from abroad changed the economic position of the United States in the world economy. In 1981 the U.S. stock of net foreign assets was about 12.3 percent of GDP. This means that the United States owned more capital abroad than foreigners owned in the United States and that the difference amounted to about one-eighth of U.S. annual income. By contrast, by 1993 the U.S. stock of net foreign assets was *negative* 8.8 percent. The United States went from being the world's largest creditor to being the world's largest debtor.

Fiscal Policy Abroad Consider now what happens to a small open economy when foreign governments increase their government purchases. If these foreign countries are a small part of the world economy, then their fiscal change has a negligible impact on other countries. But if these foreign countries are a large part of the world economy, their increase in government purchases reduces world saving and causes the world interest rate to rise.

The increase in the world interest rate raises the cost of borrowing and, thus, reduces investment in our small open economy. Because there has been no change in domestic saving, saving S now exceeds investment I, and some of our saving begins to flow abroad. Since $NX = S - I$, the reduction in I must also increase NX. Hence, reduced saving abroad leads to a trade surplus at home.

Figure 8-5 illustrates how a small open economy starting from balanced trade responds to a foreign fiscal expansion. Because the policy change is

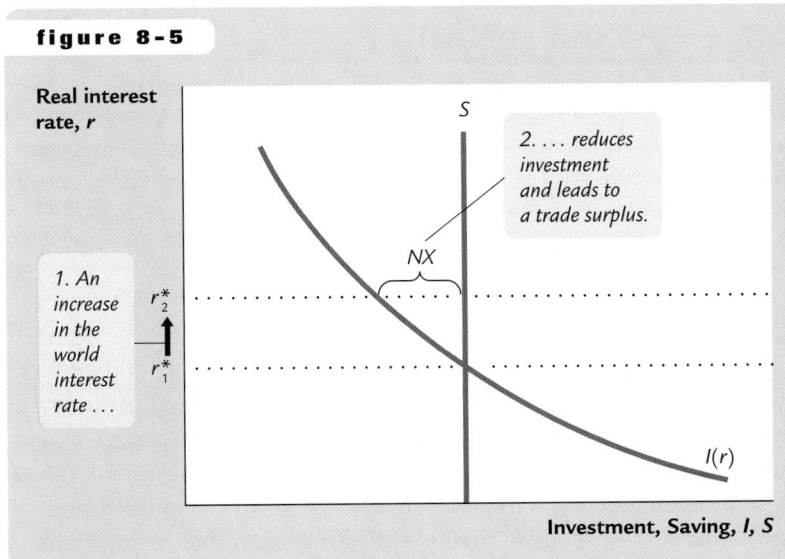

figure 8-5

Real interest rate, r

2. . . . reduces investment and leads to a trade surplus.

S

NX

1. An increase in the world interest rate . . .

r^*_2

r^*_1

$I(r)$

Investment, Saving, I, S

A Fiscal Expansion Abroad in a Small Open Economy A fiscal expansion in a foreign economy large enough to influence world saving and investment raises the world interest rate from r^*_1 to r^*_2. The higher world interest rate reduces investment in this small open economy, causing a trade surplus.

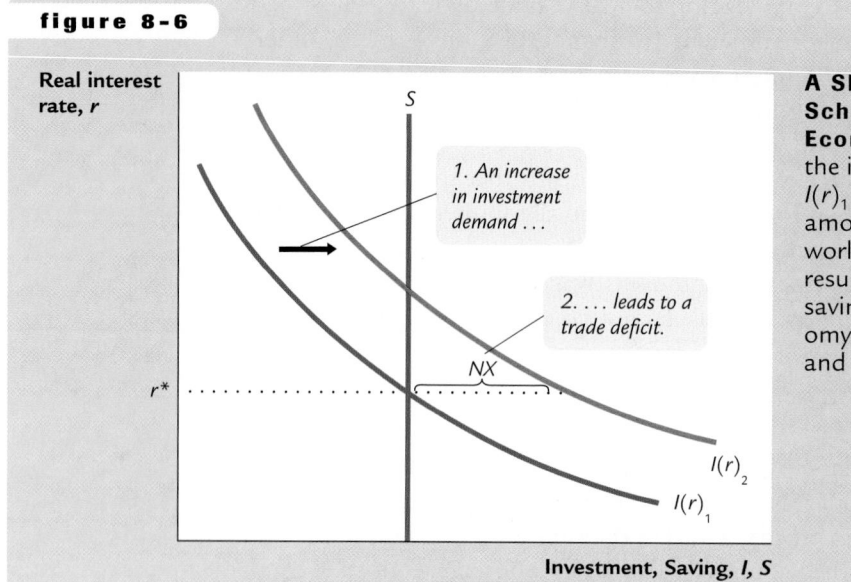

A Shift in the Investment Schedule in a Small Open Economy An outward shift in the investment schedule from $I(r)_1$ to $I(r)_2$ increases the amount of investment at the world interest rate r^*. As a result, investment now exceeds saving, which means the economy is borrowing from abroad and running a trade deficit.

occurring abroad, the domestic saving and investment schedules remain the same. The only change is an increase in the world interest rate from r_1^* to r_2^*. The trade balance is the difference between the saving and investment schedules; because saving exceeds investment at r_2^*, there is a trade surplus. *Hence, an increase in the world interest rate due to a fiscal expansion abroad leads to a trade surplus.*

Shifts in Investment Demand Consider what happens to our small open economy if its investment schedule shifts outward—that is, if the demand for investment goods at every interest rate increases. This shift would occur if, for example, the government changed the tax laws to encourage investment by providing an investment tax credit. Figure 8-6 illustrates the impact of a shift in the investment schedule. At a given world interest rate, investment is now higher. Because saving is unchanged, some investment must now be financed by borrowing from abroad, which means net foreign investment is negative. Put differently, because $NX = S - I$, the increase in I implies a decrease in NX. Hence, *an outward shift in the investment schedule causes a trade deficit.*

Evaluating Economic Policy

Our model of the open economy shows that the flow of goods and services measured by the trade balance is inextricably connected to the flow of funds for capital accumulation measured by net foreign investment. Net foreign investment is the difference between domestic saving and domestic investment. Thus, the impact of economic policies on the trade balance can always be found by examining their impact on domestic saving and domestic investment. Policies that increase investment or decrease saving tend to cause a trade deficit, and policies that decrease investment or increase saving tend to cause a trade surplus.

Our analysis of the open economy has been positive, not normative. That is, our analysis of how economic policies influence the international flows of capital and goods has not told us whether these policies are desirable. Evaluating economic policies and their impact on the open economy is a frequent topic of debate among economists and policymakers.

When a country runs a trade deficit, as the United States did throughout the 1980s and 1990s, policymakers must confront the question of whether the trade deficit represents a national problem. Most economists view a trade deficit not as a problem in itself, but perhaps as a symptom of a problem. The U.S. trade deficits of the 1980s and 1990s reflected a low saving rate. A low saving rate means that we are putting away less for the future. In a closed economy, low saving leads to low investment and a smaller future capital stock. In an open economy, low saving leads to a trade deficit and a growing foreign debt, which eventually must be repaid. In both cases, high current consumption leads to lower future consumption, implying that future generations bear the burden of low national saving.

Yet trade deficits are not always a reflection of economic malady. When poor rural economies develop into modern industrial economies, they sometimes finance their high levels of investment with foreign borrowing. In these cases, trade deficits are a sign of economic development. For example, South Korea ran large trade deficits throughout the 1970s, and it became one of the success stories of economic growth. The lesson is that one cannot judge economic performance from the trade balance alone. Instead, one must look at the underlying causes of the international flows.

8-3 | Exchange Rates

Having examined the international flows of capital and of goods and services, we now extend the analysis by considering the prices that apply to these transactions. The *exchange rate* between two countries is the price at which residents of those countries trade with each other. In this section we first examine precisely what the exchange rate measures, and we then discuss how exchange rates are determined.

Nominal and Real Exchange Rates

Economists distinguish between two exchange rates: the nominal exchange rate and the real exchange rate. Let's discuss each in turn and see how they are related.

The Nominal Exchange Rate The **nominal exchange rate** is the relative price of the currency of two countries. For example, if the exchange rate between the U.S. dollar and the Japanese yen is 120 yen per dollar, then you can exchange 1 dollar for 120 yen in world markets for foreign currency. A Japanese who wants to obtain dollars would pay 120 yen for each dollar he bought. An American who wants to obtain yen would get 120 yen for each dollar he paid. When people refer to "the exchange rate" between two countries, they usually mean the nominal exchange rate.

The Real Exchange Rate   The **real exchange rate** is the relative price of the goods of two countries. That is, the real exchange rate tells us the rate at which we can trade the goods of one country for the goods of another. The real exchange rate is sometimes called the *terms of trade*.

To see the relation between the real and nominal exchange rates, consider a single good produced in many countries: cars. Suppose an American car costs $10,000 and a similar Japanese car costs 2,400,000 yen. To compare the prices of the two cars, we must convert them into a common currency. If a dollar is worth 120 yen, then the American car costs 1,200,000 yen. Comparing the price of the American car (1,200,000 yen) and the price of the Japanese car (2,400,000 yen), we conclude that the American car costs one-half of what the Japanese car costs. In other words, at current prices, we can exchange 2 American cars for 1 Japanese car.

We can summarize our calculation above as follows:

$$\text{Real Exchange Rate} = \frac{(120 \text{ yen/dollar}) \times (10,000 \text{ dollars/American Car})}{(2,400,000 \text{ yen/Japanese Car})}$$

$$= 0.5 \frac{\text{Japanese Car}}{\text{American Car}}.$$

At these prices and this exchange rate, we obtain one-half of a Japanese car per American car. More generally, we can write this calculation as

$$\frac{\text{Real Exchange}}{\text{Rate}} = \frac{\text{Nominal Exchange Rate} \times \text{Price of Domestic Good}}{\text{Price of Foreign Good}}.$$

The rate at which we exchange foreign and domestic goods depends on the prices of the goods in the local currencies and on the rate at which the currencies are exchanged.

This calculation of the real exchange rate for a single good suggests how we should define the real exchange rate for a broader basket of goods. Let e be the nominal exchange rate (the number of yen per dollar), P be the price level in the United States (measured in dollars), and P^* be the price level in Japan (measured in yen). Then the real exchange rate ϵ is

$$
\begin{matrix}
\text{Real} & & \text{Nominal} & & \text{Ratio of} \\
\text{Exchange} & = & \text{Exchange} & \times & \text{Price} \\
\text{Rate} & & \text{Rate} & & \text{Levels} \\
\epsilon & = & e & \times & (P/P^*).
\end{matrix}
$$

The real exchange rate between two countries is computed from the nominal exchange rate and the price levels in the two countries. *If the real exchange rate is*

f y i

HOW NEWSPAPERS REPORT THE EXCHANGE RATE

You can find nominal exchange rates reported daily in many newspapers. Here's how they are reported in the *Wall Street Journal*:

Notice that each exchange rate is reported in two ways. On this Wednesday, 1 dollar bought 120.55 yen, and 1 yen bought 0.008295 dollars. We can say the exchange rate is 120.55 yen per dollar, or we can say the exchange rate is 0.008295 dollars per yen. Since 0.008295 equals 1/120.55, these two ways of expressing the exchange rate are equivalent. This book always expresses the exchange rate in units of foreign currency per dollar.

The exchange rate on this Wednesday of 120.55 yen per dollar was down from 130.18 yen per dollar on Tuesday. Such a fall in the exchange rate is called a *depreciation* of the dollar; a rise in the exchange rate is called an *appreciation*.

CURRENCY TRADING

EXCHANGE RATES

Wednesday, October 7, 1998

The New York foreign exchange selling rates below apply to trading amount banks in amounts of $1 million and more, as quoted at 4 p.m. Eastern time by Telerate and other sources. Retail transactions provide fewer units of foreign currency per dollar.

Country	U.S. $ equiv. Wed	U.S. $ equiv. Tue	Currency per U.S. $ Wed	Currency per U.S. $ Tue
Argentina (Peso)	1.0002	1.0001	.9998	.9999
Australia (Dollar)	.6234	.5920	1.6041	1.6892
Austria (Shilling)	.08812	0.8718	11.348	11.471
Bahrain (Dinar)	2.6525	2.6525	.3770	.3770
Belgium (Franc)	.02999	.02968	33.340	33.692
Brazil (Real)	.8442	.8457	1.1846	1.1824
Britain (Pound)	1.7051	1.6830	.5865	.5942
1-month forward	1.7025	1.6802	.5874	.5952
3-months forward	1.6976	1.6749	.5891	.5971
6-months forward	1.6899	1.6675	.5918	.5998
Canada (Dollar)	.6562	.6460	1.5240	1.5480
1-month forward	.6561	.6460	1.5241	1.5481
3-months forward	.6562	.6459	1.5240	1.5482
6-months forward	.6561	.6458	1.5241	1.5484
Chile (Peso)	.002163	.002151	462.35	464.95
China (Renminbi)	.1208	.1208	8.2780	8.2779
Colombia (Peso)	.0006295	.0006307	1588.64	1584.64
Czech. Rep. (Koruna)				
Commercial rate	.03401	.03330	29.400	30.027
Denmark (Krone)	.1627	.1614	6.1450	6.1950
Ecuador (Sucre)				
Floating rate	.0001582	.0001582	6323.00	6323.00
Finland (Markka)	.2035	.2015	4.9137	4.9621
France (Franc)	.1845	.1831	5.4196	5.4625
1-month forward	.1848	.1834	5.4104	5.4530
3-months forward	.1854	.1839	5.3942	5.4375
6-months forward	.1860	.1845	5.3759	5.4188
Germany (Mark)	.6186	.6143	1.6165	1.6279
1-month forward	.6197	.6154	1.6137	1.6250
3-months forward	.6215	.6171	1.6090	1.6205
6-months forward	.6236	.6192	1.6035	1.6150
Greece (Drachma)	.003569	.003530	280.17	283.32
Hong Kong (Dollar)	.1291	.1291	7.7470	7.7483
Hungary (Forint)	.004664	.004644	214.40	215.33
India (Rupee)	.02362	.02359	42.345	42.385
Indonesia (Rupiah)	.0001042	.0001015	9600.00	9850.00
Ireland (Punt)	1.5492	1.5333	.6455	.6522
Israel (Shekel)	.2433	.2466	4.1108	4.0553
Italy (Lira)	.0006258	.0006206	1598.00	1611.26
Japan (Yen)	.008295	.007682	120.55	130.18
1-month forward	.008334	.007717	119.99	129.59

Country	U.S. $ equiv. Wed	U.S. $ equiv. Tue	Currency per U.S. $ Wed	Currency per U.S. $ Tue
3-months forward	.008411	.007789	118.89	128.38
6-months forward	.008515	.007881	117.45	126.88
Jordan (Dinar)	1.4094	1.4094	.7095	.7095
Kuwait (Dinar)	3.3113	3.3014	.3020	.3029
Lebanon (Pound)	.0006626	.0006626	1509.25	1509.25
Malaysia (Ringgit-b)	.2631	.2631	3.8005	3.8003
Malta (Lira)	2.7211	2.7027	.3675	.3700
Mexico (Peso)				
Floating rate	.09770	.09804	10.235	10.200
Netherland (Guilder)	.5501	.5445	1.8177	1.8367
New Zealand (Dollar)	.5172	.4974	1.9335	2.0105
Norway (Krone)	.1359	.1341	7.3558	7.4568
Pakistan (Rupee)	.02022	.02022	49.450	49.450
Peru (new Sol)	.3317	.3314	3.0148	3.0178
Philippines (Peso)	.02289	.02284	43.680	43.790
Poland (Zloty)	.2834	.2816	3.5280	3.5510
Portugal (Escudo)	.006075	.005987	164.60	167.03
Russia (Ruble) (a)	.06329	.06329	15.800	15.800
Saudi Arabia (Riyal)	.2666	.2666	3.7509	3.7505
Singapore (Dollar)	.6105	.5983	1.6380	1.6715
Slovak Rep. (Koruna)	.02694	.02680	37.124	37.309
South Africa (Rand)	.1661	.1661	6.0200	6.0200
South Korea (Won)	.0007246	.0007199	1380.00	1389.00
Spain (Peseta)	.007281	.007222	137.34	138.46
Sweden (Krona)	.1287	.1252	7.7726	7.9876
Switzerland (Franc)	.7642	.7465	1.3085	1.3396
1-month forward	.7670	.7492	1.3037	1.3347
3-months forward	.7723	.7539	1.2949	1.3265
6-months forward	.7788	.7601	1.2840	1.3156
Taiwan (Dollar)	.02999	.02989	33.346	33.457
Thailand (Baht)	.02584	.02571	38.700	38.895
Turkey (Lira)	.00000366	.00000362	273500.00	275915.00
United Arab (Dirham)	.2723	.2723	3.6730	3.6730
Uruguay (New Peso)				
Financial	.09363	.09363	10.680	10.680
Venezuela (Bolivar)	.001753	.001751	570.38	571.00
	— — —			
SDR	1.4053	1.3837	.7116	.7227
ECU	1.2177	1.2088		

Special Drawing Rights (SDR) are based on exchange rates for the U.S., German, British, French, and Japanese currencies. Source: International Monetary Fund.

European Currency Unit (ECU) is based on a basket of community currencies.

a-Russian Central Bank rate. Trading band lowered on 8/17/98. b-Government rate.

The Wall Street Journal daily foreign exchange data for 1996 and 1997 may be purchased through the Readers' Reference Service (413) 592-3600.

Source: The Wall Street Journal, Thursday October 8, 1998. Reprinted by permission of the *Wall Street Journal,* © 1998 Dow Jones & Company, Inc. All Rights Reserved Worldwide.

high, foreign goods are relatively cheap, and domestic goods are relatively expensive. If the real exchange rate is low, foreign goods are relatively expensive, and domestic goods are relatively cheap.

The Real Exchange Rate and the Trade Balance

What macroeconomic influence does the real exchange rate exert? To answer this question, remember that the real exchange rate is nothing more than a relative price. Just as the relative price of hamburgers and pizza determines which you choose for lunch, the relative price of domestic and foreign goods affects the demand for these goods.

Suppose first that the real exchange rate is low. In this case, because domestic goods are relatively cheap, domestic residents will want to purchase few imported goods: they will buy Fords rather than Toyotas, drink Coors rather than Heineken, and vacation in Florida rather than Europe. For the same reason, foreigners will want to buy many of our goods. As a result of both of these actions, the quantity of our net exports demanded will be high.

"How about Nebraska? The dollar's still strong in Nebraska."

The opposite occurs if the real exchange rate is high. Because domestic goods are expensive relative to foreign goods, domestic residents will want to

figure 8-7

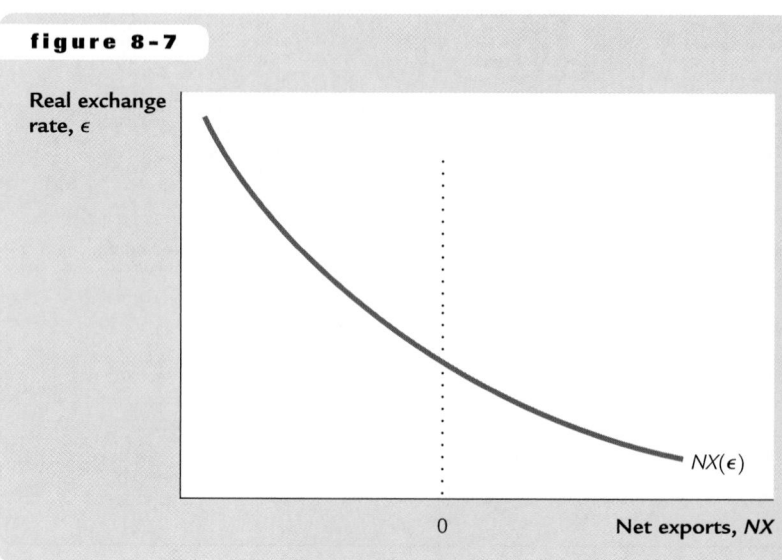

Real exchange rate, ϵ

$NX(\epsilon)$

0   Net exports, *NX*

Net Exports and the Real Exchange Rate The figure shows the relationship between the real exchange rate and net exports: the lower the real exchange rate, the less expensive are domestic goods relative to foreign goods, and thus the greater are our net exports. Note that a portion of the horizontal axis measures negative values of *NX*: because imports can exceed exports, net exports can be less than zero.

buy many imported goods, and foreigners will want to buy few of our goods. Therefore, the quantity of our net exports demanded will be low.

We write this relationship between the real exchange rate and net exports as

$$NX = NX(\epsilon).$$

This equation states that net exports are a function of the real exchange rate. Figure 8-7 illustrates this negative relationship between the trade balance and the real exchange rate.

The Determinants of the Real Exchange Rate

We now have all the pieces needed to construct a model that explains what factors determine the real exchange rate. In particular, we combine the relationship between net exports and the real exchange rate we just discussed with the model of the trade balance we developed earlier in the chapter. We can summarize the analysis as follows:

> ➤ The real exchange rate is related to net exports. When the real exchange rate is lower, domestic goods are less expensive relative to foreign goods, and net exports are greater.

> ➤ The trade balance (net exports) must equal net foreign investment, which in turn equals saving minus investment. Saving is fixed by the consumption function and fiscal policy; investment is fixed by the investment function and the world interest rate.

Figure 8-8 illustrates these two conditions. The line showing the relationship between net exports and the real exchange rate slopes downward because a low real exchange rate makes domestic goods relatively inexpensive. The line

figure 8-8

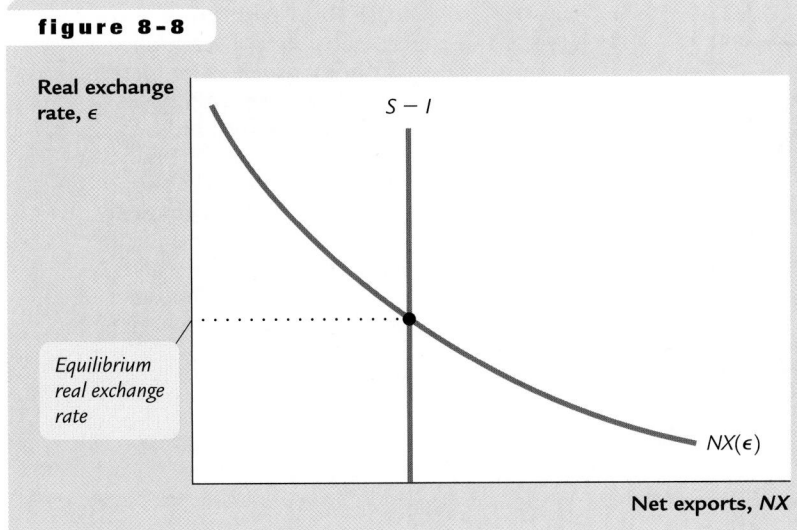

How the Real Exchange Rate Is Determined The real exchange rate is determined by the intersection of the vertical line representing saving minus investment and the downward-sloping net-exports schedule. At this intersection, the quantity of dollars supplied for net foreign investment equals the quantity of dollars demanded for the net export of goods and services.

representing the excess of saving over investment, $S - I$, is vertical because neither saving nor investment depends on the real exchange rate. The crossing of these two lines determines the equilibrium exchange rate.

Figure 8-8 looks like an ordinary supply-and-demand diagram. In fact, you can think of this diagram as representing the supply and demand for foreign-currency exchange. The vertical line, $S - I$, represents the excess of domestic saving over domestic investment, and thus the supply of dollars to be exchanged into foreign currency and invested abroad. The downward-sloping line, NX, represents the net demand for dollars coming from foreigners who want dollars to buy our goods. *At the equilibrium real exchange rate, the supply of dollars available for net foreign investment balances the demand for dollars by foreigners buying our net exports.*

How Policies Influence the Real Exchange Rate

We can use this model to show how the changes in economic policy we discussed earlier affect the real exchange rate.

Fiscal Policy at Home What happens to the real exchange rate if the government reduces national saving by increasing government purchases or cutting taxes? As we discussed earlier, this reduction in saving lowers $S - I$ and thus NX. That is, the reduction in saving causes a trade deficit.

Figure 8-9 shows how the equilibrium real exchange rate adjusts to ensure that NX falls. The change in policy shifts the vertical $S - I$ line to the left,

figure 8-9

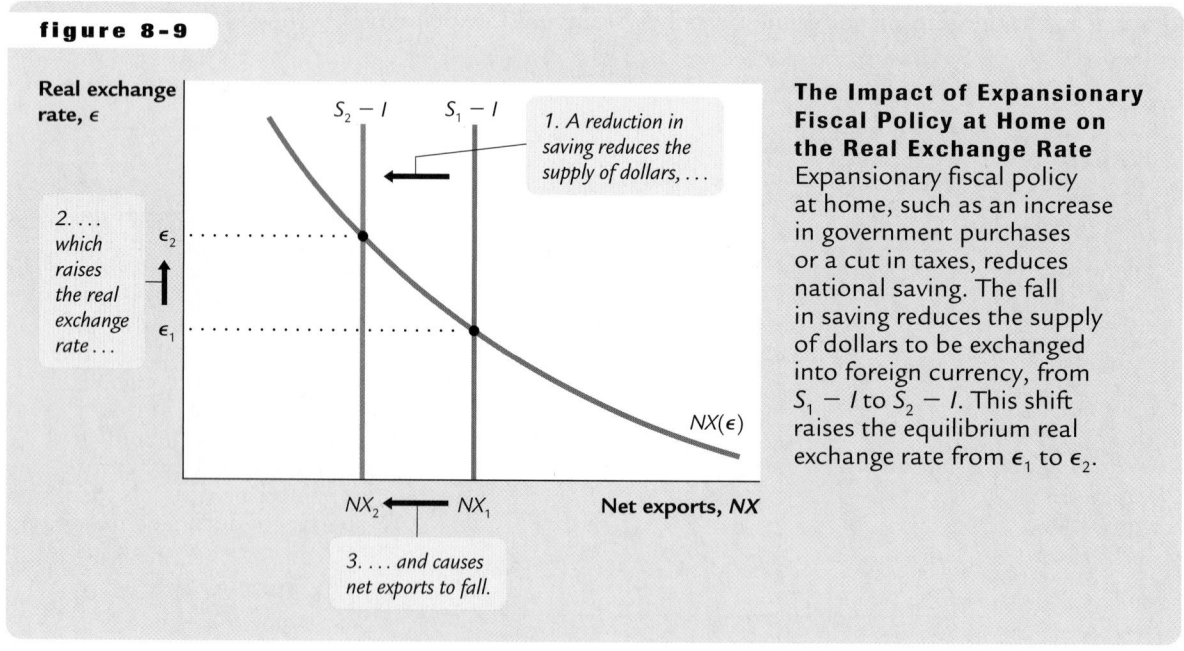

Real exchange rate, ϵ

$S_2 - I$ $S_1 - I$

1. A reduction in saving reduces the supply of dollars, . . .

2. . . . which raises the real exchange rate . . .

ϵ_2

ϵ_1

$NX(\epsilon)$

NX_2 ← NX_1 **Net exports, NX**

3. . . . and causes net exports to fall.

The Impact of Expansionary Fiscal Policy at Home on the Real Exchange Rate Expansionary fiscal policy at home, such as an increase in government purchases or a cut in taxes, reduces national saving. The fall in saving reduces the supply of dollars to be exchanged into foreign currency, from $S_1 - I$ to $S_2 - I$. This shift raises the equilibrium real exchange rate from ϵ_1 to ϵ_2.

lowering the supply of dollars to be invested abroad. The lower supply causes the equilibrium real exchange rate to rise from ϵ_1 to ϵ_2—that is, the dollar becomes more valuable. Because of the rise in the value of the dollar, domestic goods become more expensive relative to foreign goods, which causes exports to fall and imports to rise. The change in exports and the change in imports both act to reduce net exports.

Fiscal Policy Abroad What happens to the real exchange rate if foreign governments increase government purchases or cut taxes? This change in fiscal policy reduces world saving and raises the world interest rate. The increase in the world interest rate reduces domestic investment I, which raises $S - I$ and thus NX. That is, the increase in the world interest rate causes a trade surplus.

Figure 8-10 shows that this change in policy shifts the vertical $S - I$ line to the right, raising the supply of dollars to be invested abroad. The equilibrium real exchange rate falls. That is, the dollar becomes less valuable, and domestic goods become less expensive relative to foreign goods.

Shifts in Investment Demand What happens to the real exchange rate if investment demand at home increases, perhaps because Congress passes an investment tax credit? At the given world interest rate, the increase in investment demand leads to higher investment. A higher value of I means lower values of $S - I$ and NX. That is, the increase in investment demand causes a trade deficit.

Figure 8-11 shows that the increase in investment demand shifts the vertical $S - I$ line to the left, reducing the supply of dollars to be invested abroad. The

figure 8-10

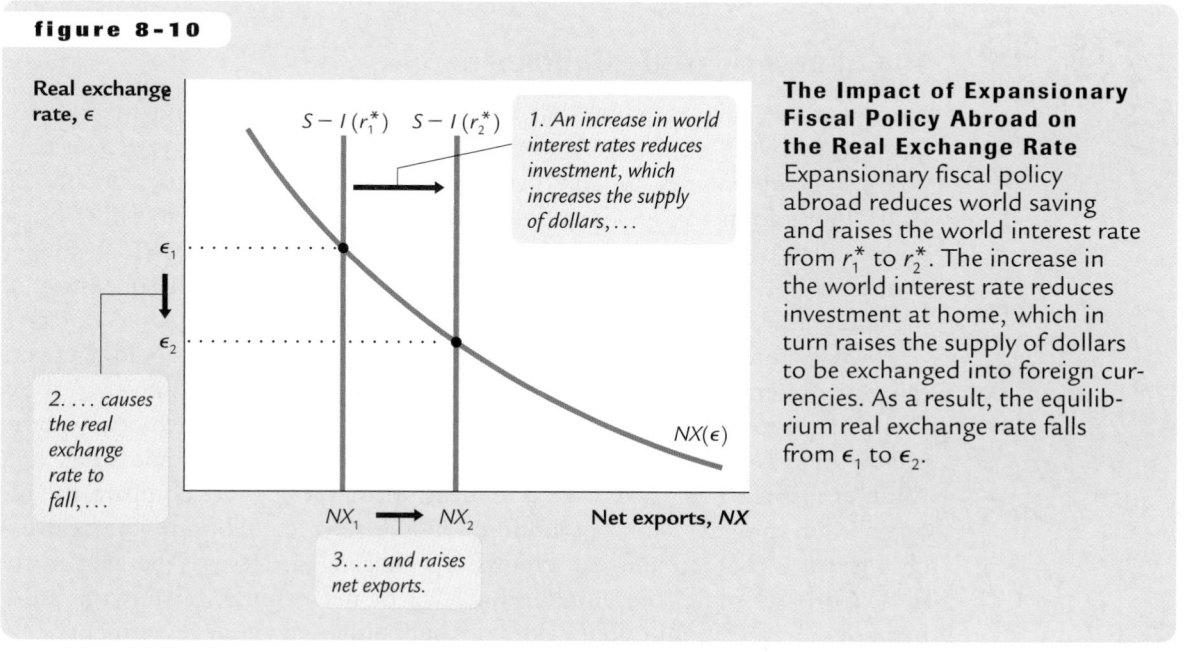

The Impact of Expansionary Fiscal Policy Abroad on the Real Exchange Rate Expansionary fiscal policy abroad reduces world saving and raises the world interest rate from r_1^* to r_2^*. The increase in the world interest rate reduces investment at home, which in turn raises the supply of dollars to be exchanged into foreign currencies. As a result, the equilibrium real exchange rate falls from ϵ_1 to ϵ_2.

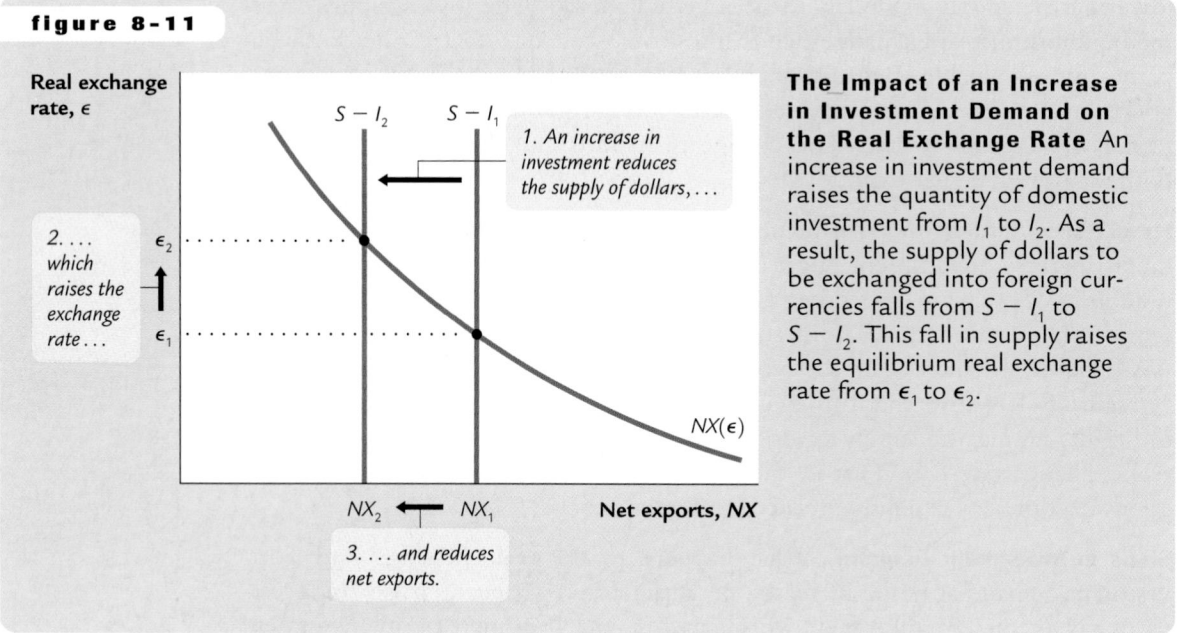

Real exchange rate, ε

1. An increase in investment reduces the supply of dollars, . . .

2. . . . which raises the exchange rate . . .

3. . . . and reduces net exports.

Net exports, NX

The Impact of an Increase in Investment Demand on the Real Exchange Rate An increase in investment demand raises the quantity of domestic investment from I_1 to I_2. As a result, the supply of dollars to be exchanged into foreign currencies falls from $S - I_1$ to $S - I_2$. This fall in supply raises the equilibrium real exchange rate from ϵ_1 to ϵ_2.

equilibrium real exchange rate rises. Hence, when the investment tax credit makes investing in the United States more attractive, it also increases the value of the U.S. dollars necessary to make these investments. When the dollar appreciates, domestic goods become more expensive relative to foreign goods, and net exports fall.

The Effects of Trade Policies

Now that we have a model that explains the trade balance and the real exchange rate, we have the tools to examine the macroeconomic effects of trade policies. Trade policies, broadly defined, are policies designed to influence directly the amount of goods and services exported or imported. Most often, trade policies take the form of protecting domestic industries from foreign competition—either by placing a tax on foreign imports (a tariff) or restricting the amount of goods and services that can be imported (a quota).

As an example of a protectionist trade policy, consider what would happen if the government prohibited the import of foreign cars. For any given real exchange rate, imports would now be lower, implying that net exports (exports minus imports) would be higher. Thus, the net-exports schedule shifts outward, as in Figure 8-12. To see the effects of the policy, we compare the old equilibrium and the new equilibrium. In the new equilibrium, the real exchange rate is higher, and net exports are unchanged. Despite the shift in the net-exports schedule, the equilibrium level of net exports remains the same, because the protectionist policy does not alter either saving or investment.

figure 8-12

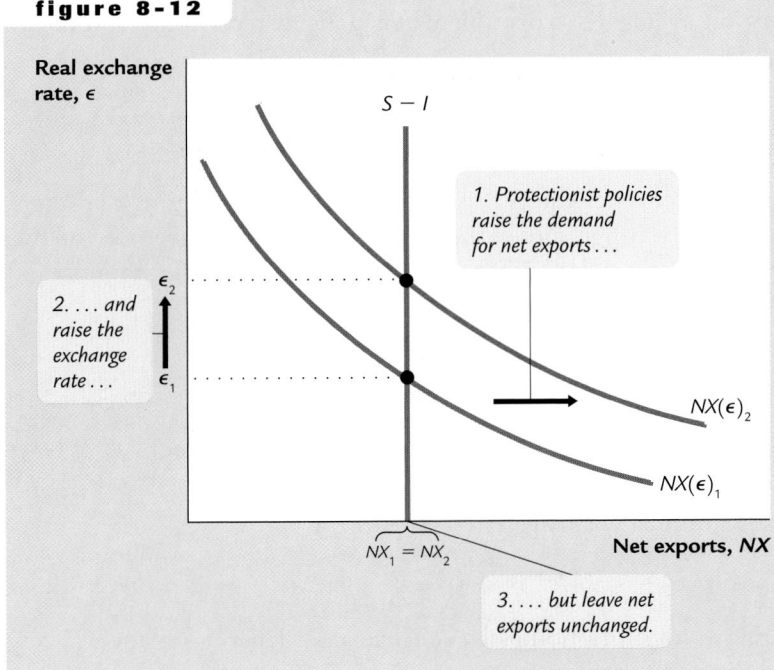

Real exchange rate, ε

S − I

1. Protectionist policies raise the demand for net exports . . .

ε₂

2. . . . and raise the exchange rate . . .

ε₁

NX(ε)₂

NX(ε)₁

NX₁ = NX₂

Net exports, NX

3. . . . but leave net exports unchanged.

The Impact of Protectionist Trade Policies on the Real Exchange Rate A protectionist trade policy, such as a ban on imported cars, shifts the net-exports schedule from $NX(\epsilon)_1$ to $NX(\epsilon)_2$, which raises the real exchange rate from ϵ_1 to ϵ_2. Notice that, despite the shift in the net-exports schedule, the equilibrium level of net exports is unchanged.

This analysis shows that protectionist trade policies do not affect the trade balance. This surprising conclusion is often overlooked in the popular debate over trade policies. Because a trade deficit reflects an excess of imports over exports, one might guess that reducing imports—such as by prohibiting the import of foreign cars—would reduce a trade deficit. Yet our model shows that protectionist policies lead only to an appreciation of the real exchange rate. The increase in the price of domestic goods relative to foreign goods tends to lower net exports by stimulating imports and depressing exports. Thus, the appreciation offsets the increase in net exports that is directly attributable to the trade restriction.

Although protectionist trade policies do not alter the trade balance, they do affect the amount of trade. As we have seen, because the real exchange rate appreciates, the goods and services we produce become more expensive relative to foreign goods and services. We therefore export less in the new equilibrium. Since net exports are unchanged, we must import less as well. (The appreciation of the exchange rate does stimulate imports to some extent, but this only partly offsets the decrease in imports due to the trade restriction.) Thus, protectionist policies reduce both the quantity of imports and the quantity of exports.

This fall in the total amount of trade is the reason economists almost always oppose protectionist policies. International trade benefits all countries by allowing each country to specialize in what it produces best and by providing each country with a greater variety of goods and services. Protectionist policies diminish these gains from trade. Although these policies benefit certain groups within society—for example, a ban on imported cars helps domestic car producers—society on average is worse off when policies reduce the amount of international trade.

The Determinants of the Nominal Exchange Rate

Having seen what determines the real exchange rate, we now turn our attention to the nominal exchange rate—the rate at which the currencies of two countries trade. Recall the relationship between the real and the nominal exchange rate:

$$
\begin{array}{ccc}
\text{Real} & \text{Nominal} & \text{Ratio of} \\
\text{Exchange} = \text{Exchange} \times & \text{Price} \\
\text{Rate} & \text{Rate} & \text{Levels} \\
\epsilon & = \quad e & \times \ (P/P^*).
\end{array}
$$

We can write the nominal exchange rate as

$$e = \epsilon \times (P^*/P).$$

This equation shows that the nominal exchange rate depends on the real exchange rate and the price levels in the two countries. Given the value of the real exchange rate, if the domestic price level P rises, then the nominal exchange rate e will fall: because a dollar is worth less, a dollar will buy fewer yen. On the other hand, if the Japanese price level P^* rises, then the nominal exchange rate will increase: because the yen is worth less, a dollar will buy more yen.

It is instructive to consider changes in exchange rates over time. The exchange rate equation can be written

% Change in e = % Change in ϵ + % Change in P^* − % Change in P.

The percentage change in ϵ is the change in the real exchange rate. The percentage change in P is the domestic inflation rate π, and the percentage change in P^* is the foreign country's inflation rate π^*. Thus, the percentage change in the nominal exchange rate is

$$
\begin{array}{ccc}
\text{\% Change in } e & = & \text{\% Change in } \epsilon & + & (\pi^* - \pi) \\
\text{Percentage Change in} & = & \text{Percentage Change in} & + & \text{Difference in} \\
\text{Nominal Exchange Rate} & & \text{Real Exchange Rate} & & \text{Inflation Rates.}
\end{array}
$$

This equation states that the percentage change in the nominal exchange rate between the currencies of two countries equals the percentage change in the real exchange rate plus the difference in their inflation rates. *If a country has a high rate of inflation relative to the United States, a dollar will buy an increasing amount of the foreign currency over time. If a country has a low rate of inflation relative to the United States, a dollar will buy a decreasing amount of the foreign currency over time.*

This analysis shows how monetary policy affects the nominal exchange rate. We know from Chapter 7 that high growth in the money supply leads to high inflation. Here, we have just seen that one consequence of high inflation is a depreciating currency: high π implies falling e. In other words, just as growth in the amount of money raises the price of goods measured in terms of money, it also tends to raise the price of foreign currencies measured in terms of the domestic currency.

CASE STUDY

Inflation and Nominal Exchange Rates

If we look at data on exchange rates and price levels of different countries, we quickly see the importance of inflation for explaining changes in the nominal exchange rate. The most dramatic examples come from periods of very high inflation. For example, the price level in Mexico rose by 2,300 percent from 1983 to 1988. Because of this inflation, the number of pesos a person could buy with a U.S. dollar rose from 144 in 1983 to 2,281 in 1988.

The same relationship holds true for countries with more moderate inflation. Figure 8-13 is a scatterplot showing the relationship between inflation and the

figure 8-13

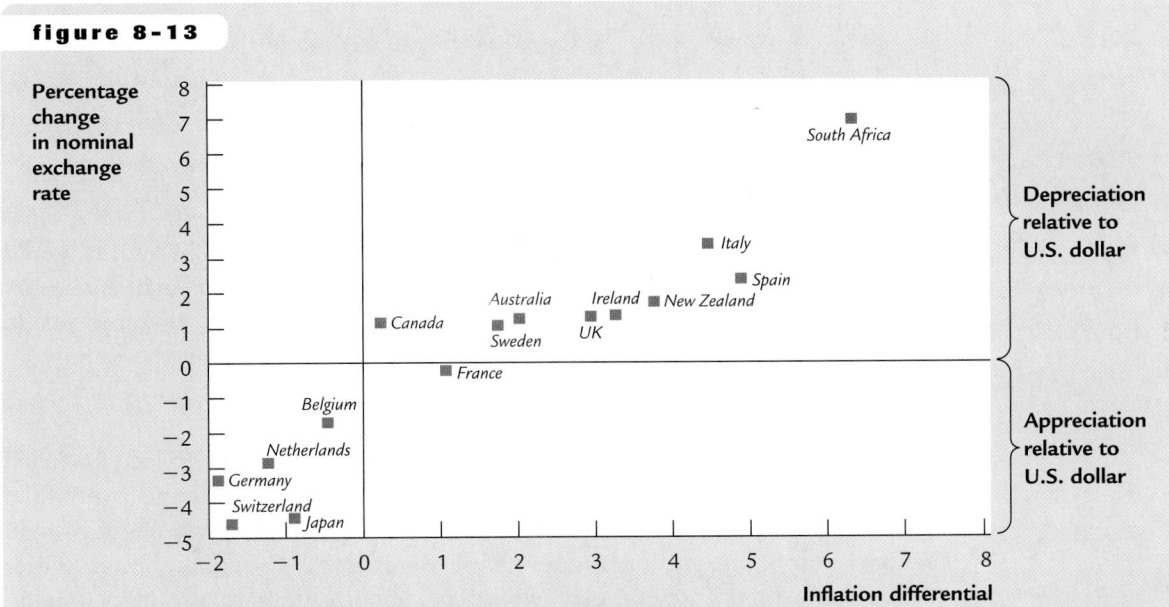

Inflation Differentials and the Exchange Rate This scatterplot shows the relationship between inflation and the nominal exchange rate. The horizontal axis shows the country's average inflation rate minus the U.S. average inflation rate over the period 1970–1996. The vertical axis is the average percentage change in the country's exchange rate (per U.S. dollar) over that period. This figure shows that countries with relatively high inflation tend to have depreciating currencies, and that countries with relatively low inflation tend to have appreciating currencies.

Source: International Financial Statistics.

exchange rate for 15 countries. On the horizontal axis is the difference between each country's average inflation rate and the average inflation rate of the United States ($\pi^* - \pi$). On the vertical axis is the average percentage change in the exchange rate between each country's currency and the U.S. dollar (% Change in e). The positive relationship between these two variables is clear in this figure. Countries with relatively high inflation tend to have depreciating currencies (you can buy more of them for your dollars over time), and countries with relatively low inflation tend to have appreciating currencies (you can buy less of them for your dollars over time).

As an example, consider the exchange rate between German marks and U.S. dollars. Both Germany and the United States have experienced inflation over the past twenty years, so both the mark and the dollar buy fewer goods than they once did. But, as Figure 8-13 shows, inflation in Germany has been lower than inflation in the United States. This means that the value of the mark has fallen less than the value of the dollar. Therefore, the number of German marks you can buy with a U.S. dollar has been falling over time.

The Special Case of Purchasing-Power Parity

A famous hypothesis in economics, called the *law of one price,* states that the same good cannot sell for different prices in different locations at the same time. If a bushel of wheat sold for less in New York than in Chicago, it would be profitable to buy wheat in New York and then sell it in Chicago. Astute arbitrageurs would take advantage of such an opportunity and, thereby, would increase the demand for wheat in New York and increase the supply in Chicago. This would drive the price up in New York and down in Chicago—thereby ensuring that prices are equalized in the two markets.

The law of one price applied to the international marketplace is called **purchasing-power parity.** It states that if international arbitrage is possible, then a dollar (or any other currency) must have the same purchasing power in every country. The argument goes as follows. If a dollar could buy more wheat domestically than abroad, there would be opportunities to profit by buying wheat domestically and selling it abroad. Profit-seeking arbitrageurs would drive up the domestic price of wheat relative to the foreign price. Similarly, if a dollar could buy more wheat abroad than domestically, the arbitrageurs would buy wheat abroad and sell it domestically, driving down the domestic price relative to the foreign price. Thus, profit-seeking by international arbitrageurs causes wheat prices to be the same in all countries.

We can interpret the doctrine of purchasing-power parity using our model of the real exchange rate. The quick action of these international arbitrageurs implies that net exports are highly sensitive to small movements in the real exchange rate. A small decrease in the price of domestic goods relative to foreign goods—that is, a small decrease in the real exchange rate—causes arbitrageurs to buy goods domestically and sell them abroad. Similarly, a small increase in the relative price of domestic goods causes arbitrageurs to import goods from abroad. Therefore, as in Figure 8-14, the net-exports schedule is very flat at the real exchange rate that equalizes purchasing power among countries: any small movement in the real exchange rate leads to a large change in net exports. This extreme sensitivity of net exports guarantees that the equilibrium real exchange rate is always close to the level ensuring purchasing-power parity.

Purchasing-power parity has two important implications. First, since the net-exports schedule is flat, changes in saving or investment do not influence the real or nominal exchange rate. Second, since the real exchange rate is fixed, all changes in the nominal exchange rate result from changes in price levels.

Is this doctrine of purchasing-power parity realistic? Most economists believe that, despite its appealing logic, purchasing-power parity does not provide a completely accurate description of the world. First, many goods are not easily traded. A haircut can be more expensive in Tokyo than in New York, yet there is no room for international arbitrage since it is impossible to transport haircuts. Second, even tradable goods are not always perfect substitutes. Some consumers prefer Toyotas, and others prefer Fords. Thus, the relative price of Toyotas and Fords can vary to some extent without leaving any profit opportunities. For these reasons, real exchange rates do in fact vary over time.

Although the doctrine of purchasing-power parity does not describe the world perfectly, it does provide a reason why movement in the real exchange rate will be limited. There is much validity to its underlying logic: the farther the real exchange rate drifts from the level predicted by purchasing-power

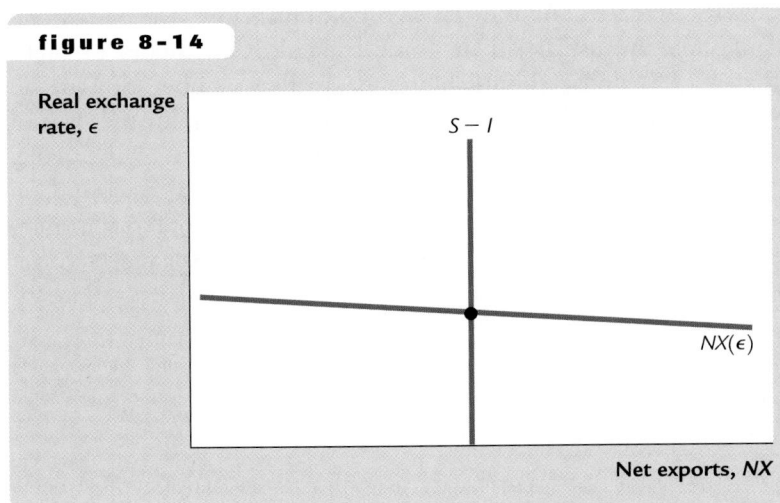

figure 8-14

Real exchange rate, ϵ

$S - I$

$NX(\epsilon)$

Net exports, NX

Purchasing-Power Parity
The law of one price applied to the international marketplace suggests that net exports are highly sensitive to small movements in the real exchange rate. This high sensitivity is reflected here with a very flat net-exports schedule.

parity, the greater the incentive for individuals to engage in international arbitrage in goods. Although we cannot rely on purchasing-power parity to eliminate all changes in the real exchange rate, this doctrine does provide a reason to expect that fluctuations in the real exchange rate will typically be small or temporary.[1]

CASE STUDY

The Big Mac Around the World

The doctrine of purchasing-power parity says that after we adjust for exchange rates, we should find that goods sell for the same price everywhere. Conversely, it says that the exchange rate between two currencies should depend on the price levels in the two countries.

To see how well this doctrine works, *The Economist,* an international newsmagazine, regularly collects data on the price of a good sold in many countries: the McDonald's Big Mac hamburger. According to purchasing-power parity, the price of a Big Mac should be closely related to the country's nominal exchange rate. The higher the price of a Big Mac in the local currency, the higher the exchange rate (measured in units of local currency per U.S. dollar) should be.

Table 8-1 presents the international prices in 1997, when a Big Mac sold for $2.42 in the United States. With these data we can use the doctrine of purchasing-power parity to predict nominal exchange rates. For example, because a Big Mac cost 294 yen in Japan, we would predict that the exchange rate between the dollar and the yen was 294/2.42, or 121, yen per dollar. At this exchange rate, a Big Mac would have cost the same in Japan and the United States.

Table 8-1 shows the predicted and actual exchange rates for 32 countries, ranked by the predicted exchange rate. You can see that the evidence on purchasing-power parity is mixed. As the last two columns show, the actual and predicted exchange rate are usually in the same ballpark. Our theory predicts, for instance, that a U.S. dollar should buy the greatest number of Russian rubles and fewest British pounds, and this turns out to be true. In the case of Japan, the predicted exchange rate of 121 yen per dollar is close to the actual exchange rate of 126. Yet the theory's predictions are far from exact and, in many cases, are off by 20 percent or more. Hence, although the theory of purchasing-power parity provides a rough guide to the level of exchange rates, it does not explain exchange rates completely.

---

[1] To learn more about purchasing-power parity, see Kenneth A. Froot and Kenneth Rogoff, "Perspectives on PPP and Long-Run Real Exchange Rates," in Gene M. Grossman and Kenneth Rogoff, eds., *Handbook of International Economics,* vol. 3 (Amsterdam: North-Holland, 1995).

table 8-1

Big Mac Prices and the Exchange Rate: An Application of Purchasing-Power Parity

Country	Currency	Price of a Big Mac	EXCHANGE RATE (PER U.S. DOLLAR)	
			Predicted	Actual
Russia	Ruble	11,000	4,545	5,739
Italy	Lira	4,600	1,901	1,683
South Korea	Won	2,300	950	894
Chile	Peso	1,200	496	417
Spain	Peseta	375	155	144
Japan	Yen	294	121	126
Hungary	Forint	271	112	178
Belgium	Franc	109	45.0	35.3
Taiwan	Dollar	68.0	28.1	27.6
Czech Republic	Crown	53.0	21.9	29.2
Thailand	Baht	46.7	19.3	26.1
Austria	Schilling	34.00	14.0	12.0
Sweden	Crown	26.0	10.7	7.72
Denmark	Crown	25.75	10.6	6.52
France	Franc	17.5	7.23	5.76
Mexico	Peso	14.9	6.16	7.90
Israel	Shekel	11.5	4.75	3.38
China	Yuan	9.70	4.01	8.33
South Africa	Rand	7.80	3.22	4.43
Switzerland	Franc	5.90	2.44	1.47
Netherlands	Guilder	5.45	2.25	1.92
Germany	Mark	4.90	2.02	1.71
Poland	Zloty	4.30	1.78	3.10
Malaysia	Ringgit	3.87	1.60	2.50
New Zealand	Dollar	3.25	1.34	1.45
Singapore	Dollar	3.00	1.24	1.44
Brazil	Real	2.97	1.23	1.06
Canada	Dollar	2.88	1.19	1.39
Argentina	Peso	2.50	1.03	1.00
Australia	Dollar	2.50	1.03	1.29
United States	Dollar	2.42	1.00	1.00
Britain	Pound	1.81	0.75	0.61

Note: The predicted exchange rate is the exchange rate that would make the price of a Big Mac in that country equal to its price in the United States.
Source: The Economist, April 12, 1997, 71.

8-4 | Conclusion: The United States as a Large Open Economy

In this chapter we have seen how a small open economy works. We have examined the determinants of the international flow of funds for capital accumulation and the international flow of goods and services. We have also examined the determinants of a country's real and nominal exchange rates. Our analysis shows how various policies—monetary policies, fiscal policies, and trade policies—affect the trade balance and the exchange rate.

The economy we have studied is "small" in the sense that its interest rate is fixed by world financial markets. That is, we have assumed that this economy does not affect the world interest rate, and that the economy can borrow and lend at the world interest rate in unlimited amounts. This assumption contrasts with the assumption we made when we studied the closed economy in Chapter 3. In the closed economy, the domestic interest rate equilibrates domestic saving and domestic investment, implying that policies that influence saving or investment alter the equilibrium interest rate.

Which of these analyses should we apply to an economy like the United States? The answer is a little of both. The United States is neither so large nor so isolated that it is immune to developments occurring abroad. The large trade deficits of the 1980s and 1990s show the importance of international financial markets for funding U.S. investment. Hence, the closed-economy analysis of Chapter 3 cannot by itself fully explain the impact of policies on the U.S. economy.

Yet the U.S. economy is not so small and so open that the analysis of this chapter applies perfectly either. First, the United States is large enough that it can influence world financial markets. For example, large U.S. budget deficits were often blamed for the high real interest rates that prevailed throughout the world in the 1980s. Second, capital may not be perfectly mobile across countries. If individuals prefer holding their wealth in domestic rather than foreign assets, funds for capital accumulation will not flow freely to equate interest rates in all countries. For these two reasons, we cannot directly apply our model of the small open economy to the United States.

When analyzing policy for a country like the United States, we need to combine the closed-economy logic of Chapter 3 and the small-open-economy logic of this chapter. The appendix to this chapter builds a model of an economy between these two extremes. In this intermediate case, there is international borrowing and lending, but the interest rate is not fixed by world financial markets. Instead, the more the economy borrows from abroad, the higher the interest rate it must offer foreign investors. The results, not surprisingly, are a mixture of the two polar cases we have already examined.

Consider, for example, a reduction in national saving due to a fiscal expansion. As in the closed economy, this policy raises the real interest rate and crowds out domestic investment. As in the small open economy, it also reduces net foreign investment, leading to a trade deficit and an appreciation of the exchange rate. Hence, although the model of the small open economy examined here does not precisely describe an economy like the United States, it does provide approximately the right answer to how policies affect the trade balance and the exchange rate.

Summary

1. Net exports are the difference between exports and imports. They are equal to the difference between what we produce and what we demand for consumption, investment, and government purchases.

2. Net foreign investment is the excess of domestic saving over domestic investment. The trade balance is the amount received for our net exports of goods and services. The national income accounts identity shows that net foreign investment always equals the trade balance.

3. The impact of any policy on the trade balance can be determined by examining its impact on saving and investment. Policies that raise saving or lower investment lead to a trade surplus, and policies that lower saving or raise investment lead to a trade deficit.

4. The nominal exchange rate is the rate at which people trade the currency of one country for the currency of another country. The real exchange rate is the rate at which people trade the goods produced by the two countries. The real exchange rate equals the nominal exchange rate multiplied by the ratio of the price levels in the two countries.

5. Because the real exchange rate is the price of domestic goods relative to foreign goods, an appreciation of the real exchange rate tends to reduce net exports. The equilibrium real exchange rate is the rate at which the quantity of net exports demanded equals net foreign investment.

6. The nominal exchange rate is determined by the real exchange rate and the price levels in the two countries. Other things equal, a high rate of inflation leads to a depreciating currency.

KEY CONCEPTS

Net exports	Balanced trade	Real exchange rate
Trade balance	Small open economy	Purchasing-power parity
Net foreign investment	World interest rate	
Trade surplus and trade deficit	Nominal exchange rate	

QUESTIONS FOR REVIEW

1. What are net foreign investment and the trade balance? Explain how they are related.

2. Define the nominal exchange rate and the real exchange rate.

3. If a small open economy cuts defense spending, what happens to saving, investment, the trade balance, the interest rate, and the exchange rate?

4. If a small open economy bans the import of Japanese VCRs, what happens to saving, investment, the trade balance, the interest rate, and the exchange rate?

5. If Germany has low inflation and Italy has high inflation, what will happen to the exchange rate between the German mark and the Italian lira?

PROBLEMS AND APPLICATIONS

1. Use the model of the small open economy to predict what would happen to the trade balance, the real exchange rate, and the nominal exchange rate in response to each of the following events.

   a. A fall in consumer confidence about the future induces consumers to spend less and save more.

   b. The introduction of a stylish line of Toyotas makes some consumers prefer foreign cars over domestic cars.

   c. The introduction of automatic teller machines reduces the demand for money.

2. Consider an economy described by the following equations:

$$Y = C + I + G + NX,$$
$$Y = 5,000,$$
$$G = 1,000,$$
$$T = 1,000,$$
$$C = 250 + 0.75(Y - T),$$
$$I = 1,000 - 50r,$$
$$NX = 500 - 500\epsilon,$$
$$r = r^* = 5.$$

   a. In this economy, solve for national saving, investment, the trade balance, and the equilibrium exchange rate.

   b. Suppose now that G rises to 1,250. Solve for national saving, investment, the trade balance, and the equilibrium exchange rate. Explain what you find.

   c. Now suppose that the world interest rate rises from 5 to 10 percent. (G is again 1,000). Solve for national saving, investment, the trade balance, and the equilibrium exchange rate. Explain what you find.

3. The country of Leverett is a small open economy. Suddenly, a change in world fashions makes the exports of Leverett unpopular.

   a. What happens in Leverett to saving, investment, net exports, the interest rate, and the exchange rate?

   b. The citizens of Leverett like to travel abroad. How will this change in the exchange rate affect them?

   c. The fiscal policymakers of Leverett want to adjust taxes to maintain the exchange rate at its previous level. What should they do? If they do this, what are the overall effects on saving, investment, net exports, and the interest rate?

4. What will happen to the trade balance and the real exchange rate of a small open economy when government purchases increase, such as during a war? Does your answer depend on whether this is a local war or a world war?

5. In 1995, President Clinton considered placing a 100-percent tariff on the import of Japanese luxury cars. Discuss the economics and politics of such a policy. In particular, how would the policy affect the U.S. trade deficit? How would it affect the exchange rate? Who would be hurt by such a policy? Who would benefit?

6. Suppose that some foreign countries begin to subsidize investment by instituting an investment tax credit.

   a. What happens to world investment demand as a function of the world interest rate?

   b. What happens to the world interest rate?

   c. What happens to investment in our small open economy?

   d. What happens to our trade balance?

   e. What happens to our real exchange rate?

7. "Traveling in Italy is much cheaper now than it was ten years ago," says a friend. "Ten years ago, a dollar bought 1,000 lire; this year, a dollar buys 1,500 lire."

   Is your friend right or wrong? Given that total inflation over this period was 25 percent in the United States and 100 percent in Italy, has it become more or less expensive to travel in Italy? Write your answer using a concrete example — like a cup of American coffee versus a cup of Italian espresso — that will convince your friend.

8. You read in a newspaper that the nominal interest rate is 12 percent per year in Canada and 8 percent per year in the United States. Suppose that the real interest rates are equalized in the two countries and that purchasing-power parity holds.

   a. Using the Fisher equation (discussed in Chapter 7), what can you infer about expected inflation in Canada and in the United States?

   b. What can you infer about the expected change in the exchange rate between the Canadian dollar and the U.S. dollar?

   c. A friend proposes a get-rich-quick scheme: borrow from a U.S. bank at 8 percent, deposit the money in a Canadian bank at 12 percent, and make a 4 percent profit. What's wrong with this scheme?

The Large Open Economy

When analyzing policy for a country like the United States, we need to combine the closed-economy logic of Chapter 3 and the small-open-economy logic of this chapter. This appendix presents a model of an economy between these two extremes, called the *large open economy*.

Net Foreign Investment

The key difference between the small and large open economies is the behavior of net foreign investment. In the model of the small open economy, capital flows freely into or out of the economy at a fixed world interest rate r^*. The model of the large open economy makes a different assumption about international capital flows. To understand that assumption, keep in mind that net foreign investment is the amount that domestic investors lend abroad minus the amount that foreign investors lend here.

Imagine that you are a domestic investor—such as the portfolio manager of a university endowment—deciding where to invest your funds. You could invest domestically (for example, by making loans to U.S. companies), or you could invest abroad (by making loans to foreign companies). Many factors may affect your decision, but surely one of them is the interest rate you can earn. The higher the interest rate you can earn domestically, the less attractive you would find foreign investment.

Investors abroad face a similar decision. They have a choice between investing in their home country or lending to someone in the United States. The higher the interest rate in the United States, the more willing foreigners are to lend to U.S. companies and to buy U.S. assets.

Thus, because of the behavior of both domestic and foreign investors, net foreign investment NFI is negatively related to the domestic real interest rate r. As the interest rate rises, less of our saving flows abroad, and more funds for capital accumulation flow in from other countries. We write this as

$$NFI = NFI(r).$$

This equation states that net foreign investment is a function of the domestic interest rate. Figure 8-15 illustrates this relationship. Notice that NFI can be either positive or negative, depending on whether the economy is a lender or borrower in world financial markets.

To see how this NFI function relates to our previous models, consider Figure 8-16. This figure shows two special cases: a vertical NFI function and a horizontal NFI function.

figure 8-15

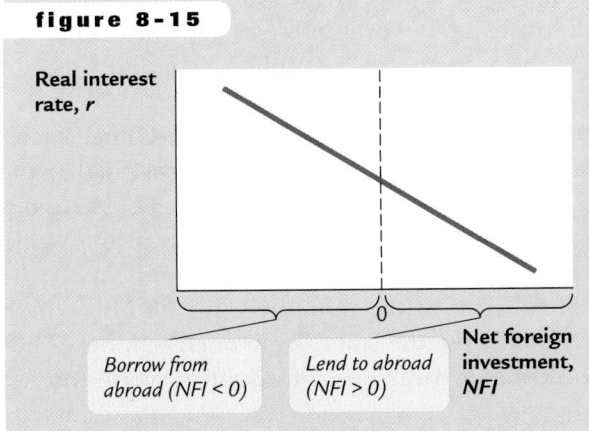

How Net Foreign Investment Depends on the Interest Rate A higher domestic interest rate discourages domestic investors from lending abroad and encourages foreign investors to lend here. Therefore, net foreign investment is negatively related to the interest rate.

The closed economy is the special case shown in panel (a) of Figure 8-16. In the closed economy, there is no international borrowing or lending, and the interest rate adjusts to equilibrate domestic saving and investment. This means that $NFI = 0$ at all interest rates. This situation would arise if investors here and abroad were unwilling to hold foreign assets, regardless of the return. It might also arise if the government prohibited its citizens from transacting in foreign financial markets, as some governments do.

The small open economy with perfect capital mobility is the special case shown in panel (b) of Figure 8-16. In this case, capital flows freely into and out of the country at the fixed world interest rate r^*. This situation would arise if

figure 8-16

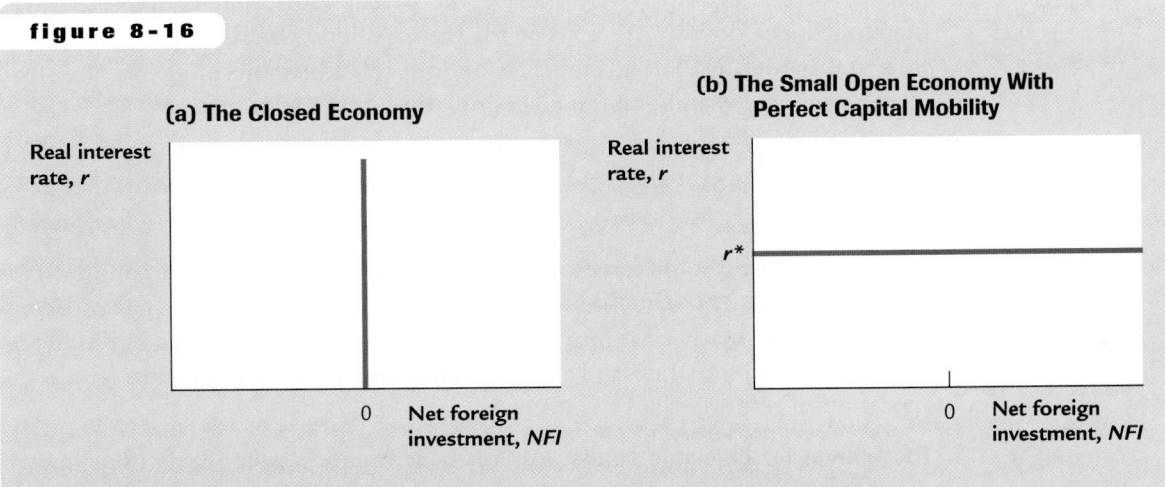

Two Special Cases In the closed economy, shown in panel (a), net foreign investment is zero for all interest rates. In the small open economy with perfect capital mobility, shown in panel (b), net foreign investment is perfectly elastic at the world interest rate r^*.

investors here and abroad bought whatever asset yielded the highest return, and if this economy were too small to affect the world interest rate. The economy's interest rate would be fixed at the interest rate prevailing in world financial markets.

Why isn't the interest rate of a large open economy like the United States fixed by the world interest rate? There are two reasons. The first is that the United States is large enough to influence world financial markets. The more the United States lends abroad, the greater is the supply of loans in the world economy, and the lower interest rates become around the world. The more the United States borrows from abroad (that is, the more negative *NFI* becomes), the higher are world interest rates. We use the label "large open economy" because this model applies to an economy large enough to affect world interest rates.

There is, however, a second reason that the interest rate in an economy may not be fixed by the world interest rate: capital may not be perfectly mobile. That is, investors here and abroad prefer holding their wealth in domestic rather than foreign assets. Such a preference for domestic assets could arise because of imperfect information about foreign assets or because of government impediments to international borrowing and lending. In either case, funds for capital accumulation will not flow freely to equalize interest rates in all countries. Instead, net foreign investment will depend on domestic interest rates relative to foreign interest rates. U.S. investors will lend abroad only if U.S. interest rates are comparatively low, and foreign investors will lend in the United States only if U.S. interest rates are comparatively high. The large-open-economy model, therefore, may apply even to a small economy if capital does not flow freely into and out of the economy.

Hence, either because the large open economy affects world interest rates, or because capital is imperfectly mobile, or perhaps for both reasons, the *NFI* function slopes downward. Except for this new downward-sloping *NFI* function, the model of the large open economy resembles the model of the small open economy. We put all the pieces together in the next section.

The Model

To understand how the large open economy works, we need to consider two key markets: the market for loanable funds (where the interest rate is determined) and the market for foreign exchange (where the exchange rate is determined). The interest rate and the exchange rate are two prices that guide the allocation of resources.

The Market for Loanable Funds An open economy's saving S is used in two ways: to finance domestic investment I and to finance net foreign investment NFI. We can write

$$S = I + NFI.$$

Consider how these three variables are determined. National saving is fixed by the level of output, fiscal policy, and the consumption function. Investment

figure 8-17

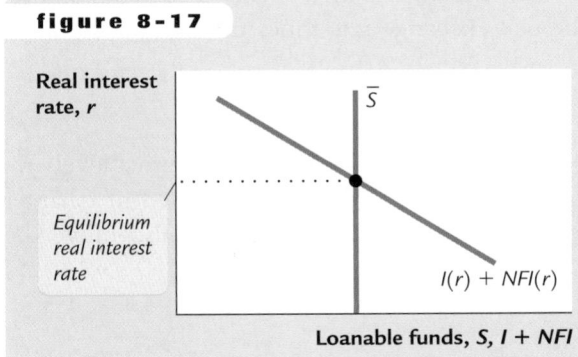

Real interest rate, r

$\bar{S}$

Equilibrium real interest rate

$I(r) + NFI(r)$

Loanable funds, S, I + NFI

The Market for Loanable Funds in the Large Open Economy At the equilibrium interest rate, the supply of loanable funds from saving S balances the demand for loanable funds from domestic investment I and net foreign investment NFI.

and net foreign investment both depend on the domestic real interest rate. We can write

$$\bar{S} = I(r) + NFI(r).$$

Figure 8-17 shows the market for loanable funds. The supply of loanable funds is national saving. The demand for loanable funds is the sum of the demand for domestic investment and the demand for net foreign investment. The interest rate adjusts to equilibrate supply and demand.

The Market for Foreign Exchange   Next, consider the relationship between net foreign investment and the trade balance. The national income accounts identity tells us

$$NX = S - I.$$

Because NX is a function of the real exchange rate, and because $NFI = S - I$, we can write

$$NX(\epsilon) = NFI.$$

Figure 8-18 shows the equilibrium in the market for foreign exchange. Once again, the real exchange rate is the price that equilibrates the trade balance and net foreign investment.

figure 8-18

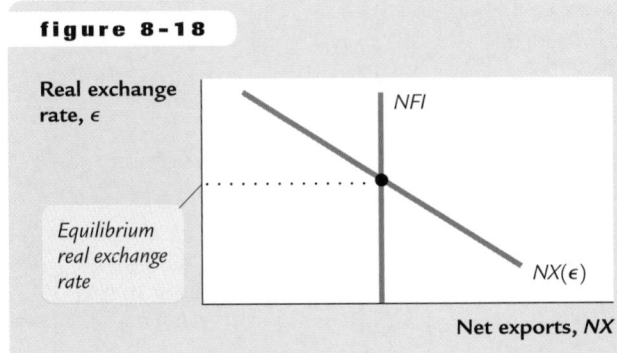

Real exchange rate, ϵ

NFI

Equilibrium real exchange rate

$NX(\epsilon)$

Net exports, NX

The Market for Foreign Currency Exchange in the Large Open Economy At the equilibrium exchange rate, the supply of dollars from net foreign investment, NFI, balances the demand for dollars from our net exports of goods and services, NX.

The last variable we should consider is the nominal exchange rate. As before, the nominal exchange rate is the real exchange rate times the ratio of the price levels:

$$e = \epsilon \times (P^*/P).$$

The real exchange rate is determined as in Figure 8-18, and the price levels are determined by monetary policies here and abroad, as we discussed in Chapter 7. Forces that move the real exchange rate or the price levels also move the nominal exchange rate.

Policies in the Large Open Economy

We can now consider how economic policies influence the large open economy. Figure 8-19 shows the three diagrams we need for the analysis. Panel (a) shows the equilibrium in the market for loanable funds; panel (b) shows the relationship between the equilibrium interest rate and net foreign investment; and panel (c) shows the equilibrium in the market for foreign exchange.

Fiscal Policy at Home Consider the effects of expansionary fiscal policy—an increase in government purchases or a decrease in taxes. Figure 8-20 shows

figure 8-19

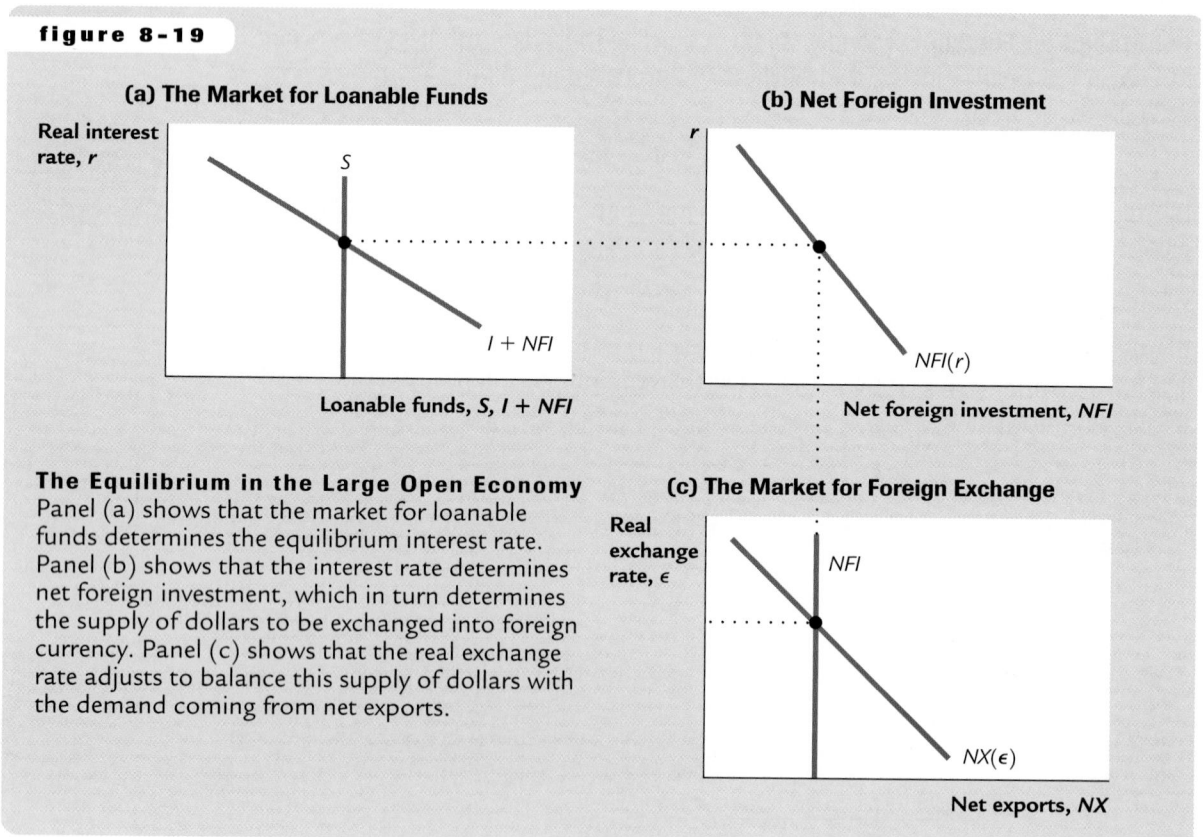

(a) The Market for Loanable Funds

(b) Net Foreign Investment

The Equilibrium in the Large Open Economy
Panel (a) shows that the market for loanable funds determines the equilibrium interest rate. Panel (b) shows that the interest rate determines net foreign investment, which in turn determines the supply of dollars to be exchanged into foreign currency. Panel (c) shows that the real exchange rate adjusts to balance this supply of dollars with the demand coming from net exports.

(c) The Market for Foreign Exchange

figure 8-20

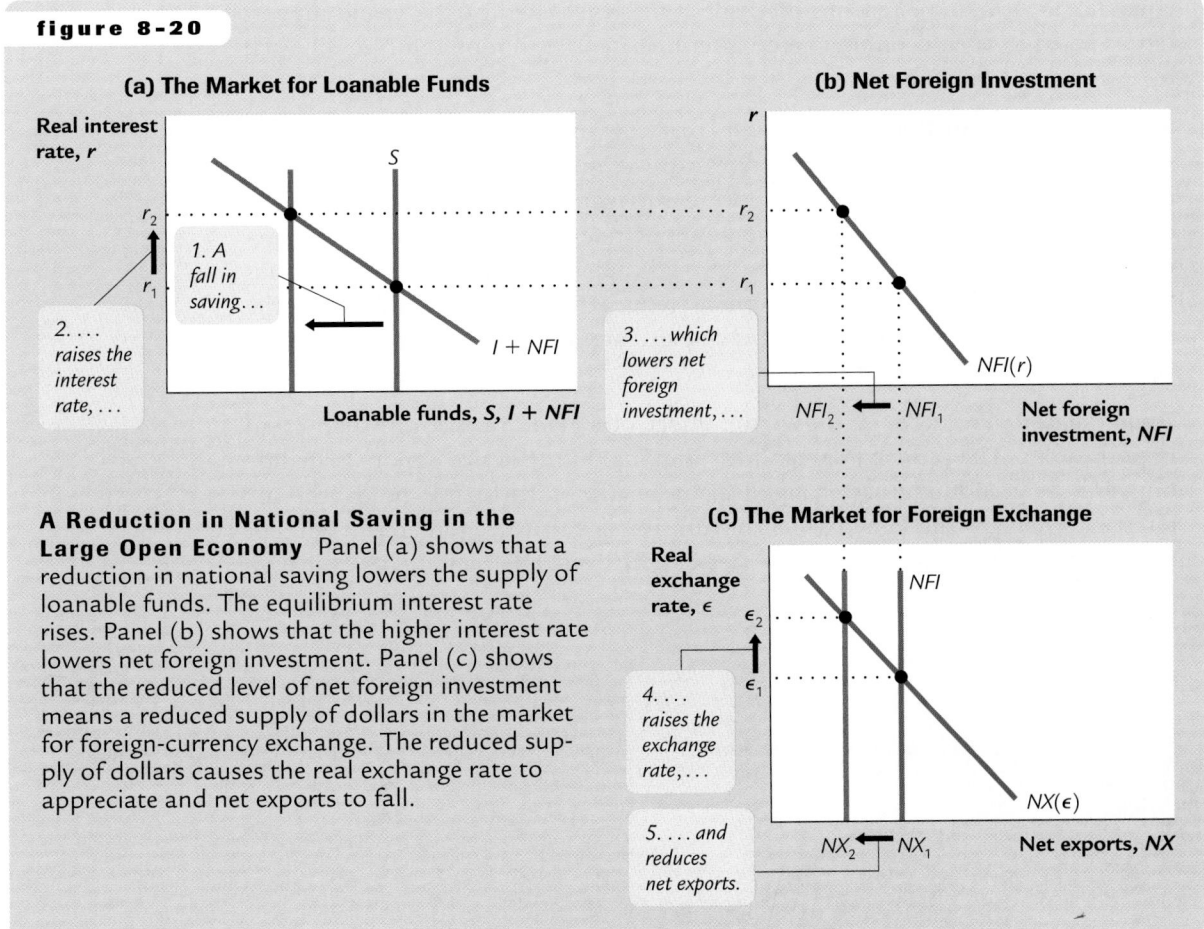

(a) The Market for Loanable Funds

Real interest rate, *r*

S

r_2

1. A fall in saving...

2. ... raises the interest rate, ...

I + NFI

Loanable funds, *S, I + NFI*

(b) Net Foreign Investment

r

r_2

r_1

3. ... which lowers net foreign investment, ...

NFI(r)

NFI_2 NFI_1

Net foreign investment, *NFI*

(c) The Market for Foreign Exchange

Real exchange rate, ϵ

NFI

ϵ_2

ϵ_1

4. ... raises the exchange rate, ...

5. ... and reduces net exports.

NX_2 NX_1

NX(ϵ)

Net exports, *NX*

A Reduction in National Saving in the Large Open Economy Panel (a) shows that a reduction in national saving lowers the supply of loanable funds. The equilibrium interest rate rises. Panel (b) shows that the higher interest rate lowers net foreign investment. Panel (c) shows that the reduced level of net foreign investment means a reduced supply of dollars in the market for foreign-currency exchange. The reduced supply of dollars causes the real exchange rate to appreciate and net exports to fall.

what happens. The policy reduces national saving *S*, thereby reducing the supply of loanable funds and raising the equilibrium interest rate *r*. The higher interest rate reduces both domestic investment *I* and net foreign investment *NFI*. The fall in net foreign investment reduces the supply of dollars to be exchanged into foreign currency. The exchange rate appreciates, and net exports fall.

Note that the impact of fiscal policy in this model combines its impact in the closed economy and its impact in the small open economy. As in the closed economy, a fiscal expansion in a large open economy raises the interest rate and crowds out investment. As in the small open economy, a fiscal expansion causes a trade deficit and an appreciation in the exchange rate.

One way to see how the three types of economy are related is to consider the identity

$$S = I + NX.$$

In all three cases, expansionary fiscal policy reduces national saving *S*. In the closed economy, the fall in *S* coincides with an equal fall in *I*, and *NX* stays constant at zero. In the small open economy, the fall in *S* coincides with an equal fall in *NX,* and *I* remains constant at the level fixed by the world interest rate. The large open economy is the intermediate case: both *I* and *NX* fall, each by less than the fall in *S.*

Shifts in Investment Demand Suppose that the investment demand schedule shifts outward, perhaps because Congress passes an investment tax credit. Figure 8-21 shows the effect. The demand for loanable funds rises, raising the equilibrium interest rate. The higher interest rate reduces net foreign investment: Americans make fewer loans abroad, and foreigners make more loans here. The fall in net foreign investment reduces the supply of dollars in the market for foreign exchange. The exchange rate appreciates, and net exports fall.

Trade Policies Figure 8-22 shows the effect of a trade restriction, such as an import quota. The reduced demand for imports shifts the net-exports schedule outward. Since nothing has changed in the market for loanable funds, the interest rate remains the same, which in turn implies that net foreign investment remains the same. The shift in the net-exports schedule causes the exchange

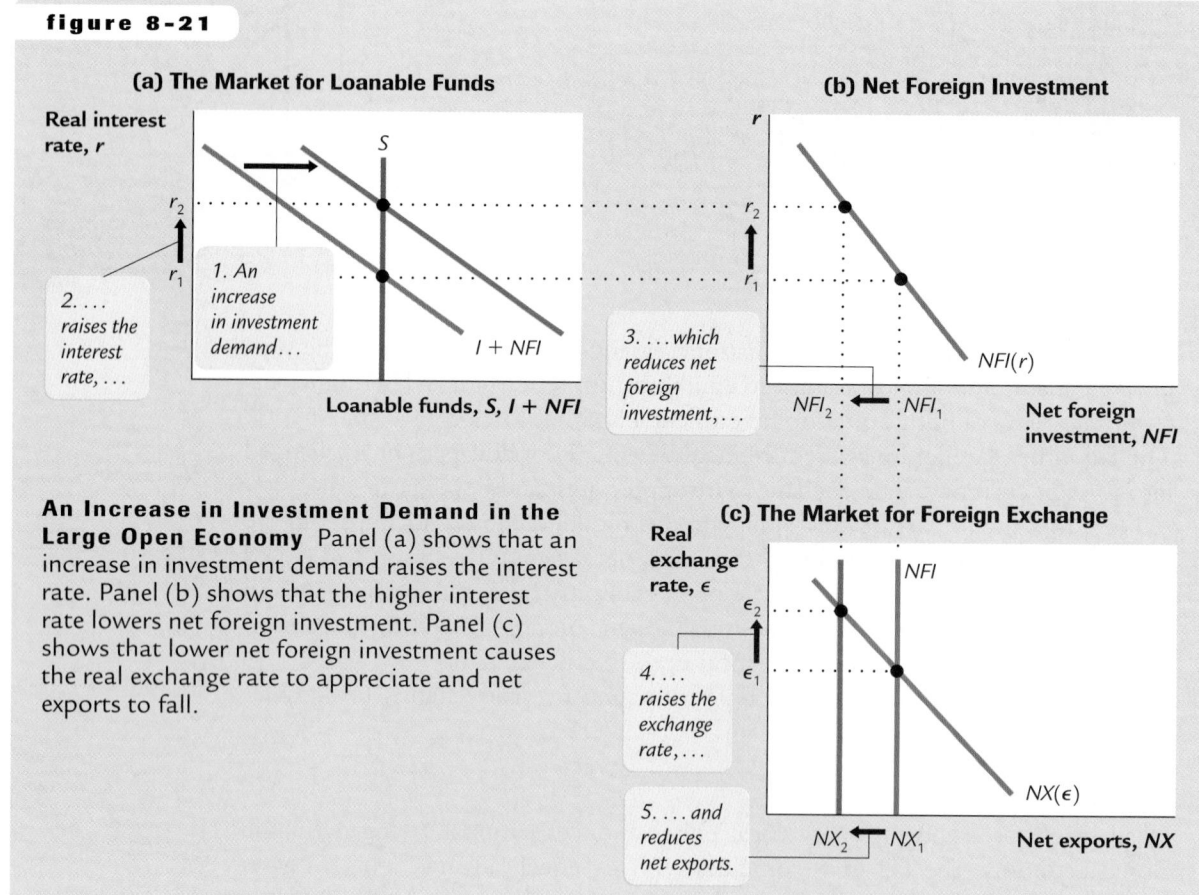

figure 8-21

(a) The Market for Loanable Funds

(b) Net Foreign Investment

(c) The Market for Foreign Exchange

An Increase in Investment Demand in the Large Open Economy Panel (a) shows that an increase in investment demand raises the interest rate. Panel (b) shows that the higher interest rate lowers net foreign investment. Panel (c) shows that lower net foreign investment causes the real exchange rate to appreciate and net exports to fall.

figure 8-22

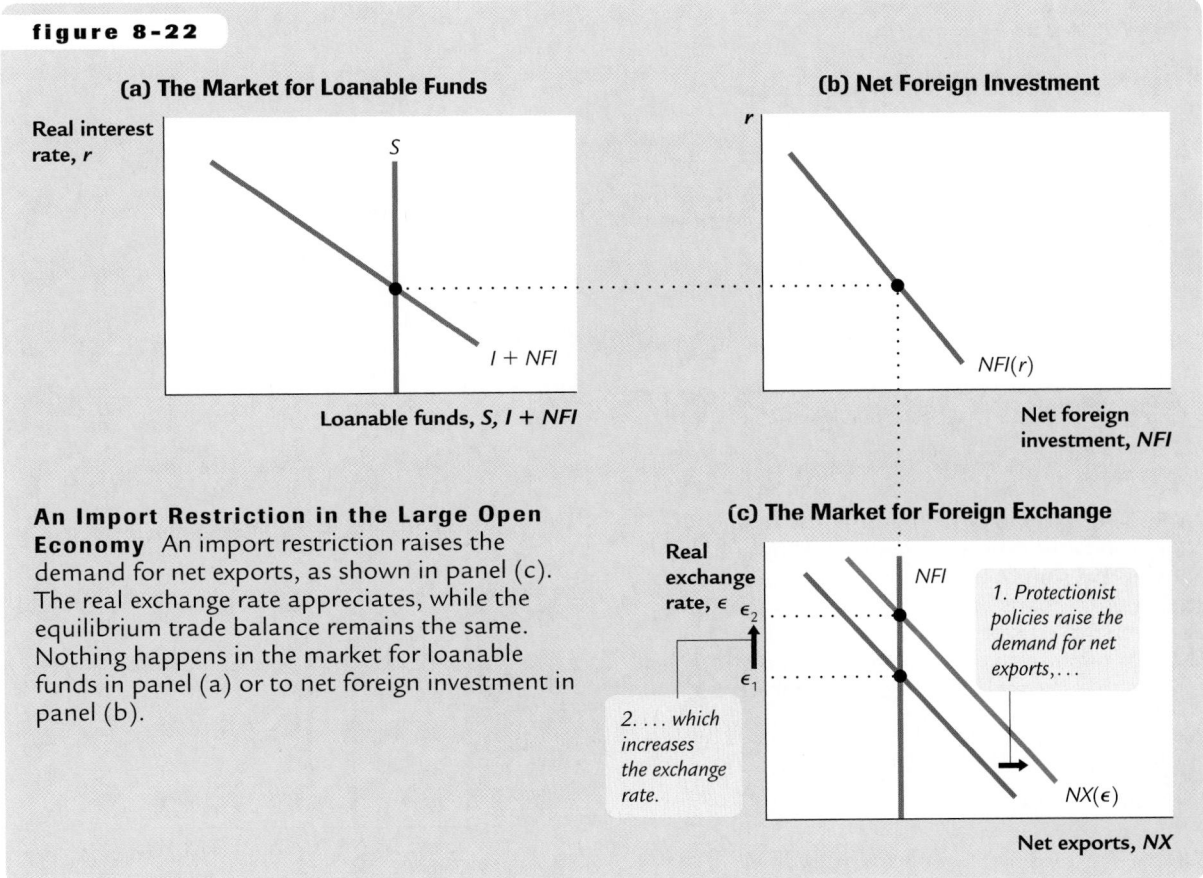

(a) The Market for Loanable Funds

Real interest rate, r

S

$I + NFI$

Loanable funds, $S, I + NFI$

(b) Net Foreign Investment

r

$NFI(r)$

Net foreign investment, NFI

An Import Restriction in the Large Open Economy An import restriction raises the demand for net exports, as shown in panel (c). The real exchange rate appreciates, while the equilibrium trade balance remains the same. Nothing happens in the market for loanable funds in panel (a) or to net foreign investment in panel (b).

(c) The Market for Foreign Exchange

Real exchange rate, ϵ

NFI

ϵ_2

ϵ_1

1. Protectionist policies raise the demand for net exports, . . .

2. . . . which increases the exchange rate.

$NX(\epsilon)$

Net exports, NX

rate to appreciate. The rise in the exchange rate makes U.S. goods expensive relative to foreign goods, which depresses exports and stimulates imports. In the end, the trade restriction does not affect the trade balance.

Shifts in Net Foreign Investment There are various reasons that the *NFI* schedule might shift. One reason is fiscal policy abroad. For example, suppose that Germany pursues a fiscal policy that raises German saving. This policy reduces the German interest rate. The lower German interest rate discourages American investors from lending in Germany and encourages German investors to lend in the United States. For any given U.S. interest rate, U.S. net foreign investment falls.

Another reason the *NFI* schedule might shift is political instability abroad. Suppose that a war or revolution breaks out in another country. Investors around the world will try to withdraw their assets from that country and seek a "safe haven" in a stable country such as the United States. The result is a reduction in U.S. net foreign investment.

Figure 8-23 shows the impact of a shift in the *NFI* schedule. The reduced demand for loanable funds lowers the equilibrium interest rate. The lower

figure 8-23

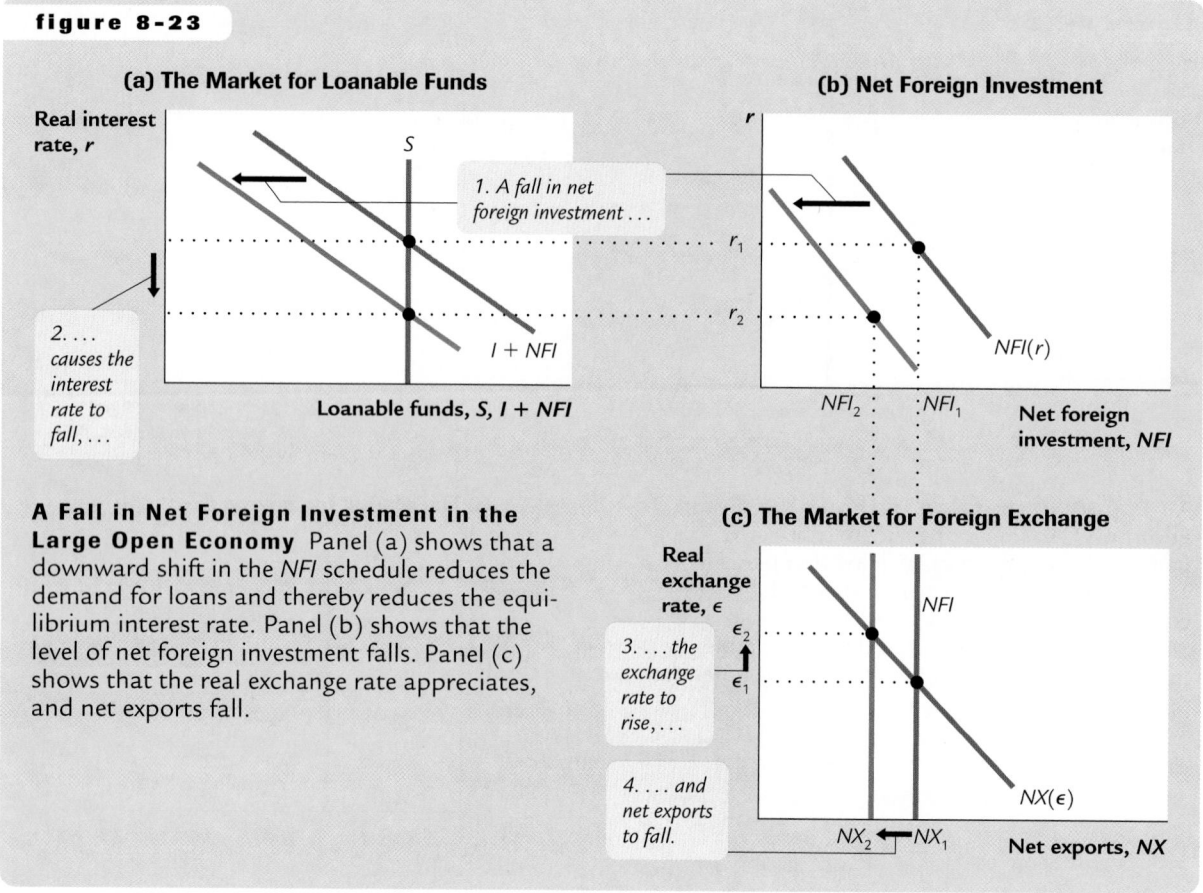

(a) The Market for Loanable Funds

Real interest rate, r

S

1. A fall in net foreign investment . . .

r_1

r_2

2. . . . causes the interest rate to fall, . . .

$I + NFI$

Loanable funds, S, $I + NFI$

(b) Net Foreign Investment

r

r_1

r_2

$NFI(r)$

NFI_2 NFI_1 Net foreign investment, NFI

A Fall in Net Foreign Investment in the Large Open Economy Panel (a) shows that a downward shift in the *NFI* schedule reduces the demand for loans and thereby reduces the equilibrium interest rate. Panel (b) shows that the level of net foreign investment falls. Panel (c) shows that the real exchange rate appreciates, and net exports fall.

(c) The Market for Foreign Exchange

Real exchange rate, ϵ

NFI

ϵ_2

3. . . . the exchange rate to rise, . . .

ϵ_1

4. . . . and net exports to fall.

$NX(\epsilon)$

NX_2 NX_1 Net exports, NX

interest rate tends to raise net foreign investment, but this only partly mitigates the shift in the *NFI* schedule. The reduced level of net foreign investment reduces the supply of dollars in the market for foreign exchange. The exchange rate appreciates, and net exports fall.

Conclusion

How different are large and small open economies? Certainly, policies affect the interest rate in a large open economy, unlike in a small open economy. But, in other ways, the two models yield similar conclusions. In both large and small open economies, policies that raise saving or lower investment lead to trade surpluses. Similarly, policies that lower saving or raise investment lead to trade deficits. In both economies, protectionist trade policies cause the exchange rate to appreciate and do not influence the trade balance. Because the results are so similar, for most questions one can use the simpler model of the small open economy, even if the economy being examined is not really small.

MORE PROBLEMS AND APPLICATIONS

1. If a war broke out abroad, it would affect the U.S. economy in many ways. Use the model of the large open economy to examine each of the following effects of such a war. What happens in the United States to saving, investment, the trade balance, the interest rate, and the exchange rate? (To keep things simple, consider each of the following effects separately.)

   a. The U.S. government, fearing it may need to enter the war, increases its purchases of military equipment.

   b. Other countries raise their demand for high-tech weapons, a major export of the United States.

   c. The war makes U.S. firms uncertain about the future, and the firms delay some investment projects.

   d. The war makes U.S. consumers uncertain about the future, and the consumers save more in response.

   e. Americans become apprehensive about traveling abroad, so more of them spend their vacations in the United States.

   f. Foreign investors seek a safe haven for their portfolios in the United States.

2. On September 21, 1995, "House Speaker Newt Gingrich threatened to send the United States into default on its debt for the first time in the nation's history, to force the Clinton Administration to balance the budget on Republican terms" (*New York Times,* September 22, 1995, A1). That same day, the interest rate on 30-year U.S. government bonds rose from 6.46 to 6.55 percent, and the dollar fell in value from 102.7 to 99.0 yen. Use the model of the large open economy to explain this event.

part THREE

The Economy in the Short Run

In Part Two we developed theories to explain how the economy behaves in the long run. Those theories were based on the classical dichotomy—the premise that real variables such as output and employment are not affected by what happens to nominal variables such as the money supply and the price level. Although classical theories are useful for explaining long-run trends, including the economic growth we observe from decade to decade, most economists believe that the classical dichotomy does not hold in the short run and, therefore, that classical theories cannot explain year-to-year fluctuations in output and employment. Here, in Part Three, we see how economists explain these short-run fluctuations.

Chapter 9 begins our analysis by discussing the key differences between the long run and the short run and by introducing the model of aggregate supply and aggregate demand. With this model we can show how shocks to the economy lead to short-run fluctuations in output and employment. We can also show how policymakers can potentially cause or cure those fluctuations.

The next four chapters develop more fully the model of aggregate supply and aggregate demand. Chapters 10 and 11 present the IS—LM model, which shows how monetary and fiscal policy affect the aggregate demand for goods and services. Chapter 12 presents the Mundell—Fleming model, which describes how aggregate demand is determined in an open economy. Chapter 13 discusses theories of aggregate supply and their implications.

Introduction to Economic Fluctuations

The modern world regards business cycles much as the ancient Egyptians regarded the overflowing of the Nile. The phenomenon recurs at intervals, it is of great importance to everyone, and natural causes of it are not in sight.

—*John Bates Clark, 1898*

Economic fluctuations present a recurring problem for economists and policy-makers. This problem is illustrated in Figure 9-1, which shows growth in real GDP for the U.S. economy. As you can see, although the economy experiences long-run growth that averages about 3 percent per year, this growth is not at all steady. Recessions—periods of falling incomes and rising unemployment—are frequent. In the recession of 1990, for instance, real GDP fell 2.2 percent from its peak to its trough, and the unemployment rate rose to 7.7 percent. During recessions, not only are more people unemployed, but those who are employed have shorter workweeks, as more workers have to accept part-time jobs, and fewer workers have the opportunity to work overtime. When recessions end and the economy enters a boom, these effects work in reverse: incomes rise, unemployment falls, and workweeks expand.

Economists call these short-run fluctuations in output and employment the *business cycle*. Although this term suggests that economic fluctuations are regular and predictable, neither is the case. Recessions are as irregular as they are common. Sometimes they are close together, such as the recessions of 1980 and 1982. Sometimes they are far apart, such as the recessions of 1982 and 1990.

In Part Two of this book, we developed models to identify the long-run determinants of national income, unemployment, inflation, and other economic variables. Yet we did not examine why these variables fluctuate so much from year to year. Here in Part Three we develop a model to explain these short-run fluctuations. Because real GDP is the best single measure of economic well-being, it is the focus of our model.

Just as Egypt now controls the flooding of the Nile Valley with the Aswan Dam, modern society tries to control the business cycle with appropriate eco-

figure 9-1

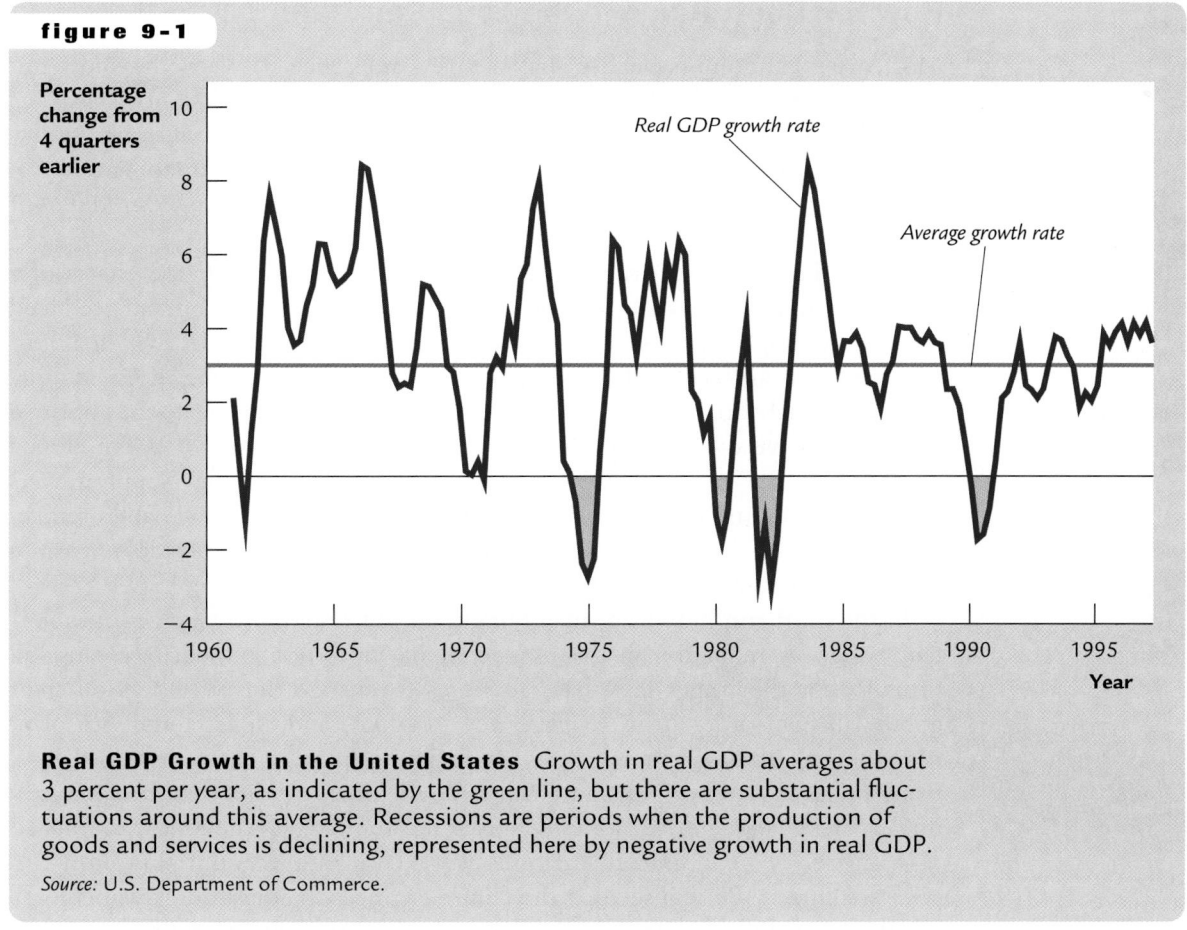

Real GDP Growth in the United States Growth in real GDP averages about 3 percent per year, as indicated by the green line, but there are substantial fluctuations around this average. Recessions are periods when the production of goods and services is declining, represented here by negative growth in real GDP.

Source: U.S. Department of Commerce.

nomic policies. The model we develop over the next several chapters shows how monetary and fiscal policies influence the business cycle. We will see that these policies can potentially stabilize the economy or, if poorly conducted, make the problem of economic instability even worse.

9-1 | Time Horizons in Macroeconomics

Before we start building a model of short-run economic fluctuations, let's step back and ask a fundamental question: Why do economists need different models for different time horizons? Why can't we stop the course here and be content with the classical models developed in Chapters 3 through 8? The answer, as this book has consistently reminded its reader, is that classical macroeconomic theory applies to the long run but not to the short run. But why is this so?

How the Short Run and the Long Run Differ

Most macroeconomists believe that the key difference between the short run and the long run is the behavior of prices. *In the long run, prices are flexible and can respond to changes in supply or demand. In the short run, many prices are "sticky" at some predetermined level.* Because prices behave differently in the short run than in the long run, economic policies have different effects over different time horizons.

To see how the short run and the long run differ, consider the effects of a change in monetary policy. Suppose that the Federal Reserve suddenly reduced the money supply by 5 percent. According to the classical model, which almost all economists agree describes the economy in the long run, the money supply affects nominal variables—variables measured in terms of money—but not real variables. As we discussed in Chapter 7, this principle is known as the *classical dichotomy*. In the long run, a 5-percent reduction in the money supply lowers all prices (including nominal wages) by 5 percent while all real variables remain the same. Thus, in the long run, changes in the money supply do not cause fluctuations in output or employment.

In the short run, however, many prices do not respond to changes in monetary policy. A reduction in the money supply does not immediately cause all firms to cut the wages they pay, all stores to change the price tags on their goods, all mail-order firms to issue new catalogs, and all restaurants to print new menus. Instead, there is little immediate change in many prices; that is, many prices are sticky. This short-run price stickiness implies that the short-run impact of a change in the money supply is not the same as the long-run impact.

A model of economic fluctuations must take into account this short-run price stickiness. We will see that the failure of prices to adjust quickly and completely means that, in the short run, output and employment must do some of the adjusting instead. In other words, during the time horizon over which prices are sticky, the classical dichotomy no longer holds: nominal variables can influence real variables, and the economy can deviate from the equilibrium predicted by the classical model.

CASE STUDY

The Puzzle of Sticky Magazine Prices

How sticky are prices? The answer to this question depends on what price we consider. Some commodities, such as wheat, soybeans, and pork bellies, are traded on organized exchanges, and their prices change every minute. No one would call these prices sticky. Yet the prices of most goods and services change much less frequently. One survey found that 39 percent of firms change their prices once a year, and another 10 percent change their prices less than once a year.[1]

---

[1] Alan S. Blinder, "On Sticky Prices: Academic Theories Meet the Real World," in *Monetary Policy,* N.G. Mankiw, ed. (Chicago: University of Chicago Press, 1994): 117–154. A case study in Chapter 19 discusses this survey in more detail.

The reasons for price stickiness are not always apparent. Consider, for example, the market for magazines. A study has documented that magazines change their newsstand prices very infrequently. The typical magazine allows inflation to erode its real price by about 25 percent before it raises its nominal price. When inflation is 4 percent per year, the typical magazine changes its price about every six years.[2]

Why do magazines leave their prices unchanged for so long? Economists do not have a definitive answer. The question is puzzling because it would seem that for magazines, the cost of a price change is small. To change prices, a mail-order firm must issue a new catalog and a restaurant must print a new menu, but a magazine publisher can simply print a new price on the cover of the next issue. Perhaps the cost to the publisher of charging the wrong price is also not very great. Or maybe customers would find it inconvenient if the price of their favorite magazine changed every month.

The magazine example shows that explaining at the microeconomic level why prices are sticky can sometimes be difficult. The cause of price stickiness is, therefore, an active area of research, which we discuss more fully in Chapter 19. In this chapter, however, we simply assume that prices are sticky so we can start developing the link between sticky prices and the business cycle. Although not yet fully explained, short-run price stickiness is widely believed to be crucial for understanding short-run economic fluctuations.

The Model of Aggregate Supply and Aggregate Demand

How does introducing sticky prices change our view of how the economy works? We can answer this question by considering economists' two favorite words — supply and demand.

In classical macroeconomic theory, the amount of output depends on the economy's ability to *supply* goods and services, which in turn depends on the supplies of capital and labor and on the available production technology. This is the essence of the models developed in Chapters 3, 4, and 5. Flexible prices are a crucial assumption of classical theory. The theory posits, sometimes implicitly, that prices adjust to ensure that the quantity of output demanded equals the quantity supplied.

The economy works quite differently when prices are sticky. In this case, as we will see, output also depends on the *demand* for goods and services. Demand, in turn, is influenced by monetary policy, fiscal policy, and various other factors. Because monetary and fiscal policy can influence the economy's output over the time horizon when prices are sticky, price stickiness provides a rationale for why these policies may be useful in stabilizing the economy in the short run.

---

[2] Stephen G. Cecchetti, "The Frequency of Price Adjustment: A Study of the Newsstand Prices of Magazines," *Journal of Econometrics* 31 (1986): 255–274.

In the rest of this chapter, we develop a model that makes these ideas more precise. The model of supply and demand, which we used in Chapter 1 to discuss the market for pizza, offers some of the most fundamental insights in economics. This model shows how the supply and demand for any good jointly determine the good's price and the quantity sold, and how shifts in supply and demand affect the price and quantity. In the rest of this chapter, we introduce the "economy-size" version of this model—*the model of aggregate supply and aggregate demand*. This macroeconomic model allows us to study how the aggregate price level and the quantity of aggregate output are determined. It also provides a way to contrast how the economy behaves in the long run and how it behaves in the short run.

Although the model of aggregate supply and aggregate demand resembles the model of supply and demand for a single good, the analogy is not exact. The model of supply and demand for a single good considers only one good within a large economy. By contrast, as we will see in the coming chapters, the model of aggregate supply and aggregate demand is a sophisticated model that incorporates the interactions among many markets.

---

f y i

THE SHORT RUN, THE LONG RUN, AND THE VERY LONG RUN

This book discusses many models of the economy, each with its own set of simplifying assumptions. Sometimes it's hard to keep all the models straight. One way to do so is to categorize the models by the time horizon over which they apply. The models fall into three categories:

➤ *The Short Run* This chapter and those that follow present the short-run theory of the economy. This theory assumes that prices are sticky and that, because of this price stickiness, capital and labor are sometimes not fully employed. Price stickiness is widely viewed as being important for explaining the economic fluctuations we observe from month to month or from year to year.

➤ *The Long Run* Chapter 3 presented the basic long-run theory of the economy, called the classical model. Chapter 7 presented the classical theory of money, and Chapter 8 presented the classical theory of the open economy. These chapters assumed that prices are flexible and, therefore, that capital and labor are fully employed. These chapters also took as fixed the quantities of capital and labor, as well as the technology for turning capital and labor into output. These assumptions are best suited for a time horizon of several years. Over this period, prices can adjust to equilibrium levels, yet capital, labor, and technology are relatively constant.

➤ *The Very Long Run* Chapters 4 and 5 presented the basic theory of economic growth, called the Solow model. This model analyzes the time horizon over which the capital stock, the labor force, and the available technology can change. This model is designed to explain how the economy works over a period of several decades.

When analyzing economic policies, it is important to keep in mind that they influence the economy over all time horizons. We must, therefore, draw on the insights of all these models.

9-2 | Aggregate Demand

Aggregate demand (*AD*) is the relationship between the quantity of output demanded and the aggregate price level. In other words, the aggregate demand curve tells us the quantity of goods and services people want to buy at any given level of prices. We examine the theory of aggregate demand in detail in Chapters 10 through 12. Here we use the quantity theory of money to provide a simple, although incomplete, derivation of the aggregate demand curve.

The Quantity Equation as Aggregate Demand

Recall from Chapter 7 that the quantity theory says that

$$MV = PY,$$

where *M* is the money supply, *V* is the velocity of money, *P* is the price level, and *Y* is the amount of output. If the velocity of money is constant, then this equation states that the money supply determines the nominal value of output, which in turn is the product of the price level and the amount of output.

You might recall that the quantity equation can be rewritten in terms of the supply and demand for real money balances:

$$M/P = (M/P)^{\mathrm{d}} = kY,$$

where $k = 1/V$ is a parameter determining how much money people want to hold for every dollar of income. In this form, the quantity equation states that the supply of real money balances M/P equals the demand $(M/P)^{\mathrm{d}}$ and that the demand is proportional to output *Y*. The velocity of money *V* is the "flip side" of the money demand parameter *k*.

For any fixed money supply and velocity, the quantity equation yields a negative relationship between the price level *P* and output *Y*. Figure 9-2 graphs the combinations of *P* and *Y* that satisfy the quantity equation holding *M* and *V* constant. This downward-sloping curve is called the aggregate demand curve.

Why the Aggregate Demand Curve Slopes Downward

As a strictly mathematical matter, the quantity equation explains the downward slope of the aggregate demand curve very simply. The money supply *M* and the velocity of money *V* determine the nominal value of output *PY*. Once *PY* is fixed, if *P* goes up, *Y* must go down.

What is the economics that lies behind this mathematical relationship? For a complete answer, we have to wait a couple of chapters. For now, however, consider the following logic: Because we have assumed that the velocity of money is fixed, the money supply determines the dollar value of all transactions in the economy. (This conclusion should be familiar from Chapter 7.) If the price level rises for some reason, so that each transaction requires more dollars, the number of transactions and thus the quantity of goods and services purchased must fall.

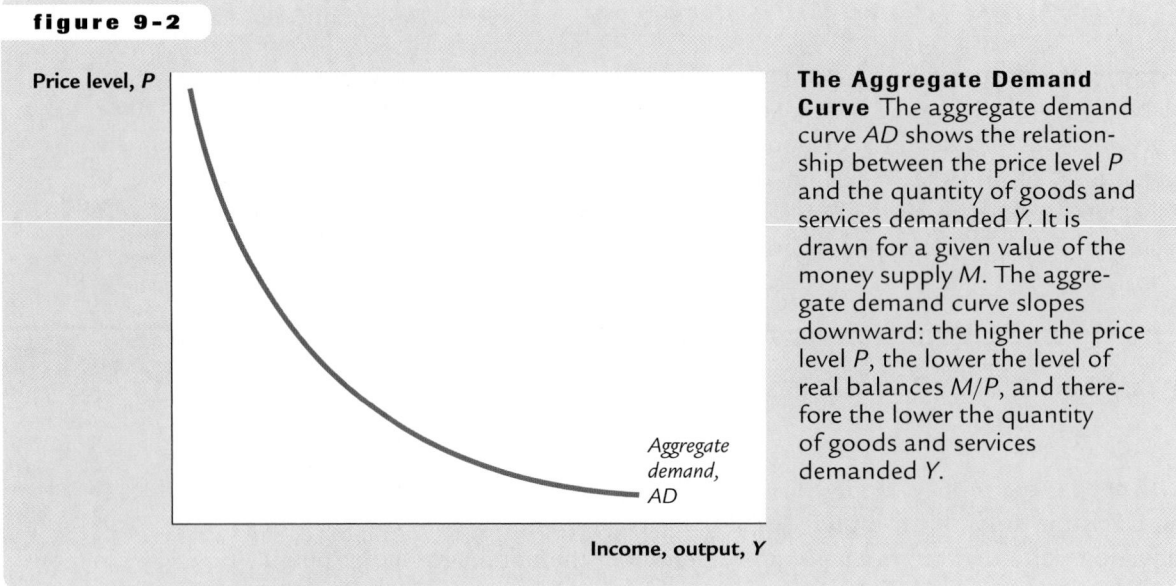

figure 9-2

Price level, *P*

Aggregate demand, *AD*

Income, output, *Y*

The Aggregate Demand Curve The aggregate demand curve *AD* shows the relationship between the price level *P* and the quantity of goods and services demanded *Y*. It is drawn for a given value of the money supply *M*. The aggregate demand curve slopes downward: the higher the price level *P*, the lower the level of real balances *M/P*, and therefore the lower the quantity of goods and services demanded *Y*.

We can also explain the downward slope of the aggregate demand curve by thinking about the supply and demand for real money balances. If output is higher, people engage in more transactions and need higher real balances *M/P*. For a fixed money supply *M*, higher real balances imply a lower price level. Conversely, if the price level is lower, real money balances are higher; the higher level of real balances allows a greater volume of transactions, which means a greater quantity of output is demanded.

Shifts in the Aggregate Demand Curve

The aggregate demand curve is drawn for a fixed value of the money supply. In other words, it tells us the possible combinations of *P* and *Y* for a given value of *M*. If the Fed changes the money supply, then the possible combinations of *P* and *Y* change, which means the aggregate demand curve shifts.

For example, consider what happens if the Fed reduces the money supply. The quantity equation, $MV = PY$, tells us that the reduction in the money supply leads to a proportionate reduction in the nominal value of output *PY*. For any given price level, the amount of output is lower, and for any given amount of output, the price level is lower. As in Figure 9–3, the aggregate demand curve relating *P* and *Y* shifts inward.

The opposite occurs if the Fed increases the money supply. The quantity equation tells us that an increase in *M* leads to an increase in *PY*. For any given price level, the amount of output is higher, and for any given amount of output, the price level is higher. As shown in Figure 9–4, the aggregate demand curve shifts outward.

figure 9-3

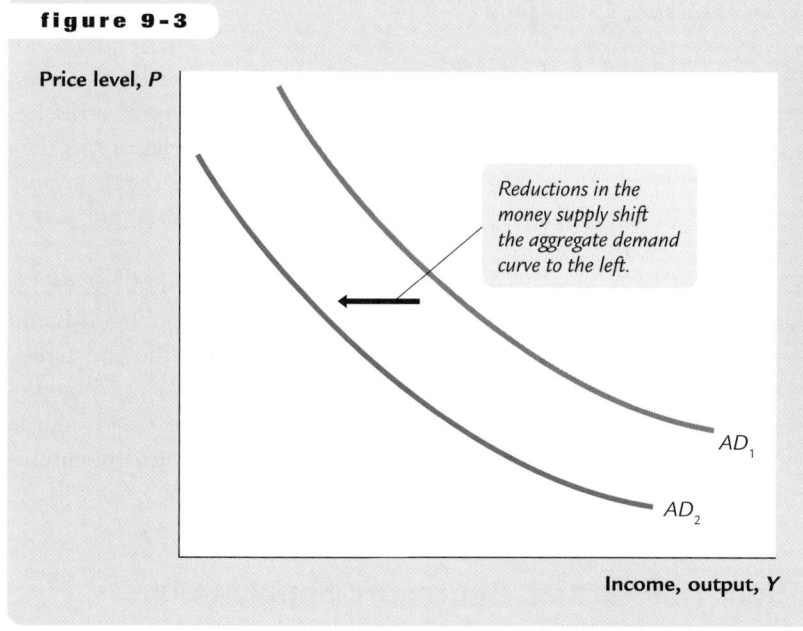

Inward Shifts in the Aggregate Demand Curve A change in the money supply shifts the aggregate demand curve. For any given price level P, a reduction in the money supply M implies that real balances M/P are lower and thus that output Y is lower. Therefore, a reduction in the money supply shifts the aggregate demand curve inward from AD_1 to AD_2.

Fluctuations in the money supply are not the only source of fluctuations in aggregate demand. Even if the money supply is held constant, the aggregate demand curve shifts if some event causes a change in the velocity of money. Over the next three chapters, we consider many possible reasons for shifts in the aggregate demand curve.

figure 9-4

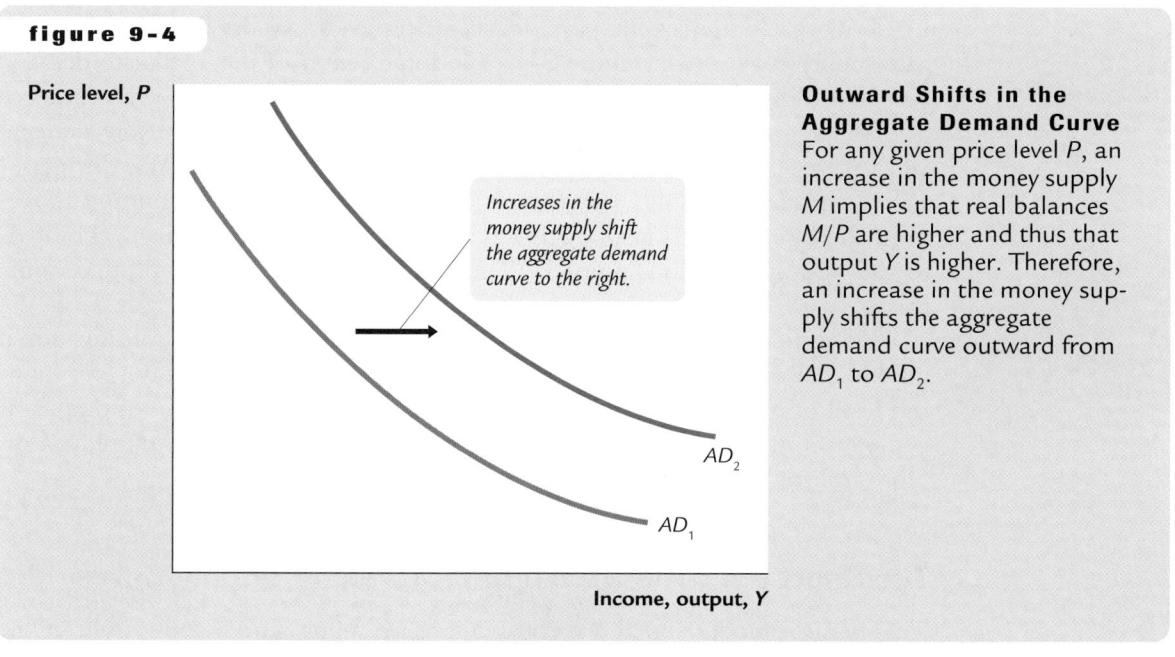

Outward Shifts in the Aggregate Demand Curve For any given price level P, an increase in the money supply M implies that real balances M/P are higher and thus that output Y is higher. Therefore, an increase in the money supply shifts the aggregate demand curve outward from AD_1 to AD_2.

9-3 | Aggregate Supply

By itself, the aggregate demand curve does not tell us the price level or the amount of output; it merely gives a relationship between these two variables. To accompany the aggregate demand curve, we need another relationship between P and Y that crosses the aggregate demand curve—an aggregate supply curve. The aggregate demand and aggregate supply curves together pin down the economy's price level and quantity of output.

Aggregate supply (AS) is the relationship between the quantity of goods and services supplied and the price level. Because the firms that supply goods and services have flexible prices in the long run but sticky prices in the short run, the aggregate supply relationship depends on the time horizon. We need to discuss two different aggregate supply curves: the long-run aggregate supply curve $LRAS$ and the short-run aggregate supply curve $SRAS$. We also need to discuss how the economy makes the transition from the short run to the long run.

The Long Run: The Vertical Aggregate Supply Curve

Because the classical model describes how the economy behaves in the long run, we derive the long-run aggregate supply curve from the classical model. Recall from Chapter 3 that the amount of output produced depends on the fixed amounts of capital and labor and on the available technology. To show this, we write

$$Y = F(\overline{K}, \overline{L})$$
$$= \overline{Y}.$$

According to the classical model, output does not depend on the price level. To show that output is the same for all price levels, we draw a vertical aggregate supply curve, as in Figure 9-5. The intersection of the aggregate demand curve with this vertical aggregate supply curve determines the price level.

If the aggregate supply curve is vertical, then changes in aggregate demand affect prices but not output. For example, if the money supply falls, the aggregate demand curve shifts downward, as in Figure 9-6. The economy moves from the old intersection of aggregate supply and aggregate demand, point A, to the new intersection, point B. The shift in aggregate demand affects only prices.

The vertical aggregate supply curve satisfies the classical dichotomy, for it implies that the level of output is independent of the money supply. This long-run level of output, $\overline{Y}$, is called the *full-employment* or *natural* level of output. It is the level of output at which the economy's resources are fully employed or, more realistically, at which unemployment is at its natural rate.

The Short Run: The Horizontal Aggregate Supply Curve

The classical model and the vertical aggregate supply curve apply only in the long run. In the short run, some prices are sticky and, therefore, do not adjust

figure 9-5

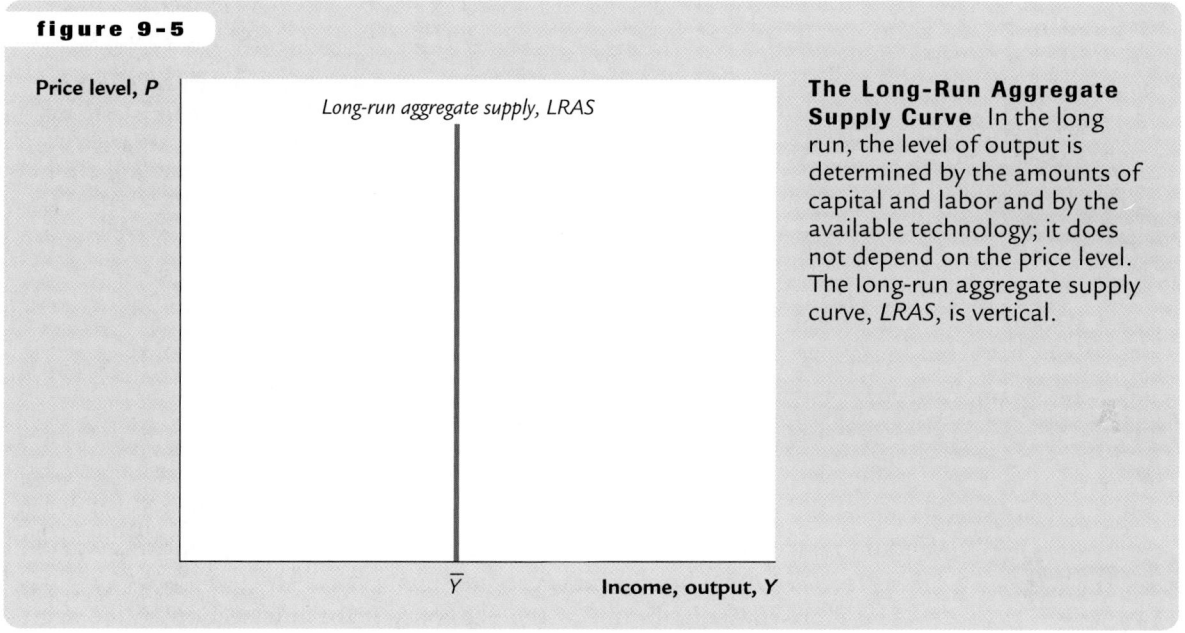

The Long-Run Aggregate Supply Curve In the long run, the level of output is determined by the amounts of capital and labor and by the available technology; it does not depend on the price level. The long-run aggregate supply curve, *LRAS*, is vertical.

to changes in demand. Because of this price stickiness, the short-run aggregate supply curve is not vertical.

As an extreme example, suppose that all firms have issued price catalogs and that it is costly for them to issue new ones. Thus, all prices are stuck at predetermined levels. At these prices, firms are willing to sell as much as their customers are willing to buy, and they hire just enough labor to produce the

figure 9-6

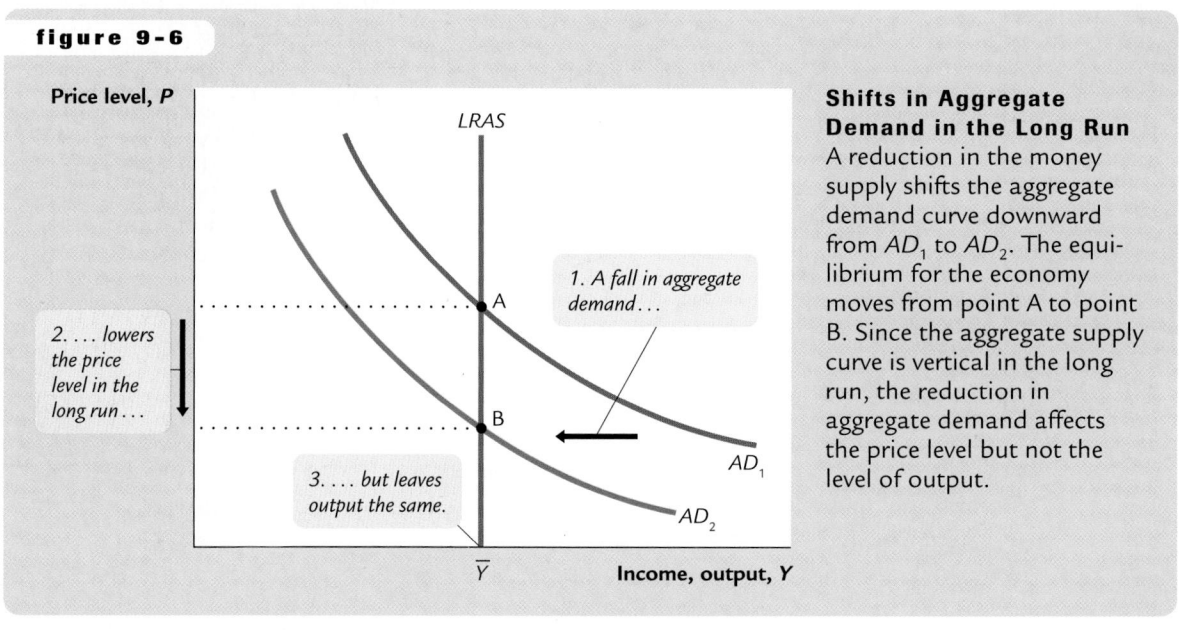

Shifts in Aggregate Demand in the Long Run A reduction in the money supply shifts the aggregate demand curve downward from AD_1 to AD_2. The equilibrium for the economy moves from point A to point B. Since the aggregate supply curve is vertical in the long run, the reduction in aggregate demand affects the price level but not the level of output.

figure 9-7

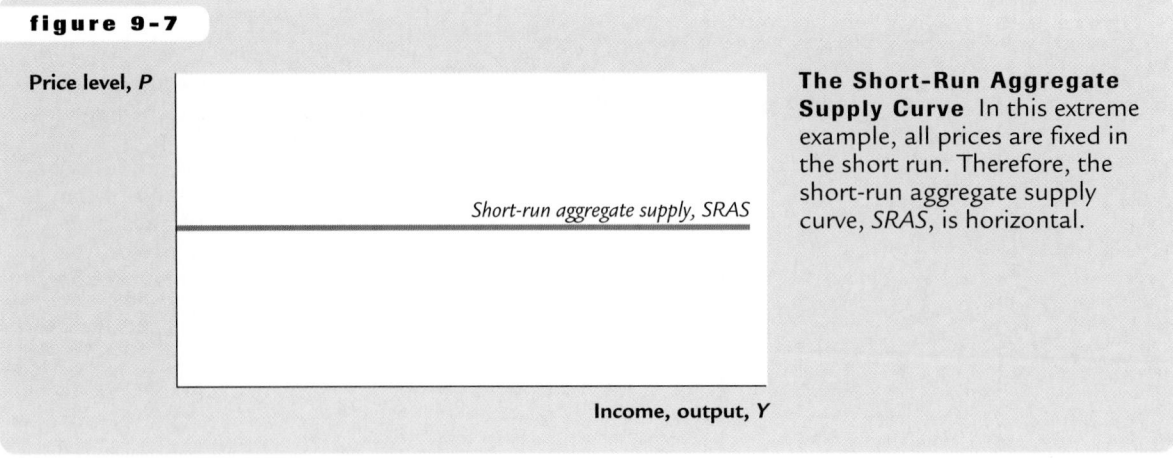

Price level, *P*

Short-run aggregate supply, *SRAS*

Income, output, *Y*

The Short-Run Aggregate Supply Curve In this extreme example, all prices are fixed in the short run. Therefore, the short-run aggregate supply curve, *SRAS*, is horizontal.

amount demanded. Because the price level is fixed, we represent this situation in Figure 9-7 with a horizontal aggregate supply curve.

The short-run equilibrium of the economy is the intersection of the aggregate demand curve and this horizontal short-run aggregate supply curve. In this case, changes in aggregate demand do affect the level of output. For example, if the Fed suddenly reduces the money supply, the aggregate demand curve shifts inward, as in Figure 9-8. The economy moves from the old intersection of aggregate demand and aggregate supply, point A, to the new intersection,

figure 9-8

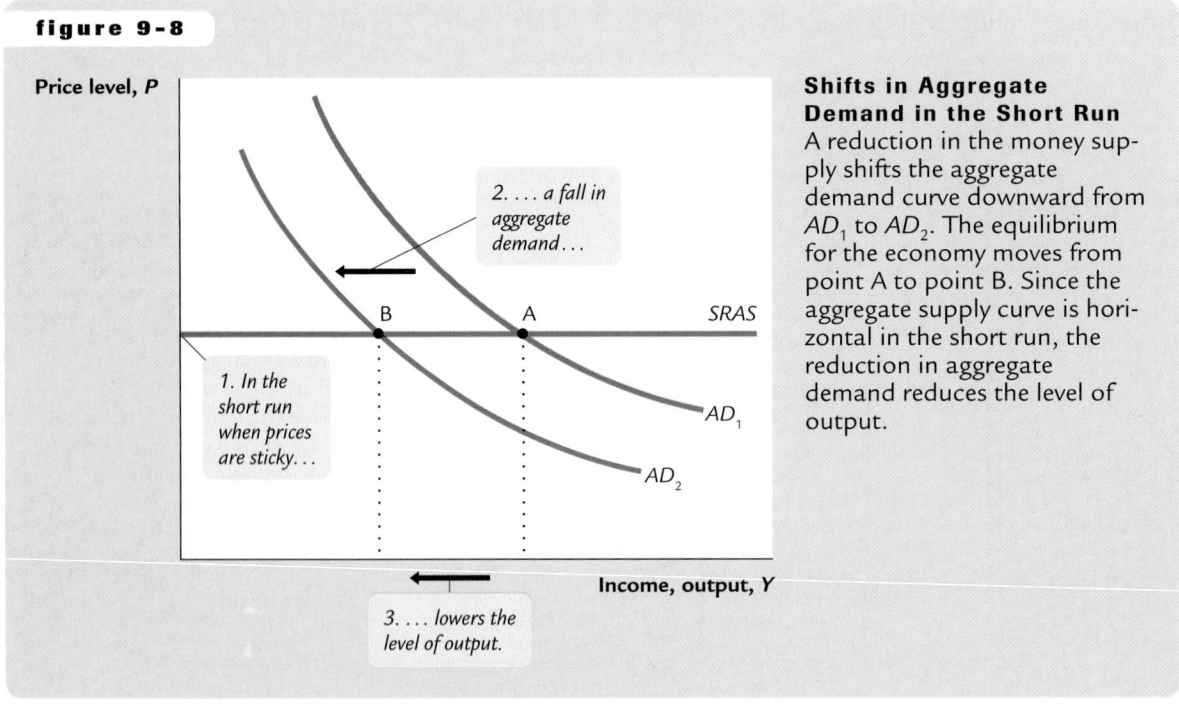

Price level, *P*

2. . . . a fall in aggregate demand . . .

B   A   *SRAS*

1. In the short run when prices are sticky . . .

*AD*₁

*AD*₂

Income, output, *Y*

3. . . . lowers the level of output.

Shifts in Aggregate Demand in the Short Run A reduction in the money supply shifts the aggregate demand curve downward from *AD*₁ to *AD*₂. The equilibrium for the economy moves from point A to point B. Since the aggregate supply curve is horizontal in the short run, the reduction in aggregate demand reduces the level of output.

point B. The movement from point A to point B represents a decline in output at a fixed price level.

Thus, a fall in aggregate demand reduces output in the short run because prices do not adjust instantly. After the sudden fall in aggregate demand, firms are stuck with prices that are too high. With demand low and prices high, firms sell less of their product, so they reduce production and lay off workers. The economy experiences a recession.

From the Short Run to the Long Run

We can summarize our analysis so far as follows: *Over long periods of time, prices are flexible, the aggregate supply curve is vertical, and changes in aggregate demand affect the price level but not output. Over short periods of time, prices are sticky, the aggregate supply curve is flat, and changes in aggregate demand do affect the economy's output of goods and services.*

How does the economy make the transition from the short run to the long run? Let's trace the effects over time of a fall in aggregate demand. Suppose that the economy is initially in long-run equilibrium, as shown in Figure 9-9. In this figure, there are three curves: the aggregate demand curve, the long-run aggregate supply curve, and the short-run aggregate supply curve. The long-run equilibrium is the point at which aggregate demand crosses the long-run aggregate supply curve. Prices have adjusted to reach this equilibrium. Therefore, when the economy is in its long-run equilibrium, the short-run aggregate supply curve must cross this point as well.

Now suppose that the Fed reduces the money supply and the aggregate demand curve shifts downward, as in Figure 9-10. In the short run, prices are sticky, so the economy moves from point A to point B. Output and employment fall below their natural levels, which means the economy is in a recession.

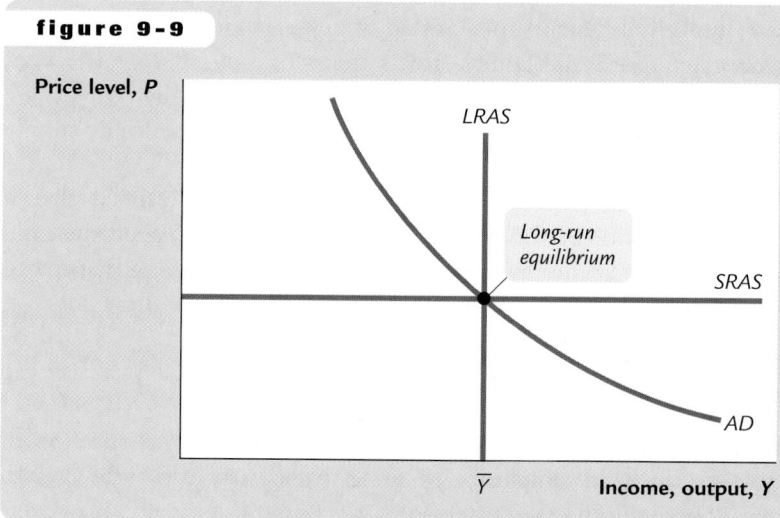

figure 9-9

Price level, *P*

LRAS

Long-run equilibrium

SRAS

AD

$\overline{Y}$ Income, output, *Y*

Long-Run Equilibrium In the long run, the economy finds itself at the intersection of the long-run aggregate supply curve and the aggregate demand curve. Because prices have adjusted to this level, the short-run aggregate supply curve crosses this point as well.

figure 9-10

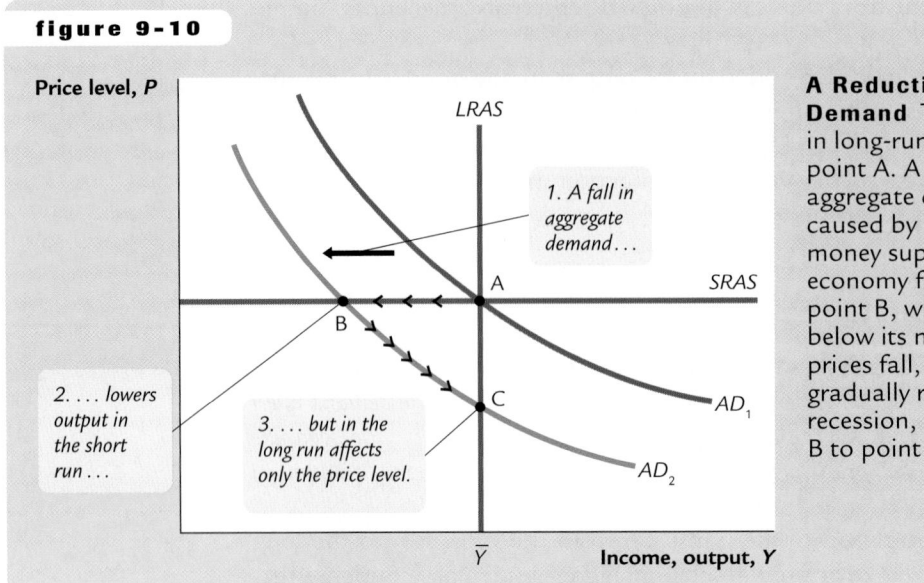

Price level, *P*

LRAS

1. *A fall in aggregate demand...*

A

SRAS

B

2. *...lowers output in the short run...*

3. *...but in the long run affects only the price level.*

C

AD₁

AD₂

$\overline{Y}$ Income, output, *Y*

A Reduction in Aggregate Demand The economy begins in long-run equilibrium at point A. A reduction in aggregate demand, perhaps caused by a decrease in the money supply, moves the economy from point A to point B, where output is below its natural level. As prices fall, the economy gradually recovers from the recession, moving from point B to point C.

Over time, in response to the low demand, wages and prices fall. The gradual reduction in the price level moves the economy downward along the aggregate demand curve to point C, which is the new long-run equilibrium. In the new long-run equilibrium (point C), output and employment are back to their natural levels, but prices are lower than in the old long-run equilibrium (point A). Thus, a shift in aggregate demand affects output in the short run, but this effect dissipates over time as firms adjust their prices.

CASE STUDY

Gold, Greenbacks, and the Contraction of the 1870s

The aftermath of the Civil War in the United States provides a vivid example of how contractionary monetary policy affects the economy. Before the war, the United States was on a gold standard. Paper dollars were readily convertible into gold. Under this policy, the quantity of gold determined the money supply and the price level.

In 1862, after the Civil War broke out, the Treasury announced that it would no longer redeem dollars for gold. In essence, this act replaced the gold standard with a system of fiat money. Over the next few years, the government printed large quantities of paper currency — called *greenbacks* for their color — and used the seigniorage to finance wartime expenditure. Because of this increase in the money supply, the price level approximately doubled during the war.

When the war was over, much political debate centered on the question of whether to return to the gold standard. The Greenback Party was formed with the primary goal of maintaining the system of fiat money. Eventually, however, the Greenback Party lost the debate. Policymakers decided to retire the greenbacks over time in order to reinstate the gold standard at the rate of exchange between dollars and gold that had prevailed before the war. Their goal was to return the value of the dollar to its former level.

Returning to the gold standard in this way required reversing the wartime rise in prices, which meant aggregate demand had to fall. (To be more precise, the growth in aggregate demand needed to fall short of the growth in the natural rate of output.) As the price level fell, the economy experienced a recession from 1873 to 1879, the longest on record. By 1879, the price level was back to its level before the war, and the gold standard was reinstated.

9-4 | Stabilization Policy

Fluctuations in the economy as a whole come from changes in aggregate supply or aggregate demand. Economists call exogenous changes in these curves **shocks** to the economy. A shock that shifts the aggregate demand curve is called a **demand shock,** and a shock that shifts the aggregate supply curve is called a **supply shock.** These shocks disrupt economic well-being by pushing output and employment away from their natural rates. One goal of the model of aggregate supply and aggregate demand is to show how shocks cause economic fluctuations.

Another goal of the model is to evaluate how macroeconomic policy can respond to these shocks. Economists use the term **stabilization policy** to refer to policy actions aimed at reducing the severity of short-run economic fluctuations. Because output and employment fluctuate around their long-run natural rates, stabilization policy dampens the business cycle by keeping output and employment as close to their natural rates as possible.

In the coming chapters, we examine in detail how stabilization policy works and what practical problems arise in its use. Here we begin our analysis of stabilization policy by examining how monetary policy might respond to shocks. Monetary policy is an important component of stabilization policy because, as we have seen, the money supply has a powerful impact on aggregate demand.

Shocks to Aggregate Demand

Consider an example of a demand shock: the introduction and expanded availability of credit cards. Because credit cards are often a more convenient way to make purchases than using cash, they reduce the quantity of money that people choose to hold. This reduction in money demand is equivalent to an increase in the velocity of money. When each person holds less money, the money demand parameter k falls. This means that each dollar of money moves from hand to hand more quickly, so velocity $V (= 1/k)$ rises.

figure 9-11

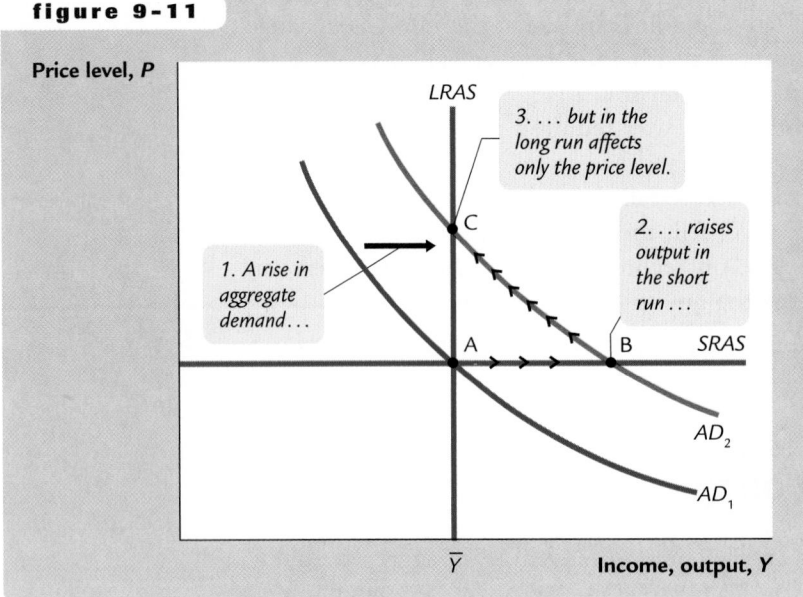

Price level, *P*

An Increase in Aggregate Demand The economy begins in long-run equilibrium at point A. An increase in aggregate demand, due to an increase in the velocity of money, moves the economy from point A to point B, where output is above its natural level. As prices rise, output gradually returns to its natural rate, and the economy moves from point B to point C.

If the money supply is held constant, the increase in velocity causes nominal spending to rise and the aggregate demand curve to shift outward, as in Figure 9-11. In the short run, the increase in demand raises the output of the economy—it causes an economic boom. At the old prices, firms now sell more output. Therefore, they hire more workers, ask their existing workers to work longer hours and make greater use of their factories and equipment.

Over time, the high level of aggregate demand pulls up wages and prices. As the price level rises, the quantity of output demanded declines, and the economy gradually approaches the natural rate of production. But during the transition to the higher price level, the economy's output is higher than the natural rate.

What can the Fed do to dampen this boom and keep output closer to the natural rate? The Fed might reduce the money supply to offset the increase in velocity. Offsetting the change in velocity would stabilize aggregate demand. Thus, the Fed can reduce or even eliminate the impact of demand shocks on output and employment if it can skillfully control the money supply. Whether the Fed in fact has the necessary skill is a more difficult question, which we take up in Chapter 14.

Shocks to Aggregate Supply

Shocks to aggregate supply, as well as shocks to aggregate demand, can cause economic fluctuations. A supply shock is a shock to the economy that alters the cost of producing goods and services and, as a result, the prices that firms charge. Because supply shocks have a direct impact on the price level, they are sometimes called *price shocks*. Here are some examples:

➤ A drought that destroys crops. The reduction in food supply pushes up food prices.

➤ A new environmental protection law that requires firms to reduce their emissions of pollutants. Firms pass on the added costs to customers in the form of higher prices.

➤ An increase in union aggressiveness. This pushes up wages and the prices of the goods produced by union workers.

➤ The organization of an international oil cartel. By curtailing competition, the major oil producers can raise the world price of oil.

All these events are *adverse* supply shocks, which means they push costs and prices upward. A *favorable* supply shock, such as the breakup of an international oil cartel, reduces costs and prices.

Figure 9-12 shows how an adverse supply shock affects the economy. The short-run aggregate supply curve shifts upward. (The supply shock may also lower the natural level of output and thus shift the long-run aggregate supply curve to the left, but we ignore that effect here.) If aggregate demand is held constant, the economy moves from point A to point B: the price level rises and the amount of output falls below the natural rate. An experience like this is called *stagflation,* because it combines stagnation (falling output) with inflation (rising prices).

figure 9-12

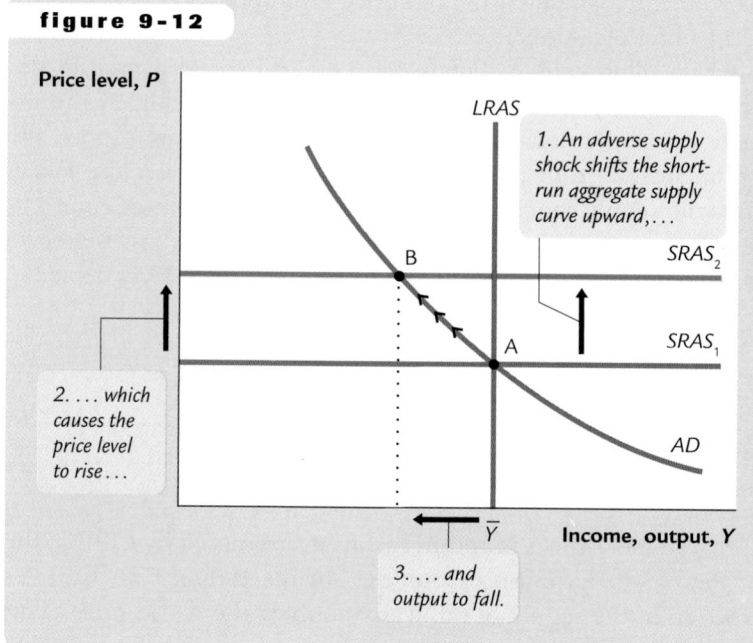

An Adverse Supply Shock An adverse supply shock pushes up costs and thus prices. If aggregate demand is held constant, the economy moves from point A to point B, leading to stagflation—a combination of increasing prices and falling output. Eventually, as prices fall, the economy returns to the natural rate, point A.

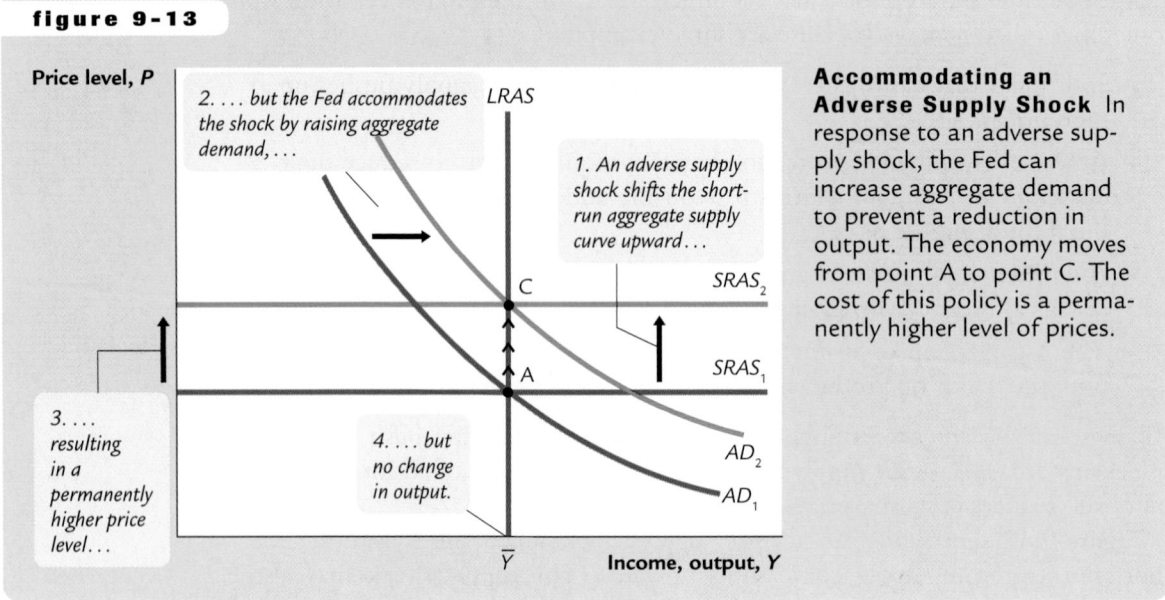

figure 9-13

Price level, *P*

2. . . . but the Fed accommodates the shock by raising aggregate demand, . . .

LRAS

1. An adverse supply shock shifts the short-run aggregate supply curve upward . . .

SRAS₂

C

SRAS₁

A

3. . . . resulting in a permanently higher price level . . .

4. . . . but no change in output.

AD₂

AD₁

Ȳ   Income, output, *Y*

Accommodating an Adverse Supply Shock In response to an adverse supply shock, the Fed can increase aggregate demand to prevent a reduction in output. The economy moves from point A to point C. The cost of this policy is a permanently higher level of prices.

Faced with an adverse supply shock, a policymaker controlling aggregate demand, such as the Fed, has a difficult choice between two options. The first option, implicit in Figure 9-12, is to hold aggregate demand constant. In this case, output and employment are lower than the natural rate. Eventually, prices will fall to restore full employment at the old price level (point A). But the cost of this process is a painful recession.

The second option, illustrated in Figure 9-13, is to expand aggregate demand to bring the economy toward the natural rate more quickly. If the increase in aggregate demand coincides with the shock to aggregate supply, the economy goes immediately from point A to point C. In this case, the Fed is said to *accommodate* the supply shock. The drawback of this option, of course, is that the price level is permanently higher. There is no way to adjust aggregate demand both to maintain full employment and to keep the price level stable.

CASE STUDY

How OPEC Helped Cause Stagflation in the 1970s and Euphoria in the 1980s

The most disruptive supply shocks in recent history were caused by OPEC, the Organization of Petroleum Exporting Countries. In the early 1970s, OPEC's coordinated reduction in the supply of oil nearly doubled the world price. This increase in oil prices caused stagflation in most industrial countries. These statistics show what happened in the United States:

Year	Change in Oil Prices	Inflation Rate (CPI)	Unemployment Rate
1973	11.0%	6.2%	4.9%
1974	68.0	11.0	5.6
1975	16.0	9.1	8.5
1976	3.3	5.8	7.7
1977	8.1	6.5	7.1

The 68-percent increase in the price of oil in 1974 was an adverse supply shock of major proportions. As one would have expected, it led to both higher inflation and higher unemployment.

A few years later, when the world economy had nearly recovered from the first OPEC recession, almost the same thing happened again. OPEC raised oil prices, causing further stagflation. Here are the statistics for the United States:

Year	Change in Oil Prices	Inflation Rate (CPI)	Unemployment Rate
1978	9.4%	7.7%	6.1%
1979	25.4	11.3	5.8
1980	47.8	13.5	7.0
1981	44.4	10.3	7.5
1982	−8.7	6.1	9.5

The increases in oil prices in 1979, 1980, and 1981 again led to double-digit inflation and higher unemployment.

In the mid-1980s, political turmoil among the Arab countries weakened OPEC's ability to restrain supplies of oil. Oil prices fell, reversing the stagflation of the 1970s and the early 1980s. Here's what happened:

Year	Changes in Oil Prices	Inflation Rate (CPI)	Unemployment Rate
1983	−7.1%	3.2%	9.5%
1984	−1.7	4.3	7.4
1985	−7.5	3.6	7.1
1986	−44.5	1.9	6.9
1987	18.3	3.6	6.1

In 1986 oil prices fell by nearly half. This favorable supply shock led to one of the lowest inflation rates experienced in recent U.S. history and to falling unemployment.

More recently, OPEC has not been a major cause of economic fluctuations. With the exception of a brief period after Iraq invaded Kuwait in the summer of 1990, the price of oil has been relatively stable. Yet the experience of the 1970s and 1980s could always repeat itself. Events in the Middle East are a potential source of shocks to economies around the world.[3]

---

[3] Some economists have suggested that changes in oil prices played a major role in economic fluctuations even before the 1970s. See James D. Hamilton, "Oil and the Macroeconomy Since World War II," *Journal of Political Economy* 91 (April 1983): 228–248.

9-5 | Conclusion

This chapter has introduced a framework to study economic fluctuations: the model of aggregate supply and aggregate demand. The model is built on the assumption that prices are sticky in the short run and flexible in the long run. It shows how shocks to the economy cause output to deviate temporarily from the level implied by the classical model.

The model also highlights the role of monetary policy. Poor monetary policy can be a source of shocks to the economy. A well-run monetary policy can respond to shocks and stabilize the economy.

In the chapters that follow, we refine our understanding of this model and our analysis of stabilization policy. Chapters 10 through 12 go beyond the quantity equation to refine our theory of aggregate demand. This refinement shows that aggregate demand depends on fiscal policy as well as monetary policy. Chapter 13 examines aggregate supply in more detail. Chapter 14 examines the debate over the virtues and limits of stabilization policy.

Summary

1. The crucial difference between the long run and the short run is that prices are flexible in the long run but sticky in the short run. The model of aggregate supply and aggregate demand provides a framework to analyze economic fluctuations and see how the impact of policies varies over different time horizons.

2. The aggregate demand curve slopes downward. It tells us that the lower the price level, the greater the aggregate quantity of goods and services demanded.

3. In the long run, the aggregate supply curve is vertical because output is determined by the amounts of capital and labor and by the available technology, but not by the level of prices. Therefore, shifts in aggregate demand affect the price level but not output or employment.

4. In the short run, the aggregate supply curve is horizontal, because wages and prices are sticky at predetermined levels. Therefore, shifts in aggregate demand affect output and employment.

5. Shocks to aggregate demand and aggregate supply cause economic fluctuations. Because the Fed can shift the aggregate demand curve, it can attempt to offset these shocks to maintain output and employment at their natural rates.

KEY CONCEPTS

Aggregate demand	Shocks	Supply shocks
Aggregate supply	Demand shocks	Stabilization policy

QUESTIONS FOR REVIEW

1. Give an example of a price that is sticky in the short run and flexible in the long run.

2. Why does the aggregate demand curve slope downward?

3. Explain the impact of an increase in the money supply in the short run and in the long run.

4. Why is it easier for the Fed to deal with demand shocks than with supply shocks?

PROBLEMS AND APPLICATIONS

1. Suppose that a change in government regulations allows banks to start paying interest on checking accounts. Recall that the money stock is the sum of currency and demand deposits, including checking accounts, so this regulatory change makes holding money more attractive.

   a. How does this change affect the demand for money?

   b. What happens to the velocity of money?

   c. If the Fed keeps the money supply constant, what will happen to output and prices in the short run and in the long run?

   d. Should the Fed keep the money supply constant in response to this regulatory change? Why or why not?

2. Suppose the Fed reduces the money supply by 5 percent.

   a. What happens to the aggregate demand curve?

   b. What happens to the level of output and the price level in the short run and in the long run?

   c. According to Okun's law, what happens to unemployment in the short run and in the long run? (*Hint:* Okun's law is the relationship between output and unemployment discussed in Chapter 2.)

   d. What happens to the real interest rate in the short run and in the long run? (*Hint:* Use the model of the real interest rate in Chapter 3 to see what happens when output changes.)

3. Let's examine how the goals of the Fed influence its response to shocks. Suppose Fed A cares only about keeping the price level stable, and Fed B cares only about keeping output and employment at their natural rates. Explain how each Fed would respond to

   a. An exogenous decrease in the velocity of money.

   b. An exogenous increase in the price of oil.

10

Aggregate Demand I

I shall argue that the postulates of the classical theory are applicable to a special case only and not to the general case. . . . Moreover, the characteristics of the special case assumed by the classical theory happen not to be those of the economic society in which we actually live, with the result that its teaching is misleading and disastrous if we attempt to apply it to the facts of experience.

—*John Maynard Keynes,* The General Theory

Of all the economic fluctuations in world history, the one that stands out as particularly large, painful, and intellectually significant is the Great Depression of the 1930s. During this time, the United States and many other countries experienced massive unemployment and greatly reduced incomes. In the worst year, 1933, one-fourth of the U.S. labor force was unemployed, and real GDP was 30 percent below its 1929 level.

This devastating episode caused many economists to question the validity of classical economic theory—the theory we examined in Chapters 3 through 8. Classical theory seemed incapable of explaining the Depression. According to that theory, national income depends on factor supplies and the available technology, neither of which changed substantially from 1929 to 1933. After the onset of the Depression, many economists believed that a new model was needed to explain such a large and sudden economic downturn and to suggest government policies that might reduce the economic hardship so many people faced.

In 1936 the British economist John Maynard Keynes revolutionized economics with his book *The General Theory of Employment, Interest, and Money.* Keynes proposed a new way to analyze the economy, which he presented as an alternative to classical theory. His vision of how the economy works quickly became a center of controversy. Yet, as economists debated *The General Theory,* a new understanding of economic fluctuations gradually developed.

Keynes proposed that low aggregate demand is responsible for the low income and high unemployment that characterize economic downturns. He criticized classical theory for assuming that aggregate supply alone—capital, labor, and technology—determines national income. Economists today reconcile these two views with the model of aggregate demand and aggregate supply introduced in Chapter 9. In the long run, prices are flexible, and aggregate supply determines income. But in the short run, prices are sticky, so changes in aggregate demand influence income.

In this chapter and the next, we continue our study of economic fluctuations by looking more closely at aggregate demand. Our goal is to identify the variables that shift the aggregate demand curve, causing fluctuations in national income. We also examine more fully the tools policymakers can use to influence aggregate demand. In Chapter 9 we derived the aggregate demand curve from the quantity theory of money, and we showed that monetary policy can shift the aggregate demand curve. In this chapter we see that the government can influence aggregate demand with both monetary and fiscal policy.

The model of aggregate demand developed in this chapter, called the **IS–LM model,** is the leading interpretation of Keynes's theory. The goal of the model is to show what determines national income for any given price level. There are two ways to view this exercise. We can view the *IS–LM* model as showing what causes income to change in the short run when the price level is fixed. Or we can view the model as showing what causes the aggregate demand curve to shift. These two views of the model are equivalent: as Figure 10-1 shows, in the short run when the price level is fixed, shifts in the aggregate demand curve lead to changes in national income.

The two parts of the *IS–LM* model are, not surprisingly, the **IS curve** and the **LM curve.** *IS* stands for "investment" and "saving," and the *IS* curve represents what's going on in the market for goods and services (which we first discussed in Chapter 3). *LM* stands for "liquidity" and "money," and the *LM*

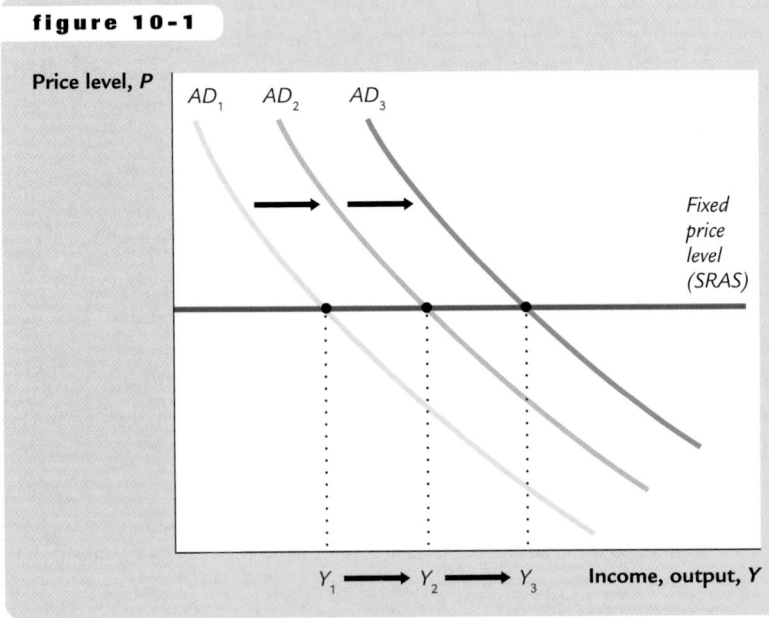

figure 10-1

Shifts in Aggregate Demand For a given price level, national income fluctuates because of shifts in the aggregate demand curve. The *IS–LM* model takes the price level as given and shows what causes income to change. The model therefore shows what causes aggregate demand to shift.

curve represents what's happening to the supply and demand for money (which we first discussed in Chapter 7). Because the interest rate influences both investment and money demand, it is the variable that links the two halves of the *IS–LM* model. The model shows how interactions between these markets determine the position and slope of the aggregate demand curve and, therefore, the level of national income in the short run.[1]

10-1 | The Goods Market and the *IS* Curve

The *IS* curve plots the relationship between the interest rate and the level of income that arises in the market for goods and services. To develop this relationship, we start with a basic model called the **Keynesian cross.** This model is the simplest interpretation of Keynes's theory of national income and is a building block for the more complex and realistic *IS–LM* model.

The Keynesian Cross

In *The General Theory* Keynes proposed that an economy's total income was, in the short run, determined largely by the desire to spend by households, firms, and the government. The more people want to spend, the more goods and services firms can sell. The more firms can sell, the more output they will choose to produce and the more workers they will choose to hire. Thus, the problem during recessions and depressions, according to Keynes, was inadequate spending. The Keynesian cross is an attempt to model this insight.

Planned Expenditure We begin our derivation of the Keynesian cross by drawing a distinction between actual and planned expenditure. *Actual expenditure* is the amount households, firms, and the government spend on goods and services, and as we first saw in Chapter 2, it equals the economy's gross domestic product (GDP). *Planned expenditure* is the amount households, firms, and the government would like to spend on goods and services.

Why would actual expenditure ever differ from planned expenditure? The answer is that firms might engage in unplanned inventory investment because their sales do not meet their expectations. When firms sell less of their product than they planned, their stock of inventories automatically rises; conversely, when firms sell more than planned, their stock of inventories falls. Because these unplanned changes in inventory are counted as investment spending by firms, actual expenditure can be either above or below planned expenditure.

Now consider the determinants of planned expenditure. Assuming that the economy is closed, so that net exports are zero, we write planned expenditure

---

[1] The *IS–LM* model was introduced in a classic article by the Nobel-prize-winning economist John R. Hicks, "Mr. Keynes and the Classics: A Suggested Interpretation," *Econometrica* 5 (1937): 147–159.

E as the sum of consumption C, planned investment I, and government pur-chases G:

$$E = C + I + G.$$

To this equation, we add the consumption function

$$C = C(Y - T).$$

This equation states that consumption depends on disposable income $(Y - T)$, which is total income Y minus taxes T. To keep things simple, for now we take planned investment as exogenously fixed:

$$I = \bar{I}.$$

And as in Chapter 3, we assume that fiscal policy—the levels of government purchases and taxes—is fixed:

$$G = \bar{G},$$
$$T = \bar{T}.$$

Combining these five equations, we obtain

$$E = C(Y - \bar{T}) + \bar{I} + \bar{G}.$$

This equation shows that planned expenditure is a function of income Y, the level of planned investment $\bar{I}$, and the fiscal policy variables $\bar{G}$ and $\bar{T}$.

Figure 10-2 graphs planned expenditure as a function of the level of income. This line slopes upward because higher income leads to higher consumption and thus higher planned expenditure. The slope of this line is the marginal propensity to consume, the *MPC*: it shows how much planned expenditure in-creases when income rises by \$1. This planned-expenditure function is the first piece of the model called the Keynesian cross.

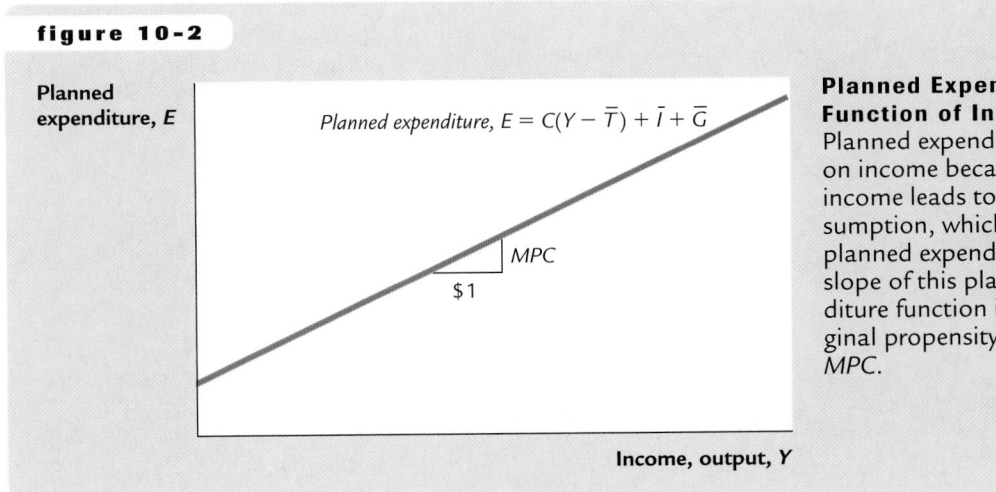

figure 10-2

Planned expenditure, *E*

Planned expenditure, $E = C(Y - \bar{T}) + \bar{I} + \bar{G}$

MPC

\$1

Income, output, *Y*

Planned Expenditure as a Function of Income
Planned expenditure depends on income because higher income leads to higher con-sumption, which is part of planned expenditure. The slope of this planned-expen-diture function is the mar-ginal propensity to consume, *MPC*.

The Economy in Equilibrium The next piece of the Keynesian cross is the assumption that the economy is in equilibrium when actual expenditure equals planned expenditure. This assumption is based on the idea that when people's plans have been realized, they have no reason to change what they are doing. Recalling that Y as GDP equals not only total income but also total actual expenditure on goods and services, we can write this equilibrium condition as

$$\text{Actual Expenditure} = \text{Planned Expenditure}$$
$$Y = E.$$

The 45-degree line in Figure 10-3 plots the points where this condition holds. With the addition of the planned-expenditure function, this diagram becomes the Keynesian cross. The equilibrium of this economy is at point A, where the planned-expenditure function crosses the 45-degree line.

How does the economy get to the equilibrium? In this model, inventories play an important role in the adjustment process. Whenever the economy is not in equilibrium, firms experience unplanned changes in inventories, and this induces them to change production levels. Changes in production in turn influence total income and expenditure, moving the economy toward equilibrium.

For example, suppose the economy were ever to find itself with GDP at a level greater than the equilibrium level, such as the level Y_1 in Figure 10-4. In this case, planned expenditure E_1 is less than production Y_1, so firms are selling less than they are producing. Firms add the unsold goods to their stock of inventories. This unplanned rise in inventories induces firms to lay off workers and reduce production, and these actions in turn reduce GDP. This process of

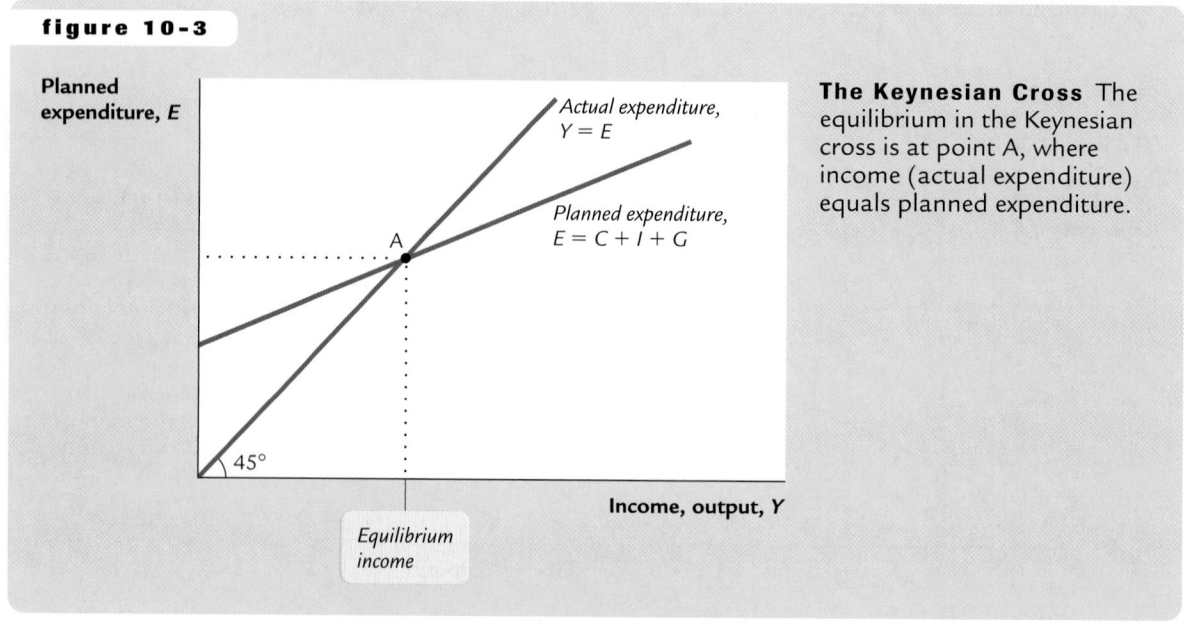

figure 10-3

Planned expenditure, E

Actual expenditure, $Y = E$

Planned expenditure, $E = C + I + G$

A

45°

Income, output, Y

Equilibrium income

The Keynesian Cross The equilibrium in the Keynesian cross is at point A, where income (actual expenditure) equals planned expenditure.

unintended inventory accumulation and falling income continues until income Y falls to the equilibrium level.

Similarly, suppose GDP were at a level lower than the equilibrium level, such as the level Y_2 in Figure 10-4. In this case, planned expenditure E_2 is greater than production Y_2. Firms meet the high level of sales by drawing down their inventories. But when firms see their stock of inventories dwindle, they hire more workers and increase production. GDP rises, and the economy approaches the equilibrium.

figure 10-4

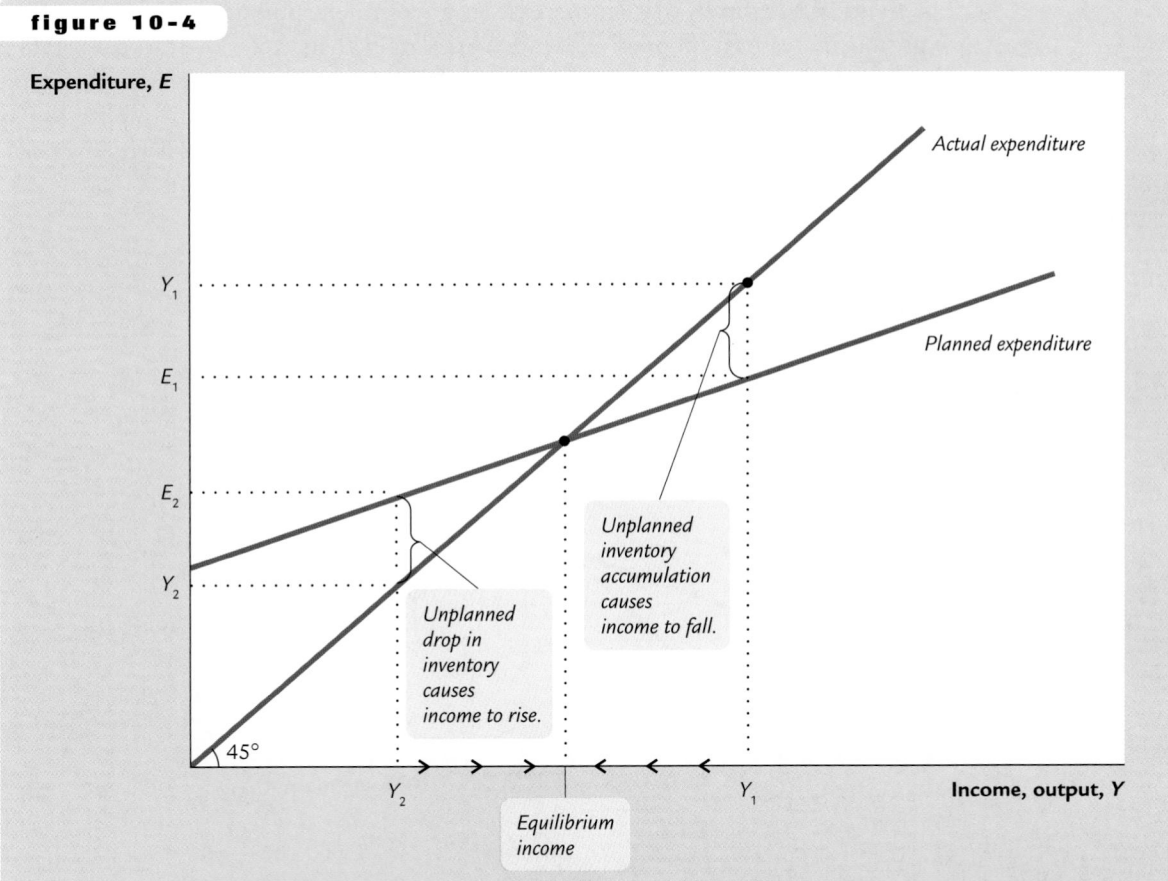

The Adjustment to Equilibrium in the Keynesian Cross If firms were producing at level Y_1, then planned expenditure E_1 would fall short of production, and firms would accumulate inventories. This inventory accumulation would induce firms to reduce production. Similarly, if firms were producing at level Y_2, then planned expenditure E_2 would exceed production, and firms would run down their inventories. This fall in inventories would induce firms to raise production. In both cases, the firms' decisions drive the economy toward equilibrium.

In summary, the Keynesian cross shows how income Y is determined for given levels of planned investment I and fiscal policy G and T. We can use this model to show how income changes when one of these exogenous variables changes.

Fiscal Policy and the Multiplier: Government Purchases Consider how changes in government purchases affect the economy. Because government purchases are one component of expenditure, higher government purchases result in higher planned expenditure for any given level of income. If government purchases rise by ΔG, then the planned-expenditure schedule shifts upward by ΔG, as in Figure 10-5. The equilibrium of the economy moves from point A to point B.

This graph shows that an increase in government purchases leads to an even greater increase in income. That is, ΔY is larger than ΔG. The ratio $\Delta Y/\Delta G$ is called the **government-purchases multiplier;** it tells us how much income rises in response to a $1 increase in government purchases. An implication of the Keynesian cross is that the government-purchases multiplier is larger than 1.

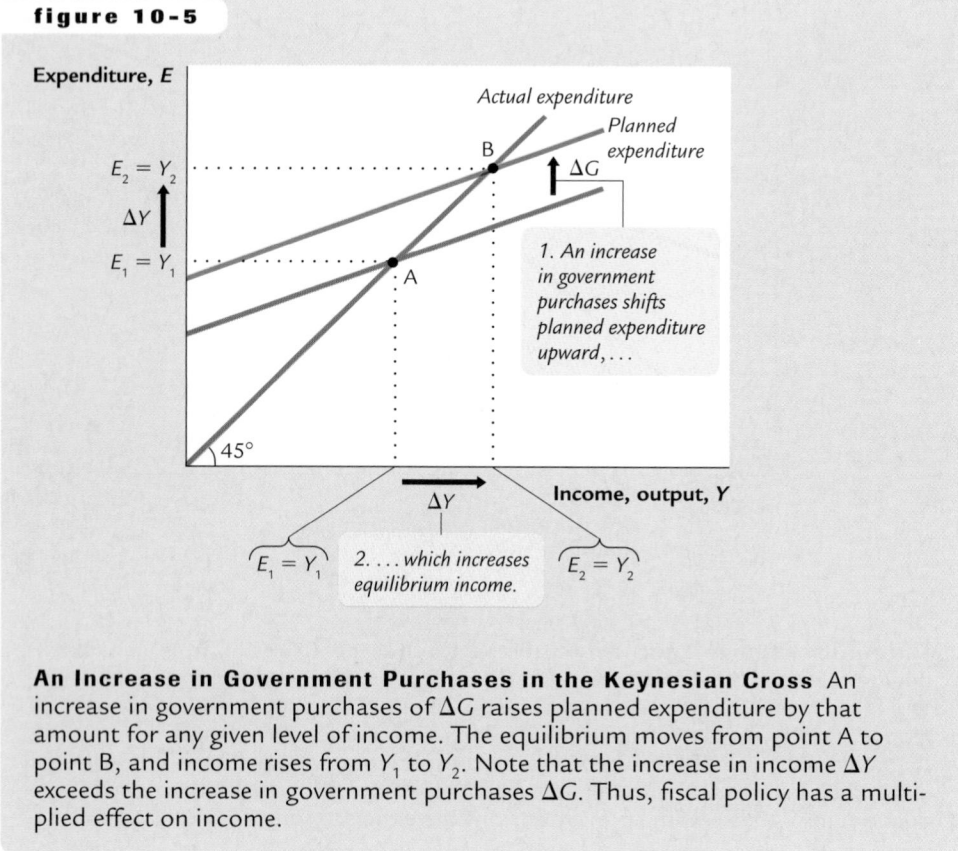

figure 10-5

An Increase in Government Purchases in the Keynesian Cross An increase in government purchases of ΔG raises planned expenditure by that amount for any given level of income. The equilibrium moves from point A to point B, and income rises from Y_1 to Y_2. Note that the increase in income ΔY exceeds the increase in government purchases ΔG. Thus, fiscal policy has a multiplied effect on income.

"Your Majesty, my voyage will not only forge a new route to the spices of the East but also create over three thousand new jobs."

Why does fiscal policy have a multiplied effect on income? The reason is that, according to the consumption function, $C = C(Y - T)$, higher income causes higher consumption. When an increase in government purchases raises income, it also raises consumption, which further raises income, which further raises consumption, and so on. Therefore, in this model, an increase in government purchases causes a greater increase in income.

How big is the multiplier? To answer this question, we trace through each step of the change in income. The process begins when expenditure rises by ΔG, which implies that income rises by ΔG as well. This increase in income in turn raises consumption by $MPC \times \Delta G$, where MPC is the marginal propensity to consume. This increase in consumption raises expenditure and income once again. This second increase in income of $MPC \times \Delta G$ again raises consumption, this time by $MPC \times (MPC \times \Delta G)$, which again raises expenditure and income, and so on. This feedback from consumption to income to consumption continues indefinitely. The total effect on income is

Initial Change in Government Purchases =	ΔG
First Change in Consumption	= $MPC \times \Delta G$
Second Change in Consumption	= $MPC^2 \times \Delta G$
Third Change in Consumption	= $MPC^3 \times \Delta G$
$\vdots$	$\vdots$

$$\Delta Y = (1 + MPC + MPC^2 + MPC^3 + \cdots)\Delta G.$$

The government-purchases multiplier is

$$\Delta Y/\Delta G = 1 + MPC + MPC^2 + MPC^3 + \cdots.$$

This expression for the multiplier is an example of an *infinite geometric series*. A result from algebra allows us to write the multiplier as[2]

$$\Delta Y/\Delta G = 1/(1 - MPC).$$

For example, if the marginal propensity to consume is 0.6, the multiplier is

$$\Delta Y/\Delta G = 1 + 0.6 + 0.6^2 + 0.6^3 + \cdots$$
$$= 1/(1 - 0.6)$$
$$= 2.5.$$

In this case, a $1.00 increase in government purchases raises equilibrium income by $2.50.[3]

Fiscal Policy and the Multiplier: Taxes Consider now how changes in taxes affect equilibrium income. A decrease in taxes of ΔT immediately raises disposable income $Y - T$ by ΔT and, therefore, increases consumption by $MPC \times \Delta T$. For any given level of income Y, planned expenditure is now higher. As Figure 10-6 shows, the planned-expenditure schedule shifts upward by $MPC \times \Delta T$. The equilibrium of the economy moves from point A to point B.

---

[2] *Mathematical note:* We prove this algebraic result as follows. Let

$$z = 1 + x + x^2 + \cdots.$$

Multiply both sides of this equation by x:

$$xz = x + x^2 + x^3 + \cdots.$$

Subtract the second equation from the first:

$$z - xz = 1.$$

Rearrange this last equation to obtain

$$z(1 - x) = 1,$$

which implies

$$z = 1/(1 - x).$$

This completes the proof.

[3] *Mathematical note:* The government-purchases multiplier is most easily derived using a little calculus. Begin with the equation

$$Y = C(Y - T) + I + G.$$

Holding T and I fixed, differentiate to obtain

$$dY = C'dY + dG,$$

and then rearrange to find

$$dY/dG = 1/(1 - C').$$

This is the same as the equation in the text.

figure 10-6

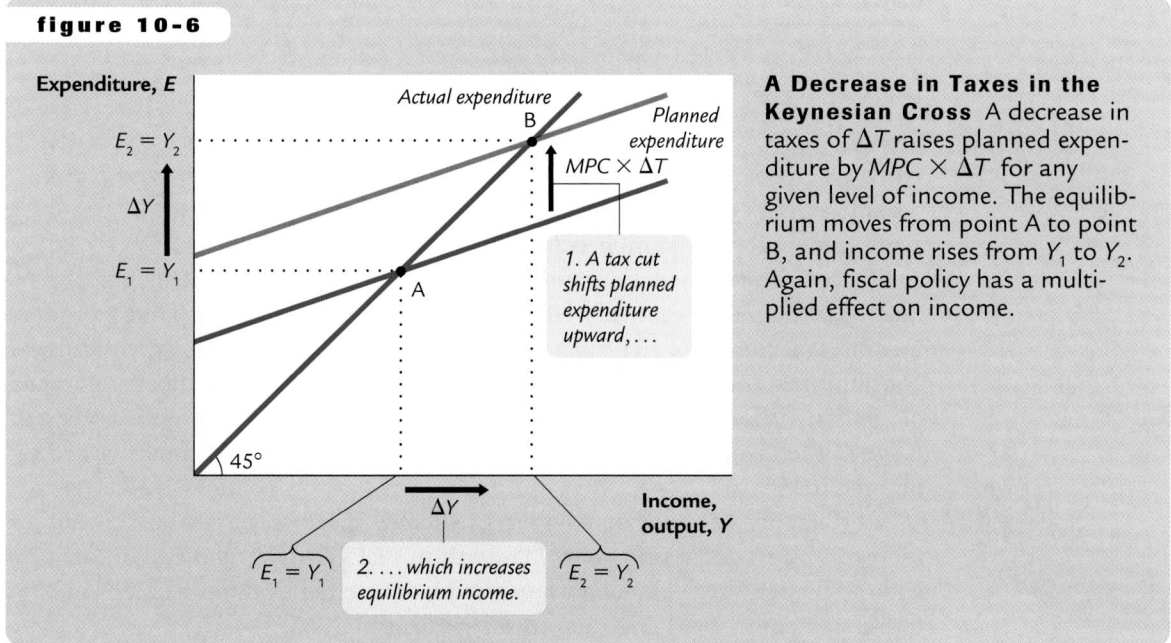

A Decrease in Taxes in the Keynesian Cross A decrease in taxes of ΔT raises planned expenditure by $MPC \times \Delta T$ for any given level of income. The equilibrium moves from point A to point B, and income rises from Y_1 to Y_2. Again, fiscal policy has a multiplied effect on income.

Just as an increase in government purchases has a multiplied effect on income, so does a decrease in taxes. As before, the initial change in expenditure, now $MPC \times \Delta T$, is multiplied by $1/(1 - MPC)$. The overall effect on income of the change in taxes is

$$\Delta Y/\Delta T = -MPC/(1 - MPC).$$

This expression is the **tax multiplier,** the amount income changes in response to a $1 change in taxes. For example, if the marginal propensity to consume is 0.6, then the tax multiplier is

$$\Delta Y/\Delta T = -0.6/(1 - 0.6) = -1.5.$$

In this example, a $1.00 cut in taxes raises equilibrium income by $1.50.[4]

---

[4] *Mathematical note:* As before, the multiplier is most easily derived using a little calculus. Begin with the equation

$$Y = C(Y - T) + I + G.$$

Holding I and G fixed, differentiate to obtain

$$dY = C'(dY - dT),$$

and then rearrange to find

$$dY/dT = -C'/(1 - C').$$

This is the same as the equation in the text.

CASE STUDY

Kennedy, Keynes, and the 1964 Tax Cut

When John F. Kennedy became President of the United States in 1961, he brought to Washington some of the brightest young economists of the day to work on his Council of Economic Advisers. These economists, who had been schooled in the economics of Keynes, brought Keynesian ideas to discussions of economic policy at the highest level.

One of the Council's first proposals was to expand national income by reducing taxes. This eventually led to a substantial cut in personal and corporate income taxes in 1964. The tax cut was intended to stimulate expenditure on consumption and investment and thus lead to higher levels of income and employment. When a reporter asked Kennedy why he advocated a tax cut, Kennedy replied, "To stimulate the economy. Don't you remember your Economics 101?"

As Kennedy's economic advisers predicted, the passage of the tax cut was followed by an economic boom. Growth in real GDP was 5.3 percent in 1964 and 6.0 percent in 1965. The unemployment rate fell from 5.7 percent in 1963 to 5.2 percent in 1964 and then to 4.5 percent in 1965.

Economists continue to debate the source of this rapid growth in the early 1960s. A group called *supply-siders* argues that the economic boom resulted from the incentive effects of the cut in income tax rates. According to supply-siders, when workers are allowed to keep a higher fraction of their earnings, they supply substantially more labor and expand the aggregate supply of goods and services. Keynesians, however, emphasize the impact of tax cuts on aggregate demand. They view the 1964 tax cut as a successful experiment with expansionary fiscal policy and as a confirmation of Keynesian economics.[5]

The Interest Rate, Investment, and the *IS* Curve

The Keynesian cross is only a steppingstone on our path to the *IS–LM* model. The Keynesian cross is useful because it shows how the spending plans of households, firms, and the government determine the economy's income. Yet it makes the simplifying assumption that the level of planned investment I is fixed. As we discussed in Chapter 3, an important macroeconomic relationship is that planned investment depends on the interest rate r.

To add this relationship between the interest rate and investment to our model, we write the level of planned investment as

$$I = I(r).$$

---

[5] For an analysis of the 1964 tax cut by one of Kennedy's economists, see Arthur Okun, "Measuring the Impact of the 1964 Tax Reduction," in W. W. Heller, ed., *Perspectives on Economic Growth* (New York: Random House, 1968); reprinted in Arthur M. Okun, *Economics for Policymaking* (Cambridge, MA: MIT Press, 1983), 405–423.

This investment function is graphed in panel (a) of Figure 10-7. Because the interest rate is the cost of borrowing to finance investment projects, an increase in the interest rate reduces planned investment. As a result, the investment function slopes downward.

To determine how income changes when the interest rate changes, we can combine the investment function with the Keynesian-cross diagram. Because investment is inversely related to the interest rate, an increase in the interest rate from r_1 to r_2 reduces the quantity of investment from $I(r_1)$ to $I(r_2)$. The reduction in planned investment, in turn, shifts the planned-expenditure function downward, as in panel (b) of Figure 10-7. The shift in the planned-expenditure function causes the level of income to fall from Y_1 to Y_2. Hence, an increase in the interest rate lowers income.

The *IS* curve, shown in panel (c) of Figure 10-7, summarizes this relationship between the interest rate and the level of income. In essence, the *IS* curve combines the interaction between r and I expressed by the investment function

figure 10-7

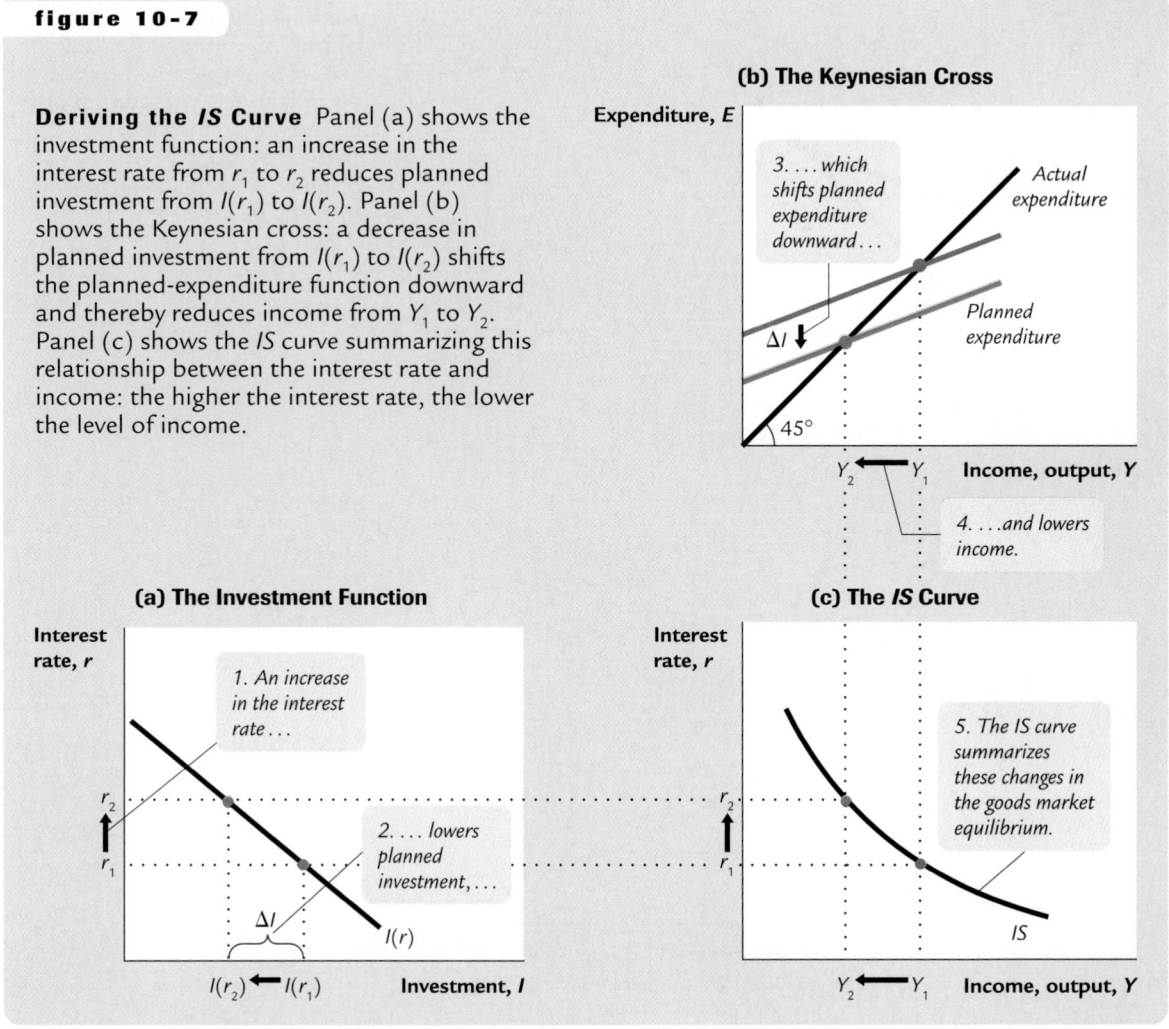

Deriving the *IS* Curve Panel (a) shows the investment function: an increase in the interest rate from r_1 to r_2 reduces planned investment from $I(r_1)$ to $I(r_2)$. Panel (b) shows the Keynesian cross: a decrease in planned investment from $I(r_1)$ to $I(r_2)$ shifts the planned-expenditure function downward and thereby reduces income from Y_1 to Y_2. Panel (c) shows the *IS* curve summarizing this relationship between the interest rate and income: the higher the interest rate, the lower the level of income.

and the interaction between I and Y demonstrated by the Keynesian cross. Because an increase in the interest rate causes planned investment to fall, which in turn causes income to fall, the IS curve slopes downward.

How Fiscal Policy Shifts the *IS* Curve

The IS curve shows us, for any given interest rate, the level of income that brings the goods market into equilibrium. As we learned from the Keynesian cross, the level of income also depends on fiscal policy. The IS curve is drawn

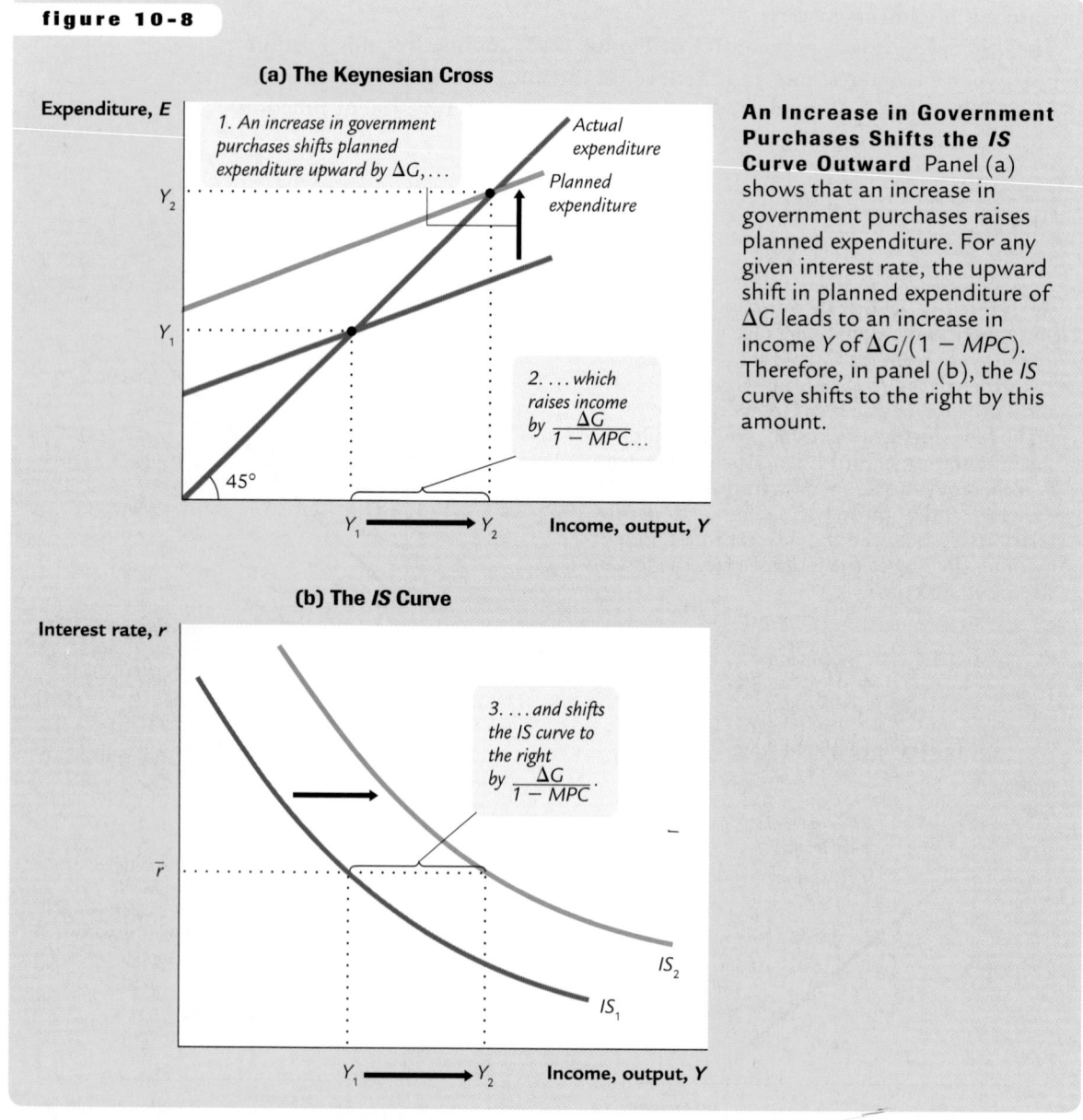

figure 10-8

(a) The Keynesian Cross

Expenditure, E

1. An increase in government purchases shifts planned expenditure upward by ΔG, ...

Y_2

Actual expenditure

Planned expenditure

Y_1

2. ... which raises income by $\frac{\Delta G}{1 - MPC}$ ...

45°

$Y_1 \longrightarrow Y_2$ Income, output, Y

(b) The *IS* Curve

Interest rate, r

3. ... and shifts the IS curve to the right by $\frac{\Delta G}{1 - MPC}$.

$\bar{r}$

IS_2

IS_1

$Y_1 \longrightarrow Y_2$ Income, output, Y

An Increase in Government Purchases Shifts the *IS* Curve Outward Panel (a) shows that an increase in government purchases raises planned expenditure. For any given interest rate, the upward shift in planned expenditure of ΔG leads to an increase in income Y of $\Delta G/(1 - MPC)$. Therefore, in panel (b), the IS curve shifts to the right by this amount.

for a given fiscal policy; that is, when we construct the *IS* curve, we hold *G* and *T* fixed. When fiscal policy changes, the *IS* curve shifts.

Figure 10-8 uses the Keynesian cross to show how an increase in government purchases from G_1 to G_2 shifts the *IS* curve. This figure is drawn for a given interest rate $\bar{r}$ and thus for a given level of planned investment. The Keynesian cross shows that this change in fiscal policy raises planned expenditure and thereby increases equilibrium income from Y_1 to Y_2. Therefore, an increase in government purchases shifts the *IS* curve outward.

We can use the Keynesian cross to see how other changes in fiscal policy shift the *IS* curve. Because a decrease in taxes also expands expenditure and income, it too shifts the *IS* curve outward. A decrease in government purchases or an increase in taxes reduces income; therefore, such a change in fiscal policy shifts the *IS* curve inward.

In summary, the IS curve shows the combinations of the interest rate and the level of income that are consistent with equilibrium in the market for goods and services. The IS curve is drawn for a given fiscal policy. Changes in fiscal policy that raise the demand for goods and services shift the IS curve to the right. Changes in fiscal policy that reduce the demand for goods and services shift the IS curve to the left.

A Loanable-Funds Interpretation of the *IS* Curve

When we first studied the market for goods and services in Chapter 3, we noted an equivalence between the supply and demand for goods and services and the supply and demand for loanable funds. This equivalence provides another way to interpret the *IS* curve.

Recall that the national income accounts identity can be written as

$$Y - C - G = I$$
$$S = I.$$

The left-hand side of this equation is national saving *S,* and the right-hand side is investment *I.* National saving represents the supply of loanable funds, and investment represents the demand for these funds.

To see how the market for loanable funds produces the *IS* curve, substitute the consumption function for *C* and the investment function for *I:*

$$Y - C(Y - T) - G = I(r).$$

The left-hand side of this equation shows that the supply of loanable funds depends on income and fiscal policy. The right-hand side shows that the demand for loanable funds depends on the interest rate. The interest rate adjusts to equilibrate the supply and demand for loans.

As Figure 10-9 illustrates, we can interpret the *IS* curve as showing the interest rate that equilibrates the market for loanable funds for any given level of income. When income rises from Y_1 to Y_2, national saving, which equals $Y - C - G$, increases. (Consumption rises by less than income, because the marginal propensity to consume is less than 1.) As panel (a) shows, the increased

figure 10-9

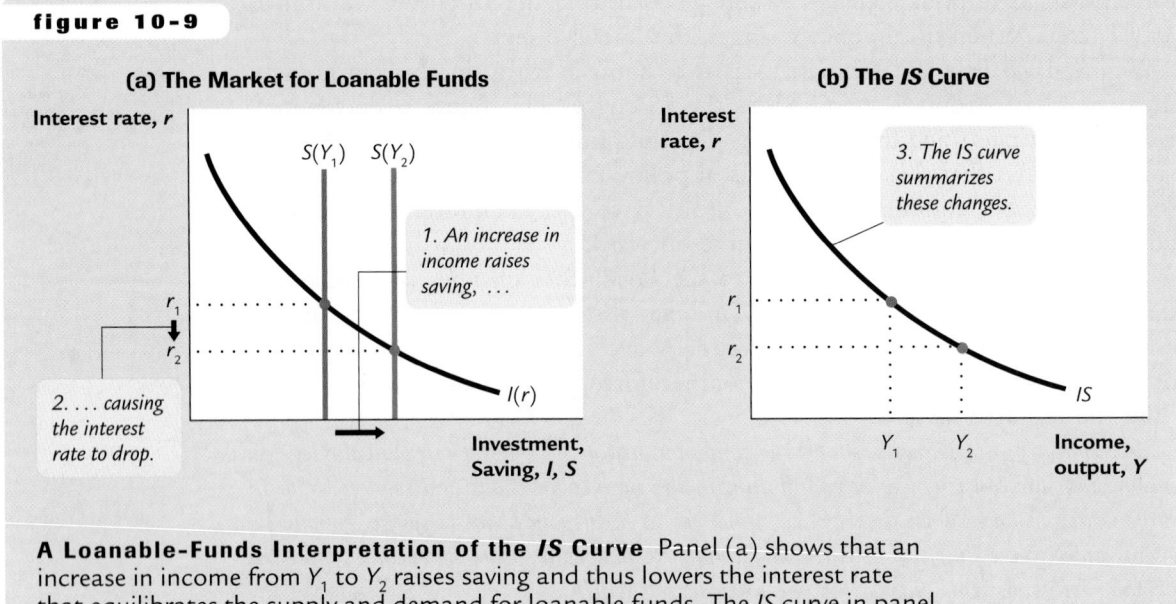

A Loanable-Funds Interpretation of the *IS* Curve Panel (a) shows that an increase in income from Y_1 to Y_2 raises saving and thus lowers the interest rate that equilibrates the supply and demand for loanable funds. The *IS* curve in panel (b) expresses this negative relationship between income and the interest rate.

supply of loanable funds drives down the interest rate from r_1 to r_2. The *IS* curve in panel (b) summarizes this relationship: higher income implies higher saving, which in turn implies a lower equilibrium interest rate. For this reason, the *IS* curve slopes downward.

This alternative interpretation of the *IS* curve also explains why a change in fiscal policy shifts the *IS* curve. An increase in government purchases or a decrease in taxes reduces national saving for any given level of income. The reduced supply of loanable funds raises the interest rate that equilibrates the market. Because the interest rate is now higher for any given level of income, the *IS* curve shifts upward in response to the expansionary change in fiscal policy.

Finally, note that the *IS* curve does not determine either income Y or the interest rate r. Instead, the *IS* curve is a relationship between Y and r arising in the market for goods and services or, equivalently, the market for loanable funds. To determine the equilibrium of the economy, we need another relationship between these two variables, to which we now turn.

10-2| The Money Market and the *LM* Curve

The *LM* curve plots the relationship between the interest rate and the level of income that arises in the market for money balances. To understand this relationship, we begin by looking at a theory of the interest rate, called the **theory of liquidity preference**.

The Theory of Liquidity Preference

In his classic work *The General Theory,* Keynes offered his view of how the in-terest rate is determined in the short run. That explanation is called the theory of liquidity preference, because it posits that the interest rate adjusts to balance the supply and demand for the economy's most liquid asset—money. Just as the Keynesian cross is a building block for the *IS* curve, the theory of liquidity preference is a building block for the *LM* curve.

To develop this theory, we begin with the supply of real money balances. If M stands for the supply of money and P stands for the price level, then M/P is the supply of real money balances. The theory of liquidity preference assumes there is a fixed supply of real balances. That is,

$$(M/P)^s = \overline{M}/\overline{P}.$$

The money supply M is an exogenous policy variable chosen by a central bank, such as the Federal Reserve. The price level P is also an exogenous variable in this model. (We take the price level as given because the $IS-LM$ model—our ultimate goal in this chapter—explains the short run when the price level is fixed.) These assumptions imply that the supply of real balances is fixed and, in particular, does not depend on the interest rate. Thus, when we plot the supply of real money balances against the interest rate in Figure 10-10, we obtain a vertical supply curve.

Next, consider the demand for real money balances. The theory of liquidity preference posits that the interest rate is one determinant of how much money people choose to hold. The reason is that the interest rate is the opportunity cost of holding money: it is what you forgo by holding some of your assets as money, which does not bear interest, instead of as interest-bearing bank deposits or bonds. When the interest rate rises, people want to hold less of their wealth in the form of money. Thus, we can write the demand for real money balances as

$$(M/P)^d = L(r),$$

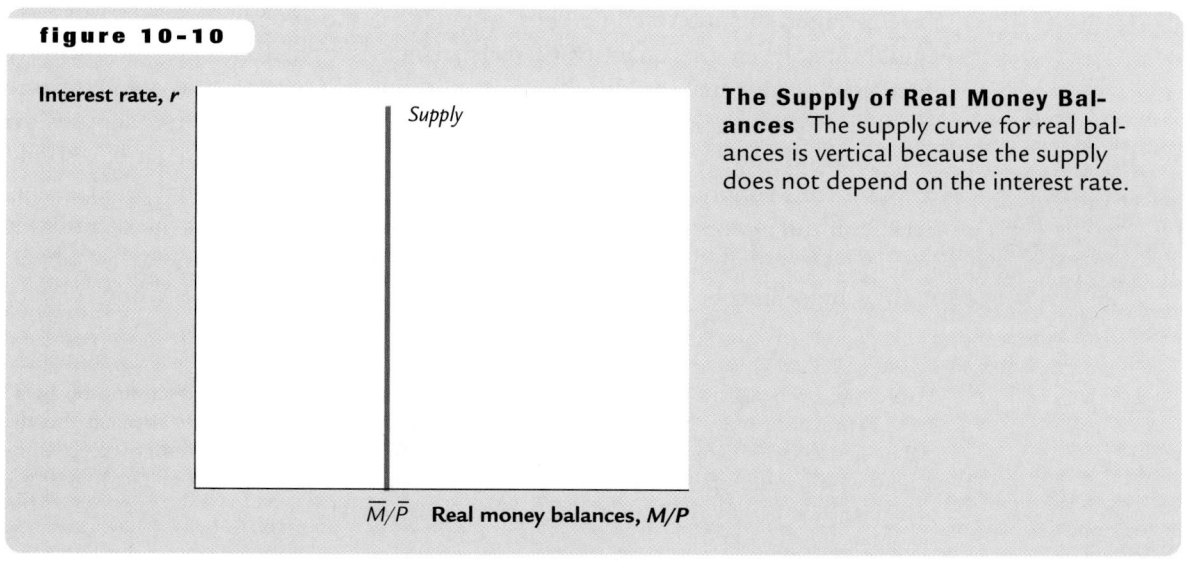

figure 10-10

The Supply of Real Money Bal-ances The supply curve for real bal-ances is vertical because the supply does not depend on the interest rate.

figure 10-11

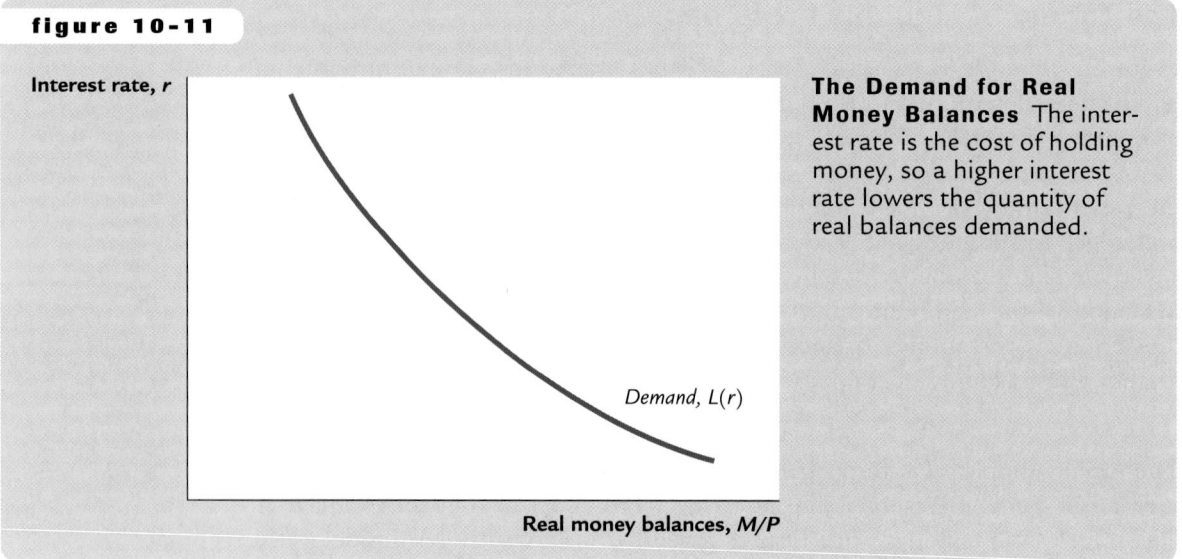

Interest rate, *r*

The Demand for Real Money Balances The interest rate is the cost of holding money, so a higher interest rate lowers the quantity of real balances demanded.

Demand, L(r)

Real money balances, *M/P*

where the function $L(\ )$ shows that the quantity of money demanded depends on the interest rate. Figure 10-11 illustrates this relationship. This demand curve slopes downward because higher interest rates reduce the quantity of real balances demanded.[6]

To explain what interest rate prevails in the economy, we combine the supply and demand for real money balances in Figure 10-12. According to the theory of liquidity preference, the interest rate adjusts to equilibrate the money market. At the equilibrium interest rate, the quantity of real balances demanded equals the quantity supplied.

How does the interest rate get to this equilibrium of money supply and money demand? The adjustment occurs because whenever the money market is not in equilibrium, people try to adjust their portfolios of assets and, in the process, alter the interest rate. For instance, if the interest rate is above the equilibrium level, the quantity of real balances supplied exceeds the quantity demanded. Individuals holding the excess supply of money try to convert some of their non-interest-bearing money into interest-bearing bank deposits or bonds. Banks and bond issuers, who prefer to pay lower interest rates, respond to this excess supply of money by lowering the interest rates they offer. Conversely, if the interest rate is below the equilibrium level, so that the quantity of money demanded exceeds the quantity supplied, individuals try to obtain money by selling bonds or making bank withdrawals. To attract now scarcer

---

[6] Note that *r* is being used to denote the interest rate here, as it was in our discussion of the *IS* curve. More accurately, it is the nominal interest rate that determines money demand and the real interest rate that determines investment. To keep things simple, we are ignoring expected inflation, which creates the difference between the real and nominal interest rates. The role of expected inflation in the *IS–LM* model is explored in Chapter 11.

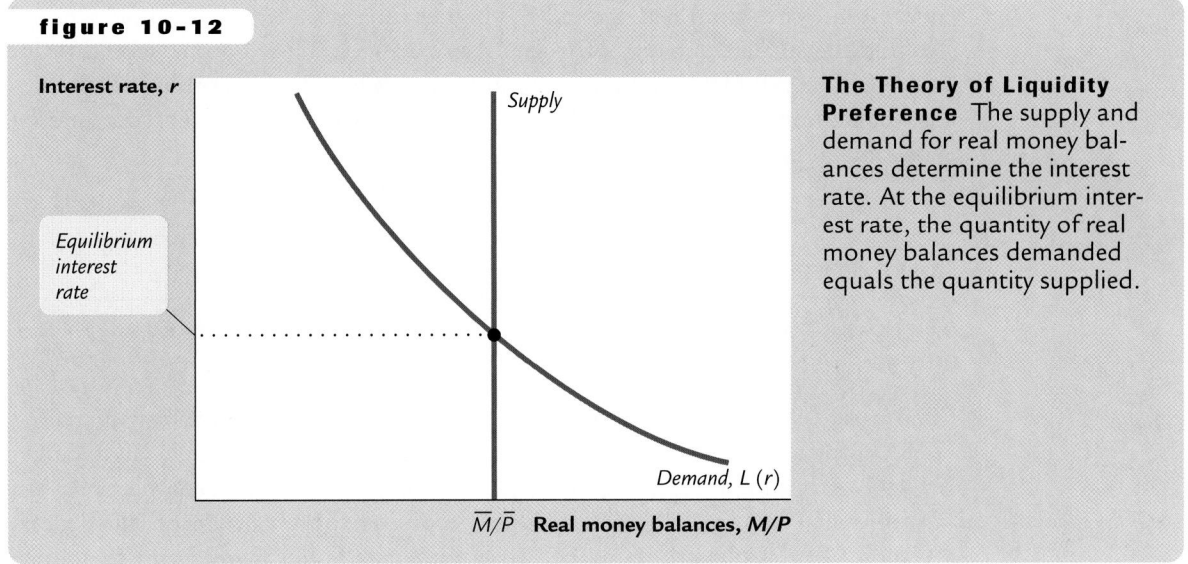

figure 10-12

The Theory of Liquidity Preference The supply and demand for real money balances determine the interest rate. At the equilibrium interest rate, the quantity of real money balances demanded equals the quantity supplied.

funds, banks and bond issuers respond by increasing the interest rates they offer. Eventually, the interest rate reaches the equilibrium level, at which people are content with their portfolios of monetary and nonmonetary assets.

Now that we have seen how the interest rate is determined, we can use the theory of liquidity preference to show how the interest rate responds to changes in the supply of money. Suppose, for instance, that the Fed suddenly decreases the money supply. A fall in M reduces M/P, because P is fixed in the model. The supply of real balances shifts to the left, as in Figure 10–13. The equilibrium

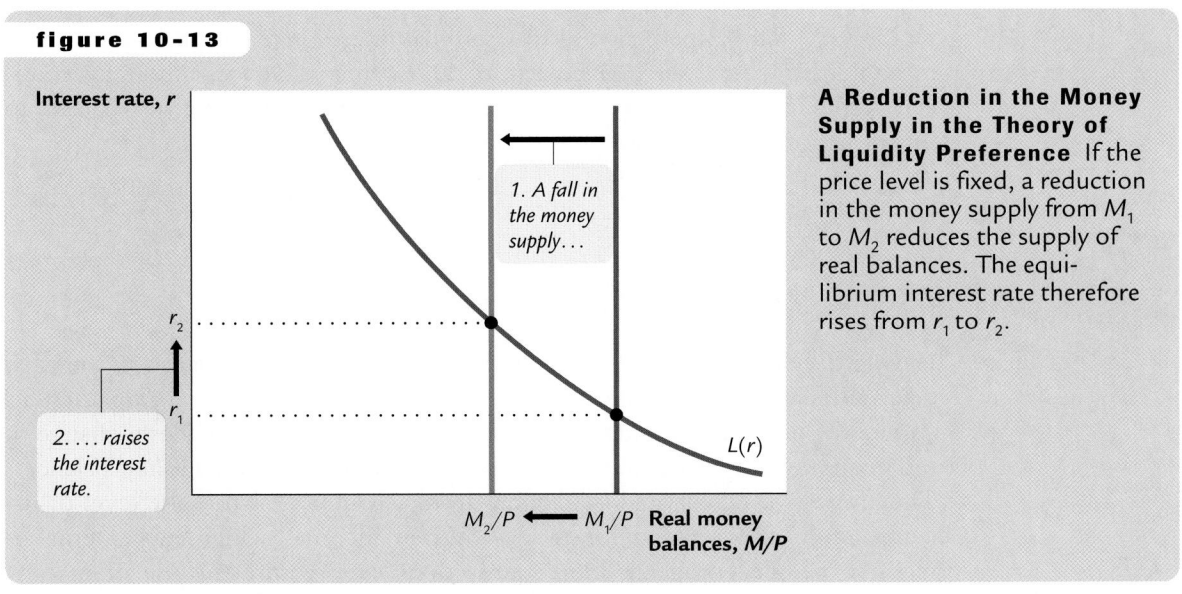

figure 10-13

A Reduction in the Money Supply in the Theory of Liquidity Preference If the price level is fixed, a reduction in the money supply from M_1 to M_2 reduces the supply of real balances. The equilibrium interest rate therefore rises from r_1 to r_2.

interest rate rises from r_1 to r_2, and the higher interest rate makes people satisfied to hold the smaller quantity of real money balances. The opposite would occur if the Fed had suddenly increased the money supply. Thus, according to the theory of liquidity preference, a decrease in the money supply raises the interest rate, and an increase in the money supply lowers the interest rate.

CASE STUDY

Did Paul Volcker's Monetary Tightening Raise or Lower Interest Rates?

The early 1980s saw the largest and quickest reduction in inflation in recent U.S. history. By the late 1970s inflation had reached the double-digit range; in 1979, consumer prices were rising at a rate of 11.3 percent per year. In October 1979, only two months after becoming the chairman of the Federal Reserve, Paul Volcker announced that monetary policy would aim to reduce the rate of inflation. This announcement began a period of tight money that, by 1983, brought the inflation rate down to about 3 percent.

How does such a monetary tightening influence interest rates? According to the theories we have been developing, the answer depends on the time horizon. Our analysis of the Fisher effect in Chapter 7 suggests that in the long run Volcker's change in monetary policy would lower inflation, and this in turn would lead to lower nominal interest rates. Yet the theory of liquidity preference predicts that, in the short run when prices are sticky, anti-inflationary monetary policy would lead to falling real balances and higher nominal interest rates.

Both conclusions are consistent with experience. Nominal interest rates did fall in the 1980s as inflation fell. But comparing the year before the October 1979 announcement and the year after, we find that real balances ($M1$ divided by the CPI) fell 8.3 percent and the nominal interest rate (on short-term commercial loans) rose from 10.1 percent to 11.9 percent. Hence, although a monetary tightening leads to lower nominal interest rates in the long run, it leads to higher nominal interest rates in the short run.

Income, Money Demand, and the *LM* Curve

Having developed the theory of liquidity preference as an explanation for what determines the interest rate, we can now use the theory to derive the *LM* curve. We begin by considering the following question: how does a change in the economy's level of income Y affect the market for real money balances? The answer (which should be familiar from Chapter 7) is that the level of income affects the demand for money. When income is high, expenditure is high, so people engage in more transactions that require the use of money.

figure 10-14

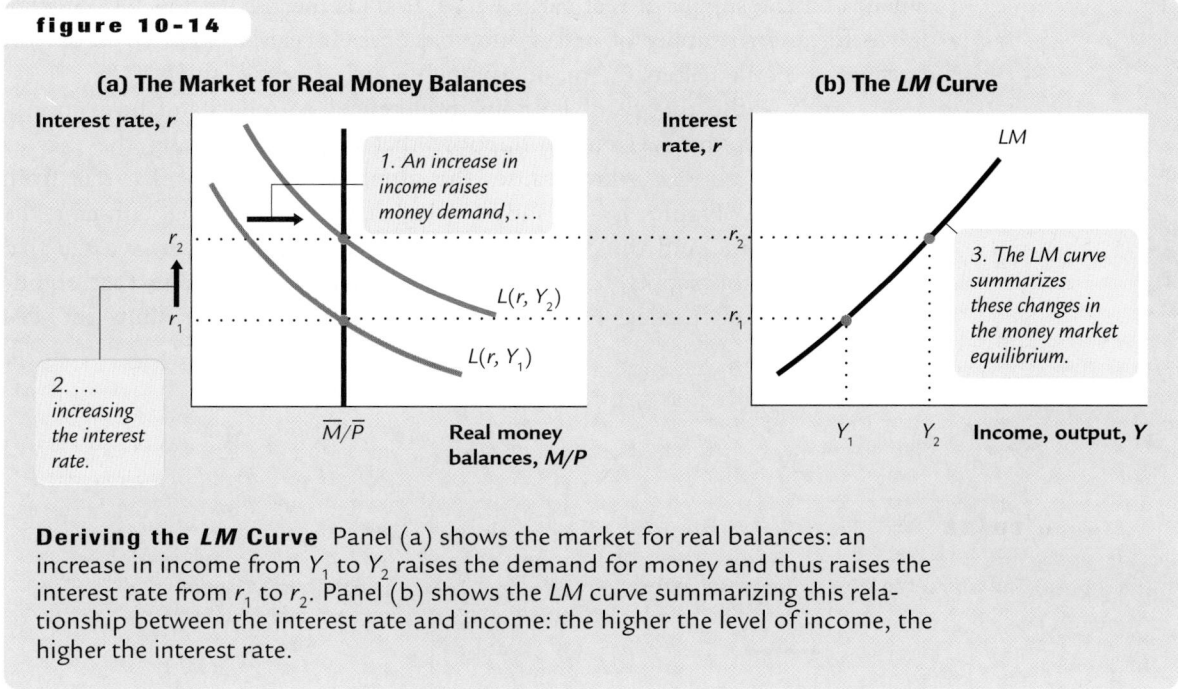

Deriving the *LM* Curve Panel (a) shows the market for real balances: an increase in income from Y_1 to Y_2 raises the demand for money and thus raises the interest rate from r_1 to r_2. Panel (b) shows the *LM* curve summarizing this relationship between the interest rate and income: the higher the level of income, the higher the interest rate.

Thus, greater income implies greater money demand. We can express these ideas by writing the money demand function as

$$(M/P)^d = L(r, Y).$$

The quantity of real money balances demanded is negatively related to the interest rate and positively related to income.

Using the theory of liquidity preference, we can figure out what happens to the equilibrium interest rate when the level of income changes. For example, consider what happens in Figure 10-14 when income increases from Y_1 to Y_2. As panel (a) illustrates, this increase in income shifts the money demand curve to the right. With the supply of real money balances unchanged, the interest rate must rise from r_1 to r_2 to equilibrate the money market. Therefore, according to the theory of liquidity preference, higher income leads to a higher interest rate.

The *LM* curve plots this relationship between the level of income and the interest rate. The higher the level of income, the higher the demand for real money balances, and the higher the equilibrium interest rate. For this reason, the *LM* curve slopes upward, as in panel (b) of Figure 10-14.

How Monetary Policy Shifts the *LM* Curve

The *LM* curve tells us the interest rate that equilibrates the money market at any level of income. Yet, as we saw earlier, the equilibrium interest rate also depends on the supply of real balances, M/P. This means that the LM curve is drawn for a *given* supply of real money balances. If real balances change—for example, if the Fed alters the money supply—the LM curve shifts.

We can use the theory of liquidity preference to understand how monetary policy shifts the LM curve. Suppose that the Fed decreases the money supply from M_1 to M_2, which causes the supply of real balances to fall from M_1/P to M_2/P. Figure 10-15 shows what happens. Holding constant the amount of income and thus the demand curve for real balances, we see that a reduction in the supply of real balances raises the interest rate that equilibrates the money market. Hence, a decrease in real balances shifts the LM curve upward.

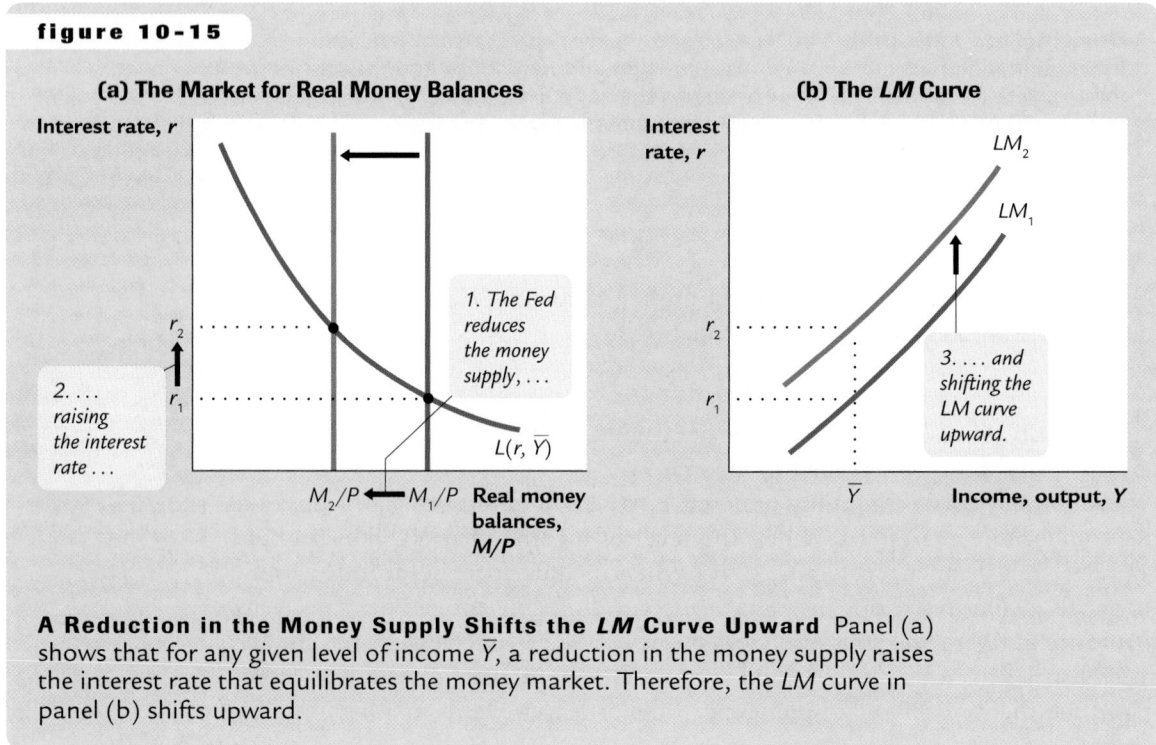

figure 10-15

(a) The Market for Real Money Balances

(b) The *LM* Curve

A Reduction in the Money Supply Shifts the *LM* Curve Upward Panel (a) shows that for any given level of income $\overline{Y}$, a reduction in the money supply raises the interest rate that equilibrates the money market. Therefore, the LM curve in panel (b) shifts upward.

In summary, the LM curve shows the combinations of the interest rate and the level of income that are consistent with equilibrium in the market for real money balances. The LM curve is drawn for a given supply of real money balances. Decreases in the supply of real money balances shift the LM curve upward. Increases in the supply of real money balances shift the LM curve downward.

A Quantity-Equation Interpretation of the *LM* Curve

When we first discussed aggregate demand and the short-run determination of income in Chapter 9, we derived the aggregate demand curve from the quantity theory of money. We described the money market with the quantity equation,

$$MV = PY,$$

and assumed that velocity V is constant. This assumption implies that, for any given price level P, the supply of money M by itself determines the level of income Y. Because the level of income does not depend on the interest rate, the quantity theory is equivalent to a vertical LM curve.

We can derive the more realistic upward-sloping LM curve from the quantity equation by relaxing the assumption that velocity is constant. The assumption of constant velocity is based on the assumption that the demand for real money balances depends only on the level of income. Yet, as we have noted in our discussion of the liquidity-preference model, the demand for real money balances also depends on the interest rate: a higher interest rate raises the cost of holding money and reduces money demand. When people respond to a higher interest rate by holding less money, each dollar they do hold must be used more often to support a given volume of transactions—that is, the velocity of money must increase. We can write this as

$$MV(r) = PY.$$

The velocity function $V(r)$ indicates that velocity is positively related to the interest rate.

This form of the quantity equation yields an LM curve that slopes upward. Because an increase in the interest rate raises the velocity of money, it raises the level of income for any given money supply and price level. The LM curve expresses this positive relationship between the interest rate and income.

This equation also shows why changes in the money supply shift the LM curve. For any given interest rate and price level, the money supply and the level of income must move together. Thus, increases in the money supply shift the LM curve to the right, and decreases in the money supply shift the LM curve to the left.

Keep in mind that the quantity equation is merely another way to express the theory behind the LM curve. This quantity-theory interpretation of the LM curve is substantively the same as that provided by the theory of liquidity preference. In both cases, the LM curve represents a positive relationship between income and the interest rate that arises from the money market.

Finally, remember that the LM curve by itself does not determine either income Y or the interest rate r that will prevail in the economy. Like the IS curve, the LM curve is only a relationship between these two endogenous variables. The IS and LM curves together determine the economy's equilibrium.

10-3 | Conclusion: The Short-Run Equilibrium

We now have all the pieces of the $IS-LM$ model. The two equations of this model are

$$Y = C(Y - T) + I(r) + G \qquad IS,$$
$$M/P = L(r, Y) \qquad\qquad LM.$$

The model takes fiscal policy, G and T, monetary policy M, and the price level P as exogenous. Given these exogenous variables, the IS curve provides the combinations of r and Y that satisfy the equation representing the goods market, and the LM curve provides the combinations of r and Y that satisfy the equation representing the money market. These two curves are shown together in Figure 10-16.

The equilibrium of the economy is the point at which the IS curve and the LM curve cross. This point gives the interest rate r and the level of income Y that satisfy conditions for equilibrium in both the goods market and the money market. In other words, at this intersection, actual expenditure equals planned expenditure, and the demand for real money balances equals the supply.

As we conclude this chapter, let's recall that our ultimate goal in developing the $IS-LM$ model is to analyze short-run fluctuations in economic activity. Figure 10-17 illustrates how the different pieces of our theory fit together. In this chapter we developed the Keynesian cross and the theory of liquidity preference as building blocks for the $IS-LM$ model. As we see more fully in the next chapter, the $IS-LM$ model helps explain the position and slope of the ag-

figure 10-16

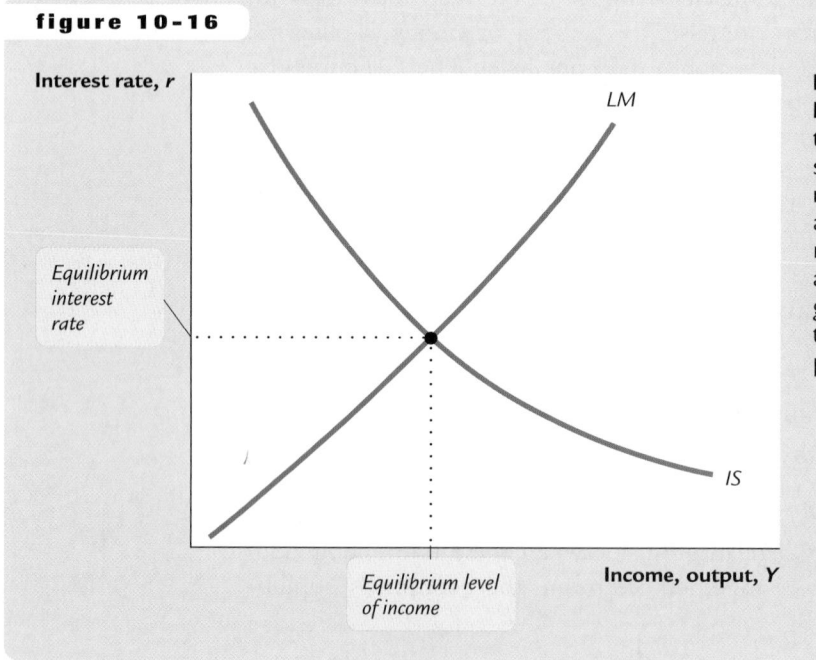

Equilibrium in the _IS–LM_ Model The intersection of the _IS_ and _LM_ curves represents simultaneous equilibrium in the market for goods and services and in the market for real money balances for given values of government spending, taxes, the money supply, and the price level.

figure 10-17

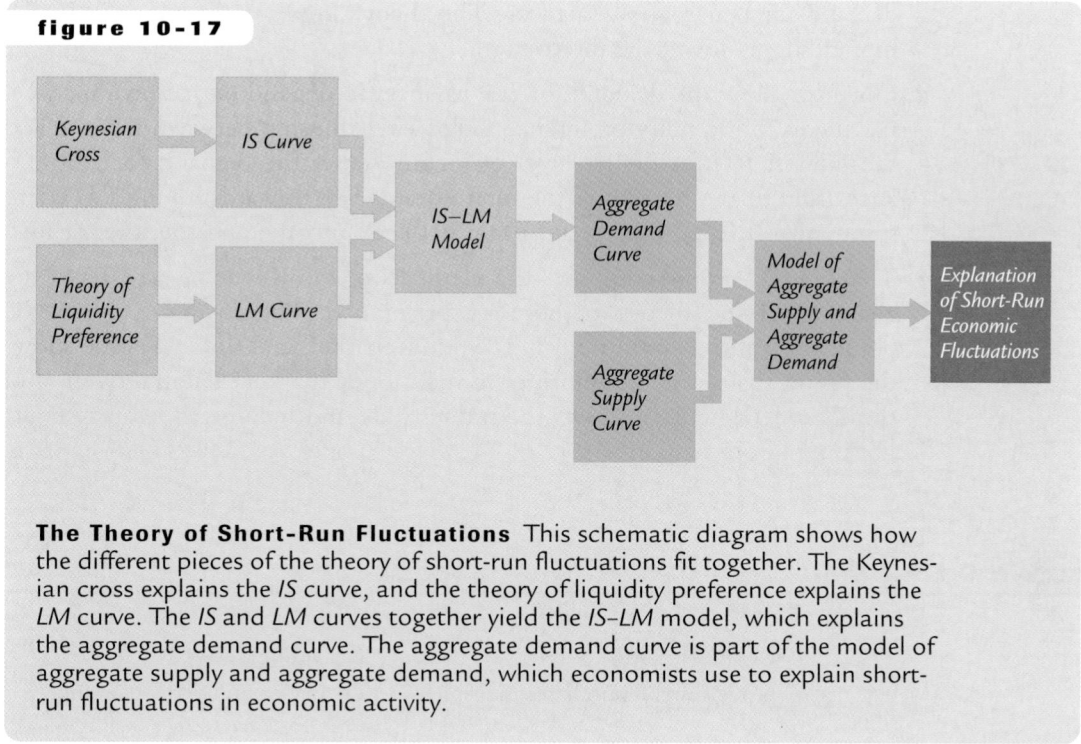

The Theory of Short-Run Fluctuations This schematic diagram shows how the different pieces of the theory of short-run fluctuations fit together. The Keynesian cross explains the *IS* curve, and the theory of liquidity preference explains the *LM* curve. The *IS* and *LM* curves together yield the *IS–LM* model, which explains the aggregate demand curve. The aggregate demand curve is part of the model of aggregate supply and aggregate demand, which economists use to explain short-run fluctuations in economic activity.

gregate demand curve. The aggregate demand curve, in turn, is a piece of the model of aggregate supply and aggregate demand, which economists use to explain the short-run effects of policy changes and other events on national income.

Summary

1. The Keynesian cross is a basic model of income determination. It takes fiscal policy and planned investment as exogenous and then shows that there is one level of national income at which actual expenditure equals planned expenditure. It shows that changes in fiscal policy have a multiplied impact on income.

2. Once we allow planned investment to depend on the interest rate, the Keynesian cross yields a relationship between the interest rate and national income. A higher interest rate lowers planned investment, and this in turn lowers national income. The downward-sloping *IS* curve summarizes this negative relationship between the interest rate and income.

3. The theory of liquidity preference is a basic model of the determination of the interest rate. It takes the money supply and the price level as exogenous and assumes that the interest rate adjusts to equilibrate the supply and

demand for real money balances. The theory implies that increases in the money supply lower the interest rate.

4. Once we allow the demand for real balances to depend on national income, the theory of liquidity preference yields a relationship between income and the interest rate. A higher level of income raises the demand for real balances, and this in turn raises the interest rate. The upward-sloping *LM* curve summarizes this positive relationship between income and the interest rate.

5. The *IS–LM* model combines the elements of the Keynesian cross and the elements of the theory of liquidity preference. The *IS* curve shows the points that satisfy equilibrium in the goods market, and the *LM* curve shows the points that satisfy equilibrium in the money market. The intersection of the *IS* and *LM* curves shows the interest rate and income that satisfy equilibrium in both markets.

KEY CONCEPTS

IS–LM model

IS curve

LM curve

Keynesian cross

Government-purchases multiplier

Tax multiplier

Theory of liquidity preference

QUESTIONS FOR REVIEW

1. Use the Keynesian cross to explain why fiscal policy has a multiplied effect on national income.

2. Use the theory of liquidity preference to explain why an increase in the money supply lowers the

interest rate. What does this explanation assume about the price level?

3. Why does the *IS* curve slope downward?

4. Why does the *LM* curve slope upward?

PROBLEMS AND APPLICATIONS

1. Use the Keynesian cross to predict the impact of

   a. An increase in government purchases.

   b. An increase in taxes.

   c. An equal increase in government purchases and taxes.

2. In the Keynesian cross, assume that the consumption function is given by

$$C = 200 + 0.75\,(Y - T).$$

Planned investment is 100; government purchases and taxes are both 100.

   a. Graph planned expenditure as a function of income.

   b. What is the equilibrium level of income?

   c. If government purchases increase to 125, what is the new equilibrium income?

   d. What level of government purchases is needed to achieve an income of 1,600?

3. Although our development of the Keynesian cross in this chapter assumes that taxes are a fixed amount, in many countries (including the United States) taxes depend on income. Let's represent the tax system by writing tax revenue as

$$T = \overline{T} + tY,$$

where $\overline{T}$ and t are parameters of the tax code. The parameter t is the marginal tax rate: if income rises by \$1, taxes rise by $t \times \$1$.

a. How does this tax system change the way consumption responds to changes in GDP?

b. In the Keynesian cross, how does this tax system alter the government-purchases multiplier?

c. In the $IS-LM$ model, how does this tax system alter the slope of the IS curve?

4. Consider the impact of an increase in thriftiness in the Keynesian cross. Suppose the consumption function is

$$C = \overline{C} + c(Y - T),$$

where $\overline{C}$ is a parameter called *autonomous consumption* and c is the marginal propensity to consume.

a. What happens to equilibrium income when the society becomes more thrifty, as represented by a decline in $\overline{C}$?

b. What happens to equilibrium saving?

c. Why do you suppose this result is called the *paradox of thrift?*

d. Does this paradox arise in the classical model of Chapter 3? Why or why not?

5. Suppose that the money demand function is

$$(M/P)^d = 1,000 - 100r,$$

where r is the interest rate in percent. The money supply M is 1,000 and the price level P is 2.

a. Graph the supply and demand for real money balances.

b. What is the equilibrium interest rate?

c. Assume that the price level is fixed. What happens to the equilibrium interest rate if the supply of money is raised from 1,000 to 1,200?

d. If the Fed wishes to raise the interest rate to 7 percent, what money supply should it set?

chapter

Aggregate Demand II

Science is a parasite: the greater the patient population the better the advance in physiology and pathology; and out of pathology arises therapy. The year 1932 was the trough of the great depression, and from its rotten soil was belatedly begot a new subject that today we call macroeconomics.

— *Paul Samuelson*

In Chapter 10 we assembled the pieces of the *IS–LM* model. We saw that the *IS* curve represents the equilibrium in the market for goods and services, that the *LM* curve represents the equilibrium in the market for real money balances, and that the *IS* and *LM* curves together determine the interest rate and national income in the short run when the price level is fixed. Now we turn our attention to applying the *IS–LM* model to analyze three issues.

First, we examine the potential causes of fluctuations in national income. We use the *IS–LM* model to see how changes in the exogenous variables (government purchases, taxes, and the money supply) influence the endogenous variables (the interest rate and national income). We also examine how various shocks to the goods markets (the *IS* curve) and the money market (the *LM* curve) affect the interest rate and national income in the short run.

Second, we discuss how the *IS–LM* model fits into the model of aggregate supply and aggregate demand we introduced in Chapter 9. In particular, we examine how the *IS–LM* model provides a theory of the slope and position of the aggregate demand curve. Here we relax the assumption that the price level is fixed, and we show that the *IS–LM* model implies a negative relationship between the price level and national income. The model can also tell us what events shift the aggregate demand curve and in what direction.

Third, we examine the Great Depression of the 1930s. As this chapter's opening quotation indicates, this episode gave birth to short-run macroeconomic theory, for it led Keynes and his many followers to think that aggregate demand was the key to understanding fluctuations in national income. With the benefit of hindsight, we can use the *IS–LM* model to discuss the various explanations of this traumatic economic downturn.

11-1| Explaining Fluctuations With the *IS–LM* Model

The intersection of the *IS* curve and the *LM* curve determines the level of national income. When one of these curves shifts, the short-run equilibrium of the economy changes, and national income fluctuates. In this section we examine how changes in policy and shocks to the economy can cause these curves to shift.

How Fiscal Policy Shifts the *IS* Curve and Changes the Short-Run Equilibrium

We begin by examining how changes in fiscal policy (government purchases and taxes) alter the economy's short-run equilibrium. Recall that changes in fiscal policy influence planned expenditure and thereby shift the *IS* curve. The *IS–LM* model shows how these shifts in the *IS* curve affect income and the interest rate.

Changes in Government Purchases   Consider an increase in government purchases of ΔG. The government-purchases multiplier in the Keynesian cross tells us that, at any given interest rate, this change in fiscal policy raises the level of income by $\Delta G/(1 - MPC)$. Therefore, as Figure 11-1 shows, the *IS* curve shifts to the right by this amount. The equilibrium of the economy moves from point A to point B. The increase in government purchases raises both income and the interest rate.

figure 11-1

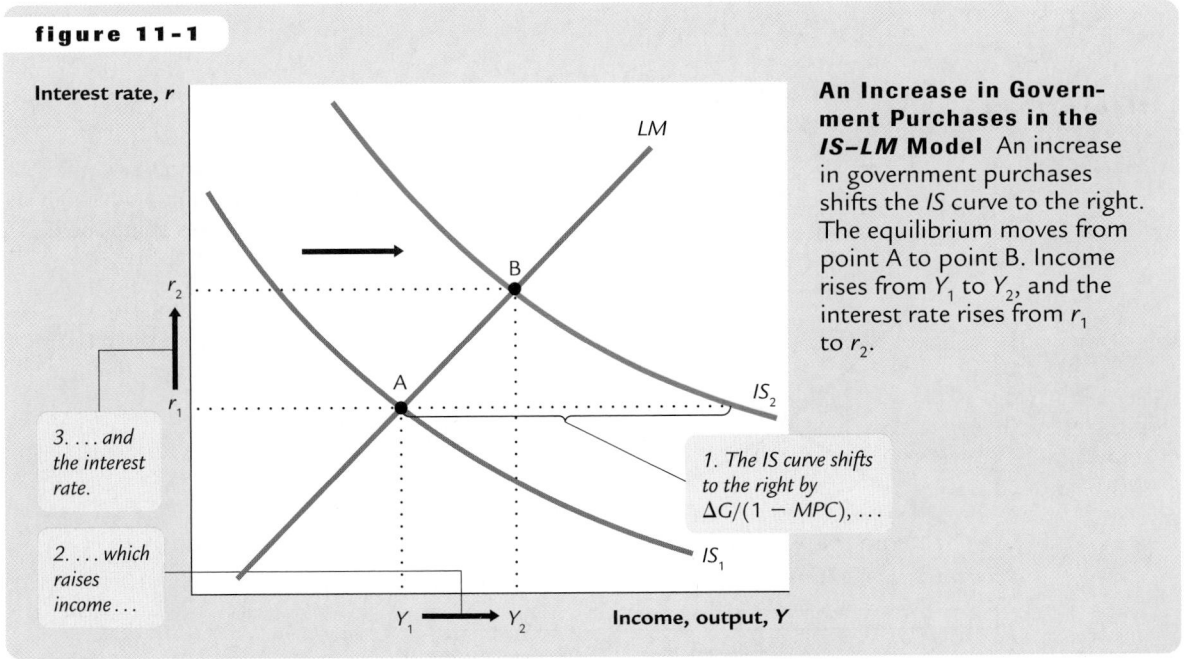

An Increase in Government Purchases in the *IS–LM* Model An increase in government purchases shifts the *IS* curve to the right. The equilibrium moves from point A to point B. Income rises from Y_1 to Y_2, and the interest rate rises from r_1 to r_2.

Interest rate, *r*

LM

B

r_2

A

IS_2

r_1

3. . . . and the interest rate.

1. The IS curve shifts to the right by $\Delta G/(1 - MPC)$, . . .

2. . . . which raises income . . .

IS_1

Y_1 ⟶ Y_2 Income, output, *Y*

To understand fully what's happening in Figure 11-1, it helps to keep in mind the building blocks for the $IS-LM$ model from the preceding chapter—the Keynesian cross and the theory of liquidity preference. Here is the story. When the government increases its purchases of goods and services, the economy's planned expenditure rises. The increase in planned expenditure stimulates the production of goods and services, which causes total income Y to rise. These effects should be familiar from the Keynesian cross.

Now consider the money market, as described by the theory of liquidity preference. Because the economy's demand for money depends on income, the rise in total income increases the quantity of money demanded at every interest rate. The supply of money has not changed, however, so higher money demand causes the equilibrium interest rate r to rise.

The higher interest rate arising in the money market, in turn, has ramifications back in the goods market. When the interest rate rises, firms cut back on their investment plans. This fall in investment partially offsets the expansionary effect of the increase in government purchases. Thus, the increase in income in response to a fiscal expansion is smaller in the $IS-LM$ model than it is in the Keynesian cross (where investment is assumed to be fixed). You can see this in Figure 11-1. The horizontal shift in the IS curve equals the rise in equilibrium income in the Keynesian cross. This amount is larger than the increase in equilibrium income here in the $IS-LM$ model. The difference is explained by the crowding out of investment due to a higher interest rate.

Changes in Taxes In the $IS-LM$ model, changes in taxes affect the economy much the same as changes in government purchases do, except that taxes affect expenditure through consumption. Consider, for instance, a decrease in taxes

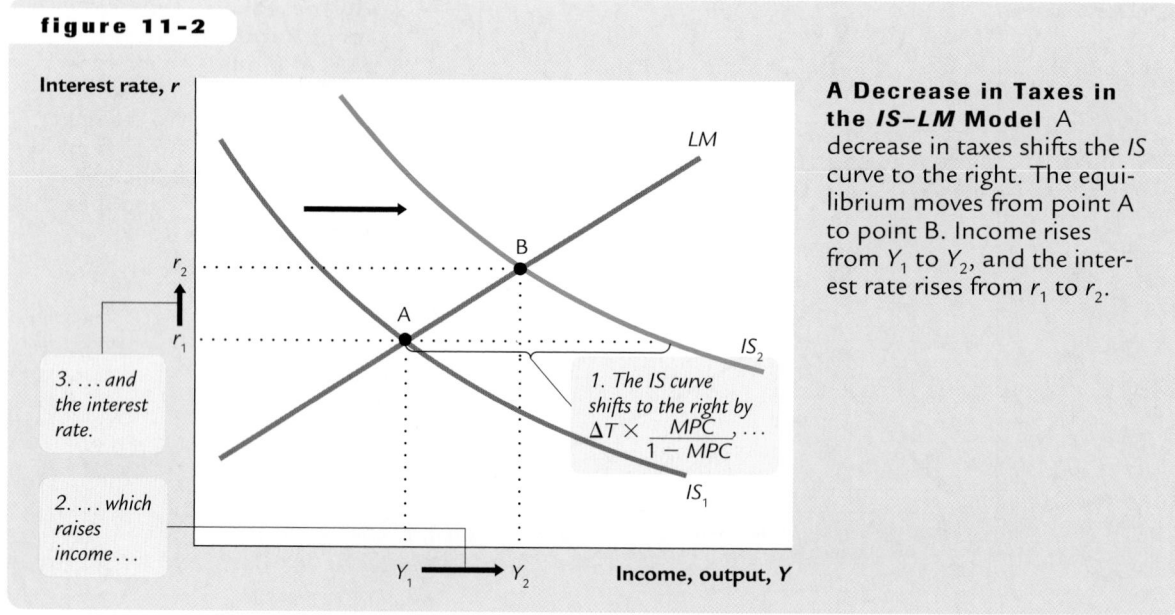

figure 11-2

A Decrease in Taxes in the *IS–LM* Model A decrease in taxes shifts the *IS* curve to the right. The equilibrium moves from point A to point B. Income rises from Y_1 to Y_2, and the interest rate rises from r_1 to r_2.

of ΔT. The tax cut encourages consumers to spend more and, therefore, increases planned expenditure. The tax multiplier in the Keynesian cross tells us that, at any given interest rate, this change in policy raises the level of income by $\Delta T \times MPC/(1 - MPC)$. Therefore, as Figure 11-2 illustrates, the *IS* curve shifts to the right by this amount. The equilibrium of the economy moves from point A to point B. The tax cut raises both income and the interest rate. Once again, because the higher interest rate depresses investment, the increase in income is smaller in the *IS–LM* model than it is in the Keynesian cross.

How Monetary Policy Shifts the *LM* Curve and Changes the Short-Run Equilibrium

We now examine the effects of monetary policy. Recall that a change in the money supply alters the interest rate that equilibrates the money market for any given level of income and, thereby, shifts the *LM* curve. The *IS–LM* model shows how a shift in the *LM* curve affects income and the interest rate.

Consider an increase in the money supply. An increase in M leads to an increase in real money balances M/P, because the price level P is fixed in the short run. The theory of liquidity preference shows that for any given level of income, an increase in real money balances leads to a lower interest rate. Therefore, the *LM* curve shifts downward, as in Figure 11-3. The equilibrium moves from point A to point B. The increase in the money supply lowers the interest rate and raises the level of income.

Once again, to tell the story that explains the economy's adjustment from point A to point B, we rely on the building blocks of the *IS–LM* model—the Keynesian cross and the theory of liquidity preference. This time, we begin

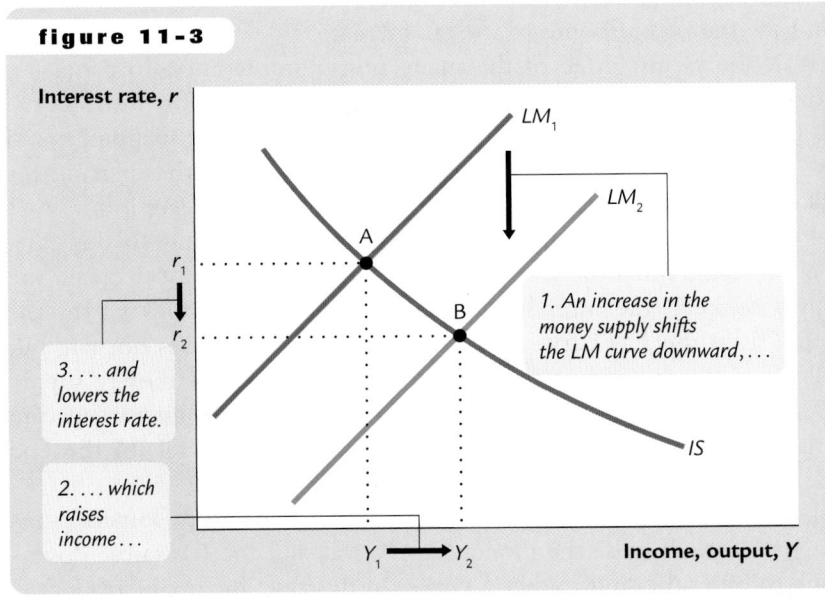

figure 11-3

An Increase in the Money Supply in the *IS–LM* Model An increase in the money supply shifts the *LM* curve downward. The equilibrium moves from point A to point B. Income rises from Y_1 to Y_2, and the interest rate falls from r_1 to r_2.

with the money market, where the monetary policy action occurs. When the Federal Reserve increases the supply of money, people have more money than they want to hold at the prevailing interest rate. As a result, they start depositing this extra money in banks or use it to buy bonds. The interest rate r then falls until people are willing to hold all the extra money that the Fed has created; this brings the money market to a new equilibrium. The lower interest rate, in turn, has ramifications for the goods market. A lower interest rate stimulates planned investment, which increases planned expenditure, production, and income Y.

Thus, the $IS-LM$ model shows that monetary policy influences income by changing the interest rate. This conclusion sheds light on our analysis of monetary policy in Chapter 9. In that chapter we showed that in the short run, when prices are sticky, an expansion in the money supply raises income. But we did not discuss *how* a monetary expansion induces greater spending on goods and services—a process that is called the **monetary transmission mechanism.** The $IS-LM$ model shows that an increase in the money supply lowers the interest rate, which stimulates investment and thereby expands the demand for goods and services.

The Interaction Between Monetary and Fiscal Policy

When analyzing any change in monetary or fiscal policy, it is important to keep in mind that the policymakers who control these policy tools are aware of what the other policymakers are doing. A change in one policy, therefore, may influence the other, and this interdependence may alter the impact of a policy change.

For example, suppose the Congress were to raise taxes. What effect should this policy have on the economy? According to the $IS-LM$ model, the answer depends on how the Fed responds to the tax increase.

Figure 11-4 shows just three of the many possible outcomes. In panel (a), the Fed holds the money supply constant. The tax increase shifts the IS curve to the left. Income falls (because higher taxes reduce consumer spending), and the interest rate falls (because lower income shifts downward the demand for money). The fall in income indicates that the tax hike causes a recession.

In panel (b), the Fed wants to hold the interest rate constant. In this case, when the tax increase shifts the IS curve to the left, the Fed must decrease the money supply to keep the interest rate at its original level. This fall in the money supply shifts the LM curve upward. The interest rate does not fall, but income falls by a larger amount than if the Fed had held the money supply constant. Whereas in panel (a) the lower interest rate stimulated investment and partially offset the contractionary effect of the tax hike, in panel (b) the Fed deepens the recession by keeping the interest rate high.

In panel (c), the Fed wants to prevent the tax increase from lowering income. It must, therefore, raise the money supply and shift the LM curve downward enough to offset the shift in the IS curve. In this case, the tax increase does not cause a recession, but it does cause a large fall in the interest rate. Although

figure 11-4

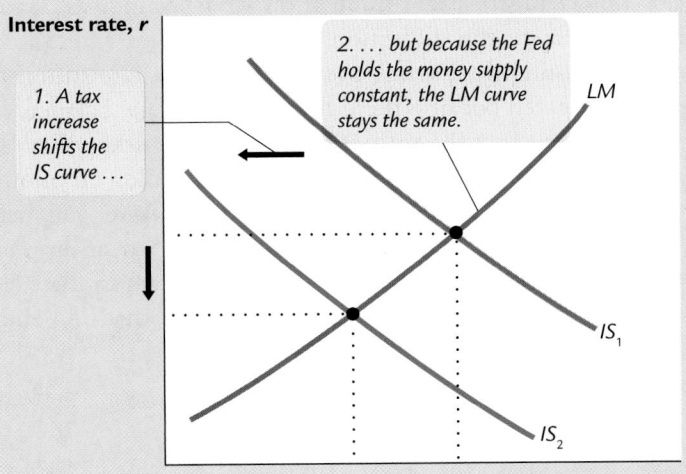

(a) Fed Holds Money Supply Constant

Interest rate, *r*

1. A tax increase shifts the IS curve . . .

2. . . . but because the Fed holds the money supply constant, the LM curve stays the same.

LM

IS_1

IS_2

Income, output, *Y*

The Response of the Economy to a Tax Increase How the economy responds to a tax increase depends on how the monetary authority responds. In panel (a) the Fed holds the money supply constant. In panel (b) the Fed holds the interest rate constant by reducing the money supply. In panel (c) the Fed holds the level of income constant by raising the money supply.

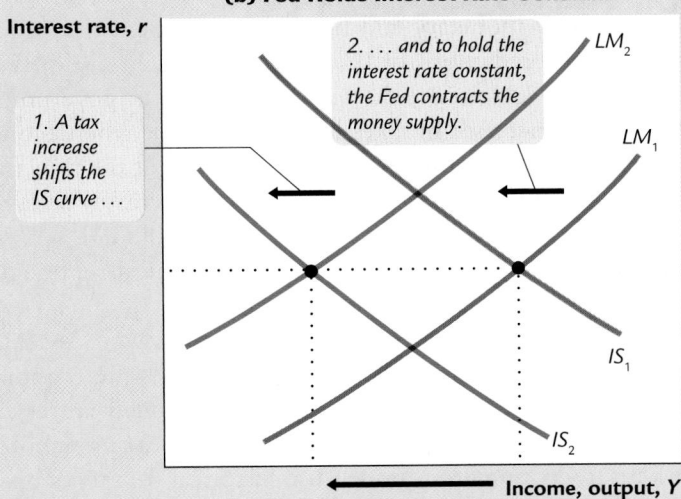

(b) Fed Holds Interest Rate Constant

Interest rate, *r*

1. A tax increase shifts the IS curve . . .

2. . . . and to hold the interest rate constant, the Fed contracts the money supply.

LM_2

LM_1

IS_1

IS_2

Income, output, *Y*

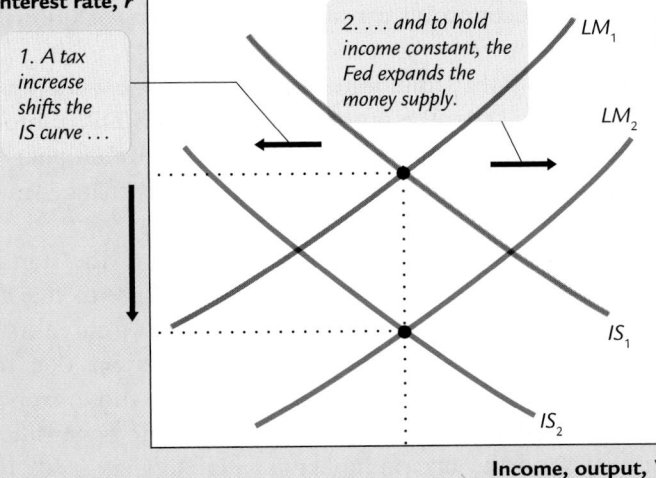

(c) Fed Holds Income Constant

Interest rate, *r*

1. A tax increase shifts the IS curve . . .

2. . . . and to hold income constant, the Fed expands the money supply.

LM_1

LM_2

IS_1

IS_2

Income, output, *Y*

| 287

the level of income is not changed, the combination of a tax increase and a monetary expansion does change the allocation of the economy's resources. The higher taxes depress consumption, while the lower interest rate stimulates investment. Income is not affected because these two effects exactly balance.

From this example we can see that the impact of a change in fiscal policy depends on the policy the Fed pursues — that is, on whether it holds the money supply, the interest rate, or the level of income constant. More generally, whenever analyzing a change in one policy, we must make an assumption about its effect on the other policy. What assumption is most appropriate depends on the case at hand and the many political considerations that lie behind economic policymaking.

CASE STUDY

Policy Analysis With Macroeconometric Models

The *IS–LM* model shows how monetary and fiscal policy influence the equilibrium level of income. The predictions of the model, however, are qualitative, not quantitative. The *IS–LM* model shows that increases in government purchases raise GDP and that increases in taxes lower GDP. But when economists analyze specific policy proposals, they need to know not just the direction of the effect but the size as well. For example, if Congress increases taxes by $100 billion and if monetary policy is not altered, how much will GDP fall? To answer this question, economists need to go beyond the graphical representation of the *IS–LM* model.

Macroeconometric models of the economy provide one way to evaluate policy proposals. A *macroeconometric model* is a model that describes the economy quantitatively, rather than just qualitatively. Many of these models are essentially more complicated and more realistic versions of our *IS–LM* model. The economists who build macroeconometric models use historical data to estimate parameters such as the marginal propensity to consume, the sensitivity of investment to the interest rate, and the sensitivity of money demand to the interest rate. Once a model is built, economists can simulate the effects of alternative policies with the help of a computer.

Table 11-1 shows the fiscal-policy multipliers implied by one widely used macroeconometric model, the Data Resources Incorporated (DRI) model, named for the economic forecasting firm that developed it. The multipliers are given for two assumptions about how the Fed might respond to changes in fiscal policy.

One assumption about monetary policy is that the Fed keeps the nominal interest rate constant. That is, when fiscal policy shifts the *IS* curve to the right or to the left, the Fed adjusts the money supply to shift the *LM* curve in the same direction. Because there is no crowding out of investment due to a changing interest rate, the fiscal-policy multipliers are similar to those from the Keynesian cross. The DRI model indicates that, in this case, the government-purchases multiplier is 1.93 and the tax multiplier is −1.19. That is, a $100-

table 11-1

The Fiscal-Policy Multipliers in the DRI Model

Assumption About Monetary Policy	$\Delta Y/\Delta G$	$\Delta Y/\Delta T$
Nominal interest rate held constant	1.93	−1.19
Money supply held constant	0.60	−0.26

Note: This table gives the fiscal-policy multipliers for a sustained change in government purchases or in personal income taxes. These multipliers are for the fourth quarter after the policy change is made.
Source: Otto Eckstein, *The DRI Model of the U.S. Economy* (New York: McGraw-Hill, 1983), 169.

billion increase in government purchases raises GDP by $193 billion, and a $100-billion increase in taxes lowers GDP by $119 billion.

The second assumption about monetary policy is that the Fed keeps the money supply constant so that the *LM* curve does not shift. In this case, there is substantial crowding out, so the multipliers are much smaller. The government-purchases multiplier is only 0.60, and the tax multiplier is only −0.26. That is, a $100-billion increase in government purchases raises GDP by $60 billion, and a $100-billion increase in taxes lowers GDP by $26 billion.

Table 11-1 shows that the fiscal-policy multipliers are very different under the two assumptions about monetary policy. The impact of any change in fiscal policy depends crucially on how the Fed responds to that change.

Shocks in the *IS–LM* Model

Because the *IS–LM* model shows how national income is determined in the short run, we can use the model to examine how various economic disturbances affect income. So far we have seen how changes in fiscal policy shift the *IS* curve and how changes in monetary policy shift the *LM* curve. Similarly, we can group other disturbances into two categories: shocks to the *IS* curve and shocks to the *LM* curve.

Shocks to the *IS* curve are exogenous changes in the demand for goods and services. Some economists, including Keynes, have emphasized that such changes in demand can arise from investors' *animal spirits*—exogenous and perhaps self-fulfilling waves of optimism and pessimism. For example, suppose that firms become pessimistic about the future of the economy and that this pessimism causes them to build fewer new factories. This reduction in the demand for investment goods causes a contractionary shift in the investment function: at every interest rate, firms want to invest less. The fall in investment reduces planned expenditure and shifts the *IS* curve to the left, reducing income and employment. This fall in equilibrium income in part validates the firms' initial pessimism.

---

f y i

WHAT IS THE FED'S POLICY INSTRUMENT—THE MONEY SUPPLY OR THE INTEREST RATE?

Our analysis of monetary policy has been based on the assumption that the Fed influences the economy by controlling the money supply. By contrast, when you hear about Fed policy in the media, the policy instrument mentioned most often is the *federal funds rate,* which is the interest rate that banks charge one another for overnight loans. Which is right? The answer is both.

In recent years, the Fed has used the federal funds rate as its short-term policy instrument. This means that when the Federal Open Market Committee meets every six weeks to set monetary policy, it votes on a target for this interest rate that will apply until the next meeting. After the meeting is over, the Fed's bond traders in New York are told to conduct the open-market operations necessary to hit that target. These open-market operations change the money supply and shift the *LM* curve so that the equilibrium interest rate (determined by the intersection of the *IS* and *LM* curves) equals the target interest rate that the Federal Open Market Committee has chosen.

As a result of this operating procedure, Fed policy is often discussed in terms of changing interest rates. Keep in mind, however, that behind these changes in interest rates are the necessary changes in the money supply. A newspaper might report, for instance, that "the Fed has lowered interest rates." To be more precise, we can translate this statement as meaning "the Federal Open Market Committee has instructed the Fed bond traders to buy bonds in open-market operations so as to increase the money supply, shift the *LM* curve, and reduce the equilibrium interest rate to hit a new lower target."

Why has the Fed chosen to use an interest rate, rather than the money supply, as its short-term policy instrument? One possible answer is that shocks to the *LM* curve are more prevalent than shocks to the *IS* curve. If so, a policy of targeting the interest rate leads to greater macroeconomic stability than a policy of targeting the money supply. (Problem 7 at the end of this chapter asks you to analyze this issue.) Another possible answer is that interest rates are easier to measure than the money supply. As we saw in Chapter 7, the Fed has several different measures of money—M1, M2, and so on—which sometimes move in different directions. Rather than deciding which measure is best, the Fed avoids the question by using the federal funds rate as its short-term policy instrument.

Shocks to the *IS* curve may also arise from changes in the demand for consumer goods. Suppose, for instance, that the election of a popular president increases consumer confidence in the economy. This induces consumers to save less for the future and consume more today. We can interpret this change as an upward shift in the consumption function. This shift in the consumption function increases planned expenditure and shifts the *IS* curve to the right, and this raises income.

Shocks to the *LM* curve arise from exogenous changes in the demand for money. For example, suppose that new restrictions on credit-card availability increase the amount of money people choose to hold. According to the theory of liquidity preference, when money demand rises, the interest rate necessary to equilibrate the money market is higher (for any given level of income and money supply). Hence, an increase in money demand shifts the *LM* curve upward, which tends to raise the interest rate and depress income.

In summary, several kinds of events can cause economic fluctuations by shifting the *IS* curve or the *LM* curve. Remember, however, that such fluctuations are not inevitable. Policymakers can try to use the tools of monetary and fiscal policy to offset exogenous shocks. If policymakers are sufficiently quick and skillful (admittedly, a big if), shocks to the *IS* or *LM* curves need not lead to fluctuations in income or employment.

11-2 *IS–LM* as a Theory of Aggregate Demand

We have been using the *IS–LM* model to explain national income in the short run when the price level is fixed. To see how the *IS–LM* model fits into the model of aggregate supply and aggregate demand introduced in Chapter 9, we now examine what happens in the *IS–LM* model if the price level is allowed to change. As was promised when we began our study of this model, the *IS–LM* model provides a theory to explain the position and slope of the aggregate demand curve.

From the *IS–LM* Model to the Aggregate Demand Curve

Recall from Chapter 9 that the aggregate demand curve describes a relationship between the price level and the level of national income. In Chapter 9 this relationship was derived from the quantity theory of money. The analysis showed that for a given money supply, a higher price level implies a lower level of income. Increases in the money supply shift the aggregate demand curve to the right, and decreases in the money supply shift the aggregate demand curve to the left.

To understand the determinants of aggregate demand more fully, we now use the *IS–LM* model, rather than the quantity theory, to derive the aggregate demand curve. First, we use the *IS–LM* model to show why national income falls as the price level rises—that is, why the aggregate demand curve is downward sloping. Second, we examine what causes the aggregate demand curve to shift.

To explain why the aggregate demand curve slopes downward, we examine what happens in the *IS–LM* model when the price level changes. This is done in Figure 11-5. For any given money supply *M,* a higher price level *P* reduces the supply of real money balances *M/P.* A lower supply of real money balances shifts the *LM* curve upward, which raises the equilibrium interest rate and lowers the equilibrium level of income, as shown in panel (a). Here the price level rises from P_1 to P_2, and income falls from Y_1 to Y_2. The aggregate demand curve in panel (b) plots this negative relationship between national income and the price level. In other words, the aggregate demand curve shows the set of equilibrium points that arise in the *IS–LM* model as we vary the price level and see what happens to income.

What causes the aggregate demand curve to shift? Because the aggregate demand curve is merely a summary of results from the *IS–LM* model, events that shift the *IS* curve or the *LM* curve (for a given price level) cause the aggregate demand curve to shift. For instance, an increase in the money supply raises income in the *IS–LM* model for any given price level; it thus shifts the aggregate demand curve to the right, as shown in panel (a) of Figure 11-6. Similarly, an increase in government purchases or a decrease in taxes raises income in the

figure 11-5

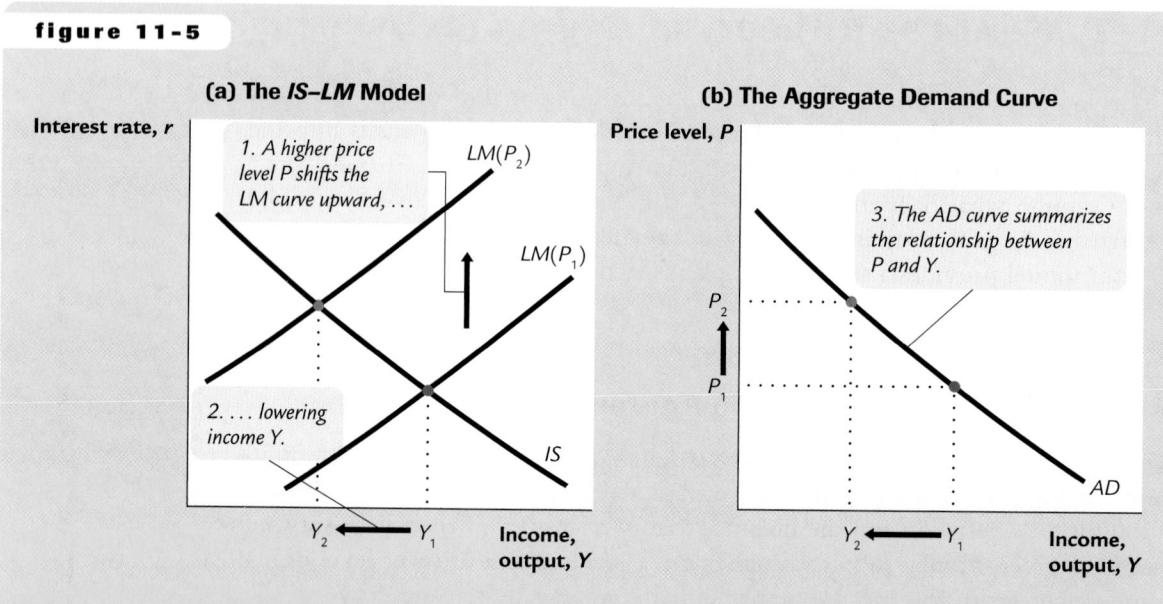

Deriving the Aggregate Demand Curve With the *IS–LM* Model Panel (a) shows the *IS–LM* model: an increase in the price level from P_1 to P_2 lowers real money balances and thus shifts the *LM* curve upward. The shift in the *LM* curve lowers income from Y_1 to Y_2. Panel (b) shows the aggregate demand curve summarizing this relationship between the price level and income: the higher the price level, the lower the level of income.

IS–LM model for a given price level; it also shifts the aggregate demand curve to the right, as shown in panel (b) of Figure 11-6. Conversely, a decrease in the money supply, a decrease in government purchases, or an increase in taxes lowers income in the *IS–LM* model and shifts the aggregate demand curve to the left.

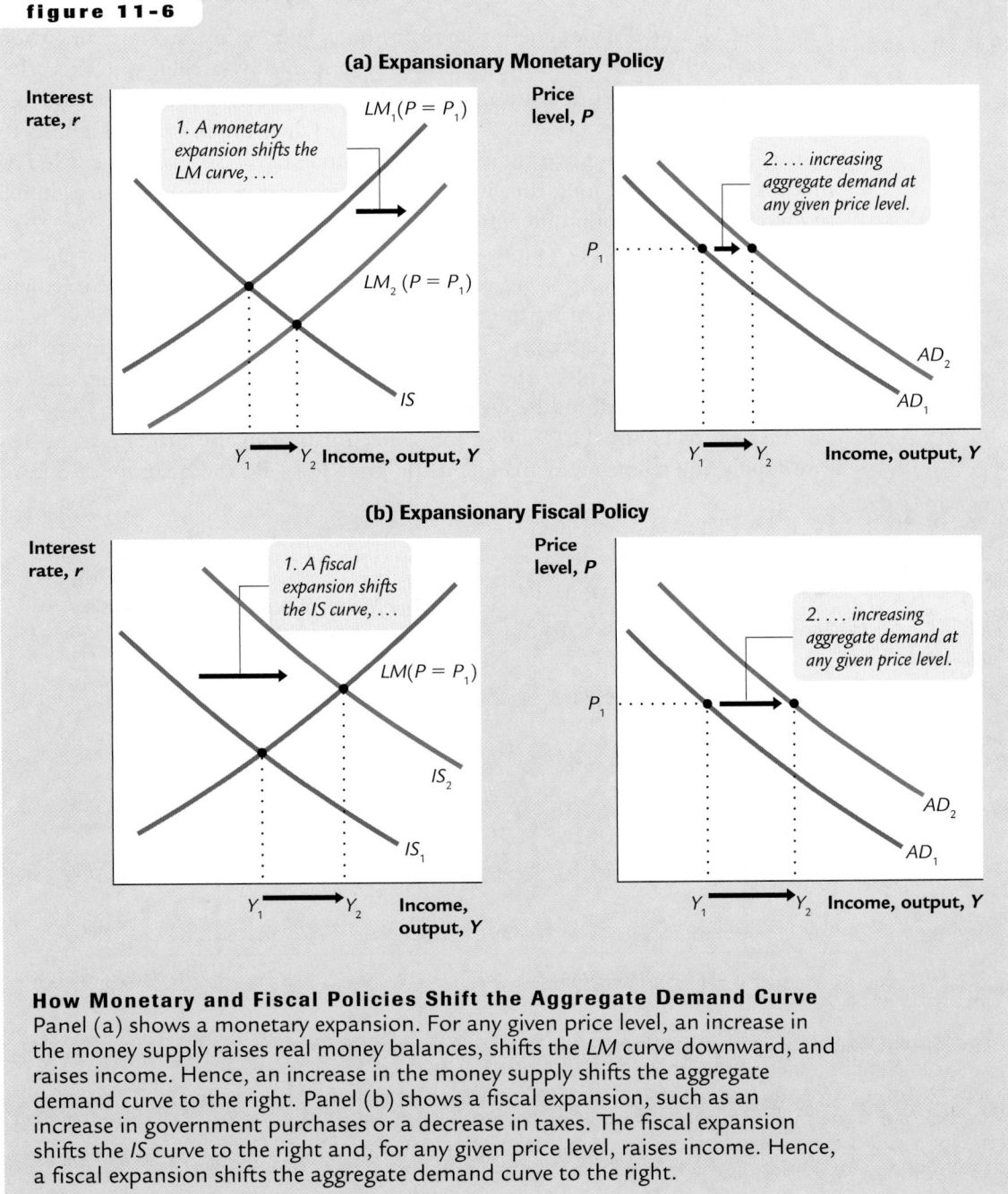

How Monetary and Fiscal Policies Shift the Aggregate Demand Curve
Panel (a) shows a monetary expansion. For any given price level, an increase in the money supply raises real money balances, shifts the *LM* curve downward, and raises income. Hence, an increase in the money supply shifts the aggregate demand curve to the right. Panel (b) shows a fiscal expansion, such as an increase in government purchases or a decrease in taxes. The fiscal expansion shifts the *IS* curve to the right and, for any given price level, raises income. Hence, a fiscal expansion shifts the aggregate demand curve to the right.

We can summarize these results as follows: *A change in income in the IS–LM model resulting from a change in the price level represents a movement along the aggregate demand curve. A change in income in the IS–LM model for a fixed price level represents a shift in the aggregate demand curve.*

The *IS–LM* Model in the Short Run and the Long Run

The *IS–LM* model is designed to explain the economy in the short run when the price level is fixed. Yet, now that we have seen how a change in the price level influences the equilibrium in the *IS–LM* model, we can also use the model to describe the economy in the long run when the price level adjusts to ensure that the economy produces at its natural rate. By using the *IS–LM* model to describe the long run, we can show clearly how the Keynesian model of income determination differs from the classical model of Chapter 3.

Panel (a) of Figure 11-7 shows the three curves that are necessary for understanding the short-run and long-run equilibria: the *IS* curve, the *LM* curve, and the vertical line representing the natural rate of output $\overline{Y}$. The *LM* curve is, as always, drawn for a fixed price level, P_1. The short-run equilibrium of the economy is point K, where the *IS* curve crosses the *LM* curve. Notice that in this short-run equilibrium, the economy's income is less than its natural rate.

Panel (b) of Figure 11-7 shows the same situation in the diagram of aggregate supply and aggregate demand. At the price level P_1, the quantity of output

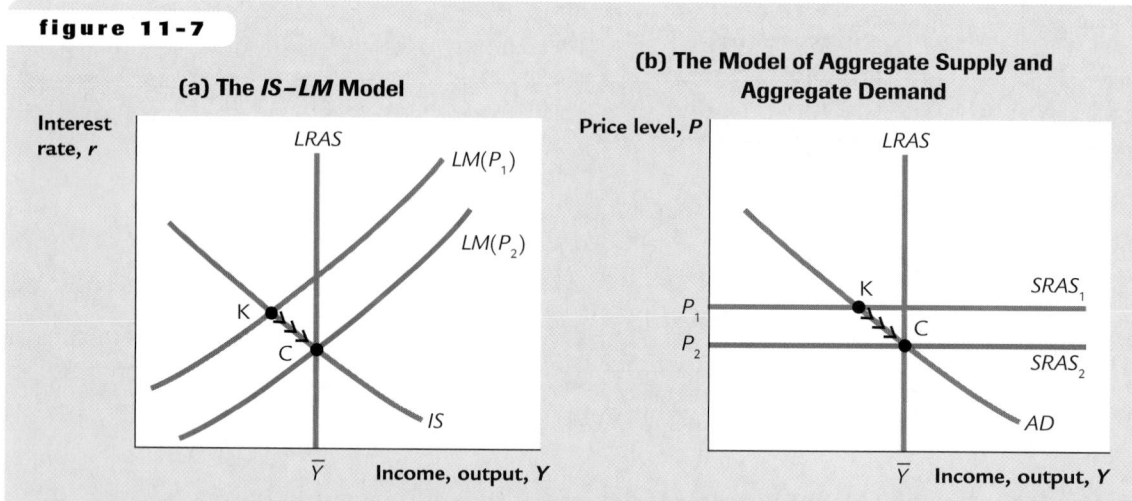

figure 11-7

(a) The *IS–LM* Model

(b) The Model of Aggregate Supply and Aggregate Demand

The Short-Run and Long-Run Equilibria We can compare the short-run and long-run equilibria using either the *IS–LM* diagram in panel (a) or the aggregate supply–aggregate demand diagram in panel (b). In the short run, the price level is stuck at P_1. The short-run equilibrium of the economy is therefore point K. In the long run, the price level adjusts so that the economy is at the natural rate. The long-run equilibrium is therefore point C.

demanded is below the natural rate. In other words, at the existing price level, there is insufficient demand for goods and services to keep the economy producing at its potential.

In these two diagrams we can examine the short-run equilibrium at which the economy finds itself and the long-run equilibrium toward which the economy gravitates. Point K describes the short-run equilibrium, because it assumes that the price level is stuck at P_1. Eventually, the low demand for goods and services causes prices to fall, and the economy moves back toward its natural rate. When the price level reaches P_2, the economy is at point C, the long-run equilibrium. The diagram of aggregate supply and aggregate demand shows that at point C, the quantity of goods and services demanded equals the natural rate of output. This long-run equilibrium is achieved in the $IS-LM$ diagram by a shift in the LM curve: the fall in the price level raises real money balances and therefore shifts the LM curve to the right.

We can now see the key difference between Keynesian and classical approaches to the determination of national income. The Keynesian assumption (represented by point K) is that the price level is stuck. Depending on monetary policy, fiscal policy, and the other determinants of aggregate demand, output may deviate from the natural rate. The classical assumption (represented by point C) is that the price level is fully flexible. The price level adjusts to ensure that national income is always at the natural rate.

To make the same point somewhat differently, we can think of the economy as being described by three equations. The first two are the IS and LM equations:

$$Y = C(Y - T) + I(r) + G \qquad IS,$$
$$M/P = L(r, Y) \qquad\qquad LM.$$

The IS equation describes the goods market, and the LM equation describes the money market. These two equations contain three endogenous variables: Y, P, and r. The Keynesian approach is to complete the model with the assumption of fixed prices, so the Keynesian third equation is

$$P = P_1.$$

This assumption implies that r and Y must adjust to satisfy the IS and LM equations. The classical approach is to complete the model with the assumption that output reaches the natural rate, so the classical third equation is

$$Y = \overline{Y}.$$

This assumption implies that r and P must adjust to satisfy the IS and LM equations.

Which assumption is most appropriate? The answer depends on the time horizon. The classical assumption best describes the long run. Hence, our long-run analysis of national income in Chapter 3 and prices in Chapter 7 assumes that output equals the natural rate. The Keynesian assumption best describes the short run. Therefore, our analysis of economic fluctuations relies on the assumption of a fixed price level.

What Happened During the Great Depression?

Year	Unemployment Rate (1)	Real GNP (2)	Consumption (2)	Investment (2)	Government Purchases (2)
1929	3.2	203.6	139.6	40.4	22.0
1930	8.9	183.5	130.4	27.4	24.3
1931	16.3	169.5	126.1	16.8	25.4
1932	24.1	144.2	114.8	4.7	24.2
1933	25.2	141.5	112.8	5.3	23.3
1934	22.0	154.3	118.1	9.4	26.6
1935	20.3	169.5	125.5	18.0	27.0
1936	17.0	193.2	138.4	24.0	31.8
1937	14.3	203.2	143.1	29.9	30.8
1938	19.1	192.9	140.2	17.0	33.9
1939	17.2	209.4	148.2	24.7	35.2
1940	14.6	227.2	155.7	33.0	36.4

Source: Historical Statistics of the United States, Colonial Times to 1970, Parts I and II (Washington, DC: U.S. Department of Commerce, Bureau of Census, 1975).
Note: (1) The unemployment rate is series D9. (2) Real GNP, consumption, investment, and government purchases are series F3, F48, F52, and F66, and are measured in billions of 1958 dollars. (3) The interest rate is the prime Commercial

11-3 | The Great Depression

Now that we have developed the model of aggregate demand, let's use it to address the question that originally motivated Keynes: what caused the Great Depression? Even today, more than half a century after the event, economists continue to debate the cause of this major economic downturn. The Great Depression provides an extended case study to show how economists use the *IS–LM* model to analyze economic fluctuations.[1]

Before turning to the explanations economists have proposed, look at Table 11-2, which presents some statistics regarding the Depression. These statistics are the battlefield on which debate about the Depression takes place. What do you think happened? An *IS* shift? An *LM* shift? Or something else?

---

[1] For a flavor of the debate, see Milton Friedman and Anna J. Schwartz, *A Monetary History of the United States, 1867–1960* (Princeton, NJ: Princeton University Press, 1963); Peter Temin, *Did Monetary Forces Cause the Great Depression?* (New York: W. W. Norton, 1976); the essays in Karl Brunner, ed., *The Great Depression Revisited* (Boston: Martinus Nijhoff, 1981); and the symposium on the Great Depression in the Spring 1993 issue of the *Journal of Economic Perspectives*.

Year	Nominal Interest Rate (3)	Money Supply (4)	Price Level (5)	Inflation (6)	Real Money Balances (7)
1929	5.9	26.6	50.6	—	52.6
1930	3.6	25.8	49.3	−2.6	52.3
1931	2.6	24.1	44.8	−10.1	54.5
1932	2.7	21.1	40.2	−9.3	52.5
1933	1.7	19.9	39.3	−2.2	50.7
1934	1.0	21.9	42.2	7.4	51.8
1935	0.8	25.9	42.6	0.9	60.8
1936	0.8	29.6	42.7	0.2	62.9
1937	0.9	30.9	44.5	4.2	69.5
1938	0.8	30.5	43.9	−1.3	69.5
1939	0.6	34.2	43.2	−1.6	79.1
1940	0.6	39.7	43.9	1.6	90.3

Paper rate, 4–6 months, series x445. (4) The money supply is series x414, currency plus demand deposits, measured in billions of dollars. (5) The price level is the GNP deflator (1958 = 100), series E1. (6) The inflation rate is the percentage change in the price level series. (7) Real money balances, calculated by dividing the money supply by the price level and multiplying by 100, are in billions of 1958 dollars.

The Spending Hypothesis: Shocks to the *IS* Curve

Table 11-2 shows that the decline in income in the early 1930s coincided with falling interest rates. This fact has led some economists to suggest that the cause of the decline may have been a contractionary shift in the *IS* curve. This view is sometimes called the *spending hypothesis,* because it places primary blame for the Depression on an exogenous fall in spending on goods and services.

Economists have attempted to explain this decline in spending in several ways. Some argue that a downward shift in the consumption function caused the contractionary shift in the *IS* curve. The stock market crash of 1929 may have been partly responsible for this shift: by reducing wealth and increasing uncertainty about the future prospects of the U.S. economy, the crash may have induced consumers to save more of their income rather than spending it.

Others explain the decline in spending by pointing to the large drop in investment in housing. Some economists believe that the residential investment boom of the 1920s was excessive and that once this "overbuilding" became apparent, the demand for residential investment declined drastically. Another possible explanation for the fall in residential investment is the reduction in immigration in the 1930s: a more slowly growing population demands less new housing.

Once the Depression began, several events occurred that could have reduced spending further. First, many banks failed in the early 1930s, in part because of inadequate bank regulation, and these bank failures may have exacerbated the fall in investment spending. Banks play the crucial role of getting the funds available for investment to those households and firms that can best use them. The closing of many banks in the early 1930s may have prevented some businesses from getting the funds they needed for capital investment and, therefore, may have led to a further contractionary shift in the investment function.[2]

In addition, the fiscal policy of the 1930s caused a contractionary shift in the *IS* curve. Politicians at that time were more concerned with balancing the budget than with using fiscal policy to keep production and employment at their natural rates. The Revenue Act of 1932 increased various taxes, especially those falling on lower- and middle-income consumers.[3] The Democratic platform of that year expressed concern about the budget deficit and advocated an "immediate and drastic reduction of governmental expenditures." In the midst of historically high unemployment, policymakers searched for ways to raise taxes and reduce government spending.

There are, therefore, several ways to explain a contractionary shift in the *IS* curve. Keep in mind that these different views may all be true. There may be no single explanation for the decline in spending. It is possible that all of these changes coincided and that together they led to a massive reduction in spending.

The Money Hypothesis: A Shock to the *LM* Curve

Table 11-2 shows that the money supply fell 25 percent from 1929 to 1933, during which time the unemployment rate rose from 3.2 percent to 25.2 percent. This fact provides the motivation and support for what is called the *money hypothesis*, which places primary blame for the Depression on the Federal Reserve for allowing the money supply to fall by such a large amount.[4] The best-known advocates of this interpretation are Milton Friedman and Anna Schwartz, who defend it in their treatise on U.S. monetary history. Friedman and Schwartz argue that contractions in the money supply have caused most economic downturns and that the Great Depression is a particularly vivid example.

Using the *IS–LM* model, we might interpret the money hypothesis as explaining the Depression by a contractionary shift in the *LM* curve. Seen in this way, however, the money hypothesis runs into two problems.

---

[2] Ben Bernanke, "Non-Monetary Effects of the Financial Crisis in the Propagation of the Great Depression," *American Economic Review* 73 (June 1983): 257–276.

[3] E. Cary Brown, "Fiscal Policy in the 'Thirties: A Reappraisal," *American Economic Review* 46 (December 1956): 857–879.

[4] We discuss the reasons for this large decrease in the money supply in Chapter 18, where we examine the money supply process in more detail. In particular, see the case study "Bank Failures and the Money Supply in the 1930s."

The first problem is the behavior of *real* money balances. Monetary policy leads to a contractionary shift in the *LM* curve only if real money balances fall. Yet from 1929 to 1931 real money balances rose slightly, since the fall in the money supply was accompanied by an even greater fall in the price level. Although the monetary contraction may be responsible for the rise in unemployment from 1931 to 1933, when real money balances did fall, it cannot easily explain the initial downturn from 1929 to 1931.

The second problem for the money hypothesis is the behavior of interest rates. If a contractionary shift in the *LM* curve triggered the Depression, we should have observed higher interest rates. Yet nominal interest rates fell continuously from 1929 to 1933.

These two reasons appear sufficient to reject the view that the Depression was instigated by a contractionary shift in the *LM* curve. But was the fall in the money stock irrelevant? Next, we turn to another mechanism through which monetary policy might have been responsible for the severity of the Depression—the deflation of the 1930s.

The Money Hypothesis Again: The Effects of Falling Prices

From 1929 to 1933 the price level fell 25 percent. Many economists blame this deflation for the severity of the Great Depression. They argue that the deflation may have turned what in 1931 was a typical economic downturn into an unprecedented period of high unemployment and depressed income. If correct, this argument gives new life to the money hypothesis. Because the falling money supply was, plausibly, responsible for the falling price level, it could have been responsible for the severity of the Depression. To evaluate this argument, we must discuss how changes in the price level affect income in the *IS–LM* model.

The Stabilizing Effects of Deflation In the *IS–LM* model we have developed so far, falling prices raise income. For any given supply of money *M,* a lower price level implies higher real money balances M/P. An increase in real money balances causes an expansionary shift in the *LM* curve, which leads to higher income.

Another channel through which falling prices expand income is called the **Pigou effect.** Arthur Pigou, a prominent classical economist in the 1930s, pointed out that real money balances are part of households' wealth. As prices fall and real money balances rise, consumers should feel wealthier and spend more. This increase in consumer spending should cause an expansionary shift in the *IS* curve, also leading to higher income.

These two reasons led some economists in the 1930s to believe that falling prices would help stabilize the economy. That is, they thought that a decline in the price level would automatically push the economy back toward full employment. Yet other economists were less confident in the economy's ability to correct itself. They pointed to other effects of falling prices, to which we now turn.

The Destabilizing Effects of Deflation　Economists have proposed two theories to explain how falling prices could depress income rather than raise it. The first, called the **debt-deflation theory,** describes the effects of unexpected falls in the price level. The second explains the effects of expected deflation.

The debt-deflation theory begins with an observation from Chapter 7: unanticipated changes in the price level redistribute wealth between debtors and creditors. If a debtor owes a creditor $1,000, then the real amount of this debt is $1,000/P, where P is the price level. A fall in the price level raises the real amount of this debt—the amount of purchasing power the debtor must repay the creditor. Therefore, an unexpected deflation enriches creditors and impoverishes debtors.

The debt-deflation theory then posits that this redistribution of wealth affects spending on goods and services. In response to the redistribution from debtors to creditors, debtors spend less and creditors spend more. If these two groups have equal spending propensities, there is no aggregate impact. But it seems reasonable to assume that debtors have higher propensities to spend than creditors—perhaps that is why the debtors are in debt in the first place. In this case, debtors reduce their spending by more than creditors raise theirs. The net effect is a reduction in spending, a contractionary shift in the *IS* curve, and lower national income.

To understand how *expected* changes in prices can affect income, we need to add a new variable to the *IS–LM* model. Our discussion of the model so far has not distinguished between the nominal and real interest rates. Yet we know from previous chapters that investment depends on the real interest rate and that money demand depends on the nominal interest rate. If i is the nominal interest rate and π^e is expected inflation, then the *ex ante* real interest rate is $i - \pi^e$. We can now write the *IS–LM* model as

$$Y = C(Y - T) + I(i - \pi^e) + G \qquad IS,$$
$$M/P = L(i, Y) \qquad\qquad\qquad LM.$$

Expected inflation enters as a variable in the *IS* curve. Thus, changes in expected inflation shift the *IS* curve.

Let's use this extended *IS–LM* model to examine how changes in expected inflation influence the level of income. We begin by assuming that everyone expects the price level to remain the same. In this case, there is no expected inflation ($\pi^e = 0$), and these two equations produce the familiar *IS–LM* model. Figure 11-8 depicts this initial situation with the *LM* curve and the *IS* curve labeled IS_1. The intersection of these two curves determines the nominal and real interest rates, which for now are the same.

Now suppose that everyone suddenly expects that the price level will fall in the future, so that π^e becomes negative. The real interest rate is now higher at any given nominal interest rate. This increase in the real interest rate depresses planned investment spending, shifting the *IS* curve from IS_1 to IS_2. Thus, an expected deflation leads to a reduction in national income from Y_1 to Y_2. The

figure 11-8

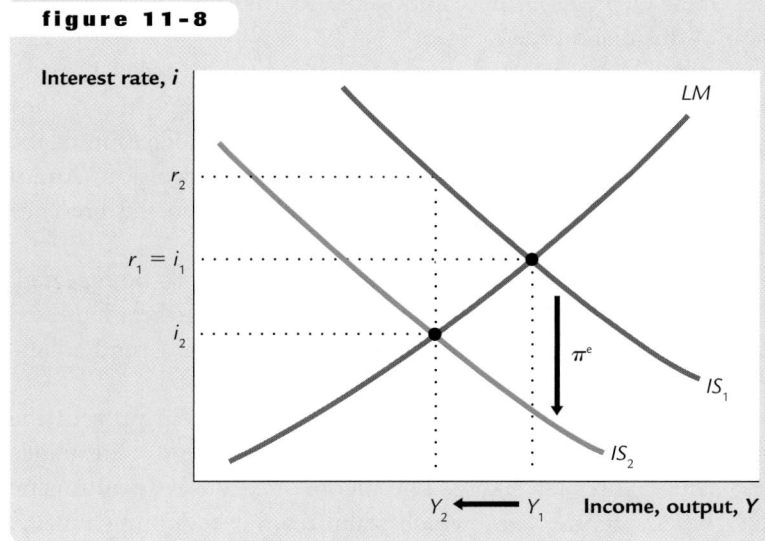

Expected Deflation in the *IS–LM* Model An expected deflation (a negative value of π^e) raises the real interest rate for any given nominal interest rate, and this depresses investment spending. The reduction in investment shifts the *IS* curve downward. The level of income falls from Y_1 to Y_2. The nominal interest rate falls from i_1 to i_2, and the real interest rate rises from r_1 to r_2.

nominal interest rate falls from i_1 to i_2, while the real interest rate rises from r_1 to r_2.

Here is the story behind this figure. When firms come to expect deflation, they become reluctant to borrow to buy investment goods because they believe they will have to repay these loans later in more valuable dollars. The fall in investment depresses planned expenditure, which in turn depresses income. The fall in income reduces the demand for money, and this reduces the nominal interest rate that equilibrates the money market. The nominal interest rate falls by less than the expected deflation, so the real interest rate rises.

Note that there is a common thread in these two stories of destabilizing deflation. In both, falling prices depress national income by causing a contractionary shift in the *IS* curve. Because a deflation of the size observed from 1929 to 1933 is unlikely except in the presence of a major contraction in the money supply, these two explanations give some of the responsibility for the Depression—especially its severity—to the Fed. In other words, if falling prices are destabilizing, then a contraction in the money supply can lead to a fall in income, even without a decrease in real money balances or a rise in nominal interest rates.

Could the Depression Happen Again?

Economists study the Depression both because of its intrinsic interest as a major economic event and to provide guidance to policymakers so that it will not happen again. To state with confidence whether this event could recur, we would need to know why it happened. Because there is not yet agreement on the causes of the Great Depression, it is impossible to rule out with certainty another depression of this magnitude.

Yet most economists believe that the mistakes that led to the Great Depression are unlikely to be repeated. The Fed seems unlikely to allow the money supply to fall by one-fourth. Many economists believe that the deflation of the early 1930s was responsible for the depth and length of the Depression. And it seems likely that such a prolonged deflation was possible only in the presence of a falling money supply.

The fiscal-policy mistakes of the Depression are also unlikely to be repeated. Fiscal policy in the 1930s not only failed to help but actually further depressed aggregate demand. Few economists today would advocate such a rigid adherence to a balanced budget in the face of massive unemployment.

In addition, there are many institutions today that would help prevent the events of the 1930s from recurring. The system of Federal Deposit Insurance makes widespread bank failures less likely. The income tax causes an automatic reduction in taxes when income falls, which stabilizes the economy. Finally, economists know more today than they did in the 1930s. Our knowledge of how the economy works, limited as it still is, should help policymakers formulate better policies to combat such widespread unemployment.

CASE STUDY

The Japanese Slump of the 1990s

During the 1990s, after many years of rapid growth and enviable prosperity, the Japanese economy experienced a prolonged downturn. The unemployment rate, which had historically been very low in Japan, rose from 2 percent in 1990 to 4 percent in 1998. Industrial production, which had doubled in the two decades before 1990, was about the same in 1998 as it was in 1990. Real GDP also stagnated, and even fell for a while.

Although the Japanese slump of the 1990s is not even close in magnitude to the Great Depression of the 1930s, the episodes are similar in several ways. First, both episodes are traced in part to a large decline in stock prices. In Japan, stock prices in 1998 were less than half the peak level they had reached about a decade earlier. Like the stock market, Japanese land prices had also skyrocketed in the 1980s before crashing in the 1990s. (At the peak of Japan's land bubble, it was said that the land under the Imperial Palace was worth more than the entire state of California.) When stock and land prices collapsed, Japanese citizens saw their wealth plummet. This decline in wealth, like that during the Great Depression, depressed consumer spending.

Second, during both episodes, banks ran into trouble and exacerbated the slump in economic activity. Japanese banks in the 1980s had made many loans that were backed by stock or land. When the value of this collateral fell, borrowers started defaulting on their loans. These defaults on the old loans reduced the banks' ability to make new loans. The resulting "credit crunch" made it harder for firms to finance investment projects and, thus, depressed investment spending.

Third, both episodes saw a fall in economic activity coincide with very low interest rates. In Japan in 1998, as in the United States in 1935, short-term nominal interest rates were less than 1 percent. This fact suggests that the cause of the slump was primarily a contractionary shift in the *IS* curve, because such a shift reduces both income and the interest rate. The obvious suspects to explain the *IS* shift are the crashes in stock and land prices and the problems in the banking system.

Finally, the policy debate in Japan mirrored the debate over the Great Depression. Some economists recommended that the Japanese government pass large tax cuts to encourage more consumer spending. Although this advice was followed to some extent, Japanese policymakers were reluctant to enact very large tax cuts because, like the U.S. policymakers in the 1930s, they wanted to avoid budget deficits. In Japan, this reluctance to increase government debt arose in part because the government was facing a large unfunded pension liability and a rapidly aging population.

Other economists recommended that the Bank of Japan expand the money supply more rapidly. Even if nominal interest rates could not go much lower, then perhaps more rapid money growth could raise expected inflation, lower real interest rates, and stimulate investment spending. Thus, although economists differed about whether fiscal or monetary policy was more likely to be effective, there was wide agreement that the solution to Japan's slump, like the solution to the Great Depression, rested in more aggressive expansion of aggregate demand.[5]

11-4 Conclusion

The purpose of this chapter and the previous one has been to deepen our understanding of aggregate demand. We now have the tools to analyze the effects of monetary and fiscal policy in the long run and in the short run. In the long run, prices are flexible, and we use the classical analysis of Part Two of this book. In the short run, prices are sticky, and we use the *IS–LM* model to examine how changes in policy influence the economy.

Although the model presented in this chapter provides the basic framework for analyzing aggregate demand, it is not the whole story. In later chapters, we examine in more detail the elements of this model and thereby refine our understanding of aggregate demand. In Chapter 16, for example, we study theories of consumption. Because the consumption function is a crucial piece of the

---

[5] To learn more about this episode, see Adam S. Posen, *Restoring Japan's Economic Growth* (Washington, DC: Institute for International Economics, 1998).

IS–LM model, a deeper analysis of consumption may modify our view of the impact of monetary and fiscal policy on the economy. The simple *IS–LM* model presented in Chapters 10 and 11 provides the starting point for this further analysis.

Summary

1. The *IS–LM* model is a general theory of the aggregate demand for goods and services. The exogenous variables in the model are fiscal policy, monetary policy, and the price level. The model explains two endogenous variables: the interest rate and the level of national income.

2. The *IS* curve represents the negative relationship between the interest rate and the level of income that arises from equilibrium in the market for goods and services. The *LM* curve represents a positive relationship between the interest rate and the level of income that arises from equilibrium in the market for real money balances. Equilibrium in the *IS–LM* model—the intersection of the *IS* and *LM* curves—represents simultaneous equilibrium in the market for goods and services and in the market for real money balances.

3. The aggregate demand curve summarizes the results from the *IS–LM* model by showing equilibrium income at any given price level. The aggregate demand curve slopes downward because a lower price level increases real money balances, lowers the interest rate, stimulates investment spending, and thereby raises equilibrium income.

4. Expansionary fiscal policy—an increase in government purchases or a decrease in taxes—shifts the *IS* curve to the right. This shift in the *IS* curve increases the interest rate and income. The increase in income represents a rightward shift in the aggregate demand curve. Similarly, contractionary fiscal policy shifts the *IS* curve to the left, lowers the interest rate and income, and shifts the aggregate demand curve to the left.

5. Expansionary monetary policy shifts the *LM* curve downward. This shift in the *LM* curve lowers the interest rate and raises income. The increase in income represents a rightward shift of the aggregate demand curve. Similarly, contractionary monetary policy shifts the *LM* curve upward, raises the interest rate, lowers income, and shifts the aggregate demand curve to the left.

KEY CONCEPTS

Monetary transmission
   mechanism
Pigou effect

Debt-deflation theory

QUESTIONS FOR REVIEW

1. Explain why the aggregate demand curve slopes downward.

2. What is the impact of an increase in taxes on the interest rate, income, consumption, and investment?

3. What is the impact of a decrease in the money supply on the interest rate, income, consumption, and investment?

4. Describe the possible effects of falling prices on equilibrium income.

PROBLEMS AND APPLICATIONS

1. According to the *IS–LM* model, what happens to the interest rate, income, consumption, and investment under the following circumstances?

   a. The central bank increases the money supply.

   b. The government increases government purchases.

   c. The government increases taxes.

   d. The government increases government purchases and taxes by equal amounts.

2. Use the *IS–LM* model to predict the effects of each of the following shocks on income, the interest rate, consumption, and investment. In each case, explain what the Fed should do to keep income at its initial level.

   a. After the invention of a new high-speed computer chip, many firms decide to upgrade their computer systems.

   b. A wave of credit-card fraud increases the frequency with which people make transactions in cash.

   c. A best-seller titled *Retire Rich* convinces the public to increase the percentage of their income devoted to saving.

3. Consider the economy of Hicksonia.

   a. The consumption function is given by

   $$C = 200 + 0.75(Y - T).$$

   The investment function is

   $$I = 200 - 25r.$$

   Government purchases and taxes are both 100. For this economy, graph the *IS* curve for *r* ranging from 0 to 8.

   b. The money demand function in Hicksonia is

   $$(M/P)^d = Y - 100r.$$

   The money supply *M* is 1,000 and the price level *P* is 2. For this economy, graph the *LM* curve for *r* ranging from 0 to 8.

   c. Find the equilibrium interest rate *r* and the equilibrium level of income *Y*.

   d. Suppose that government purchases are raised from 100 to 150. How much does the *IS* curve shift? What are the new equilibrium interest rate and level of income?

   e. Suppose instead that the money supply is raised from 1,000 to 1,200. How much does the *LM* curve shift? What are the new equilibrium interest rate and level of income?

   f. With the initial values for monetary and fiscal policy, suppose that the price level rises from 2 to 4. What happens? What are the new equilibrium interest rate and level of income?

   g. Derive and graph an equation for the aggregate demand curve. What happens to this aggregate demand curve if fiscal or monetary policy changes, as in parts (d) and (e)?

4. Explain why each of the following statements is true. Discuss the impact of monetary and fiscal policy in each of these special cases.

   a. If investment does not depend on the interest rate, the *IS* curve is vertical.

   b. If money demand does not depend on the interest rate, the *LM* curve is vertical.

   c. If money demand does not depend on income, the *LM* curve is horizontal.

d. If money demand is extremely sensitive to the interest rate, the *LM* curve is horizontal.

5. Suppose that the government wants to raise investment but keep output constant. In the *IS–LM* model, what mix of monetary and fiscal policy will achieve this goal? In the early 1980s, the U.S. government cut taxes and ran a budget deficit while the Fed pursued a tight monetary policy. What effect should this policy mix have?

6. Use the *IS–LM* diagram to describe the short-run and long-run effects of the following changes on national income, the interest rate, the price level, consumption, investment, and real money balances.

   a. An increase in the money supply.

   b. An increase in government purchases.

   c. An increase in taxes.

7. The Fed is considering two alternative monetary policies:

   ➤ holding the money supply constant and letting the interest rate adjust, or

   ➤ adjusting the money supply to hold the interest rate constant.

   In the *IS–LM* model, which policy will better stabilize output under the following conditions?

   a. All shocks to the economy arise from exogenous changes in the demand for goods and services.

   b. All shocks to the economy arise from exogenous changes in the demand for money.

8. Suppose that the demand for real money balances depends on disposable income. That is, the money demand function is

$$M/P = L(r, Y - T).$$

   Using the *IS–LM* model, discuss whether this change in the money demand function alters the following:

   a. The analysis of changes in government purchases.

   b. The analysis of changes in taxes.

The Simple Algebra of the *IS–LM* Model and the Aggregate Demand Curve

The chapter analyzes the *IS–LM* model with graphs of the *IS* and *LM* curves. Here we analyze the model algebraically rather than graphically. This alternative presentation offers additional insight into how monetary and fiscal policy influence aggregate demand.

The *IS* Curve

One way to think about the *IS* curve is that it describes the combinations of income Y and the interest rate r that satisfy an equation we first saw in Chapter 3:

$$Y = C(Y - T) + I(r) + G.$$

This equation combines the national income accounts identity, the consumption function, and the investment function. It states that the quantity of goods produced, Y, must equal the quantity of goods demanded, $C + I + G$.

We can learn more about the *IS* curve by considering the special case in which the consumption function and investment function are linear. We begin with the national income accounts identity

$$Y = C + I + G.$$

Now suppose that the consumption function is

$$C = a + b(Y - T),$$

where a and b are numbers greater than zero, and the investment function is

$$I = c - dr,$$

where c and d also are numbers greater than zero. The parameter b is the marginal propensity to consume, so we expect b to be between zero and one. The parameter d determines how much investment responds to the interest rate; because investment rises when the interest rate falls, there is a minus sign in front of d.

From these three equations, we can derive an algebraic expression for the *IS* curve and see what influences the *IS* curve's position and slope. If we substitute the consumption and investment functions into the national income accounts identity, we obtain

$$Y = [a + b(Y - T)] + (c - dr) + G.$$

Note that Y shows up on both sides of this equation. We can simplify this equation by bringing all the Y terms to the left-hand side and rearranging the terms on the right-hand side:

$$Y - bY = (a + c) + (G - bT) - dr.$$

We solve for Y to get

$$Y = \frac{a + c}{1 - b} + \frac{1}{1 - b} G + \frac{-b}{1 - b} T + \frac{-d}{1 - b} r.$$

This equation expresses the IS curve algebraically. It tells us the level of income Y for any given interest rate r and fiscal policy G and T. Holding fiscal policy fixed, the equation gives us a relationship between the interest rate and the level of income: the higher the interest rate, the lower the level of income. The IS curve graphs this equation for different values of Y and r given fixed values of G and T.

Using this last equation, we can verify our previous conclusions about the IS curve. First, because the coefficient of the interest rate is negative, the IS curve slopes downward: higher interest rates reduce income. Second, because the coefficient of government purchases is positive, an increase in government purchases shifts the IS curve to the right. Third, because the coefficient of taxes is negative, an increase in taxes shifts the IS curve to the left.

The coefficient of the interest rate, $-d/(1 - b)$, tells us what determines whether the IS curve is steep or flat. If investment is highly sensitive to the interest rate, then d is large, and income is highly sensitive to the interest rate as well. In this case, small changes in the interest rate lead to large changes in income: the IS curve is relatively flat. Conversely, if investment is not very sensitive to the interest rate, then d is small, and income is also not very sensitive to the interest rate. In this case, large changes in interest rates lead to small changes in income: the IS curve is relatively steep.

Similarly, the slope of the IS curve depends on the marginal propensity to consume b. The larger the marginal propensity to consume, the larger the change in income resulting from a given change in the interest rate. The reason is that a large marginal propensity to consume leads to a large multiplier for changes in investment. The larger the multiplier, the larger the impact of a change in investment on income and the flatter the IS curve.

The marginal propensity to consume b also determines how much changes in fiscal policy shift the IS curve. The coefficient of G, $1/(1 - b)$, is the government-purchases multiplier in the Keynesian cross. Similarly, the coefficient of T, $-b/(1 - b)$, is the tax multiplier in the Keynesian cross. The larger the marginal propensity to consume, the greater the multiplier, and thus the greater the shift in the IS curve that arises from a change in fiscal policy.

The *LM* Curve

The LM curve describes the combinations of income Y and the interest rate r that satisfy the money market equilibrium condition

$$M/P = L(r, Y).$$

This equation simply equates money supply and money demand.

We can learn more about the *LM* curve by considering the case in which the money demand function is linear—that is,

$$L(r, Y) = eY - fr,$$

where *e* and *f* are numbers greater than zero. The value of *e* determines how much the demand for money rises when income rises. The value of *f* determines how much the demand for money falls when the interest rate rises. There is a minus sign in front of the interest rate term because money demand is inversely related to the interest rate.

The equilibrium in the money market is now described by

$$M/P = eY - fr.$$

To see what this equation implies, rearrange the terms so that *r* is on the left-hand side. We obtain

$$r = (e/f)Y - (1/f)M/P.$$

This equation gives us the interest rate that equilibrates the money market for any values of income and real money balances. The *LM* curve graphs this equation for different values of *Y* and *r* given a fixed value of *M/P*.

From this last equation, we can verify some of our conclusions about the *LM* curve. First, because the coefficient of income is positive, the *LM* curve slopes upward: higher income requires a higher interest rate to equilibrate the money market. Second, because the coefficient of real money balances is negative, decreases in real balances shift the *LM* curve upward, and increases in real balances shift the *LM* curve downward.

From the coefficient of income, *e/f*, we can see what determines whether the *LM* curve is steep or flat. If money demand is not very sensitive to the level of income, then *e* is small. In this case, only a small change in the interest rate is necessary to offset the small increase in money demand caused by a change in income: the *LM* curve is relatively flat. Similarly, if the quantity of money demanded is not very sensitive to the interest rate, then *f* is small. In this case, a shift in money demand due to a change in income leads to a large change in the equilibrium interest rate: the *LM* curve is relatively steep.

The Aggregate Demand Curve

To find the aggregate demand equation, we must find the level of income that satisfies both the *IS* equation and the *LM* equation. To do this, substitute the *LM* equation for the interest rate *r* into the *IS* equation to obtain

$$Y = \frac{a+c}{1-b} + \frac{1}{1-b}G + \frac{-b}{1-b}T + \frac{-d}{1-b}\left(\frac{e}{f}Y - \frac{1}{f}\frac{M}{P}\right).$$

With some algebraic manipulation, we can solve for Y. The final equation for Y is

$$Y = \frac{z(a + c)}{1 - b} + \frac{z}{1 - b}\,G + \frac{-zb}{1 - b}\,T + \frac{d}{(1 - b)[f + de/(1 - b)]}\,\frac{M}{P},$$

where $z = f/[f + de/(1 - b)]$ is a composite of some of the parameters and is between zero and one.

This last equation expresses the aggregate demand curve algebraically. It says that income depends on fiscal policy G and T, monetary policy M, and the price level P. The aggregate demand curve graphs this equation for different values of Y and P given fixed values of G, T, and M.

We can explain the slope and position of the aggregate demand curve with this equation. First, the aggregate demand curve slopes downward, since an increase in P lowers M/P and thus lowers Y. Second, increases in the money supply raise income and shift the aggregate demand curve to the right. Third, increases in government purchases or decreases in taxes also raise income and shift the aggregate demand curve to the right. Note that, because z is less than one, the multipliers for fiscal policy are smaller in the $IS-LM$ model than in the Keynesian cross. Hence, the parameter z reflects the crowding out of investment discussed earlier.

Finally, this equation shows the relationship between the aggregate demand curve derived in this chapter from the $IS-LM$ model and the aggregate demand curve derived in Chapter 9 from the quantity theory of money. The quantity theory assumes that the interest rate does not influence the quantity of real money balances demanded. Put differently, the quantity theory assumes that the parameter f equals zero. If f equals zero, then the composite parameter z also equals zero, so fiscal policy does not influence aggregate demand. Thus, the aggregate demand curve derived in Chapter 9 is a special case of the aggregate demand curve derived here.

CASE STUDY

The Effectiveness of Monetary and Fiscal Policy

Economists have long debated whether monetary or fiscal policy exerts a more powerful influence on aggregate demand. According to the $IS-LM$ model, the answer to this question depends on the parameters of the IS and LM curves. Therefore, economists have spent much energy arguing about the size of these parameters. The most hotly contested parameters are those that describe the influence of the interest rate on economic decisions.

Those economists who believe that fiscal policy is more potent than monetary policy argue that the responsiveness of investment to the interest rate— measured by the parameter d—is small. If you look at the algebraic equation for aggregate demand, you will see that a small value of d implies a small effect of the money supply on income. The reason is that when d is small, the IS curve is nearly vertical, and shifts in the LM curve do not cause much of a change in income. In addition, a small value of d implies a large value of z, which in turn implies that fiscal policy has a large effect on income. The reason for this large effect is that when investment is not very responsive to the interest rate, there is little crowding out.

Those economists who believe that monetary policy is more potent than fiscal policy argue that the responsiveness of money demand to the interest rate—measured by the parameter f—is small. When f is small, z is small and fiscal policy has a small effect on income; in this case, the *LM* curve is nearly vertical. In addition, when f is small, changes in the money supply have a large effect on income.

Few economists today endorse either of these extreme views. The evidence indicates that the interest rate affects both investment and money demand. This finding implies that both monetary and fiscal policy are important determinants of aggregate demand.

MORE PROBLEMS AND APPLICATIONS

1. Give an algebraic answer to each of the following questions. Then explain in words the economics that underlies your answer.

   a. How does the sensitivity of investment to the interest rate affect the slope of the aggregate demand curve?

   b. How does the sensitivity of money demand to the interest rate affect the slope of the aggregate demand curve?

   c. How does the marginal propensity to consume affect the response of aggregate demand to changes in government purchases?

chapter 12

Aggregate Demand in the Open Economy

When conducting monetary and fiscal policy, policymakers often look beyond their own country's borders. Even if domestic prosperity is their sole objective, it is necessary for them to consider the rest of the world. The international flow of goods and services (measured by net exports) and the international flow of capital (measured by net foreign investment) can affect an economy in profound ways. Policymakers ignore these effects at their peril.

In this chapter we extend our analysis of aggregate demand to include international trade and finance. The model developed in this chapter, called the **Mundell–Fleming model,** is an open-economy version of the *IS–LM* model. Both models stress the interaction between the goods market and the money market. Both models assume that the price level is fixed and then show what causes short-run fluctuations in aggregate income (or, equivalently, shifts in the aggregate demand curve). The key difference is that the *IS–LM* model assumes a closed economy, whereas the Mundell–Fleming model assumes an open economy. The Mundell–Fleming model extends the short-run model of national income from Chapters 10 and 11 by including the effects of international trade and finance from Chapter 8.

The Mundell–Fleming model makes one important and extreme assumption: it assumes that the economy being studied is a small open economy with perfect capital mobility. That is, the economy can borrow or lend as much as it wants in world financial markets and, as a result, the economy's interest rate is determined by the world interest rate. One virtue of this assumption is that it simplifies the analysis: once the interest rate is determined, we can concentrate our attention on the role of the exchange rate. In addition, for some economies, such as Belgium or the Netherlands, the assumption of a small open economy with perfect capital mobility is a good one. Yet this assumption—and thus the Mundell–Fleming model—does not apply exactly to a large open economy such as the United States. In the conclusion to this chapter (and more fully in the appendix), we consider what happens in the more complex case in which international capital mobility is less than perfect or a nation is so large it can influence world financial markets.

One lesson from the Mundell–Fleming model is that the behavior of an economy depends on the exchange-rate system it has adopted. We begin by assuming that the economy operates with a floating exchange rate. That is, we assume that the central bank allows the exchange rate to adjust to changing economic conditions. We then examine how the economy operates under a fixed exchange rate, and we discuss whether a floating or fixed exchange rate is better. This question has been extraordinarily important in recent years, as many nations around the world have debated what exchange-rate system to adopt.

12-1 The Mundell – Fleming Model

In this section we build the Mundell–Fleming model, and in the following sections we use the model to examine the impact of various policies. As you will see, the Mundell–Fleming model is built from components we have used in previous chapters. But these pieces are put together in a new way to address a new set of questions.[1]

The Key Assumption: Small Open Economy With Perfect Capital Mobility

Let's begin with the assumption of a small open economy with perfect capital mobility. As we saw in Chapter 8, this assumption means that the interest rate in this economy r is determined by the world interest rate r^*. Mathematically, we can write this assumption as

$$r = r^*.$$

This world interest rate is assumed to be exogenously fixed because the economy is sufficiently small relative to the world economy that it can borrow or lend as much as it wants in world financial markets without affecting the world interest rate.

Although the idea of perfect capital mobility is expressed mathematically with a simple equation, it is important not to lose sight of the sophisticated process that this equation represents. Imagine that some event were to occur that would normally raise the interest rate (such as a decline in domestic saving). In a small open economy, the domestic interest rate might rise by a little bit for a short time, but as soon as it did, foreigners would see the higher interest rate and start lending to this country (by, for instance, buying this country's bonds). The capital inflow would drive the domestic interest rate back toward r^*. Similarly, if any event were ever to start driving the domestic interest rate downward, capital would flow out of the country to earn a higher return abroad, and this capital outflow would drive the domestic interest rate back upward toward r^*. Hence, the $r = r^*$ equation represents the assumption that the international flow of capital is sufficiently rapid as to keep the domestic interest rate equal to the world interest rate.

---

[1] The Mundell–Fleming model was developed in the early 1960s. Mundell's contributions are collected in Robert A. Mundell, *International Economics* (New York: Macmillan, 1968). For Fleming's contribution, see J. Marcus Fleming, "Domestic Financial Policies Under Fixed and Under Floating Exchange Rates," *IMF Staff Papers* 9 (November 1962): 369–379.

The Goods Market and the *IS* * Curve

The Mundell–Fleming model describes the market for goods and services much as the *IS–LM* model does, but it adds a new term for net exports. In particular, the goods market is represented with the following equation:

$$Y = C(Y - T) + I(r^*) + G + NX(e).$$

This equation states that aggregate income Y is the sum of consumption C, investment I, government purchases G, and net exports NX. Consumption depends positively on disposable income $Y - T$. Investment depends negatively on the interest rate, which equals the world interest rate r^*. Net exports depend negatively on the exchange rate e. As before, we define the exchange rate e as the amount of foreign currency per unit of domestic currency—for example, e might be 100 yen per dollar.

You may recall that in Chapter 8 we related net exports to the real exchange rate (the relative price of goods at home and abroad) rather than the nominal exchange rate (the relative price of domestic and foreign currencies). If e is the nominal exchange rate, then the real exchange rate ϵ equals eP/P^*, where P is the domestic price level and P^* is the foreign price level. The Mundell–Fleming model, however, assumes that the price levels at home and abroad are fixed, so the real exchange rate is proportional to the nominal exchange rate. That is, when the nominal exchange rate appreciates (say, from 100 to 120 yen per dollar), foreign goods become cheaper compared to domestic goods, and this causes exports to fall and imports to rise.

We can illustrate this equation for goods market equilibrium on a graph in which income is on the horizontal axis and the exchange rate is on the vertical axis. This curve is shown in panel (c) of Figure 12-1 and is called the *IS* * curve. The new label reminds us that the curve is drawn holding the interest rate constant at the world interest rate r^*.

The *IS* * curve slopes downward because a higher exchange rate reduces net exports, which in turn lowers aggregate income. To show how this works, the other panels of Figure 12-1 combine the net-exports schedule and the Keynesian cross to derive the *IS* * curve. In panel (a), an increase in the exchange rate from e_1 to e_2 lowers net exports from $NX(e_1)$ to $NX(e_2)$. In panel (b), the reduction in net exports shifts the planned-expenditure schedule downward and thus lowers income from Y_1 to Y_2. The *IS* * curves summarizes this relationship between the exchange rate e and income Y.

The Money Market and the *LM* * Curve

The Mundell–Fleming model represents the money market with an equation that should be familiar from the *IS–LM* model, with the additional assumption that the domestic interest rate equals the world interest rate:

$$M/P = L(r^*, Y).$$

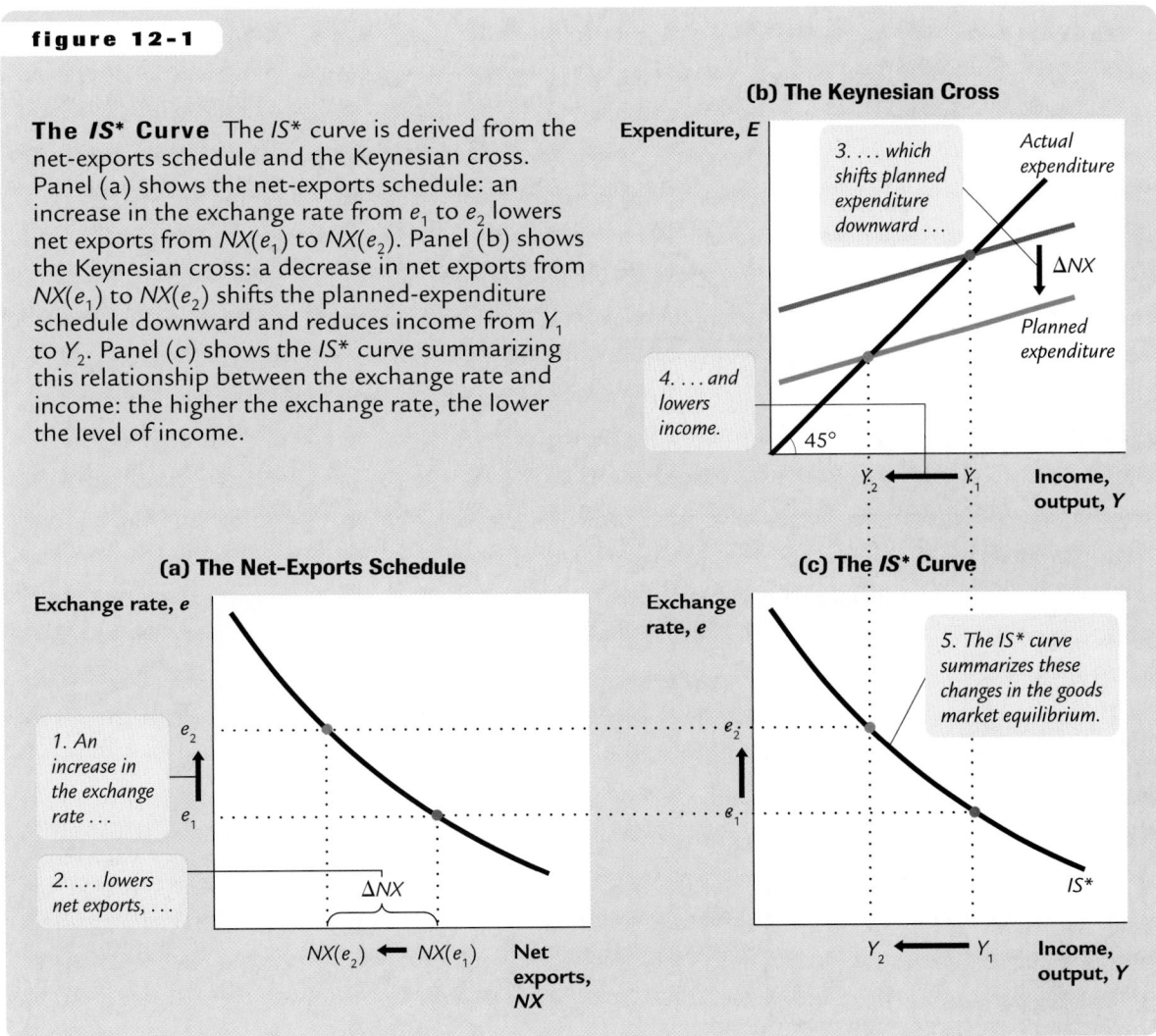

The IS* Curve The IS* curve is derived from the net-exports schedule and the Keynesian cross. Panel (a) shows the net-exports schedule: an increase in the exchange rate from e_1 to e_2 lowers net exports from $NX(e_1)$ to $NX(e_2)$. Panel (b) shows the Keynesian cross: a decrease in net exports from $NX(e_1)$ to $NX(e_2)$ shifts the planned-expenditure schedule downward and reduces income from Y_1 to Y_2. Panel (c) shows the IS* curve summarizing this relationship between the exchange rate and income: the higher the exchange rate, the lower the level of income.

This equation states that the supply of real money balances, M/P, equals the demand, $L(r, Y)$. The demand for real balances depends negatively on the interest rate, which is now set equal to the world interest rate r^*, and positively on income Y. The money supply M is an exogenous variable controlled by the central bank, and because the Mundell–Fleming model is designed to analyze short-run fluctuations, the price level P is also assumed to be exogenously fixed.

We can represent this equation graphically with a vertical LM* curve, as in panel (b) of Figure 12-2. The LM* curve is vertical because the exchange rate does not enter into the LM* equation. Given the world interest rate, the LM* equation determines aggregate income, regardless of the exchange rate. Figure 12-2 shows how the LM* curve arises from the world interest rate and the LM curve, which relates the interest rate and income.

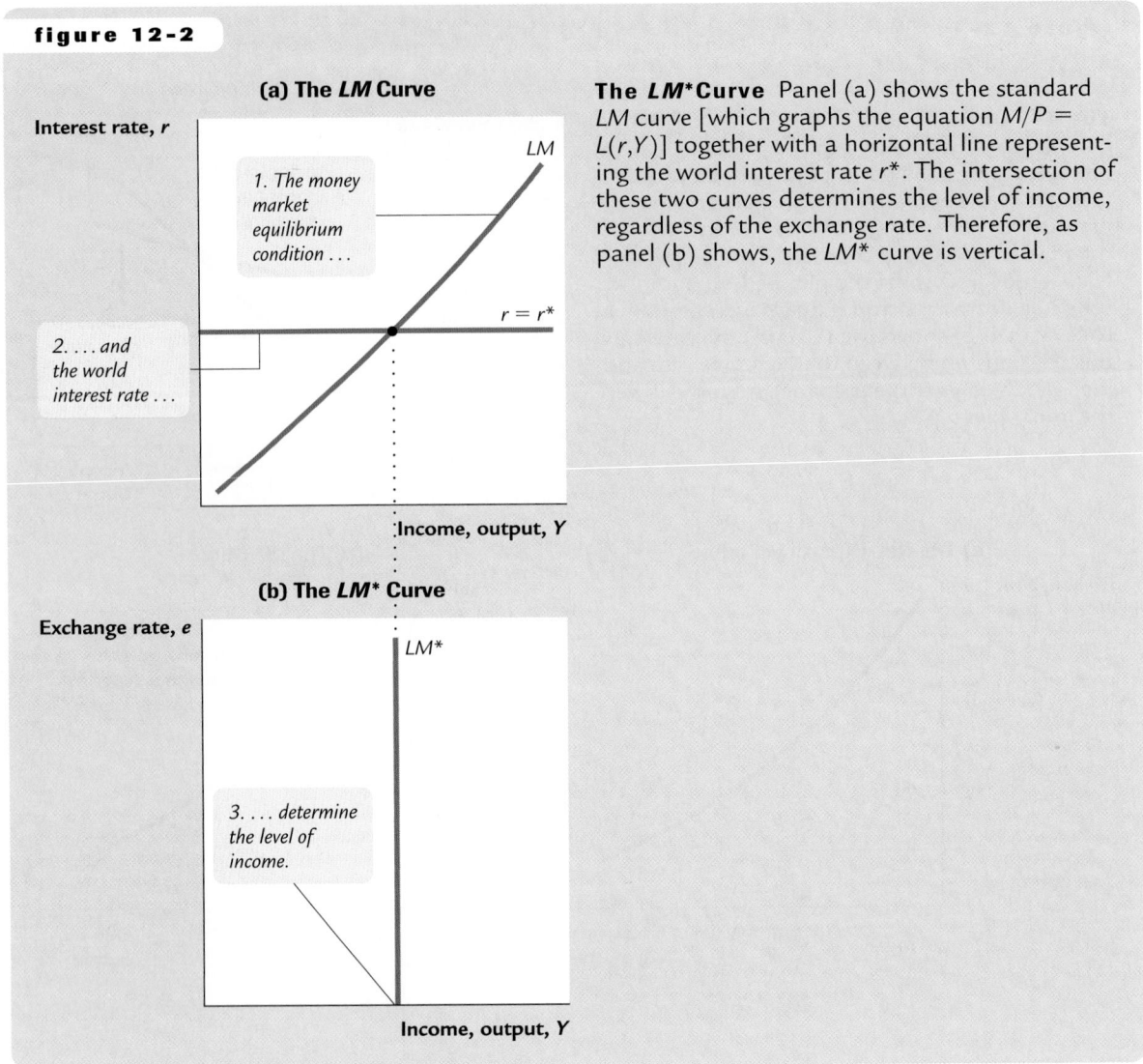

figure 12-2

(a) The *LM* Curve

Interest rate, *r*

1. The money market equilibrium condition . . .

LM

r = *r**

2. . . . and the world interest rate . . .

Income, output, *Y*

(b) The *LM** Curve

Exchange rate, *e*

LM*

3. . . . determine the level of income.

Income, output, *Y*

The *LM**Curve Panel (a) shows the standard *LM* curve [which graphs the equation $M/P = L(r,Y)$] together with a horizontal line representing the world interest rate r^*. The intersection of these two curves determines the level of income, regardless of the exchange rate. Therefore, as panel (b) shows, the *LM** curve is vertical.

Putting the Pieces Together

According to the Mundell–Fleming model, a small open economy with perfect capital mobility can be described by two equations:

$$Y = C(Y - T) + I(r^*) + G + NX(e) \qquad IS^*,$$
$$M/P = L(r^*, Y) \qquad\qquad\qquad LM^*.$$

The first equation describes equilibrium in the goods market, and the second equation describes equilibrium in the money market. The exogenous variables are fiscal policy G and T, monetary policy M, the price level P, and the world interest rate r^*. The endogenous variables are income Y and the exchange rate e.

These two relationships are illustrated together in Figure 12-3. The equilibrium for the economy is found where the IS^* curve and the LM^* curve inter-

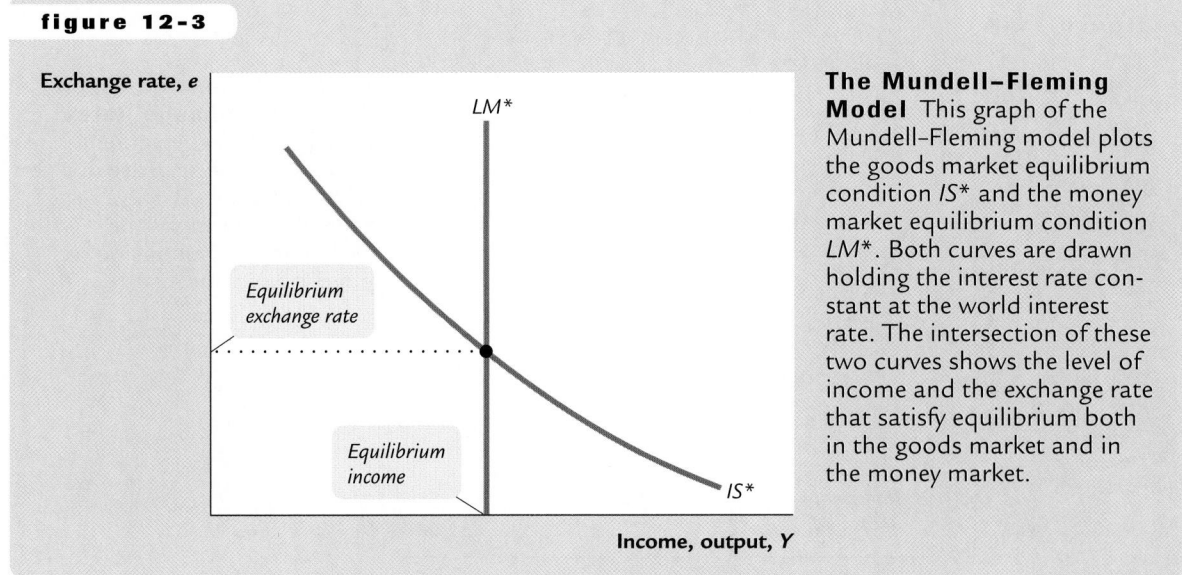

figure 12-3

The Mundell–Fleming Model This graph of the Mundell–Fleming model plots the goods market equilibrium condition IS* and the money market equilibrium condition LM*. Both curves are drawn holding the interest rate constant at the world interest rate. The intersection of these two curves shows the level of income and the exchange rate that satisfy equilibrium both in the goods market and in the money market.

sect. This intersection shows the exchange rate and the level of income at which both the goods market and the money market are in equilibrium. With this diagram, we can use the Mundell–Fleming model to show how aggregate income Y and the exchange rate e respond to changes in policy.

12-2 | The Small Open Economy Under Floating Exchange Rates

Before analyzing the impact of policies in an open economy, we must specify the international monetary system in which the country has chosen to operate. We start with the system relevant for most major economies today: **floating exchange rates.** Under floating exchange rates, the exchange rate is allowed to fluctuate freely in response to changing economic conditions.

Fiscal Policy

Suppose that the government stimulates domestic spending by increasing government purchases or by cutting taxes. Because such expansionary fiscal policy increases planned expenditure, it shifts the IS* curve to the right, as in Figure 12-4. As a result, the exchange rate appreciates, while the level of income remains the same.

Notice that fiscal policy has very different effects in a small open economy than it does in a closed economy. In the closed-economy IS–LM model, a

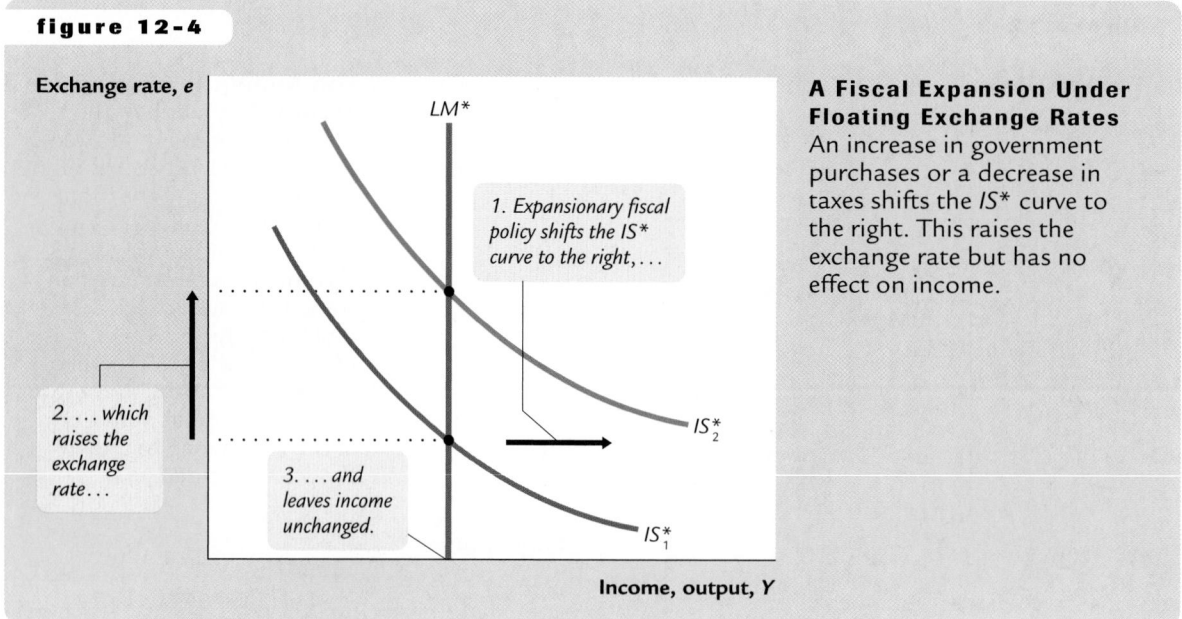

figure 12-4

Exchange rate, e

LM*

1. Expansionary fiscal policy shifts the IS* curve to the right, . . .

IS_2^*

2. . . . which raises the exchange rate . . .

3. . . . and leaves income unchanged.

IS_1^*

Income, output, Y

A Fiscal Expansion Under Floating Exchange Rates An increase in government purchases or a decrease in taxes shifts the IS* curve to the right. This raises the exchange rate but has no effect on income.

fiscal expansion raises income, whereas in a small open economy with a floating exchange rate, a fiscal expansion leaves income at the same level. Why the difference? In a closed economy, when income rises, the interest rate rises, because higher income increases the demand for money. That is not possible in a small open economy: as soon as the interest rate tries to increase above the world interest rate r^*, capital flows in from abroad. This capital inflow increases the demand for the domestic currency in the market for foreign-currency exchange and, thus, bids up the value of the domestic currency. The appreciation of the exchange rate makes domestic goods expensive relative to foreign goods, and this reduces net exports. The fall in net exports offsets the effects of the expansionary fiscal policy on income.

Why is the fall in net exports so great as to render fiscal policy completely powerless to influence income? To answer this question, consider the equation that describes the money market:

$$M/P = L(r, Y).$$

In both closed and open economies, the quantity of real money balances supplied M/P is fixed, and the quantity demanded (determined by r and Y) must equal this fixed supply. In a closed economy, a fiscal expansion causes the equilibrium interest rate to rise. This increase in the interest rate (which reduces the quantity of money demanded) allows equilibrium income to rise (which increases the quantity of money demanded). By contrast, in a small open economy, r is fixed at r^*, so there is only one level of income that can satisfy this equation, and this level of income does not change when fiscal policy changes.

Thus, when the government increases spending or cuts taxes, the appreciation of the exchange rate and the fall in net exports must be exactly large enough to offset fully the normal expansionary effect of the policy on income.

Monetary Policy

Suppose now that the central bank increases the money supply. Because the price level is assumed to be fixed, the increase in the money supply means an increase in real balances. The increase in real balances shifts the LM^* curve to the right, as in Figure 12-5. Hence, an increase in the money supply raises income and lowers the exchange rate.

Although monetary policy influences income in an open economy, as it does in a closed economy, the monetary transmission mechanism is different. Recall that in a closed economy an increase in the money supply increases spending because it lowers the interest rate and stimulates investment. In a small open economy, the interest rate is fixed by the world interest rate. As soon as an increase in the money supply puts downward pressure on the domestic interest rate, capital flows out of the economy, as investors seek a higher return elsewhere. This capital outflow prevents the domestic interest rate from falling. In addition, because the capital outflow increases the supply of the domestic currency in the market for foreign-currency exchange, the exchange rate depreciates. The fall in the exchange rate makes domestic goods inexpensive relative to foreign goods and, thereby, stimulates net exports. Hence, in a small open economy, monetary policy influences income by altering the exchange rate rather than the interest rate.

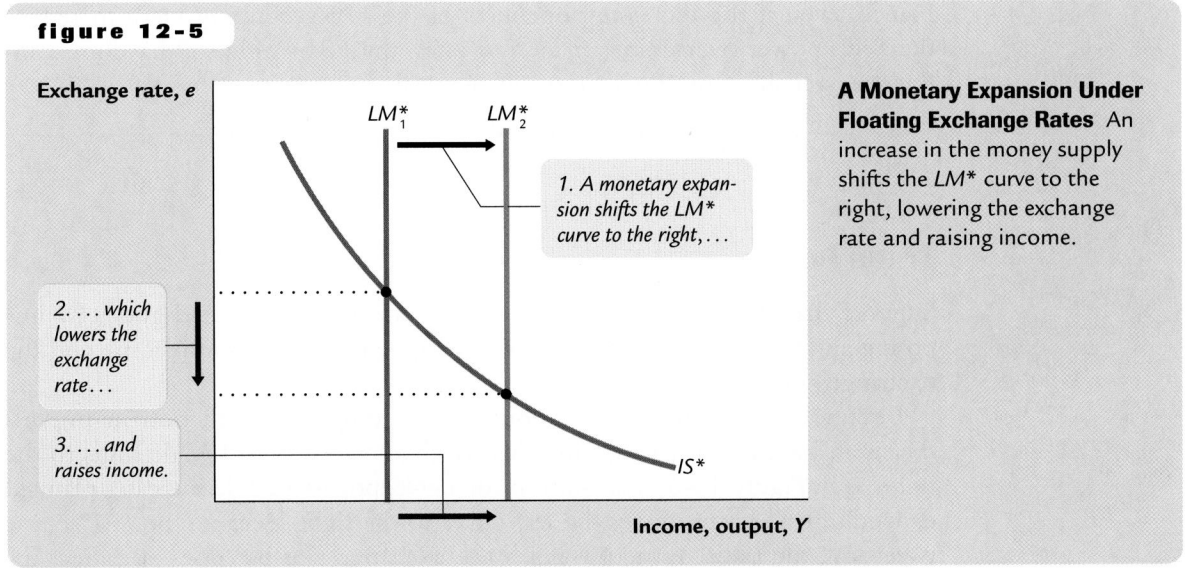

figure 12-5

A Monetary Expansion Under Floating Exchange Rates An increase in the money supply shifts the LM^* curve to the right, lowering the exchange rate and raising income.

CASE STUDY

Can World Financial Markets Usurp the Power of the Federal Reserve?

Some commentators in the media have suggested that the Federal Reserve has less influence over the U.S. economy today than it had in the past. Their argument goes roughly as follows:

1. As world financial sophistication rises and barriers to international trade and finance fall, the U.S. economy is increasingly open to international capital flows.

2. As a result, U.S. interest rates are more determined by developments in world financial market and less determined by domestic monetary policy than they were previously.

3. With less control over interest rates, the Fed may soon find itself powerless in the fight against short-run economic fluctuations.

Does this argument makes sense? Should U.S. policymakers worry that world financial markets will soon hold the U.S. economy hostage?

The Mundell–Fleming model tells us not to worry. We can interpret statement 1 in the above argument as claiming that the U.S. economy is becoming less like the closed economy described by the *IS–LM* model and more like the small open economy described by the Mundell–Fleming model. Let's imagine that this were to occur completely. Statement 2 would then be correct: the $r = r^*$ equation means that world financial markets would determine the domestic interest rate. But statement 3 does not follow from these assumptions. In the Mundell–Fleming model, the central bank has great influence over aggregate income, but this influence arises because the central bank can control the money supply, which affects aggregate income through the exchange rate. Hence, even if the increasing openness of the U.S. economy were to reduce the Fed's power over domestic interest rates, the Fed would still have great influence over short-run fluctuations in aggregate income.

Trade Policy

Suppose that the government reduces the demand for imported goods by imposing an import quota or a tariff. What happens to aggregate income and the exchange rate?

Because net exports equal exports minus imports, a reduction in imports means an increase in net exports. That is, the net-exports schedule shifts to the right, as in Figure 12-6. This shift in the net-exports schedule increases planned expenditure and thus moves the *IS** curve to the right. Because the *LM** curve is vertical, the trade restriction raises the exchange rate but does not affect income.

figure 12-6

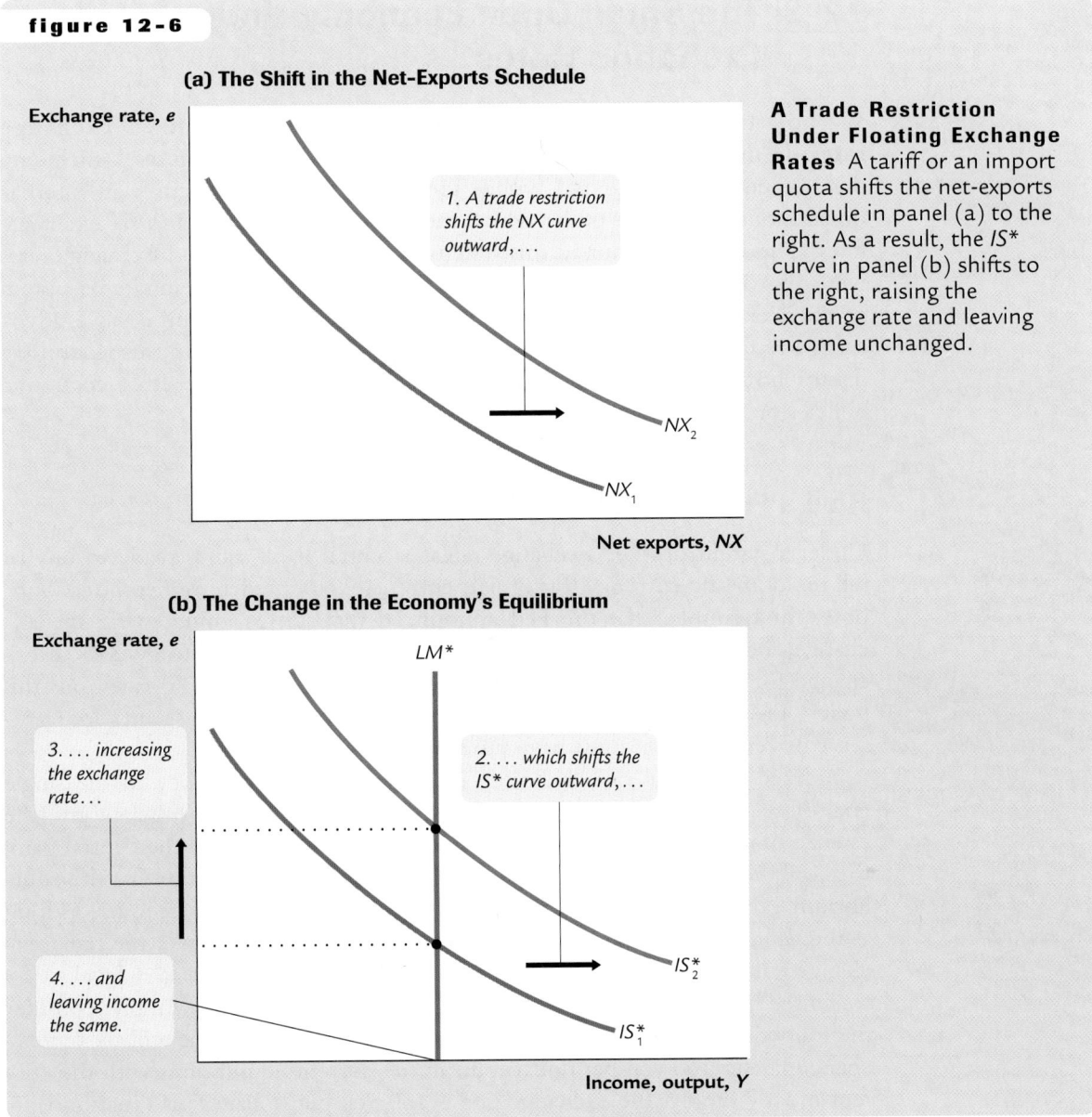

(a) The Shift in the Net-Exports Schedule

Exchange rate, *e*

1. A trade restriction shifts the NX curve outward,...

NX_2

NX_1

Net exports, *NX*

A Trade Restriction Under Floating Exchange Rates A tariff or an import quota shifts the net-exports schedule in panel (a) to the right. As a result, the *IS** curve in panel (b) shifts to the right, raising the exchange rate and leaving income unchanged.

(b) The Change in the Economy's Equilibrium

Exchange rate, *e*

LM*

3. ... increasing the exchange rate...

2. ... which shifts the IS* curve outward,...

IS_2^*

IS_1^*

4. ... and leaving income the same.

Income, output, *Y*

Often a stated goal of policies to restrict trade is to alter the trade balance *NX*. Yet, as we first saw in Chapter 8, such policies do not necessarily have that effect. The same conclusion holds in the Mundell–Fleming model under floating exchange rates. Recall that

$$NX(e) = Y - C(Y - T) - I(r^*) - G.$$

Because a trade restriction does not affect income, consumption, investment, or government purchases, it does not affect the trade balance. Although the shift in the net-exports schedule tends to raise *NX*, the increase in the exchange rate reduces *NX* by the same amount.

12-3| The Small Open Economy Under Fixed Exchange Rates

We now turn to the second type of exchange-rate system: **fixed exchange rates.** In the 1950s and 1960s, most of the world's major economies, including the United States, operated within the Bretton Woods system—an international monetary system under which most governments agreed to fix exchange rates. The world abandoned this system in the early 1970s, and exchange rates were allowed to float freely. Some European countries later reinstated a system of fixed exchange rates among themselves, and some economists have advocated a return to a worldwide system of fixed exchange rates. In this section we discuss how such a system works, and we examine the impact of economic policies on an economy with a fixed exchange rate.

How a Fixed-Exchange-Rate System Works

Under a system of fixed exchange rates, a central bank stands ready to buy or sell the domestic currency for foreign currencies at a predetermined price. Suppose, for example, that the Fed announced that it was going to fix the exchange rate at 100 yen per dollar. It would then stand ready to give $1 in exchange for 100 yen or to give 100 yen in exchange for $1. To carry out this policy, the Fed would need a reserve of dollars (which it can print) and a reserve of yen (which it must have purchased previously).

A fixed exchange rate dedicates a country's monetary policy to the single goal of keeping the exchange rate at the announced level. In other words, the essence of a fixed-exchange-rate system is the commitment of the central bank to allow the money supply to adjust to whatever level will ensure that the equilibrium exchange rate equals the announced exchange rate. Moreover, as long as the central bank stands ready to buy or sell foreign currency at the fixed exchange rate, the money supply adjusts automatically to the necessary level.

To see how fixing the exchange rate determines the money supply, consider the following example. Suppose that the Fed announces that it will fix the exchange rate at 100 yen per dollar, but, in the current equilibrium with the current money supply, the exchange rate is 150 yen per dollar. This situation is illustrated in panel (a) of Figure 12-7. Notice that there is a profit opportunity: an arbitrageur could buy 300 yen in the marketplace for $2, and then sell the yen to the Fed for $3, making a $1 profit. When the Fed buys these yen from the arbitrageur, the dollars it pays for them automatically increase the money supply. The rise in the money supply shifts the LM^* curve to the right, lowering the equilibrium exchange rate. In this way, the money supply continues to rise until the equilibrium exchange rate falls to the announced level.

Conversely, suppose that when the Fed announces that it will fix the exchange rate at 100 yen per dollar, the equilibrium is 50 yen per dollar. Panel (b) of Figure 12-7 shows this situation. In this case, an arbitrageur could make a profit by buying 100 yen from the Fed for $1 and then selling the yen in the marketplace for $2. When the Fed sells these yen, the $1 it receives automati-

figure 12-7

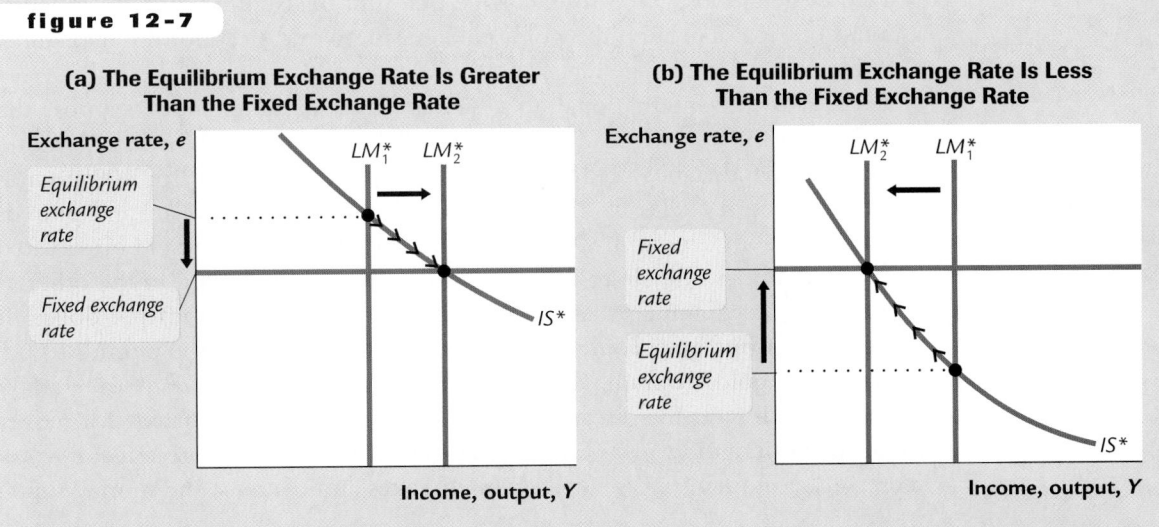

(a) The Equilibrium Exchange Rate Is Greater Than the Fixed Exchange Rate

(b) The Equilibrium Exchange Rate Is Less Than the Fixed Exchange Rate

How a Fixed Exchange Rate Governs the Money Supply In panel (a), the equilibrium exchange rate initially exceeds the fixed level. Arbitrageurs will buy foreign currency in foreign-exchange markets and sell it to the Fed for a profit. This process automatically increases the money supply, shifting the LM^* curve to the right and lowering the exchange rate. In panel (b), the equilibrium exchange rate is below the fixed level. Arbitrageurs will buy dollars in foreign-exchange markets and use them to buy foreign currency from the Fed. This process automatically reduces the money supply, shifting the LM^* curve to the left and raising the exchange rate.

cally reduces the money supply. The fall in the money supply shifts the LM^* curve to the left, raising the equilibrium exchange rate. The money supply continues to fall until the equilibrium exchange rate rises to the announced level.

It is important to understand that this exchange-rate system fixes the nominal exchange rate. Whether it also fixes the real exchange rate depends on the time horizon under consideration. If prices are flexible, as they are in the long run, then the real exchange rate can change even while the nominal exchange rate is fixed. Therefore, in the long run described in Chapter 8, a policy to fix the nominal exchange rate would not influence any real variable, including the real exchange rate. A fixed nominal exchange rate would influence only the money supply and the price level. Yet in the short run described by the Mundell–Fleming model, prices are fixed, so a fixed nominal exchange rate implies a fixed real exchange rate as well.

CASE STUDY

The International Gold Standard

During the late nineteenth and early twentieth centuries, most of the world's major economies operated under a gold standard. Each country maintained a reserve of gold and agreed to exchange one unit of its currency for a specified amount of gold. Through the gold standard, the world's economies maintained a system of fixed exchange rates.

To see how an international gold standard fixes exchange rates, suppose that the U.S. Treasury stands ready to buy or sell 1 ounce of gold for $100, and the Bank of England stands ready to buy or sell 1 ounce of gold for 100 pounds. Together, these policies fix the rate of exchange between dollars and pounds: $1 must trade for 1 pound. Otherwise, the law of one price would be violated, and it would be profitable to buy gold in one country and sell it in the other.

Suppose, for example, that the exchange rate were 2 pounds per dollar. In this case, an arbitrageur could buy 200 pounds for $100, use the pounds to buy 2 ounces of gold from the Bank of England, bring the gold to the United States, and sell it to the Treasury for $200—making a $100 profit. Moreover, by bringing the gold to the United States from England, the arbitrageur would increase the money supply in the United States and decrease the money supply in England.

Thus, during the era of the gold standard, the international transport of gold by arbitrageurs was an automatic mechanism adjusting the money supply and stabilizing exchange rates. This system did not completely fix exchange rates, because shipping gold across the Atlantic was costly. Yet the international gold standard did keep the exchange rate within a range dictated by transportation costs. It thereby prevented large and persistent movements in exchange rates.[2]

Fiscal Policy

Let's now examine how economic policies affect a small open economy with a fixed exchange rate. Suppose that the government stimulates domestic spending by increasing government purchases or by cutting taxes. This policy shifts the IS^* curve to the right, as in Figure 12-8, putting upward pressure on the exchange rate. But because the central bank stands ready to trade foreign and domestic currency at the fixed exchange rate, arbitrageurs quickly respond to the rising exchange rate by selling foreign currency to the central bank, leading to an automatic monetary expansion. The rise in the money supply shifts the LM^* curve to the right. Thus, in contrast to the situation under floating exchange rates, a fiscal expansion under fixed exchange rates raises aggregate income.

Monetary Policy

Imagine that a central bank operating with a fixed exchange rate were to try to increase the money supply—for example, by buying bonds from the public. What would happen? The initial impact of this policy is to shift the LM^* curve

---

[2] For more on how the gold standard worked, see the essays in Barry Eichengreen, ed., *The Gold Standard in Theory and History* (New York: Methuen, 1985).

figure 12-8

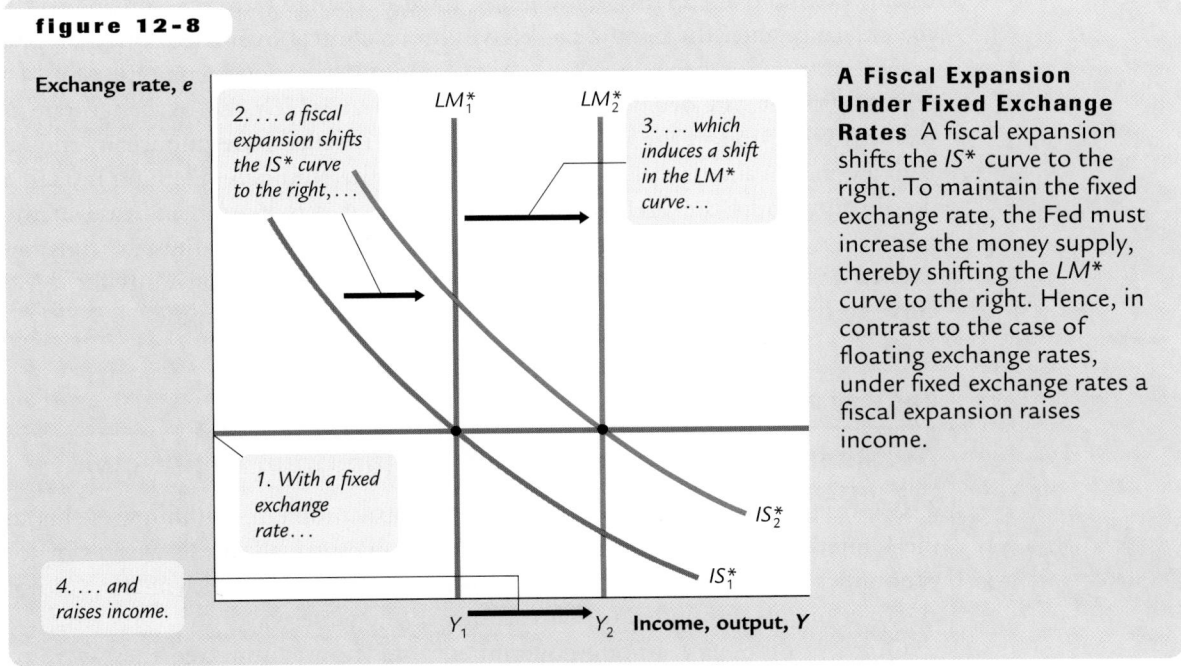

2. . . . a fiscal expansion shifts the IS* curve to the right, . . .

3. . . . which induces a shift in the LM* curve. . .

1. With a fixed exchange rate . . .

4. . . . and raises income.

A Fiscal Expansion Under Fixed Exchange Rates A fiscal expansion shifts the IS* curve to the right. To maintain the fixed exchange rate, the Fed must increase the money supply, thereby shifting the LM* curve to the right. Hence, in contrast to the case of floating exchange rates, under fixed exchange rates a fiscal expansion raises income.

to the right, lowering the exchange rate, as in Figure 12-9. But, because the central bank is committed to trading foreign and domestic currency at a fixed exchange rate, arbitrageurs quickly respond to the falling exchange rate by selling the domestic currency to the central bank, causing the money supply and the LM* curve to return to their initial positions. Hence, monetary policy as

figure 12-9

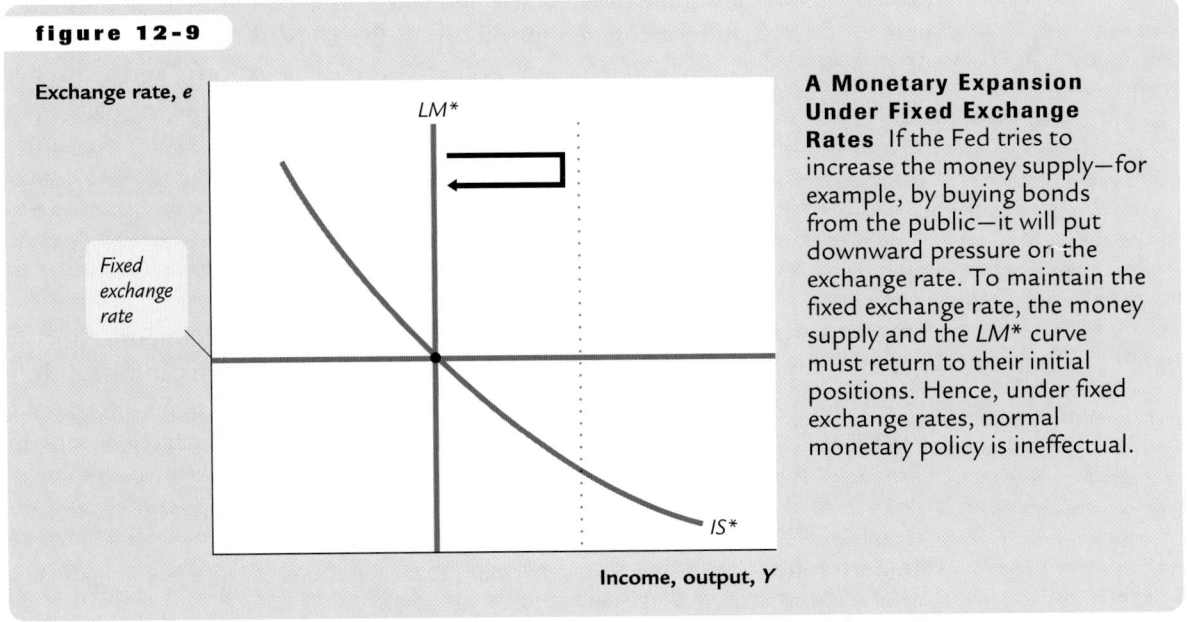

Fixed exchange rate

A Monetary Expansion Under Fixed Exchange Rates If the Fed tries to increase the money supply—for example, by buying bonds from the public—it will put downward pressure on the exchange rate. To maintain the fixed exchange rate, the money supply and the LM* curve must return to their initial positions. Hence, under fixed exchange rates, normal monetary policy is ineffectual.

usually conducted is ineffectual under a fixed exchange rate. By agreeing to fix the exchange rate, the central bank gives up its control over the money supply.

A country with a fixed exchange rate can, however, conduct a type of monetary policy: it can decide to change the level at which the exchange rate is fixed. A reduction in the value of the currency is called a **devaluation,** and an increase in its value is called a **revaluation.** In the Mundell–Fleming model, a devaluation shifts the LM^* curve to the right; it acts like an increase in the money supply under a floating exchange rate. A devaluation thus expands net exports and raises aggregate income. Conversely, a revaluation shifts the LM^* curve to the left, reduces net exports, and lowers aggregate income.

CASE STUDY

Devaluation and the Recovery From the Great Depression

The Great Depression of the 1930s was a global problem. Although events in the United States may have precipitated the downturn, all of the world's major economies experienced huge declines in production and employment. Yet not all governments responded to this calamity in the same way.

One key difference among governments was how committed they were to the fixed exchange rate set by the international gold standard. Some countries, such as France, Germany, Italy, and the Netherlands, maintained the old rate of exchange between gold and currency. Other countries, such as Denmark, Finland, Norway, Sweden, and the United Kingdom, reduced the amount of gold they would pay for each unit of currency by about 50 percent. By reducing the gold content of their currencies, these governments devalued their currencies relative to those of other countries.

The subsequent experience of these two groups of countries conforms to the prediction of the Mundell–Fleming model. Those countries that pursued a policy of devaluation recovered quickly from the Depression. The lower value of the currency raised the money supply, stimulated exports, and expanded production. By contrast, those countries that maintained the old exchange rate suffered longer with a depressed level of economic activity.[3]

Trade Policy

Suppose that the government reduces imports by imposing an import quota or a tariff. This policy shifts the net-exports schedule to the right and thus shifts the IS^* curve to the right, as in Figure 12-10. The shift in the IS^* curve tends to raise the exchange rate. To keep the exchange rate at the fixed level, the money supply must rise, shifting the LM^* curve to the right.

---

[3] Barry Eichengreen and Jeffrey Sachs, "Exchange Rates and Economic Recovery in the 1930s," *Journal of Economic History* 45 (December 1985): 925–946.

figure 12-10

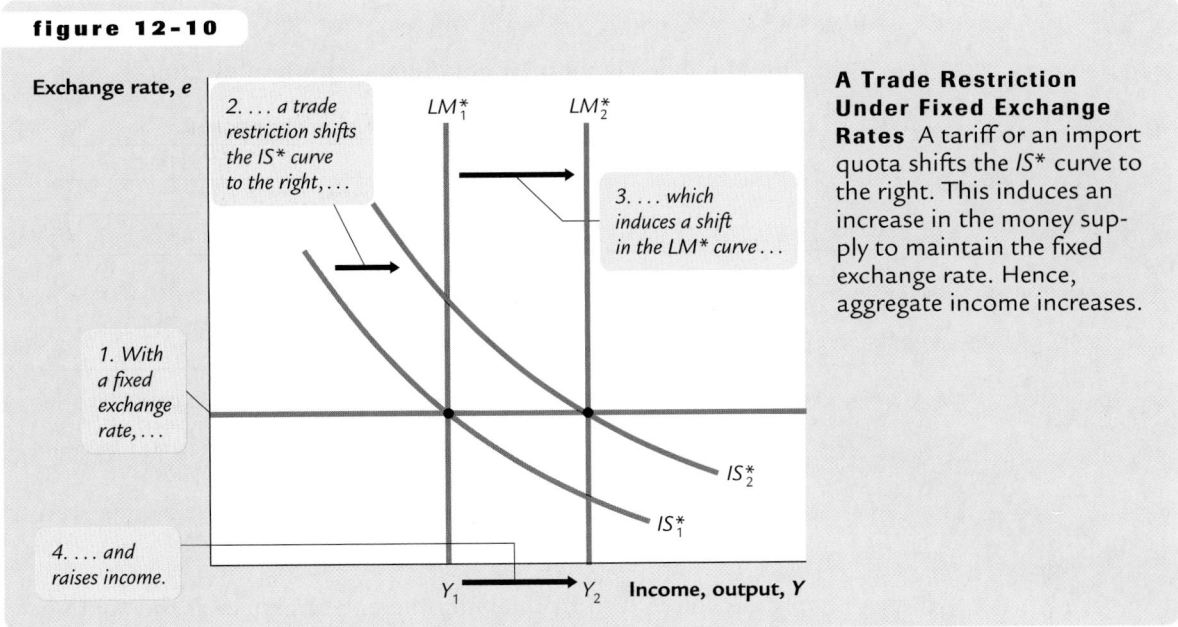

Exchange rate, e

2. . . . a trade restriction shifts the IS^* curve to the right, . . .

LM_1^*

LM_2^*

3. . . . which induces a shift in the LM^* curve . . .

1. With a fixed exchange rate, . . .

IS_2^*

IS_1^*

4. . . . and raises income.

Y_1 Y_2 Income, output, Y

A Trade Restriction Under Fixed Exchange Rates A tariff or an import quota shifts the IS^* curve to the right. This induces an increase in the money supply to maintain the fixed exchange rate. Hence, aggregate income increases.

The result of a trade restriction under a fixed exchange rate is very different from that under a floating exchange rate. In both cases, a trade restriction shifts the net-exports schedule to the right, but only under a fixed exchange rate does a trade restriction increase net exports NX. The reason is that a trade restriction under a fixed exchange rate induces monetary expansion rather than an appreciation of the exchange rate. The monetary expansion, in turn, raises aggregate income. Recall the accounting identity

$$NX = S - I.$$

When income rises, saving also rises, and this implies an increase in net exports.

Policy in the Mundell–Fleming Model: A Summary

The Mundell–Fleming model shows that the effect of almost any economic policy on a small open economy depends on whether the exchange rate is floating or fixed. Table 12-1 summarizes our analysis of the short-run effects of fiscal, monetary, and trade policies on income, the exchange rate, and the trade balance. What is most striking is that all of the results are different under floating and fixed exchange rates.

To be more specific, the Mundell–Fleming model shows that the power of monetary and fiscal policy to influence aggregate income depends on the exchange-rate regime. Under floating exchange rates, only monetary policy can affect income. The usual expansionary impact of fiscal policy is offset by a rise in the value of the currency. Under fixed exchange rates, only fiscal policy can affect income. The normal potency of monetary policy is lost because the

table 12-1

The Mundell-Fleming Model: Summary of Policy Effects

	EXCHANGE-RATE REGIME					
	FLOATING			FIXED		
	IMPACT ON:					
Policy	Y	e	NX	Y	e	NX
Fiscal expansion	0	↑	↓	↑	0	0
Monetary expansion	↑	↓	↑	0	0	0
Import restriction	0	↑	0	↑	0	↑

Note: This table shows the direction of impact of various economic policies on income Y, the exchange rate e, and the trade balance NX. A " ↑ " indicates that the variable increases; a " ↓ " indicates that it decreases; a "0" indicates no effect. Remember that the exchange rate is defined as the amount of foreign currency per unit of domestic currency (for example, 100 yen per dollar).

money supply is dedicated to maintaining the exchange rate at the announced level.

12-4 | Interest-Rate Differentials

So far, our analysis has assumed that the interest rate in a small open economy is equal to the world interest rate: $r = r^*$. To some extent, however, interest rates differ around the world. We now extend our analysis by considering the causes and effects of international interest-rate differentials.

Country Risk and Exchange-Rate Expectations

When we assumed earlier that the interest rate in our small open economy is determined by the world interest rate, we were applying the law of one price. We reasoned that if the domestic interest rate were above the world interest rate, people from abroad would lend to that country, driving the domestic interest rate down. And if the domestic interest rate were below the world interest rate, domestic residents would lend abroad to earn a higher return, driving the domestic interest rate up. In the end, the domestic interest rate would equal the world interest rate.

Why doesn't this logic always apply? There are two reasons.

One reason is country risk. When investors buy U.S. government bonds or make loans to U.S. corporations, they are fairly confident that they will be repaid with interest. By contrast, in some less-developed countries, it is plausible to fear that a revolution or other political upheaval might lead to a default on loan repayments. Borrowers in such countries often have to pay higher interest rates to compensate lenders for this risk.

Another reason interest rates differ across countries is expected changes in the exchange rate. For example, suppose that people expect the French franc to fall in value relative to the U.S. dollar. Then loans made in francs will be repaid in a less valuable currency than loans made in dollars. To compensate for this expected fall in the French currency, the interest rate in France will be higher than the interest rate in the United States.

Thus, because of both country risk and expectations of future exchange-rate changes, the interest rate of a small open economy can differ from interest rates in other economies around the world. Let's now see how this fact affects our analysis.

Differentials in the Mundell–Fleming Model

To incorporate interest-rate differentials into the Mundell–Fleming model, we assume that the interest rate in our small open economy is determined by the world interest rate plus a risk premium θ:

$$r = r^* + \theta.$$

The risk premium is determined by the perceived political risk of making loans in a country and the expected change in the real exchange rate. For our purposes here, we can take the risk premium as exogenous in order to examine how changes in the risk premium affect the economy.

The model is largely the same as before. The two equations are

$$Y = C(Y - T) + I(r^* + \theta) + G + NX(e) \qquad IS^*,$$
$$M/P = L(r^* + \theta, Y) \qquad\qquad\qquad\qquad LM^*.$$

For any given fiscal policy, monetary policy, price level, and risk premium, these two equations determine the level of income and exchange rate that equilibrate the goods market and the money market. Holding constant the risk premium, monetary policy, fiscal policy, and trade policy work as we have already seen.

Now suppose that political turmoil causes the country's risk premium θ to rise. The most direct effect is that the domestic interest rate r rises. The higher interest rate, in turn, has two effects. First, the IS^* curve shifts to the left, because the higher interest rate reduces investment. Second, the LM^* curve shifts to the right, because the higher interest rate reduces the demand for money, and this allows a higher level of income for any given money supply. [Recall that Y must satisfy the equation $M/P = L(r^* + \theta, Y)$.] As Figure 12-11 shows, these two shifts cause income to rise and the currency to depreciate.

This analysis has an important implication: expectations of the exchange rate are partially self-fulfilling. For example, suppose that people come to believe that the French franc will not be valuable in the future. Investors will place a larger risk premium on French assets: θ will rise in France. This expectation will drive up French interest rates and, as we have just seen, will drive down the value of the French currency. Thus, the expectation that a currency will lose value in the future causes it to lose value today.

figure 12-11

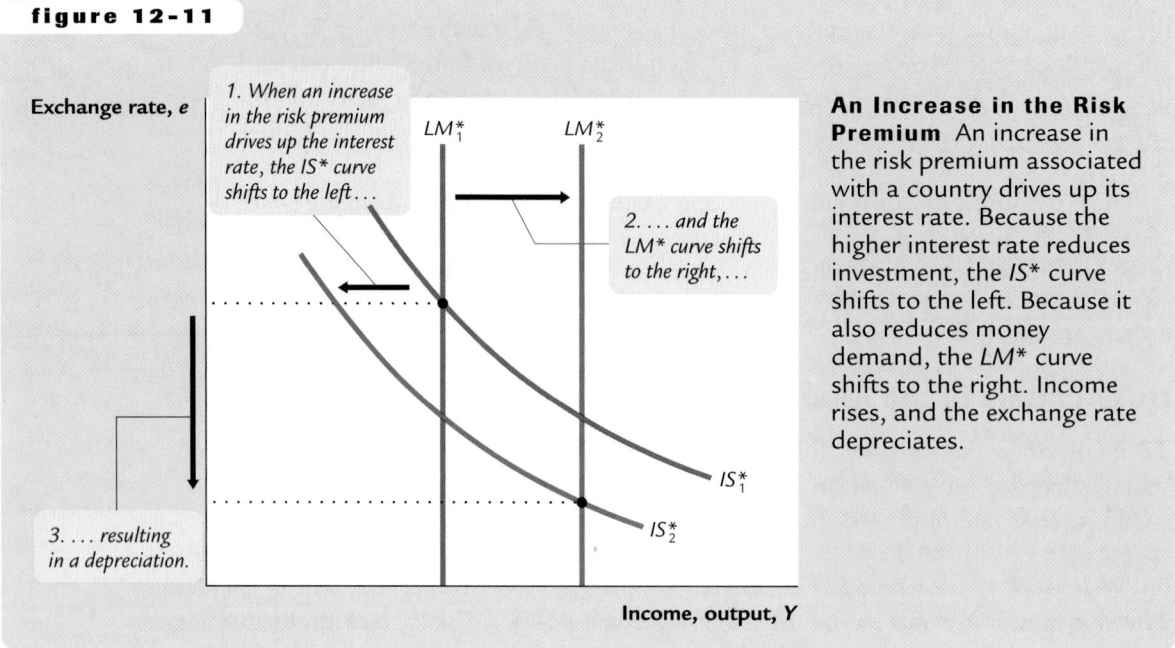

Exchange rate, e

1. When an increase in the risk premium drives up the interest rate, the IS* curve shifts to the left...

LM_1^* LM_2^*

2. ... and the LM* curve shifts to the right, ...

IS_1^*

IS_2^*

3. ... resulting in a depreciation.

Income, output, Y

An Increase in the Risk Premium An increase in the risk premium associated with a country drives up its interest rate. Because the higher interest rate reduces investment, the IS* curve shifts to the left. Because it also reduces money demand, the LM* curve shifts to the right. Income rises, and the exchange rate depreciates.

One surprising—and perhaps inaccurate—prediction of this analysis is that an increase in country risk as measured by θ will cause the economy's income to increase. This occurs in Figure 12-11 because of the rightward shift in the LM^* curve. Although higher interest rates depress investment, the depreciation of the currency stimulates net exports by an even greater amount. As a result, aggregate income rises.

There are three reasons why, in practice, such a boom in income does not occur. First, the central bank might want to avoid the large depreciation of the domestic currency and, therefore, may respond by decreasing the money supply M. Second, the depreciation of the domestic currency may suddenly increase the price of imported goods, causing an increase in the price level P. Third, when some event increases the country risk premium θ, residents of the country might respond to the same event by increasing their demand for money (for any given income and interest rate), because money is often the safest asset available. All three of these changes would tend to shift the LM^* curve toward the left, which mitigates the fall in the exchange rate but also tends to depress income.

Thus, increases in country risk are not desirable. In the short run, they typically lead to a depreciating currency and, through the three channels just described, falling aggregate income. In addition, because a higher interest rate reduces investment, the long-run implication is reduced capital accumulation and lower economic growth.

CASE STUDY

International Financial Crisis: Mexico 1994–1995

In August 1994, a Mexican peso was worth 30 cents. A year later, it was worth only 16 cents. What explains this massive fall in the value of the Mexican currency? Country risk is a large part of the story.

At the beginning of 1994, Mexico was a country on the rise. The recent passage of the North American Free Trade Agreement (NAFTA), which reduced trade barriers among the United States, Canada, and Mexico, made many confident about the future of the Mexican economy. Investors around the world were eager to make loans to the Mexican government and to Mexican corporations.

Political developments soon changed that perception. A violent uprising in the Chiapas region of Mexico made the political situation in Mexico seem precarious. Then Luis Donaldo Colosio, the leading presidential candidate, was assassinated. The political future looked less certain, and many investors started placing a larger risk premium on Mexican assets.

At first, the rising risk premium did not affect the value of the peso, for Mexico was operating with a fixed exchange rate. As we have seen, under a fixed exchange rate, the central bank agrees to trade the domestic currency (pesos) for a foreign currency (dollars) at a predetermined rate. Thus, when an increase in the country risk premium put downward pressure on the value of the peso, the Mexican central bank had to accept pesos and pay out dollars. This automatic exchange-market intervention contracted the Mexican money supply (shifting the LM^* curve to the left) when the currency might otherwise have depreciated.

Yet Mexico's reserves of foreign currency were too small to maintain its fixed exchange rate. When Mexico ran out of dollars at the end of 1994, the Mexican government announced a devaluation of the peso. This choice had repercussions, however, because the government had repeatedly promised that it would not devalue. Investors became even more distrustful of Mexican policymakers and feared further Mexican devaluations.

Investors around the world (including those in Mexico) avoided buying Mexican assets. The country risk premium rose once again, adding to the upward pressure on interest rates and the downward pressure on the peso. The Mexican stock market plummeted. When the Mexican government needed to roll over some of its debt that was coming due, investors were unwilling to buy the new debt. Default appeared to be the government's only option. In just a few months, Mexico had gone from being a promising emerging economy to being a risky economy with a government on the verge of bankruptcy.

Then the United States stepped in. The U.S. government had three motives: to help its neighbor to the south, to prevent the massive illegal immigration that might follow government default and economic collapse, and to prevent the investor pessimism regarding Mexico from spreading to other developing countries. The U.S. government, together with the International Monetary

Fund (IMF), led an international effort to bail out the Mexican government. In particular, the United States provided loan guarantees for Mexican government debt, which allowed the Mexican government to refinance the debt that was coming due. These loan guarantees helped restore confidence in the Mexican economy, thereby reducing to some extent the country risk premium.

Although the U.S. loan guarantees may well have stopped a bad situation from getting worse, they did not prevent the Mexican meltdown of 1994–1995 from being a painful experience for the Mexican people. Not only did the Mexican currency lose much of its value, but Mexico also went through a deep recession. Fortunately, by the late 1990s, aggregate income was growing again, and the worst appeared to be over. But the lesson from this experience is clear and could well apply again in the future: changes in perceived country risk, often attributable to political instability, are an important determinant of interest rates and exchange rates in small open economies.

CASE STUDY

International Financial Crisis: Asia 1997–1998

Toward the end of 1997, as the Mexican economy was recovering from its financial crisis, a similar story started to unfold in several Asian economies, including Thailand, South Korea, and especially Indonesia. The symptoms were familiar: high interest rates, falling asset values, and a depreciating currency. In Indonesia, for instance, short-term nominal interest rates rose above 50 percent, the stock market lost about 90 percent of its value (measured in U.S. dollars), and the rupiah fell against the dollar by more than 80 percent. The crisis led to rising inflation in these countries (as the depreciating currency made imports more expensive) and to falling GDP (as high interest rates and reduced confidence depressed spending). According to preliminary estimates, real GDP in Indonesia fell about 15 percent in 1998, making the downturn larger than any U.S. recession since the Great Depression of the 1930s.

What sparked this firestorm? The problem began in the Asian banking systems. For many years, the governments in the Asian nations had been more involved in managing the allocation of resources—in particular, financial resources—than is true in the United States and other developed countries. Some commentators had applauded this "partnership" between government and private enterprise and had even suggested that the United States should follow the example. Over time, however, it became clear that many Asian banks had been extending loans to those with the most political clout rather than to those with the most profitable investment projects. Once rising default rates started to expose this "crony capitalism," as it was then called, international investors started to lose confidence in the future of these economies. The risk premiums for Asian assets rose, causing interest rates to skyrocket and currencies to collapse.

International crises of confidence often involve a vicious circle that can amplify the problem. Here is one theory about what happened in Asia:

1. Problems in the banking system eroded international confidence in these economies.

2. Loss of confidence raised risk premiums and interest rates.

3. Rising interest rates, together with the loss of confidence, depressed the prices of stock and other assets.

4. Falling asset prices reduced the value of collateral being used for bank loans.

5. Reduced collateral increased default rates on bank loans.

6. Greater defaults exacerbated problems in the banking system. Now return to step 1 to complete and continue the circle.

Some economists have used this vicious-circle argument to suggest that the Asian crisis was a self-fulfilling prophecy: bad things happened merely because people expected bad things to happen. Most economists, however, thought the political corruption of the banking system was a real problem, which was then compounded by this vicious circle of reduced confidence.

As the Asian crisis developed, the IMF and the United States tried to restore confidence, much as they had with Mexico a few years earlier. In particular, the IMF made loans to the Asian countries to help them over the crisis; in exchange for these loans, it exacted promises that the governments would reform their banking systems and eliminate crony capitalism. The IMF's hope was that the short-term loans and longer-term reforms would restore confidence, lower the risk premium, and turn the vicious circle into a virtuous circle. As this book was going to press, it was still to be seen how well this policy would work.

12-5 | Should Exchange Rates Be Floating or Fixed?

Having analyzed how an economy works under floating and fixed exchange rates, we turn to the question of which exchange-rate regime is preferable. The international monetary system is often a topic of heated debate among international economists and policymakers. Historically, most economists have favored a system of floating exchange rates. Yet, in recent years, some have advocated a return to fixed exchange rates.

The primary argument for a floating exchange rate is that it allows monetary policy to be used for other purposes. Under fixed rates, monetary policy is committed to the single goal of maintaining the exchange rate at its announced level. Yet the exchange rate is only one of many macroeconomic variables that

"Then it's agreed. Until the dollar firms up, we let the clamshell float."

monetary policy can influence. A system of floating exchange rates leaves monetary policymakers free to pursue other goals, such as stabilizing employment or prices.

Advocates of fixed exchange rates argue that exchange-rate uncertainty makes international trade more difficult. After the world abandoned the Bretton Woods system of fixed exchange rates in the early 1970s, both real and nominal exchange rates became (and remained) much more volatile than anyone had expected. Some economists attribute this volatility to irrational and destabilizing speculation by international investors. Business executives often claim that this volatility is harmful because it increases the uncertainty that accompanies international business transactions. Yet, despite this exchange-rate volatility, the amount of world trade has continued to rise under floating exchange rates.

Advocates of fixed exchange rates sometimes argue that a commitment to a fixed exchange rate is one way to discipline a nation's monetary authority and prevent excessive growth in the money supply. Yet there are many other policy rules to which the central bank could be committed. In Chapter 14, for instance, we discuss policy rules such as targets for nominal GDP or the inflation rate. Fixing the exchange rate has the advantage of being simpler to implement than these other policy rules, because the money supply adjusts automatically, but this policy may lead to greater volatility in income and employment.

In the end, the choice between floating and fixed rates is not as stark as it may seem at first. During periods of fixed exchange rates, countries can change the value of their currency if maintaining the exchange rate conflicts too severely with other goals. During periods of floating exchange rates, countries often use formal or informal targets for the exchange rate when deciding whether to expand or contract the money supply. We rarely observe exchange rates that are completely fixed or completely floating. Instead, under both systems, stability of the exchange rate is usually one among many of the central bank's objectives.

CASE STUDY

Monetary Union in the United States and Europe

If you have ever driven the 3,000 miles from New York City to San Francisco, you may recall that you never needed to change your money from one form of currency to another. In all fifty U.S. states, local residents are happy to accept the U.S. dollar for the items you might buy. Such a *monetary union* is the most extreme form of a fixed exchange rate. The exchange rate between New York dollars and San Francisco dollars is so irrevocably fixed that you may not even know that there is a difference between the two. (What's the difference? Each dollar bill is issued by one of the dozen local Federal Reserve Banks. Although the bank of origin can be identified from the bill's markings, you don't care which type of dollar you hold because everyone else, including the Federal Reserve system, is ready to trade them one for one.)

If you have ever made a similar 3,000-mile trip across Europe, however, your experience was probably very different. You didn't have to travel far before needing to exchange your French francs for German marks, Dutch guilders, Spanish pesetas, or Italian lira. The large number of currencies in Europe made traveling less convenient and more expensive. Every time you crossed a border, you had to wait in line at a bank to get the local money, and you had to pay the bank a fee for the service.

Recently, however, this has started to change. Many countries in Europe have decided to form their own monetary union and use a common currency called the euro, which was introduced in January 1999. The adoption of the euro is an extension of the *European Monetary System (EMS)*, which during the previous two decades had attempted to limit exchange-rate fluctuations among participating countries. When the euro is fully adopted, this goal will be achieved: the exchange rate between France and Germany will be as fixed as the exchange rate between New York City and San Francisco.

The introduction of a common currency has its costs. The most important is that the nations of Europe will no longer be able to conduct their own monetary policies. Instead, a European central bank, with participation of all member countries, will set a single monetary policy for all of Europe. The central banks of the individual countries will play a role similar to that of regional Federal Reserve Banks: they will monitor local conditions but they will have no control over the money supply or interest rates. Critics of the move toward a common currency argue that the cost of losing national monetary policy is large. If a recession hits one country but not others in Europe, that country may wish it had the tool of monetary policy to combat the downturn.

Why, according to these economists, is monetary union a bad idea for Europe if it works so well in the United States? These economists argue that the United States is different from Europe in two important ways. First, labor is more mobile among U.S. states than among European countries. This is in part because the United States has a common language and in part because most Americans are descended from immigrants, who have shown a willingness to move. Therefore, when a regional recession occurs, U.S. workers are more likely to move from high-unemployment states to low-unemployment states. Second, the United States has a strong central government that can use fiscal policy—such as the federal income tax—to redistribute resources among regions. Because Europe does not have these two advantages, it will suffer more when it restricts itself to a single monetary policy.

Advocates of a common currency believe that the loss of national monetary policy is more than offset by other gains. With a single currency in all of Europe, travelers and businesses will no longer need to worry about exchange rates, and this should encourage more international trade. In addition, a common currency may have the political advantage of making Europeans feel more connected to one another. The twentieth century was marked by two world wars, both of which were sparked by European discord. If a common currency makes the nations of Europe more harmonious, it will benefit the entire world.

12-6 | The Mundell–Fleming Model With a Changing Price Level

So far we have been using the Mundell–Fleming model to study the small open economy in the short run when the price level is fixed. To see how this model relates to models we have examined previously, let's consider what happens when the price level changes.

To examine price adjustment in an open economy, we must distinguish between the nominal exchange rate e and the real exchange rate ϵ, which equals eP/P^*. We can write the Mundell–Fleming model as

$$Y = C(Y - T) + I(r^*) + G + NX(\epsilon) \qquad IS^*,$$
$$M/P = L(r^*, Y) \qquad\qquad\qquad\qquad LM^*.$$

These equations should be familiar by now. The first equation describes the IS^* curve, and the second equation describes the LM^* curve. Note that net exports depend on the real exchange rate.

Figure 12-12 shows what happens when the price level falls. Because a lower price level raises the level of real money balances, the LM^* curve shifts to the right, as in panel (a) of Figure 12-12. The real exchange rate depreciates, and the equilibrium level of income rises. The aggregate demand curve summarizes this negative relationship between the price level and the level of income, as shown in panel (b) of Figure 12-12.

Thus, just as the IS–LM model explains the aggregate demand curve in a closed economy, the Mundell–Fleming model explains the aggregate demand curve for a small open economy. In both cases, the aggregate demand curve shows the set of equilibria that arise as the price level varies. And in both cases, anything that changes the equilibrium for a given price level shifts the aggregate demand curve. Policies that raise income shift the aggregate demand curve to

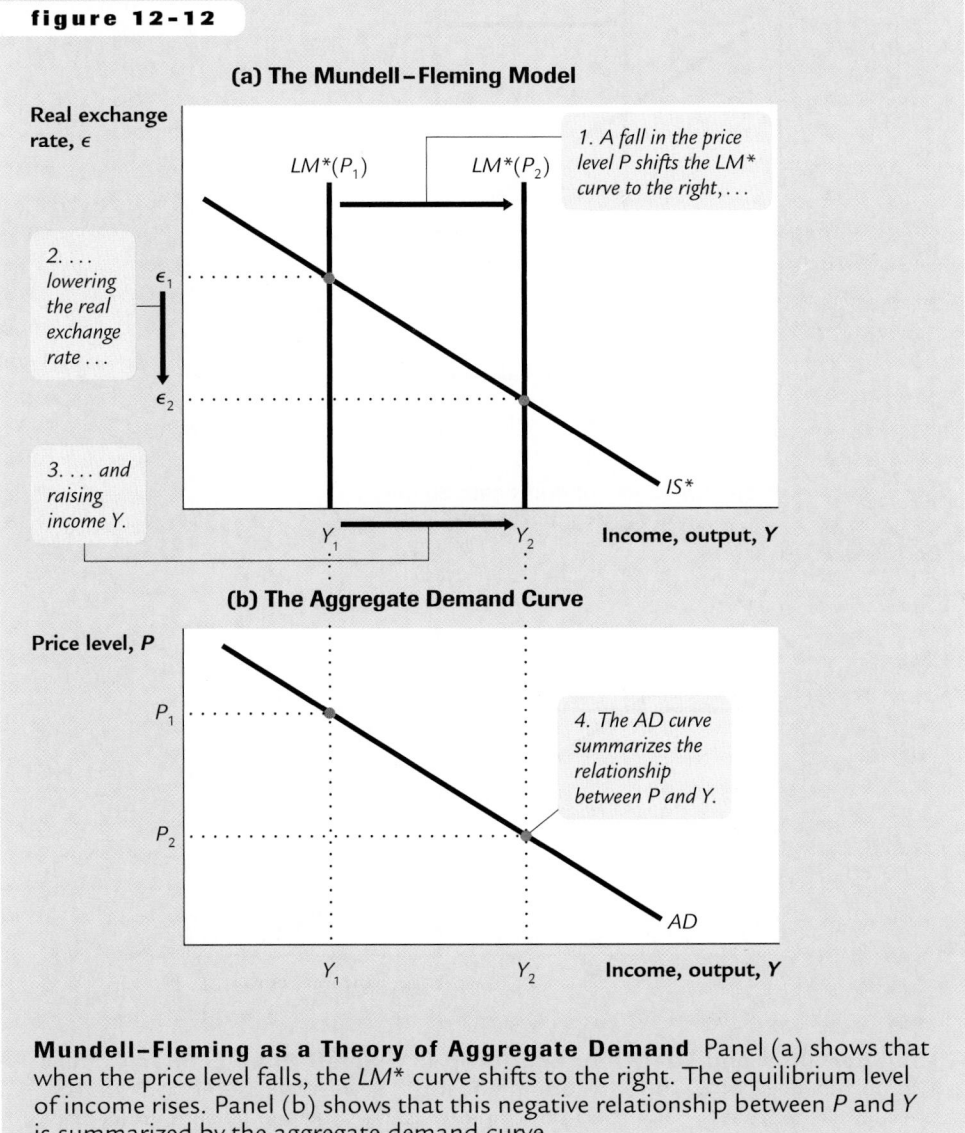

figure 12-12

(a) The Mundell–Fleming Model

Real exchange rate, ϵ

$LM^*(P_1)$ $LM^*(P_2)$

1. *A fall in the price level P shifts the LM* curve to the right, . . .*

2. *. . . lowering the real exchange rate . . .* ϵ_1

ϵ_2

3. *. . . and raising income Y.*

IS^*

Y_1 Y_2 **Income, output, Y**

(b) The Aggregate Demand Curve

Price level, **P**

P_1

4. *The AD curve summarizes the relationship between P and Y.*

P_2

AD

Y_1 Y_2 **Income, output, Y**

Mundell–Fleming as a Theory of Aggregate Demand Panel (a) shows that when the price level falls, the LM^* curve shifts to the right. The equilibrium level of income rises. Panel (b) shows that this negative relationship between P and Y is summarized by the aggregate demand curve.

the right; policies that lower income shift the aggregate demand curve to the left.

We can use this diagram to show how the short-run model in this chapter is related to the long-run model in Chapter 8. Figure 12-13 shows the short-run and long-run equilibria. In both panels of the figure, point K describes the

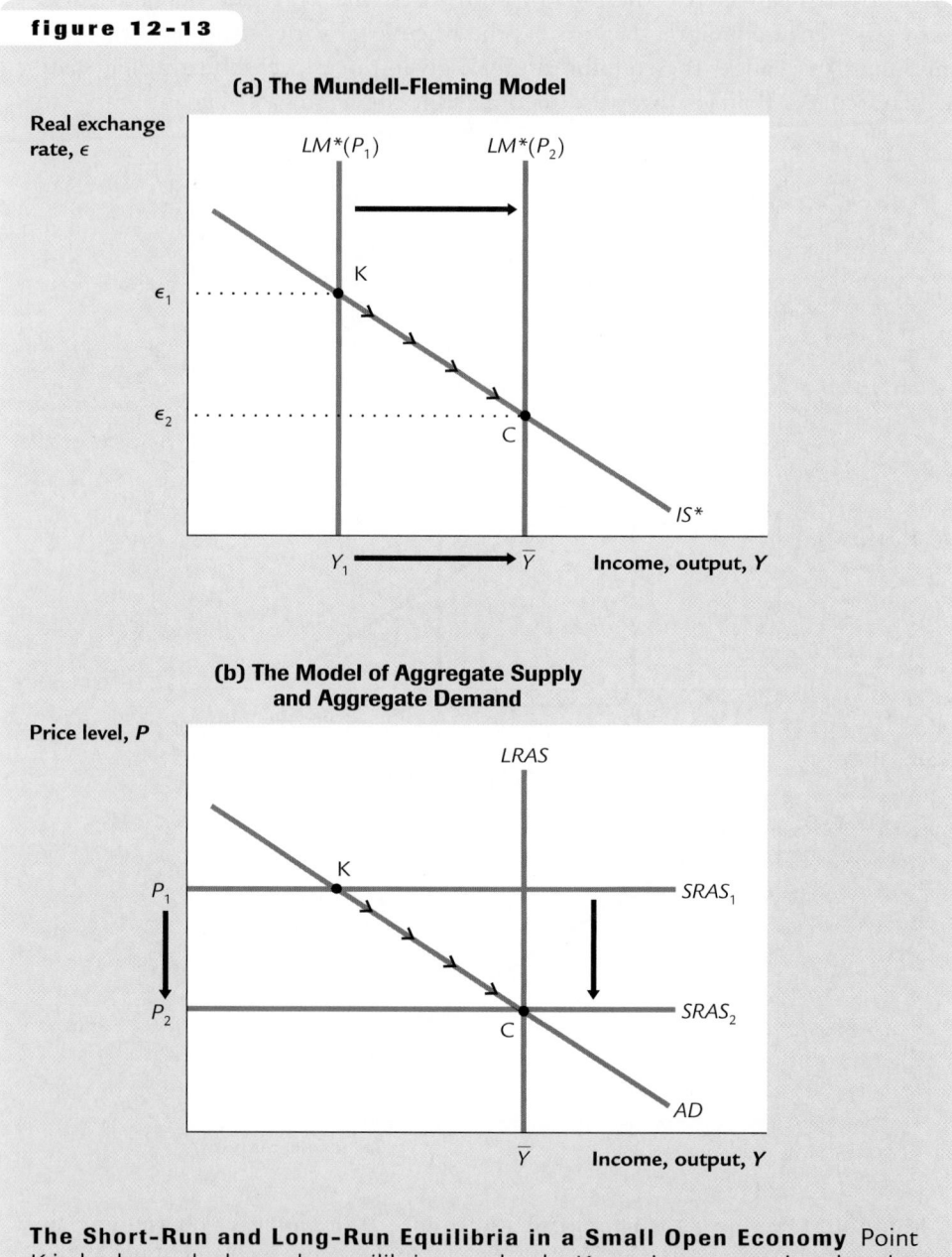

figure 12-13

The Short-Run and Long-Run Equilibria in a Small Open Economy Point K in both panels shows the equilibrium under the Keynesian assumption that the price level is fixed at P_1. Point C in both panels shows the equilibrium under the classical assumption that the price level adjusts to maintain income at its natural rate $\overline{Y}$.

short-run equilibrium, because it assumes a fixed price level. At this equilibrium, the demand for goods and services is too low to keep the economy producing at its natural rate. Over time, low demand causes the price level to fall. The fall in the price level raises real money balances, shifting the *LM** curve to the right. The real exchange rate depreciates, so net exports rises. Eventually, the economy reaches point C, the long-run equilibrium. The speed of transition between the short-run and long-run equilibria depends on how quickly the price level adjusts to restore the economy to the natural rate.

The levels of income at point K and point C are both of interest. Our central concern in this chapter has been how policy influences point K, the short-run equilibrium. In Chapter 8 we examined the determinants of point C, the long-run equilibrium. Whenever policymakers consider any change in policy, they need to consider both the short-run and long-run effects of their decision.

12-7 | A Concluding Reminder

In this chapter we have examined how a small open economy works in the short run when prices are sticky. We have seen how monetary and fiscal policy influence income and the exchange rate, and how the behavior of the economy depends on whether the exchange rate is floating or fixed. In closing, it is worth repeating a lesson from Chapter 8. Many countries, including the United States, are neither closed economies nor small open economies: they lie somewhere in between.

A large open economy like the United States combines the behavior of a closed economy and the behavior of a small open economy. When analyzing policies in a large open economy, we need to consider both the closed-economy logic of Chapter 11 and the open-economy logic developed in this chapter. The appendix to this chapter presents a model for the intermediate case of a large open economy. The results of that model are, as one would guess, a mixture of the two polar cases we have already examined.

To see how we can draw on the logic of both the closed and small open economies and apply these insights to the United States, consider how a monetary contraction affects the economy in the short run. In a closed economy, a monetary contraction raises the interest rate, lowers investment, and thus lowers aggregate income. In a small open economy with a floating exchange rate, a monetary contraction raises the exchange rate, lowers net exports, and thus lowers aggregate income. The interest rate is unaffected, however, because it is determined by world financial markets.

The U.S. economy contains elements of both cases. Because the United States is large enough to affect the world interest rate and because capital is not perfectly mobile across countries, a monetary contraction does raise the interest rate and depress investment. At the same time, a monetary contraction also raises the value of the dollar, thereby depressing net exports. Hence, although the Mundell–Fleming model does not precisely describe an economy like that of the United States, it does predict correctly what happens to international variables such as the exchange rate, and it shows how international interactions alter the effects of monetary and fiscal policies.

Summary

1. The Mundell–Fleming model is the *IS–LM* model for a small open economy. It takes the price level as given and then shows what causes fluctuations in income and the exchange rate.

2. The Mundell–Fleming model shows that fiscal policy does not influence aggregate income under floating exchange rates. A fiscal expansion causes the currency to appreciate, reducing net exports and offsetting the usual expansionary impact on aggregate income. Fiscal policy does influence aggregate income under fixed exchange rates.

3. The Mundell–Fleming model shows that monetary policy does not influence aggregate income under fixed exchange rates. Any attempt to expand the money supply is futile, because the money supply must adjust to ensure that the exchange rate stays at its announced level. Monetary policy does influence aggregate income under floating exchange rates.

4. If investors are wary of holding assets in a country, the interest rate in that country may exceed the world interest rate by some risk premium. According to the Mundell–Fleming model, an increase in the risk premium causes the interest rate to rise and the currency of that country to depreciate.

5. There are advantages to both floating and fixed exchange rates. Floating exchange rates leave monetary policymakers free to pursue objectives other than exchange-rate stability. Fixed exchange rates reduce some of the uncertainty in international business transactions.

KEY CONCEPTS

Mundell–Fleming model	Fixed exchange rates	Revaluation
Floating exchange rates	Devaluation	

QUESTIONS FOR REVIEW

1. In the Mundell–Fleming model with floating exchange rates, explain what happens to aggregate income, the exchange rate, and the trade balance when taxes are raised. What would happen if exchange rates were fixed rather than floating?

2. In the Mundell–Fleming model with floating exchange rates, explain what happens to aggregate income, the exchange rate, and the trade balance when the money supply is reduced. What would happen if exchange rates were fixed rather than floating?

3. In the Mundell–Fleming model with floating exchange rates, explain what happens to aggregate income, the exchange rate, and the trade balance when a quota on imported cars is removed. What would happen if exchange rates were fixed rather than floating?

4. What are the advantages of floating exchange rates and fixed exchange rates?

PROBLEMS AND APPLICATIONS |

1. Use the Mundell–Fleming model to predict what would happen to aggregate income, the exchange rate, and the trade balance under both floating and fixed exchange rates in response to each of the following shocks:

   a. A fall in consumer confidence about the future induces consumers to spend less and save more.

   b. The introduction of a stylish line of Toyotas makes some consumers prefer foreign cars over domestic cars.

   c. The introduction of automatic teller machines reduces the demand for money.

2. The Mundell–Fleming model takes the world interest rate r^* as an exogenous variable. Let's consider what happens when this variable changes.

   a. What might cause the world interest rate to rise?

   b. In the Mundell–Fleming model with a floating exchange rate, what happens to aggregate income, the exchange rate, and the trade balance when the world interest rate rises?

   c. In the Mundell–Fleming model with a fixed exchange rate, what happens to aggregate income, the exchange rate, and the trade balance when the world interest rate rises?

3. Business executives and policymakers are often concerned about the "competitiveness" of American industry (the ability of U.S. industries to sell their goods profitably in world markets).

   a. How would a change in the exchange rate affect competitiveness?

   b. Suppose you wanted to make domestic industries more competitive but did not want to alter aggregate income. According to the Mundell–Fleming model, what combination of monetary and fiscal policies should you pursue?

4. Suppose that higher income implies higher imports and thus lower net exports. That is, the net exports function is

$$NX = NX(e, Y).$$

Examine the effects in a small open economy of a fiscal expansion on income and the trade balance under

   a. A floating exchange rate.

   b. A fixed exchange rate.

   How does your answer compare to the results in Table 12-1?

5. Suppose that money demand depends on disposable income, so that the equation for the money market becomes

$$M/P = L(r, Y - T).$$

Analyze the impact of a tax cut in a small open economy on the exchange rate and income under both floating and fixed exchange rates.

6. Suppose that the price level relevant for money demand includes the price of imported goods and that the price of imported goods depends on the exchange rate. That is, the money market is

described by

$$M/P = L(r, Y),$$

where

$$P = \lambda P_d + (1 - \lambda) P_f / e.$$

The parameter λ is the share of domestic goods in the price index P. Assume that the price of domestic goods P_d and the price of foreign goods measured in foreign currency P_f are fixed.

a. Suppose we graph the LM^* curve for given values of P_d and P_f (instead of the usual P). Explain why in this model this LM^* curve is upward sloping rather than vertical.

b. What is the effect of expansionary fiscal policy under floating exchange rates in this model? Explain. Contrast with the standard Mundell–Fleming model.

c. Suppose that political instability increases the country risk premium and, thereby, the inter-

est rate. What is the effect on the exchange rate, the price level, and aggregate income in this model? Contrast with the standard Mundell–Fleming model.

7. Use the Mundell–Fleming model to answer the following questions about the state of California (a small open economy).

a. If California suffers from a recession, should the state government use monetary or fiscal policy to stimulate employment? Explain. (*Note:* For this question, assume that the state government can print dollar bills.)

b. If California prohibited the import of wines from the state of Washington, what would happen to income, the exchange rate, and the trade balance? Consider both the short-run and the long-run impacts.

Appendix: A Short-Run Model of the Large Open Economy

When analyzing policies in an economy such as the United States, we need to combine the closed-economy logic of the $IS-LM$ model and the small-open-economy logic of the Mundell–Fleming model. This appendix presents a model for the intermediate case of a large open economy.

As we discussed in the appendix to Chapter 8, a large open economy differs from a small open economy because its interest rate is not fixed by world financial markets. In a large open economy, we must consider the relationship between the interest rate and net foreign investment. Net foreign investment is the amount that domestic investors lend abroad minus the amount that foreign investors lend here. As the domestic interest rate falls, domestic investors find foreign lending more attractive, and foreign investors find lending here less attractive. Thus, net foreign investment is negatively related to the interest rate. Here we add this relationship to our short-run model of national income.

The three equations of the model are

$$Y = C(Y - T) + I(r) + G + NX(e),$$
$$M/P = L(r, Y),$$
$$NX(e) = NFI(r).$$

The first two equations are the same as those used in the Mundell–Fleming model of this chapter. The third equation, taken from the appendix to Chapter 8, states that the trade balance NX equals net foreign investment NFI and that net foreign investment depends on the domestic interest rate.

To see what this model implies, substitute the third equation into the first, so the model becomes

$$Y = C(Y - T) + I(r) + G + NFI(r) \qquad IS,$$
$$M/P = L(r, Y) \qquad\qquad\qquad\qquad LM.$$

These two equations are much like the two equations of the closed-economy $IS-LM$ model. The only difference is that expenditure now depends on the interest rate for two reasons. As before, a higher interest rate reduces investment. But now, a higher interest rate also reduces net foreign investment and thus lowers net exports.

To analyze this model, we can use the three graphs in Figure 12-14. Panel (a) shows the $IS-LM$ diagram. As in the closed-economy model in Chapters 10 and 11, the interest rate r is on the vertical axis, and income Y is on the horizontal axis. The IS and LM curves together determine the equilibrium level of income and the equilibrium interest rate.

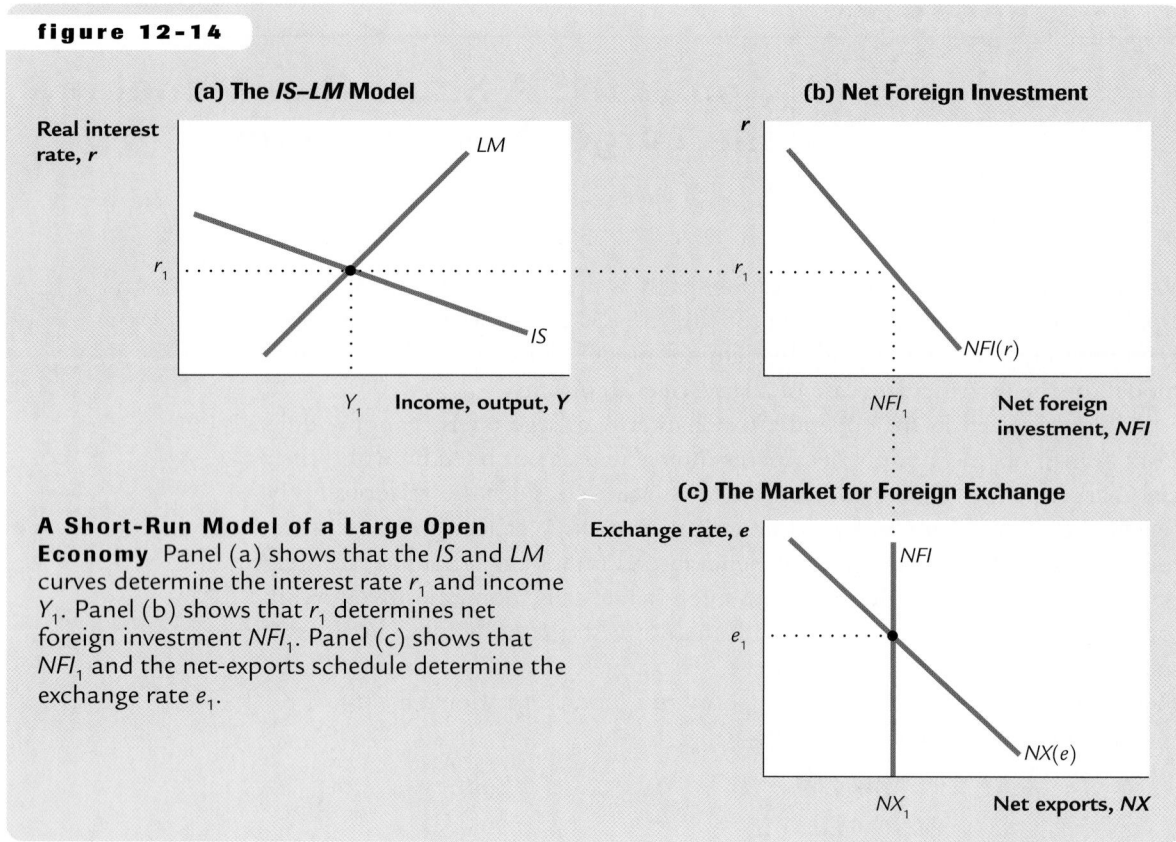

figure 12-14

(a) The *IS–LM* Model

Real interest rate, r

LM

r_1

IS

Y_1 Income, output, Y

(b) Net Foreign Investment

r

r_1

$NFI(r)$

NFI_1 Net foreign investment, *NFI*

(c) The Market for Foreign Exchange

Exchange rate, e

NFI

e_1

$NX(e)$

NX_1 Net exports, *NX*

A Short-Run Model of a Large Open Economy Panel (a) shows that the *IS* and *LM* curves determine the interest rate r_1 and income Y_1. Panel (b) shows that r_1 determines net foreign investment NFI_1. Panel (c) shows that NFI_1 and the net-exports schedule determine the exchange rate e_1.

The new net-foreign-investment term in the *IS* equation, *NFI(r)*, makes this *IS* curve flatter than it would be in a closed economy. The more responsive net foreign investment is to the interest rate, the flatter the *IS* curve is. You might recall from the Chapter 8 appendix that the small open economy represents the extreme case in which net foreign investment is infinitely elastic at the world interest rate. In this extreme case, the *IS* curve is completely flat. Hence, a small open economy would be depicted in this figure with a horizontal *IS* curve.

Panels (b) and (c) show how the equilibrium from the *IS–LM* model determines net foreign investment, the trade balance, and the exchange rate. In panel (b) we see that the interest rate determines net foreign investment. This curve slopes downward because a higher interest rate discourages domestic investors from lending abroad and encourages foreign investors to lend here. In panel (c) we see that the exchange rate adjusts to ensure that net exports of goods and services equal net foreign investment.

Now let's use this model to examine the impact of various policies. We assume that the economy has a floating exchange rate, since this assumption is correct for most large open economies such as the United States.

Fiscal Policy

Figure 12-15 examines the impact of a fiscal expansion. An increase in government purchases or a cut in taxes shifts the *IS* curve to the right. As panel (a) illustrates, this shift in the *IS* curve leads to an increase in the level of income and an increase in the interest rate. These two effects are similar to those in a closed economy.

Yet, in the large open economy, the higher interest rate reduces net foreign investment, as in panel (b). The fall in net foreign investment reduces the supply of dollars in the market for foreign exchange. The exchange rate appreciates, as in panel (c). Because domestic goods become more expensive relative to foreign goods, net exports fall.

Figure 12-15 shows that a fiscal expansion does raise income in the large open economy, unlike in a small open economy under a floating exchange rate. The impact on income, however, is smaller than in a closed economy. In a closed economy, the expansionary impact of fiscal policy is partially offset by the crowding out of investment: as the interest rate rises, investment falls,

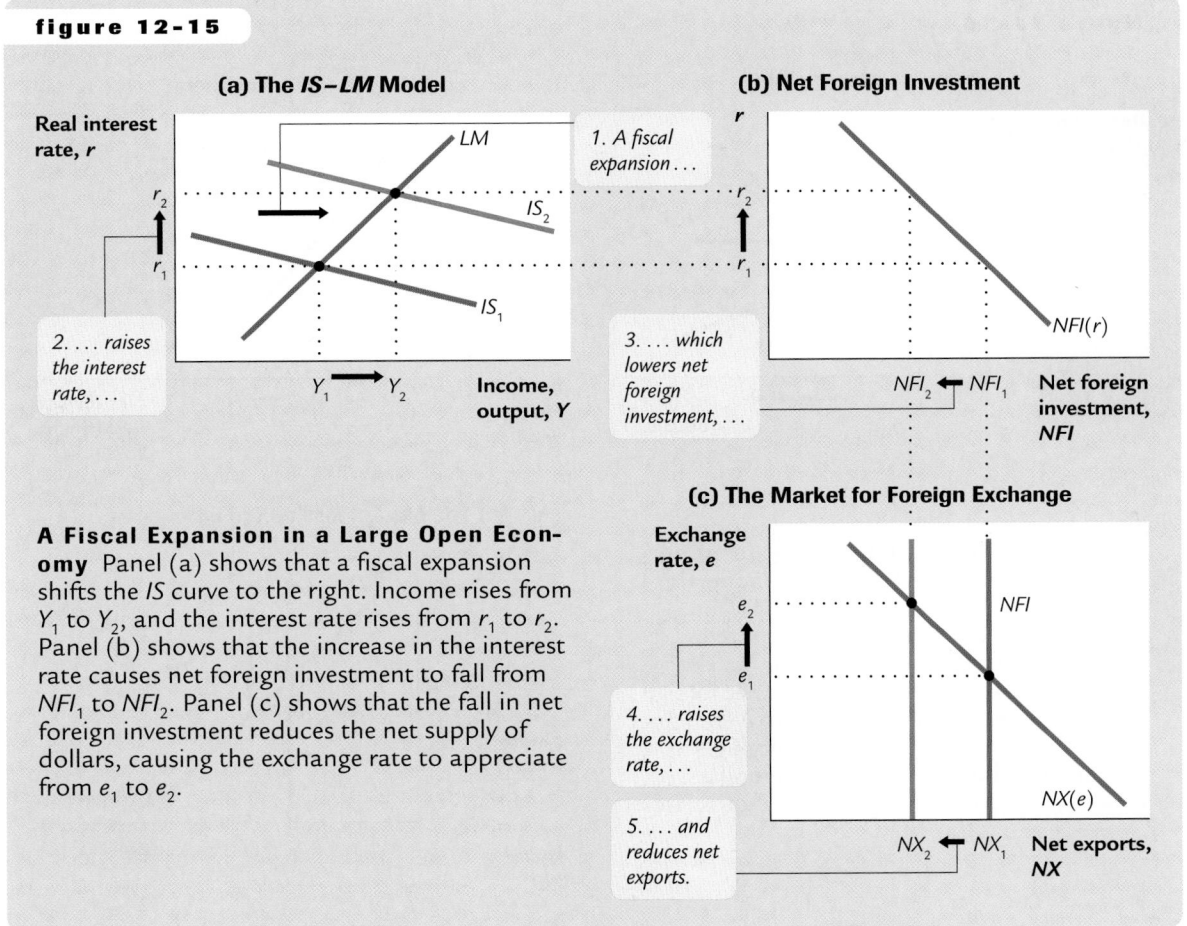

figure 12-15

A Fiscal Expansion in a Large Open Economy Panel (a) shows that a fiscal expansion shifts the *IS* curve to the right. Income rises from Y_1 to Y_2, and the interest rate rises from r_1 to r_2. Panel (b) shows that the increase in the interest rate causes net foreign investment to fall from NFI_1 to NFI_2. Panel (c) shows that the fall in net foreign investment reduces the net supply of dollars, causing the exchange rate to appreciate from e_1 to e_2.

reducing the fiscal-policy multipliers. In a large open economy, there is yet another offsetting factor: as the interest rate rises, net foreign investment falls, the exchange rate appreciates, and net exports fall. Together these effects are not large enough to make fiscal policy powerless, as it is in a small open economy, but they do reduce fiscal policy's impact.

Monetary Policy

Figure 12-16 examines the effect of a monetary expansion. An increase in the money supply shifts the LM curve to the right, as in panel (a). The level of income rises, and the interest rate falls. Once again, these effects are similar to those in a closed economy.

Yet, as panel (b) shows, the lower interest rate leads to higher net foreign investment. The increase in NFI raises the supply of dollars in the market for foreign exchange. The exchange rate depreciates, as in panel (c). As domestic goods become cheaper relative to foreign goods, net exports rise.

figure 12-16

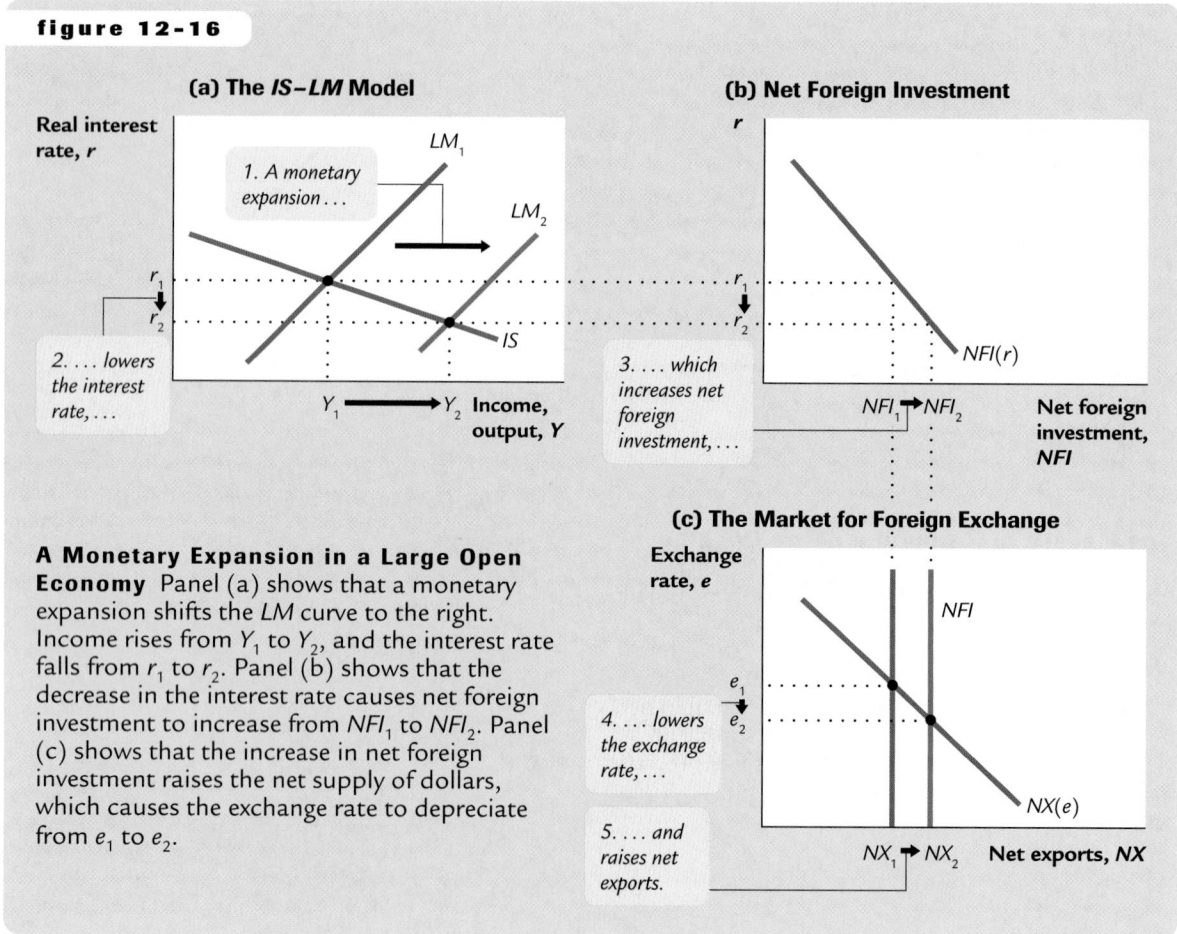

A Monetary Expansion in a Large Open Economy Panel (a) shows that a monetary expansion shifts the LM curve to the right. Income rises from Y_1 to Y_2, and the interest rate falls from r_1 to r_2. Panel (b) shows that the decrease in the interest rate causes net foreign investment to increase from NFI_1 to NFI_2. Panel (c) shows that the increase in net foreign investment raises the net supply of dollars, which causes the exchange rate to depreciate from e_1 to e_2.

We can now see that the monetary transmission mechanism has two parts in a large open economy. As in a closed economy, a monetary expansion lowers the interest rate. As in a small open economy, a monetary expansion causes the currency to depreciate in the market for foreign exchange. The lower interest rate stimulates investment, and the lower exchange rate stimulates net exports.

A Rule of Thumb

This model of the large open economy describes well the U.S. economy today. Yet it is somewhat more complicated and cumbersome than the model of the closed economy we studied in Chapters 10 and 11 and the model of the small open economy we developed in this chapter. Fortunately, there is a useful rule of thumb to help you determine how policies influence a large open economy without remembering all the details of the model: *The large open economy is an average of the closed economy and the small open economy. To find how any policy will affect any variable, find the answer in the two extreme cases and take an average.*

For example, how does a monetary contraction affect the interest rate and investment in the short run? In a closed economy, the interest rate rises and investment falls. In a small open economy, neither the interest rate nor investment changes. The effect in the large open economy is an average of these two cases: a monetary contraction raises the interest rate and reduces investment, but only somewhat. The fall in net foreign investment mitigates the rise in the interest rate and the fall in investment that would occur in a closed economy. But unlike in a small open economy, the international flow of capital is not so strong as to negate fully these effects.

This rule of thumb makes the simple models all the more valuable. Although they do not describe perfectly the world in which we live, they do provide a useful guide to the effects of economic policy.

MORE PROBLEMS AND APPLICATIONS

1. Imagine that you run the central bank in a large open economy. Your goal is to stabilize income, and you adjust the money supply accordingly. Under your policy, what happens to the money supply, the interest rate, the exchange rate, and the trade balance in response to each of the following shocks?

   a. The president raises taxes to reduce the budget deficit.

   b. The president restricts the import of Japanese cars.

2. Over the past several decades, investors around the world have become more willing to take advantage of opportunities in other countries. Because of this increasing sophistication, economies are more open today than in the past. Consider how this development affects the ability of monetary policy to influence the economy.

a. If investors become more willing to substitute foreign and domestic assets, what happens to the slope of the *NFI* function?

b. If the *NFI* function changes in this way, what happens to the slope of the *IS* curve?

c. How does this change in the *IS* curve affect the Fed's ability to control the interest rate?

d. How does this change in the *IS* curve affect the Fed's ability to control national income?

3. Suppose that policymakers in a large open economy want to raise the level of investment without changing aggregate income or the exchange rate.

a. Is there any combination of domestic monetary and fiscal policies that would achieve this goal?

b. Is there any combination of domestic monetary, fiscal, and trade policies that would achieve this goal?

c. Is there any combination of monetary and fiscal policies at home and abroad that would achieve this goal?

4. Suppose that a large open economy has a fixed exchange rate.

a. Describe what happens in response to a fiscal contraction, such as a tax increase. Compare your answer to the case of a small open economy.

b. Describe what happens if the central bank expands the money supply by buying bonds from the public. Compare your answer to the case of a small open economy.

13

Aggregate Supply

There is always a temporary tradeoff between inflation and unemployment; there is no permanent tradeoff. The temporary tradeoff comes not from inflation per se, but from unanticipated inflation, which generally means, from a rising rate of inflation.

— *Milton Friedman*

Most economists analyze short-run fluctuations in aggregate income and the price level using the model of aggregate demand and aggregate supply. In the previous three chapters, we examined aggregate demand in some detail. The *IS–LM* model—together with its open-economy cousin the Mundell–Fleming model—shows how changes in monetary and fiscal policy and shocks to the money and goods markets shift the aggregate demand curve. In this chapter, we turn our attention to aggregate supply and develop theories that explain the position and slope of the aggregate supply curve.

When we introduced the aggregate supply curve in Chapter 9, we established that aggregate supply behaves very differently in the short run than in the long run. In the long run, prices are flexible, and the aggregate supply curve is vertical. When the aggregate supply curve is vertical, shifts in the aggregate demand curve affect the price level, but the output of the economy remains at its natural rate. By contrast, in the short run, prices are sticky, and the aggregate supply curve is not vertical. In this case, shifts in aggregate demand do cause fluctuations in output. In Chapter 9 we took a simplified view of price stickiness by drawing the short-run aggregate supply curve as a horizontal line, representing the extreme situation in which all prices are fixed. Our task now is to refine this understanding of short-run aggregate supply.

Unfortunately, one fact makes this task more difficult: economists disagree about how best to explain aggregate supply. As a result, this chapter begins by presenting four prominent models of the short-run aggregate supply curve. Among economists, each of these models has some prominent adherents (as well as some prominent critics), and you can decide for yourself which you find most plausible. Although these models differ in some significant details, they are also related in an important way: they share a common theme about what makes the short-run and long-run aggregate supply curves differ and a common conclusion that the short-run aggregate supply curve is upward sloping.

After examining the models, we examine an implication of the short-run aggregate supply curve. We show that this curve implies a tradeoff between two measures of economic performance—inflation and unemployment. According to this tradeoff, to reduce the rate of inflation policymakers must temporarily raise unemployment, and to reduce unemployment they must accept higher inflation. As the quotation at the beginning of the chapter suggests, the tradeoff between inflation and unemployment is only temporary. One goal of this chapter is to explain why policymakers face such a tradeoff in the short run and, just as important, why they do not face it in the long run.

13-1 Four Models of Aggregate Supply

Classes in physics often begin by assuming away the existence of friction, but no good engineer would ever take this assumption as a literal description of how the world works. Similarly, this book began with classical macroeconomic theory, but it would be a mistake to assume that this model is true in all circumstances. Our job now is to look more deeply into the "frictions" of macroeconomics.

We do this by examining four prominent models of aggregate supply, roughly in the order of their development. In all the models, some market imperfection (that is, some type of friction) causes the output of the economy to deviate from the classical benchmark. As a result, the short-run aggregate supply curve is upward sloping, rather than vertical, and shifts in the aggregate demand curve cause the level of output to deviate temporarily from the natural rate. These temporary deviations represent the booms and busts of the business cycle.

Although each of the four models takes us down a different theoretical route, each route ends up in the same place. That final destination is a short-run aggregate supply equation of the form

$$Y = \overline{Y} + \alpha(P - P^e), \qquad \alpha > 0,$$

where Y is output, $\overline{Y}$ is the natural rate of output, P is the price level, and P^e is the expected price level. This equation states that output deviates from its natural rate when the price level deviates from the expected price level. The parameter α indicates how much output responds to unexpected changes in the price level; $1/\alpha$ is the slope of the aggregate supply curve.

Each of the four models tells a different story about what lies behind this short-run aggregate supply equation. In other words, each highlights a particular reason why unexpected movements in the price level are associated with fluctuations in aggregate output.

The Sticky-Wage Model

To explain why the short-run aggregate supply curve is upward sloping, many economists stress the sluggish adjustment of nominal wages. In many industries, nominal wages are set by long-term contracts, so wages cannot adjust quickly when economic conditions change. Even in industries not covered by formal contracts, implicit agreements between workers and firms may limit wage changes. Wages may also depend on social norms and notions of fairness that evolve slowly. For these reasons, many economists believe that nominal wages are sticky in the short run.

The **sticky-wage model** shows what a sticky nominal wage implies for aggregate supply. To preview the model, consider what happens to the amount of output produced when the price level rises:

1. When the nominal wage is stuck, a rise in the price level lowers the real wage, making labor cheaper.

2. The lower real wage induces firms to hire more labor.

3. The additional labor hired produces more output.

This positive relationship between the price level and the amount of output means that the aggregate supply curve slopes upward during the time when the nominal wage cannot adjust.

To develop this story of aggregate supply more formally, assume that workers and firms bargain over and agree on the nominal wage before they know what the price level will be when their agreement takes effect. The bargaining parties—the workers and the firms—have in mind a target real wage. The target may be the real wage that equilibrates labor supply and demand. More likely, the target real wage is higher than the equilibrium real wage: as discussed in Chapter 6, union power and efficiency-wage considerations tend to keep real wages above the level that brings supply and demand into balance.

The workers and firms set the nominal wage W based on the target real wage ω and on their expectation of the price level P^e. The nominal wage they set is

$$W \quad = \quad \omega \quad \times \quad P^e$$

Nominal Wage = Target Real Wage $\times$ Expected Price Level.

After the nominal wage has been set and before labor has been hired, firms learn the actual price level P. The real wage turns out to be

$$W/P \quad = \quad \omega \quad \times \quad (P^e/P)$$

Real Wage = Target Real Wage $\times \dfrac{\text{Expected Price Level}}{\text{Actual Price Level}}$.

This equation shows that the real wage deviates from its target if the actual price level differs from the expected price level. When the actual price level is greater than expected, the real wage is less than its target; when the actual price level is less than expected, the real wage is greater than its target.

The final assumption of the sticky-wage model is that employment is determined by the quantity of labor that firms demand. In other words, the bargain between the workers and the firms does not determine the level of employment in advance; instead, the workers agree to provide as much labor as the firms wish to buy at the predetermined wage. We describe the firms' hiring decisions by the labor demand function

$$L = L^d(W/P),$$

which states that the lower the real wage, the more labor firms hire. The labor demand curve is shown in panel (a) of Figure 13-1. Output is determined by the production function

$$Y = F(L),$$

which states that the more labor is hired, the more output is produced. This is shown in panel (b) of Figure 13-1.

Panel (c) of Figure 13-1 shows the resulting aggregate supply curve. Because the nominal wage is sticky, an unexpected change in the price level moves the real wage away from the target real wage, and this change in the real wage influences the amounts of labor hired and output produced. The aggregate supply curve can be written as

$$Y = \overline{Y} + \alpha(P - P^e).$$

figure 13-1

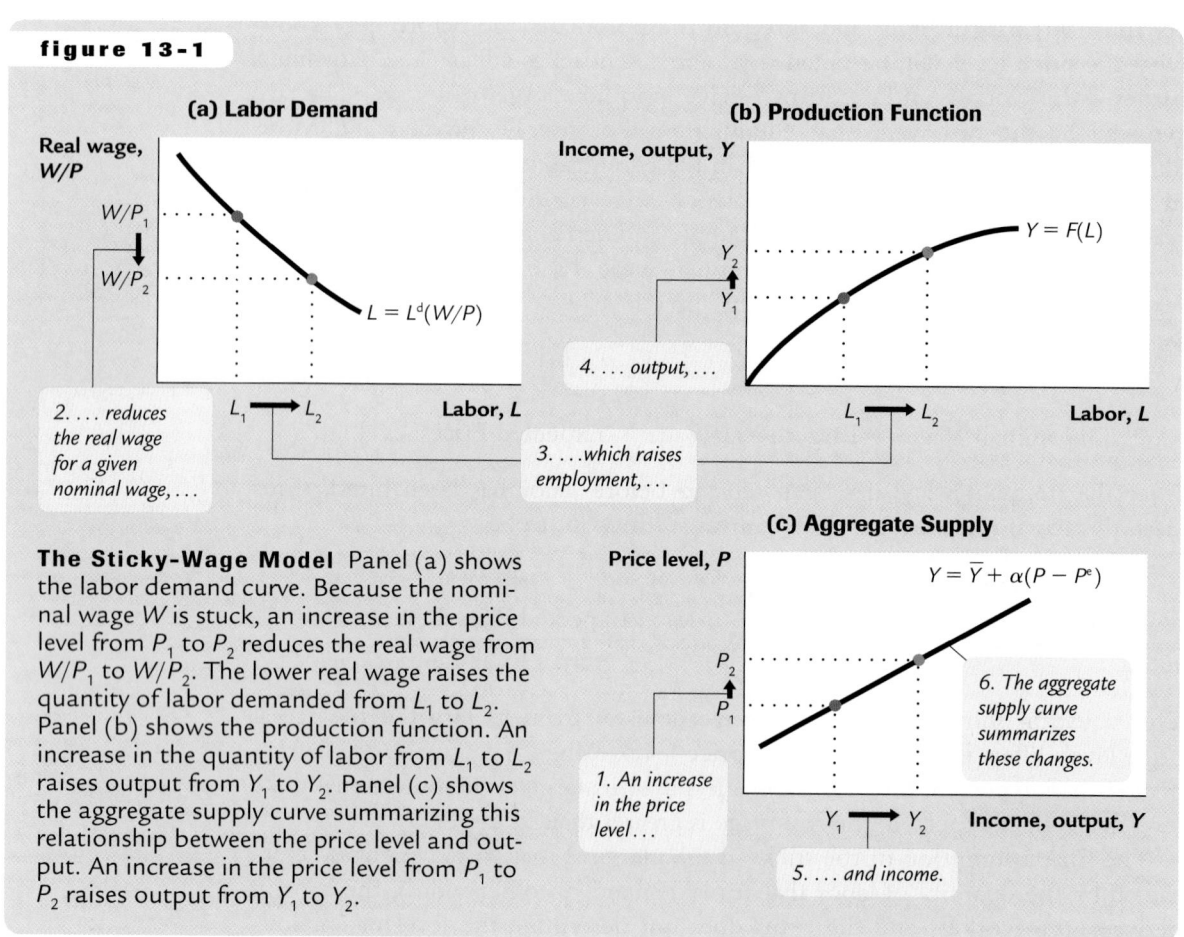

The Sticky-Wage Model Panel (a) shows the labor demand curve. Because the nominal wage W is stuck, an increase in the price level from P_1 to P_2 reduces the real wage from W/P_1 to W/P_2. The lower real wage raises the quantity of labor demanded from L_1 to L_2. Panel (b) shows the production function. An increase in the quantity of labor from L_1 to L_2 raises output from Y_1 to Y_2. Panel (c) shows the aggregate supply curve summarizing this relationship between the price level and output. An increase in the price level from P_1 to P_2 raises output from Y_1 to Y_2.

Output deviates from its natural level when the price level deviates from the expected price level.[1]

The Worker-Misperception Model

The next model also explains the upward-sloping short-run aggregate supply curve by focusing on the labor market. Unlike the sticky-wage model, however, the **worker-misperception model** assumes that wages can adjust freely and quickly to balance the supply and demand for labor. Its key assumption is that unexpected movements in the price level influence labor supply because workers temporarily confuse real and nominal wages.

The two components of the worker-misperception model are labor supply and labor demand. As before, the quantity of labor firms demand depends on the real wage:

$$L^d = L^d(W/P).$$

The labor supply curve is new:

$$L^s = L^s(W/P^e).$$

This equation states that the quantity of labor supplied depends on the real wage that workers expect to earn. Workers know their nominal wage W, but they do not know the overall price level P. When deciding how much to work, they consider the expected real wage, which equals the nominal wage W divided by their expectation of the price level P^e. We can also write the expected real wage as

$$\frac{W}{P^e} = \frac{W}{P} \times \frac{P}{P^e}.$$

The expected real wage is the product of the actual real wage W/P and the variable P/P^e. Notice that P/P^e measures workers' misperception of the price level: if P/P^e is greater than one, the price level is greater than what workers expected, and if P/P^e is less than one, the price level is less than expected. To see what determines labor supply, we can substitute this expression for W/P^e and write

$$L^s = L^s[(W/P) \times (P/P^e)].$$

The quantity of labor supplied depends on the real wage and on worker misperceptions of the price level.

To see what this model says about aggregate supply, consider the equilibrium in the labor market, shown in Figure 13-2. As is usual, the labor demand curve slopes downward, the labor supply curve slopes upward, and the wage

---

[1] For more on the sticky-wage model, see Jo Anna Gray, "Wage Indexation: A Macroeconomic Approach," *Journal of Monetary Economics* 2 (April 1976): 221–235; and Stanley Fischer, "Long-Term Contracts, Rational Expectations, and the Optimal Money Supply Rule," *Journal of Political Economy* 85 (February 1977): 191–205.

figure 13-2

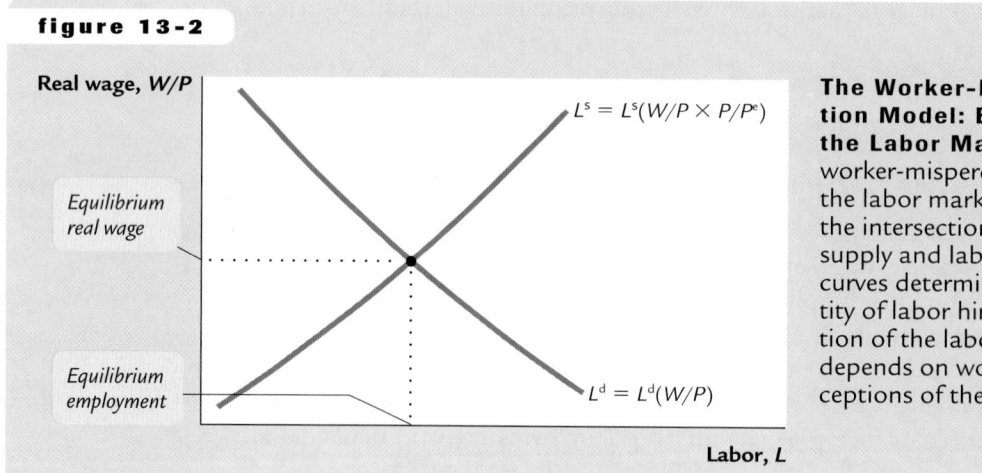

figure 13-2

Real wage, *W/P*

$L^s = L^s(W/P \times P/P^e)$

Equilibrium
real wage

$L^d = L^d(W/P)$

Equilibrium
employment

Labor, *L*

The Worker-Mispercep-tion Model: Equilibrium in the Labor Market In the worker-misperception model, the labor market clears, so the intersection of the labor supply and labor demand curves determines the quantity of labor hired. The position of the labor supply curve depends on worker misperceptions of the price level.

adjusts to equilibrate supply and demand. Note that the position of the labor supply curve and thus the equilibrium in the labor market depend on worker misperception P/P^e.

Whenever the price level P rises, the reaction of the economy depends on whether workers anticipate the change. If they do, then P^e rises proportionately with P. In this case, workers' perceptions are accurate, and neither labor supply nor labor demand changes. The nominal wage rises by the same amount as prices, and the real wage and the level of employment remain the same.

By contrast, if the price increase catches workers by surprise, then P^e remains the same when P rises. The increase in P/P^e shifts the labor supply curve to the right, as in Figure 13-3, lowering the real wage and raising the level of employment. In essence, workers believe that the price level is lower, and thus the real wage is higher, than actually is the case. This misperception induces them to supply more labor. Firms are assumed to be better informed than workers and to recognize the fall in the real wage, so they hire more labor and produce more output.

To sum up, the worker-misperception model says that deviations of prices from expected prices induce workers to alter their supply of labor and that this change in labor supply alters the quantity of output firms produce. The model implies an aggregate supply curve of the form:

$$Y = \overline{Y} + \alpha(P - P^e).$$

Once again, as with the sticky-wage model but for different reasons, output deviates from the natural rate when the price level deviates from the expected price level.[2]

---

[2] The worker-misperception model as presented here comes from the classic article by Milton Friedman, "The Role of Monetary Policy," *American Economic Review* 58 (March 1968): 1–17.

figure 13-3

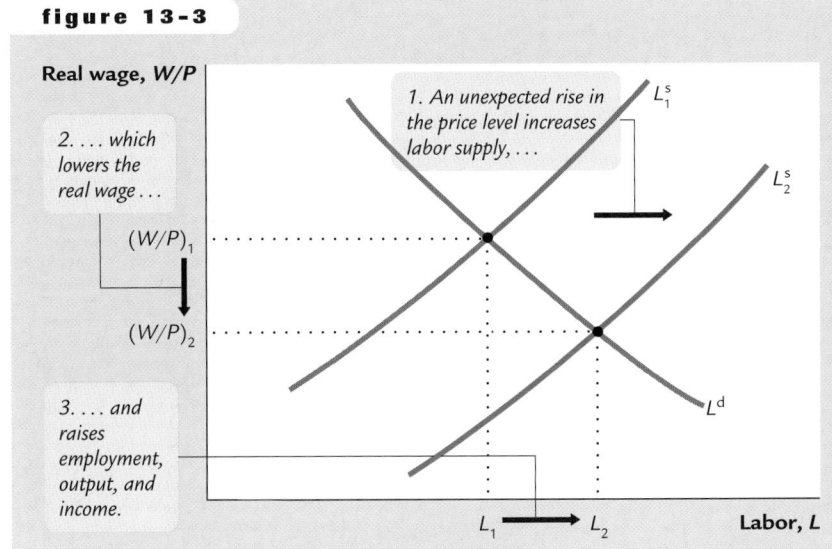

Real wage, W/P

1. An unexpected rise in the price level increases labor supply, . . .

L_1^s

L_2^s

2. . . . which lowers the real wage . . .

$(W/P)_1$

$(W/P)_2$

L^d

3. . . . and raises employment, output, and income.

$L_1 \longrightarrow L_2$　　**Labor, L**

The Worker-Misperception Model: An Unexpected Increase in the Price Level If the price level rises unexpectedly, workers are willing to supply more labor at any given real wage, since they believe the real wage is higher than it actually is. The equilibrium level of employment therefore rises.

CASE STUDY

The Cyclical Behavior of the Real Wage

In any model with an unchanging labor demand curve, such as the two models we have just discussed, employment rises when the real wage falls. In the sticky-wage and worker-misperception models, an unexpected rise in the price level lowers the real wage and thereby raises the quantity of labor hired and the amount of output produced. Thus, the real wage should be *countercyclical*: it should fluctuate in the opposite direction from employment and output. Keynes himself wrote in *The General Theory* that "an increase in employment can only occur to the accompaniment of a decline in the rate of real wages."

The earliest attacks on *The General Theory* came from economists challenging Keynes's prediction. Figure 13-4 is a scatterplot of the percentage change in real compensation per hour and the percentage change in real GDP using annual data for the U.S. economy from 1960 to 1997. If Keynes's prediction were correct, this figure would show a negative relationship. Yet it shows only a weak correlation between the real wage and output. If the real wage is cyclical at all, it is slightly *procyclical*: the real wage tends to rise when output rises. Thus, abnormally high labor costs cannot explain the low employment and output observed in recessions.

How should we interpret this evidence? Most economists conclude that the sticky-wage and worker-misperception models cannot, by themselves, fully explain aggregate supply. They advocate models in which the labor demand

figure 13-4

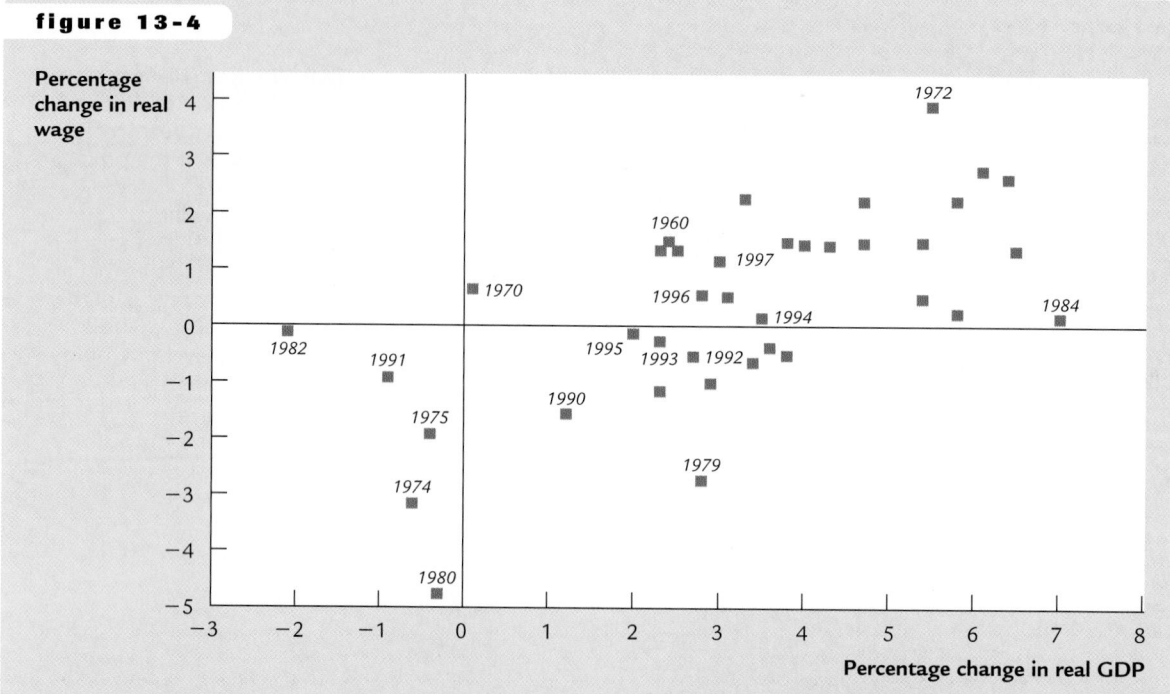

The Cyclical Behavior of the Real Wage This scatterplot shows the percentage change in real GDP and the percentage change in the real wage (measured here as real private hourly earnings). As output fluctuates, the real wage typically moves in the same direction. That is, the real wage is somewhat procyclical. This observation is inconsistent with the sticky-wage and worker-misperception models.

curve shifts over the business cycle. These shifts may arise because firms have sticky prices and cannot sell all they want at those prices; we discuss this possibility below. Alternatively, the labor demand curve may shift because of shocks to technology, which alter labor productivity. The theory we discuss in Chapter 19, called the theory of real business cycles, gives a prominent role to technology shocks as a source of economic fluctuations.[3]

---

[3] For some of the recent work on the cyclical behavior of the real wage, see Mark J. Bils, "Real Wages Over the Business Cycle: Evidence From Panel Data," *Journal of Political Economy* 93 (1985): 666–689; Scott Sumner and Stephen Silver, "Real Wages, Employment, and the Phillips Curve," *Journal of Political Economy* 97 (June 1989): 706–720; and Gary Solon, Robert Barsky, and Jonathan A. Parker, "Measuring the Cyclicality of Real Wages: How Important Is Composition Bias?" *Quarterly Journal of Economics* 109 (February 1994): 1–25.

The Imperfect-Information Model

The third explanation for the upward slope of the short-run aggregate supply curve, the **imperfect-information model,** again assumes that markets clear and that the short-run and long-run aggregate supply curves differ because of temporary misperceptions about prices. But unlike the worker-misperception model, it does not assume that firms are better informed about the price level than their workers. In its simplest form, the model does not distinguish between workers and firms at all.

The imperfect-information model assumes that each supplier in the economy produces a single good and consumes many goods. Because the number of goods is so large, suppliers cannot observe all prices at all times. They monitor closely the prices of what they produce but less closely the prices of all the goods they consume. Because of imperfect information, they sometimes confuse changes in the overall level of prices with changes in relative prices. This confusion influences decisions about how much to supply, and it leads to a short-run relationship between the price level and output.

Consider the decision facing a single supplier—a wheat farmer, for instance. Because the farmer earns income from selling wheat and uses this income to buy goods and services, the amount of wheat she chooses to produce depends on the price of wheat relative to the prices of other goods and services in the economy. If the relative price of wheat is high, the farmer is motivated to work hard and produce more wheat, because the reward is great. If the relative price of wheat is low, she prefers to enjoy more leisure and produce less wheat.

Unfortunately, when the farmer makes her production decision, she does not know the relative price of wheat. As a wheat producer, she monitors the wheat market closely and always knows the nominal price of wheat. But she does not know the prices of all the other goods in the economy. She must, therefore, estimate the relative price of wheat using the nominal price of wheat and her expectation of the overall price level.

Consider how the farmer responds if all prices in the economy, including the price of wheat, increase. One possibility is that she expected this change in prices. When she observes an increase in the price of wheat, her estimate of its relative price is unchanged. She does not work any harder.

The other possibility is that the farmer did not expect the price level to increase (or to increase by this much). When she observes the increase in the price of wheat, she is not sure whether other prices have risen (in which case wheat's relative price is unchanged) or whether only the price of wheat has risen (in which case its relative price is higher). The rational inference is that some of each has happened. In other words, the farmer infers from the increase in the nominal price of wheat that its relative price has risen somewhat. She works harder and produces more.

Our wheat farmer is not unique. When the price level rises unexpectedly, all suppliers in the economy observe increases in the prices of the goods they produce. They all infer, rationally but mistakenly, that the relative prices of the goods they produce have risen. They work harder and produce more.

To sum up, the imperfect-information model says that when prices exceed expected prices, suppliers raise their output. The model implies an aggregate supply curve that is now familiar:

$$Y = \overline{Y} + \alpha(P - P^e).$$

Output deviates from the natural rate when the price level deviates from the expected price level.[4]

The Sticky-Price Model

Our fourth and final explanation for why the short-run aggregate supply curve is upward sloping, the **sticky-price model,** emphasizes that firms do not instantly adjust the prices they charge in response to changes in demand. Sometimes prices are set by long-term contracts between firms and customers. Even without formal agreements, firms may hold prices steady in order not to annoy their regular customers with frequent price changes. Some prices are sticky because of the way markets are structured: once a firm has printed and distributed its catalog or price list, it is costly to alter prices.

To see how sticky prices can help explain an upward-sloping aggregate supply curve, we first consider the pricing decisions of individual firms and then add together the decisions of many firms to explain the behavior of the economy as a whole. Notice that this model encourages us to depart from the assumption of perfect competition, which we have used since Chapter 3. Perfectly competitive firms are price takers rather than price setters. If we want to consider how firms set prices, it is natural to assume that these firms have at least some monopoly control over the prices they charge.

Consider the pricing decision facing a typical firm. The firm's desired price p depends on two macroeconomic variables:

➤ The overall level of prices P. A higher price level implies that the firm's costs are higher. Hence, the higher the overall price level, the more the firm would like to charge for its product.

➤ The level of aggregate income Y. A higher level of income raises the demand for the firm's product. Because marginal cost increases at higher levels of production, the greater the demand, the higher the firm's desired price.

We write the firm's desired price as

$$p = P + a(Y - \overline{Y}).$$

This equation says that the desired price p depends on the overall level of prices P and on the level of aggregate output relative to the natural rate $Y - \overline{Y}$.

---

[4] To read more on the imperfect-information model, see Robert E. Lucas, Jr., "Understanding Business Cycles," *Stabilization of the Domestic and International Economy,* vol. 5 of Carnegie-Rochester Conference on Public Policy (Amsterdam: North-Holland, 1977).

The parameter a (which is greater than zero) measures how much the firm's desired price responds to the level of aggregate output.[5]

Now assume that there are two types of firms. Some have flexible prices: they always set their prices according to this equation. Others have sticky prices: they announce their prices in advance based on what they expect economic conditions to be. Firms with sticky prices set prices according to

$$p = P^e + a(Y^e - \overline{Y^e}),$$

where, as before, a superscript "e" represents the expected value of a variable. For simplicity, assume that these firms expect output to be at its natural rate, so that the last term, $a(Y^e - \overline{Y^e})$, is zero. Then these firms set the price

$$p = P^e.$$

That is, firms with sticky prices set their prices based on what they expect other firms to charge.

We can use the pricing rules of the two groups of firms to derive the aggregate supply equation. To do this, we find the overall price level in the economy, which is the weighted average of the prices set by the two groups. If s is the fraction of firms with sticky prices and $1 - s$ the fraction with flexible prices, then the overall price level is

$$P = sP^e + (1 - s)[P + a(Y - \overline{Y})].$$

The first term is the price of the sticky-price firms weighted by their fraction in the economy, and the second term is the price of the flexible-price firms weighted by their fraction. Now subtract $(1 - s)P$ from both sides of this equation to obtain

$$sP = sP^e + (1 - s)[a(Y - \overline{Y})].$$

Divide both sides by s to solve for the overall price level:

$$P = P^e + [(1 - s)a/s](Y - \overline{Y}).$$

The two terms in this equation are explained as follows:

➤ When firms expect a high price level, they expect high costs. Those firms that fix prices in advance set their prices high. These high prices cause the other firms to set high prices also. Hence, a high expected price level P^e leads to a high actual price level P.

➤ When output is high, the demand for goods is high. Those firms with flexible prices set their prices high, which leads to a high price level. The effect of output on the price level depends on the proportion of firms with flexible prices.

---

[5] *Mathematical note:* The firm cares most about its relative price, which is the ratio of its nominal price to the overall price level. If we interpret p and P as the logarithms of the firm's price and the price level, then this equation states that the desired relative price depends on the deviation of output from the natural rate.

Hence, the overall price level depends on the expected price level and on the level of output.

Algebraic rearrangement puts this aggregate pricing equation into a more familiar form:

$$Y = \overline{Y} + \alpha(P - P^e),$$

where $\alpha = s/[(1 - s)a]$. Like the other models, the sticky-price model says that the deviation of output from the natural rate is positively associated with the deviation of the price level from the expected price level.

Although the sticky-price model emphasizes the goods market, consider briefly what is happening in the labor market. If a firm's price is stuck in the short run, then a reduction in aggregate demand reduces the amount that the firm is able to sell. The firm responds to the drop in sales by reducing its production and its demand for labor. Note the contrast to the sticky-wage and worker-misperception models: the firm here does not move along a fixed labor demand curve. Instead, fluctuations in output are associated with shifts in the labor demand curve. Because of these shifts in labor demand, employment, production, and the real wage can all move in the same direction. Thus, the real wage can be procyclical.[6]

CASE STUDY

International Differences in the Aggregate Supply Curve

Although all countries experience economic fluctuations, these fluctuations are not exactly the same everywhere. International differences are intriguing puzzles in themselves, and they often provide a way to test alternative economic theories. Examining international differences has been especially fruitful in research on aggregate supply.

When economist Robert Lucas proposed the imperfect-information model, he derived a surprising interaction between aggregate demand and aggregate supply: according to his model, the slope of the aggregate supply curve should depend on the variability of aggregate demand. In countries where aggregate demand fluctuates widely, the aggregate price level fluctuates widely as well. Because most movements in prices in these countries do not represent movements in relative prices, suppliers should have learned not to respond much to unexpected changes in the price level. Therefore, the aggregate supply curve should be relatively steep (that is, α will be small). Conversely, in countries where aggregate demand is relatively stable, suppliers should have learned that most price changes are relative price changes. Accordingly, in these countries, suppliers should be more responsive to unexpected price changes, making the aggregate supply curve relatively flat (that is, α will be large).

---

[6] For a more advanced development of the sticky-price model, see Julio Rotemberg, "Monopolistic Price Adjustment and Aggregate Output," *Review of Economic Studies* 49 (1982): 517–531.

Lucas tested this prediction by examining international data on output and prices. He found that changes in aggregate demand have the biggest effect on output in those countries where aggregate demand and prices are most stable. Lucas concluded that the evidence supports the imperfect-information model.[7]

The sticky-price model also makes predictions about the slope of the short-run aggregate supply curve. In particular, it predicts that the average rate of inflation should influence the slope of the short-run aggregate supply curve. When the average rate of inflation is high, it is very costly for firms to keep prices fixed for long intervals. Thus, firms adjust prices more frequently. More frequent price adjustment in turn allows the overall price level to respond more quickly to shocks to aggregate demand. Hence, a high rate of inflation should make the short-run aggregate supply curve steeper.

International data support this prediction of the sticky-price model. In countries with low average inflation, the short-run aggregate supply curve is relatively flat: fluctuations in aggregate demand have large effects on output and are slowly reflected in prices. High-inflation countries have steep short-run aggregate supply curves. In other words, high inflation appears to erode the frictions that cause prices to be sticky.[8]

Note that the sticky-price model can also explain Lucas's finding that countries with variable aggregate demand have steep aggregate supply curves. If the price level is highly variable, few firms will commit to prices in advance (s will be small). Hence, the aggregate supply curve will be steep (α will be small).

Summary and Implications

Figure 13-5 lists the four models of aggregate supply and the market imperfection that each uses to explain why the short-run aggregate supply curve is upward sloping. The figure divides the models according to two characteristics. The first is whether the model assumes that markets clear—that is, whether wages and prices are free to equilibrate supply and demand. The second is whether the model emphasizes the labor or the goods market as the source of the market imperfection. Keep in mind that these models of aggregate supply are not necessarily incompatible with one another. We need not accept one model and reject the others. The world may contain all four of these market imperfections, and all may contribute to the behavior of short-run aggregate supply.

Although the four models of aggregate supply differ in their assumptions and emphases, their implications for aggregate output are similar. All can be summarized by the equation

$$Y = \overline{Y} + \alpha(P - P^e).$$

[7] Robert E. Lucas, Jr., "Some International Evidence on Output-Inflation Tradeoffs," *American Economic Review* 63 (June 1973): 326–334.

[8] Laurence Ball, N. Gregory Mankiw, and David Romer, "The New Keynesian Economics and the Output-Inflation Tradeoff," *Brookings Papers on Economic Activity* (1988:1): 1–65.

figure 13-5

| | | **Market With Imperfection** | |
		Labor	Goods
Markets Clear?	Yes	**Worker-Misperception Model:** Workers confuse nominal wage changes with real wage changes.	**Imperfect-Information Model:** Suppliers confuse changes in the price level with changes in relative prices.
	No	**Sticky-Wage Model:** Nominal wages adjust slowly.	**Sticky-Price Model:** The prices of goods and services adjust slowly.

Comparison of Models of Aggregate Supply The four models of aggregate supply differ in two characteristics: whether they assume that markets clear and whether the key market imperfection lies in the goods market or in the labor market.

This equation states that deviations of output from the natural rate are related to deviations of the price level from the expected price level. *If the price level is higher than the expected price level, output exceeds its natural rate. If the price level is lower than the expected price level, output falls short of its natural rate.* Figure 13-6 graphs this equation. Notice that the short-run aggregate supply curve is drawn for a given expectation P^e and that a change in P^e would shift the curve.

figure 13-6

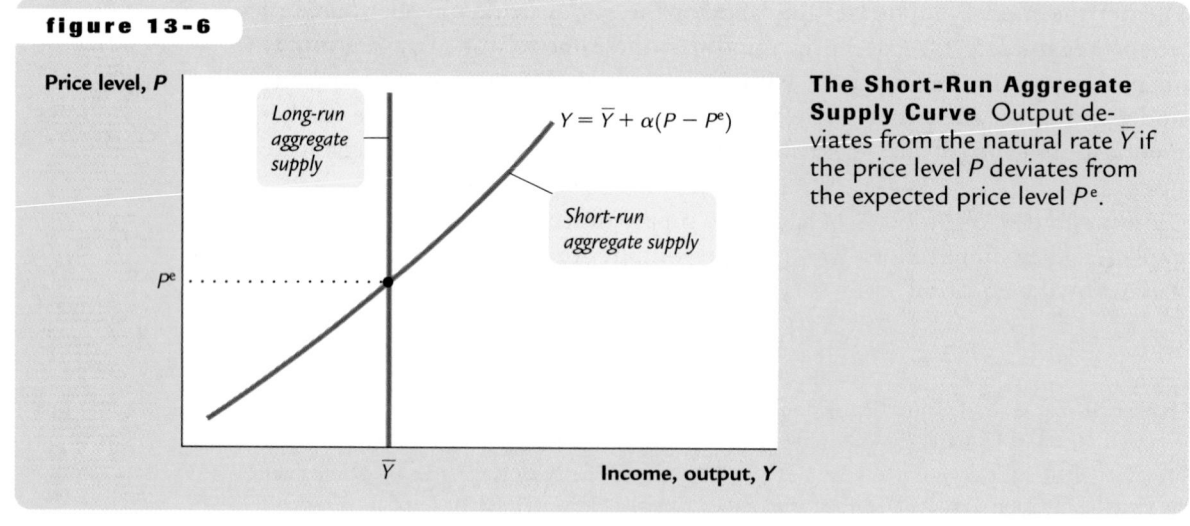

The Short-Run Aggregate Supply Curve Output deviates from the natural rate $\bar{Y}$ if the price level P deviates from the expected price level P^e.

$$Y = \bar{Y} + \alpha(P - P^e)$$

Now that we have a better understanding of aggregate supply, let's put aggregate supply and aggregate demand back together. Figure 13-7 uses our aggregate supply equation to show how the economy responds to an unexpected increase in aggregate demand attributable, say, to an unexpected monetary expansion. In the short run, the equilibrium moves from point A to point B. The increase in aggregate demand raises the actual price level from P_1 to P_2. Because people did not expect this increase in the price level, the expected price level remains at P_2^e, and output rises from Y_1 to Y_2, which is above the natural rate $\overline{Y}$. Thus, the unexpected expansion in aggregate demand causes the economy to boom.

Yet the boom does not last forever. In the long run, the expected price level rises to catch up with reality, causing the short-run aggregate supply curve to shift upward. As the expected price level rises from P_2^e to P_3^e, the equilibrium of the economy moves from point B to point C. The actual price level rises from P_2 to P_3, and output falls from Y_2 to Y_3. In other words, the economy returns to the natural level of output in the long run, but at a much higher price level.

This analysis shows an important principle, which holds for each of the four models of aggregate supply: long-run monetary neutrality and short-run monetary *non*neutrality are perfectly compatible. Short-run nonneutrality is represented here by the movement from point A to point B, and long-run monetary neutrality is represented by the movement from point A to point C. We reconcile the short-run and long-run effects of money by emphasizing the adjustment of expectations about the price level.

figure 13-7

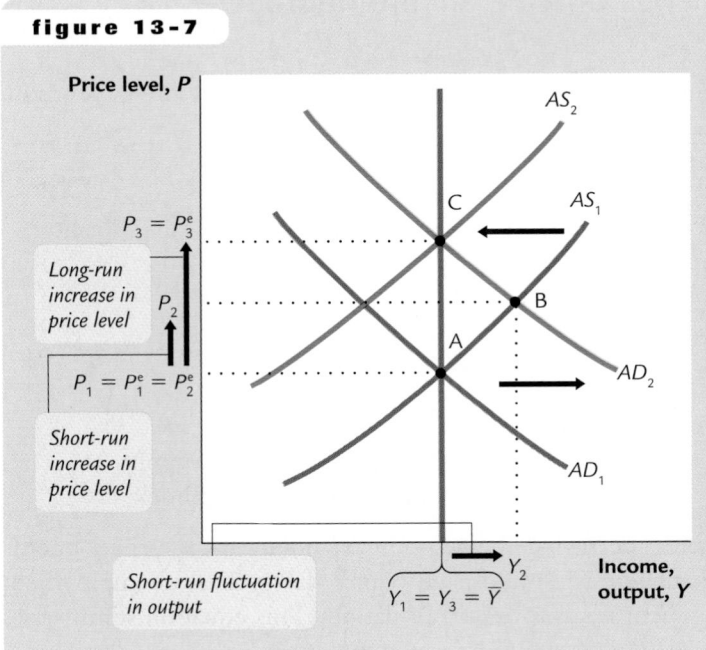

How Shifts in Aggregate Demand Lead to Short-Run Fluctuations Here the economy begins in a long-run equilibrium, point A. When aggregate demand increases unexpectedly, the price level rises from P_1 to P_2. Because the price level P_2 is above the expected price level P_2^e, output rises temporarily above the natural rate, as the economy moves along the short-run aggregate supply curve from point A to point B. In the long run, the expected price level rises to P_3^e, causing the short-run aggregate supply curve to shift upward. The economy returns to a new long-run equilibrium, point C, where output is back at its natural rate.

13-2 | Inflation, Unemployment, and the Phillips Curve

Two goals of economic policymakers are low inflation and low unemployment, but often these goals conflict. Suppose, for instance, that policymakers were to use monetary or fiscal policy to expand aggregate demand. This policy would move the economy along the short-run aggregate supply curve to a point of higher output and a higher price level. (Figure 13-7 shows this as the change from point A to point B.) Higher output means lower unemployment, because firms need more workers when they produce more. A higher price level, given the previous year's price level, means higher inflation. Thus, when policymakers move the economy up along the short-run aggregate supply curve, they reduce the unemployment rate and raise the inflation rate. Conversely, when they contract aggregate demand and move the economy down the short-run aggregate supply curve, unemployment rises and inflation falls.

This tradeoff between inflation and unemployment, called the *Phillips curve,* is our topic in this section. As we have just seen (and will derive more formally in a moment), the Phillips curve is a reflection of the short-run aggregate supply curve: as policymakers move the economy along the short-run aggregate supply curve, unemployment and inflation move in opposite directions. The Phillips curve is a useful way to express aggregate supply because inflation and unemployment are such important measures of economic performance.

Deriving the Phillips Curve From the Aggregate Supply Curve

The **Phillips curve** in its modern form states that the inflation rate depends on three forces:

➤ Expected inflation

➤ The deviation of unemployment from the natural rate, called cyclical unemployment

➤ Supply shocks.

These three forces are expressed in the following equation:

$$\pi = \pi^e - \beta(u - u^n) + v$$

$$\text{Inflation} = \frac{\text{Expected}}{\text{Inflation}} - \left(\beta \times \frac{\text{Cyclical}}{\text{Unemployment}}\right) + \frac{\text{Supply}}{\text{Shock,}}$$

where β is a parameter measuring the response of inflation to cyclical unemployment. Notice that there is a minus sign before the cyclical unemployment term: high unemployment tends to reduce inflation. This equation summarizes the relationship between inflation and unemployment.

Where does this equation for the Phillips curve come from? Although it may not seem familiar, we can derive it from our equation for aggregate supply. To see how, write the aggregate supply equation as

$$P = P^e + (1/\alpha)(Y - \overline{Y}).$$

With one addition, one subtraction, and one substitution, we can manipulate this equation to yield a relationship between inflation and unemployment.

Here are the three steps. First, add to the right-hand side of the equation a supply shock ν to represent exogenous events (such as a change in world oil prices) that alter the price level and shift the short-run aggregate supply curve:

$$P = P^e + (1/\alpha)(Y - \overline{Y}) + \nu.$$

Next, to go from the price level to inflation rates, subtract last year's price level P_{-1} from both sides of the equation to obtain

$$(P - P_{-1}) = (P^e - P_{-1}) + (1/\alpha)(Y - \overline{Y}) + \nu.$$

The term on the left-hand side, $P - P_{-1}$, is the difference between the current price level and last year's price level, which is inflation π.[9] The term on the right-hand side, $P^e - P_{-1}$, is the difference between the expected price level and last year's price level, which is expected inflation π^e. Therefore, we can replace $P - P_{-1}$ with π and $P^e - P_{-1}$ with π^e:

$$\pi = \pi^e + (1/\alpha)(Y - \overline{Y}) + \nu.$$

Third, to go from output to unemployment, recall from Chapter 2 that Okun's law gives a relationship between these two variables. One version of Okun's law states that the deviation of output from its natural rate is inversely related to the deviation of unemployment from its natural rate; that is, when output is higher than the natural rate of output, unemployment is lower than the natural rate of unemployment. We can write this as

$$(1/\alpha)(Y - \overline{Y}) = -\beta(u - u^n).$$

Using this Okun's law relationship, we can substitute $-\beta(u - u^n)$ for $(1/\alpha)(Y - \overline{Y})$ in the previous equation to obtain:

$$\pi = \pi^e - \beta(u - u^n) + \nu.$$

Thus, we can derive the Phillips curve equation from the aggregate supply equation.

All this algebra is meant to show one thing: the Phillips curve equation and the short-run aggregate supply equation represent essentially the same macroeconomic ideas. In particular, both equations show a link between real and nominal variables that causes the classical dichotomy (the theoretical separation of real and nominal variables) to break down in the short run. According to the

[9] *Mathematical note:* This statement is not precise, because inflation is really the *percentage* change in the price level. To make the statement more precise, interpret P as the logarithm of the price level. By the properties of logarithms, the change in P is roughly the inflation rate. The reason is that $dP = d(\log$ price level$) = d($price level$)/$price level.

f y i

THE HISTORY OF THE MODERN PHILLIPS CURVE

The Phillips curve is named after New Zealand-born economist A. W. Phillips. In 1958 Phillips observed a negative relationship between the unemployment rate and the rate of wage inflation in data for the United Kingdom.[10] The Phillips curve that economists use today differs in three ways from the relationship Phillips examined.

First, the modern Phillips curve substitutes price inflation for wage inflation. This difference is not crucial, because price inflation and wage inflation are closely related. In periods when wages are rising quickly, prices are rising quickly as well.

Second, the modern Phillips curve includes expected inflation. This addition is due to the work of Milton Friedman and Edmund Phelps. In developing the worker-misperception model in the 1960s, these two economists emphasized the importance of expectations for aggregate supply.

Third, the modern Phillips curve includes supply shocks. Credit for this addition goes to OPEC, the Organization of Petroleum Exporting Countries. In the 1970s OPEC caused large increases in the world price of oil, which made economists more aware of the importance of shocks to aggregate supply.

short-run aggregate supply equation, output is related to unexpected movements in the price level. According to the Phillips curve equation, unemployment is related to unexpected movements in the inflation rate. The aggregate supply curve is more convenient when we are studying output and the price level, whereas the Phillips curve is more convenient when we are studying unemployment and inflation. But we should not lose sight of the fact that the Phillips curve and the aggregate supply curve are merely two sides of the same coin.

Adaptive Expectations and Inflation Inertia

To make the Phillips curve useful for analyzing the choices facing policymakers, we need to say what determines expected inflation. A simple and often plausible assumption is that people form their expectations of inflation based on recently observed inflation. This assumption is called **adaptive expectations.** For example, suppose that people expect prices to rise this year at the same rate as they did last year. Then expected inflation π^e equals last year's inflation π_{-1}:

$$\pi^e = \pi_{-1}.$$

In this case, we can write the Phillips curve as

$$\pi = \pi_{-1} - \beta(u - u^n) + \nu,$$

---

[10] A. W. Phillips, "The Relationship Between Unemployment and the Rate of Change of Money Wages in the United Kingdom, 1861–1957," *Economica* 25 (November 1958): 283–299.

which states that inflation depends on past inflation, cyclical unemployment, and a supply shock.

The first term in this form of the Phillips curve, π_{-1}, implies that inflation has inertia. That is, like an object moving through space, inflation keeps going unless something acts to stop it. In particular, if unemployment is at its natural rate and if there are no supply shocks, the price level will continue to rise at the rate it has been rising. This inertia arises because past inflation influences expectations of future inflation and because these expectations influence the wages and prices that people set. Robert Solow captured the concept of inflation inertia well when, during the high inflation of the 1970s, he wrote, "Why is our money ever less valuable? Perhaps it is simply that we have inflation because we expect inflation, and we expect inflation because we've had it."

In the model of aggregate supply and aggregate demand, inflation inertia is interpreted as persistent upward shifts in both the aggregate supply curve and the aggregate demand curve. Consider first aggregate supply. If prices have been rising quickly, people will expect them to continue to rise quickly. Because the position of the short-run aggregate supply curve depends on the expected price level, the short-run aggregate supply curve will shift upward over time. It will continue to shift upward until some event, such as a recession or a supply shock, changes inflation and thereby changes expectations of inflation.

The aggregate demand curve must also shift upward to confirm the expectations of inflation. Most often, the continued rise in aggregate demand is due to persistent growth in the money supply. If the Fed suddenly halted money growth, aggregate demand would stabilize, and the upward shift in aggregate supply would cause a recession. The high unemployment in the recession would reduce inflation and expected inflation, causing inflation inertia to subside.

Two Causes of Rising and Falling Inflation

The second and third terms in the Phillips curve equation show the two forces that can change the rate of inflation.

The second term, $\beta(u - u^n)$, shows that cyclical unemployment—the deviation of unemployment from its natural rate—exerts upward or downward pressure on inflation. Low unemployment pulls the inflation rate up. This is called **demand-pull inflation** because high aggregate demand is responsible for this type of inflation. High unemployment pulls the inflation rate down. The parameter β measures how responsive inflation is to cyclical unemployment.

The third term, ν, shows that inflation also rises and falls because of supply shocks. An adverse supply shock, such as the rise in world oil prices in the 1970s, implies a positive value of ν and causes inflation to rise. This is called **cost-push inflation** because adverse supply shocks are typically events that push up the costs of production. A beneficial supply shock, such as the oil glut that led to a fall in oil prices in the 1980s, makes ν negative and causes inflation to fall.

CASE STUDY

Inflation and Unemployment in the United States

Because inflation and unemployment are such important measures of economic performance, macroeconomic developments are often viewed through the lens of the Phillips curve. Figure 13-8 displays the history of inflation and unemployment in the United States since 1961. These nearly four decades of data illustrate some of the causes of rising or falling inflation.

The 1960s showed how policymakers can, in the short run, lower unemployment at the cost of higher inflation. The tax cut of 1964, together with expansionary monetary policy, expanded aggregate demand and pushed the unemployment rate below 5 percent. This expansion of aggregate demand continued in the late 1960s largely as a by-product of government spending for the Vietnam War. Unemployment fell lower and inflation rose higher than policymakers intended.

figure 13-8

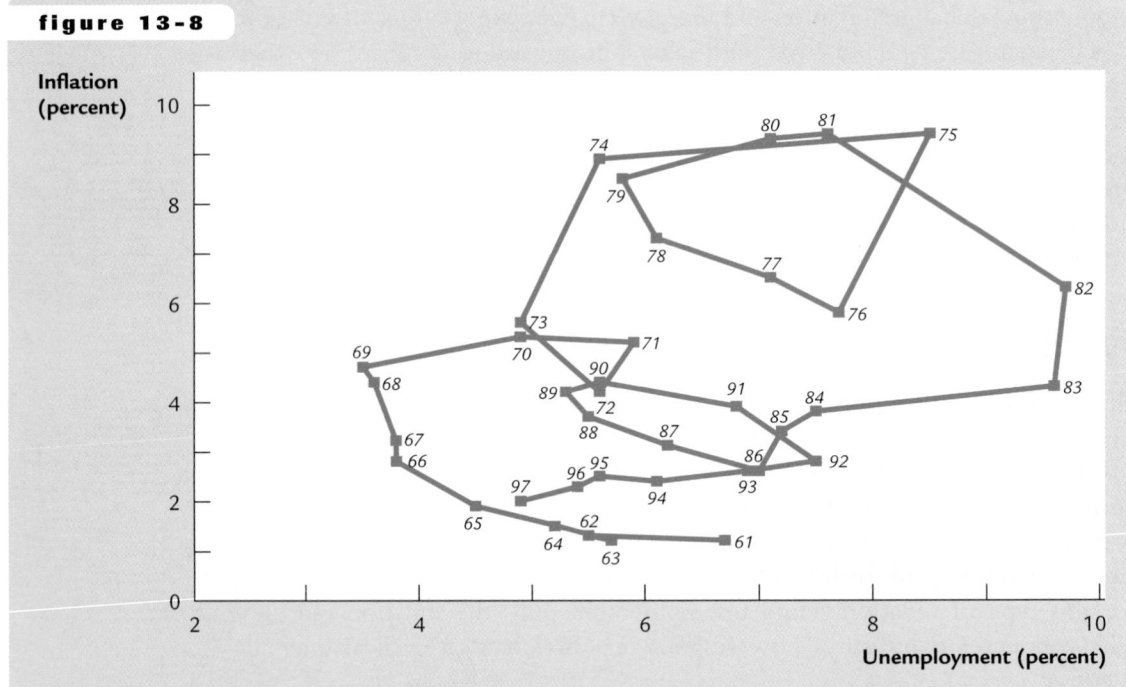

Inflation and Unemployment in the United States Since 1961 This figure uses annual data on the unemployment rate and the inflation rate (percentage change in the GDP deflator) to illustrate macroeconomic developments over the past three decades.

Source: U.S. Department of Commerce and U.S. Department of Labor.

The 1970s were a period of economic turmoil. The decade began with poli-cymakers trying to lower the inflation inherited from the 1960s. President Nixon imposed temporary controls on wages and prices, and the Federal Reserve engineered a recession through contractionary monetary policy, but the inflation rate fell only slightly. The effects of wage and price controls ended when the controls were lifted, and the recession was too small to counteract the inflationary impact of the boom that had preceded it. By 1972 the unemployment rate was the same as a decade earlier, while inflation was 3 percentage points higher.

Beginning in 1973 policymakers had to cope with the large supply shocks caused by the Organization of Petroleum Exporting Countries (OPEC). OPEC first raised oil prices in the mid–1970s, pushing the inflation rate up to about 10 percent. This adverse supply shock, together with temporarily tight monetary policy, led to a recession in 1975. High unemployment during the recession reduced inflation somewhat, but further OPEC price hikes pushed inflation up again in the late 1970s.

The 1980s began with high inflation and high expectations of inflation. Under the leadership of Chairman Paul Volcker, the Federal Reserve doggedly pursued monetary policies aimed at reducing inflation. In 1982 and 1983 the unemployment rate reached its highest level in 40 years. High unemployment, aided by a fall in oil prices in 1986, pulled the inflation rate down from about 10 percent to about 3 percent. By 1987 the unemployment rate of about 6 percent was close to most estimates of the natural rate. Unemployment continued to fall through the 1980s, however, reaching a low of 5.2 percent in 1989 and beginning a new round of demand-pull inflation.

Compared to the previous 30 years, the 1990s were relatively quiet. The decade began with a recession caused by several contractionary shocks to aggregate demand. (A case study in Chapter 14 examines these shocks.) The unemployment rate rose to 7.3 percent in 1992. Inflation fell, but only slightly. Unlike in the 1982 recession, unemployment in the 1990 recession was never far above the natural rate, so the effect on inflation was small.

As the 1990s drew to a close, inflation and unemployment both reached their lowest levels in many years. Some economists have explained this fortunate development by claiming (as we saw in Chapter 6) that the aging of the baby-boom generation has reduced the economy's natural rate of unemployment. If so, perhaps unemployment can remain below 5 percent without causing inflation to rise. Other economists have argued that a variety of temporary factors (such as a strong U.S. dollar due to a financial crisis in Asia) have held down inflation and that a new round of demand-pull inflation is around the corner. Only time will tell which intepretation is right.

Thus, recent macroeconomic history exhibits the many causes of inflation. The 1960s and the 1980s show the two sides of demand-pull inflation: in the 1960s low unemployment pulled inflation up, and in the 1980s high unemployment pulled inflation down. The 1970s show the effects of cost-push inflation.

The Short-Run Tradeoff Between Inflation and Unemployment

Consider the options the Phillips curve gives to a policymaker who can influence aggregate demand with monetary or fiscal policy. At any moment, expected inflation and supply shocks are beyond the policymaker's immediate control. Yet, by changing aggregate demand, the policymaker can alter output, unemployment, and inflation. The policymaker can expand aggregate demand to lower unemployment and raise inflation. Or the policymaker can depress aggregate demand to raise unemployment and lower inflation.

Figure 13-9 plots the Phillips-curve equation and shows the short-run tradeoff between inflation and unemployment. The policymaker can manipulate aggregate demand to choose a combination of inflation and unemployment on this curve, called the *short-run Phillips curve.*

Notice that the position of the short-run Phillips curve depends on the expected rate of inflation. If expected inflation rises, the curve shifts upward, and the policymaker's tradeoff becomes less favorable: inflation is higher for any level of unemployment. Figure 13-10 shows how the tradeoff depends on expected inflation.

Because people adjust their expectations of inflation over time, the tradeoff between inflation and unemployment holds only in the short run. The policymaker cannot keep inflation above expected inflation (and thus unemployment below its natural rate) forever. Eventually, expectations adapt to whatever inflation rate the policymaker has chosen. In the long run, the classical dichotomy holds, unemployment returns to its natural rate, and there is no tradeoff between inflation and unemployment.

figure 13-9

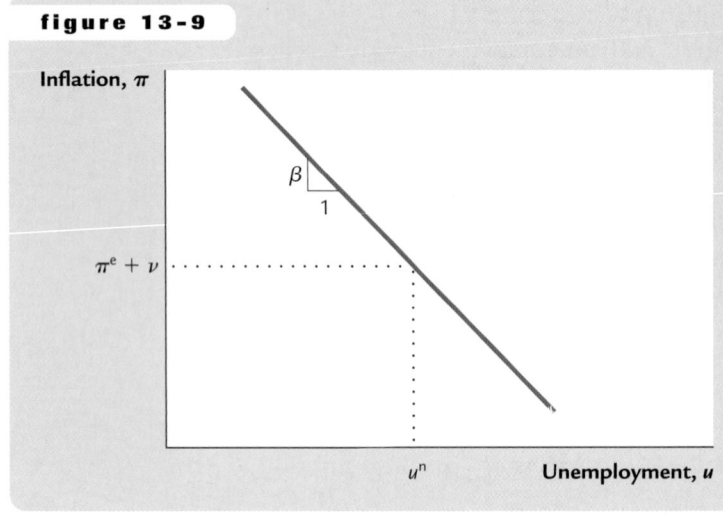

The Short-Run Tradeoff Between Inflation and Unemployment In the short run, there is a negative relationship between inflation and unemployment. At any point in time, a policymaker who controls aggregate demand can choose a combination of inflation and unemployment on this short-run Phillips curve.

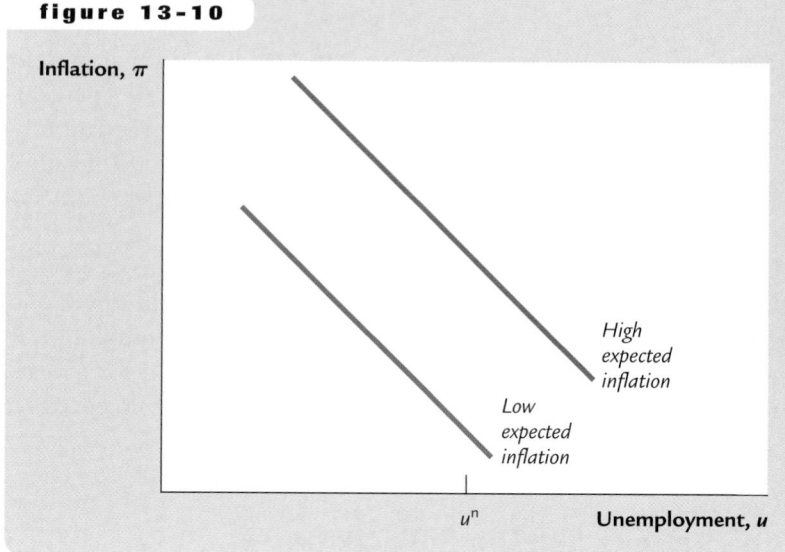

figure 13-10

Inflation, π

**Shifts in the Short-Run
Tradeoff** The short-run tradeoff between inflation and
unemployment depends on
expected inflation. The curve is
higher when expected inflation
is higher.

High
expected
inflation

Low
expected
inflation

u^n

Unemployment, u

Disinflation and the Sacrifice Ratio

Imagine an economy in which unemployment is at its natural rate and inflation
is running at 6 percent. What would happen to unemployment and output if
the central bank pursued a policy to reduce inflation from 6 to 2 percent?

The Phillips curve shows that in the absence of a beneficial supply shock,
lowering inflation requires a period of high unemployment and reduced output. But by how much and for how long would unemployment need to rise
above the natural rate? Before deciding whether to reduce inflation, policymakers must know how much output would be lost during the transition to
lower inflation. This cost can then be compared with the benefits of lower inflation.

Much research has used the available data to examine the Phillips curve
quantitatively. The results of these studies are often summarized in a number
called the **sacrifice ratio,** the percentage of a year's real GDP that must be forgone to reduce inflation by 1 percentage point. Although estimates of the sacrifice ratio vary substantially, a typical estimate is about 5: for every percentage
point that inflation is to fall, 5 percent of one year's GDP must be sacrificed.[11]

We can also express the sacrifice ratio in terms of unemployment. Okun's
law says that a change of 1 percentage point in the unemployment rate translates into a change of 2 percentage points in GDP. Therefore, reducing

[11] Arthur M. Okun, "Efficient Disinflationary Policies," *American Economic Review* 68 (May
1978): 348–352; Robert J. Gordon and Stephen R. King, "The Output Cost of Disinflation in
Traditional and Vector Autoregressive Models," *Brookings Papers on Economic Activity* (1982:1):
205–245.

inflation by 1 percentage point requires about 2.5 percentage points of cyclical unemployment.

We can use the sacrifice ratio to estimate by how much and for how long unemployment must rise to reduce inflation. If reducing inflation by 1 percentage point requires a sacrifice of 5 percent of a year's GDP, reducing inflation by 4 percentage points requires a sacrifice of 20 percent of a year's GDP. Equivalently, this reduction in inflation requires a sacrifice of 10 percentage points of cyclical unemployment.

This disinflation could take various forms, each totaling the same sacrifice of 20 percent of a year's GDP. For example, a rapid disinflation would lower output by 10 percent for 2 years: this is sometimes called the *cold-turkey* solution to inflation. A moderate disinflation would lower output by 5 percent for 4 years. An even more gradual disinflation would depress output by 2 percent for a decade.

Rational Expectations and the Possibility of Painless Disinflation

Because the expectation of inflation influences the short-run tradeoff between inflation and unemployment, it is crucial to understand how people form expectations. So far, we have been assuming that expected inflation depends on recently observed inflation. Although this assumption of adaptive expectations is plausible, it is probably too simple to apply in all circumstances.

An alternative approach is to assume that people have **rational expectations.** That is, we might assume that people optimally use all the available information, including information about current government policies, to forecast the future. Because monetary and fiscal policies influence inflation, expected inflation should also depend on the monetary and fiscal policies in effect. According to the theory of rational expectations, a change in monetary or fiscal policy will change expectations, and an evaluation of any policy change must incorporate this effect on expectations. If people do form their expectations rationally, then inflation may have less inertia than it first appears.

Here is how Thomas Sargent, a prominent advocate of rational expectations, describes its implications for the Phillips curve:

> An alternative "rational expectations" view denies that there is any inherent momentum to the present process of inflation. This view maintains that firms and workers have now come to expect high rates of inflation in the future and that they strike inflationary bargains in light of these expectations. However, it is held that people expect high rates of inflation in the future precisely because the government's current and prospective monetary and fiscal policies warrant those expectations. . . . Thus inflation only seems to have a momentum of its own; it is actually the long-term government policy of persistently running large deficits and creating money at high rates which imparts the momentum to the inflation rate. An implication of this view is that inflation can be stopped much more quickly than advocates of the "momentum" view have indicated and that their estimates of the length of time and the costs of stopping inflation in terms of

foregone output are erroneous. . . . [Stopping inflation] would require a change in the policy regime: there must be an abrupt change in the continuing government policy, or strategy, for setting deficits now and in the future that is sufficiently binding as to be widely believed. . . . How costly such a move would be in terms of foregone output and how long it would be in taking effect would depend partly on how resolute and evident the government's commitment was.[12]

Thus, advocates of rational expectations argue that the short-run Phillips curve does not accurately represent the options that policymakers have available. They believe that if policymakers are credibly committed to reducing inflation, rational people will understand the commitment and will quickly lower their expectations of inflation. Inflation can then come down without a rise in unemployment and fall in output. According to the theory of rational expectations, traditional estimates of the sacrifice ratio are not useful for evaluating the impact of alternative policies. Under a credible policy, the costs of reducing inflation may be much lower than estimates of the sacrifice ratio suggest.

In the most extreme case, one can imagine reducing the rate of inflation without causing any recession at all. A painless disinflation has two requirements. First, the plan to reduce inflation must be announced before the workers and firms who set wages and prices have formed their expectations. Second, the workers and firms must believe the announcement; otherwise, they will not reduce their expectations of inflation. If both requirements are met, the announcement will immediately shift the short-run tradeoff between inflation and unemployment downward, permitting a lower rate of inflation without higher unemployment.

Although the rational-expectations approach remains controversial, almost all economists agree that expectations of inflation influence the short-run tradeoff between inflation and unemployment. The credibility of a policy to reduce inflation is therefore one determinant of how costly the policy will be. Unfortunately, it is often difficult to predict whether the public will view the announcement of a new policy as credible. The central role of expectations makes forecasting the results of alternative policies far more difficult.

CASE STUDY

The Sacrifice Ratio in Practice

The Phillips curve with adaptive expectations implies that reducing inflation requires a period of high unemployment and low output. By contrast, the rational-expectations approach suggests that reducing inflation can be much less costly. What happens during actual disinflations?

Consider the U.S. disinflation in the early 1980s. This decade began with some of the highest rates of inflation in U.S. history. Yet because of the tight monetary policies the Fed pursued under Chairman Paul Volcker, the rate of inflation fell substantially in the first few years of the decade. This episode

---

[12] Thomas J. Sargent, "The Ends of Four Big Inflations," in Robert E. Hall, ed., *Inflation: Causes and Effects* (Chicago: University of Chicago Press, 1982).

provides a natural experiment with which to estimate how much output is lost during the process of disinflation.

The first question is, how much did inflation fall? As measured by the GDP deflator, inflation reached a peak of 9.7 percent in 1981. It is natural to end the episode in 1985 because oil prices plunged in 1986—a large, beneficial supply shock unrelated to Fed policy. In 1985, inflation was 3.0 percent, so we can estimate that the Fed engineered a reduction in inflation of 6.7 percentage points over four years.

The second question is, how much output was lost during this period? Table 13-1 shows the unemployment rate from 1982 to 1985. Assuming that the natural rate of unemployment was 6 percent, we can compute the amount of cyclical unemployment in each year. In total over this period, there were 9.5 percentage points of cyclical unemployment. Okun's law says that 1 percentage point of unemployment translates into 2 percentage points of GDP. Therefore, 19.0 percentage points of annual GDP were lost during the disinflation.

Now we can compute the sacrifice ratio for this episode. We know that 19.0 percentage points of GDP were lost and that inflation fell by 6.7 percentage points. Hence, 19.0/6.7, or 2.8, percentage points of GDP were lost for each percentage-point reduction in inflation. The estimate of the sacrifice ratio from the Volcker disinflation is 2.8.

This estimate of the sacrifice ratio is smaller than the estimates made before Volcker was appointed Fed chairman. In other words, Volcker reduced inflation at a smaller cost than many economists had predicted. One explanation is that Volcker's tough stand was credible enough to influence expectations of inflation directly. Yet the change in expectations was not large enough to make the disinflation painless: in 1982 unemployment reached its highest level since the Great Depression.

Although the Volcker disinflation is only one historical episode, this kind of analysis can be applied to other disinflations. A recent study documented the results of 65 disinflations in 19 countries. In almost all cases, the reduction in inflation came at the cost of temporarily lower output. Yet the size of the output loss varied from episode to episode. Rapid disinflations usually had smaller

---

table 13-1

Unemployment During the Volcker Disinflation

Year	Unemployment Rate, u	Natural Rate, u^n	Cyclical Unemployment, $u - u^n$
1982	9.5%	6.0%	3.5%
1983	9.5	6.0	3.5
1984	7.4	6.0	1.4
1985	7.1	6.0	1.1
		Total	9.5%

sacrifice ratios than slower ones. That is, in contrast to what the Phillips curve with adaptive expectations suggests, a cold-turkey approach appears less costly than a gradual one. Moreover, countries with more flexible wage-setting institutions, such as shorter labor contracts, had smaller sacrifice ratios. These findings indicate that reducing inflation always has some cost, but that policies and institutions can affect its magnitude.[13]

Hysteresis and the Challenge to the Natural-Rate Hypothesis

Our discussion of the cost of disinflation—and indeed our entire discussion of economic fluctuations in the past four chapters—has been based on an assumption called the **natural-rate hypothesis.** This hypothesis is summarized in the following statement:

> *Fluctuations in aggregate demand affect output and employment only in the short run. In the long run, the economy returns to the levels of output, employment, and unemployment described by the classical model.*

The natural-rate hypothesis allows macroeconomists to study separately short-run and long-run developments in the economy. It is one expression of the classical dichotomy.

Recently, some economists have challenged the natural-rate hypothesis by suggesting that aggregate demand may affect output and employment even in the long run. They have pointed out a number of mechanisms through which recessions might leave permanent scars on the economy by altering the natural rate of unemployment. **Hysteresis** is the term used to describe the long-lasting influence of history on the natural rate.

A recession can have permanent effects if it changes the people who become unemployed. For instance, workers might lose valuable job skills when unemployed, lowering their ability to find a job even after the recession ends. Alternatively, a long period of unemployment may change an individual's attitude toward work and reduce his desire to find employment. In either case, the recession permanently inhibits the process of job search and raises the amount of frictional unemployment.

Another way in which a recession can permanently affect the economy is by changing the process that determines wages. Those who become unemployed may lose their influence on the wage-setting process. Unemployed workers may lose their status as union members, for example. More generally, some of the *insiders* in the wage-setting process become *outsiders*. If the smaller group of insiders cares more about high real wages and less about high employment, then the recession may permanently push real wages further above the equilibrium level and raise the amount of wait unemployment.

---

[13] Laurence Ball, "What Determines the Sacrifice Ratio?" in N. Gregory Mankiw, ed., *Monetary Policy* (Chicago: University of Chicago Press, 1994).

Hysteresis remains a controversial theory. Some economists believe the theory helps explain persistently high unemployment in Europe, for the rise in European unemployment starting in the early 1980s coincided with disinflation but continued after inflation stabilized. Moreover, the increase in unemployment tended to be larger for those countries that experienced the greatest reductions in inflations, such as Ireland, Italy, and Spain. Yet there is still no consensus whether the hysteresis phenomenon is significant, or why it might be more pronounced in some countries than in others. (Other explanations of high European unemployment, discussed in Chapter 6, give little role to the disinflation.) If true, however, the theory is important, because hysteresis greatly increases the cost of recessions. Put another way, hysteresis raises the sacrifice ratio, because output is lost even after the period of disinflation is over.[14]

13-3 | Conclusion

We began this chapter by discussing four models of aggregate supply, each of which focuses on a different reason why the short-run aggregate supply curve is upward sloping. The four models have similar predictions for the aggregate economy, and all of them yield a short-run tradeoff between inflation and unemployment. A convenient way to express and analyze that tradeoff is with the Phillips-curve equation, according to which inflation depends on expected inflation, cyclical unemployment, and supply shocks.

Keep in mind that not all economists endorse all the ideas discussed here. There is widespread disagreement, for instance, about the practical importance of rational expectations and the relevance of hysteresis. If you find it difficult to fit all the pieces together, you are not alone. The study of aggregate supply remains one of the most unsettled—and therefore one of the most exciting—research areas in macroeconomics.

Summary

1. The four theories of aggregate supply—the sticky-wage, worker-misperception, imperfect-information, and sticky-price models—attribute deviations of output and employment from the natural rate to various market imperfections. According to all four theories, output rises above the natural rate when the price level exceeds the expected price level, and output falls below the natural rate when the price level is less than the expected price level.

---

[14] Olivier J. Blanchard and Lawrence H. Summers, "Beyond the Natural Rate Hypothesis," *American Economic Review* 78 (May 1988): 182–187; Laurence Ball, "Disinflation and the NAIRU," in Christina D. Romer and David H. Romer, eds., *Reducing Inflation: Motivation and Strategy* (Chicago: University of Chicago Press, 1997): 167–185.

2. Economists often express aggregate supply in a relationship called the Phillips curve. The Phillips curve says that inflation depends on expected inflation, the deviation of unemployment from its natural rate, and supply shocks. According to the Phillips curve, policymakers who control aggregate demand face a short-run tradeoff between inflation and unemployment.

3. If expected inflation depends on recently observed inflation, then inflation has inertia, which means that reducing inflation requires either a beneficial supply shock or a period of high unemployment and reduced output. If people have rational expectations, however, then a credible announcement of a change in policy might be able to influence expectations directly and, therefore, reduce inflation without causing a recession.

4. Most economists accept the natural-rate hypothesis, according to which fluctuations in aggregate demand have only short-run effects on output and unemployment. Yet some economists have suggested ways in which recessions can leave permanent scars on the economy by raising the natural rate of unemployment.

KEY CONCEPTS

Sticky-wage model	Phillips curve	Sacrifice ratio
Worker-misperception model	Adaptive expectations	Rational expectations
Imperfect-information model	Demand-pull inflation	Natural-rate hypothesis
Sticky-price model	Cost-push inflation	Hysteresis

QUESTIONS FOR REVIEW

1. Explain the four theories of aggregate supply. On what market imperfection does each theory rely? What do the theories have in common?

2. How is the Phillips curve related to aggregate supply?

3. Why might inflation be inertial?

4. Explain the differences between demand-pull inflation and cost-push inflation.

5. Under what circumstances might it be possible to reduce inflation without causing a recession?

6. Explain two ways in which a recession might raise the natural rate of unemployment.

PROBLEMS AND APPLICATIONS

1. Consider the following changes in the sticky-wage model.

   a. Suppose that labor contracts specify that the nominal wage be fully indexed for inflation. That is, the nominal wage is to be adjusted to fully compensate for changes in the consumer price index. How does full indexation alter the aggregate supply curve in this model?

   b. Suppose now that indexation is only partial. That is, for every increase in the CPI, the nominal wage rises, but by a smaller percentage. How does partial indexation alter the aggregate supply curve in this model?

2. In the sticky-price model, describe the aggregate supply curve in the following special cases. How do these cases compare to the short-run aggregate supply curve we discussed in Chapter 9?

   a. No firms have flexible prices ($s = 1$).

   b. The desired price does not depend on aggregate output ($a = 0$).

3. Suppose that an economy has the Phillips curve

   $$\pi = \pi_{-1} - 0.5(u - 0.06).$$

   a. What is the natural rate of unemployment?

   b. Graph the short-run and long-run relationships between inflation and unemployment.

   c. How much cyclical unemployment is necessary to reduce inflation by 5 percentage points? Using Okun's law, compute the sacrifice ratio.

   d. Inflation is running at 10 percent. The Fed wants to reduce it to 5 percent. Give two scenarios that will achieve that goal.

4. According to the rational-expectations approach, if everyone believes that policymakers are committed to reducing inflation, the cost of reducing inflation—the sacrifice ratio—will be lower than if the public is skeptical about the policymakers' intentions. Why might this be true? How might credibility be achieved?

5. Assume that people have rational expectations and that the economy is described by the sticky-wage or sticky-price model. Explain why each of the following propositions is true:

   a. Only unanticipated changes in the money supply affect real GDP. Changes in the money supply that were anticipated when wages and prices were set do not have any real effects.

   b. If the Fed chooses the money supply at the same time as people are setting wages and prices, so that everyone has the same information about the state of the economy, then monetary policy cannot be used systematically to stabilize output. Hence, a policy of keep-

ing the money supply constant will have the same real effects as a policy of adjusting the money supply in response to the state of the economy. (This is called the *policy irrelevance proposition*.)

   c. If the Fed sets the money supply well after people have set wages and prices, so the Fed has collected more information about the state of the economy, then monetary policy can be used systematically to stabilize output.

6. Suppose that an economy has the Phillips curve

   $$\pi = \pi_{-1} - 0.5(u - u^n),$$

   and that the natural rate of unemployment is given by an average of the past two years' unemployment:

   $$u^n = 0.5(u_{-1} + u_{-2}).$$

   a. Why might the natural rate of unemployment depend on recent unemployment (as is assumed in the above equation)?

   b. Suppose that the Fed follows a policy to reduce permanently the inflation rate by 1 percentage point. What effect will that policy have on the unemployment rate over time?

   c. What is the sacrifice ratio in this economy? Explain.

   d. What do these equations imply about the short-run and long-run tradeoffs between inflation and unemployment?

7. Some economists believe that taxes have an important effect on labor supply. They argue that higher taxes cause people to want to work less and that lower taxes cause them to want to work more. Consider how this effect alters the macroeconomic analysis of tax changes.

   a. If this view is correct, how does a tax cut affect the natural rate of output?

   b. How does a tax cut affect the aggregate demand curve? The long-run aggregate supply curve? The short-run aggregate supply curve?

   c. What is the short-run impact of a tax cut on output and the price level? How does your answer differ from the case without the labor-supply effect?

d. What is the long-run impact of a tax cut on output and the price level? How does your answer differ from the case without the labor-supply effect?

8. Economist Alan Blinder, whom Bill Clinton appointed to be Vice Chairman of the Federal Reserve, once wrote the following:

> The costs that attend the low and moderate inflation rates experienced in the United States and in other industrial countries appear to be quite modest—more like a bad cold than a cancer on society. . . . As rational individuals, we do not volunteer for a lobotomy to cure a head cold. Yet, as a collectivity, we routinely prescribe the economic equivalent of lobotomy (high unemployment) as a cure for the inflationary cold.[15]

What do you think Blinder meant by this? What are the policy implications of the viewpoint Blinder is advocating? Do you agree? Why or why not?

---

[15] Alan Blinder, *Hard Heads, Soft Hearts: Tough-Minded Economics for a Just Society* (Reading, MA: Addison-Wesley, 1987): 51.

FOUR

Macroeconomic Policy Debates

Discussions among economists are most heated — and most fun — when the topic turns to economic policy. So far in this book we have developed the theories that economists use to study the long-run and short-run behavior of key macroeconomic variables. We can now apply these tools to some of the debates over macroeconomic policy.

Chapter 14 examines the debate over how policymakers should respond to short-run fluctuations by considering two questions. Should monetary and fiscal policy take an active role in taming the business cycle, or should it remain passive? Should policy be conducted by discretion, or should it be governed by a rule set out in advance? As we will see, there are good arguments on both sides of these questions.

Chapter 15 considers the debate over government debt and budget deficits. From 1980 to 1995, the debt of the U.S. federal government roughly doubled as a percentage of GDP. Although some economists view this fact as relatively insignificant, others see it as the most troubling aspect of recent U.S. policy. This chapter discusses the wide range of views about how government debt affects the economy.

14

Stabilization Policy

The Federal Reserve's job is to take away the punch bowl just as the party gets going.

— *William McChesney Martin*

What we need is not a skilled monetary driver of the economic vehicle continuously turning the steering wheel to adjust to the unexpected irregularities of the route, but some means of keeping the monetary passenger who is in the back seat as ballast from occasionally leaning over and giving the steering wheel a jerk that threatens to send the car off the road.

— *Milton Friedman*

How should government policymakers respond to the business cycle? The two quotations above—the first from a former chairman of the Federal Reserve, the second from a prominent critic of the Fed—show the diversity of opinion over how this question is best answered.

Some economists, such as William McChesney Martin, view the economy as inherently unstable. They argue that the economy experiences frequent shocks to aggregate demand and aggregate supply. Unless policymakers use monetary and fiscal policy to stabilize the economy, these shocks will lead to unnecessary and inefficient fluctuations in output, unemployment, and inflation. According to the popular saying, macroeconomic policy should "lean against the wind," stimulating the economy when it is depressed and slowing the economy when it is overheated.

Other economists, such as Milton Friedman, view the economy as naturally stable. They blame bad economic policies for the large and inefficient fluctuations we have sometimes experienced. They argue that economic policy should not try to "fine tune" the economy. Instead, economic policymakers should admit their limited abilities and be satisfied if they do no harm.

This debate has persisted for decades with numerous protagonists advancing various arguments for their positions. The fundamental issue is how policymakers should use the theory of short-run economic fluctuations developed in the preceding chapters. In this chapter we ask two questions that arise in this debate. First, should monetary and fiscal policy take an active role in trying to stabilize the economy, or should policy remain passive? Second, should policymakers be free to use their discretion in responding to changing economic conditions, or should they be committed to following a fixed policy rule?

14-1 Should Policy Be Active or Passive?

Policymakers in the federal government view economic stabilization as one of their primary responsibilities. The analysis of macroeconomic policy is a regular duty of the Council of Economic Advisers, the Congressional Budget Office, the Federal Reserve, and other government agencies. When Congress or the president is considering a major change in fiscal policy, or when the Federal Reserve is considering a major change in monetary policy, foremost in the discussion are how the change will influence inflation and unemployment and whether aggregate demand needs to be stimulated or restrained.

Although the government has long conducted monetary and fiscal policy, the view that it should use these policy instruments to try to stabilize the economy is more recent. The Employment Act of 1946 was a key piece of legislation in which the government first held itself accountable for macroeconomic performance. The act states that "it is the continuing policy and responsibility of the Federal Government to . . . promote full employment and production." This law was written when the memory of the Great Depression was still fresh. The lawmakers who wrote it believed, as many economists do, that in the absence of an active government role in the economy, events like the Great Depression could occur regularly.

To many economists the case for active government policy is clear and simple. Recessions are periods of high unemployment, low incomes, and increased economic hardship. The model of aggregate demand and aggregate supply shows how shocks to the economy can cause recessions. It also shows how monetary and fiscal policy can prevent recessions by responding to these shocks. These economists consider it wasteful not to use these policy instruments to stabilize the economy.

Other economists are critical of the government's attempts to stabilize the economy. These critics argue that the government should take a hands-off approach to macroeconomic policy. At first, this view might seem surprising. If our model shows how to prevent or reduce the severity of recessions, why do these critics want the government to refrain from using monetary and fiscal policy for economic stabilization? To find out, let's consider some of their arguments.

Lags in the Implementation and Effects of Policies

Economic stabilization would be easy if the effects of policy were immediate. Making policy would be like driving a car: policymakers would simply adjust their instruments to keep the economy on the desired path.

Making economic policy, however, is less like driving a car than it is like piloting a large ship. A car changes direction almost immediately after the steering wheel is turned. By contrast, a ship changes course long after the pilot adjusts the rudder, and once the ship starts to turn, it continues turning long after the rudder is set back to normal. A novice pilot is likely to oversteer and, after noticing the mistake, overreact by steering too much in the opposite direction. The ship's path could become unstable, as the novice responds to previous mistakes by making larger and larger corrections.

Like a ship's pilot, economic policymakers face the problem of long lags. Indeed, the problem for policymakers is even more difficult, because the lengths of the lags are hard to predict. These long and variable lags greatly complicate the conduct of monetary and fiscal policy.

Economists distinguish between two lags in the conduct of stabilization policy: the inside lag and the outside lag. The **inside lag** is the time between a shock to the economy and the policy action responding to that shock. This lag arises because it takes time for policymakers first to recognize that a shock has occurred and then to put appropriate policies into effect. The **outside lag** is the time between a policy action and its influence on the economy. This lag arises because policies do not immediately influence spending, income, and employment.

A long inside lag is a central problem with using fiscal policy for economic stabilization. This is especially true in the United States, where changes in spending or taxes require the approval of the president and both houses of Congress. The slow and cumbersome legislative process often leads to delays, which make fiscal policy an imprecise tool for stabilizing the economy. This inside lag is shorter in countries with parliamentary systems, such as the United Kingdom, because there the party in power can often enact policy changes more rapidly.

Monetary policy has a much shorter inside lag than fiscal policy, for a central bank can decide on and implement a policy change in less than a day, but monetary policy has a substantial outside lag. Monetary policy works by changing the money supply and thereby interest rates, which in turn influence investment. But many firms make investment plans far in advance. Therefore, a change in monetary policy is thought not to affect economic activity until about six months after it is made.

The long and variable lags associated with monetary and fiscal policy certainly make stabilizing the economy more difficult. Advocates of passive policy argue that, because of these lags, successful stabilization policy is almost impossible. Indeed, attempts to stabilize the economy can be destabilizing. Suppose that the economy's condition changes between the beginning of a policy action and its impact on the economy. In this case, active policy may end up stimulating the economy when it is overheated or depressing the economy when it is cooling off. Advocates of active policy admit that such lags do require policy-makers to be cautious. But, they argue, these lags do not necessarily mean that policy should be completely passive, especially in the face of a severe and protracted economic downturn.

Some policies, called **automatic stabilizers,** are designed to reduce the lags associated with stabilization policy. Automatic stabilizers are policies that stimulate or depress the economy when necessary without any deliberate policy change. For example, the system of income taxes automatically reduces taxes when the economy goes into a recession, without any change in the tax laws, because individuals and corporations pay less tax when their incomes fall. Similarly, the unemployment-insurance and welfare systems automatically raise transfer payments when the economy moves into a recession, because more people apply for benefits. One can view these automatic stabilizers as a type of fiscal policy without any inside lag.

CASE STUDY

The 1990 Recession

When President Clinton took office in 1993, the United States was recovering from a recent recession, which had begun in the middle of 1990. Unemployment rose from 5.1 percent in June 1990 to 7.7 percent in June 1992. Although not severe by historical standards, the recession was a cause of much concern among policymakers. High unemployment lingered throughout 1992, and the state of the economy became a central issue in that year's presidential campaign.

What caused this recession? No single culprit is apparent, but there is a group of likely suspects that may have been responsible for a fall in aggregate demand.

One early cause of the recession was a contractionary shift in the *LM* curve due to monetary policy. The low unemployment rate in the late 1980s was, by most estimates, below the natural rate, and inflation appeared to be heating up. This caused the Fed to slow the rate of money growth. Short-term interest rates rose from 6 percent in the middle of 1988 to almost 9 percent a year later, putting downward pressure on investment spending and thereby aggregate demand.

Shortly after the Fed's tightening, two shocks to the *IS* curve appear to have contributed to the downturn. First, for various reasons (including inadequate previous regulation), many financial institutions, especially savings and loans associations, found themselves at or near the point of bankruptcy. This made bankers and bank regulators more cautious in approving loans. The resulting "credit crunch" forced some firms to forgo investment projects, thereby reducing the demand for investment goods. Second, when Iraq invaded Kuwait in the summer of 1990, consumer confidence fell. The uncertainty caused by the Gulf War may have induced consumers to delay spending until the uncertainty was resolved. The fall in consumer spending added to the decline in aggregate demand.

Could the recession have been avoided? In retrospect, it is clear that a more expansionary monetary policy would have helped. The Fed did lower interest rates, but only gradually as the recession unfolded. Short-term interest rates fell to about 3 percent in 1992. Yet, at the same time, growth in some measures of the money supply was quite low. One interpretation of these events is that the Fed was unaware of the magnitude of the *IS* shocks. When the Fed saw falling interest rates, it might have misinterpreted this as evidence of expansionary shifts in the *LM* curve rather than contractionary shifts in the *IS* curve. Because data on income are available only after a lag, and because income responds to monetary policy with a lag, the Fed would have learned of its mistake after it was too late to prevent the recession.

The 1990 recession shows some of the difficulties in short-run stabilization policy. There are many sources of shocks to the economy, and the magnitudes of the shocks are not easily observed. Because policymakers can recognize and offset the shocks only after a substantial lag, their ability to stabilize the economy is limited.

The Difficult Job of Economic Forecasting

Because policy influences the economy only after a substantial lag, successful stabilization policy requires the ability to predict accurately future economic conditions. If we cannot predict whether the economy will be in a boom or a recession in six months or a year, we cannot evaluate whether monetary and fiscal policy should now be trying to expand or contract aggregate demand. Unfortunately, economic developments are often unpredictable, at least given our current understanding of the economy.

One way forecasters try to look ahead is with **leading indicators.** A leading indicator is a data series that usually fluctuates in advance of the economy. A large fall in a leading indicator signals that a recession is more likely.

Another way forecasters look ahead is with macroeconometric models, which have been developed both by government agencies and by private firms for forecasting and policy analysis. As we discussed in Chapter 11, these large-scale computer models are made up of many equations, each representing a part of the economy. After making assumptions about the path of the exogenous variables, such as monetary

"It's true, Caesar. Rome is declining, but I expect it to pick up in the next quarter."

Drawing by Dana Fradon; © 1988 The New Yorker Magazine, Inc.

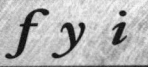

WHAT'S IN THE INDEX OF LEADING ECONOMIC INDICATORS?

Each month the Conference Board, a private economics research group, announces the *index of leading economic indicators*. This index is made up from 11 data series that are often used to forecast changes in economic activity about six to nine months ahead. Here is a list of the 11 series. Can you explain why each of these might help predict changes in real GDP?

1. Average workweek of production workers in manufacturing.

2. Average initial weekly claims for state unemployment insurance. This series is inverted in computing the index, so that a decrease in the series raises the index.

3. New orders for consumer goods and materials, adjusted for inflation.

4. Vendor performance. This is a measure of the number of companies receiving slower deliveries from suppliers.

5. Contracts and orders for plant and equipment, adjusted for inflation.

6. New building permits issued.

7. Change in manufacturers' unfilled orders.

8. Change in sensitive materials prices.

9. Index of stock prices.

10. Money supply (*M2*), adjusted for inflation.

11. Index of consumer expectations.

---

policy, fiscal policy, and oil prices, these models yield predictions about unemployment, inflation, and other endogenous variables. Keep in mind, however, that the validity of these predictions is only as good as the model and the forecasters' assumptions about the exogenous variables.

CASE STUDY

Mistakes in Forecasting

"Light showers, bright intervals, and moderate winds." This was the forecast offered by the renowned British national weather service on October 14, 1987. The next day Britain was hit by the worst storm in over two centuries.

Like weather forecasts, economic forecasts are a crucial input to private and public decisionmaking. Business executives rely on economic forecasts when deciding how much to produce and how much to invest in plant and equipment. Government policymakers also rely on them when developing economic policies. Yet also like weather forecasts, economic forecasts are far from precise.

The most severe economic downturn in U.S. history, the Great Depression of the 1930s, caught economic forecasters completely by surprise. Even after the stock market crash of 1929, they remained confident that the economy would not suffer a substantial setback. In late 1931, when the economy was clearly in bad shape, the eminent economist Irving Fisher predicted that it would recover quickly. Subsequent events showed that these forecasts were much too optimistic.[1]

Figure 14-1 shows how economic forecasters did during the recession of 1982, the most severe economic downturn in the United States since the Great

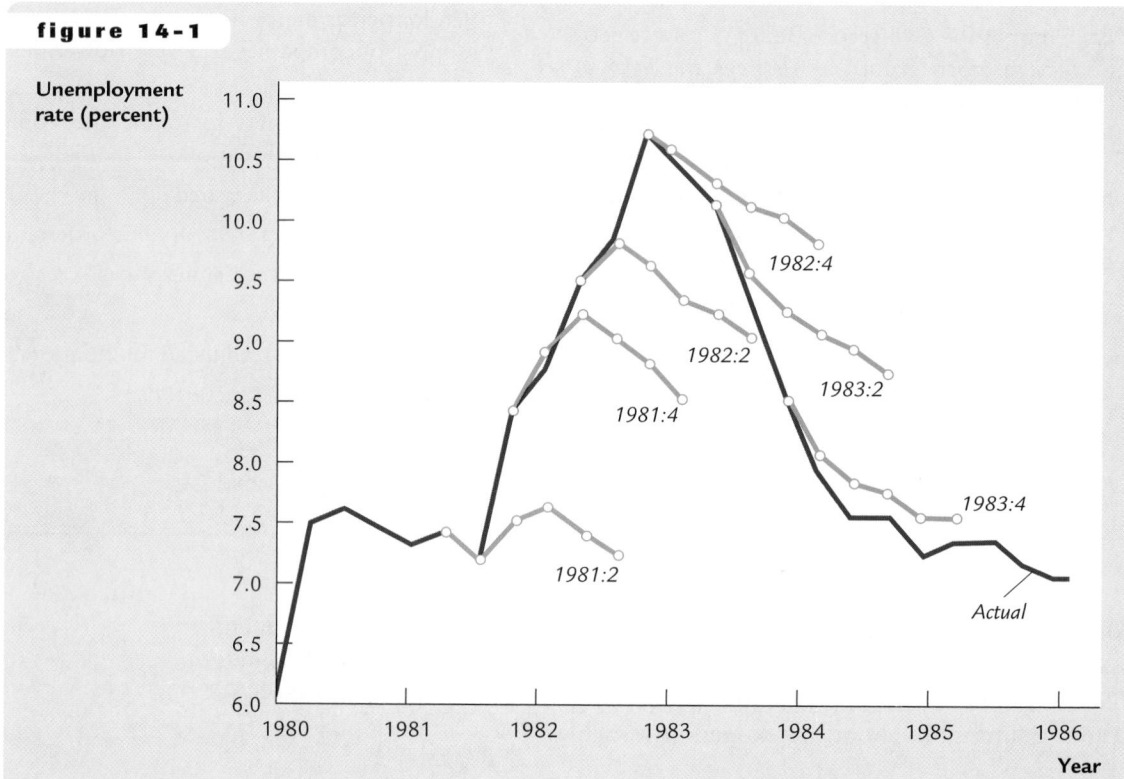

figure 14-1

Forecasting the Recession of 1982 The red line shows the actual unemployment rate from the first quarter of 1980 to the first quarter of 1986. The green lines show the unemployment rate predicted at six points in time: the second quarter of 1981, the fourth quarter of 1981, the second quarter of 1982, and so on. For each forecast, the symbols mark the current unemployment rate and the forecast for the subsequent five quarters. Notice that the forecasters failed to predict both the rapid rise in the unemployment rate and the subsequent rapid decline.

Source: The unemployment rate is from the Department of Commerce. The predicted unemployment rate is the median forecast of about 20 forecasters surveyed by the American Statistical Association and the National Bureau of Economic Research.

---

[1] Kathryn M. Dominguez, Ray C. Fair, and Matthew D. Shapiro, "Forecasting the Depression: Harvard Versus Yale," *American Economic Review* 78 (September 1988): 595–612. This article shows how badly economic forecasters did during the Great Depression, and it argues that they could not have done any better with the modern forecasting techniques available today.

Depression. This figure shows the actual unemployment rate (in red) and six attempts to predict it for the following five quarters (in green). You can see that the forecasters did well predicting unemployment one quarter ahead. The more distant forecasts, however, were often inaccurate. For example, in the second quarter of 1981, forecasters were predicting little change in the unemployment rate over the next five quarters; yet only two quarters later unemployment began to rise sharply. The rise in unemployment to almost 11 percent in the fourth quarter of 1982 caught the forecasters by surprise. After the depth of the recession became apparent, the forecasters failed to predict how rapid the subsequent decline in unemployment would be.

These two episodes—the Great Depression and the recession of 1982—show that many of the most dramatic economic events are unpredictable. Although private and public decisionmakers have little choice but to rely on economic forecasts, they must always keep in mind that these forecasts come with a large margin of error.

Ignorance, Expectations, and the Lucas Critique

The prominent economist Robert Lucas once wrote, "As an advice-giving profession we are in way over our heads." Even many of those who advise policymakers would agree with this assessment. Economics is a young science, and there is still much that we do not know. Economists cannot be completely confident when they assess the effects of alternative policies. This ignorance suggests that economists should be cautious when offering policy advice.

Although there are many topics about which economists' knowledge is limited, Lucas has emphasized the issue of how people form expectations of the future. Expectations play a crucial role in the economy because they influence all sorts of economic behavior. For instance, households decide how much to consume based on expectations of future income, and firms decide how much to invest based on expectations of future profitability. These expectations depend on many things, including the economic policies being pursued by the government. Thus, when policymakers estimate the effect of any policy change, they need to know how people's expectations will respond to the policy change. Lucas has argued that traditional methods of policy evaluation—such as those that rely on standard macroeconometric models—do not adequately take into account this impact of policy on expectations. This criticism of traditional policy evaluation is known as the **Lucas critique**.[2]

---

[2] Robert E. Lucas, Jr., "Econometric Policy Evaluation: A Critique," *Carnegie Rochester Conference on Public Policy* 1 (Amsterdam: North-Holland, 1976), 19–46.

An important example of the Lucas critique arises in the analysis of disinflation. As you may recall from Chapter 13, the cost of reducing inflation is often measured by the sacrifice ratio, which is the number of percentage points of GDP that must be forgone to reduce inflation by 1 percentage point. Because these estimates of the sacrifice ratio are often large, they have led some economists to argue that policymakers should learn to live with inflation, rather than incurring the large cost of reducing it.

According to advocates of the rational-expectations approach, however, these estimates of the sacrifice ratio are unreliable because they are subject to the Lucas critique. Traditional estimates of the sacrifice ratio are based on adaptive expectations, that is, on the assumption that expected inflation depends on past inflation. Adaptive expectations may be a reasonable premise in some circumstances, but if the policymakers make a credible change in policy, workers and firms setting wages and prices will rationally respond by adjusting their expectations of inflation appropriately. This change in inflation expectations will quickly alter the short-run tradeoff between inflation and unemployment. As a result, reducing inflation can potentially be much less costly than is suggested by traditional estimates of the sacrifice ratio.

The Lucas critique leaves us with two lessons. The more narrow lesson is that economists evaluating alternative policies need to consider how policy affects expectations and, thereby, behavior. The broader lesson is that policy evaluation is hard, so economists engaged in this task should be sure to show the requisite humility.

The Historical Record

In judging whether government policy should play an active or passive role in the economy, we must give some weight to the historical record. If the economy has experienced many large shocks to aggregate supply and aggregate demand, and if policy has successfully insulated the economy from these shocks, then the case for active policy should be clear. Conversely, if the economy has experienced few large shocks, and if the fluctuations we have observed can be traced to inept economic policy, then the case for passive policy should be clear. In other words, our view of stabilization policy should be influenced by whether policy has historically been stabilizing or destabilizing. For this reason, the debate over macroeconomic policy frequently turns into a debate over macroeconomic history.

Yet history does not settle the debate over stabilization policy. Disagreements over history arise because it is not easy to identify the sources of economic fluctuations. The historical record often permits more than one interpretation.

The Great Depression is a case in point. Economists' views on macroeconomic policy are often related to their views on the cause of the Depression. Some economists believe that a large contractionary shock to private spending caused the Depression. They assert that policymakers should have responded by stimulating aggregate demand. Other economists believe that the large fall in the money supply caused the Depression. They assert that the Depression would have been avoided if the Fed had been pursuing a passive monetary policy of increasing the money supply at a steady rate. Hence, depending on one's beliefs about its cause, the Great Depression can be viewed either as an example of why active monetary and fiscal policy is necessary or as an example of why it is dangerous.

CASE STUDY

Is the Stabilization of the Economy a Figment of the Data?

Keynes wrote *The General Theory* in the 1930s, and in the wake of the Keynesian revolution, governments around the world began to view economic stabilization as a primary responsibility. Some economists believe that the development of Keynesian theory has had a profound influence on the behavior of the economy. Comparing data from before World War I and after World War II, they find that real GDP and unemployment have become much more stable. This, some Keynesians claim, is the best argument for active stabilization policy: it has worked.

In a series of provocative and influential papers, economist Christina Romer has challenged this assessment of the historical record. She argues that the measured reduction in volatility reflects not an improvement in economic policy and performance but rather an improvement in the economic data. The older data are much less accurate than the newer data. Romer claims that the higher volatility of unemployment and real GDP reported for the period before World War I is largely a figment of the data.

Romer uses various techniques to make her case. One is to construct more accurate data for the earlier period. This task is difficult because data sources are not readily available. A second way is to construct *less* accurate data for the recent period—that is, data that are comparable to the older data and thus suffer from the same imperfections. After constructing new "bad" data, Romer finds that the recent period appears almost as volatile as the early period, suggesting that the volatility of the early period may be largely an artifact of data construction.

Romer's work is an important part of the continuing debate over whether macroeconomic policy has improved the performance of the economy. Although her work remains controversial, most economists now believe that the economy is only slightly more stable than it was in the past.[3]

---

[3] Christina D. Romer, "Spurious Volatility in Historical Unemployment Data," *Journal of Political Economy* 94 (February 1986): 1–37; Christina D. Romer, "Is the Stabilization of the Postwar Economy a Figment of the Data?" *American Economic Review* 76 (June 1986): 314–334.

14-2 | Should Policy Be Conducted by Rule or by Discretion?

A second topic of debate among economists is whether economic policy should be conducted by rule or by discretion. Policy is conducted by rule if policymakers announce in advance how policy will respond to various situations and commit themselves to following through on this announcement. Policy is conducted by discretion if policymakers are free to size up events as they occur and choose whatever policy seems appropriate at the time.

The debate over rules versus discretion is distinct from the debate over passive versus active policy. Policy can be conducted by rule and yet be either passive or active. For example, a passive policy rule might specify steady growth in the money supply of 3 percent per year. An active policy rule might specify that

$$\text{Money Growth} = 3\% + (\text{Unemployment Rate} - 6\%).$$

Under this rule, the money supply grows at 3 percent if the unemployment rate is 6 percent, but for every percentage point by which the unemployment rate exceeds 6 percent, money growth increases by an extra percentage point. This rule tries to stabilize the economy by raising money growth when the economy is in a recession.

We begin this section by discussing why policy might be improved by a commitment to a policy rule. We then examine several possible policy rules.

Distrust of Policymakers and the Political Process

Some economists believe that economic policy is too important to be left to the discretion of policymakers. Although this view is more political than economic, evaluating it is central to how we judge the role of economic policy. If politicians are incompetent or opportunistic, then we may not want to give them the discretion to use the powerful tools of monetary and fiscal policy.

Incompetence in economic policy arises for several reasons. Some economists view the political process as erratic, perhaps because it reflects the shifting power of special interest groups. In addition, macroeconomics is complicated, and politicians often do not have sufficient knowledge of it to make informed judgments. This ignorance allows charlatans to propose incorrect but superficially appealing solutions to complex problems. The political process often cannot weed out the advice of charlatans from that of competent economists.

Opportunism in economic policy arises when the objectives of policymakers conflict with the well-being of the public. Some economists fear that politicians use macroeconomic policy to further their own electoral ends. If citizens vote on the basis of economic conditions prevailing at the time of the election, then politicians have an incentive to pursue policies that will make the economy look good during election years. A president might cause a recession soon after coming into office to lower inflation and then stimulate the economy as the next election approaches to lower unemployment; this would ensure that both inflation and unemployment are low on election day. Manipulation of the economy for electoral gain, called the **political business cycle,** has been the subject of extensive research by economists and political scientists.[4]

Distrust of the political process leads some economists to advocate placing economic policy outside the realm of politics. Some have proposed constitutional amendments, such as a balanced-budget amendment, that would tie the hands of legislators and insulate the economy from both incompetence and opportunism.

CASE STUDY

The Economy Under Republican and Democratic Presidents

How does the political party in power affect the economy? Researchers working at the boundary between economics and political science have been studying this question. One intriguing finding is that the two political parties in the United States appear to conduct systematically different macroeconomic policies.

Table 14-1 presents the growth in real GDP in each of the four years of the presidential terms since 1948. Notice that growth is usually low, and often negative, in the second year of Republican administrations. Six of the eight years in which real GDP fell are second or third years of Republican administrations. By contrast, the economy is usually booming in the second and third years of Democratic administrations.

One interpretation of this finding is that the two parties have different preferences regarding inflation and unemployment. That is, rather than viewing politicians as opportunistic, perhaps we should view them as merely partisan. Republicans seem to dislike inflation more than Democrats do. Therefore, Republicans pursue contractionary policies soon after coming into office and are willing to endure a recession to reduce inflation. Democrats pursue more expansionary policies to reduce unemployment and are willing to endure the higher inflation that results. Examining growth in the money supply shows that monetary policy is, in fact, less inflationary during Republican administrations. Thus, it seems that the two political parties pursue dramatically different policies, and that the political process is one source of economic fluctuations.

Even if we accept this interpretation of the evidence, it is not clear whether it argues for or against fixed policy rules. On the one hand, a policy rule would insulate the economy from these political shocks. Under a fixed rule, the Fed would be unable to alter monetary policy in response to the changing political

---

[4] William Nordhaus, "The Political Business Cycle," *Review of Economic Studies* 42 (1975): 169–190; Edward Tufte, *Political Control of the Economy* (Princeton, NJ: Princeton University Press, 1978).

table 14-1

Real GDP Growth During Democratic and Republican Administrations

President	YEAR OF TERM			
	First	Second	Third	Fourth
Democratic Administrations				
Truman	−0.8	8.9	7.6	3.7
Kennedy/Johnson	2.3	6.1	4.3	5.8
Johnson	6.4	6.5	2.5	4.7
Carter	4.7	5.4	2.8	−0.3
Clinton I	2.3	3.5	2.3	3.4
Clinton II	3.9			
Average	3.1	6.1	3.9	3.5
Republican Administrations				
Eisenhower I	4.6	−0.7	7.1	2.0
Eisenhower II	1.9	−1.0	7.4	2.4
Nixon	3.0	0.1	3.3	5.5
Nixon/Ford	5.8	−0.6	−0.4	5.4
Reagan I	2.3	−2.1	4.0	7.0
Reagan II	3.6	3.1	2.9	3.8
Bush	3.4	1.2	−0.9	2.7
Average	3.5	0.0	3.3	4.1

Source: Department of Commerce

climate. The economy might be more stable, and long-run economic performance might be improved. On the other hand, a fixed policy rule would reduce the voice of the electorate in influencing macroeconomic policy.[5]

The Time Inconsistency of Discretionary Policy

If we assume that we can trust our policymakers, discretion at first glance appears superior to a fixed policy rule. Discretionary policy is, by its nature, flexible. As long as policymakers are intelligent and benevolent, there might appear to be little reason to deny them flexibility in responding to changing conditions.

Yet a case for rules over discretion arises from the problem of **time inconsistency** of policy. In some situations policymakers may want to announce in advance the policy they will follow in order to influence the expectations of

[5]Alberto Alesina, "Macroeconomics and Politics," *NBER Macroeconomics Annual* 3 (1988): 13–52.

private decisionmakers. But later, after the private decisionmakers have acted on the basis of their expectations, these policymakers may be tempted to renege on their announcement. Understanding that policymakers may be inconsistent over time, private decisionmakers are led to distrust policy announcements. In this situation, to make their announcements credible, policymakers may want to make a commitment to a fixed policy rule.

Time inconsistency is illustrated most simply in a political rather than an economic example—specifically, public policy about negotiating with terrorists over the release of hostages. The announced policy of many nations is that they will not negotiate over hostages. Such an announcement is intended to deter terrorists: if there is nothing to be gained from kidnapping hostages, rational terrorists won't kidnap any. In other words, the purpose of the announcement is to influence the expectations of terrorists and thereby their behavior.

But, in fact, unless the policymakers are credibly committed to the policy, the announcement has little effect. Terrorists know that once hostages are taken, policymakers face an overwhelming temptation to make some concession to obtain the hostages' release. The only way to deter rational terrorists is to take away the discretion of policymakers and commit them to a rule of never negotiating. If policymakers were truly unable to make concessions, the incentive for terrorists to take hostages would be largely eliminated.

The same problem arises less dramatically in the conduct of monetary policy. Consider the dilemma of a Federal Reserve that cares about both inflation and unemployment. According to the Phillips curve, the tradeoff between inflation and unemployment depends on expected inflation. The Fed would prefer everyone to expect low inflation so that it will face a favorable tradeoff. To reduce expected inflation, the Fed might announce that low inflation is the paramount goal of monetary policy.

But an announcement of a policy of low inflation is by itself not credible. Once households and firms have formed their expectations of inflation and set wages and prices accordingly, the Fed has an incentive to renege on its announcement and implement expansionary monetary policy to reduce unemployment. People understand the Fed's incentive to renege and therefore do not believe the announcement in the first place. Just as a president facing a hostage crisis is sorely tempted to negotiate their release, a Federal Reserve with discretion is sorely tempted to inflate in order to reduce unemployment. And just as terrorists discount announced policies of never negotiating, households and firms discount announced policies of low inflation.

The surprising outcome of this analysis is that policymakers can sometimes better achieve their goals by having their discretion taken away from them. In the case of rational terrorists, fewer hostages will be taken and killed if policymakers are committed to following the seemingly harsh rule of refusing to negotiate for hostages' freedom. In the case of monetary policy, there will be lower inflation without higher unemployment if the Fed is committed to a policy of zero inflation. (This conclusion about monetary policy is modeled more explicitly in the appendix to this chapter.)

The time inconsistency of policy arises in many other contexts. Here are some examples:

➤ To encourage investment, the government announces that it will not tax income from capital. But after factories have been built, the government is tempted to renege on its promise to raise more tax revenue from them.

➤ To encourage research, the government announces that it will give a temporary monopoly to companies that discover new drugs. But after a drug has been discovered, the government is tempted to revoke the patent or to regulate the price to make the drug more affordable.

➤ To encourage good behavior, a parent announces that he or she will punish a child whenever the child breaks a rule. But after the child has misbehaved, the parent is tempted to forgive this transgression, because punishment is unpleasant for the parent as well as for the child.

➤ To encourage you to work hard, your professor announces that this course will end with an exam. But after you have studied and learned all the material, the professor is tempted to cancel the exam so that he or she won't have to grade it.

In each case, rational agents understand the incentive for the policymaker to renege, and this expectation affects their behavior. And in each case, the solution is to take away the policymaker's discretion with a credible commitment to a fixed policy rule.

CASE STUDY

Alexander Hamilton Versus Time Inconsistency

Time inconsistency has long been a problem associated with discretionary policy. In fact, it was one of the first problems that confronted Alexander Hamilton when President George Washington appointed him the first U.S. Secretary of the Treasury in 1789.

Hamilton faced the question of how to deal with the debts that the new nation had accumulated as it fought for its independence from Britain. When the revolutionary government incurred the debts, it promised to honor them when the war was over. But after the war, many Americans advocated defaulting on the debt because repaying the creditors would require taxation, which is always costly and unpopular.

Hamilton opposed the time-inconsistent policy of repudiating the debt. He knew that the nation would likely need to borrow again sometime in the future. In his *First Report on the Public Credit,* which he presented to Congress in 1790, he wrote

If the maintenance of public credit, then, be truly so important, the next inquiry which suggests itself is: By what means is it to be effected? The ready answer to which question is, by good faith; by a punctual performance of contracts. States, like individuals, who observe their engagements are respected and trusted, while the reverse is the fate of those who pursue an opposite conduct.

Thus, Hamilton proposed that the nation make a commitment to the policy rule of honoring its debts.

The policy rule that Hamilton originally proposed has continued for over two centuries. Today, unlike in Hamilton's time, when Congress debates spending priorities, no one seriously proposes defaulting on the public debt as a way to reduce taxes. In the case of public debt, everyone now agrees that the government should be committed to a fixed policy rule.

Rules for Monetary Policy

Even if we are convinced that policy rules are superior to discretion, the debate over macroeconomic policy is not over. If the Fed were to commit to a rule for monetary policy, what rule should it choose? Let's discuss briefly three policy rules that various economists advocate.

Some economists, called **monetarists,** advocate that the Fed keep the money supply growing at a steady rate. The quotation at the beginning of this chapter from Milton Friedman—the most famous monetarist—exemplifies this view of monetary policy. Monetarists believe that fluctuations in the money supply are responsible for most large fluctuations in the economy. They argue that slow and steady growth in the money supply would yield stable output, employment, and prices.

Although a monetarist policy rule might have prevented many of the economic fluctuations we have experienced historically, most economists believe that it is not the best possible policy rule. Steady growth in the money supply stabilizes aggregate demand only if the velocity of money is stable. But sometimes the economy experiences shocks, such as shifts in money demand, that cause velocity to be unstable. Most economists believe that a policy rule needs to allow the money supply to adjust to various shocks to the economy.

A second policy rule that economists widely advocate is nominal GDP targeting. Under this rule, the Fed announces a planned path for nominal GDP. If nominal GDP rises above the target, the Fed reduces money growth to dampen aggregate demand. If it falls below the target, the Fed raises money growth to stimulate aggregate demand. Since a nominal GDP target allows monetary policy to adjust to changes in the velocity of money, most economists believe it would lead to greater stability in output and prices than a monetarist policy rule.

A third policy rule that is often advocated is inflation targeting. Under this rule, the Fed would announce a target for the inflation rate (usually a low one) and then adjust the money supply when the actual inflation deviates from the target. Like nominal GDP targeting, inflation targeting insulates the economy from changes in the velocity of money. In addition, an inflation target has the political advantage that it is easy to explain to the public.

Notice that all these rules are expressed in terms of some nominal variable— the money supply, nominal GDP, or the price level. One can also imagine policy rules expressed in terms of real variables. For example, the Fed might try to target the unemployment rate at 5 percent. The problem with such a rule is that no one knows exactly what the natural rate of unemployment is. If the Fed chose a target for the unemployment rate below the natural rate, the result would be accelerating inflation. Conversely, if the Fed chose a target for the unemployment rate above the natural rate, the result would be accelerating deflation. For this reason, economists rarely advocate rules for monetary policy expressed solely in terms of real variables, even though real variables such as unemployment and real GDP are the best measures of economic performance.

CASE STUDY

Inflation Targeting: Rule or Constrained Discretion?

Throughout the 1990s, many of the world's central banks—including those of Australia, Canada, Finland, Israel, New Zealand, Spain, Sweden, and the United Kingdom—have adopted some form of an inflation target. Sometimes inflation targeting takes the form of a central bank announcing its policy intentions. Other times it takes the form of a national law that spells out the goals of monetary policy. For example, the Reserve Bank of New Zealand Act of 1989 told the central bank "to formulate and implement monetary policy directed to the economic objective of achieving and maintaining stability in the general level of prices." The act conspicuously omitted any mention of any other competing objective, such as stability in output, employment, interest rates, or exchange rates. Although the U.S. Federal Reserve has not adopted inflation targeting, some members of Congress have proposed bills that would require the Fed to do so.

Should we interpret inflation targeting as a type of precommitment to a policy rule? Not completely. In all the countries that have adopted inflation targeting, central banks are left are with a fair amount of discretion. Inflation targets are usually set as a range—an inflation rate of 1 to 3 percent, for instance—rather than a particular number. Thus, the central bank can choose where in the range it wants to be. In addition, the central banks are sometimes allowed to adjust their targets for inflation, at least temporarily, if some exogenous event (such as an easily identified supply shock) pushes inflation outside of the range that was previously announced.

In light of this flexibility, what is the purpose of inflation targeting? Although inflation targeting does leave the central bank with some discretion, the policy does constrain how this discretion is used. When a central bank is told to "do the right thing," it is hard to hold the central bank accountable, for people can argue forever about what the right thing is in any specific circumstance. By contrast, when a central bank has announced an inflation target, the public can more easily judge whether the central bank is meeting that target. Thus, although inflation targeting does not tie the hands of the central bank, it does increase the transparency of monetary policy and, by doing so, makes central bankers more accountable for their actions.[6]

---

[6] See Ben S. Bernanke and Frederic S. Mishkin, "Inflation Targeting: A New Framework for Monetary Policy?" *Journal of Economic Perspectives* 11 (Spring 1997): 97–116.

CASE STUDY

Central-Bank Independence

Suppose you were put in charge of writing the constitution and laws for a country. Would you give the president of the country authority over the policies of the central bank? Or would you allow the central bank to make decisions free from such political influence? In other words, assuming that monetary policy is made by discretion rather than by rule, who should exercise that discretion?

Countries vary greatly in how they choose to answer this question. In some countries, the central bank is a branch of the government; in others, the central bank is largely independent. In the United States, Fed governors are appointed by the president for 14-year terms, and they cannot be recalled if the president is unhappy with their decisions. This institutional structure gives the Fed a degree of independence similar to that of the Supreme Court.

Many researchers have investigated the effects of constitutional design on monetary policy. They have examined the laws of different countries to construct an index of central-bank independence. This index is based on various characteristics, such as the length of bankers' terms, the role of government officials on the bank board, and the frequency of contact between the government and the central bank. The researchers have then examined the correlation between central-bank independence and macroeconomic performance.

The results of these studies are striking: more independent central banks are strongly associated with lower and more stable inflation. Figure 14-2 shows a scatterplot of central-bank independence and average inflation for the period 1955 to 1988. Countries that had an independent central bank, such as Germany, Switzerland, and the United States, tended to have low average inflation. Countries that had central banks with less independence, such as New Zealand and Spain, tended to have higher average inflation.

Researchers have also found there is no relationship between central-bank independence and real economic activity. In particular, central-bank independence is not correlated with average unemployment, the volatility of unemployment, the average growth of real GDP, or the volatility of real GDP. Central-bank independence appears to offer countries a free lunch: it has the benefit of lower inflation without any apparent cost. This finding has led some countries, such as New Zealand, to rewrite their laws to give their central banks greater independence.[7]

---

[7] For a more complete presentation of these findings and references to the large literature on central-bank independence, see Alberto Alesina and Lawrence H. Summers, "Central Bank Independence and Macroeconomic Performance: Some Comparative Evidence," *Journal of Money, Credit, and Banking* 25 (May 1993): 151–162. For a study that questions the link between inflation and central-bank independence, see Marta Campillo and Jeffrey A. Miron, "Why Does Inflation Differ Across Countries?" in Christina D. Romer and David H. Romer, eds., *Reducing Inflation: Motivation and Strategy* (Chicago: University of Chicago Press, 1997): 335–362.

figure 14-2

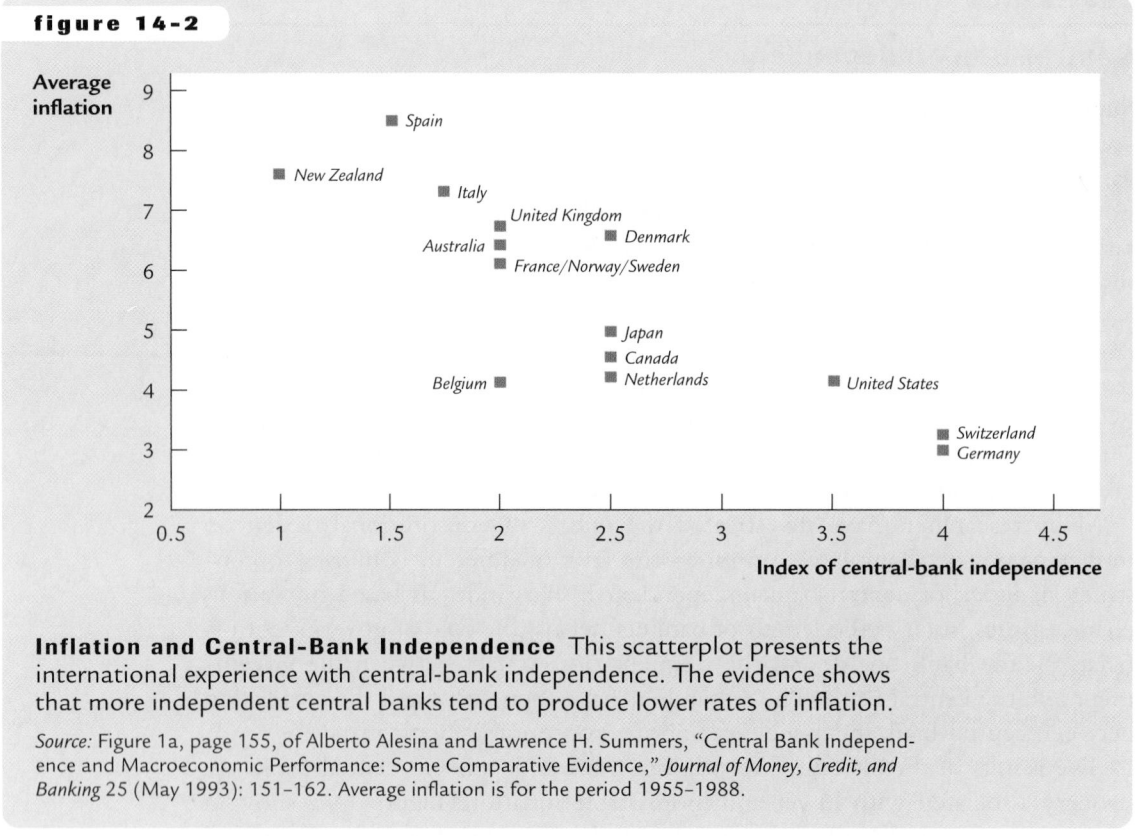

Inflation and Central-Bank Independence This scatterplot presents the international experience with central-bank independence. The evidence shows that more independent central banks tend to produce lower rates of inflation.

Source: Figure 1a, page 155, of Alberto Alesina and Lawrence H. Summers, "Central Bank Independence and Macroeconomic Performance: Some Comparative Evidence," *Journal of Money, Credit, and Banking* 25 (May 1993): 151–162. Average inflation is for the period 1955–1988.

Rules for Fiscal Policy

Although most discussion of policy rules centers on monetary policy, economists and politicians also frequently propose rules for fiscal policy. The rule that has received the most attention is the balanced-budget rule. Under a balanced-budget rule, the government would not be allowed to spend more than it receives in tax revenue. In the United States, many state governments operate under such a fiscal policy rule, since state constitutions often require a balanced budget. A recurring topic of political debate is whether the federal constitution should require a balanced budget for the federal government.

Most economists oppose a strict rule requiring the government to balance its budget. There are three reasons to believe that a budget deficit or surplus is sometimes appropriate.

First, a budget deficit or surplus can help stabilize the economy. In essence, a balanced-budget rule would revoke the automatic stabilizing powers of the system of taxes and transfers. When the economy goes into a recession, taxes automatically fall, and transfers automatically rise. While these automatic responses help stabilize the economy, they push the budget into deficit. A strict balanced–budget rule would require that the government raise taxes or reduce spending in a recession, but these actions would further depress aggregate demand.

Second, a budget deficit or surplus can be used to reduce the distortion of incentives caused by the tax system. As you probably learned in courses in microeconomics, high tax rates impose a cost on society by discouraging economic activity. A tax on labor earnings, for instance, reduces the incentive that people have to work long hours. Because this disincentive becomes particularly large at very high tax rates, the total social cost of taxes is minimized by keeping tax rates relatively stable rather than making them high in some years and low in others. Economists call this policy *tax smoothing*. To keep tax rates smooth, a deficit is necessary in years of unusually low income (recessions) or unusually high expenditure (wars).

Third, a budget deficit can be used to shift a tax burden from current to future generations. For example, some economists argue that if the current generation fights a war to maintain freedom, future generations benefit as well and should bear some of the burden. To pass on some of the war's costs, the current generation can finance the war with a budget deficit. The government can later retire the debt by levying taxes on the next generation.

These considerations lead most economists to reject a strict balanced-budget rule. At the very least, a rule for fiscal policy needs to take account of the recurring episodes, such as recessions and wars, during which a budget deficit is a reasonable policy response.

14-3 | Conclusion: Making Policy in an Uncertain World

In this chapter we have examined whether policy should take an active or passive role in responding to economic fluctuations and whether policy should be conducted by rule or by discretion. There are many arguments on both sides of these questions. Perhaps the only clear conclusion is that there is no simple and compelling case for any particular view of macroeconomic policy. In the end, you must weigh the various arguments, both economic and political, and decide for yourself what kind of role the government should play in trying to stabilize the economy.

For better or worse, economists play a key role in the formulation of economic policy. Because the economy is complex, this role is often difficult. Yet it is also inevitable. Economists cannot sit back and wait until our knowledge of the economy has been perfected before giving advice. In the meantime, someone must advise economic policymakers. That job, difficult as it sometimes is, falls to economists.

The role of economists in the policymaking process goes beyond giving advice to policymakers. Even economists cloistered in academia influence policy indirectly through their research and writing. In the conclusion of *The General Theory,* John Maynard Keynes wrote that

> the ideas of economists and political philosophers, both when they are right and when they are wrong, are more powerful than is commonly understood. Indeed, the world is ruled by little else. Practical men, who believe themselves to be quite exempt from intellectual influences, are usually the slaves of some defunct economist. Madmen in authority, who hear voices in the air, are distilling their frenzy from some academic scribbler of a few years back.

This is as true today as it was when Keynes wrote it in 1936—except now that academic scribbler is often Keynes himself.

Summary

1. Advocates of active policy view the economy as subject to frequent shocks that will lead to unnecessary fluctuations in output and employment unless monetary or fiscal policy responds. Many believe that economic policy has been successful in stabilizing the economy.

2. Advocates of passive policy argue that because monetary and fiscal policies work with long and variable lags, attempts to stabilize the economy are likely to end up being destabilizing. In addition, they believe that our present understanding of the economy is too limited to be useful in formulating successful stabilization policy and that inept policy is a frequent source of economic fluctuations.

3. Advocates of discretionary policy argue that discretion gives more flexibility to policymakers in responding to various unforeseen situations.

4. Advocates of policy rules argue that the political process cannot be trusted. They believe that politicians make frequent mistakes in conducting economic policy and sometimes use economic policy for their own political ends. In addition, advocates of policy rules argue that a commitment to a fixed policy rule is necessary to solve the problem of time inconsistency.

KEY CONCEPTS

Inside and outside lags

Automatic stabilizers

Leading indicators

Lucas critique

Political business cycle

Time inconsistency

Monetarists

QUESTIONS FOR REVIEW

1. What are the inside lag and the outside lag? Which has the longer inside lag—monetary or fiscal policy? Which has the longer outside lag? Why?

2. Why would more accurate economic forecasting make it easier for policymakers to stabilize the economy? Describe two ways economists try to forecast developments in the economy.

3. Describe the Lucas critique.

4. How does a person's interpretation of macroeconomic history affect his view of macroeconomic policy?

5. What is meant by the "time inconsistency" of economic policy? Why might policymakers be tempted to renege on an announcement they made earlier? In this situation, what is the advantage of a policy rule?

6. List three policy rules that the Fed might follow. Which of these would you advocate? Why?

7. Give three reasons why requiring a balanced budget might be too restrictive a rule for fiscal policy.

PROBLEMS AND APPLICATIONS

1. Suppose that the tradeoff between unemployment and inflation is determined by the Phillips curve:

$$u = u^n - \alpha(\pi - \pi^e),$$

where u denotes the unemployment rate, u^n the natural rate of unemployment, π the rate of inflation, and π^e the expected rate of inflation. In addition, suppose that the Democratic party always follows a policy of high money growth and the Republican party always follows a policy of low money growth. What "political business cycle" pattern of inflation and unemployment would you predict under the following conditions?

   a. Every four years, one of the parties takes control based on a random flip of a coin. [*Hint:* What will expected inflation be prior to the election?]

   b. The two parties take turns.

2. When cities pass laws limiting the rent landlords can charge on apartments, the laws usually apply to existing buildings and exempt any buildings not yet built. Advocates of rent control argue that this exemption ensures that rent control does not discourage the construction of new housing. Evaluate this argument in light of the time-inconsistency problem.

3. The *cyclically adjusted budget deficit* is the budget deficit corrected for the effects of the business cycle. In other words, it is the budget deficit that the government would be running if unemployment were at the natural rate. (It is also called the *full-employment budget deficit*.) Some economists have proposed the rule that the cyclically adjusted budget deficit always be balanced. Compare this proposal to a strict balanced-budget rule. Which is preferable? What problems do you see with the rule requiring a balanced cyclically adjusted budget?

Time Inconsistency and the Tradeoff Between Inflation and Unemployment

In this appendix, we examine more analytically the time-inconsistency argument for rules rather than discretion. This material is relegated to an appendix because we will need to use some calculus.[8]

Suppose that the Phillips curve describes the relationship between inflation and unemployment. Letting u denote the unemployment rate, u^n the natural rate of unemployment, π the rate of inflation, and π^e the expected rate of inflation, unemployment is determined by

$$u = u^n - \alpha(\pi - \pi^e).$$

Unemployment is low when inflation exceeds expected inflation and high when inflation falls below expected inflation.

For simplicity, suppose also that the Fed chooses the rate of inflation. Of course, more realistically, the Fed controls inflation only imperfectly through its control of the money supply. But for the purposes of illustration, it is useful to assume that the Fed can control inflation perfectly.

The Fed likes low unemployment and low inflation. Suppose that the cost of unemployment and inflation, as perceived by the Fed, can be represented as

$$L(u, \pi) = u + \gamma\pi^2,$$

where the parameter γ represents how much the Fed dislikes inflation relative to unemployment. $L(u, \pi)$ is called the *loss function*. The Fed's objective is to make the loss as small as possible.

Having specified how the economy works and the Fed's objective, let's compare monetary policy made under a fixed rule and under discretion.

First, consider policy under a fixed rule. A rule commits the Fed to a particular level of inflation. As long as private agents understand that the Fed is committed to this rule, the expected level of inflation will be the level the Fed is committed to produce. Since expected inflation equals actual inflation ($\pi^e = \pi$), unemployment will be at its natural rate ($u = u^n$).

What is the optimal rule? Since unemployment is at its natural rate regardless of the level of inflation legislated by the rule, there is no benefit to having any

---

[8] The material in this appendix is derived from Finn E. Kydland and Edward C. Prescott, "Rules Rather Than Discretion: The Inconsistency of Optimal Plans," *Journal of Political Economy* 85 (June 1977): 473–492; and Robert J. Barro and David Gordon, "A Positive Theory of Monetary Policy in a Natural Rate Model," *Journal of Political Economy* 91 (August 1983): 589–610.

inflation at all. Therefore, the optimal fixed rule requires that the Fed produce zero inflation.

Second, consider discretionary monetary policy. Under discretion, the economy works as follows:

1. Private agents form their expectations of inflation π^e.

2. The Fed chooses the actual level of inflation π.

3. Based on expected and actual inflation, unemployment is determined.

Under this arrangement, the Fed minimizes its loss $L(u, \pi)$ subject to the constraint that the Phillips curve imposes. When making its decision about the rate of inflation, the Fed takes expected inflation as already determined.

To find what outcome we would obtain under discretionary policy, we must examine what level of inflation the Fed would choose. By substituting the Phillips curve into the Fed's loss function, we obtain

$$L(u, \pi) = u^n - \alpha(\pi - \pi^e) + \gamma\pi^2.$$

Notice that the Fed's loss is negatively related to unexpected inflation (the second term in the equation) and positively related to actual inflation (the third term). To find the level of inflation that minimizes this loss, differentiate with respect to π to obtain

$$dL/d\pi = -\alpha + 2\gamma\pi.$$

The loss is minimized when this derivative equals zero. Solving for π, we get

$$\pi = \alpha/(2\gamma).$$

Whatever level of inflation private agents expected, this is the "optimal" level of inflation for the Fed to choose. Of course, rational private agents understand the objective of the Fed and the constraint that the Phillips curve imposes. They therefore expect that the Fed will choose this level of inflation. Expected inflation equals actual inflation [$\pi^e = \pi = \alpha/(2\gamma)$], and unemployment equals its natural rate ($u = u^n$).

Now compare the outcome under optimal discretion to the outcome under the optimal rule. In both cases, unemployment is at its natural rate. Yet discretionary policy produces more inflation than does policy under the rule. *Thus, optimal discretion is worse than the optimal rule.* This is true even though the Fed under discretion was attempting to minimize its loss, $L(u, \pi)$.

At first it may seem bizarre that the Fed can achieve a better outcome by being committed to a fixed rule. Why can't the Fed with discretion mimic the Fed committed to a zero-inflation rule? The answer is that the Fed is playing a game against private decisionmakers who have rational expectations. Unless it is committed to a fixed rule of zero inflation, the Fed cannot get private agents to expect zero inflation.

Suppose, for example, that the Fed simply announces that it will follow a zero-inflation policy. Such an announcement by itself cannot be credible. After private agents have formed their expectations of inflation, the Fed has the incentive to renege on its announcement in order to decrease unemployment. (As we have just seen, once expectations are given, the Fed's optimal policy is to set inflation at $\pi = \alpha/(2\gamma)$, regardless of π^e.) Private agents understand the incentive to renege and therefore do not believe the announcement in the first place.

This theory of monetary policy has an important corollary. Under one circumstance, the Fed with discretion achieves the same outcome as the Fed committed to a fixed rule of zero inflation. If the Fed dislikes inflation much more than it dislikes unemployment (so that γ is very large), inflation under discretion is near zero, since the Fed has little incentive to inflate. This finding provides some guidance to those who have the job of appointing central bankers. An alternative to imposing a fixed rule is to appoint an individual with a fervent distaste for inflation. Perhaps this is why even liberal politicians (Jimmy Carter, Bill Clinton) who are more concerned about unemployment than inflation sometimes appoint conservative central bankers (Paul Volcker, Alan Greenspan) who are more concerned about inflation.

MORE PROBLEMS AND APPLICATIONS

1. In the 1970s in the United States, the inflation rate and the natural rate of unemployment both rose. Let's use this model of time inconsistency to examine this phenomenon. Assume that policy is discretionary.

   a. In the model as developed so far, what happens to the inflation rate when the natural rate of unemployment rises?

   b. Let's now change the model slightly by supposing that the Fed's loss function is quadratic in both inflation and unemployment. That is,

   $$L(u, \pi) = u^2 + \gamma\pi^2.$$

   Follow steps similar to those in the text to solve for the inflation rate under discretionary policy.

   c. Now what happens to the inflation rate when the natural rate of unemployment rises?

   d. In 1979, President Jimmy Carter appointed the conservative central banker Paul Volcker to head the Federal Reserve. According to this model, what should have happened to inflation and unemployment?

Government Debt and Budget Deficits

Blessed are the young, for they shall inherit the national debt.

— *Herbert Hoover*

When a government spends more than it collects in taxes, it borrows from the private sector to finance the budget deficit. The accumulation of past borrowing is the government debt. Debate about the appropriate amount of government debt in the United States is as old as the country itself. Alexander Hamilton believed that "a national debt, if it is not excessive, will be to us a national blessing," while James Madison argued that "a public debt is a public curse." Indeed, the location of the nation's capital was chosen as part of a deal in which the federal government assumed the Revolutionary War debts of the states: because the northern states had larger outstanding debts, the capital was located in the South.

Although attention to the national debt has waxed and waned over the years, it has been especially intense during the past two decades. Beginning in the early 1980s, the U.S. federal government began running large budget deficits—in part because of increased spending and in part because of reduced taxes. As a result, the government debt expressed as a percentage of GDP roughly doubled from 26 percent in 1980 to 50 percent in 1995. By the late 1990s, the budget deficit had come under control and had even turned into a budget surplus, but the level of debt remained high.

This large increase in government debt during a period of peace and prosperity is unprecedented in U.S. history. Not surprisingly, it sparked a renewed interest among economists and policymakers in the economic effects of government debt. Some view the large budget deficits of the 1980s and 1990s as the worst mistake of economic policy since the Great Depression, while others think that the deficits matter very little. This chapter considers various facets of this debate.

We begin simply by looking at the numbers. Section 15-1 examines the size of the U.S. government debt, comparing it to the debt of other countries and to the debt that the United States has had during its own past. It also takes a brief look at what the future may hold. Section 15-2 discusses why measuring changes in government indebtedness is not as straightforward as it might seem. Indeed, some economists have argued that traditional measures are so misleading that they should be completely ignored.

We then look at how government debt affects the economy. Section 15-3 describes the traditional view of government debt, according to which government borrowing reduces national saving and crowds out capital accumulation. This view is held by most economists and has been implicit in the discussion of fiscal policy throughout this book. Section 15-4 discusses an alternative view, called *Ricardian equivalence,* which is held by a small but influential minority of economists. According to the Ricardian view, government debt does not influence national saving and capital accumulation. As we will see, the debate between the traditional and Ricardian views of government debt arises from disagreements over how consumers respond to the government's debt policy. Section 15-5 then looks at various other possible effects of government debt, including effects on monetary policy, the political process, and the role of a country in the world economy.

15-1 | The Size of the Government Debt

Let's begin by putting the government debt in perspective. In 1998, the debt of the U.S. federal government was $3.8 trillion. If we divide this number by 270

table 15-1

How Indebted Are the World's Governments?

Country	Government Debt as a Percentage of GDP
Belgium	125%
Italy	123
Greece	103
Canada	94
Japan	93
Sweden	76
Spain	74
Netherlands	73
Austria	73
Ireland	67
Denmark	67
Germany	66
Portugal	65
France	65
United States	65
United Kingdom	60
Finland	59
Australia	40
Norway	34

Source: OECD Economic Outlook. Figures are based on estimates of gross government debt and GDP for 1998.

million, the number of people in the United States, we find that each person's share of the government debt was about $14,000. Obviously, this is not a trivial number—few people sneeze at $14,000. Yet if we compare this debt to the roughly $1 million a typical person will earn over his or her working life, the government debt does not look like the catastrophe it is sometimes made out to be.

One way to judge the size of a government's debt is to compare it to the amount of debt other countries have accumulated. Table 15-1 shows the amount of government debt for 19 major countries expressed as a percentage of each country's GDP. On the top of the list are the heavily indebted countries of Belgium and Italy, who have accumulated a debt that exceeds annual GDP. At the bottom are Norway and Australia, who have accumulated relatively small debts. The United States is in the middle of the pack. By international standards, the U.S. government is neither especially profligate nor especially frugal.

Over the course of U.S. history, the indebtedness of the federal government has varied substantially. Figure 15-1 shows the ratio of the federal debt to GDP

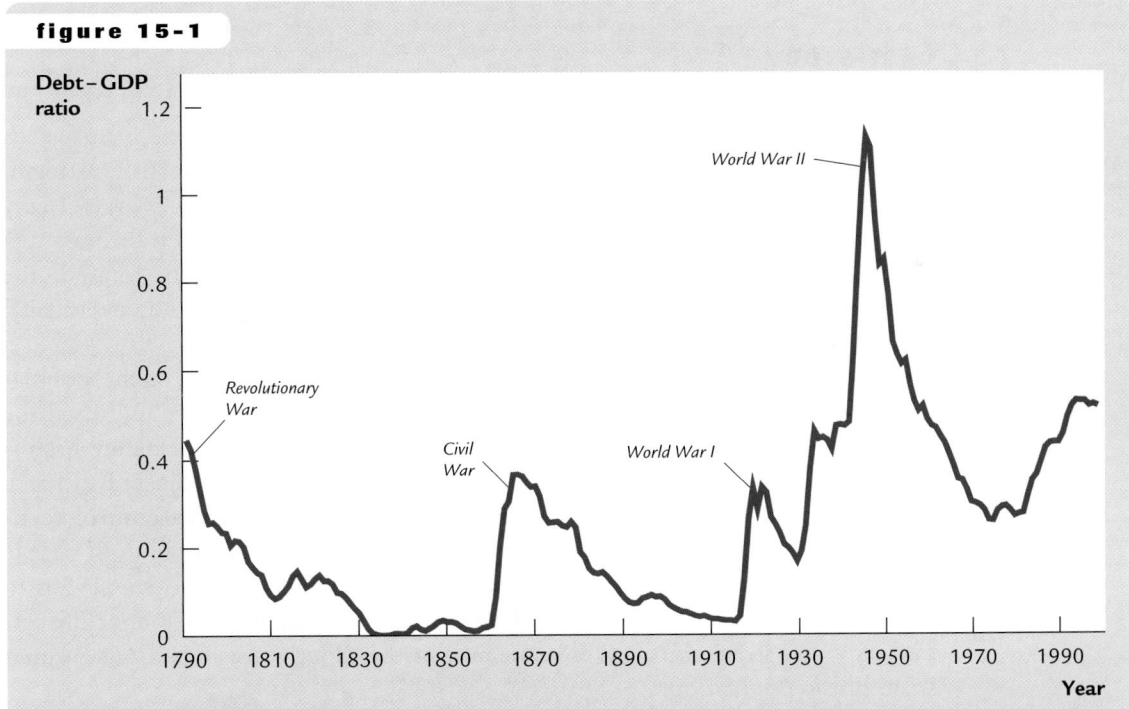

figure 15-1

The Ratio of Government Debt to GDP Since 1790 The U.S. federal government debt held by the public, relative to the size of the U.S. economy, rises sharply during wars and declines slowly during peacetime. The exception is the period since 1980, when the debt–GDP ratio rose without the occurrence of a major military conflict.

Source: U.S. Department of the Treasury, U.S. Department of Commerce, and T.S. Berry, "Production and Population Since 1789," Bostwick Paper No. 6, Richmond, 1988.

since 1790. The government debt, relative to the size of the economy, varies from close to zero in the 1830s to a maximum of 129 percent of GDP in 1946.

Historically, the primary cause of increases in the government debt is war. The debt–GDP ratio rises sharply during major wars and falls slowly during peacetime. Many economists think that this historical pattern is the appropriate way to run fiscal policy. As we discussed in Chapter 14, deficit financing of wars appears optimal for reasons of both tax smoothing and generational equity. The one instance of a large increase in government debt in peacetime occurred during the 1980s and early 1990s, when the federal government ran substantial budget deficits. Many economists have criticized this increase in government debt as imposing a burden on future generations without justification.

During the middle of the 1990s, the U.S. federal government started to get its budget deficit under control. A combination of tax hikes, spending cuts, and rapid economic growth caused the ratio of debt to GDP to stabilize and even decline a bit. Recent experience has tempted some observers to think that exploding government debt is a thing of the past. But as the next case study suggests, the worst may be yet to come.

CASE STUDY

The Fiscal Future

What does the future hold for fiscal policymakers? Economic forecasting is far from precise, but all indicators suggest there is reason to worry. Many economists believe that current policies are not sustainable. They forecast that unless the laws governing taxes and spending are substantially revised, the government's debts will take off over the next half century and, eventually, will spiral out of control.

This projection is based largely on changes in the age profile of the population. Healthier lifestyles and advances in medical technology have increased the length of the average person's life. In the United States, life expectancy has increased from 70 years in 1965 to 75 years in 1990, and it is projected to reach to 78 years in 2010. At the same time, improvements in birth-control techniques and changing social norms have reduced the number of children people have. Birth rates have fallen from about 25 per 1,000 people in the 1950s to about 15 per 1,000 people in the 1990s. These two changes—longer life expectancy and lower birth rates—mean that the elderly are becoming a larger share of the population.

Table 15-2 shows the magnitude of this demographic trend in seven major countries. In the United States in 1990, for instance, there were 21 elderly for every 100 people aged 20 to 64. Yet as the baby-boom generation born in the 1950s retires, the number of elderly will rise to 36 per 100 working-age people by the year 2030. Even more dramatic changes are expected in Germany, Italy, Japan, and Canada, where the relative size of the elderly population will more than double.

table 15-2

The Elderly as a Percentage of the Working-Age Population

Country	1990	2030
Germany	24	54
Italy	24	52
Japan	19	49
Canada	19	44
United Kingdom	27	43
France	23	43
United States	21	36

Source: Long-Term Budgetary Pressures and Policy Options, Congressional Budget Office, May 1998, p. 4. This table shows the number of people age 65 and older expressed as a percentage of the number of people ages 20 to 64.

This aging of the population will have a profound impact on fiscal policy. In most countries, the government provides benefits to the elderly in the form of pensions and health care. In the United States, for instance, Social Security and Medicare already make up about one-third of the budget of the federal government. As more people become eligible for these "entitlements," as they are sometimes called, government spending will rise automatically over time.

Table 15-3 shows what will happen in the United States under current policies, as projected by the Congressional Budget Office (CBO). These projections incorporate not only the CBO's projections of fiscal policy but also the

table 15-3

Fiscal Policy Projections: U.S. Federal Government (All Variables Expressed as a Percentage of GDP)

	YEAR					
	2000	2010	2020	2030	2040	2050
Government receipts	21	20	20	20	20	20
Government expenditure	21	20	22	25	30	43
Budget deficit	0	−1	1	5	10	23
Government debt	42	21	17	40	93	206

Source: Long-Term Budgetary Pressures and Policy Options, Congressional Budget Office, May 1998, p. 20. These projections show what will happen over time if no policy changes are made. They assume that discretionary spending, such as spending on defense, science, the environment, and education, will fall as a percentage of GDP from 6 percent in 1997 to 4 percent in 2008 (as current law requires) and will thereafter remain constant as a percentage of GDP. Note that the budget deficit is not exactly equal to expenditure minus receipts because of rounding.

CBO's estimate of the feedback from fiscal policy to the economy. That is, they include the reduction in GDP that takes place as increased government debt crowds out capital accumulation and depresses long-run economic growth.

The results are nothing short of alarming. As the population ages, government expenditure automatically rises from 21 percent of GDP in the year 2000 to 43 percent in the year 2050, and the budget goes from approximate balance to a deficit of 23 percent of GDP. The good news is that the government debt relative to the economy shrinks for the first two decades: an approximately balanced budget coupled with normal economic growth reduces the debt–GDP ratio from 42 percent in the year 2000 to 17 percent in the year 2020. But after that, the fiscal picture deteriorates, with the debt reaching 206 percent of GDP in the year 2050. This level of government debt is higher than the United States has experienced at any time in its history, and it is higher than the indebtedness of any major country today.

As economist Herbert Stein once noted, things that can't go on forever eventually come to an end. The increasing government indebtedness shown in Table 15-3 is one example. At some time, U.S. fiscal policymakers will have to steer the economy toward an alternative course. The open questions are how quickly they will act and what course they will choose. According to the CBO, reaching long-term fiscal balance would require an immediate increase in taxes or cut in spending equal to about 1.6 percent of GDP, or about 8 percent of taxes or spending. If no action is taken until 2030 (when the long-term fiscal problem becomes truly apparent), the size of the required adjustment would be almost three times as large. Deciding how to handle the aging of the population and the resulting fiscal imbalance will surely be one of the great challenges facing the next generation of policymakers in the United States and around the world.

15-2 | Problems in Measurement

The government budget deficit equals government spending minus government revenue, which in turn equals the amount of new debt the government needs to issue to finance its operations. This definition may sound simple enough, but in fact debates over fiscal policy sometimes arise over how the budget deficit should be measured. Some economists believe that the deficit as currently measured is not a good indicator of the stance of fiscal policy. That is, they believe that the budget deficit does not accurately gauge either the impact of fiscal policy on today's economy or the burden being placed on future generations of taxpayers. In this section we discuss four problems with the usual measure of the budget deficit.

Measurement Problem 1: Inflation

The least controversial of the measurement issues is the correction for inflation. Almost all economists agree that the government's indebtedness should be measured in real terms, not in nominal terms. The measured deficit should equal the change in the government's real debt, not the change in its nominal debt.

The budget deficit as commonly measured, however, does not correct for inflation. To see how large an error this induces, consider the following example. Suppose that the real government debt is not changing; in other words, in real terms, the budget is balanced. In this case, the nominal debt must be rising at the rate of inflation. That is,

$$\Delta D/D = \pi,$$

where π is the inflation rate and D is the stock of government debt. This implies

$$\Delta D = \pi D.$$

The government would look at the change in the nominal debt ΔD and would report a budget deficit of πD. Hence, most economists believe that the reported budget deficit is overstated by the amount πD.

We can make the same argument in another way. The deficit is government expenditure minus government revenue. Part of expenditure is the interest paid on the government debt. Expenditure should include only the real interest paid on the debt rD, not the nominal interest paid iD. Because the difference between the nominal interest rate i and the real interest rate r is the inflation rate π, the budget deficit is overstated by πD.

This correction for inflation can be large, especially when inflation is high, and it can often change our evaluation of fiscal policy. For example, in 1979, the federal government reported a budget deficit of $28 billion. Inflation was 8.6 percent, and the government debt held at the beginning of the year by the public (excluding the Federal Reserve) was $495 billion. The deficit was therefore overstated by

$$\pi D = 0.086 \times \$495 \text{ billion}$$
$$= \$43 \text{ billion}.$$

Corrected for inflation, the reported budget deficit of $28 billion turns into a budget surplus of $15 billion! In other words, even though nominal government debt was rising, real government debt was falling.

Measurement Problem 2: Capital Assets

Many economists believe that an accurate assessment of the government's budget deficit requires accounting for the government's assets as well as its liabilities. In particular, when measuring the government's overall indebtedness, we should subtract government assets from government debt. Therefore, the budget deficit should be measured as the change in debt minus the change in assets.

Certainly, individuals and firms treat assets and liabilities symmetrically. When a person borrows to buy a house, we do not say that he is running a budget deficit. Instead, we offset the increase in assets (the house) against the increase in debt (the mortgage) and record no change in net wealth. Perhaps we should treat the government's finances the same way.

A budget procedure that accounts for assets as well as liabilities is called **capital budgeting,** because it takes into account changes in capital. For example, suppose that the government sells one of its office buildings or some of its land and uses the proceeds to reduce the government debt. Under current budget procedures, the reported deficit would be lower. Under capital budgeting, the revenue received from the sale would not lower the deficit, because the reduction in debt would be offset by a reduction in assets. Similarly, under capital budgeting, government borrowing to finance the purchase of a capital good would not raise the deficit.

The major difficulty with capital budgeting is that it is hard to decide which government expenditures should count as capital expenditures. For example, should the interstate highway system be counted as an asset of the government? If so, what is its value? What about the stockpile of nuclear weapons? Should spending on education be treated as expenditure on human capital? These difficult questions must be answered if the government is to adopt a capital budget.

Economists and policymakers disagree about whether the federal government should use capital budgeting. (Many state governments already use it.) Opponents of capital budgeting argue that, although the system is superior in principle to the current system, it is too difficult to implement in practice. Proponents of capital budgeting argue that even an imperfect treatment of capital assets would be better than ignoring them altogether.

Measurement Problem 3: Uncounted Liabilities

Some economists argue that the measured budget deficit is misleading because it excludes some important government liabilities. For example, consider the pensions of government workers. These workers provide labor services to the government today, but part of their compensation is deferred to the future. In essence, these workers are providing a loan to the government. Their future pension benefits represent a government liability not very different from government debt. Yet this liability is not included as part of the government debt, and the accumulation of this liability is not included as part of the budget deficit. According to estimates of the Office of Management and Budget for 1995, if pension liabilities were counted, the reported debt of the federal government would be about 50 percent larger than it is.

Similarly, consider the Social Security system. In some ways, the system is like a pension plan. People pay some of their income into the system when young and expect to receive benefits when old. Perhaps accumulated future Social Security benefits should be included in the government's liabilities. Estimates suggest that the government's future Social Security liabilities (less future Social Security taxes) equal about three times the government debt as officially measured.

One might argue that Social Security liabilities are different from government debt because the government can change the laws determining Social Security benefits. Yet, in principle, the government could always choose not to repay all of its debt: the government honors its debt only because it chooses to do so. Promises to pay the holders of government debt may not be fundamentally different from promises to pay the future recipients of Social Security.

A particularly difficult form of government liability to measure is the *contingent liability*—the liability that is due only if a specified event occurs. For example, the government guarantees many forms of private credit, such as student loans, mortgages for low- and moderate-income families, and deposits in banks and savings and loan institutions. If the borrower repays the loan, the government pays nothing; if the borrower defaults, the government makes the repayment. When the government provides this guarantee, it undertakes a liability contingent on the borrower's default. Yet this contingent liability is not reflected in the budget deficit, in part because it is not clear what dollar value to attach to it.

Measurement Problem 4: The Business Cycle

Many changes in the government's budget deficit occur automatically in response to a fluctuating economy. For example, when the economy goes into a recession, incomes fall, so people pay less in personal income taxes. Profits fall, so corporations pay less in corporate income taxes. More people become eligible for government assistance, such as welfare and unemployment insurance, so government spending rises. Even without any change in the laws governing taxation and spending, the budget deficit increases.

These automatic changes in the deficit are not errors in measurement, for the government truly borrows more when a recession depresses tax revenue and boosts government spending. But these changes do make it more difficult to use the deficit to monitor changes in fiscal policy. That is, the deficit can rise or fall either because the government has changed policy or because the economy has changed direction. For some purposes, it would be good to know which is occurring.

To solve this problem, the government calculates a **cyclically adjusted budget deficit** (sometimes called the *full-employment budget deficit*). The cyclically adjusted deficit is based on estimates of what government spending and tax revenue would be if the economy were operating at its natural rate of output and employment. The cyclically adjusted deficit is a useful measure because it reflects policy changes but not the current stage of the business cycle.

Summing Up

Economists differ in the importance they place on these measurement problems. Some believe that the problems are so severe that the measured budget deficit is almost meaningless. Most take these measurement problems seriously but still view the measured budget deficit as a useful indicator of fiscal policy.

The undisputed lesson is that to evaluate fully what fiscal policy is doing, economists and policymakers must look at more than just the measured budget deficit. And, in fact, they do. The budget documents prepared annually by the Office of Management and Budget contain much detailed information about the government's finances, including data on capital expenditures and credit programs.

No economic statistic is perfect. Whenever we see a number reported in the media, we need to know what it is measuring and what it is leaving out. This is especially true for data on government debt and budget deficits.

CASE STUDY

Generational Accounting

One harsh critic of current measures of the budget deficit is economist Laurence Kotlikoff. Kotlikoff argues that the budget deficit is like the fabled emperor who wore no clothes: everyone should plainly see the problem, but no one is willing to admit to it. He writes, "On the conceptual level, the budget deficit is intellectually bankrupt. On the practical level, there are so many official deficits that 'balanced budget' has lost any true meaning." He sees an "urgent need to switch from an outdated, misleading, and fundamentally noneconomic measure of fiscal policy, namely the budget deficit, to generational accounting."

Generational accounting, Kotlikoff's new way to gauge the influence of fiscal policy, is based on the idea that a person's economic well-being depends on his or her lifetime income. (This idea is founded on Modigliani's life-cycle theory of consumer behavior, which we examine in Chapter 16.) When evaluating fiscal policy, therefore, we should not be concerned with taxes or spending in any single year. Instead, we should look at the taxes paid, and transfers received, by people over their entire lives. Generational accounts measure the impact of fiscal policy on the lifetime incomes of different generations.

Generational accounts tell a very different story than the budget deficit about the history of U.S. fiscal policy. In the early 1980s, the U.S. government cut taxes, beginning a long period of large budget deficits. Most commentators claim that older generations benefited at the expense of younger generations during this period, since the young inherited the government debt. Kotlikoff agrees that these tax cuts raised the burden on the young, but he claims that this standard analysis ignores the impact of many other policy changes. His generational accounts show that the young were hit even harder during the 1950s, 1960s, and 1970s. During these years, the government raised Social Security benefits for the elderly and financed the higher spending by taxing the working-age population. This policy redistributed income away from the young, even though it did not affect the budget deficit. During the 1980s, Social Security reforms reversed this trend, benefiting younger generations.

Despite Kotlikoff's advocacy, generational accounting is not likely to replace the budget deficit. This alternative system also has flaws. For example, to calculate the total tax burden on different generations, one needs to make assumptions about future policy, which are open to dispute. Nonetheless, generational accounting offers a useful perspective in the debate over fiscal policy.[1]

15-3| The Traditional View of Government Debt

Imagine that you are an economist working for the Congressional Budget Office (CBO). You receive a letter from the chair of the Senate Budget Committee:

> Dear CBO Economist:
>   Congress is about to consider the president's request to cut all taxes by 20 percent. Before deciding whether to endorse the request, my committee would like your analysis. We see little hope of reducing government spending, so the tax cut would mean an increase in the budget deficit. How would the tax cut and budget deficit affect the economy and the economic well-being of the country?
>   Sincerely,
>   Committee Chair

Before responding to the senator, you open your favorite economics textbook—this one, of course—to see what the models predict for such a change in fiscal policy.

To analyze the long-run effects of this policy change, you turn to the models in Chapters 3, 4, and 5. The model in Chapter 3 shows that a tax cut stimulates consumer spending and reduces national saving. The reduction in saving raises the interest rate, which crowds out investment. The Solow growth model introduced in Chapter 4 shows that lower investment eventually leads to a lower steady-state capital stock and a lower level of output. Because we concluded in Chapter 5 that the U.S. economy has less capital than in the Golden Rule steady state (the steady state with maximum consumption), the fall in steady-state capital means lower consumption and reduced economic well-being.

To analyze the short-run effects of the policy change, you turn to the *IS–LM* model in Chapters 10 and 11. This model shows that a tax cut stimulates consumer spending, which implies an expansionary shift in the *IS* curve. If there is no change in monetary policy, the shift in the *IS* curve leads to an expansionary shift in the aggregate demand curve. In the short run, when prices are sticky, the expansion in aggregate demand leads to higher output and lower unemployment. Over time, as prices adjust, the economy returns to the natural rate of output, and the higher aggregate demand results in a higher price level.

---

[1] Laurence J. Kotlikoff, *Generational Accounting: Knowing Who Pays, and When, for What We Spend* (New York: The Free Press, 1992). For an appraisal of the book, see David M. Cutler, Book Review, *National Tax Journal* 56 (March 1993): 61–67. See also the symposium on generational accounting in the Winter 1994 issue of the *Journal of Economic Perspectives*.

To see how international trade affects your analysis, you turn to the open-economy models in Chapters 8 and 12. The model in Chapter 8 shows that when national saving falls, people start financing investment by borrowing from abroad, causing a trade deficit. Although the inflow of capital from abroad lessens the effect of the fiscal-policy change on U.S. capital accumulation, the United States becomes indebted to foreign countries. The fiscal policy change also causes the dollar to appreciate, which makes foreign goods cheaper in the United States and domestic goods more expensive abroad. The Mundell–Fleming model in Chapter 12 shows that the appreciation of the dollar and the resulting fall in net exports reduce the short-run expansionary impact of the fiscal change on output and employment.

With all these models in mind, you draft a response:

Dear Senator:

A tax cut financed by government borrowing would have many effects on the economy. The immediate impact of the tax cut would be to stimulate consumer spending. Higher consumer spending affects the economy in both the short run and the long run.

In the short run, higher consumer spending would raise the demand for goods and services and thus raise output and employment. Interest rates would also rise, however, as investors competed for a smaller flow of saving. Higher interest rates would discourage investment and would encourage capital to flow in from abroad. The dollar would rise in value against foreign currencies, and U.S. firms would become less competitive in world markets.

In the long run, the smaller national saving caused by the tax cut would mean a smaller capital stock and a greater foreign debt. Therefore, the output of the nation would be smaller, and a greater share of that output would be owed to foreigners.

The overall effect of the tax cut on economic well-being is hard to judge. Current generations would benefit from higher consumption and higher employment, although inflation would likely be higher as well. Future generations would bear much of the burden of today's budget deficits: they would be born into a nation with a smaller capital stock and a larger foreign debt.

Your faithful servant,
CBO Economist

The senator replies:

Dear CBO Economist:

Thank you for your letter. It made sense to me. But yesterday my committee heard testimony from a prominent economist who called herself a "Ricardian" and who reached quite a different conclusion. She said that a tax cut by itself would not stimulate consumer spending. She concluded that the budget deficit would therefore not have all the effects you listed. What's going on here?

Sincerely,
Committee Chair

After studying the next section, you write back to the senator, explaining in detail the debate over Ricardian equivalence.

15-4| The Ricardian View of Government Debt

The traditional view of government debt presumes that when the government cuts taxes and runs a budget deficit, consumers respond to their higher after-tax income by spending more. An alternative view, called **Ricardian equivalence,** questions this presumption. According to the Ricardian view, consumers are forward-looking and, therefore, base their spending not only on their current income but also on their expected future income. As we explore more fully in Chapter 16, the forward-looking consumer is at the heart of many modern theories of consumption. The Ricardian view of government debt applies the logic of the forward-looking consumer to analyze the effects of fiscal policy.

The Basic Logic of Ricardian Equivalence

Consider the response of a forward-looking consumer to the tax cut that the Senate Budget Committee is considering. The consumer might reason as follows:

> The government is cutting taxes without any plans to reduce government spending. Does this policy alter my set of opportunities? Am I richer because of this tax cut? Should I consume more?
>
> Maybe not. The government is financing the tax cut by running a budget deficit. At some point in the future, the government will have to raise taxes to pay off the debt and accumulated interest. So the policy really represents a tax cut today coupled with a tax hike in the future. The tax cut merely gives me transitory income that eventually will be taken back. I am not any better off, so I will leave my consumption unchanged.

The forward-looking consumer understands that government borrowing today means higher taxes in the future. A tax cut financed by government debt does not reduce the tax burden; it merely reschedules it. It therefore should not encourage the consumer to spend more.

One can view this argument another way. Suppose that the government borrows $1,000 from the typical citizen to give that citizen a $1,000 tax cut. In essence, this policy is the same as giving the citizen a $1,000 government bond as a gift. One side of the bond says, "The government owes you, the bondholder, $1,000 plus interest." The other side says, "You, the taxpayer, owe the government $1,000 plus interest." Overall, the gift of a bond from the government to the typical citizen does not make the citizen richer or poorer, because the value of the bond is offset by the value of the future tax liability.

The general principle is that government debt is equivalent to future taxes, and if consumers are sufficiently forward-looking, future taxes are equivalent to current taxes. Hence, financing the government by debt is equivalent to financing it by taxes. This view is called *Ricardian equivalence* after the famous nineteenth-century economist David Ricardo, because he first noted the theoretical argument.

The implication of Ricardian equivalence is that a debt-financed tax cut leaves consumption unaffected. Households save the extra disposable income to pay the future tax liability that the tax cut implies. This increase in private saving just offsets the decrease in public saving. National saving—the sum of private and public saving—remains the same. The tax cut therefore has none of the effects that the traditional analysis predicts.

The logic of Ricardian equivalence does not mean that all changes in fiscal policy are irrelevant. Changes in fiscal policy do influence consumer spending if they influence present or future government purchases. For example, suppose that the government cuts taxes today because it plans to reduce government purchases in the future. If the consumer understands that this tax cut does not require an increase in future taxes, he feels richer and raises his consumption. But note that it is the reduction in government purchases, rather than the reduction in taxes, that stimulates consumption: the announcement of a future reduction in government purchases would raise consumption today even if current taxes were unchanged, because it would imply lower taxes at some time in the future.

Consumers and Future Taxes

The essence of the Ricardian view is that when people choose their consumption, they rationally look ahead to the future taxes implied by government debt. But how forward-looking are consumers? Defenders of the traditional view of government debt believe that the prospect of future taxes does not have as large an influence on current consumption as the Ricardian view assumes. Here are some of their arguments.[2]

Myopia Proponents of the Ricardian view of fiscal policy assume that people are rational when making decisions such as choosing how much of their income to consume and how much to save. When the government borrows to pay for current spending, rational consumers look ahead to the future taxes required to support this debt. Thus, the Ricardian view presumes that people have substantial knowledge and foresight.

One possible argument for the traditional view of tax cuts is that people are shortsighted, perhaps because they do not fully comprehend the implications of government budget deficits. It is possible that some people follow simple and not fully rational rules of thumb when choosing how much to save. Suppose, for example, that a person acts on the assumption that future taxes will be the same as current taxes. This person will fail to take account of future changes in taxes required by current government policies. A debt-financed tax cut will lead this person to believe that his lifetime income has increased, even if it

---

[2] For a survey of the debate over Ricardian equivalence, see Douglas Bernheim, "Ricardian Equivalence: An Evaluation of Theory and Evidence," *NBER Macroeconomics Annual* (1987): 263–303. See also the symposium on budget deficits in the Spring 1989 issue of the *Journal of Economic Perspectives*.

hasn't. The tax cut will therefore lead to higher consumption and lower national saving.

Borrowing Constraints   The Ricardian view of government debt assumes that consumers base their spending not only on current income but on their lifetime income, which includes both current and expected future income. According to the Ricardian view, a debt-financed tax cut increases current income, but it does not alter lifetime income or consumption. Advocates of the traditional view of government debt argue that current income is more important than lifetime income for those consumers who face binding borrowing constraints. A *borrowing constraint* is a limit on how much an individual can borrow from banks or other finanical institutions.

A person who would like to consume more than his current income—perhaps because he expects higher income in the future—has to do so by borrowing. If he cannot borrow to finance current consumption, or can borrow only a limited amount, his current income determines his spending, regardless of what his lifetime income might be. In this case, a debt-financed tax cut raises current income and thus consumption, even though future income is lower. In essence, when the government cuts current taxes and raises future taxes, it is giving taxpayers a loan. For a person who wanted to obtain a loan but was unable to, the tax cut expands his opportunities and stimulates consumption.

CASE STUDY

George Bush's Withholding Experiment

In early 1992, President George Bush pursued a novel policy to deal with the lingering recession in the United States. By executive order, he lowered the amount of income taxes that were being withheld from workers' paychecks. The order did not reduce the amount of taxes that workers owed; it merely delayed payment. The higher take-home pay that workers received during 1992 was to be offset by higher tax payments, or smaller tax refunds, when income taxes were due in April 1993.

What effect would you predict for this policy? According to the logic of Ricardian equivalence, consumers should realize that their lifetime resources were unchanged and, therefore, save the extra take-home pay to meet the upcoming tax liability. Yet George Bush claimed his policy would provide "money people can use to help pay for clothing, college, or to get a new car." That is, he believed that consumers would spend the extra income, thereby stimulating aggregate demand and helping the economy recover from the recession. Bush seemed to be assuming that consumers were shortsighted or faced binding borrowing constraints.

Gauging the actual effects of this policy is difficult with aggregate data, because many other things were happening at the same time. Yet some evidence comes from a survey two economists conducted shortly after the policy was announced. The survey asked people what they would do with the extra income. Fifty-seven percent of the respondents said they would save it, use it to repay debts, or adjust their withholding in order to reverse the effect of Bush's executive order. Forty-three percent said they would spend the extra income. Thus, for this policy change, a majority of the population was planning to act as Ricardian theory posits. Nonetheless, Bush was partly right: many people planned to spend the extra income, even though they understood that the following year's tax bill would be higher.[3]

Future Generations Besides myopia and borrowing constraints, a third argument for the traditional view of government debt is that consumers expect the implied future taxes to fall not on them but on future generations. Suppose, for example, that the government cuts taxes today, issues 30-year bonds to finance the budget deficit, and then raises taxes in 30 years to repay the loan. In this case, the government debt represents a transfer of wealth from the next generation of taxpayers (which faces the tax hike) to the current generation of taxpayers (which gets the tax cut). This transfer raises the lifetime resources of the current generation, so it raises their consumption. In essence, a debt-financed tax cut stimulates consumption because it gives the current generation the opportunity to consume at the expense of the next generation.

Economist Robert Barro has provided a clever rejoinder to this argument to support the Ricardian view. Barro argues that because future generations are the children and grandchildren of the current generation, we should not view them as independent economic actors. Instead, he argues, the appropriate assumption is that current generations care about future generations. This altruism between generations is evidenced by the gifts that many people give their children, often in the form of bequests at the time of their death. The existence of bequests suggests that many people are not eager to take advantage of the opportunity to consume at their children's expense.

According to Barro's analysis, the relevant decisionmaking unit is not

"What's this I hear about you adults mortgaging my future?"

Drawing by Dave Carpenter. From *The Wall Street Journal.* Permission, Cartoon Features Syndicate.

---

[3] Matthew D. Shapiro and Joel Slemrod, "Consumer Response to the Timing of Income: Evidence From a Change in Tax Withholding," *American Economic Review* 85 (March 1995): 274–283.

the individual, who lives only a finite number of years, but the family, which continues forever. In other words, an individual decides how much to consume based not only on his own income but also on the income of future members of his family. A debt-financed tax cut may raise the income an individual receives in his lifetime, but it does not raise his family's overall resources. Instead of consuming the extra income from the tax cut, the individual saves it and leaves it as a bequest to his children, who will bear the future tax liability.

We can see now that the debate over government debt is really a debate over consumer behavior. The Ricardian view assumes that consumers have a long time horizon. Barro's analysis of the family implies that the consumer's time horizon, like the government's, is effectively infinite. Yet it is possible that consumers do not look ahead to the tax liabilities of future generations. Perhaps they expect their children to be richer than they are and, therefore, welcome the opportunity to consume at their children's expense. The fact that many people leave zero or minimal bequests to their children is consistent with this hypothesis. For these zero-bequest families, a debt-financed tax cut alters consumption by redistributing wealth among generations.[4]

CASE STUDY

Why Do Parents Leave Bequests?

The debate over Ricardian equivalence is partly a debate over how different generations are linked to one another. Robert Barro's defense of the Ricardian view is based on the assumption that parents leave their children bequests because they care about them. But is altruism really the reason that parents leave bequests?

One group of economists has suggested that parents use bequests to control their children. Parents often want their children to do certain things for them, such as phoning home regularly and visiting on holidays. Perhaps parents use the implicit threat of disinheritance to induce their children to be more attentive.

To test this "strategic bequest motive," these economists examined data on how often children visit their parents. They found that the more wealthy the parent, the more often the children visit. Even more striking was another result: only wealth that can be left as a bequest induces more frequent visits. Wealth that cannot be bequeathed, such as pension wealth, which reverts to the pension company in the event of an early death, does not encourage children to visit. These findings suggest that there may be more to the relationships among generations than mere altruism.[5]

---

[4] Robert J. Barro, "Are Government Bonds Net Wealth?" *Journal of Political Economy* 81 (1974): 1095–1117.

[5] B. Douglas Bernheim, Andrei Shleifer, and Lawrence H. Summers, "The Strategic Bequest Motive," *Journal of Political Economy* 93 (1985): 1045–1076.

Making a Choice

Having seen the traditional and Ricardian views of government debt, you should ask yourself two sets of questions.

First, which view do you agree with? If the government cuts taxes today, runs a budget deficit, and raises taxes in the future, how will the policy affect the economy? Will it stimulate consumption, as the traditional view holds? Or will consumers understand that their lifetime income is unchanged and, therefore, offset the budget deficit with higher private saving?

---

f y i

RICARDO ON RICARDIAN EQUIVALENCE

David Ricardo was a millionaire stockbroker and one of the great economists of all time. His most important contribution was his 1817 book *Principles of Political Economy and Taxation,* in which he developed the theory of comparative advantage, which economists still use to explain the gains from international trade. Ricardo was also a member of the British Parliament, where he put his own theories to work and opposed the corn laws, which restricted international trade in grain.

Ricardo was interested in the alternative ways in which a government might pay for its expenditure. In an 1820 article called "Essay on the Funding System," he considered an example of a war that cost 20 million pounds. He noted that if the interest rate were 5 percent, this expense could be financed with a one-time tax of 20 million pounds, a perpetual tax of 1 million pounds, or a tax of 1.2 million pounds for 45 years. He wrote:

> In point of economy, there is no real difference in either of the modes; for twenty million in one payment, one million per annum for ever, or 1,200,0000 pounds for 45 years, are precisely of the same value.

Ricardo was aware that the issue involved the linkages among generations:

> It would be difficult to convince a man possessed of 20,000 pounds, or any other sum, that a perpetual payment of 50 pounds per annum was equally burdensome with a single tax of 1000 pounds. He would have some vague notion that the 50 pounds per annum would be paid by posterity, and would not be paid by him; but if he leaves his fortune to his son, and leaves it charged with this perpetual tax, where is the difference whether he leaves him 20,000 pounds with the tax, or 19,000 pounds without it?

Although Ricardo viewed these alternative methods of government finance as equivalent, he did not think other people would view them as such:

> The people who pay taxes . . . do not manage their private affairs accordingly. We are apt to think that the war is burdensome only in proportion to what we are at the moment called to pay for it in taxes, without reflecting on the probable duration of such taxes.

Thus, Ricardo doubted that people were rational and farsighted enough to look ahead fully to their future tax liabilities.

As a policymaker, Ricardo took seriously the government debt. Before the British Parliament, he once declared,

> This would be the happiest country in the world, and its progress in prosperity would go beyond the powers of imagination to conceive, if we got rid of two great evils—the national debt and the corn laws.

It is one of the great ironies in the history of economic thought that Ricardo rejected the theory that now bears his name!

Second, why do you hold the view that you do? If you agree with the traditional view of government debt, what is the reason? Do consumers fail to understand that higher government borrowing today means higher taxes tomorrow? Or do they ignore future taxes, either because they are borrowing-constrained or because future taxes fall on future generations with which they do not feel an economic link? If you hold the Ricardian view, do you believe that consumers have the foresight to see that government borrowing today will result in future taxes levied on them or their descendants? Do you believe that consumers will save the extra income to offset that future tax liability?

We might hope that the evidence could help us decide between these two views of government debt. Yet when economists examine historical episodes of large budget deficits, the evidence is inconclusive. History can be interpreted in different ways.

Consider, for example, the experience of the 1980s. The large budget deficits, caused partly by the Reagan tax cut of 1981, seem to offer a natural experiment to test the two views of government debt. At first glance, this episode appears decisively to support the traditional view. The large budget deficits coincided with low national saving, high real interest rates, and a large trade deficit. Indeed, advocates of the traditional view of government debt often claim that the experience of the 1980s confirms their position.

Yet those who hold the Ricardian view of government debt interpret these events differently. Perhaps saving was low in the 1980s because people were optimistic about future economic growth—an optimism that was also reflected in a booming stock market. Or perhaps saving was low because people expected that the tax cut would eventually lead not to higher taxes but, as Reagan promised, to lower government spending. Because it is hard to rule out any of these interpretations, both views of government debt survive.

15-5 Other Perspectives on Government Debt

The policy debates over government debt have many facets. So far we have considered the traditional and Ricardian views of government debt. According to the traditional view, a government budget deficit expands aggregate demand and stimulates output in the short run but crowds out capital and depresses economic growth in the long run. According to the Ricardian view, a government budget deficit has none of these effects, because consumers understand that a budget deficit represents merely postponement of a tax burden. Here we consider several other perspectives on government debt, which could be used to modify either the traditional or the Ricardian viewpoint.

Effects on Monetary Policy

In 1985, Paul Volcker told Congress that "the actual and prospective size of the budget deficit . . . heightens skepticism about our ability to control the money supply and contain inflation." A decade later, Alan Greenspan claimed that "a substantial reduction in the long-term prospective deficit of the United States will significantly lower very long-term inflation expectations." Both of these Fed chairmen apparently saw a link between fiscal policy and monetary policy.

We first discussed such a possibility in Chapter 7. As we saw, one way for a government to finance a budget deficit is simply to print money—a policy that leads to higher inflation. Indeed, when countries experience hyperinflation, the typical reason is that fiscal policymakers are relying on the inflation tax to pay for some of their spending. The ends of hyperinflations almost always coincide with fiscal reforms that include large cuts in government spending and, therefore, a reduced need for seigniorage.

In addition to this link between the budget deficit and inflation, some economists have suggested that a high level of debt might also encourage the government to create inflation. Because most government debt is specified in nominal terms, the real value of the debt falls when the price level rises. This is the usual redistribution between creditors and debtors caused by unexpected inflation—here the debtor is the government and the creditor is the private sector. But this debtor, unlike others, has access to the monetary printing press. A high level of debt might encourage the government to print money, thereby raising the price level and reducing the real value of its debts.

Despite these concerns about a possible link between government debt and monetary policy, there is little evidence that this link is important in most developed countries. In the United States, for instance, inflation was high in the 1970s, even though government debt was low relative to GDP. Monetary policymakers got inflation under control in the early 1980s, just as fiscal policymakers started running large budget deficits and increasing the government debt. Thus, although monetary policy might be driven by fiscal policy in some situations, such as during the classic hyperinflations, this situation appears not to be the norm in most countries today. There are several reasons for this. First, most governments can finance deficits by selling debt and don't need to rely on seigniorage. Second, central banks often have enough independence to resist political pressure for more expansionary monetary policy. Third, and most important, policymakers in all parts of government know that inflation is a poor solution to fiscal problems.

Debt and the Political Process

Fiscal policy is made not by angels but by an imperfect political process. Some economists worry that the possibility of financing government spending by issuing debt makes that political process all the worse.

This idea has a long history. Nineteenth-century economist Knut Wicksell claimed that if the benefit of some type of government spending exceeded its cost, it should be possible to finance that spending in a way that would receive unanimous support from the voters. He concluded that government spending should be undertaken only when support was, in fact, nearly unanimous. In the case of debt finance, however, Wicksell was concerned that "the interests [of future taxpayers] are not represented at all or are represented inadequately in the tax-approving assembly."

Many economists have echoed this theme more recently. In their 1977 book *Democracy in Deficit,* James Buchanan and Richard Wagner argued for a balanced-budget rule for fiscal policy on the grounds that it "will have the effect of bringing the real costs of public outlays to the awareness of decision makers; it will tend to dispel the illusory 'something for nothing' aspects of fiscal choice." Similarly, Martin Feldstein (once an economic adviser to Ronald Reagan and a long-time critic of budget deficits) argues that "only the 'hard budget constraint' of having to balance the budget" can force politicians to judge whether spending's "benefits really justify its costs."

These arguments have led some economists to favor a constitutional amendment that would require Congress to pass a balanced budget. Often these proposals have escape clauses for times of national emergency, such as wars and depressions, when a budget deficit is a reasonable policy response. Some critics of these proposals argue that, even with the escape clauses, such a constitutional amendment would tie the hands of policymakers too severely. Others claim that Congress would easily evade the balanced-budget requirement with accounting tricks. As this discussion makes clear, the debate over the desirability of a balanced-budget amendment is as much political as economic.

International Dimensions

Government debt may affect a nation's role in the world economy. As we first saw in Chapter 8, when a government budget deficit reduces national saving, it often leads to a trade deficit, which in turn is financed by borrowing from abroad. For instance, many observers have blamed U.S. fiscal policy for the recent switch of the United States from a major creditor in the world economy to a major debtor. This link between the budget deficit and the trade deficit leads to two further effects of government debt.

First, high levels of government debt may increase the risk that an economy will experience capital flight—an abrupt decline in the demand for a country's assets in world financial markets. International investors are aware that a government can always deal with its debt simply by defaulting. This approach was used as far back as 1335, when England's King Edward III defaulted on his debt to Italian bankers. More recently, several Latin American countries defaulted on their debts in the 1980s, and Russia did the same in 1998. The higher the level of the government debt, the greater the temptation of default. Thus, as government debt increases, international investors may come to fear default and curtail their lending. If this loss of confidence occurs suddenly, the result could be the classic symptoms of capital flight: a collapse in the value of the currency and an increase in interest rates. As we discussed in Chapter 12, this is precisely what happened to Mexico in the early 1990s when default appeared likely.

Second, high levels of government debt financed by foreign borrowing may reduce a nation's political clout in world affairs. This fear was emphasized by economist Ben Friedman in his 1988 book *Day of Reckoning.* He wrote, "World power and influence have historically accrued to creditor countries. It is not coincidental that America emerged as a world power simultaneously with our transition from a debtor nation . . . to a creditor supplying investment capital to the rest of the world." Friedman suggests that if the United States continues to run large trade deficits, it will eventually lose some of its international influence. So far, the record has not been kind to this hypothesis: the United States has run another decade of trade deficits and remains a leading superpower. But perhaps other events—such as the collapse of the Soviet Union—offset the fall in political clout that the United States would have experienced from its increased indebtedness.

CASE STUDY

The Benefits of Indexed Bonds

In 1997, the U.S. Treasury Department started to issue bonds that pay a return based on the consumer price index. These bonds pay a low interest rate of about 3.5 percent, so a $1,000 bond pays only $35 per year in interest. But that interest payment grows with the overall price level as measured by the CPI. In addition, when the $1,000 of principal is repaid, that amount is also adjusted for changes in the CPI. The 3.5 percent, therefore, is a real interest rate. No longer do professors of macroeconomics need to define the real interest rate as an abstract construct. They can open up the *New York Times,* point to the credit report, and say, "Look here, this is a nominal interest rate, and this is a real interest rate." (Professors in the United Kingdom and several other countries have long enjoyed this luxury because indexed bonds have been trading in other countries for years.)

Of course, making macroeconomics easier to teach was not the reason that the Treasury chose to index some of the government debt. That was just a positive externality. Its goal was to introduce a new type of government bond that should benefit bondholder and taxpayer alike. These bonds are a win–win proposition because they insulate both sides of the transaction from inflation risk. Bondholders should care about the real interest rate they earn, and taxpayers should care about the real interest rate they pay. When government bonds are specified in nominal terms, both sides take on risk that is neither productive nor necessary. The new indexed bonds eliminate this inflation risk.

In addition, the new bonds have three other benefits:

First, the bonds may encourage the private sector to begin issuing its own indexed securities. Financial innovation is, to some extent, a public good. Once an innovation has been introduced into the market, the idea is nonexcludable (people cannot be prevented from using it) and nonrival (one person's use of the idea does not diminish other people's use of it). Just as a free market will not adequately supply the public goods of national defense and basic research, it will not adequately supply financial innovation. The Treasury's new bonds can be viewed as a remedy for that market failure.

Second, the bonds reduce the government's incentive to produce surprise inflation. After the large budget deficits of the 1980s and 1990s, the U.S. government is now a substantial debtor, and its debts are specified almost entirely in dollar terms. What is unique about the federal government, in contrast to most debtors, is that it can just print the money it needs. The greater the government's nominal debts, the more incentive the government has to inflate away its debt. The Treasury's switch toward indexed debt reduces this potentially problematic incentive.

Third, the bonds provide data that might be useful for monetary policy. Many macroeconomic theories point to expected inflation as a key variable to explain the relationship between inflation and unemployment. But what is expected inflation? One way to measure it is to survey private forecasters. Another way is to look at the difference between the yield on nominal bonds and the yield on real bonds.

In the past, economists have proposed a variety of rules that could be used to conduct monetary policy, as we discussed in the preceding chapter. The new indexed bonds expand the number of possible rules. Here is one idea: The Fed announces a target for the inflation rate. Then, every day, the Fed measures expected inflation as the spread between the yield on nominal debt and the yield on indexed debt. If expected inflation is above the target, the Fed contracts the money supply. If expected inflation is below the target, the Fed expands the money supply. In this way, the Fed can use the bond market's inflation forecast to ensure that the money supply is growing at the rate needed to keep inflation close to its target.

The Treasury's new indexed bonds, therefore, will likely produce many benefits: less inflation risk, more financial innovation, better government incentives, more informed monetary policy, and easier lives for students and teachers of macroeconomics.[6]

15-6 Conclusion

Fiscal policy and government debt have been central in the U.S. political debate over the past decade. When Bill Clinton became president in 1993, he made reducing the budget deficit a high priority of his administration. When the Republicans took control of Congress in 1995, they pushed for even faster deficit reduction than Clinton had advocated. Although these efforts together with some good luck turned the federal government budget from deficit to surplus by the late 1990s, this is far from the end of the story. There is wide

---

[6] To read more about indexed bonds, see John Y. Campbell and Robert J. Shiller, "A Scorecard for Indexed Government Debt," *NBER Macroeconomics Annual,* (1996): 155–197; and David W. Wilcox, "Policy Watch: The Introduction of Indexed Government Debt in the United States," *The Journal of Economic Perspectives* 12 (Winter 1998): 219–227.

agreement that unless major changes in policy are enacted, large budget deficits loom on the horizon.

This chapter has discussed the debate among economists over government debt and budget deficits. Economists disagree about how fiscal policy is best measured and how fiscal policy affects the economy. To be sure, these are among the most important and controversial questions facing policymakers today. Given the fiscal prognosis, there seems little doubt that these debates will continue in the years to come.

Summary

1. The current debt of the U.S. federal government is of moderate size compared to the debt of other countries or compared to the debt that the United States has had throughout its own history. The 1980s and 1990s were unusual, however, in that the ratio of debt to GDP increased substantially during a period of peace and prosperity.

2. Standard measures of the budget deficit are imperfect measures of fiscal policy because they do not correct for the effects of inflation, do not offset changes in government liabilities with changes in government assets, omit some liabilities altogether, and do not correct for the effects of the business cycle.

3. According to the traditional view of government debt, a debt-financed tax cut stimulates consumer spending and lowers national saving. This increase in consumer spending leads to greater aggregate demand and higher income in the short run, but it leads to a lower capital stock and lower income in the long run.

4. According to the Ricardian view of government debt, a debt-financed tax cut does not stimulate consumer spending because it does not raise consumers' overall resources—it merely reschedules taxes from the present to the future. The debate between the traditional and Ricardian views of government debt is ultimately a debate over how consumers behave. Are consumers rational or shortsighted? Do they face binding borrowing constraints? Are they economically linked to future generations through altruistic bequests? Economists' views of government debt hinge on their answers to these questions.

5. Government debt can potentially have various additional effects. Large government debt or budget deficits may encourage excessively expansionary monetary policy and, therefore, lead to greater inflation. The possibility of running budget deficits may encourage politicians to unduly burden future generations when setting government spending and taxes. A high level of government debt may risk capital flight and diminish a nation's influence around the world. Economists differ in which of these effects they consider most important.

KEY CONCEPTS |

Capital budgeting
Cyclically adjusted budget deficit
Ricardian equivalence

QUESTIONS FOR REVIEW |

1. What is unusual about U.S. fiscal policy since 1980?

2. Why do many economists project increasing budget deficits and government debt over the next several decades?

3. Describe four problems affecting measurement of the government budget deficit.

4. According to the traditional view of government debt, how does a debt-financed tax cut affect public saving, private saving, and national saving?

5. According to the Ricardian view of government debt, how does a debt-financed tax cut affect public saving, private saving, and national saving?

6. Do you believe the traditional or the Ricardian view of government debt? Why?

7. Why might the level of government debt affect the government's incentives regarding money creation?

PROBLEMS AND APPLICATIONS |

1. On April 1, 1996, Taco Bell, the fast-food chain, ran a full-page ad in the *New York Times* with this news: "In an effort to help the national debt, Taco Bell is pleased to announce that we have agreed to purchase the Liberty Bell, one of our country's most historic treasures. It will now be called the *Taco Liberty Bell* and will still be accessible to the American public for viewing. We hope our move will prompt other corporations to take similar action to do their part to reduce the country's debt." Would such actions by U.S. corporations actually reduce the national debt as it is now measured? How would your answer change if the U.S. government adopted capital budgeting? Do you think these actions represent a true reduction in the government's indebtedness? Do you think Taco Bell was serious about this plan? (*Hint:* Note the date.)

2. Draft a letter to the senator described in Section 15-1, explaining and evaluating the Ricardian view of government debt.

3. The Social Security system levies a tax on workers and pays benefits to the elderly. Suppose that Congress increases both the tax and the benefits. For simplicity, assume that the Congress announces that the increases will last for one year only.

   a. How do you suppose this change would affect the economy? (*Hint:* Think about the marginal propensities to consume of the young and the old.)

   b. Does your answer depend on whether generations are altruistically linked?

4. Evaluate the usefulness of generational accounting from the perspective of someone who believes that generations are altruistically linked. Now evaluate the usefulness of generational accounting from the perspective of someone who believes that many consumers face binding borrowing constraints.

part FIVE

More on the Microeconomics Behind Macroeconomics

To understand the economy as a whole, we must understand the households and firms that make up the economy. In the next four chapters we look more closely at the behavior of households and firms. These chapters present microeconomic models that help refine our macroeconomic analysis.

Chapter 16 looks at how consumers behave. It begins with the simple consumption function that we have used throughout much of this book and then discusses more sophisticated models of consumer behavior.

Chapter 17 examines the determinants of the three types of investment spending—business fixed investment, residential investment, and inventory investment. It discusses why investment depends on the interest rate, what might cause the investment function to shift, and why investment fluctuates so much over the business cycle.

Chapter 18 studies the supply and demand for money. It discusses the role of the banking system in determining the money supply, as well as the various theories of the money demand function. This discussion offers new insights into the instruments and problems of monetary policy.

Chapter 19 presents some recent developments in the theory of short-run economic fluctuations. It discusses the avenues of research that economists are now exploring to improve our understanding of the business cycle, and it highlights the disagreements about which avenues are likely to prove most fruitful.

chapter **16**

Consumption

Consumption is the sole end and purpose of all production.

— *Adam Smith*

How do households decide how much of their income to consume today and how much to save for the future? This is a microeconomic question because it addresses the behavior of individual decisionmakers. Yet its answer has macroeconomic consequences. As we have seen in previous chapters, households' consumption decisions affect the way the economy as a whole behaves both in the long run and in the short run.

The consumption decision is crucial for long-run analysis because of its role in economic growth. The Solow growth model of Chapters 4 and 5 shows that the saving rate is a key determinant of the steady-state capital stock and thus of the level of economic well-being. The saving rate measures how much of its income the present generation is putting aside for its own future and for future generations.

The consumption decision is crucial for short-run analysis because of its role in determining aggregate demand. Consumption is two-thirds of GDP, so fluctuations in consumption are a key element of booms and recessions. The *IS–LM* model of Chapters 10 and 11 shows that changes in consumers' spending plans can be a source of shocks to the economy, and that the marginal propensity to consume is a determinant of the fiscal-policy multipliers.

In previous chapters we explained consumption with a function that relates consumption to disposable income: $C = C(Y - T)$. This approximation allowed us to develop simple models for long-run and short-run analysis. But it is too simple to provide a complete explanation of consumer behavior. In this chapter we examine the consumption function in greater detail and develop a more thorough explanation of what determines aggregate consumption.

Since macroeconomics began as a field of study, many economists have written about the theory of consumer behavior and suggested alternative ways of interpreting the data on consumption and income. This chapter presents the views of four prominent economists, roughly in historical order. By examining the theories of consumer behavior developed by John Maynard Keynes, Irving

Fisher, Franco Modigliani, and Milton Friedman, this chapter provides an overview of the diverse approaches to explaining consumption.

16-1 | John Maynard Keynes and the Consumption Function

We begin our study of consumption with John Maynard Keynes's *General Theory,* which was published in 1936. Keynes made the consumption function central to his theory of economic fluctuations, and it has played a key role in macroeconomic analysis ever since. Let's consider what Keynes thought about the consumption function, and then see what puzzles arose when his ideas were confronted with the data.

Keynes's Conjectures

Today, economists who study consumption rely on sophisticated techniques of data analysis. With the help of computers, they analyze aggregate data on the behavior of the overall economy from the national income accounts and detailed data on the behavior of individual households from surveys. Because Keynes wrote in the 1930s, however, he had neither the advantage of these data nor the computers necessary to analyze such large data sets. Instead of relying on statistical analysis, Keynes made conjectures about the consumption function based on introspection and casual observation.

First and most important, Keynes conjectured that the **marginal propensity to consume**—the amount consumed out of an additional dollar of income—is between zero and one. He wrote that the "fundamental psychological law, upon which we are entitled to depend with great confidence, . . . is that men are disposed, as a rule and on the average, to increase their consumption as their income increases, but not by as much as the increase in their income." That is, when a person earns an extra dollar, he typically spends some of it and saves some of it. As we saw in Chapter 10 when we developed the Keynesian cross, the marginal propensity to consume was crucial to Keynes's policy recommendations for how to reduce widespread unemployment. The power of fiscal policy to influence the economy—as expressed by the fiscal-policy multipliers—arises from the feedback between income and consumption.

Second, Keynes posited that the ratio of consumption to income, called the **average propensity to consume,** falls as income rises. He believed that saving was a luxury, so he expected the rich to save a higher proportion of their income than the poor. Although not essential for Keynes's own analysis, the postulate that the average propensity to consume falls as income rises became a central part of early Keynesian economics.

Third, Keynes thought that income is the primary determinant of consumption and that the interest rate does not have an important role. This conjecture stood in stark contrast to the beliefs of the classical economists who preceded him. The classical economists held that a higher interest rate encourages saving and discourages consumption. Keynes admitted that the interest rate could influence consumption as a matter of theory. Yet he wrote that "the main conclusion suggested by experience, I think, is that the short-period influence of the rate of interest on individual spending out of a given income is secondary and relatively unimportant."

On the basis of these three conjectures, the Keynesian consumption function is often written as

$$C = \overline{C} + cY, \qquad \overline{C} > 0, \quad 0 < c < 1,$$

where C is consumption, Y is disposable income, $\overline{C}$ is a constant, and c is the marginal propensity to consume. This consumption function, shown in Figure 16-1, is graphed as a straight line.

Notice that this consumption function exhibits the three properties that Keynes posited. It satisfies Keynes's first property because the marginal propensity to consume c is between zero and one, so that higher income leads to higher consumption and also to higher saving. This consumption function satisfies Keynes's second property because the average propensity to consume APC is

$$APC = C/Y = \overline{C}/Y + c.$$

As Y rises, $\overline{C}/Y$ falls, and so the average propensity to consume C/Y falls. And finally, this consumption function satisfies Keynes's third property because the interest rate is not included in this equation as a determinant of consumption.

---

figure 16-1

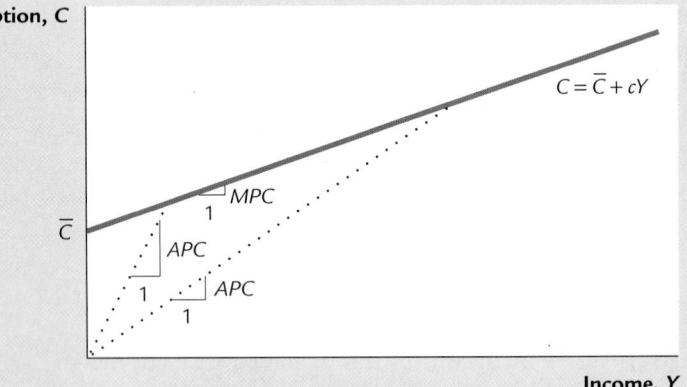

The Keynesian Consumption Function This figure graphs a consumption function with the three properties that Keynes conjectured. First, the marginal propensity to consume c is between zero and one. Second, the average propensity to consume falls as income rises. Third, consumption is determined by current income.

Note: The marginal propensity to consume, *MPC*, is the slope of the consumption function. The average propensity to consume, *APC = C/Y*, equals the slope of a line drawn from the origin to a point on the consumption function.

The Early Empirical Successes

Soon after Keynes proposed the consumption function, economists began collecting and examining data to test his conjectures. The earliest studies indicated that the Keynesian consumption function is a good approximation of how consumers behave.

In some of these studies, researchers surveyed households and collected data on consumption and income. They found that households with higher income consumed more, which confirms that the marginal propensity to consume is greater than zero. They also found that households with higher income saved more, which confirms that the marginal propensity to consume is less than one. In addition, these researchers found that higher-income households saved a larger fraction of their income, which confirms that the average propensity to consume falls as income rises. Thus, these data verified Keynes's conjectures about the marginal and average propensities to consume.

In other studies, researchers examined aggregate data on consumption and income for the period between the two world wars. These data also supported the Keynesian consumption function. In years when income was unusually low, such as during the depths of the Great Depression, both consumption and saving were low, indicating that the marginal propensity to consume is between zero and one. In addition, during those years of low income, the ratio of consumption to income was high, confirming Keynes's second conjecture. Finally, because the correlation between income and consumption was so strong, no other variable appeared to be important for explaining consumption. Thus, the data also confirmed Keynes's third conjecture that income is the primary determinant of how much people choose to consume.

Secular Stagnation, Simon Kuznets, and the Consumption Puzzle

Although the Keynesian consumption function met with early successes, two anomalies soon arose. Both concern Keynes's conjecture that the average propensity to consume falls as income rises.

The first anomaly became apparent after some economists made a dire — and, it turned out, erroneous — prediction during World War II. On the basis of the Keynesian consumption function, these economists reasoned that as incomes in the economy grew over time, households would consume a smaller and smaller fraction of their incomes. They feared that there might not be enough profitable investment projects to absorb all this saving. If so, the low consumption would lead to an inadequate demand for goods and services, resulting in a depression once the wartime demand from the government ceased. In other words, on the basis of the Keynesian consumption function, these economists predicted that the economy would experience what they called *secular stagnation* — a long depression of indefinite duration — unless fiscal policy was used to expand aggregate demand.

Fortunately for the economy, but unfortunately for the Keynesian consumption function, the end of World War II did not throw the country into another depression. Although incomes were much higher after the war than before, these higher incomes did not lead to large increases in the rate of saving. Keynes's conjecture that the average propensity to consume would fall as income rose appeared not to hold.

The second anomaly arose when economist Simon Kuznets constructed new aggregate data on consumption and income dating back to 1869. Kuznets assembled these data in the 1940s and would later receive the Nobel Prize for this work. He discovered that the ratio of consumption to income was remarkably stable from decade to decade, despite large increases in income over the period he studied. Again, Keynes's conjecture that the average propensity to consume would fall as income rose appeared not to hold.

The failure of the secular-stagnation hypothesis and the findings of Kuznets both indicated that the average propensity to consume is fairly constant over long periods of time. This fact presented a puzzle that motivated much of the subsequent work on consumption. Economists wanted to know why some studies confirmed Keynes's conjectures and others refuted them. That is, why did Keynes's conjectures hold up well in the studies of household data and in the studies of short time-series, but fail when long time-series were examined?

figure 16-2

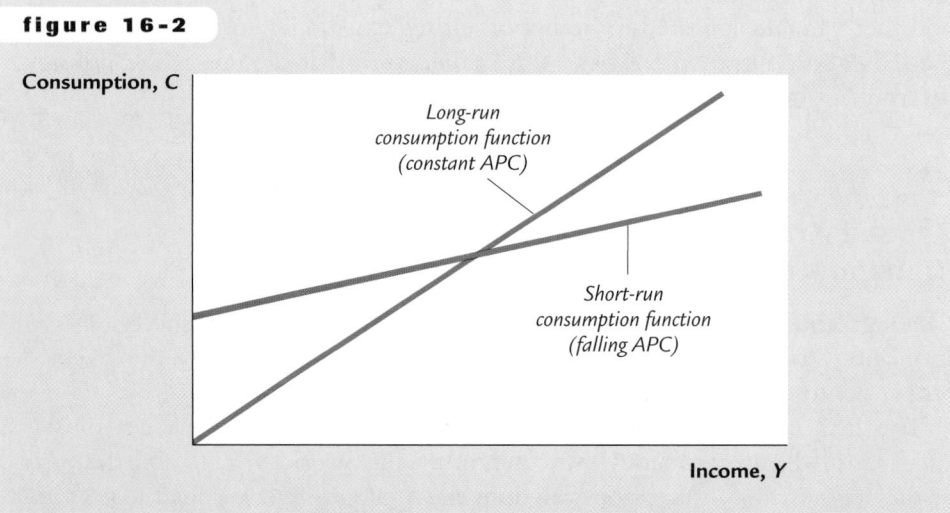

The Consumption Puzzle Studies of household data and short time-series found a relationship between consumption and income similar to the one Keynes conjectured. In the figure, this relationship is called the short-run consumption function. But studies of long time-series found that the average propensity to consume did not vary systematically with income. This relationship is called the long-run consumption function. Notice that the short-run consumption function has a falling average propensity to consume, whereas the long-run consumption function has a constant average propensity to consume.

Figure 16-2 illustrates the puzzle. The evidence suggested that there were two consumption functions. For the household data or for the short time-series, the Keynesian consumption function appeared to work well. Yet for the long time-series, the consumption function appeared to have a constant average propensity to consume. In Figure 16-2, these two relationships between consumption and income are called the short-run and long-run consumption functions. Economists needed to explain how these two consumption functions could be consistent with each other.

In the 1950s, Franco Modigliani and Milton Friedman each proposed explanations of these seemingly contradictory findings. Both economists later won Nobel Prizes, in part because of their work on consumption. But before we see how Modigliani and Friedman tried to solve the consumption puzzle, we must discuss Irving Fisher's contribution to consumption theory. Both Modigliani's life-cycle hypothesis and Friedman's permanent-income hypothesis rely on the theory of consumer behavior proposed much earlier by Irving Fisher.

16-2 | Irving Fisher and Intertemporal Choice

The consumption function introduced by Keynes relates current consumption to current income. This relationship, however, is incomplete at best. When people decide how much to consume and how much to save, they consider both the present and the future. The more consumption they enjoy today, the less they will be able to enjoy tomorrow. In making this tradeoff, households must look ahead to the income they expect to receive in the future and to the consumption of goods and services they hope to be able to afford.

The economist Irving Fisher developed the model with which economists analyze how rational, forward-looking consumers make intertemporal choices—that is, choices involving different periods of time. Fisher's model illuminates the constraints consumers face, the preferences they have, and how these constraints and preferences together determine their choices about consumption and saving.

The Intertemporal Budget Constraint

Most people would prefer to increase the quantity or quality of the goods and services they consume—to wear nicer clothes, eat at better restaurants, or see more movies. The reason people consume less than they desire is that their consumption is constrained by their income. In other words, consumers face a limit on how much they can spend, called a *budget constraint*. When they are deciding how much to consume today versus how much to save for the future, they face an **intertemporal budget constraint,** which measures the total resources available for consumption today and in the future. Our first step in developing Fisher's model is to examine this constraint in some detail.

To keep things simple, we examine the decision facing a consumer who lives for two periods. Period one represents the consumer's youth, and period two represents the consumer's old age. The consumer earns income Y_1 and consumes C_1 in period one, and earns income Y_2 and consumes C_2 in period two. (All variables are real—that is, adjusted for inflation.) Because the consumer has the opportunity to borrow and save, consumption in any single period can be either greater or less than income in that period.

Consider how the consumer's income in the two periods constrains consumption in the two periods. In the first period, saving equals income minus consumption. That is,

$$S = Y_1 - C_1,$$

where S is saving. In the second period, consumption equals the accumulated saving, including the interest earned on that saving, plus second-period income. That is,

$$C_2 = (1 + r)S + Y_2,$$

where r is the real interest rate. For example, if the interest rate is 5 percent, then for every $1 of saving in period one, the consumer enjoys an extra $1.05 of consumption in period two. Because there is no third period, the consumer does not save in the second period.

Note that the variable S can represent either saving or borrowing and that these equations hold in both cases. If first-period consumption is less than first-period income, the consumer is saving, and S is greater than zero. If first-period consumption exceeds first-period income, the consumer is borrowing, and S is less than zero. For simplicity, we assume that the interest rate for borrowing is the same as the interest rate for saving.

To derive the consumer's budget constraint, combine the two equations above. Substitute the first equation for S into the second equation to obtain

$$C_2 = (1 + r)(Y_1 - C_1) + Y_2.$$

To make the equation easier to interpret, we must rearrange terms. To place all the consumption terms together, bring $(1 + r)C_1$ from the right-hand side to the left-hand side of the equation to obtain

$$(1 + r)C_1 + C_2 = (1 + r)Y_1 + Y_2.$$

Now divide both sides by $1 + r$ to obtain

$$C_1 + \frac{C_2}{1 + r} = Y_1 + \frac{Y_2}{1 + r}.$$

This equation relates consumption in the two periods to income in the two periods. It is the standard way of expressing the consumer's intertemporal budget constraint.

The consumer's budget constraint is easily interpreted. If the interest rate is zero, the budget constraint shows that total consumption in the two periods equals total income in the two periods. In the usual case in which the interest

figure 16-3

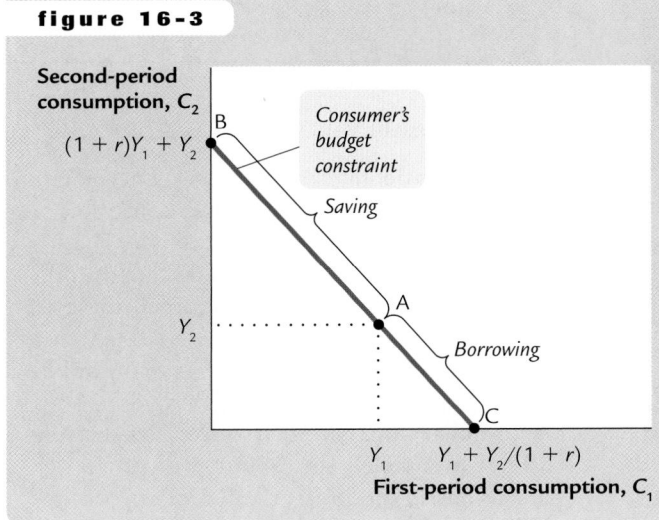

Second-period consumption, C_2

$(1 + r)Y_1 + Y_2$

B

Consumer's budget constraint

Saving

A

Y_2

Borrowing

C

Y_1 $Y_1 + Y_2/(1 + r)$

First-period consumption, C_1

The Consumer's Budget Constraint
This figure shows the combinations of first-period and second-period consumption the consumer can choose. If he chooses points between A and B, he consumes less than his income in the first period and saves the rest for the second period. If he chooses points between A and C, he consumes more than his income in the first period and borrows to make up the difference.

rate is greater than zero, future consumption and future income are discounted by a factor $1 + r$. This **discounting** arises from the interest earned on savings. In essence, because the consumer earns interest on current income that is saved, future income is worth less than current income. Similarly, because future consumption is paid for out of savings that have earned interest, future consumption costs less than current consumption. The factor $1/(1 + r)$ is the price of second-period consumption measured in terms of first-period consumption: it is the amount of first-period consumption that the consumer must forgo to obtain 1 unit of second-period consumption.

Figure 16-3 graphs the consumer's budget constraint. Three points are marked on this figure. At point A, the consumer consumes exactly his income in each period ($C_1 = Y_1$ and $C_2 = Y_2$), so there is neither saving nor borrowing between the two periods. At point B, the consumer consumes nothing in the first period ($C_1 = 0$) and saves all income, so second-period consumption C_2 is $(1 + r)Y_1 + Y_2$. At point C, the consumer plans to consume nothing in the second period ($C_2 = 0$) and borrows as much as possible against second-period income, so first-period consumption C_1 is $Y_1 + Y_2/(1 + r)$. Of course, these are only three of the many combinations of first- and second-period consumption that the consumer can afford: all the points on the line from B to C are available to the consumer.

Consumer Preferences

The consumer's preferences regarding consumption in the two periods can be represented by **indifference curves.** An indifference curve shows the combinations of first-period and second-period consumption that make the consumer equally happy.

---

f y i

PRESENT VALUE, OR WHY A $1,000,000 PRIZE IS WORTH ONLY $623,000

The use of discounting in the consumer's budget constraint illustrates an important fact of economic life: a dollar in the future is less valuable than a dollar today. This is true because a dollar today can be deposited in an interest-bearing bank account and produce more than one dollar in the future. If the interest rate is 5 percent, for instance, then a dollar today can be turned to $1.05 dollars next year, $1.1025 in two years, $1.1576 in three years, . . . , or $2.65 in 20 years.

Economists use a concept called *present value* to compare dollar amounts from different times. The present value of any amount in the future is the amount that would be needed today, given available interest rates, to produce that future amount. Thus, if you are going to be paid X dollars in T years and the interest rate is r, then the present value of that payment is

$$\text{Present Value} = X/(1+r)^T.$$

In light of this definition, we can see a new interpretation of the consumer's budget constraint in our two-period consumption problem. The intertemporal budget constraint states that the present value of consumption must equal the present value of income.

The concept of present value has many applications. Suppose, for instance, that you won a million-dollar lottery. Such prizes are usually paid out over time—say, $50,000 a year for 20 years. What is the present value of such a delayed prize? By applying the above formula for each of the 20 payments and adding up the result, we learn that the million-dollar prize, discounted at an interest rate of 5 percent, has a present value of only $623,000. (If the prize were paid out as a dollar a year for a million years, the present value would be a mere $20!) Sometimes a million dollars isn't all it's cracked up to be.

Figure 16-4 shows two of the consumer's many indifference curves. The consumer is indifferent among combinations W, X, and Y, because they are all on the same curve. Not surprisingly, if the consumer's first-period consumption is reduced, say from point W to point X, second-period consumption must increase to keep him equally happy. If first-period consumption is reduced again, from point X to point Y, the amount of extra second-period consumption he requires for compensation is greater.

The slope at any point on the indifference curve shows how much second-period consumption the consumer requires in order to be compensated for a 1-unit reduction in first-period consumption. This slope is the **marginal rate of substitution** between first-period consumption and second-period consumption. It tells us the rate at which the consumer is willing to substitute second-period consumption for first-period consumption.

Notice that the indifference curves in Figure 16-4 are not straight lines and, as a result, the marginal rate of substitution depends on the levels of consumption in the two periods. When first-period consumption is high and second-period consumption is low, as at point W, the marginal rate of substitution is low: the consumer requires only a little extra second-period consumption to

figure 16-4

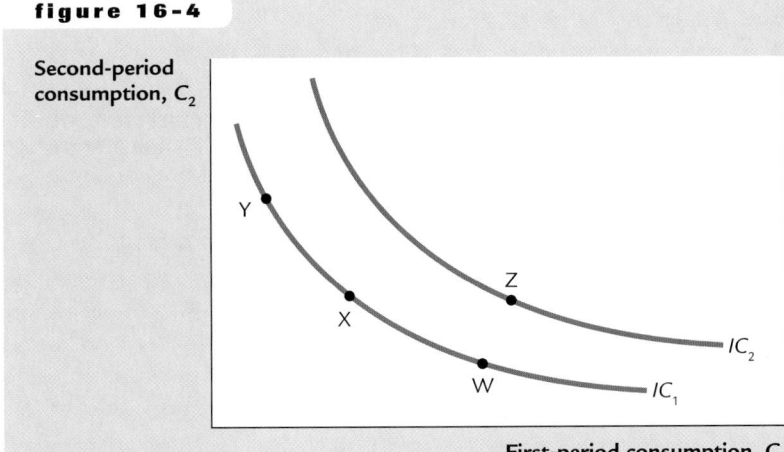

Second-period consumption, C_2

First-period consumption, C_1

The Consumer's Preferences Indifference curves represent the consumer's preferences over first-period and second-period consumption. An indifference curve gives the combinations of consumption in the two periods that make the consumer equally happy. This figure shows two of many indifference curves. Higher indifference curves such as IC_2 are preferred to lower curves such as IC_1. The consumer is equally happy at points W, X, and Y, but prefers point Z to points W, X, or Y.

give up 1 unit of first-period consumption. When first-period consumption is low and second-period consumption is high, as at point Y, the marginal rate of substitution is high: the consumer requires much additional second-period consumption to give up 1 unit of first-period consumption.

The consumer is equally happy at all points on a given indifference curve, but he prefers some indifference curves to others. Because he prefers more consumption to less, he prefers higher indifference curves to lower ones. In Figure 16-4, the consumer prefers the points on curve IC_2 to the points on curve IC_1.

The set of indifference curves gives a complete ranking of the consumer's preferences. It tells us that the consumer prefers point Z to point W, but that may be obvious because point Z has more consumption in both periods. Yet compare point Z and point Y: point Z has more consumption in period one and less in period two. Which is preferred, Z or Y? Because Z is on a higher indifference curve than Y, we know that the consumer prefers point Z to point Y. Hence, we can use the set of indifference curves to rank any combinations of first-period and second-period consumption.

Optimization

Having discussed the consumer's budget constraint and preferences, we can consider the decision about how much to consume. The consumer would like to end up with the best possible combination of consumption in the two periods—that is, on the highest possible indifference curve. But the budget constraint requires that the consumer also end up on or below the budget line, because the budget line measures the total resources available to him.

figure 16-5

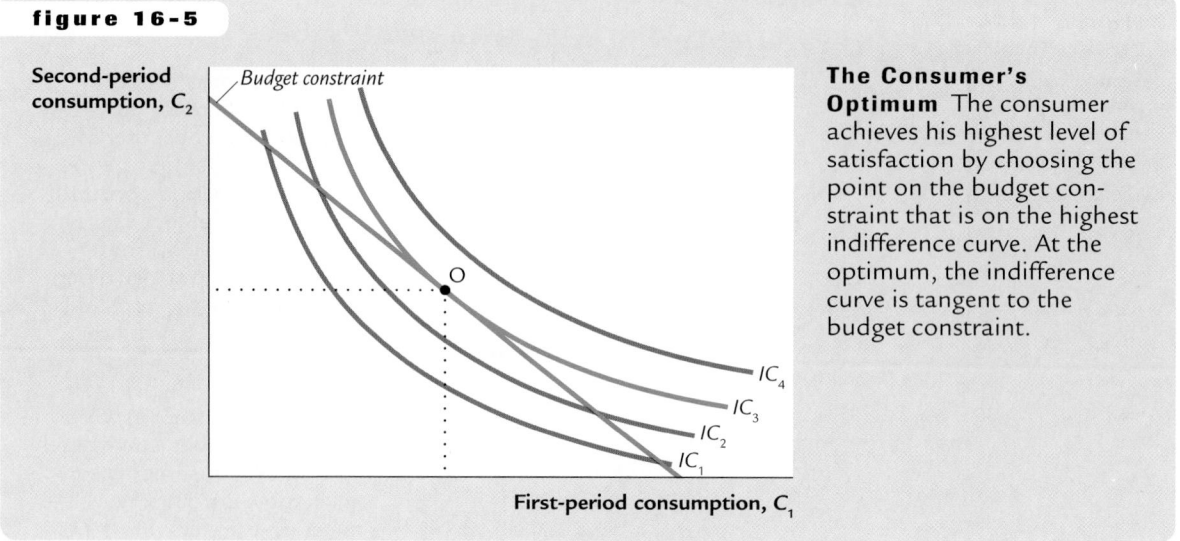

Second-period consumption, C_2

Budget constraint

O

IC_4
IC_3
IC_2
IC_1

First-period consumption, C_1

The Consumer's Optimum The consumer achieves his highest level of satisfaction by choosing the point on the budget constraint that is on the highest indifference curve. At the optimum, the indifference curve is tangent to the budget constraint.

Figure 16-5 shows that many indifference curves cross the budget line. The highest indifference curve that the consumer can obtain without violating the budget constraint is the indifference curve that just barely touches the budget line, which is curve IC_3 in the figure. The point at which the curve and line touch—point O for "optimum"—is the best combination of consumption in the two periods that the consumer can afford.

Notice that, at the optimum, the slope of the indifference curve equals the slope of the budget line. The indifference curve is *tangent* to the budget line. The slope of the indifference curve is the marginal rate of substitution *MRS,* and the slope of the budget line is 1 plus the real interest rate. We conclude that at point O,

$$MRS = 1 + r.$$

The consumer chooses consumption in the two periods so that the marginal rate of substitution equals 1 plus the real interest rate.

How Changes in Income Affect Consumption

Now that we have seen how the consumer makes the consumption decision, let's examine how consumption responds to an increase in income. An increase in either Y_1 or Y_2 shifts the budget constraint outward, as in Figure 16-6. The higher budget constraint allows the consumer to choose a better combination of first- and second-period consumption—that is, the consumer can now reach a higher indifference curve.

In Figure 16-6, the consumer responds to the shift in his budget constraint by choosing more consumption in both periods. Although not implied by the logic of the model alone, this situation is the most usual. If a consumer wants more of a good when his or her income rises, economists call it a **normal**

figure 16-6

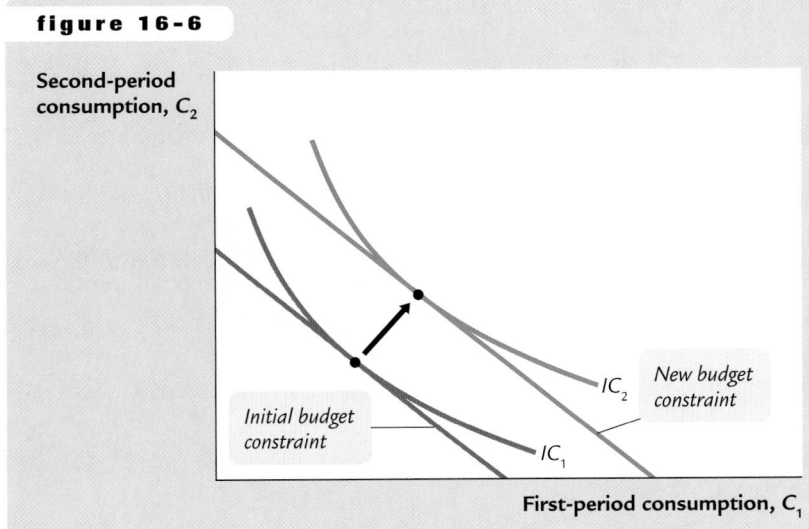

Second-period consumption, C_2

An Increase in Income
An increase in either first-period income or second-period income shifts the budget constraint outward. If consumption in period one and consumption in period two are both normal goods, this increase in income raises consumption in both periods.

IC_2 New budget constraint

Initial budget constraint

IC_1

First-period consumption, C_1

good. The indifference curves in Figure 16-6 are drawn under the assumption that consumption in period one and consumption in period two are both normal goods.

The key conclusion from Figure 16-6 is that regardless of whether the increase in income occurs in the first period or the second period, the consumer spreads it over consumption in both periods. This behavior is sometimes called *consumption smoothing.* Because the consumer can borrow and lend between periods, the timing of the income is irrelevant to how much is consumed today (except, of course, that future income is discounted by the interest rate). The lesson of this analysis is that consumption depends on the present value of current and future income—that is, on

$$\text{Present Value of Income} = Y_1 + \frac{Y_2}{1 + r}.$$

Notice that this conclusion is quite different from that reached by Keynes. *Keynes posited that a person's current consumption depends largely on his current income. Fisher's model says, instead, that consumption is based on the resources the consumer expects over his lifetime.*

How Changes in the Real Interest Rate Affect Consumption

Let's now use Fisher's model to consider how a change in the real interest rate alters the consumer's choices. There are two cases to consider: the case in which the consumer is initially saving and the case in which he is initially borrowing. Here we discuss the saving case, and Problem 1 at the end of the chapter asks you to analyze the borrowing case.

Figure 16-7 shows that an increase in the real interest rate rotates the consumer's budget line around the point (Y_1, Y_2) and, thereby, alters the amount

figure 16-7

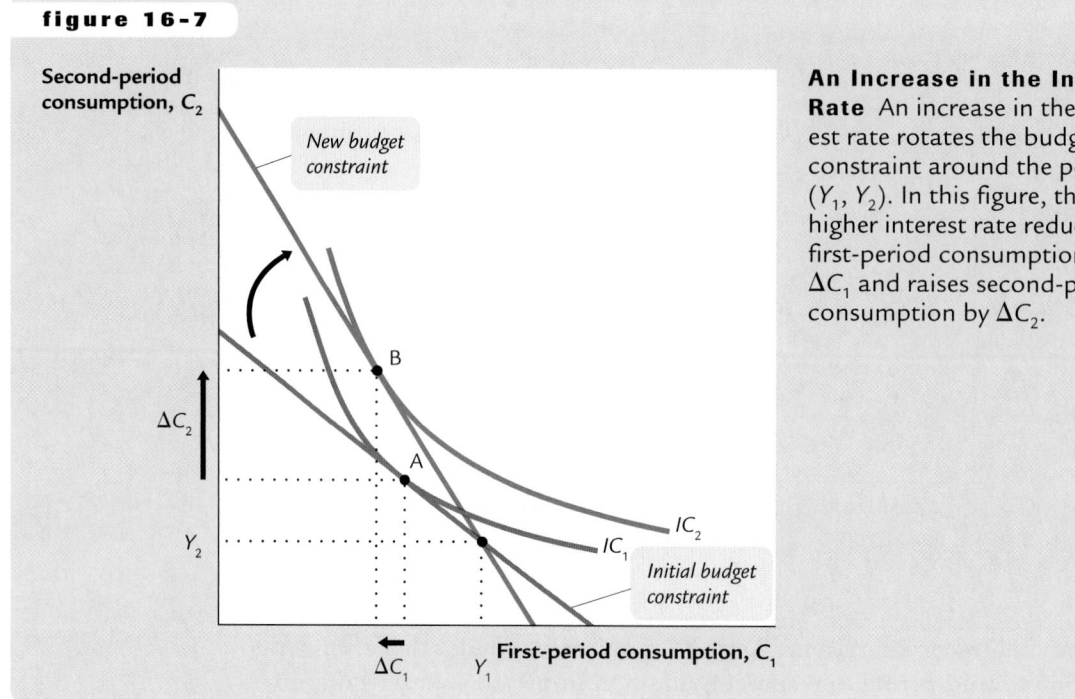

Second-period consumption, C_2

New budget constraint

B

ΔC_2

A

IC_2

Y_2

IC_1

Initial budget constraint

ΔC_1 Y_1 First-period consumption, C_1

An Increase in the Interest Rate An increase in the interest rate rotates the budget constraint around the point (Y_1, Y_2). In this figure, the higher interest rate reduces first-period consumption by ΔC_1 and raises second-period consumption by ΔC_2.

of consumption he chooses in both periods. Here, the consumer moves from point A to point B. You can see that for the indifference curves drawn in this figure first-period consumption falls and second-period consumption rises.

Economists decompose the impact of an increase in the real interest rate on consumption into two effects: an **income effect** and a **substitution effect.** Textbooks in microeconomics discuss these effects in detail. We summarize them briefly here.

The income effect is the change in consumption that results from the movement to a higher indifference curve. Because the consumer is a saver rather than a borrower (as indicated by the fact that first-period consumption is less than first-period income), the increase in the interest rate makes him better off (as reflected by the movement to a higher indifference curve). If consumption in period one and consumption in period two are both normal goods, the consumer will want to spread this improvement in his welfare over both periods. This income effect tends to make the consumer want more consumption in both periods.

The substitution effect is the change in consumption that results from the change in the relative price of consumption in the two periods. In particular, consumption in period two becomes less expensive relative to consumption in period one when the interest rate rises. That is, because the real interest rate earned on saving is higher, the consumer must now give up less first-period consumption to obtain an extra unit of second-period consumption. This substitution effect tends to make the consumer choose more consumption in period two and less consumption in period one.

The consumer's choice depends on both the income effect and the substitution effect. Both effects act to increase the amount of second-period consumption; hence, we can confidently conclude that an increase in the real interest rate raises second-period consumption. But the two effects have opposite impacts on first-period consumption. Hence, the increase in the interest rate could either lower or raise first-period consumption.

CASE STUDY

Consumption and the Real Interest Rate

Irving Fisher's model shows that, depending on the consumer's preferences, changes in the real interest rate could either raise or lower consumption. In other words, economic theory alone cannot predict how the interest rate influences consumption. Therefore, economists have devoted much energy to examining empirically how the interest rate affects consumption and saving.

Figure 16-8 presents a scatterplot of the personal saving rate and the real interest rate. This figure shows that there is no apparent relationship between the two variables. Some economists interpret these data as showing that saving does not depend on the interest rate. They explain this result by claiming that the income and substitution effects of higher interest rates approximately cancel each other.

This sort of evidence, however, is not completely persuasive. The task of estimating the sensitivity of saving to the interest rate is complicated by the identification problem discussed in Chapter 3. That is, when variables are related in more than one way, as these two variables are, it is tricky to separate one relationship from another. Nonetheless, more sophisticated examinations of the data usually find that the real interest rate has little effect on consumption

figure 16-8

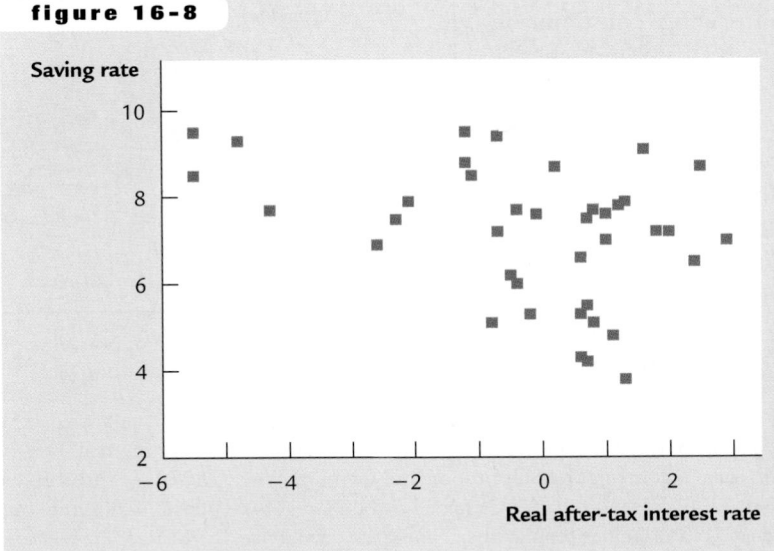

A Scatterplot of Saving and the Interest Rate This figure uses annual data from 1959 to 1997 to examine whether there is any relationship between the personal saving rate and the real interest rate. No relationship is evident.

Note: The personal saving rate is personal saving as a share of personal disposable income. The real interest rate is the after-tax interest rate on six-month Treasury bills minus inflation rate; this was calculated assuming a tax rate of 30 percent.

Source: U.S. Department of Commerce, U.S. Department of the Treasury, and author's calculations.

and saving. Keynes's third conjecture—that consumption does not depend much on the interest rate—has held up well in the face of much empirical testing.[1]

Constraints on Borrowing

Fisher's model assumes that the consumer can borrow as well as save. The ability to borrow allows current consumption to exceed current income. In essence, when the consumer borrows, he consumes some of his future income today. Yet for many people such borrowing is impossible. For example, a student wishing to enjoy spring break in Florida would probably be unable to finance this vacation with a bank loan. Let's examine how Fisher's analysis changes if the consumer cannot borrow.

The inability to borrow prevents current consumption from exceeding current income. A constraint on borrowing can therefore be expressed as

$$C_1 \leq Y_1.$$

This inequality states that consumption in period one must be less than or equal to income in period one. This additional constraint on the consumer is called a **borrowing constraint** or, sometimes, a *liquidity constraint.*

Figure 16-9 shows how this borrowing constraint restricts the consumer's set of choices. The consumer's choice must satisfy both the intertemporal budget constraint and the borrowing constraint. The shaded area represents the combinations of first-period consumption and second-period consumption that satisfy both constraints.

Figure 16-10 shows how this borrowing constraint affects the consumption decision. There are two possibilities. In panel (a), the consumer wishes to consume less in period one than he earns. The borrowing constraint is not binding in this case and, therefore, does not affect consumption. In panel (b), the consumer would like to consume more in period one than he earns. In this case, the consumer consumes all his first-period income, and the borrowing constraint prevents him from consuming more.

The analysis of borrowing constraints leads us to conclude that

"What I'd like, basically, is a temporary line of credit just to tide me over the rest of my life."

---

[1] For some of the recent research on the relationship between consumption and the real interest rate, see Robert E. Hall, "Intertemporal Substitution and Consumption," *Journal of Political Economy* 96 (April 1988): 339–357; and John Y. Campbell and N. Gregory Mankiw, "Consumption, Income, and Interest Rates: Reinterpreting the Time-Series Evidence," *NBER Macroeconomics Annual* (1989): 185–216.

figure 16-9

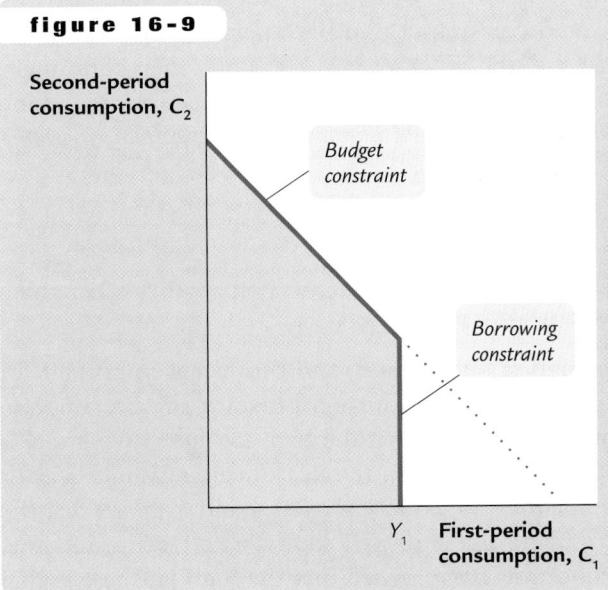

Second-period consumption, C_2

Budget constraint

Borrowing constraint

Y_1 First-period consumption, C_1

A Borrowing Constraint If the consumer cannot borrow, he faces the additional constraint that first-period consumption cannot exceed first-period income. The shaded area represents the combination of first-period and second-period consumption the consumer can choose.

figure 16-10

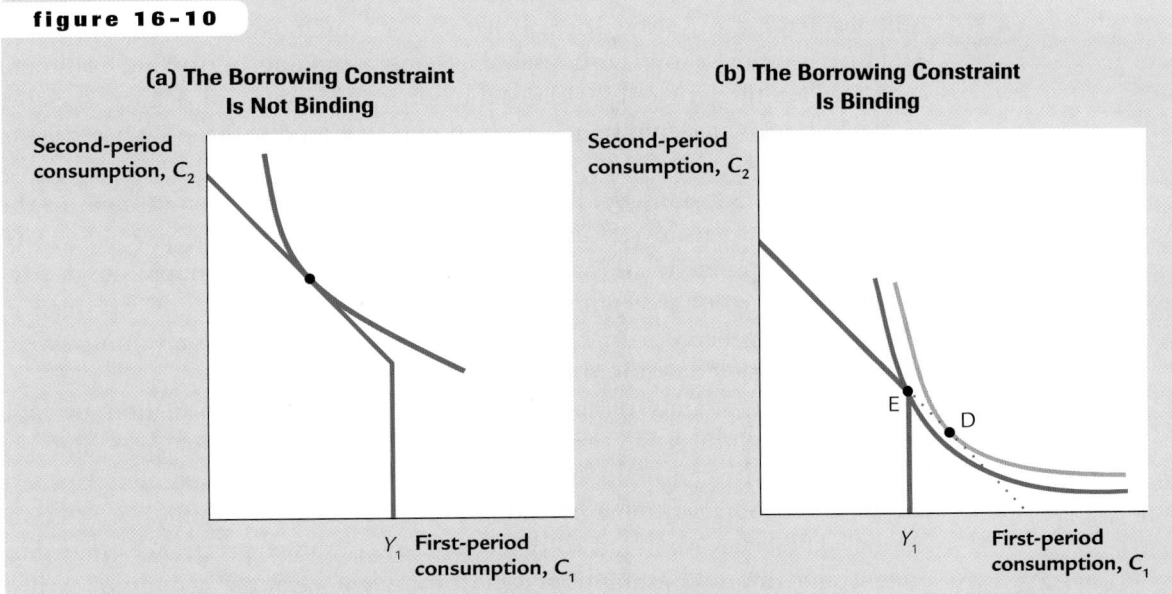

(a) The Borrowing Constraint Is Not Binding

Second-period consumption, C_2

Y_1 First-period consumption, C_1

(b) The Borrowing Constraint Is Binding

Second-period consumption, C_2

E   D

Y_1 First-period consumption, C_1

The Consumer's Optimum With a Borrowing Constraint When the consumer faces a borrowing constraint, there are two possible situations. In panel (a), the consumer chooses first-period consumption to be less than first-period income, so the borrowing constraint is not binding and does not affect consumption in either period. In panel (b), the borrowing constraint is binding. The consumer would like to borrow and choose point D. But because borrowing is not allowed, the best available choice is point E. When the borrowing constraint is binding, first-period consumption equals first-period income.

there are two consumption functions. For some consumers, the borrowing constraint is not binding, and consumption in both periods depends on the present value of lifetime income, $Y_1 + [Y_2/(1 + r)]$. For other consumers, the borrowing constraint binds, and the consumption function is $C_1 = Y_1$ and $C_2 = Y_2$. *Hence, for those consumers who would like to borrow but cannot, consumption depends only on current income.*

CASE STUDY

The High Japanese Saving Rate

Japan has one of the world's highest saving rates, and this fact is important for understanding both the long-run and short-run performance of its economy. On the one hand, many economists believe that the high Japanese saving rate is a key to the rapid growth Japan experienced in the decades after World War II. Indeed, the Solow growth model developed in Chapters 4 and 5 shows that the saving rate is a primary determinant of a country's steady-state level of income. On the other hand, some economists have argued that the high Japanese saving rate has contributed to Japan's slump during the 1990s. High saving means low consumer spending, which according to the *IS–LM* model of Chapters 10 and 11 translates into low aggregate demand and reduced income.

Why do the Japanese consume a much smaller fraction of their income than Americans? One reason is that it is harder for households to borrow in Japan. As Fisher's model shows, a household facing a binding borrowing constraint consumes less than it would without the borrowing constraint. Hence, societies in which borrowing constraints are common will tend to have higher rates of saving.

One reason that households often wish to borrow is to buy a home. In the United States, a person can usually buy a home with a down payment of 10 percent. A home buyer in Japan cannot borrow nearly this much: down payments of 40 percent are common. Moreover, housing prices are very high in Japan, primarily because land prices are high. A Japanese family must save a great deal if it is ever to afford its own home.

Although constraints on borrowing are part of the explanation of high Japanese saving, there are many other differences between Japan and the United States that contribute to the difference in the saving rates. The Japanese tax system encourages saving by taxing capital income very lightly. In addition, cultural differences may lead to differences in consumer preferences regarding present and future consumption. One prominent Japanese economist writes, "The Japanese are simply *different*. They are more risk averse and more patient. If this is true, the long-run implication is that Japan will absorb all the wealth in the world. I refuse to comment on this explanation."[2]

---

[2] Fumio Hayashi, "Why Is Japan's Saving Rate So Apparently High?" *NBER Macroeconomics Annual* (1986): 147–210.

16-3 Franco Modigliani and the Life-Cycle Hypothesis

In a series of papers written in the 1950s, Franco Modigliani and his collaborators Albert Ando and Richard Brumberg used Fisher's model of consumer behavior to study the consumption function. One of their goals was to solve the consumption puzzle—that is, to explain the apparently conflicting pieces of evidence that came to light when Keynes's consumption function was brought to the data. According to Fisher's model, consumption depends on a person's lifetime income. Modigliani emphasized that income varies systematically over people's lives and that saving allows consumers to move income from those times in life when income is high to those times when it is low. This interpretation of consumer behavior formed the basis for his **life-cycle hypothesis.**[3]

The Hypothesis

One important reason that income varies over a person's life is retirement. Most people plan to stop working at about age 65, and they expect their incomes to fall when they retire. Yet they do not want a large drop in their standard of living, as measured by their consumption. To maintain consumption after retirement, people must save during their working years. Let's see what this motive for saving implies for the consumption function.

Consider a consumer who expects to live another T years, has wealth of W, and expects to earn income Y until she retires R years from now. What level of consumption will the consumer choose if she wishes to maintain a smooth level of consumption over her life?

The consumer's lifetime resources are composed of initial wealth W and lifetime earnings of $R \times Y$. (For simplicity, we are assuming an interest rate of zero; if the interest rate were greater than zero, we would need to take account of interest earned on savings as well.) The consumer can divide up her lifetime resources among her T remaining years of life. We assume that she wishes to achieve the smoothest possible path of consumption over her lifetime. Therefore, she divides this total of $W + RY$ equally among the T years and each year consumes

$$C = (W + RY)/T.$$

We can write this person's consumption function as

$$C = (1/T)W + (R/T)Y.$$

---

[3] For references to the large body of work on the life-cycle hypothesis, a good place to start is the lecture Modigliani gave when he won the Nobel Prize. Franco Modigliani, "Life Cycle, Individual Thrift, and the Wealth of Nations," *American Economic Review* 76 (June 1986): 297–313.

For example, if the consumer expects to live for 50 more years and work for 30 of them, then $T = 50$ and $R = 30$, so her consumption function is

$$C = 0.02W + 0.6Y.$$

This equation says that consumption depends on both income and wealth. An extra $1 of income per year raises consumption by $0.60 per year, and an extra $1 of wealth raises consumption by $0.02 per year.

If every individual in the economy plans consumption like this, then the aggregate consumption function is much the same as the individual one. In particular, aggregate consumption depends on both wealth and income. That is, the economy's consumption function is

$$C = \alpha W + \beta Y,$$

where the parameter α is the marginal propensity to consume out of wealth, and the parameter β is the marginal propensity to consume out of income.

Implications

Figure 16-11 graphs the relationship between consumption and income predicted by the life-cycle model. For any given level of wealth W, the model yields a conventional consumption function similar to the one shown in Figure 16-1. Notice, however, that the intercept of the consumption function, which shows what would happen to consumption if income ever fell to zero, is not a fixed value, as it is in Figure 16-1. Instead, the intercept here is αW and, thus, depends on the level of wealth.

figure 16-11

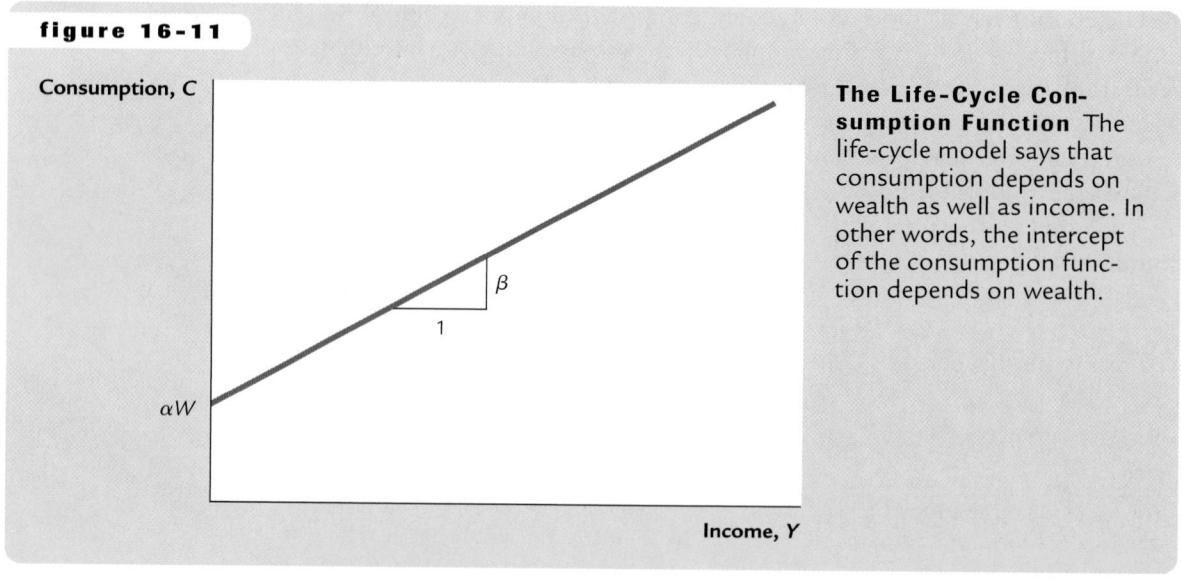

The Life-Cycle Consumption Function The life-cycle model says that consumption depends on wealth as well as income. In other words, the intercept of the consumption function depends on wealth.

This life-cycle model of consumer behavior can solve the consumption puzzle. According to the life-cycle consumption function, the average propensity to consume is

$$C/Y = \alpha(W/Y) + \beta.$$

Because wealth does not vary proportionately with income from person to person or from year to year, we should find that high income corresponds to a low average propensity to consume when looking at data across individuals or over short periods of time. But, over long periods of time, wealth and income grow together, resulting in a constant ratio W/Y and thus a constant average propensity to consume.

To make the same point somewhat differently, consider how the consumption function changes over time. As Figure 16-11 shows, for any given level of wealth, the life-cycle consumption function looks like the one Keynes suggested. But this function holds only in the short run when wealth is constant. In the long run, as wealth increases, the consumption function shifts upward, as in Figure 16-12. This upward shift prevents the average propensity to consume from falling as income increases. In this way, Modigliani resolved the consumption puzzle posed by Simon Kuznets's data.

The life-cycle model makes many other predictions as well. Most important, it predicts that saving varies over a person's lifetime. If a person begins adulthood with no wealth, she will accumulate wealth during her working years and then run down her wealth during her retirement years. Figure 16-13 illustrates the consumer's income, consumption, and wealth over her adult life.

figure 16-12

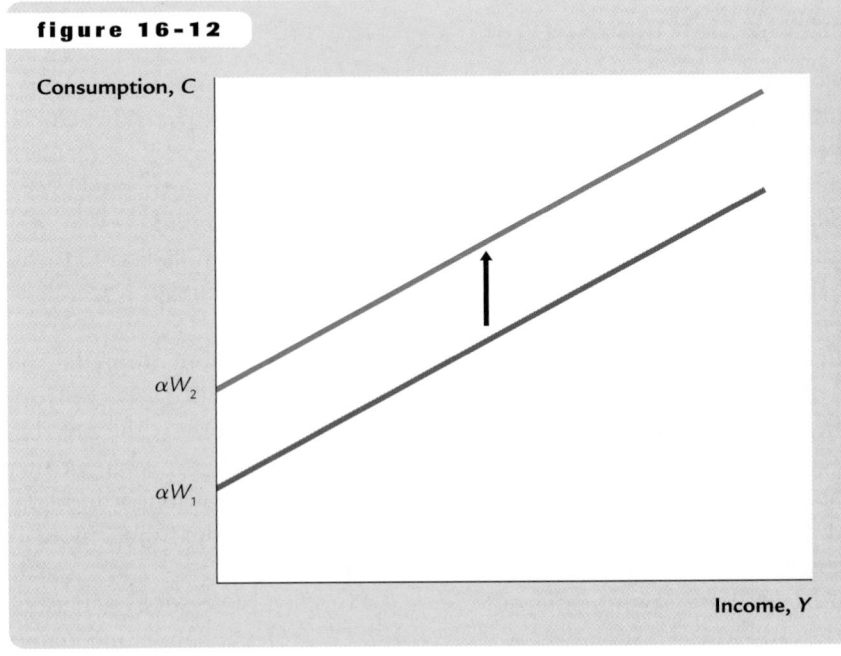

How Changes in Wealth Shift the Consumption Function If consumption depends on wealth, then an increase in wealth shifts the consumption function upward. Thus, the short-run consumption function (which holds wealth constant) will not continue to hold in the long run (as wealth rises over time).

figure 16-13

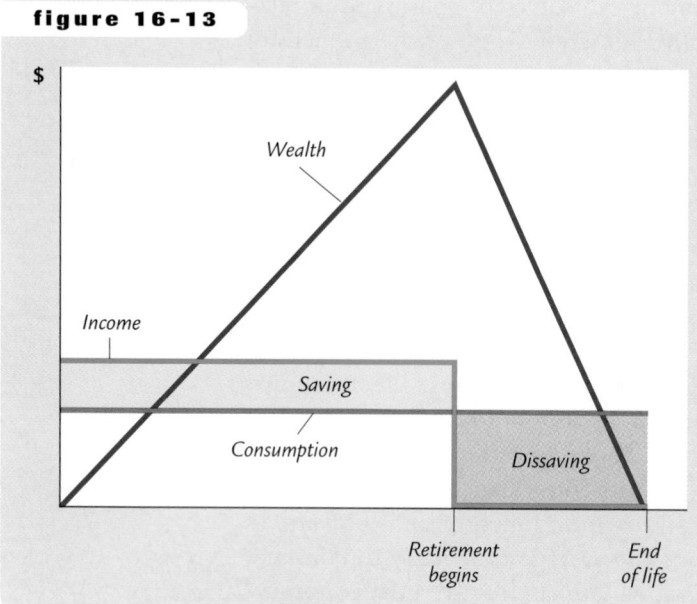

Consumption, Income, and Wealth Over the Life Cycle If the consumer smooths consumption over her life (as indicated by the horizontal consumption line), she will save and accumulate wealth during her working years and then dissave and run down her wealth during retirement.

According to the life-cycle hypothesis, because people want to smooth consumption over their lives, the young who are working save, while the old who are retired dissave.

CASE STUDY

The Consumption and Saving of the Elderly

Many economists have studied the consumption and saving of the elderly. Their findings present a problem for the life-cycle model. It appears that the elderly do not dissave as much as the model predicts. In other words, the elderly do not run down their wealth as quickly as one would expect if they were trying to smooth their consumption over their remaining years of life.

There are two chief explanations for why the elderly do not dissave to the extent that the model predicts. Each suggests a direction for further research on consumption.

The first explanation is that the elderly are concerned about unpredictable expenses. Additional saving that arises from uncertainty is called **precautionary saving.** One reason for precautionary saving by the elderly is the possibility of living longer than expected and thus having to provide for a longer than average span of retirement. Another reason is the possibility of illness and large medical bills. The elderly may respond to this uncertainty by saving more in order to be better prepared for these contingencies.

The precautionary-saving explanation is not completely persuasive, because the elderly can largely insure against these risks. To protect against uncertainty regarding life span, they can buy *annuities* from insurance companies. For a fixed fee, annuities offer a stream of income that lasts as long as the recipient lives. Uncertainty about medical expenses should be largely eliminated by Medicare, the government's health insurance plan for the elderly, and by private insurance plans.

The second explanation for the failure of the elderly to dissave is that they may want to leave bequests to their children. Economists have proposed various theories of the parent–child relationship and the bequest motive. In Chapter 15 we discussed some of these theories and their implications for consumption and fiscal policy.

Overall, research on the elderly suggests that the simplest life-cycle model cannot fully explain consumer behavior. There is no doubt that providing for retirement is an important motive for saving, but other motives, such as precautionary saving and bequests, appear important as well.[4]

16-4 Milton Friedman and the Permanent-Income Hypothesis

In a book published in 1957, Milton Friedman proposed the **permanent-income hypothesis** to explain consumer behavior. Friedman's permanent-income hypothesis complements Modigliani's life-cycle hypothesis: both use Irving Fisher's theory of the consumer to argue that consumption should not depend on current income alone. But unlike the life-cycle hypothesis, which emphasizes that income follows a regular pattern over a person's lifetime, the permanent-income hypothesis emphasizes that people experience random and temporary changes in their incomes from year to year.[5]

The Hypothesis

Friedman suggested that we view current income Y as the sum of two components, **permanent income** Y^P and **transitory income** Y^T. That is,

$$Y = Y^P + Y^T.$$

Permanent income is the part of income that people expect to persist into the future. Transitory income is the part of income that people do not expect to

---

[4] To read more about the consumption and saving of the elderly, see Albert Ando and Arthur Kennickell, "How Much (or Little) Life Cycle Saving Is There in Micro Data?" in Rudiger Dornbusch, Stanley Fischer, and John Bossons, eds., *Macroeconomics and Finance: Essays in Honor of Franco Modigliani* (Cambridge, MA: MIT Press, 1986); and Michael Hurd, "Research on the Elderly: Economic Status, Retirement, and Consumption and Saving," *Journal of Economic Literature* 28 (June 1990): 565–589.

[5] Milton Friedman, *A Theory of the Consumption Function* (Princeton, NJ: Princeton University Press, 1957).

persist. Put differently, permanent income is average income, and transitory income is the random deviation from that average.

To see how we might separate income into these two parts, consider these examples:

➤ Maria, who has a law degree, earned more this year than John, who is a high-school dropout. Maria's higher income resulted from higher permanent income, because her education will continue to provide her a higher salary.

➤ Sue, a Florida orange grower, earned less than usual this year because a freeze destroyed her crop. Bill, a California orange grower, earned more than usual because the freeze in Florida drove up the price of oranges. Bill's higher income resulted from higher transitory income, because he is no more likely than Sue to have good weather next year.

These examples show that different forms of income have different degrees of persistence. A good education provides a permanently higher income, whereas good weather provides only transitorily higher income. Although one can imagine intermediate cases, it is useful to keep things simple by supposing that there are only two kinds of income: permanent and transitory.

Friedman reasoned that consumption should depend primarily on permanent income, because consumers use saving and borrowing to smooth consumption in response to transitory changes in income. For example, if a person received a permanent raise of $10,000 per year, his consumption would rise by about as much. Yet if a person won $10,000 in a lottery, he would not consume it all in one year. Instead, he would spread the extra consumption over the rest of his life. Assuming an interest rate of zero and a remaining life span of 50 years, consumption would rise by only $200 per year in response to the $10,000 prize. Thus, consumers spend their permanent income, but they save rather than spend most of their transitory income.

Friedman concluded that we should view the consumption function as approximately

$$C = \alpha Y^P,$$

where α is a constant that measures the fraction of permanent income consumed. The permanent-income hypothesis, as expressed by this equation, states that consumption is proportional to permanent income.

Implications

The permanent-income hypothesis solves the consumption puzzle by suggesting that the standard Keynesian consumption function uses the wrong variable. According to the permanent-income hypothesis, consumption depends on permanent income; yet many studies of the consumption function try to relate consumption to current income. Friedman argued that this *errors-in-variables problem* explains the seemingly contradictory findings.

Let's see what Friedman's hypothesis implies for the average propensity to consume. Divide both sides of his consumption function by Y to obtain

$$APC = C/Y = \alpha Y^{\mathrm{p}}/Y.$$

According to the permanent-income hypothesis, the average propensity to consume depends on the ratio of permanent income to current income. When current income temporarily rises above permanent income, the average propensity to consume temporarily falls; when current income temporarily falls below permanent income, the average propensity to consume temporarily rises.

Now consider the studies of household data. Friedman reasoned that these data reflect a combination of permanent and transitory income. Households with high permanent income have proportionately higher consumption. If all variation in current income came from the permanent component, the average propensity to consume would be the same in all households. But some of the variation in income comes from the transitory component, and households with high transitory income do not have higher consumption. Therefore, researchers find that high-income households have, on average, lower average propensities to consume.

Similarly, consider the studies of time-series data. Friedman reasoned that year-to-year fluctuations in income are dominated by transitory income. Therefore, years of high income should be years of low average propensities to consume. But over long periods of time—say, from decade to decade—the variation in income comes from the permanent component. Hence, in long time-series, one should observe a constant average propensity to consume, as in fact Kuznets found.

CASE STUDY

The 1964 Tax Cut and the 1968 Tax Surcharge

The permanent-income hypothesis can help us to interpret how the economy responds to changes in fiscal policy. According to the $IS-LM$ model of Chapters 10 and 11, tax cuts stimulate consumption and raise aggregate demand, and tax increases depress consumption and reduce aggregate demand. The permanent-income hypothesis, however, predicts that consumption responds only to changes in permanent income. Therefore, transitory changes in taxes will have only a negligible effect on consumption and aggregate demand. If a change in taxes is to have a large effect on aggregate demand, it must be permanent.

Two changes in fiscal policy—the tax cut of 1964 and the tax surcharge of 1968—illustrate this principle. The tax cut of 1964 was popular. It was announced to be a major and permanent reduction in tax rates. As we discussed in Chapter 10, this policy change had the intended effect of stimulating the economy.

The tax surcharge of 1968 arose in a very different political climate. It became law because the economic advisers of President Lyndon Johnson believed that the increase in government spending from the Vietnam War had excessively stimulated aggregate demand. To offset this effect, they recommended a tax increase. But Johnson, aware that the war was already unpopular, feared the political repercussions of higher taxes. He finally agreed to a temporary tax surcharge—in essence, a one-year increase in taxes. The tax surcharge did not have the desired effect of reducing aggregate demand. Unemployment continued to fall, and inflation continued to rise.

The lesson to be learned from these episodes is that a full analysis of tax policy must go beyond the simple Keynesian consumption function; it must take into account the distinction between permanent and transitory income. If consumers expect a tax change to be temporary, it will have a smaller impact on consumption and aggregate demand.

Rational Expectations and Random-Walk Consumption

The permanent-income hypothesis is founded on Fisher's model of intertemporal choice. It builds on the idea that forward-looking consumers base their consumption decisions not only on their current income but also on the income they expect to receive in the future. Thus, the permanent-income hypothesis highlights that consumption depends on people's expectations.

Recent research on consumption has combined this view of the consumer with the assumption of rational expectations. The rational-expectations assumption states that people use all available information to make optimal forecasts about the future. You might recall from Chapter 13 that this assumption has potentially profound implications for the costs of stopping inflation. It can also have profound implications for consumption.

The economist Robert Hall was the first to derive the implications of rational expectations for consumption. He showed that if the permanent-income hypothesis is correct, and if consumers have rational expectations, then changes in consumption over time should be unpredictable. When changes in a variable are unpredictable, the variable is said to follow a *random walk*. According to Hall, the combination of the permanent-income hypothesis and rational expectations implies that consumption follows a random walk.

Hall reasoned as follows. According to the permanent-income hypothesis, consumers face fluctuating income and try their best to smooth their consumption over time. At any moment, consumers choose consumption based on their current expectations of their lifetime incomes. Over time, they change their consumption because they receive news that causes them to revise their expectations. For example, a person getting an unexpected promotion increases consumption, whereas a person getting an unexpected demotion decreases consumption. In other words, changes in consumption reflect "surprises" about lifetime income. If consumers are optimally using all available information, then they should be surprised only by events that were entirely unpredictable. Therefore, changes in their consumption should be unpredictable as well.[6]

---

[6] Robert E. Hall, "Stochastic Implications of the Life Cycle–Permanent Income Hypothesis: Theory and Evidence," *Journal of Political Economy* 86 (April 1978): 971–987.

The rational-expectations approach to consumption has implications not only for forecasting but also for the analysis of economic policies. *If consumers obey the permanent-income hypothesis and have rational expectations, then only unexpected policy changes influence consumption. These policy changes take effect when they change expectations.* For example, suppose that today Congress passes a tax increase to be effective next year. In this case, consumers receive the news about their lifetime incomes when Congress passes the law (or even earlier if the law's passage was predictable). The arrival of this news causes consumers to revise their expectations and reduce their consumption. The following year, when the tax hike goes into effect, consumption is unchanged because no news has arrived.

Hence, if consumers have rational expectations, policymakers influence the economy not only through their actions but also through the public's expectations of their actions. Expectations, however, cannot be observed directly. Therefore, it is often hard to know how and when changes in fiscal policy alter aggregate demand.

CASE STUDY

Do Predictable Changes in Income Lead to Predictable Changes in Consumption?

Of the many facts about consumer behavior, one is impossible to dispute: income and consumption fluctuate together over the business cycle. When the economy goes into a recession, both income and consumption fall, and when the economy booms, both income and consumption rise rapidly.

By itself, this fact doesn't say much about the rational-expectations version of the permanent-income hypothesis. Most short-run fluctuations are unpredictable. Thus, when the economy goes into a recession, the typical consumer is receiving bad news about his lifetime income, so consumption naturally falls. And when the economy booms, the typical consumer is receiving good news, so consumption rises. This behavior does not necessarily violate the random-walk theory that changes in consumption are impossible to forecast.

Yet suppose we could identify some *predictable* changes in income. According to the random-walk theory, these changes in income should not cause consumers to revise their spending plans. If consumers had reason to expect income to rise or fall, they should have adjusted their consumption already in response to that information. Thus, predictable changes in income should not lead to predictable changes in consumption.

Data on consumption and income, however, appear not to satisfy this implication of the random-walk theory. When income is expected to fall by $1, consumption will typically fall at the same time by about $0.50. In other words, predictable changes in income lead to predictable changes in consumption that are roughly half as large.

Why is this true? One possible explanation of this behavior is that some consumers may fail to have rational expectations. Instead, they may base their expectations of future income excessively on current income. Thus, when income rises or falls (even predictably), they act as if they received news about their lifetime resources and change their consumption accordingly. Another possible explanation is that some consumers are borrowing-constrained and, therefore, base their consumption on current income alone. Regardless of which explanation is correct, Keynes's original consumption function starts to look more attractive. That is, current income appears to have a larger role in determining consumer spending than the random-walk theory suggests.[7]

16-5 | Conclusion

In the work of Keynes, Fisher, Modigliani, and Friedman, we have seen a progression of views on consumer behavior. Keynes proposed that consumption depends largely on current income. Since then, economists have argued that consumers understand that they face an intertemporal decision. Consumers look ahead to their future resources and needs, implying a more complex consumption function than the one that Keynes proposed. Keynes suggested a consumption function of the form

$$\text{Consumption} = f(\text{Current Income}).$$

Recent work suggests instead that

Consumption

$$= f(\text{Current Income, Wealth, Expected Future Income, Interest Rates}).$$

In other words, current income is only one determinant of aggregate consumption.

Economists continue to debate the relative importance of these determinants of consumption. There remains disagreement, for example, over whether interest rates have much influence over consumer spending and over whether borrowing constraints are prevalent or rare. Economists sometimes disagree about economic policy because they assume different consumption functions. For instance, as we saw in the previous chapter, the debate over the effects of government debt is partly a debate over the determinants of consumer spending. The key role of consumption in policy evaluation is sure to maintain economists' interest in studying consumer behavior for many years to come.

---

[7] John Y. Campbell and N. Gregory Mankiw, "Consumption, Income, and Interest Rates: Reinterpreting the Time-Series Evidence," *NBER Macroeconomics Annual* (1989): 185–216; John Shea, "Union Contracts and the Life-Cycle/Permanent-Income Hypothesis," *American Economic Review* 85 (March 1995): 186–200.

Summary

1. Keynes conjectured that the marginal propensity to consume is between zero and one, that the average propensity to consume falls as income rises, and that current income is the primary determinant of consumption. Studies of household data and short time-series confirmed Keynes's conjectures. Yet studies of long time-series found no tendency for the average propensity to consume to fall as income rises over time.

2. Recent work on consumption builds on Irving Fisher's model of the consumer. In this model, the consumer faces an intertemporal budget constraint and chooses consumption for the present and the future to achieve the highest level of lifetime satisfaction. As long as the consumer can save and borrow, consumption depends on the consumer's lifetime resources.

3. Modigliani's life-cycle hypothesis emphasizes that income varies somewhat predictably over a person's life and that consumers use saving and borrowing to smooth their consumption over their lifetimes. According to this hypothesis, consumption depends on both income and wealth.

4. Friedman's permanent-income hypothesis emphasizes that individuals experience both permanent and transitory fluctuations in their income. Because consumers can save and borrow, and because they want to smooth their consumption, consumption does not respond much to transitory income. Consumption depends primarily on permanent income.

KEY CONCEPTS

Marginal propensity to consume	Marginal rate of substitution	Life-cycle hypothesis
Average propensity to consume	Normal good	Precautionary saving
Intertemporal budget constraint	Income effect	Permanent-income hypothesis
Discounting	Substitution effect	Permanent income
Indifference curves	Borrowing constraint	Transitory income

QUESTIONS FOR REVIEW

1. What were Keynes's three conjectures about the consumption function?

2. Describe the evidence that was consistent with Keynes's conjectures and the evidence that was inconsistent with them.

3. How do the life-cycle and permanent-income hypotheses resolve the seemingly contradictory pieces of evidence regarding consumption behavior?

4. Use Fisher's model of consumption to analyze an increase in second-period income. Compare the case in which the consumer faces a binding borrowing constraint and the case in which he does not.

5. Explain why changes in consumption are unpredictable if consumers obey the permanent-income hypothesis and have rational expectations.

PROBLEMS AND APPLICATIONS

1. The chapter uses the Fisher model to discuss a change in the interest rate for a consumer who saves some of his first-period income. Suppose, instead, that the consumer is a borrower. How does that alter the analysis? Discuss the income and substitution effects on consumption in both periods.

2. Jack and Jill both obey the two-period Fisher model of consumption. Jack earns $100 in the first period and $100 in the second period. Jill earns nothing in the first period and $210 in the second period. Both of them can borrow or lend at the interest rate r.

   a. You observe both Jack and Jill consuming $100 in the first period and $100 in the second period. What is the interest rate r?

   b. Suppose the interest rate increases. What will happen to Jack's consumption in the first period? Is Jack better off or worse off than before the interest-rate rise?

   c. What will happen to Jill's consumption in the first period when the interest rate increases? Is Jill better off or worse off than before the interest-rate increase?

3. The chapter analyzes Fisher's model for the case in which the consumer can save or borrow at an interest rate of r and for the case in which the consumer can save at this rate but cannot borrow at all. Consider now the intermediate case in which the consumer can save at rate r_s and borrow at rate r_b, where $r_s < r_b$.

   a. What is the consumer's budget constraint in the case in which he consumes less than his income in period one?

   b. What is the consumer's budget constraint in the case in which he consumes more than his income in period one?

   c. Graph the two budget constraints and shade the area that represents the combination of first-period and second-period consumption the consumer can choose.

   d. Now add to your graph the consumer's indifference curves. Show three possible outcomes: one in which the consumer saves, one in which he borrows, and one in which he neither saves nor borrows.

   e. What determines first-period consumption in each of the three cases?

4. Explain whether borrowing constraints increase or decrease the potency of fiscal policy to influence aggregate demand in each of the following two cases:

   a. A temporary tax cut.

   b. An announced future tax cut.

5. In the discussion of the life-cycle hypothesis in the text, income is assumed to be constant during the period before retirement. For most people, however, income grows over their lifetimes. How does this growth in income influence the lifetime pattern of consumption and wealth accumulation shown in Figure 16-13 under the following conditions?

   a. Consumers can borrow, so their wealth can be negative.

   b. Consumers face borrowing constraints that prevent their wealth from falling below zero.

   Do you consider case (a) or case (b) to be more realistic? Why?

6. Demographers predict that the fraction of the population that is elderly will increase over the next 20 years. What does the life-cycle model predict for the influence of this demographic change on the national saving rate?

7. One study found that the elderly who do not have children dissave at about the same rate as the elderly who do have children. What might this finding imply about the reason the elderly do not dissave as much as the life-cycle model predicts?

chapter **17**

Investment

Investment is the most volatile component of GDP. When expenditure on goods and services falls during a recession, much of the decline is usually due to a drop in investment spending. In the severe U.S. recession of 1982, for example, real GDP fell $105 billion from its peak in the third quarter of 1981 to its trough in the fourth quarter of 1982. Investment spending over the same period fell $152 billion, accounting for more than the entire fall in spending.

Economists study investment to better understand fluctuations in the economy's output of goods and services. The models of GDP we saw in previous chapters, such as the *IS−LM* model in Chapters 10 and 11, were based on a simple investment function relating investment to the real interest rate: $I = I(r)$. That function states that an increase in the real interest rate reduces investment. In this chapter we look more closely at the theory behind this investment function.

There are three types of investment spending. **Business fixed investment** includes the equipment and structures that businesses buy to use in production. **Residential investment** includes the new housing that people buy to live in and that landlords buy to rent out. **Inventory investment** includes those goods that businesses put aside in storage, including materials and supplies, work in process, and finished goods. Figure 17-1 plots total investment and its three components in the United States since 1970. You can see that all types of investment fall substantially during recessions, which are shown as shaded areas in the figure.

In this chapter we build models of each type of investment to explain these fluctuations. The models will shed light on the following questions:

➤ Why is investment negatively related to the interest rate?

➤ What causes the investment function to shift?

➤ Why does investment rise during booms and fall during recessions?

At the end of the chapter, we return to these questions and summarize the answers that the models offer.

17-1 Business Fixed Investment

The largest piece of investment spending, accounting for about three-quarters of the total, is business fixed investment. The term "business" means that these investment goods are bought by firms for use in future production. The term

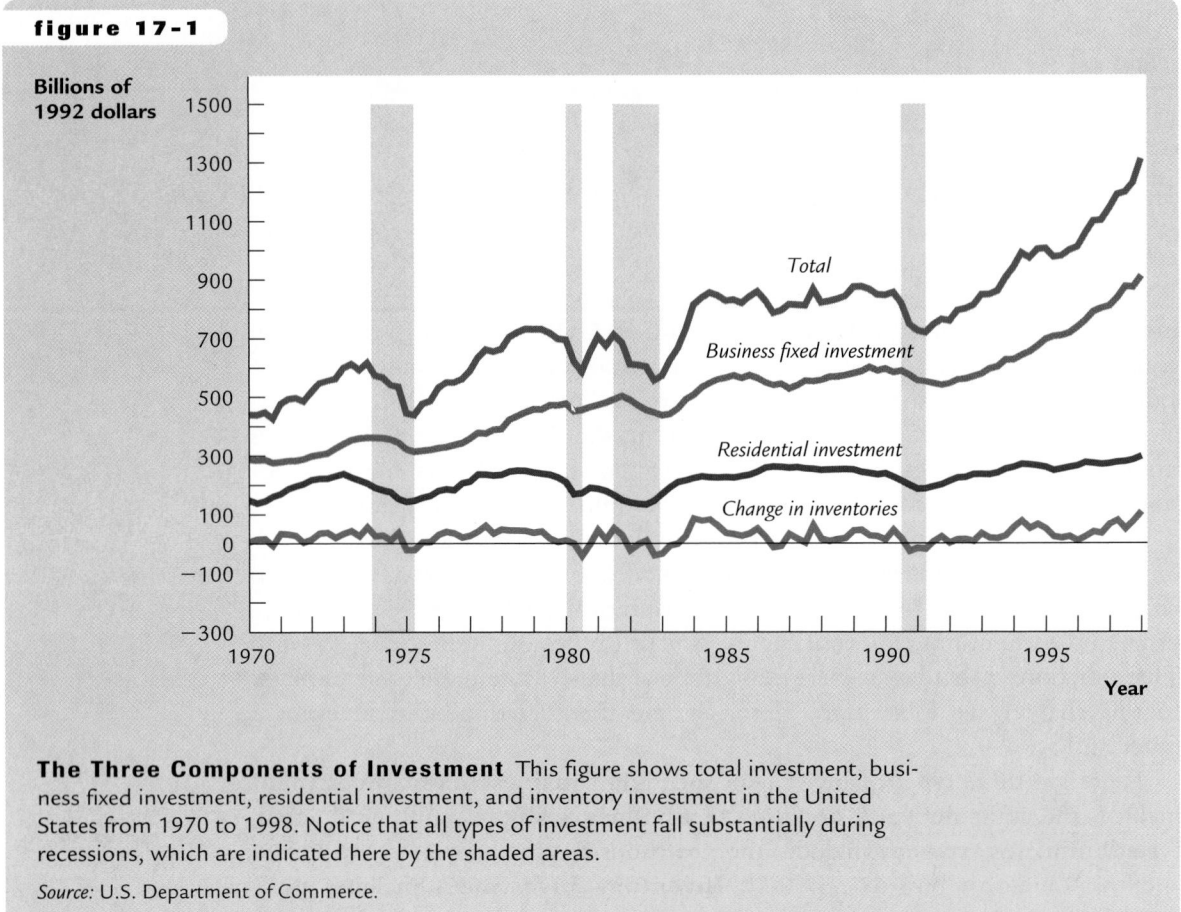

figure 17-1

Billions of 1992 dollars

The Three Components of Investment This figure shows total investment, business fixed investment, residential investment, and inventory investment in the United States from 1970 to 1998. Notice that all types of investment fall substantially during recessions, which are indicated here by the shaded areas.

Source: U.S. Department of Commerce.

"fixed" means that this spending is for capital that will stay put for a while, as opposed to inventory investment, which will be used or sold shortly later. Business fixed investment includes everything from fax machines to factories, computers to company cars.

The standard model of business fixed investment is called the **neoclassical model of investment.** The neoclassical model examines the benefits and costs to firms of owning capital goods. The model shows how the level of investment—the addition to the stock of capital—is related to the marginal product of capital, the interest rate, and the tax rules affecting firms.

To develop the model, imagine that there are two kinds of firms in the economy. *Production firms* produce goods and services using capital that they rent. *Rental firms* make all the investments in the economy; they buy capital and rent it out to the production firms. Of course, most firms in the actual economy perform both functions: they produce goods and services, and they invest in capital for future production. Our analysis is simpler, however, if we separate these two activities by imagining that they take place in different firms.

The Rental Price of Capital

Let's first consider the typical production firm. As we discussed in Chapter 3, this firm decides how much capital to rent by comparing the cost and benefit of each unit of capital. The firm rents capital at a rental rate R and sells its output at a price P; the real cost of a unit of capital to the production firm is R/P. The real benefit of a unit of capital is the marginal product of capital MPK—the extra output produced with one more unit of capital. The marginal product of capital declines as the amount of capital rises: the more capital the firm has, the less an additional unit of capital will add to its output. Chapter 3 concluded that, to maximize profit, the firm rents capital until the marginal product of capital falls to equal the real rental price.

Figure 17-2 shows the equilibrium in the rental market for capital. For the reasons just discussed, the marginal product of capital determines the demand curve. The demand curve slopes downward because the marginal product of capital is low when the level of capital is high. At any point in time, the amount of capital in the economy is fixed, so the supply curve is vertical. The real rental price of capital adjusts to equilibrate supply and demand.

To see what variables influence the equilibrium rental price, let's consider a particular production function. As the appendix to Chapter 3 discusses, many economists consider the Cobb–Douglas production function a good approximation of how the actual economy turns capital and labor into goods and services. The Cobb–Douglas production function is

$$Y = AK^\alpha L^{1-\alpha},$$

where Y is output, K capital, L labor, A a parameter measuring the level of technology, and α a parameter between zero and one that measures capital's

figure 17-2

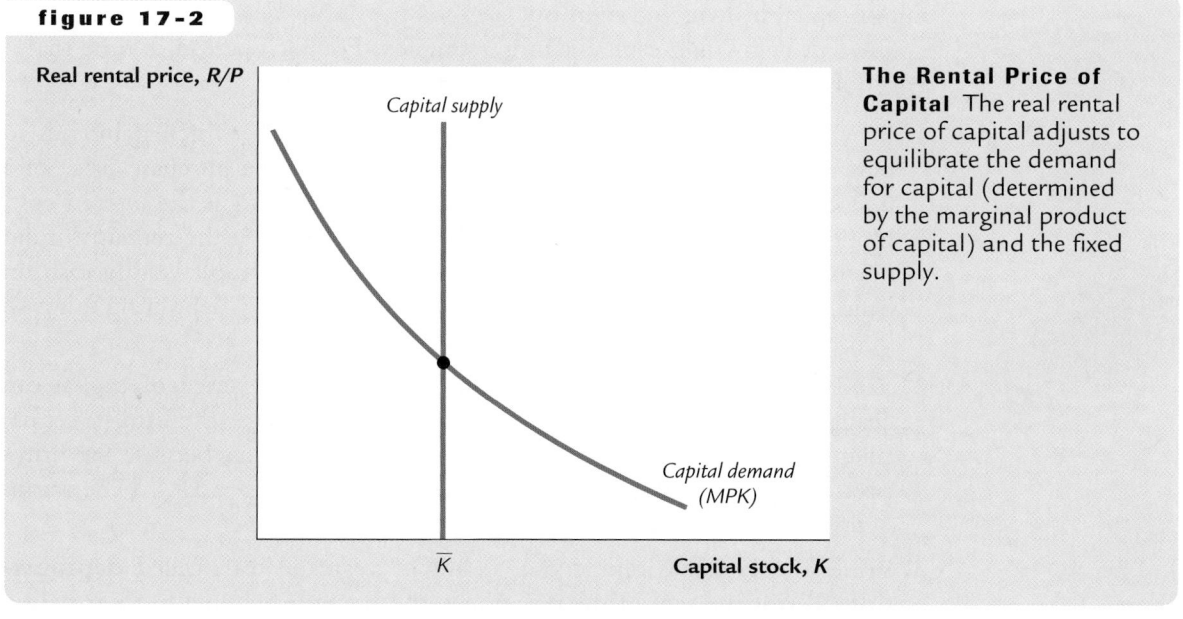

The Rental Price of Capital The real rental price of capital adjusts to equilibrate the demand for capital (determined by the marginal product of capital) and the fixed supply.

share of output. The marginal product of capital for the Cobb–Douglas production function is

$$MPK = \alpha A(L/K)^{1-\alpha}.$$

Because the real rental price equals the marginal product of capital in equilibrium, we can write

$$R/P = \alpha A(L/K)^{1-\alpha}.$$

This expression identifies the variables that determine the real rental price. It shows the following:

> ➤ The lower the stock of capital, the higher the real rental price of capital.

> ➤ The greater the amount of labor employed, the higher the real rental price of capital.

> ➤ The better the technology, the higher the real rental price of capital.

Events that reduce the capital stock (an earthquake), or raise employment (an expansion in aggregate demand), or improve the technology (a scientific discovery) raise the equilibrium real rental price of capital.

The Cost of Capital

Next consider the rental firms. These firms, like car-rental companies, merely buy capital goods and rent them out. Since our goal is to explain the investments made by the rental firms, we begin by considering the benefit and cost of owning capital.

The benefit of owning capital is the revenue from renting it to the production firms. The rental firm receives the real rental price of capital R/P for each unit of capital it owns and rents out.

The cost of owning capital is more complex. For each period of time that it rents out a unit of capital, the rental firm bears three costs:

1. When a rental firm borrows to buy a unit of capital, which it intends to rent out, it must pay interest on the loan. If P_K is the purchase price of a unit of capital and i is the nominal interest rate, then iP_K is the interest cost. Notice that this interest cost would be the same even if the rental firm did not have to borrow: if the rental firm buys a unit of capital using cash on hand, it loses out on the interest it could have earned by depositing this cash in the bank. In either case, the interest cost equals iP_K.

2. While the rental firm is renting out the capital, the price of capital can change. If the price of capital falls, the firm loses, because the firm's asset has fallen in value. If the price of capital rises, the firm gains, because the firm's asset has risen in value. The cost of this loss or gain is $-\Delta P_K$. (The minus sign is here because we are measuring costs, not benefits.)

3. While the capital is rented out, it suffers wear and tear, called **depreciation.** If δ is the rate of depreciation—the fraction of value lost per period because of wear and tear—then the dollar cost of depreciation is δP_K.

The total cost of renting out a unit of capital for one period is therefore

$$\text{Cost of Capital} = iP_\text{K} - \Delta P_\text{K} + \delta P_\text{K}$$
$$= P_\text{K}(i - \Delta P_\text{K}/P_\text{K} + \delta).$$

The cost of capital depends on the price of capital, the interest rate, the rate at which capital prices are changing, and the depreciation rate.

For example, consider the cost of capital to a car-rental company. The company buys cars for $10,000 each and rents them out to other businesses. The company faces an interest rate i of 10 percent per year, so the interest cost iP_K is $1,000 per year for each car the company owns. Car prices are rising at 6 percent per year, so, excluding wear and tear, the firm gets a capital gain ΔP_K of $600 per year. Cars depreciate at 20 percent per year, so the loss due to wear and tear δP_K is $2,000 per year. Therefore, the company's cost of capital is

$$\text{Cost of Capital} = \$1,000 - \$600 + \$2,000$$
$$= \$2,400.$$

The cost to the car-rental company of keeping a car in its capital stock is $2,400 per year.

To make the expression for the cost of capital simpler and easier to interpret, we assume that the price of capital goods rises with the prices of other goods. In this case, $\Delta P_\text{K}/P_\text{K}$ equals the overall rate of inflation π. Because $i - \pi$ equals the real interest rate r, we can write the cost of capital as

$$\text{Cost of Capital} = P_\text{K}(r + \delta).$$

This equation states that the cost of capital depends on the price of capital, the real interest rate, and the depreciation rate.

Finally, we want to express the cost of capital relative to other goods in the economy. The **real cost of capital**—the cost of buying and renting out a unit of capital measured in units of the economy's output—is

$$\text{Real Cost of Capital} = (P_\text{K}/P)(r + \delta).$$

This equation states that the real cost of capital depends on the relative price of a capital good P_K/P, the real interest rate r, and the depreciation rate δ.

The Determinants of Investment

Now consider a rental firm's decision about whether to increase or decrease its capital stock. For each unit of capital, the firm earns real revenue R/P and bears the real cost $(P_\text{K}/P)(r + \delta)$. The real profit per unit of capital is

$$\text{Profit Rate} = \text{Revenue} - \text{Cost}$$
$$= R/P - (P_\text{K}/P)(r + \delta).$$

Because the real rental price in equilibrium equals the marginal product of capital, we can write the profit rate as

$$\text{Profit Rate} = MPK - (P_\text{K}/P)(r + \delta).$$

The rental firm makes a profit if the marginal product of capital is greater than the cost of capital. It incurs a loss if the marginal product is less than the cost of capital.

We can now see the economic incentives that lie behind the rental firm's investment decision. The firm's decision regarding its capital stock—that is, whether to add to it or to let it depreciate—depends on whether owning and renting out capital is profitable. The change in the capital stock, called **net investment,** depends on the difference between the marginal product of capital and the cost of capital. *If the marginal product of capital exceeds the cost of capital, firms find it profitable to add to their capital stock. If the marginal product of capital falls short of the cost of capital, they let their capital stock shrink.*

We can also now see that the separation of economic activity between production and rental firms, although useful for clarifying our thinking, is not necessary for our conclusion regarding how firms choose how much to invest. For a firm that both uses and owns capital, the benefit of an extra unit of capital is the marginal product of capital, and the cost is the cost of capital. Like a firm that owns and rents out capital, this firm adds to its capital stock if the marginal product exceeds the cost of capital. Thus, we can write

$$\Delta K = I_n \left[MPK - (P_K/P)(r + \delta) \right],$$

where $I_n(\ )$ is the function showing how much net investment responds to the incentive to invest.

We can now derive the investment function. Total spending on business fixed investment is the sum of net investment and the replacement of depreciated capital. The investment function is

$$I = I_n \left[MPK - (P_K/P)(r + \delta) \right] + \delta K.$$

Business fixed investment depends on the marginal product of capital, the cost of capital, and the amount of depreciation.

This model shows why investment depends on the interest rate. A decrease in the real interest rate lowers the cost of capital. It therefore raises the amount of profit from owning capital and increases the incentive to accumulate more capital. Similarly, an increase in the real interest rate raises the cost of capital and leads firms to reduce their investment. For this reason, the investment schedule relating investment to the interest rate slopes downward, as in panel (a) of Figure 17-3.

The model also shows what causes the investment schedule to shift. Any event that raises the marginal product of capital increases the profitability of investment and causes the investment schedule to shift outward, as in panel (b) of Figure 17-3. For example, a technological innovation that increases the production function parameter A raises the marginal product of capital and, for any given interest rate, increases the amount of capital goods that rental firms wish to buy.

Finally, consider what happens as this adjustment of the capital stock continues over time. If the marginal product begins above the cost of capital, the capital stock will rise and the marginal product will fall. If the marginal product of

figure 17-3

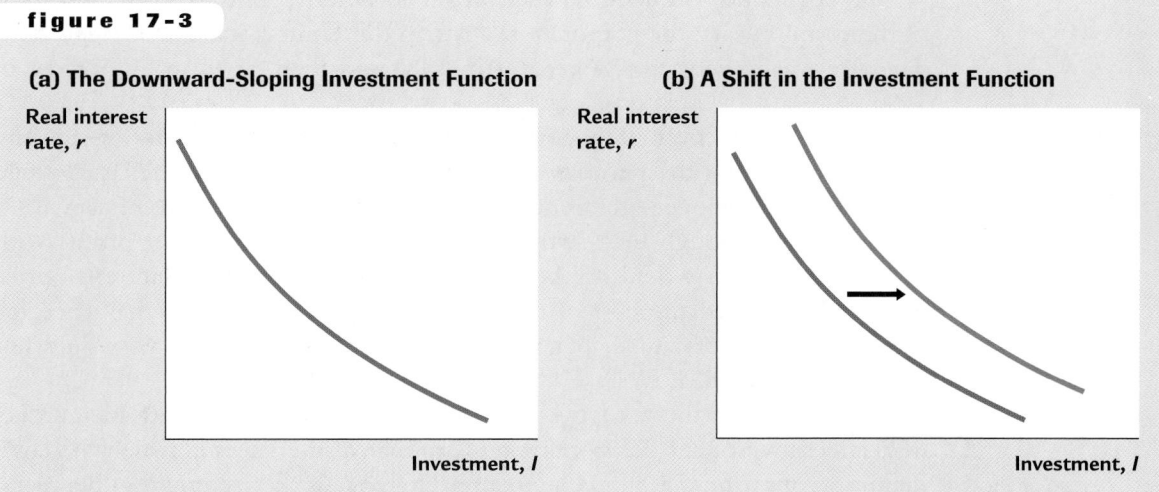

(a) The Downward-Sloping Investment Function

Real interest rate, r

Investment, I

(b) A Shift in the Investment Function

Real interest rate, r

Investment, I

The Investment Function Panel (a) shows that business fixed investment increases when the interest rate falls. This is because a lower interest rate reduces the cost of capital and therefore makes owning capital more profitable. Panel (b) shows an outward shift in the investment function, which might be due to an increase in the marginal product of capital.

capital begins below the cost of capital, the capital stock will fall and the marginal product will rise. Eventually, as the capital stock adjusts, the marginal product of capital approaches the cost of capital. When the capital stock reaches a steady-state level, we can write

$$MPK = (P_K/P)(r + \delta).$$

Thus, in the long run, the marginal product of capital equals the real cost of capital. The speed of adjustment toward the steady state depends on how quickly firms adjust their capital stock, which in turn depends on how costly it is to build, deliver, and install new capital.[1]

Taxes and Investment

Tax laws influence firms' incentives to accumulate capital in many ways. Sometimes policymakers change the tax laws in order to shift the investment function and influence aggregate demand. Here we consider two of the most important provisions of corporate taxation: the corporate income tax and the investment tax credit.

---

[1] Economists often measure capital goods in units such that the price of 1 unit of capital equals the price of 1 unit of other goods and services ($P_K = P$). This was the approach taken implicitly in Chapter 4, for example. In this case, the steady-state condition says that the marginal product of capital net of depreciation, $MPK - \delta$, equals the real interest rate r.

The **corporate income tax** is a tax on corporate profits. Throughout most of the past 40 years, the corporate tax rate in the United States was 46 percent. The rate was lowered to 34 percent in 1986 and then raised to 35 percent in 1993.

The effect of a corporate income tax on investment depends on how the law defines "profit" for the purpose of taxation. Suppose, first, that the law defined profit as we did above—the rental price of capital minus the cost of capital. In this case, even though firms would be sharing a fraction of their profits with the government, it would still be rational for them to invest if the rental price of capital exceeded the cost of capital, and to disinvest if the rental price fell short of the cost of capital. A tax on profit, measured in this way, would not alter investment incentives.

Yet, because of the tax law's definition of profit, the corporate income tax does affect investment decisions. There are many differences between the law's definition of profit and ours. One major difference is the treatment of depreciation. Our definition of profit deducts the *current* value of depreciation as a cost. That is, it bases depreciation on how much it would cost today to replace worn-out capital. By contrast, under the corporate tax laws, firms deduct depreciation using *historical* cost. That is, the depreciation deduction is based on the price of the capital when it was originally purchased. In periods of inflation, replacement cost is greater than historical cost, so the corporate tax tends to understate the cost of depreciation and overstate profit. As a result, the tax law sees a profit and levies a tax even when economic profit is zero, which makes owning capital less attractive. For this and other reasons, many economists believe that the corporate income tax discourages investment.

The **investment tax credit** is a tax provision that encourages the accumulation of capital. The investment tax credit reduces a firm's taxes by a certain amount for each dollar spent on capital goods. Because a firm recoups part of its expenditure on new capital in lower taxes, the credit reduces the effective purchase price of a unit of capital P_K. Thus, the investment tax credit reduces the cost of capital and raises investment.

Many economists believe that the investment tax credit is an effective way to stimulate investment. In 1985 the investment tax credit was 10 percent. Yet the Tax Reform Act of 1986, which reduced the corporate income tax rate, also eliminated the investment tax credit. When Bill Clinton ran for president in 1992, he campaigned on a platform of reinstituting the investment tax credit. Yet this change in tax law did not occur.[2]

CASE STUDY

The Swedish Investment Funds System

Tax incentives for investment are one tool policymakers can use to control aggregate demand. For example, an increase in the investment tax credit reduces

---

[2] To read more about how taxes influence investment, see Robert E. Hall and Dale W. Jorgenson, "Tax Policy and Investment Behavior," *American Economic Review* 57 (June 1967): 391–414.

the cost of capital, shifts the investment function outward, and raises aggregate demand. Similarly, a reduction in the tax credit reduces aggregate demand by making investment more costly.

From the mid-1950s to the mid-1970s, the government of Sweden attempted to control aggregate demand by encouraging or discouraging investment. A system called the *investment fund* subsidized investment, much like an investment tax credit, during periods of recession. When government officials decided that economic growth had slowed, they authorized a temporary investment subsidy. When the officials concluded that the economy had recovered sufficiently, they revoked the subsidy. Eventually, however, Sweden abandoned the use of temporary investment subsidies to control the business cycle, and the subsidy became a permanent feature of Swedish tax policy.

Should investment subsidies be used to combat economic fluctuations? Some economists believe that for the two decades it was in effect the Swedish policy reduced the magnitude of the business cycle. Others believe that such a policy could have had unintended and perverse effects: for example, if the economy begins to slow down, firms may anticipate a future subsidy and delay investment, making the slowdown worse. Because the use of countercyclical investment subsidies could either reduce or amplify the size of economic fluctuations, their overall impact on economic performance is hard to evaluate.[3]

The Stock Market and Tobin's q

Many economists see a link between fluctuations in investment and fluctuations in the stock market. The term **stock** refers to the shares in the ownership of corporations, and the **stock market** is the market in which these shares are traded. Stock prices tend to be high when firms have many opportunities for profitable investment, since these profit opportunities mean higher future income for the shareholders. Thus, stock prices reflect the incentives to invest.

The Nobel-Prize-winning economist James Tobin proposed that firms base their investment decisions on the following ratio, which is now called **Tobin's** q:

$$q = \frac{\text{Market Value of Installed Capital}}{\text{Replacement Cost of Installed Capital}}.$$

The numerator of Tobin's q is the value of the economy's capital as determined by the stock market. The denominator is the price of the capital if it were purchased today.

Tobin reasoned that net investment should depend on whether q is greater or less than 1. If q is greater than 1, then the stock market values installed capital at more than its replacement cost. In this case, managers can raise the market value of their firms' stock by buying more capital. Conversely, if q is less than 1, the

---

[3] John B. Taylor, "The Swedish Investment Funds System as a Stabilization Rule," *Brookings Papers on Economic Activity* (1982:1): 57–106.

stock market values capital at less than its replacement cost. In this case, managers will not replace capital as it wears out.

Although at first the q theory of investment may appear quite different from the neoclassical model developed above, in fact the two theories are closely related. To see the relationship, note that Tobin's q depends on current and future expected profits from installed capital. If the marginal product of capital exceeds the cost of capital, then firms are earning profit on their installed capital. These profits make the rental firms desirable to own, which raises the market value of these firms' stock, implying a high value of q. Similarly, if the marginal product of capital falls short of the cost of capital, then firms are incurring losses on their installed capital, implying a low market value and a low value of q.

The advantage of Tobin's q as a measure of the incentive to invest is that it reflects the expected future profitability of capital as well as the current profitability. For example, suppose that Congress legislates a reduction in the corporate income tax beginning next year. This expected fall in the corporate tax means greater profits for the owners of capital. These higher expected profits raise the value of stock today, raise Tobin's q, and therefore encourage investment today. Thus, Tobin's q theory of investment emphasizes that investment decisions depend not only on current economic policies, but also on policies expected to prevail in the future.[4]

CASE STUDY

The Stock Market as an Economic Indicator

"The stock market has predicted nine out of the last five recessions." So goes Paul Samuelson's famous quip about the stock market's reliability as an economic indicator. The stock market is in fact quite volatile, and it can give false signals about the future of the economy. Yet one should not ignore the link between the stock market and the economy. Figure 17-4 shows that changes in the stock market often reflect changes in real GDP. Whenever the stock market experiences a substantial decline, there is reason to fear that a recession may be around the corner.

Why do stock prices and economic activity tend to fluctuate together? One reason is given by Tobin's q theory, together with the model of aggregate demand and aggregate supply. Suppose, for instance, that you observe a fall in stock prices. Because the replacement cost of capital is fairly stable, a fall in the stock market is usually associated with a fall in Tobin's q. A fall in q reflects investors' pessimism about the current or future profitability of capital. This

---

[4] To read more about the relationship between the neoclassical model of investment and q theory, see Fumio Hayashi, "Tobin's Marginal q and Average q: A Neoclassical Approach," *Econometrica* 50 (January 1982): 213–224; and Lawrence H. Summers, "Taxation and Corporate Investment: A q-theory Approach," *Brookings Papers on Economic Activity* (1981:1): 67–140.

figure 17-4

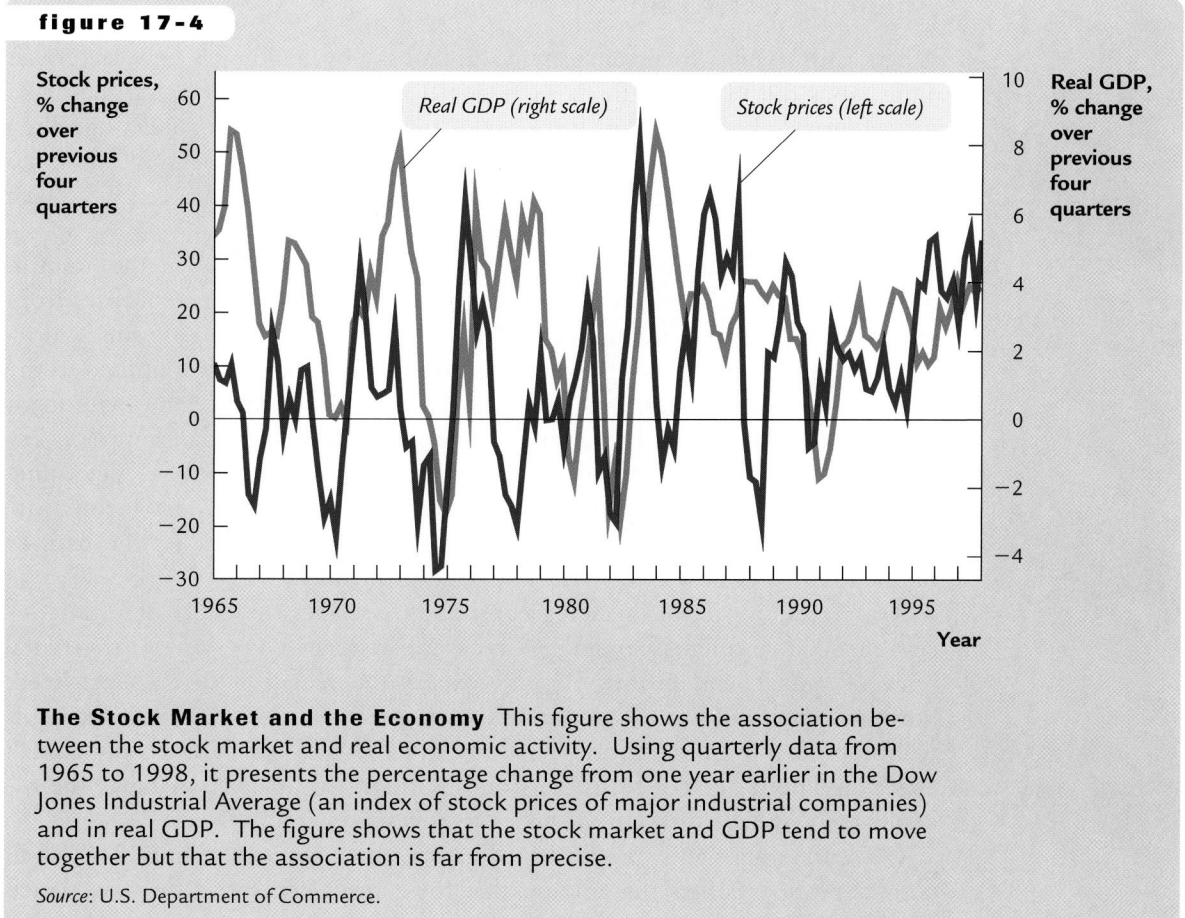

The Stock Market and the Economy This figure shows the association between the stock market and real economic activity. Using quarterly data from
1965 to 1998, it presents the percentage change from one year earlier in the Dow
Jones Industrial Average (an index of stock prices of major industrial companies)
and in real GDP. The figure shows that the stock market and GDP tend to move
together but that the association is far from precise.

Source: U.S. Department of Commerce.

means that the investment function has shifted inward: investment is lower at
any given interest rate. As a result, the aggregate demand for goods and services
contracts, leading to lower output and employment.

There are two additional reasons why stock prices are associated with economic activity. First, because stock is part of household wealth, a fall in stock
prices makes people poorer and thus depresses consumer spending, which also
reduces aggregate demand. Second, a fall in stock prices might reflect bad news
about technological progress and long-run economic growth. If so, this means
that the natural rate of output—and thus aggregate supply—will be expanding
more slowly in the future than was previously expected.

These links between the stock market and the economy are not lost on policymakers, such as those at the Federal Reserve. Indeed, because the stock market often anticipates changes in real GDP, and because data on the stock market are available more quickly than data on GDP, the stock market is a closely
watched economic indicator.

Financing Constraints

When a firm wants to invest in new capital, say by building a new factory, it often raises the necessary funds in financial markets. This financing may take several forms: obtaining loans from banks, selling bonds to the public, or selling shares in future profits on the stock market. The neoclassical model assumes that if a firm is willing to pay the cost of capital, the financial markets will make the funds available.

Yet sometimes firms face **financing constraints**—limits on the amount they can raise in financial markets. Financing constraints can prevent firms from undertaking profitable investments. When a firm is unable to raise funds in financial markets, the amount it can spend on new capital goods is limited to the amount it is currently earning. Financing constraints influence the investment behavior of firms just as borrowing constraints influence the consumption behavior of households. Borrowing constraints cause households to determine their consumption on the basis of current rather than permanent income; financing constraints cause firms to determine their investment on the basis of their current cash flow rather than expected profitability.

To see the impact of financing constraints, consider the effect of a short recession on investment spending. A recession reduces employment, the rental price of capital, and profits. If firms expect the recession to be short-lived, however, they will want to continue investing, knowing that their investments will be profitable in the future. That is, a short recession will have only a small effect on Tobin's q. For firms that can raise funds in financial markets, the recession should have only a small effect on investment.

Quite the opposite is true for firms that face financing constraints. The fall in current profits restricts the amount that these firms can spend on new capital goods and may prevent them from making profitable investments. Thus, financing constraints make investment more sensitive to current economic conditions.[5]

CASE STUDY

Banking Crises and Credit Crunches

Throughout economic history, problems in the banking system have often coincided with downturns in economic activity. This was true, for instance, during the Great Depression of the 1930s (which we discussed in Chapter 11). Soon after the Depression's onset, many banks found themselves insolvent, as the value of their assets fell below the value of their liabilities. These banks were, therefore, forced to suspend operations. Many economists believe the widespread bank failures during this period help explain the Depression's depth and persistence.

---

[5] For empirical work supporting the importance of these financing constraints, see Steven M. Fazzari, R. Glenn Hubbard, and Bruce C. Petersen, "Financing Constraints and Corporate Investment," *Brookings Papers on Economic Activity* (1988:1): 141–195.

Similar patterns, although less severe, can be observed more recently. In the United States, the 1990 recession (discussed in Chapter 14) came on the heels of the savings and loan crisis. Problems in the banking system were also part of the recent slump in Japan (Chapter 11) and the recent financial crisis in Indonesia and other Asian economies (Chapter 12).

Why are banking crises so often at the center of short-run economic fluctuations? Part of the answer lies in the fact that banks have an important role in allocating financial resources. In particular, they serve as *intermediaries* between those people who have income they want to save and those people who have profitable investment projects but need to borrow to invest. When banks become insolvent or nearly so, they are less able to serve this function. Financing constraints become more prevalent, and some investors are forced to forgo some potentially profitable investment projects. Such an increase in financing constraints is sometimes called a *credit crunch*.

The macroeconomic effects of a credit crunch are easily interpreted within the *IS–LM* model. When some would-be investors are denied credit, the demand for investment goods falls at every interest rate. The result is a contractionary shift in the *IS* curve, which in turn leads to a fall in aggregate demand and reduced production and employment. Because of these effects, policymakers at the Fed and in other parts of government are always trying to monitor the health of the nation's banking system. Their goal is to avert banking crises and credit crunches and, when they do occur, to respond as quickly as possible to minimize the resulting disruption to the economy.[6]

17-2| Residential Investment

In this section we consider the determinants of residential investment. We begin by presenting a simple model of the housing market. Residential investment includes the purchase of new housing both by people who plan to live in it themselves and by landlords who plan to rent it to others. To keep things simple, however, it is useful to imagine that all housing is owner-occupied.

The Stock Equilibrium and the Flow Supply

There are two parts to the model. First, the market for the existing stock of houses determines the equilibrium housing price. Second, the housing price determines the flow of residential investment.

Panel (a) of Figure 17-5 shows how the relative price of housing P_H/P is determined by the supply and demand for the existing stock of houses. At

[6] For an analysis of the U.S. experience in 1990, see Ben S. Bernanke and Cara Lown, "The Credit Crunch," *Brookings Papers on Economic Activity* (1991:2): 205–228.

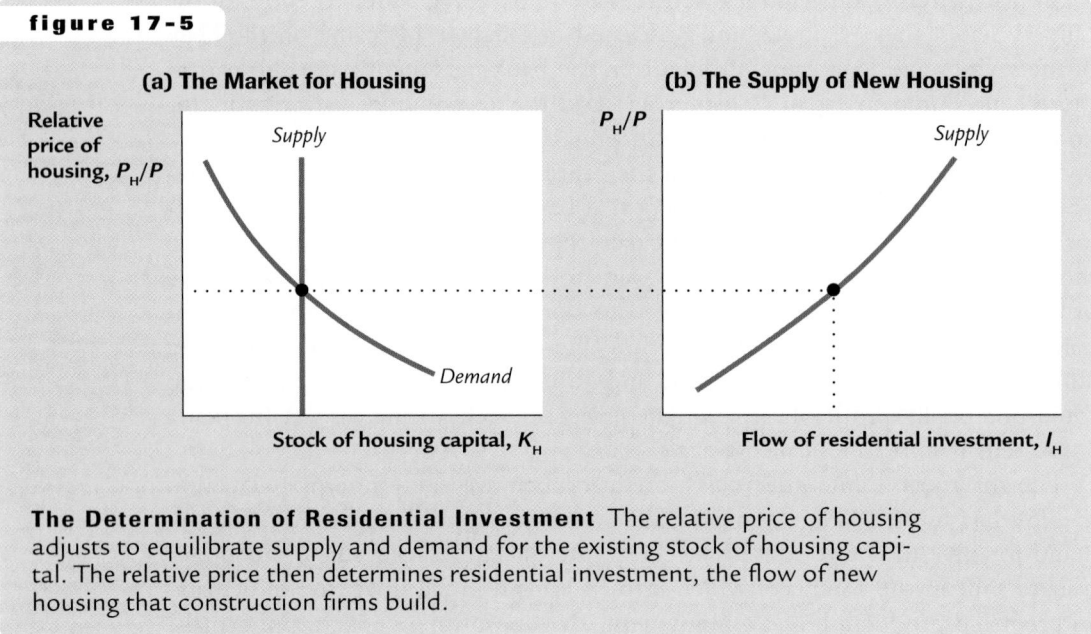

figure 17-5

(a) The Market for Housing

Relative price of housing, P_H/P

Supply

Demand

Stock of housing capital, K_H

(b) The Supply of New Housing

P_H/P

Supply

Flow of residential investment, I_H

The Determination of Residential Investment The relative price of housing adjusts to equilibrate supply and demand for the existing stock of housing capital. The relative price then determines residential investment, the flow of new housing that construction firms build.

any point in time, the supply of houses is fixed. We represent this stock with a vertical supply curve. The demand curve for houses slopes downward, because high prices cause people to live in smaller houses, to share residences, or sometimes even to become homeless. The price of housing adjusts to equilibrate supply and demand.

Panel (b) of Figure 17-5 shows how the relative price of housing determines the supply of new houses. Construction firms buy materials and hire labor to build houses, and then sell the houses at the market price. Their costs depend on the overall price level P (which reflects the cost of wood, bricks, plaster, etc.), and their revenue depends on the price of houses P_H. The higher the relative price of housing, the greater the incentive to build houses, and the more houses are built. The flow of new houses—residential investment—therefore depends on the equilibrium price set in the market for existing houses.

This model of residential investment is similar to the q theory of business fixed investment. According to q theory, business fixed investment depends on the market price of installed capital relative to its replacement cost; this relative price, in turn, depends on the expected profits from owning installed capital. According to this model of the housing market, residential investment depends on the relative price of housing. The relative price of housing, in turn, depends on the demand for housing, which depends on the imputed rent that individuals expect to receive from their housing. Hence, the relative price of housing plays much the same role for residential investment as Tobin's q does for business fixed investment.

figure 17-6

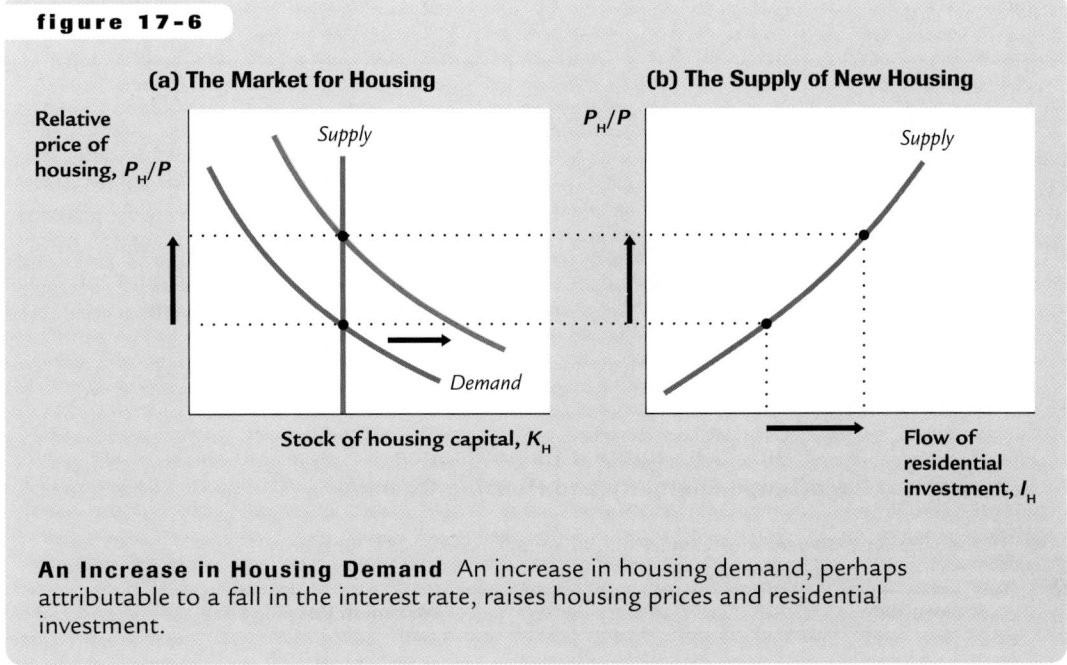

(a) The Market for Housing

Relative price of housing, P_H/P

Supply

Demand

Stock of housing capital, K_H

(b) The Supply of New Housing

P_H/P

Supply

Flow of residential investment, I_H

An Increase in Housing Demand An increase in housing demand, perhaps attributable to a fall in the interest rate, raises housing prices and residential investment.

Changes in Housing Demand

When the demand for housing shifts, the equilibrium price of housing changes, and this change in turn affects residential investment. The demand curve for housing can shift for various reasons. An economic boom raises national income and therefore the demand for housing. A large increase in the population, perhaps because of immigration, also raises the demand for housing. Panel (a) of Figure 17-6 shows that an expansionary shift in demand raises the equilibrium price. Panel (b) shows that the increase in the housing price increases residential investment.

One important determinant of housing demand is the real interest rate. Many people take out loans—mortgages—to buy their homes; the interest rate is the cost of the loan. Even the few people who do not have to borrow to purchase a home will respond to the interest rate, because the interest rate is the opportunity cost of holding their wealth in housing rather than putting it in a bank. A reduction in the interest rate therefore raises housing demand, housing prices, and residential investment.

The Tax Treatment of Housing

Just as the tax laws affect the accumulation of business fixed investment, they also affect the accumulation of residential investment. In this case, however, their effects are nearly the opposite. Rather than discouraging investment, as

---

f y i

WHAT PRICE HOUSE CAN YOU AFFORD?

When someone takes out a mortgage to buy a house, the bank often places a ceiling on the size of the loan. That ceiling depends on the person's income and the market interest rate. A typical bank requirement is that the monthly mortgage payment—including both interest and repayment of principal—not exceed 28 percent of the borrower's monthly income.

Table 17-1 shows how the interest rate affects the loan ceiling. The home buyer in the example has an income of $30,000 and is applying for a 30-year mortgage. The bank is assumed to use the standard 28-percent limit on the size of the loan.

As you can see, if the home buyer is up against the borrowing limit, as many are, small changes in the interest rate can have a large influence on the amount he or she can spend on a house. An increase in the interest rate from 8 to 10 percent reduces the maximum loan from $95,398 to $79,766—a fall of 16 percent. An increase in the interest rate therefore reduces housing demand, which in turn depresses housing prices and residential investment.

It is noteworthy—and a bit puzzling—that banks make this calculation using the nominal rather than the real interest rate. The real interest rate measures the true cost of borrowing to buy a house, because the price of the house will normally rise at the overall rate of inflation. Yet bank rules use nominal interest rates when computing mortgage eligibility. Because of these bank rules, residential investment depends on nominal as well as real interest rates.

table 17-1

How High Interest Rates Reduce Mortgage Eligibility and Housing Demand

Assumptions: 30-year mortgage, $30,000 annual income, 28% limit on mortgage payment

Interest Rate	Maximum Possible Loan
5%	$130,397
6	116,754
7	105,215
8	95,398
9	86,997
10	79,766
11	73,504
12	68,053

the corporate income tax does for businesses, the personal income tax encourages households to invest in housing.

One can view a homeowner as a landlord with himself as a tenant. But he is a landlord with a special tax treatment. The U.S. income tax does not require him to pay tax on the imputed rent (the rent he "pays" himself), yet it allows him to deduct mortgage interest. In essence, when computing his taxable income, he can subtract part of the cost of owning a home, but he does not have to add any of the benefit.

The size of this subsidy to homeownership depends on the rate of inflation. The reason is that the tax law allows homeowners to deduct their *nominal* interest payments when computing taxable income. Because the nominal interest rate on mortgages rises when inflation rises, the value of this subsidy is higher at higher rates of inflation. When inflation and nominal interest rates rose substantially in the 1970s, the tax benefits of homeownership rose as well. When inflation and nominal interest rates fell in the 1980s and early 1990s, the tax benefits became smaller.

Many economists have criticized the tax treatment of homeownership. They believe that, because of this subsidy, the United States invests too much in housing compared to other forms of capital. They advocate reducing the subsidy, perhaps by eliminating the deductibility of mortgage interest. This idea received some attention during the presidential campaign of 1996. The "flat tax" proposal advocated by Republican primary candidate Steve Forbes eliminated the mortgage-interest deduction and used the extra revenue to lower income tax rates. The political reaction to this idea was mixed: while voters like lower tax rates, homeowners were not eager to give up the mortgage-interest subsidy that they have enjoyed for many years.

17-3 | Inventory Investment

Inventory investment—the goods that businesses put aside in storage—is at the same time negligible and of great significance. It is one of the smallest components of spending, averaging about 1 percent of GDP. Yet its remarkable volatility makes it central to the study of economic fluctuations. In recessions, firms stop replenishing their inventory as goods are sold, and inventory investment becomes negative. In a typical recession, more than half the fall in spending comes from a decline in inventory investment.

Reasons for Holding Inventories

Inventories serve many purposes. Before presenting a model to explain fluctuations in inventory investment, let's discuss some of the motives firms have for holding inventories.

One use of inventories is to smooth the level of production over time. Consider a firm that experiences temporary booms and busts in sales. Rather than adjusting production to match the fluctuations in sales, the firm may find it cheaper to produce goods at a steady rate. When sales are low, the firm produces more than it sells and puts the extra goods into inventory. When sales are high, the firm produces less than it sells and takes goods out of inventory. This motive for holding inventories is called **production smoothing.**

A second reason for holding inventories is that they may allow a firm to operate more efficiently. Retail stores, for example, can sell merchandise more effectively if they have goods on hand to show to customers. Manufacturing firms keep inventories of spare parts to reduce the time that the assembly line is shut down when a machine breaks. In some ways, we can view **inventories as a factor of production:** the larger the stock of inventories a firm holds, the more output it can produce.

A third reason for holding inventories is to avoid running out of goods when sales are unexpectedly high. Firms often have to make production decisions before knowing the level of customer demand. For example, a publisher must decide how many copies of a new book to print before knowing whether the book will be popular. If demand exceeds production and there are no inventories, the good will be out of stock for a period, and the firm will lose sales and profit. Inventories can prevent this from happening. This motive for holding inventories is called **stock-out avoidance.**

A fourth explanation of inventories is dictated by the production process. Many goods require a number of steps in production and, therefore, take time to produce. When a product is only partly completed, its components are counted as part of a firm's inventory. These inventories are called **work in process.**

CASE STUDY

Seasonal Fluctuations and Production Smoothing

Economists have spent much time studying data on production, sales, and inventories to test alternative theories of inventory holding. Much of this research examines whether the production-smoothing theory accurately describes the behavior of firms. Contrary to what many economists expected, most of the evidence suggests that firms do not use inventories to smooth production over time.

The clearest evidence against production smoothing comes from industries with seasonal fluctuations in demand. In many industries, sales fluctuate regularly over the course of a year. For example, the toy industry sells more of its output in December than in January. One might expect that firms would build up inventories in times of low sales and draw them down in times of high sales.

Yet, in most industries, firms do not use inventories to smooth production over the year. Instead, the seasonal pattern in production closely matches the seasonal pattern in sales. The evidence from seasonal fluctuations suggests that, in most industries, firms see little benefit to smoothing production.[7]

---

[7] Jeffrey A. Miron and Stephen P. Zeldes, "Seasonality, Cost Shocks, and the Production Smoothing Model of Inventories," *Econometrica* 56 (July 1988): 877–908.

The Accelerator Model of Inventories

Because there are many motives for holding inventories, there are many models of inventory investment. One simple model that explains the data well, without endorsing a particular motive, is the **accelerator model.** This model was developed about half a century ago, and it is sometimes applied to all types of investment. Here we apply it to the type for which it works best—inventory investment.

The accelerator model of inventories assumes that firms hold a stock of inventories that is proportional to the firms' level of output. There are various reasons for this assumption. When output is high, manufacturing firms need more materials and supplies on hand, and they have more goods in the process of being completed. When the economy is booming, retail firms want to have more merchandise on the shelves to show customers. Thus, if N is the economy's stock of inventories and Y is output, then

$$N = \beta Y,$$

where β is a parameter reflecting how much inventory firms wish to hold as a proportion of output.

Inventory investment I is the change in the stock of inventories ΔN. Therefore,

$$I = \Delta N = \beta \, \Delta Y.$$

The accelerator model predicts that inventory investment is proportional to the change in output. When output rises, firms want to hold a larger stock of inventory, so inventory investment is high. When output falls, firms want to hold a smaller stock of inventory, so they allow their inventory to run down, and inventory investment is negative.

We can now see how the model earned its name. Because the variable Y is the rate at which firms are producing goods, ΔY is the "acceleration" of production. The model says that inventory investment depends on whether the economy is speeding up or slowing down.

CASE STUDY

The Evidence for the Accelerator Model

To see how well the accelerator model fits the data, look at Figure 17-7. This figure is a scatterplot of annual data from the national income accounts for the United States. On the horizontal axis is the change in real GDP. On the vertical axis is real inventory investment.

The positive association between the change in GDP and inventory investment supports the prediction of the accelerator model. The line drawn through these points shows the following relationship:

$$I = 0.2 \, \Delta Y.$$

For every $1 that GDP rises, there is $0.20 of inventory investment.

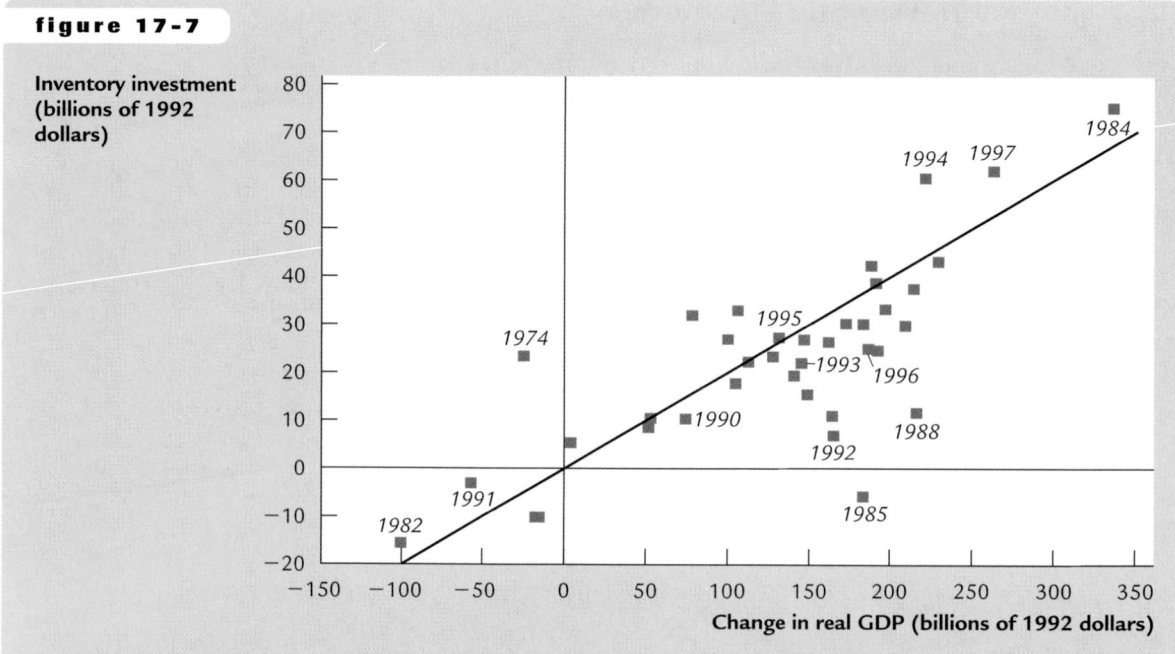

figure 17-7

Inventory investment (billions of 1992 dollars)

Change in real GDP (billions of 1992 dollars)

The Evidence for the Accelerator Model This scatterplot shows that inventory investment is high in years when real GDP rises and low in years when real GDP falls.

Source: U.S. Department of Commerce.

Inventories and the Real Interest Rate

Like other components of investment, inventory investment depends on the real interest rate. When a firm holds a good in inventory and sells it tomorrow rather than selling it today, it gives up the interest it could have earned between today and tomorrow. Thus, the real interest rate measures the opportunity cost of holding inventories.

When the real interest rate rises, holding inventories becomes more costly, so rational firms try to reduce their stock. Therefore, an increase in the real interest rate depresses inventory investment. For example, in the 1980s many firms adopted "just-in-time" production plans, which were designed to reduce the amount of inventory by producing goods just before sale. The high real interest rates that prevailed during most of this decade are one possible explanation for this change in business strategy.

17-4 Conclusion

The purpose of this chapter has been to examine the determinants of investment in more detail. Looking back on the various models of investment, we can see three themes.

First, all types of investment spending are inversely related to the real interest rate. A higher interest rate raises the cost of capital to firms that invest in plant and equipment, raises the cost of borrowing to home buyers, and raises the cost of holding inventories. Thus, the models of investment developed here justify the investment function we have used throughout this book.

Second, there are various causes of shifts in the investment function. An improvement in the available technology raises the marginal product of capital and raises business fixed investment. An increase in the population raises the demand for housing and raises residential investment. Most important, various economic policies, such as changes in the investment tax credit and the corporate income tax, alter the incentives to invest and thus shift the investment function.

Third, it is natural to expect investment to be volatile over the business cycle, because investment spending depends on the output of the economy as well as on the interest rate. In the neoclassical model of business fixed investment, higher employment raises the marginal product of capital and the incentive to invest. Higher output also raises firms' profits and, thereby, relaxes the financing constraints that some firms face. In addition, higher income raises the demand for houses, in turn raising housing prices and residential investment. Higher output raises the stock of inventories firms wish to hold, stimulating inventory investment. Our models predict that an economic boom should stimulate investment and a recession should depress it. This is exactly what we observe.

Summary

1. The marginal product of capital determines the real rental price of capital. The real interest rate, the depreciation rate, and the relative price of capital goods determine the cost of capital. According to the neoclassical model, firms invest if the rental price is greater than the cost of capital, and they disinvest if the rental price is less than the cost of capital.

2. Various parts of the federal tax code influence the incentive to invest. The corporate income tax discourages investment, and the investment tax credit—which has now been repealed in the United States—encourages it.

3. An alternative way of expressing the neoclassical model is to state that investment depends on Tobin's *q,* the ratio of the market value of installed capital to its replacement cost. This ratio reflects the current and expected future profitability of capital. The higher is *q,* the greater is the market value of installed capital relative to its replacement cost, and the greater is the incentive to invest.

4. In contrast to the assumption of the neoclassical model, firms cannot always raise funds to finance investment. Financing constraints make investment sensitive to firms' current cash flow.

5. Residential investment depends on the relative price of housing. Housing prices in turn depend on the demand for housing and the current fixed

supply. An increase in housing demand, perhaps attributable to a fall in the interest rate, raises housing prices and residential investment.

6. Firms have various motives for holding inventories of goods: smoothing production, using them as a factor of production, avoiding stock-outs, and storing work in process. One model of inventory investment that works well without endorsing a particular motive is the accelerator model. According to this model, the stock of inventories depends on the level of GDP, and inventory investment depends on the change in GDP.

KEY CONCEPTS

Business fixed investment

Residential investment

Inventory investment

Neoclassical model of investment

Depreciation

Real cost of capital

Net investment

Corporate income tax

Investment tax credit

Stock

Stock market

Tobin's q

Financing constraints

Production smoothing

Inventories as a factor of
    production

Stock-out avoidance

Work in process

Accelerator model

QUESTIONS FOR REVIEW

1. In the neoclassical model of business fixed investment, under what conditions will firms find it profitable to add to their capital stock?

2. What is Tobin's q, and what does it have to do with investment?

3. Explain why an increase in the interest rate reduces the amount of residential investment.

4. List four reasons firms might hold inventories.

PROBLEMS AND APPLICATIONS

1. Use the neoclassical model of investment to explain the impact of each of the following on the rental price of capital, the cost of capital, and investment:

   a. Anti-inflationary monetary policy raises the real interest rate.

   b. An earthquake destroys part of the capital stock.

   c. Immigration of foreign workers increases the size of the labor force.

2. Suppose that the government levies a tax on oil companies equal to a proportion of the value of the company's oil reserves. (The government assures the firms that the tax is for one time only.) According to the neoclassical model, what effect will the tax have on business fixed investment by these firms? What if these firms face financing constraints?

3. The IS–LM model developed in Chapters 10 and 11 assumes that investment depends only on the interest rate. Yet our theories of investment

suggest that investment might also depend on national income: higher income might induce firms to invest more.

a. Explain why investment might depend on national income.

b. Suppose that investment is determined by

$$I = \bar{I} + aY,$$

where *a* is a constant between zero and one, which measures the influence of national income on investment. With investment set this way, what are the fiscal-policy multipliers in the Keynesian-cross model? Explain.

c. Suppose that investment depends on both income and the interest rate. That is, the investment function is

$$I = \bar{I} + aY - br,$$

where *a* is a constant between zero and one, which measures the influence of national income on investment, and *b* is a constant greater than zero, which measures the influence of the interest rate on investment. Use the *IS–LM* model to consider the short-run impact of an increase in government purchases on national income *Y,* the interest rate *r,* consumption *C,* and investment *I.* How might this investment function alter the conclusions implied by the basic *IS–LM* model?

4. When the stock market crashes, as it did in October 1929 and October 1987, how should the Federal Reserve respond? Why?

5. It is an election year, and the economy is in a recession. The opposition candidate campaigns on a platform of passing an investment tax credit, which would be effective next year after she takes office. What impact does this campaign promise have on economic conditions during the current year?

6. The United States experienced a large increase in the number of births in the 1950s. People in this baby-boom generation reached adulthood and started forming their own households in the 1970s.

a. Use the model of residential investment to predict the impact of this event on housing prices and residential investment.

b. For the years 1970 and 1980, compute the real price of housing, measured as the residential investment deflator divided by the GDP deflator. What do you find? Is this finding consistent with the model? (*Hint:* A good source of data is the *Economic Report of the President,* which is published annually.)

7. The U.S. tax laws encourage investment in housing and discourage investment in business capital. What are the long-run effects of this policy? (*Hint:* Think about the labor market.)

chapter 18

Money Supply and Money Demand

There have been three great inventions since the beginning of time: fire, the wheel, and central banking.

— *Will Rogers*

The supply and demand for money are crucial to many issues in macroeconomics. In Chapter 7, we discussed how economists use the term "money," how the central bank controls the quantity of money, and how monetary policy affects prices and interest rates in the long run when prices are flexible. In Chapters 10 and 11, we saw that the money market is a key element of the *IS–LM* model, which describes the economy in the short run when prices are sticky.

This chapter examines money supply and money demand more closely. In Section 18-1 we see that the banking system plays a key role in determining the money supply, and we discuss various policy instruments that the central bank can use to alter the money supply. In Section 18-2 we consider the motives behind money demand, and we analyze the household's decision about how much money to hold. In Section 18-3 we discuss how recent changes in the financial system have blurred the distinction between money and other assets and how this development complicates the conduct of monetary policy.

18-1 | Money Supply

Chapter 7 introduced the concept of "money supply" in a highly simplified manner. In that chapter we defined the quantity of money as the number of dollars held by the public, and we assumed that the Federal Reserve controls the supply of money by increasing or decreasing the number of dollars in circulation through open-market operations. Although this explanation is a good first approximation, it is incomplete, for it omits the role of the banking system in determining the money supply. We now present a more complete explanation.

In this section we see that the money supply is determined not only by Fed policy, but also by the behavior of households which hold money and of banks in which money is held. We begin by recalling that the money supply includes both currency in the hands of the public and deposits at banks that households can use on demand for transactions, such as checking accounts. That is, letting M denote the money supply, C currency, and D demand deposits, we can write

$$\text{Money Supply} = \text{Currency} + \text{Demand Deposits}$$
$$M = C + D.$$

To understand the money supply, we must understand the interaction between currency and demand deposits and how Fed policy influences these two components of the money supply.

100-Percent-Reserve Banking

We begin by imagining a world without banks. In such a world, all money takes the form of currency, and the quantity of money is simply the amount of currency that the public holds. For this discussion, suppose that there is $1,000 of currency in the economy.

Now introduce banks. At first, suppose that banks accept deposits but do not make loans. The only purpose of the banks is to provide a safe place for depositors to keep their money.

The deposits that banks have received but have not lent out are called **reserves.** Some reserves are held in the vaults of local banks throughout the country, but most are held at a central bank, such as the Federal Reserve. In our hypothetical economy, all deposits are held as reserves: banks simply accept deposits, place the money in reserve, and leave the money there until the depositor makes a withdrawal or writes a check against the balance. This system is called **100-percent-reserve banking.**

Suppose that households deposit the economy's entire $1,000 in Firstbank. Firstbank's **balance sheet**—its accounting statement of assets and liabilities—looks like this:

FIRSTBANK'S BALANCE SHEET	
Assets	**Liabilities**
Reserves $1,000	Deposits $1,000

The bank's assets are the $1,000 it holds as reserves; the bank's liabilities are the $1,000 it owes to depositors. Unlike banks in our economy, this bank is not making loans, so it will not earn profit from its assets. The bank presumably charges depositors a small fee to cover its costs.

What is the money supply in this economy? Before the creation of Firstbank, the money supply was the $1,000 of currency. After the creation of Firstbank, the money supply is the $1,000 of demand deposits. A dollar deposited in a bank reduces currency by $1 and raises deposits by $1, so the money supply remains the same. *If banks hold 100 percent of deposits in reserve, the banking system does not affect the supply of money.*

Fractional-Reserve Banking

Now imagine that banks start to use some of their deposits to make loans—for example, to families who are buying houses or to firms that are investing in new plants and equipment. The advantage to banks is that they can charge interest on the loans. The banks must keep some reserves on hand so that reserves are available whenever depositors want to make withdrawals. But as long as the amount of new deposits approximately equals the amount of withdrawals, a bank need not keep all its deposits in reserve. Thus, bankers have an incentive to make loans. When they do so, we have **fractional-reserve banking,** a system under which banks keep only a fraction of their deposits in reserve.

Here is Firstbank's balance sheet after it makes a loan:

FIRSTBANK'S BALANCE SHEET

Assets		Liabilities	
Reserves	$200	Deposits	$1,000
Loans	$800		

This balance sheet assumes that the *reserve–deposit ratio*—the fraction of deposits kept in reserve—is 20 percent. Firstbank keeps $200 of the $1,000 in deposits in reserve and lends out the remaining $800.

Notice that Firstbank increases the supply of money by $800 when it makes this loan. Before the loan is made, the money supply is $1,000, equaling the deposits in Firstbank. After the loan is made, the money supply is $1,800: the depositor still has a demand deposit of $1,000, but now the borrower holds $800 in currency. *Thus, in a system of fractional-reserve banking, banks create money.*

The creation of money does not stop with Firstbank. If the borrower deposits the $800 in another bank (or if the borrower uses the $800 to pay someone who then deposits it), the process of money creation continues. Here is the balance sheet of Secondbank:

SECONDBANK'S BALANCE SHEET

Assets		Liabilities	
Reserves	$160	Deposits	$800
Loans	$640		

Secondbank receives the $800 in deposits, keeps 20 percent, or $160, in reserve, and then loans out $640. Thus, Secondbank creates $640 of money. If this $640 is eventually deposited in Thirdbank, this bank keeps 20 percent, or $128, in reserve and loans out $512, resulting in this balance sheet:

THIRDBANK'S BALANCE SHEET

Assets		Liabilities	
Reserves	$128	Deposits	$640
Loans	$512		

The process goes on and on. With each deposit and loan, more money is created.

Although this process of money creation can continue forever, it does not create an infinite amount of money. Letting rr denote the reserve–deposit ratio, the amount of money that the original $1,000 creates is

$$
\begin{aligned}
\text{Original Deposit} &= \$1,000 \\
\text{Firstbank Lending} &= (1 - rr) \times \$1,000 \\
\text{Secondbank Lending} &= (1 - rr)^2 \times \$1,000 \\
\text{Thirdbank Lending} &= (1 - rr)^3 \times \$1,000 \\
&\vdots \\
\hline
\text{Total Money Supply} &= [1 + (1 - rr) + (1 - rr)^2 \\
&\quad + (1 - rr)^3 + \cdots] \times \$1,000 \\
&= (1/rr) \times \$1,000
\end{aligned}
$$

Each $1 of reserves generates $$(1/rr)$ of money. In our example, $rr = 0.2$, so the original $1,000 generates $5,000 of money.[1]

The banking system's ability to create money is the primary difference between banks and other financial institutions. As we first discussed in Chapter 3, financial markets have the important function of transferring the economy's resources from those households that wish to save some of their income for the future to those households and firms that wish to borrow to buy investment goods to be used in future production. The process of transferring funds from savers to borrowers is called **financial intermediation.** Many institutions in the economy act as financial intermediaries: the most prominent examples are the stock market, the bond market, and the banking system. Yet, of these financial institutions, only banks have the legal authority to create assets that are part of the money supply, such as checking accounts. Therefore, banks are the only financial institutions that directly influence the money supply.

Note that although the system of fractional-reserve banking creates money, it does not create wealth. When a bank loans out some of its reserves, it gives borrowers the ability to make transactions and therefore increases the supply of money. The borrowers are also undertaking a debt obligation to the bank, however, so the loan does not make them wealthier. In other words, the creation of money by the banking system increases the economy's liquidity, not its wealth.

A Model of the Money Supply

Now that we have seen how banks create money, let's examine in more detail what determines the money supply. Here we present a model of the money

---

[1] *Mathematical note:* The last step in the derivation of the total money supply uses the algebraic result for the sum of an infinite geometric series (which we used previously in computing the multiplier in Chapter 10). According to this result, if x is a number between -1 and 1, then

$$1 + x + x^2 + x^3 + \cdots = 1/(1 - x).$$

In this application, $x = (1 - rr)$.

supply under fractional-reserve banking. The model has three exogenous variables:

- The **monetary base** B is the total number of dollars held by the public as currency C and by the banks as reserves R. It is directly controlled by the Federal Reserve.

- The **reserve–deposit ratio** rr is the fraction of deposits that banks hold in reserve. It is determined by the business policies of banks and the laws regulating banks.

- The **currency–deposit ratio** cr is the amount of currency C people hold as a fraction of their holdings of demand deposits D. It reflects the preferences of households about the form of money they wish to hold.

Our model shows how the money supply depends on the monetary base, the reserve–deposit ratio, and the currency–deposit ratio. It allows us to examine how Fed policy and the choices of banks and households influence the money supply.

We begin with the definitions of the money supply and the monetary base:

$$M = C + D,$$
$$B = C + R.$$

The first equation states that the money supply is the sum of currency and demand deposits. The second equation states that the monetary base is the sum of currency and bank reserves. To solve for the money supply as a function of the three exogenous variables (B, rr, and cr), we begin by dividing the first equation by the second to obtain

$$\frac{M}{B} = \frac{C + D}{C + R}.$$

Then divide both the top and bottom of the expression on the right by D.

$$\frac{M}{B} = \frac{C/D + 1}{C/D + R/D}.$$

Note that C/D is the currency–deposit ratio cr, and that R/D is the reserve–deposit ratio rr. Making these substitutions, and bringing the B from the left to the right side of the equation, we obtain

$$M = \frac{cr + 1}{cr + rr} \times B.$$

This equation shows how the money supply depends on the three exogenous variables.

We can now see that the money supply is proportional to the monetary base. The factor of proportionality, $(cr + 1)/(cr + rr)$, is denoted m and is called the **money multiplier.** We can write

$$M = m \times B.$$

Each dollar of the monetary base produces m dollars of money. Because the monetary base has a multiplied effect on the money supply, the monetary base is sometimes called **high-powered money.**

Here's a numerical example that approximately describes the U.S. economy today. Suppose that the monetary base B is $500 billion, the reserve–deposit ratio rr is 0.1, and the currency–deposit ratio cr is 0.6. In this case, the money multiplier is

$$m = \frac{0.6 + 1}{0.6 + 0.1} = 2.3,$$

and the money supply is

$$M = 2.3 \times \$500 \text{ billion} = \$1{,}150 \text{ billion}.$$

Each dollar of the monetary base generates 2.3 dollars of money, so the total money supply is $1,150 billion.

We can now see how changes in the three exogenous variables—B, rr, and cr—cause the money supply to change.

1. The money supply is proportional to the monetary base. Thus, an increase in the monetary base increases the money supply by the same percentage.

2. The lower the reserve–deposit ratio, the more loans banks make, and the more money banks create from every dollar of reserves. Thus, a decrease in the reserve–deposit ratio raises the money multiplier and the money supply.

3. The lower the currency–deposit ratio, the fewer dollars of the monetary base the public holds as currency, the more base dollars banks hold as reserves, and the more money banks can create. Thus, a decrease in the currency–deposit ratio raises the money multiplier and the money supply.

With this model in mind, we can discuss the ways in which the Fed influences the money supply.

The Three Instruments of Monetary Policy

In previous chapters we made the simplifying assumption that the Federal Reserve controls the money supply directly. In fact, the Fed controls the money supply indirectly by altering either the monetary base or the reserve–deposit ratio. To do this, the Fed has at its disposal three instruments of monetary policy: open-market operations, reserve requirements, and the discount rate.

Open-market operations are the purchases and sales of government bonds by the Fed. When the Fed buys bonds from the public, the dollars it pays for the bonds increase the monetary base and thereby increase the money supply. When the Fed sells bonds to the public, the dollars it receives reduce the monetary base and thus decrease the money supply. Open-market operations are the policy instrument that the Fed uses most often. In fact, the Fed conducts open-market operations in New York bond markets almost every weekday.

Reserve requirements are Fed regulations that impose on banks a minimum reserve–deposit ratio. An increase in reserve requirements raises the reserve–deposit ratio and thus lowers the money multiplier and the money supply. Changes in reserve requirements are the least frequently used of the Fed's three policy instruments.

The **discount rate** is the interest rate that the Fed charges when it makes loans to banks. Banks borrow from the Fed when they find themselves with too few reserves to meet reserve requirements. The lower the discount rate, the cheaper are borrowed reserves, and the more banks borrow at the Fed's discount window. Hence, a reduction in the discount rate raises the monetary base and the money supply.

Although these three instruments—open-market operations, reserve requirements, and the discount rate—give the Fed substantial power to influence the money supply, the Fed cannot control the money supply perfectly. Bank discretion in conducting business can cause the money supply to change in ways the Fed did not anticipate. For example, banks may choose to hold **excess reserves**—that is, reserves above the reserve requirement. The higher the amount of excess reserves, the higher the reserve–deposit ratio, and the lower the money supply. As another example, the Fed cannot precisely control the amount banks borrow from the discount window. The less banks borrow, the smaller the monetary base, and the smaller the money supply. Hence, the money supply sometimes moves in ways the Fed does not intend.

CASE STUDY

Bank Failures and the Money Supply in the 1930s

Between August 1929 and March 1933, the money supply fell 28 percent. As we discussed in Chapter 11, some economists believe that this large decline in the money supply was the primary cause of the Great Depression. But we did not discuss why the money supply fell so dramatically.

The three variables that determine the money supply—the monetary base, the reserve–deposit ratio, and the currency–deposit ratio—are shown in Table 18-1 for 1929 and 1933. You can see that the fall in the money supply cannot be attributed to a fall in the monetary base: in fact, the monetary base rose 18 percent over this period. Instead, the money supply fell because the money multiplier fell 38 percent. The money multiplier fell because the currency–deposit and reserve–deposit ratios both rose substantially.

Most economists attribute the fall in the money multiplier to the large number of bank failures in the early 1930s. From 1930 to 1933, more than 9,000 banks suspended operations, often defaulting on their depositors. The bank failures caused the money supply to fall by altering the behavior of both depositors and bankers.

Bank failures raised the currency–deposit ratio by reducing public confidence in the banking system. People feared that bank failures would continue,

table 18-1

The Money Supply and Its Determinants: 1929 and 1933

	August 1929	March 1933
Money Supply	**26.5**	**19.0**
Currency	3.9	5.5
Demand deposits	22.6	13.5
Monetary Base	**7.1**	**8.4**
Currency	3.9	5.5
Reserves	3.2	2.9
Money Multiplier	**3.7**	**2.3**
Reserve—deposit ratio	0.14	0.21
Currency—deposit ratio	0.17	0.41

Source: Adapted from Milton Friedman and Anna Schwartz, *A Monetary History of the United States, 1867–1960* (Princeton, NJ: Princeton University Press, 1963), Appendix A.

and they began to view currency as a more desirable form of money than demand deposits. When they withdrew their deposits, they drained the banks of reserves. The process of money creation reversed itself, as banks responded to lower reserves by reducing their outstanding balance of loans.

In addition, the bank failures raised the reserve–deposit ratio by making bankers more cautious. Having just observed many bank runs, bankers became apprehensive about operating with a small amount of reserves. They therefore increased their holdings of reserves to well above the legal minimum. Just as households responded to the banking crisis by holding more currency relative to deposits, bankers responded by holding more reserves relative to loans. Together these changes caused a large fall in the money multiplier.

Although it is easy to explain why the money supply fell, it is more difficult to decide whether to blame the Federal Reserve. One might argue that the monetary base did not fall, so the Fed should not be blamed. Critics of Fed policy during this period make two arguments. First, they claim that the Fed should have taken a more vigorous role in preventing bank failures by acting as a *lender of last resort* when banks needed cash during bank runs. This would have helped maintain confidence in the banking system and prevented the large fall in the money multiplier. Second, they point out that the Fed could have responded to the fall in the money multiplier by increasing the monetary base even more than it did. Either of these actions would likely have prevented such a large fall in the money supply, which in turn might have reduced the severity of the Great Depression.

Since the 1930s, many policies have been put into place that make such a large and sudden fall in the money multiplier less likely today. Most important, the system of federal deposit insurance maintains public confidence in the banking system and thus prevents large swings in the currency–deposit ratio. Deposit insurance, however, can be a costly policy: in the late 1980s and early 1990s, the federal government incurred the large expense of bailing out many insolvent savings and loan institutions. Yet deposit insurance does help stabilize the banking system and the money supply.

18-2 | Money Demand

We now turn to the other side of the money market and examine what determines money demand. In previous chapters, we used simple money demand functions. We started with the quantity theory, which assumes that the demand for real balances is proportional to income. That is, the quantity theory assumes

$$(M/P)^d = kY,$$

where k is a constant measuring how much money people want to hold for every dollar of income. We then considered a more general and realistic money demand function that assumes the demand for real money balances depends on both the interest rate and income:

$$(M/P)^d = L(i, Y).$$

We used this money demand function when we discussed the link between money and prices in Chapter 7 and when we developed the $IS-LM$ model in Chapters 10 and 11.

There is, of course, much more to say about what determines how much money people choose to hold. Just as studies of the consumption function rely on microeconomic models of the consumption decision, studies of the money demand function rely on microeconomic models of the money demand decision. In this section we first discuss in broad terms the different ways to model money demand. We then develop one prominent model.

Recall that money serves three functions: it is a unit of account, a store of value, and a medium of exchange. The first function—money as a unit of account—does not by itself generate any demand for money, because one can quote prices in dollars without holding any. By contrast, money can serve its other two functions only if people hold it. Theories of money demand emphasize the role of money either as a store of value or as a medium of exchange.

Portfolio Theories of Money Demand

Theories of money demand that emphasize the role of money as a store of value are called **portfolio theories.** According to these theories, people hold money as part of their portfolio of assets. The key insight is that money offers a different combination of risk and return than other assets. In particular, money offers a safe (nominal) return, whereas the prices of stocks and bonds may rise or fall. Thus, some economists have suggested that households choose to hold money as part of their optimal portfolio.[2]

Portfolio theories predict that the demand for money should depend on the risk and return offered by money and by the various assets households can hold instead of money. In addition, money demand should depend on total wealth, because wealth measures the size of the portfolio to be allocated among money and the alternative assets. For example, we might write the money demand function as

$$(M/P)^\mathrm{d} = L(r_\mathrm{s}, r_\mathrm{b}, \pi^\mathrm{e}, W),$$

where r_s is the expected real return on stock, r_b is the expected real return on bonds, π^e is the expected inflation rate, and W is real wealth. An increase in r_s or r_b reduces money demand, because other assets become more attractive. An increase in π^e also reduces money demand, because money becomes less attractive. (Recall that $-\pi^\mathrm{e}$ is the expected real return to holding money.) An increase in W raises money demand, because higher wealth means a larger portfolio.

From the standpoint of portfolio theories, we can view our money demand function, $L(i, Y)$, as a useful simplification. First, it uses real income Y as a proxy for real wealth W. Second, the only return variable it includes is the nominal interest rate, which is the sum of the real return on bonds and expected inflation (that is, $i = r_\mathrm{b} + \pi^\mathrm{e}$). According to portfolio theories, however, the money demand function should include the expected returns on other assets as well.

Are portfolio theories useful for studying money demand? The answer depends on which measure of money we are considering. The most narrow measures of money, such as $M1$, include only currency and deposits in checking accounts. These forms of money earn zero or very low rates of interest. There are other assets—such as savings accounts, Treasury bills, certificates of deposit, and money market mutual funds—that earn higher rates of interest and have the same risk characteristics as currency and checking accounts. Economists say that money ($M1$) is a **dominated asset:** as a store of value, it exists alongside other assets that are always better. Thus, it is not optimal for people to hold money as part of their portfolio, and portfolio theories cannot explain the demand for these dominated forms of money.

Portfolio theories are more plausible as theories of money demand if we adopt a broad measure of money. The broad measures include many of those assets that dominate currency and checking accounts. $M2$, for example, includes savings accounts and money market mutual funds. When we examine why people hold assets in the form of $M2$, rather than bonds or stock, the portfolio considerations of risk and return may be paramount. Hence, although the portfolio approach to money demand may not be plausible when applied to $M1$, it may be a good theory to explain the demand for $M2$ or $M3$.

---

[2] James Tobin, "Liquidity Preference as Behavior Toward Risk," *Review of Economic Studies* 25 (February 1958): 65–86.

CASE STUDY

Currency and the Underground Economy

How much currency are you holding right now in your wallet? How many $100 bills?

In the United States today, the amount of currency per person exceeds $1,000. About half of that is in $100 bills. Most people find this fact surprising, because they hold much smaller amounts and in smaller denominations.

Some of this currency is used by people in the underground economy—that is, by those engaged in illegal activity such as the drug trade and by those trying to hide income to evade taxes. People whose wealth was earned illegally may have fewer options for investing their portfolio, because by holding wealth in banks, bonds, or stock, they assume a greater risk of detection. For criminals, currency may not be a dominated asset: it may be the best store of value available.

Some economists point to the large amount of currency in the underground economy as one reason that some inflation may be desirable. Recall that inflation is a tax on the holders of money, because inflation erodes the real value of money. A drug dealer holding $20,000 in cash pays an inflation tax of $2,000 per year when the inflation rate is 10 percent. The inflation tax is one of the few taxes those in the underground economy cannot evade.[3]

Transactions Theories of Money Demand

Theories of money demand that emphasize the role of money as a medium of exchange are called **transactions theories.** These theories acknowledge that money is a dominated asset and stress that people hold money, unlike other assets, to make purchases. These theories best explain why people hold narrow measures of money, such as currency and checking accounts, as opposed to holding assets that dominate them, such as savings accounts or Treasury bills.

Transactions theories of money demand take many forms, depending on how one models the process of obtaining money and making transactions. All these theories assume that money has the cost of earning a low rate of return and the benefit of making transactions more convenient. People decide how much money to hold by trading off these costs and benefits.

To see how transactions theories explain the money demand function, let's develop one prominent model of this type. The **Baumol–Tobin model** was developed in the 1950s by economists William Baumol and James Tobin, and it remains a leading theory of money demand.[4]

---

[3] To read more about the large quantity of currency, see Case M. Sprenkle, "The Case of the Missing Currency," *Journal of Economic Perspectives* 7 (Fall 1993): 175–184.

[4] William Baumol, "The Transactions Demand for Cash: An Inventory Theoretic Approach," *Quarterly Journal of Economics* 66 (November 1952): 545–556; James Tobin, "The Interest Elasticity of the Transactions Demand for Cash," *Review of Economics and Statistics* (August 1956): 241–247.

The Baumol–Tobin Model of Cash Management

The Baumol–Tobin model analyzes the costs and benefits of holding money. The benefit of holding money is convenience: people hold money to avoid making a trip to the bank every time they wish to buy something. The cost of this convenience is the forgone interest they would have received had they left the money deposited in a savings account that paid interest.

To see how people trade off these benefits and costs, consider a person who plans to spend Y dollars gradually over the course of a year. (For simplicity, assume that the price level is constant, so real spending is constant over the year.) How much money should he hold in the process of spending this amount? That is, what is the optimal size of average cash balances?

Consider the possibilities. He could withdraw the Y dollars at the beginning of the year and gradually spend the money. Panel (a) of Figure 18-1 shows his money holdings over the course of the year under this plan. His money holdings begin the year at Y and end the year at zero, averaging $Y/2$ over the year.

A second possible plan is to make two trips to the bank. In this case, he withdraws $Y/2$ dollars at the beginning of the year, gradually spends this amount over the first half of the year, and then makes another trip to withdraw $Y/2$ for the second half of the year. Panel (b) of Figure 18-1 shows that money holdings over the year vary between $Y/2$ and zero, averaging $Y/4$. This plan has the advantage that less money is held on average, so the individual forgoes less interest, but it has the disadvantage of requiring two trips to the bank rather than one.

figure 18-1

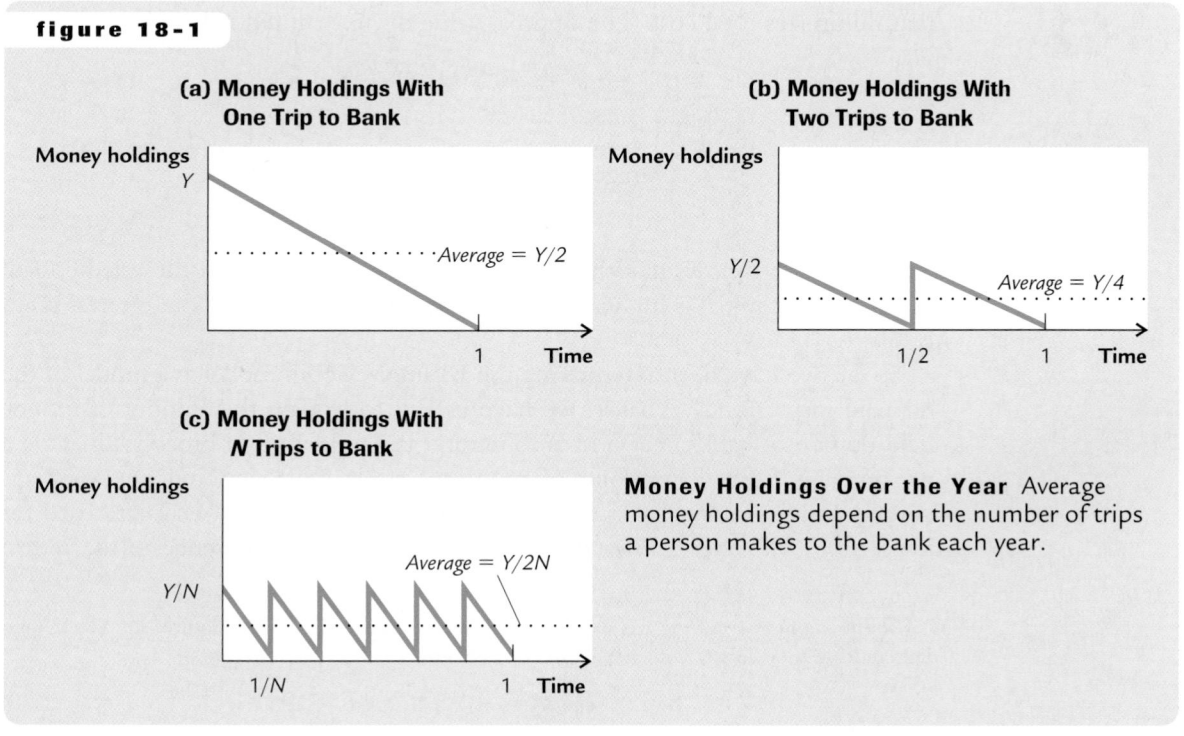

Money Holdings Over the Year Average money holdings depend on the number of trips a person makes to the bank each year.

More generally, suppose the individual makes N trips to the bank over the course of the year. On each trip, he withdraws Y/N dollars; he then spends the money gradually over the following $1/N$th of the year. Panel (c) of Figure 18-1 shows that money holdings vary between Y/N and zero, averaging $Y/(2N)$.

The question is, what is the optimal choice of N? The greater N is, the less money the individual holds on average and the less interest he forgoes. But as N increases, so does the inconvenience of making frequent trips to the bank.

Suppose that the cost of going to the bank is some fixed amount F. We can view F as representing the value of the time spent traveling to and from the bank and waiting in line to make the withdrawal. For example, if a trip to the bank takes 15 minutes and a person's wage is $12 per hour, then F is $3. Also, let i denote the interest rate; because money does not bear interest, i measures the opportunity cost of holding money.

Now we can analyze the optimal choice of N, which determines money demand. For any N, the average amount of money held is $Y/(2N)$, so the forgone interest is $iY/(2N)$. Because F is the cost per trip to the bank, the total cost of making trips to the bank is FN. The total cost the individual bears is the sum of the forgone interest and the cost of trips to the bank:

$$\text{Total Cost} = \text{Forgone Interest} + \text{Cost of Trips}$$
$$= iY/(2N) + FN.$$

The larger the number of trips N, the smaller the forgone interest, and the larger the cost of going to the bank.

Figure 18-2 shows how total cost depends on N. There is one value of N that minimizes total cost. The optimal value of N, denoted N^*, is[5]

$$N^* = \sqrt{iY/2F}.$$

Average money holding is

$$\text{Average Money Holding} = Y/(2N^*)$$
$$= \sqrt{YF/2i}.$$

This expression shows that the individual holds more money if the fixed cost of going to the bank F is higher, if expenditure Y is higher, or if the interest rate i is lower.

So far, we have been interpreting the Baumol–Tobin model as a model of the demand for currency. That is, we have used it to explain the amount of money held outside of banks. Yet one can interpret the model more broadly. Imagine a person who holds a portfolio of monetary assets (currency and checking accounts) and nonmonetary assets (stocks and bonds). Monetary assets are used for transactions but offer a low rate of return. Let i be the difference in the return

---

[5] *Mathematical note:* Deriving this expression for the optimal choice of N requires simple calculus. Differentiate total cost C with respect to N to obtain

$$dC/dN = -iYN^{-2}/2 + F.$$

At the optimum, $dC/dN = 0$, which yields the formula for N^*.

figure 18-2

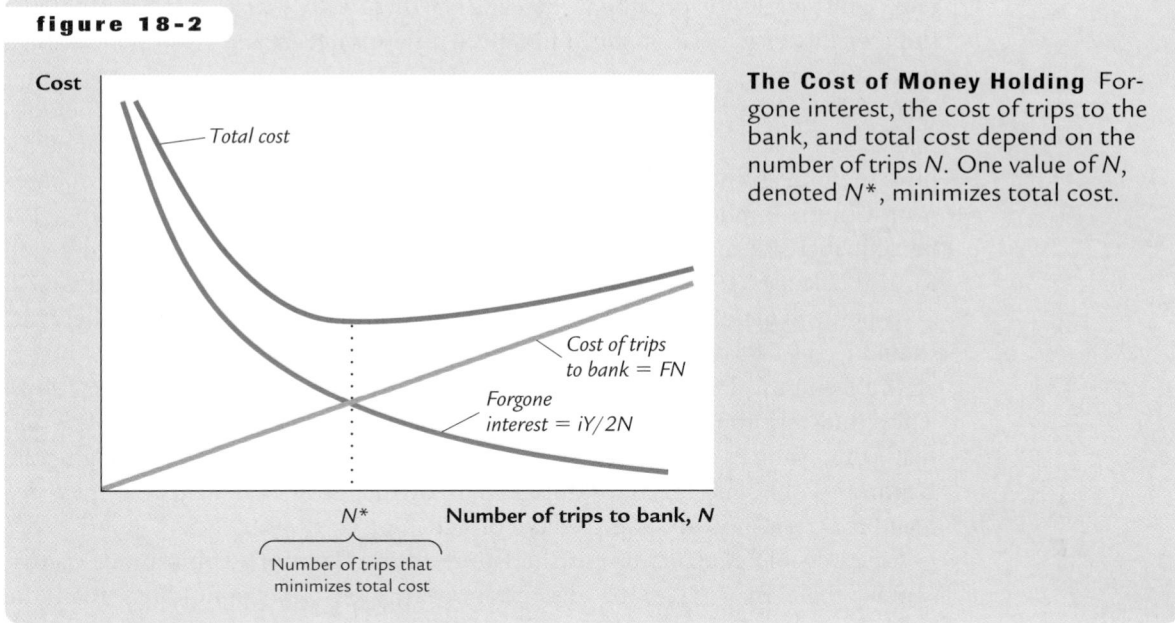

The Cost of Money Holding Forgone interest, the cost of trips to the bank, and total cost depend on the number of trips N. One value of N, denoted N^*, minimizes total cost.

between monetary and nonmonetary assets, and let F be the cost of transferring nonmonetary assets into monetary assets, such as a brokerage fee. The decision about how often to pay the brokerage fee is analogous to the decision about how often to make a trip to the bank. Therefore, the Baumol–Tobin model describes this person's demand for monetary assets. By showing that money demand depends positively on expenditure Y and negatively on the interest rate i, the model provides a microeconomic justification for the money demand function, $L(i, Y)$, that we have used throughout this book.

One implication of the Baumol–Tobin model is that any change in the fixed cost of going to the bank F alters the money demand function—that is, it changes the quantity of money demanded for any given interest rate and income. It is easy to imagine events that might influence this fixed cost. The spread of automatic teller machines, for instance, reduces F by reducing the time it takes to withdraw money. Similarly, the introduction of internet banking reduces F by makes it easier to transfer funds among accounts. On the other hand, an increase in real wages increases F by increasing the value of time. And an increase in banking fees increases F directly. Thus, although the Baumol–Tobin model gives us a very specific money demand function, it does not give us reason to believe that this function will necessarily be stable over time.

CASE STUDY

Empirical Studies of Money Demand

Many economists have studied the data on money, income, and interest rates to learn more about the money demand function. One purpose of these studies is to estimate how money demand responds to changes in income and the interest rate. The sensitivity of money demand to these two variables determines the slope of the *LM* curve; it thus influences how monetary and fiscal policy affect the economy.

Another purpose of the empirical studies is to test the theories of money demand. The Baumol–Tobin model, for example, makes precise predictions for how income and interest rates influence money demand. The model's square-root formula implies that the income elasticity of money demand is 1/2: a 10-percent increase in income should lead to a 5-percent increase in the demand for real balances. It also says that the interest elasticity of money demand is 1/2: a 10-percent increase in the interest rate (say, from 10 percent to 11 percent) should lead to a 5-percent decrease in the demand for real balances.

Most empirical studies of money demand do not confirm these predictions. They find that the income elasticity of money demand is larger than 1/2 and that the interest elasticity is smaller than 1/2. Thus, although the Baumol–Tobin model may capture part of the story behind the money demand function, it is not completely correct.

One possible explanation for the failure of the Baumol–Tobin model is that some people may have less discretion over their money holdings than the model assumes. For example, consider a person who must go to the bank once a week to deposit her paycheck; while at the bank, she takes advantage of her visit to withdraw the currency needed for the coming week. For this person, the number of trips to the bank, *N,* does not respond to changes in expenditure or the interest rate. Because *N* is fixed, average money holdings ($Y/2N$) are proportional to expenditure and insensitive to the interest rate.

Now imagine that the world is populated with two sorts of people. Some obey the Baumol–Tobin model, so they have income and interest elasticities of 1/2. The others have a fixed *N,* so they have an income elasticity of 1 and an interest elasticity of zero. In this case, the overall demand for money looks like a weighted average of the demands of the two groups. The income elasticity will be between 1/2 and 1, and the interest elasticity will be between 1/2 and zero, as the empirical studies find.[6]

18-3 | Financial Innovation and the Rise of Near Money

Traditional macroeconomic analysis groups assets into two categories: those used as a medium of exchange as well as a store of value (currency, checking accounts) and those used only as a store of value (stocks, bonds, savings ac-

---

[6] To learn more about the empirical studies of money demand, see Stephen M. Goldfeld and Daniel E. Sichel, "The Demand for Money," *Handbook of Monetary Economics,* volume 1 (Amsterdam: North-Holland, 1990): 299–356; and David Laidler, *The Demand for Money: Theories and Evidence,* 3d ed. (New York: Harper & Row, 1985).

counts). The first category of assets is called "money." In this chapter we discussed its supply and demand.

Although the distinction between monetary and nonmonetary assets remains a useful theoretical tool, in recent years it has become more difficult to use in practice. In part because of deregulation of banks and other financial institutions, and in part because of improved computer technology, the past decade has seen rapid financial innovation. Monetary assets such as checking accounts once paid no interest; today they earn market interest rates and are comparable to nonmonetary assets as stores of value. Nonmonetary assets such as stocks and bonds were once inconvenient to buy and sell; today mutual funds allow depositors to hold stocks and bonds and to make withdrawals simply by writing checks from their accounts. These nonmonetary assets that have acquired some of the liquidity of money are called **near money.**

The existence of near money complicates monetary policy by making the demand for money unstable. Since money and near money are close substitutes, households can easily switch their assets from one form to the other. Such changes can occur for minor reasons and do not necessarily reflect changes in spending. Thus, the velocity of money becomes unstable, and the quantity of money gives faulty signals about aggregate demand.

One response to this problem is to use a broad definition of money that includes near money. Yet, since there is a continuum of assets in the world with varying characteristics, it is not clear how to choose a subset to label "money." Moreover, if we adopt a broad definition of money, the Fed's ability to control this quantity may be limited, since many forms of near money have no reserve requirement.

The instability in money demand caused by near money has been an important practical problem for the Federal Reserve. In the early 1990s, different measures of the quantity of money gave conflicting signals: some measures of money grew quickly, while others grew slowly. In 1993, Fed Chairman Alan Greenspan announced that the Fed would pay less attention to short-run fluctuations in monetary aggregates. Under the new policy, the Fed uses the instruments of monetary policy to set interest rates at a level it believes to be consistent with low inflation and stable growth. The period since this announcement has, so far, been marked by better-than-average macroeconomic stability.

CASE STUDY

John Taylor's (and Alan Greenspan's?) Rule for Monetary Policy

If you wanted to set interest rates to achieve stable prices while avoiding large fluctuations in output and employment, how would you do it? This is exactly the question that Alan Greenspan and the other governors of the Federal Reserve must ask themselves every day. The short-term policy instrument that the Fed now sets is the federal funds rate—the short-term interest rate at which banks make loans to one another. Whenever the Federal Open Market

Committee meets, it chooses a target for the federal funds rate. The Fed's bond traders are then told to conduct open-market operations in order to hit the desired target.

The hard part of the Fed's job is choosing the target for the federal funds rate. Two guidelines are clear. First, when inflation heats up, the federal funds rate should rise. An increase in the interest rate will mean a smaller money supply and, eventually, lower investment, lower output, higher unemployment, and reduced inflation. Second, when real economic activity slows—as reflected in real GDP or unemployment—the federal funds rate should fall. A decrease in the interest rate will mean a larger money supply and, eventually, higher investment, higher output, and lower unemployment.

The Fed needs to go beyond these general guidelines, however, and decide how much to respond to changes in inflation and real economic activity. To help it make this decision, economist John Taylor has proposed a simple rule for the federal funds rate:

$$\text{Nominal Federal Funds Rate} = \text{Inflation} + 2.0$$
$$+ 0.5 \,(\text{Inflation} - 2.0) - 0.5 \,(\text{GDP gap}).$$

The GDP gap is the percentage shortfall of real GDP from an estimate of its natural rate.

figure 18-3

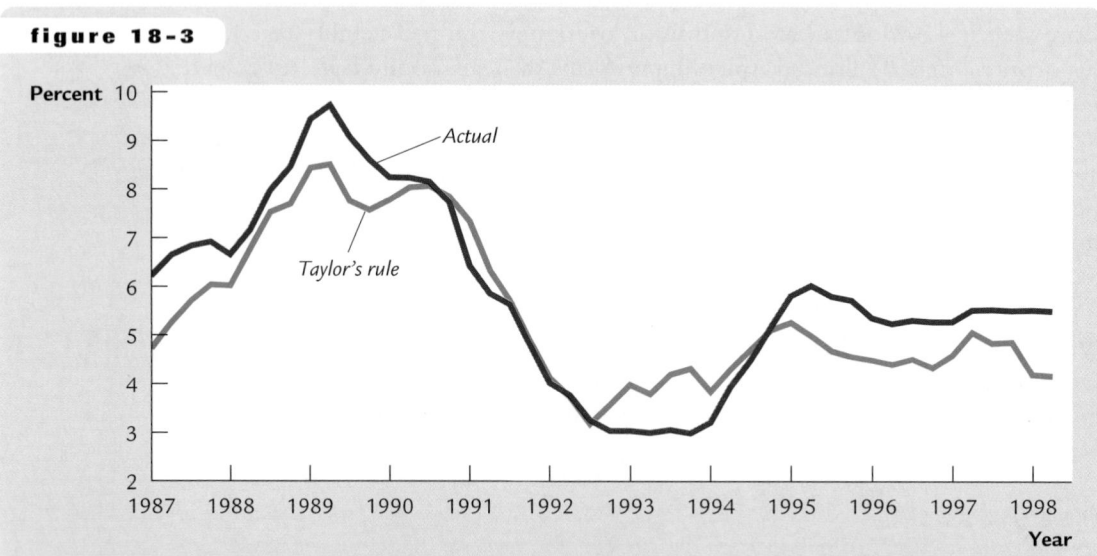

The Federal Funds Rate: Actual and Suggested This figure shows the federal funds rate—the short-term interest rate at which banks make loans to each other. It also shows the federal funds rate suggested by John Taylor's monetary rule. Notice that the two series move closely together.

Source: Federal Reserve Board, U.S. Department of Commerce, and author's calculations. To implement the Taylor rule, the inflation rate is measured as the percentage change in the GDP deflator over the previous four quarters, and the GDP gap is measured as twice the deviation of the unemployment rate from 6 percent.

Taylor's rule has the real federal funds rate—the nominal rate minus inflation—responding to inflation and the GDP gap. According to this rule, the real federal funds rate equals 2 percent when inflation is 2 percent and GDP is at its natural rate. For each percentage point by which inflation rises above 2 percent, the real federal funds rate rises by 0.5 percent. For each percentage point by which real GDP falls below its natural rate, the real federal funds rate falls by 0.5 percent. If GDP rises above its natural rate, so that the GDP gap is negative, the real federal funds rate rises accordingly.

Taylor's rule for monetary policy is not only simple and reasonable, but it also resembles actual Fed behavior in recent years. Figure 18-3 shows the actual federal funds rate and the target rate as determined by Taylor's proposed rule. Notice how closely together the two series move. John Taylor's monetary rule may be more than an academic suggestion. It may be the rule that Alan Greenspan and his colleagues subconsciously follow.[7]

18-4 Conclusion

Money is at the heart of much macroeconomic analysis. Models of money supply and money demand can help shed light on the long-run determinants of the price level and the short-run causes of economic fluctuations. The rise of near money in recent years has shown that there is still much to be learned. Building reliable microeconomic models of money and near money remains a central challenge for macroeconomists.

Summary

1. The system of fractional-reserve banking creates money, because each dollar of reserves generates many dollars of demand deposits.

2. The supply of money depends on the monetary base, the reserve–deposit ratio, and the currency–deposit ratio. An increase in the monetary base leads to a proportionate increase in the money supply. A decrease in the reserve–deposit ratio or in the currency–deposit ratio increases the money multiplier and thus the money supply.

3. The Federal Reserve changes the money supply using three policy instruments. It can increase the monetary base by making an open-market purchase of bonds or by lowering the discount rate. It can reduce the reserve–deposit ratio by relaxing reserve requirements.

---

[7] John B. Taylor, "The Inflation/Output Variability Tradeoff Revisited," in *Goals, Guidelines, and Constraints Facing Monetary Policymakers* (Federal Reserve Bank of Boston, 1994).

4. Portfolio theories of money demand stress the role of money as a store of value. They predict that the demand for money depends on the risk and return on money and alternative assets.

5. Transactions theories of money demand, such as the Baumol–Tobin model, stress the role of money as a medium of exchange. They predict that the demand for money depends positively on expenditure and negatively on the interest rate.

6. Financial innovation has led to the creation of assets with many of the attributes of money. These near monies make the demand for money less stable, which complicates the conduct of monetary policy.

KEY CONCEPTS

Reserves

100-percent-reserve banking

Balance sheet

Fractional-reserve banking

Financial intermediation

Monetary base

Reserve–deposit ratio

Currency–deposit ratio

Money multiplier

High-powered money

Open-market operations

Reserve requirements

Discount rate

Excess reserves

Portfolio theories

Dominated asset

Transactions theories

Baumol–Tobin model

Near money

QUESTIONS FOR REVIEW

1. Explain how banks create money.

2. What are the three ways in which the Federal Reserve can influence the money supply?

3. Why might a banking crisis lead to a fall in the money supply?

4. Explain the difference between portfolio and transactions theories of money demand.

5. According to the Baumol–Tobin model, what determines how often people go to the bank? What does this decision have to do with money demand?

6. In what way does the existence of near money complicate the conduct of monetary policy?

PROBLEMS AND APPLICATIONS

1. The money supply fell during the years 1929 to 1933 because both the currency–deposit ratio and the reserve–deposit ratio increased. Use the model of the money supply and the data in Table 18-1 to answer the following hypothetical questions about this episode.

   a. What would have happened to the money supply if the currency–deposit ratio had risen but the reserve–deposit ratio had remained the same?

   b. What would have happened to the money supply if the reserve–deposit ratio had risen but the currency–deposit ratio had remained the same?

c. Which of the two changes was more responsible for the fall in the money supply?

2. To increase tax revenue, the U.S. government in 1932 imposed a 2-cent tax on checks written on deposits in bank accounts. (In today's dollars, this tax was about 25 cents per check.)

a. How do you think the check tax affected the currency–deposit ratio? Explain.

b. Use the model of the money supply under fractional-reserve banking to discuss how this tax affected the money supply.

c. Now use the *IS–LM* model to discuss the impact of this tax on the economy. Was the check tax a good policy to implement in the middle of the Great Depression?

3. Suppose that an epidemic of street crime sweeps the country, making it more likely that your wallet will be stolen. Using the Baumol–Tobin model, explain (in words, not equations) how this crime wave will affect the optimal frequency of trips to the bank and the demand for money.

4. Let's see what the Baumol–Tobin model says about how often you should go to the bank to withdraw cash.

a. How much do you buy per year with currency (as opposed to checks or credit cards)? This is your value of *Y*.

b. How long does it take you to go to the bank? What is your hourly wage? Use these two figures to compute your value of *F*.

c. What interest rate do you earn on the money you leave in your bank account? This is your value of *i*. (Be sure to write *i* in decimal form—that is, 6 percent should be expressed 0.06.)

d. According to the Baumol–Tobin model, how many times should you go to the bank each year, and how much should you withdraw each time?

e. In practice, how often do you go to the bank, and how much do you withdraw?

f. Compare the predictions of the Baumol–Tobin model to your behavior. Does the model describe how you actually behave? If not, why not? How would you change the model to make it a better description of your behavior?

5. In Chapter 6, we defined the velocity of money as the ratio of nominal expenditure to the quantity of money. Let's now use the Baumol–Tobin model to examine what determines velocity.

a. Recalling that average money holdings equal $Y/(2N)$, write velocity as a function of the number of trips to the bank *N*. Explain your result.

b. Use the formula for the optimal number of trips to express velocity as a function of expenditure *Y*, the interest rate *i*, and the cost of a trip to the bank *F*.

c. What happens to velocity when the interest rate rises? Explain.

d. What happens to velocity when the price level rises? Explain.

e. As the economy grows, what should happen to the velocity of money? (*Hint:* Think about how economic growth will influence *Y* and *F*.)

f. Suppose now that the number of trips to the bank is fixed rather than discretionary. What does this assumption imply about velocity?

chapter 19

Advances in the Theory of Economic Fluctuations

What is the best way to explain short-run fluctuations in output and employment? How should monetary and fiscal policy respond to these fluctuations? Most economists believe that these questions are best answered using the model of aggregate demand and aggregate supply. This book has, therefore, developed and applied this model thoroughly. Yet as we approach the end of the book, let's take a step closer to the frontier of modern economic research and examine the continuing debate over the theory of short-run economic fluctuations. This chapter discusses two recent strands of research—**real business cycle theory** and **new Keynesian economics**.

As a matter of logic, the output of the economy can fluctuate either because the natural rate of output fluctuates or because the output of the economy has deviated from its natural rate. Throughout most of this book, we have presumed that the natural rate of output grows smoothly over time (as explained by the Solow growth model) and that most short-run fluctuations are deviations from the natural rate (as explained by the model of aggregate demand and aggregate supply). New Keynesian theory accepts these presumptions. By contrast, real business cycle theory—a viewpoint held by a small but significant minority of economists—suggests that deviations from the natural rate are not significant and that most fluctuations should be viewed as changes in the natural, or equilibrium, level of output.

We begin this chapter by examining the theory of real business cycles. According to this theory, short-run economic fluctuations should be explained while maintaining the assumptions of the classical model, which we have used to study the long run. Most important, real business cycle theory assumes that prices are fully flexible, even in the short run. Almost all microeconomic analysis is based on the premise that prices adjust to clear markets. Advocates of real business cycle theory argue that macroeconomic analysis should be based on the same assumption.

Because real business cycle theory assumes complete price flexibility, it is consistent with the classical dichotomy: in this theory, nominal variables, such as the money supply and the price level, do not influence real variables, such as output and employment. To explain fluctuations in real variables, real business cycle theory emphasizes real changes in the economy, such as changes in production technologies, that can alter the economy's natural rate. The "real" in real business cycle theory refers to the theory's exclusion of nominal variables in explaining short-run economic fluctuations.

By contrast, new Keynesian economics is based on the premise that market-clearing models such as real business cycle theory cannot explain short-run economic fluctuations. In *The General Theory,* Keynes urged economists to abandon the classical presumption that wages and prices adjust quickly to equilibrate markets. He emphasized that aggregate demand is a primary determinant of national income in the short run. New Keynesian economists accept these basic conclusions, and so they advocate models with sticky wages and prices.

In their research, new Keynesian economists try to develop more fully the Keynesian approach to economic fluctuations. Many new Keynesians accept the *IS–LM* model as the theory of aggregate demand and, in their research, try to refine the theory of aggregate supply. This work tries to explain how wages and prices behave in the short run by identifying more precisely the market imperfections that make wages and prices sticky and that cause the economy to return only slowly to the natural rate. We discuss this research in the second half of the chapter.

In presenting the work of these two schools of thought, this chapter takes an approach that is more descriptive than analytic. Studying recent theoretical developments in detail would require more mathematics than is appropriate for this book. Yet, even without the formal models, we can discuss the direction of this research and get a sense of how different economists are applying microeconomic thinking to better understand macroeconomic fluctuations.[1]

19-1 | The Theory of Real Business Cycles

When we studied economic growth in Chapter 4, we described a relatively smooth process. Output grew as population, capital, and the available technology evolved over time. In the Solow growth model, the economy approaches a steady state in which most variables grow together at a rate determined by the constant rate of technological progress.

But is the process of economic growth necessarily as steady as the Solow model assumes? Perhaps technological progress and economic growth occur unevenly. Perhaps there are shocks to the economy that induce short-run fluctuations in the natural rates of output and employment. To see how this might be so, we consider a famous allegory which economists have borrowed from author Daniel Defoe.

The Economics of Robinson Crusoe

Robinson Crusoe is a sailor stranded on a desert island. Because Crusoe lives alone, his life is simple. Yet he has to make many economic decisions. Considering Crusoe's decisions—and how they change in response to changing circumstances—sheds light on the decisions that people face in larger, more complex economies.

---

[1] For a more formal treatment of the issues discussed here, see Chapters 4 and 6 of David Romer, *Advanced Macroeconomics* (New York: McGraw-Hill, 1996).

To keep things simple, imagine that Crusoe engages in only a few activities. Crusoe spends some of his time enjoying leisure, perhaps swimming on his island's beaches. He spends the rest of his time working, either catching fish or collecting vines to make into fishing nets. Both forms of work produce a valuable good: fish are Crusoe's consumption, and nets are Crusoe's investment. If we were to compute GDP for Crusoe's island, we would add together the number of fish caught and the number of nets made (weighted by some "price" to reflect Crusoe's relative valuation of these two goods).

Crusoe allocates his time among swimming, fishing, and making nets based on his preferences and the opportunities available to him. It is reasonable to assume that Crusoe optimizes. That is, he chooses the quantities of leisure, consumption, and investment that are best for him given the constraints that nature imposes.

Over time, Crusoe's decisions change as shocks impinge on his life. For example, suppose that one day a big school of fish passes by the island. GDP rises in the Crusoe economy for two reasons. First, Crusoe's productivity rises: with a large school in the water, Crusoe catches more fish per hour of fishing. Second, Crusoe's employment rises. That is, he decides to reduce temporarily his enjoyment of leisure in order to work harder and take advantage of this unusual opportunity to catch fish. The Crusoe economy is booming.

Similarly, suppose that a storm arrives one day. Because the storm makes outdoor activity difficult, productivity falls: each hour spent fishing or making nets yields a smaller output. In response, Crusoe decides to spend less time working and to wait out the storm in his hut. Consumption of fish and investment in nets both fall, so GDP falls as well. The Crusoe economy is in recession.

Suppose that one day Crusoe is attacked by natives. While he is defending himself, Crusoe has less time to enjoy leisure. Thus, the increased demand for defense spurs employment in the Crusoe economy, especially in the "defense industry." To some extent, Crusoe spends less time fishing for consumption. To a larger extent, he spends less time making nets, because this task is easy to put off for a while. Thus, defense spending crowds out investment. Because Crusoe spends more time at work, GDP (which now includes the value of national defense) rises. The Crusoe economy is experiencing a wartime boom.

What is notable about this story of booms and recessions is its simplicity. *In this story, fluctuations in output, employment, consumption, investment, and productivity are all the natural and desirable response of an individual to the inevitable changes in his environment.* In the Crusoe economy, fluctuations have nothing to do with monetary policy, sticky prices, or any type of market failure.

According to the theory of real business cycles, fluctuations in our economy are much the same as fluctuations in Robinson Crusoe's. Shocks to our ability to produce goods and services (like the changing weather on Crusoe's island) alter the natural rates of employment and output. These shocks are not necessarily desirable, but they are inevitable. Once the shocks occur, it is desirable for GDP, employment, and other real macroeconomic variables to fluctuate in response.

The parable of Robinson Crusoe, like any model in economics, is not intended to be a literal description of how the economy works. Instead, it tries to get at the essence of the complex pheonomon that we call the business cycle. Does the parable succeed in this goal? Are the booms and recessions in modern industrial economies really like the fluctuations on Robinson Crusoe's island? Economists disagree about the answer to this question and, therefore, disagree about the validity of real business cycle theory. At the heart of the debate are four basic issues:

➤ The interpretation of the labor market: Do fluctuations in employment reflect voluntary changes in the quantity of labor supplied?

➤ The importance of technology shocks: Does the economy's production function experience large, exogenous shifts in the short run?

➤ The neutrality of money: Do changes in the money supply have only nominal effects?

➤ The flexibility of wages and prices: Do wages and prices adjust quickly and completely to balance supply and demand?

Whether or not you view the parable of Robinson Crusoe as a plausible allegory for the business cycle, considering these four issues is instructive, for each of them raises fundamental questions about how the economy works.

The Interpretation of the Labor Market

Real business cycle theory emphasizes the idea that the quantity of labor supplied at any given time depends on the incentives that workers face, just as Robinson Crusoe changes his work effort voluntarily in response to changing circumstances. When workers are well rewarded, they are willing to work more hours; when the rewards to working are less, workers are willing to work fewer hours. Sometimes, if the reward for working is sufficiently small, workers choose to forgo working altogether—at least temporarily. This willingness to reallocate hours of work over time is called the **intertemporal substitution of labor.**

To see how intertemporal substitution affects labor supply, consider the following example. A college student finishing her sophomore year has two summer vacations left before graduation. She wishes to work for one of these summers (so she can buy a car after she graduates) and to relax at the beach during the other summer. How should she choose which summer to work?

Let W_1 be her real wage in the first summer and W_2 the real wage she expects in the second summer. To choose which summer to work, the student compares these two wages. Yet, because she can earn interest on money earned earlier, a dollar earned in the first summer is more valuable than a dollar earned in the second summer. Let r be the real interest rate. If the student works in the first summer and saves her earnings, she will have $(1 + r)W_1$ a year later. If she works in the second summer, she will have W_2. The intertemporal relative wage—that is, the earnings from working the first summer relative to the earnings from working the second summer—is

$$\text{Intertemporal Relative Wage} = \frac{(1 + r)W_1}{W_2}.$$

Working the first summer is more attractive if the interest rate is high or if the wage is high relative to the wage expected to prevail in the future.

According to real business cycle theory, all workers perform this cost–benefit analysis when deciding whether to work or to enjoy leisure. If the wage is temporarily high or if the interest rate is high, it is a good time to work. If the wage is temporarily low or if the interest rate is low, it is a good time to enjoy leisure.

Real business cycle theory uses the intertemporal substitution of labor to explain why employment and output fluctuate. Shocks to the economy that cause the interest rate to rise or the wage to be temporarily high cause people to want to work more. The increase in work effort raises employment and production.

Critics of real business cycle theory believe that fluctuations in employment do not reflect changes in the amount people want to work. They believe that *desired* employment is not very sensitive to the real wage and the real interest rate. They point out that the unemployment rate fluctuates substantially over the business cycle. The high unemployment in recessions suggests that the labor market does not clear: if people were voluntarily choosing not to work in recessions, they would not call themselves unemployed. These critics conclude that wages do not adjust to equilibrate labor supply and labor demand, as real business cycle models assume.

In reply, advocates of real business cycle theory argue that unemployment statistics are difficult to interpret. The mere fact that the unemployment rate is high does not mean that intertemporal substitution of labor is unimportant. Individuals who voluntarily choose not to work may call themselves unemployed so they can collect unemployment-insurance benefits. Or they may call themselves unemployed because they would be willing to work if they were offered the wage they receive in most years.

CASE STUDY

Looking for Intertemporal Substitution

Because intertemporal substitution of labor is central to real business cycle theory, much research has been aimed at examining whether it is an important determinant of labor supply. This research looks at data on wages and hours to see whether people alter the amount they work in response to small changes in the real wage. If leisure were highly intertemporally substitutable, then individuals expecting increases in the real wage should work little today and much in the future. Those expecting decreases in their real wage should work hard today and enjoy leisure in the future.

Most studies of labor supply find that expected changes in the real wage lead to only small changes in hours worked. Individuals appear not to respond to expected real-wage changes by substantially reallocating leisure over time. This evidence suggests that intertemporal substitution is not as important a determinant of labor supply as real business cycle theorists claim.

This evidence does not convince everyone, however. One reason is that the data are often far from perfect. For example, to study labor supply, we need data on wages; yet when a person is not working, we do not observe the wage that person could have earned by taking a job. Thus, although most studies of labor supply find little evidence for intertemporal substitution, they do not end the debate over real business cycle theory.[2]

The Importance of Technology Shocks

The Crusoe economy fluctuates because of changes in the weather, which induce Crusoe to alter his work effort. Similarly, real business cycle theory assumes that our economy experiences fluctuations in technology, which determines our ability to turn inputs (capital and labor) into output (goods and services), and that these fluctuations in technology cause fluctuations in output and employment. When the available production technology improves, the economy produces more output, and real wages rise. Because of intertemporal substitution of labor, the improved technology also leads to greater employment. Real business cycle theorists often explain recessions as periods of "technological regress." According to these models, output and employment fall during recessions because the available production technology deteriorates, lowering output and reducing the incentive to work.

Critics of real business cycle theory are skeptical that the economy experiences large shocks to technology. It is a more common presumption that technological progress occurs gradually. Critics argue that technological regress is especially implausible: the accumulation of technological knowledge may slow down, but it is hard to imagine that it would go in reverse.

Advocates respond by taking a broad view of shocks to technology. They argue that there are many events that, although not literally technological, affect the economy much as technology shocks do. For example, bad weather, the passage of strict environmental regulations, or increases in world oil prices have effects similar to adverse changes in technology: they all reduce our ability to turn capital and labor into goods and services. Whether such events are sufficiently common to explain the frequency and magnitude of business cycles is an open question.

---

[2] The classic article emphasizing the role of intertemporal substitution in the labor market is Robert E. Lucas, Jr., and Leonard A. Rapping, "Real Wages, Employment, and Inflation," *Journal of Political Economy* 77 (September/October 1969): 721–754. For some of the empirical work that casts doubt on this hypothesis, see Joseph G. Altonji, "Intertemporal Substitution in Labor Supply: Evidence From Micro Data," *Journal of Political Economy* 94 (June 1986, Part 2): S176–S215; and Laurence Ball, "Intertemporal Substitution and Constraints on Labor Supply: Evidence From Panel Data," *Economic Inquiry* 28 (October 1990): 706–724. For a recent study reporting evidence in favor of the hypothesis, see Casey B. Mulligan, "Substitution Over Time: Another Look at Life Cycle Labor Supply," *NBER Macroeconomics Annual* 13 (1998).

CASE STUDY

The Solow Residual and the Business Cycle

To demonstrate the role of technology shocks in generating business cycles, economist Edward Prescott looked at data on the economy's inputs (capital and labor) and its output (GDP). For every year, he computed the **Solow residual**—the percentage change in output minus the percentage change in inputs, where the different inputs are weighted by their factor shares. The Solow residual measures the portion of output growth that cannot be explained by growth in capital or labor. Prescott interprets it as a measure of the rate of technological progress.[3]

Figure 19-1 shows the Solow residual and the growth in output for the period 1948 to 1996. Notice that the Solow residual fluctuates substantially. It tells us, for example, that technology worsened in 1982 and improved in 1984. In addition, the Solow residual moves closely with output: in years when output falls, technology worsens. According to Prescott, these large fluctuations in the Solow residual show that technology shocks are an important source of economic fluctuations.

Prescott's interpretation of this figure is controversial, however. Many economists believe that the Solow residual does not accurately represent changes in technology over short periods of time. The standard explanation of the cyclical behavior of the Solow residual is that it results from two measurement problems.

First, during recessions, firms may continue to employ workers they do not need, so that they will have these workers on hand when the economy recovers. This phenomenon, called **labor hoarding,** means that labor input is overestimated in recessions, because the hoarded workers are probably not working as hard as usual. As a result, the Solow residual is more cyclical than the available production technology. In a recession, productivity as measured by the Solow residual falls even if technology has not changed simply because hoarded workers are sitting around waiting for the recession to end.

Second, when demand is low, firms may produce things that are not easily measured. In recessions, workers may clean the factory, organize the inventory, get some training, and do other useful tasks that standard measures of output fail to include. If so, then output is underestimated in recessions, which would also make the measured Solow residual cyclical for reasons other than technology.

Thus, economists can interpret the cyclical behavior of the Solow residual in different ways. Real business cycle theorists point to the low productivity in recessions as evidence for adverse technology shocks. Other economists believe that measured productivity is low in recessions because workers are not working as hard as usual and because more of their output is not measured. Unfortu-

---

[3] The appendix to Chapter 4 shows that the Solow residual is

$$\frac{\Delta A}{A} = \frac{\Delta Y}{Y} - \alpha \frac{\Delta K}{K} - (1 - \alpha) \frac{\Delta L}{L}.$$

where A is total factor productivity, Y output, K capital, L labor, and α capital's share of income.

figure 19-1

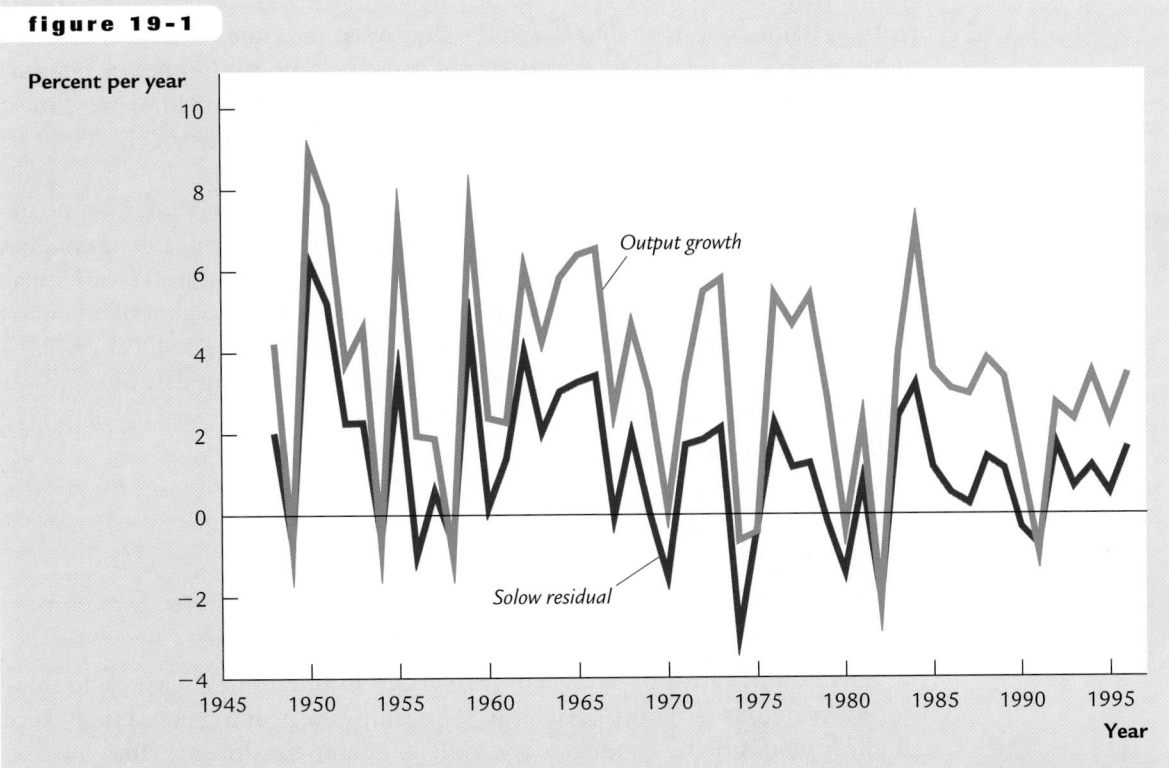

Growth in Output and the Solow Residual The Solow residual, which some economists interpret as a measure of technology shocks, fluctuates with the economy's output of goods and services.

Source: U.S. Department of Commerce, U. S. Department of Labor, and author's calculations.

nately, there is no clear evidence on the importance of labor hoarding and the cyclical mismeasurement of output. Therefore, different interpretations of Figure 19-1 persist. This disagreement is one part of the debate between advocates and critics of real business cycle theory.[4]

The Neutrality of Money

Just as money has no role in the Crusoe economy, real business cycle theory assumes that money in our economy is neutral, even in the short run. That is, monetary policy is assumed not to affect real variables such as output and

[4] For the two sides of this debate, see Edward C. Prescott, "Theory Ahead of Business Cycle Measurement," and Lawrence H. Summers, "Some Skeptical Observations on Real Business Cycle Theory." Both are in *Quarterly Review,* Federal Reserve Bank of Minneapolis (Fall 1986).

employment. Not only does the neutrality of money give real business cycle theory its name, but neutrality is also the theory's most radical assumption.

Critics argue that the evidence does not support short-run monetary neutrality. They point out that reductions in money growth and inflation are almost always associated with periods of high unemployment. Monetary policy appears to have a strong influence on the real economy.

Advocates of real business cycle theory argue that their critics confuse the direction of causation between money and output. These advocates claim that the money supply is endogenous: fluctuations in output might cause fluctuations in the money supply. For example, when output rises because of a beneficial technology shock, the quantity of money demanded rises. The Federal Reserve may respond by raising the money supply to accommodate the greater demand. This endogenous response of money to economic activity may give the illusion of monetary non-neutrality.[5]

CASE STUDY

Testing for Monetary Neutrality

The direction of causation between fluctuations in the money supply and fluctuations in output is hard to establish. The only sure way to determine cause and effect would be to conduct a controlled experiment. Imagine that the Fed set the money supply according to some random process. Every January, the Fed chairman would flip a coin. Heads would mean an expansionary monetary policy for the coming year; tails a contractionary one. After a number of years we would know with confidence the effects of monetary policy. If output and employment usually rose after the coin came up heads and usually fell after it came up tails, then we would conclude that monetary policy has real effects. Yet if the flip of the Fed's coin were unrelated to subsequent economic performance, then we would conclude that real business cycle theorists are right about the neutrality of money.

Unfortunately for scientific progress, but fortunately for the economy, economists are not allowed to conduct such experiments. Instead, we must glean what we can from the data that history gives us.

One classic study in the history of monetary policy is the 1963 book by Milton Friedman and Anna Schwartz, *A Monetary History of the United States, 1867–1960.* This book describes the historical events that shaped decisions over monetary policy and the economic events that resulted from those decisions. Friedman and Schwartz claim, for instance, that the death in 1928 of Benjamin Strong, the president of the New York Federal Reserve Bank, was one cause of the Great Depression of the 1930s: Strong's death left a power

---

[5] Robert G. King and Charles I. Plosser, "Money, Credit, and Prices in a Real Business Cycle," *American Economic Review* 74 (June 1984): 363–380.

vacuum at the Fed, which prevented the Fed from responding vigorously as economic conditions deteriorated. In other words, Strong's death, like the Fed's coin coming up tails, was a random event leading to more contractionary monetary policy.[6]

A more recent study by Christina Romer and David Romer follows in the footsteps of Friedman and Schwartz. The Romers carefully read through the minutes of the meetings of the Federal Reserve's Open Market Committee, which sets monetary policy. From these minutes, they identified dates when the Fed appears to have shifted its policy toward reducing the rate of inflation. The Romers argue that these dates are, in essence, the equivalent of the Fed's coin coming up tails. They then show that the economy experienced a decline in output and employment after each of these dates. Thus, the Romers' evidence appears to establish the short-run non-neutrality of money.[7]

Interpretations of history, however, are always open to dispute. No one can be sure what would have happened during the 1930s had Benjamin Strong lived. Similarly, not everyone is convinced that the Romers' dates are as exogenous as a coin's flip: perhaps the Fed was actually responding to events that would have caused declining output and employment even without Fed action. Thus, while most economists are convinced that monetary policy has an important role in the business cycle, this judgment is based on the accumulation of evidence from many studies. There is no "smoking gun" that convinces absolutely everyone.

The Flexibility of Wages and Prices

Real business cycle theory assumes that wages and prices adjust quickly to clear markets, just as Crusoe always achieves his optimal level of GDP without any impediment from a market imperfection. Advocates of this theory believe that the market imperfection of sticky wages and prices is not important for understanding economic fluctuations. They also believe that the assumption of flexible prices is superior methodologically to the assumption of sticky prices, because it ties macroeconomic theory more closely to microeconomic theory.

Critics point out that many wages and prices are not flexible. They believe that this inflexibility explains both the existence of unemployment and the non-neutrality of money. To explain why prices are sticky, they rely on the various new Keynesian theories that we discuss in the next section.

---

[6] Milton Friedman and Anna J. Schwartz, *A Monetary History of the United States, 1867–1960* (Princeton, NJ: Princeton University Press, 1960).

[7] Christina Romer and David Romer, "Does Monetary Policy Matter? A New Test in the Spirit of Friedman and Schwartz," *NBER Macroeconomics Annual* (1989): 121–170.

f y i

WHAT IS NEW CLASSICAL ECONOMICS?

Real business cycle theory is called **new classical economics** because it uses the assumptions of the classical model—especially flexible prices and monetary neutrality—to study short-run economic fluctuations. Yet real business cycle theory is not the only part of macroeconomics that bears the label "new classical." Most economists use the term broadly to describe the many challenges to the Keynesian orthodoxy that prevailed in the 1960s.

According to this broad definition, one can apply the label "new classical" to some of the ideas we discussed in earlier chapters, including rational expectations (Chapter 13), the Lucas critique (Chapter 14), the problem of time inconsistency (Chapter 14), and the Ricardian view of government debt (Chapter 15). Some economists apply the label "new classical" to any model in which prices are fully flexible in the short run. By this definition, the worker-misperception and imperfect-information models of aggregate sup-

ply (Chapter 13) are new classical, even though they violate the classical dichotomy.

Although real business cycle theory is widely called "new classical," in some ways the term is a misnomer, for the classical economists themselves never suggested that money was neutral in the short run. For example, David Hume, in his 1752 essay "Of Money," stressed that money was neutral only in the long run:

> In my opinion, it is only in the interval or intermediate situation, between the acquisition of money and the rise in prices, that the increasing quantity of gold or silver is favourable to industry. . . . The farmer or gardener, finding that their commodities are taken off, apply themselves with alacrity to the raising of more. . . . It is easy to trace the money in its progress through the whole commonwealth; where we shall find that it must first quicken the diligence of every individual, before it increases the price of labour.

In suggesting the hypothesis that money is neutral in the short run, real business cycle theory pushes the assumptions of classical economics further than did the classical economists themselves.[8]

19-2 | New Keynesian Economics

Most economists are skeptical of the theory of real business cycles and believe that short-run fluctuations in output and employment represent deviations from the economy's natural rate. They think these deviations occur because wages and prices are slow to adjust to changing economic conditions. As we have discussed in Chapters 9 and 13, this stickiness makes the short-run aggregate supply curve upward sloping rather than vertical. As a result, fluctuations in aggregate demand cause short-run fluctuations in output and employment.

[8] For a textbook that emphasizes the new classical approach, see Robert J. Barro, *Macroeconomics,* 5th ed. (Cambridge, MA: MIT Press, 1998). To read more about real business cycle theory, see N. Gregory Mankiw, "Real Business Cycles: A New Keynesian Perspective," *Journal of Economic Perspectives* 3 (Summer 1989): 79–90; Bennett T. McCallum, "Real Business Cycle Models," in R. Barro, ed., *Modern Business Cycle Theory* (Cambridge, MA: Harvard University Press, 1989), 16–50; and Charles I. Plosser, "Understanding Real Business Cycles," *Journal of Economic Perspectives* 3 (Summer 1989): 51–77.

But why exactly are prices sticky? New Keynesian research has attempted to answer this question by examining the microeconomics behind short-run price adjustment. By doing so, it tries to put the traditional theories of short-run fluctuations on a firmer theoretical foundation.

Small Menu Costs and Aggregate-Demand Externalities

One reason prices do not adjust immediately in the short run is that there are costs to price adjustment. To change its prices, a firm may need to send out a new catalog to customers, distribute new price lists to its sales staff, or, in the case of a restaurant, print new menus. These costs of price adjustment, called **menu costs,** lead firms to adjust prices intermittently rather than continuously.

Economists disagree about whether menu costs explain the short-run stickiness of prices. Skeptics point out that menu costs are usually very small. How can small menu costs help to explain recessions, which are very costly for society? Proponents reply that small does not mean inconsequential: even though menu costs are small for the individual firm, they can have large effects on the economy as a whole.

According to proponents of the menu-cost hypothesis, to understand why prices adjust slowly, we must acknowledge that there are externalities to price adjustment: a price reduction by one firm benefits other firms in the economy. When a firm lowers the price it charges, it slightly lowers the average price level and thereby raises real money balances. The increase in real money balances expands aggregate income (by shifting the *LM* curve outward). The economic expansion in turn raises the demand for the products of all firms. This macroeconomic impact of one firm's price adjustment on the demand for all other firms' products is called an **aggregate-demand externality.**

In the presence of this aggregate-demand externality, small menu costs can make prices sticky, and this stickiness can have a large cost to society. Suppose that a firm originally sets its price too high and later must decide whether to cut its price. The firm makes this decision by comparing the benefit of a price cut—higher sales and profit—to the cost of price adjustment. Yet because of the aggregate-demand externality, the benefit to society of the price cut would exceed the benefit to the firm. The firm ignores this externality when making its decision, so it may decide not to pay the menu cost and cut its price even though the price cut is socially desirable. *Hence, sticky prices may be optimal for those setting prices, even though they are undesirable for the economy as a whole.*[9]

---

[9] For more on this topic, see N. Gregory Mankiw, "Small Menu Costs and Large Business Cycles: A Macroeconomic Model of Monopoly," *Quarterly Journal of Economics* 100 (May 1985): 529–537; George A. Akerlof and Janet L. Yellen, "A Near Rational Model of the Business Cycle, With Wage and Price Inertia," *Quarterly Journal of Economics* 100 (Supplement 1985): 823–838; and Olivier Jean Blanchard and Nobuhiro Kiyotaki, "Monopolistic Competition and the Effects of Aggregate Demand," *American Economic Review* 77 (September 1987): 647–666.

Recessions as Coordination Failure

Some new Keynesian economists suggest that recessions result from a failure of coordination. In recessions, output is low, workers are unemployed, and factories sit idle. It is possible to imagine allocations of resources in which everyone is better off—for example, the high output and employment of the 1920s were clearly preferable to the low output and employment of the 1930s. If society fails to reach an outcome that is feasible and that everyone prefers, then the members of society have failed to coordinate in some way.

Coordination problems can arise in the setting of wages and prices because those who set them must anticipate the actions of other wage and price setters. Union leaders negotiating wages are concerned about the concessions other unions will win. Firms setting prices are mindful of the prices other firms will charge.

To see how a recession could arise as a failure of coordination, consider the following parable. The economy is made up of two firms. After a fall in the money supply, each firm must decide whether to cut its price, based on its goal of maximizing profit. Each firm's profit, however, depends not only on its pricing decision but also on the decision made by the other firm.

The choices facing each firm are listed in Figure 19-2, which shows how the profits of the two firms depend on their actions. If neither firm cuts its price, real money balances are low, a recession ensues, and each firm makes a profit of only $15. If both firms cut their prices, real money balances are high, a recession is avoided, and each firm makes a profit of $30. Although both firms prefer to avoid a recession, neither can do so by its own actions. If one firm cuts its price while the other does not, a recession follows. The firm making the price cut makes only $5, while the other firm makes $15.

figure 19-2

		Firm 2	
		Cut Price	Keep High Price
Firm 1	Cut Price	**Firm 1** makes $30 **Firm 2** makes $30	**Firm 1** makes $5 **Firm 2** makes $15
	Keep High Price	**Firm 1** makes $15 **Firm 2** makes $5	**Firm 1** makes $15 **Firm 2** makes $15

Price Setting and Coordination Failure This figure shows a hypothetical "game" between two firms, each of which is deciding whether to cut prices after a fall in the money supply. Each firm must choose a strategy without knowing the strategy the other firm will choose. What outcome would you expect?

The essence of this parable is that each firm's decision influences the set of outcomes available to the other firm. When one firm cuts its price, it improves the position of the other firm, because the other firm can then avoid the recession. This positive impact of one firm's price cut on the other firm's profit opportunities might arise from an aggregate-demand externality.

What outcome should we expect in this economy? On the one hand, if each firm expects the other to cut its price, both will cut prices, resulting in the preferred outcome in which each makes $30. On the other hand, if each firm expects the other to maintain its price, both will maintain their prices, resulting in the inferior solution in which each makes $15. Either of these outcomes is possible: economists say that there are *multiple equilibria*.

The inferior outcome, in which each firm makes $15, is an example of a **coordination failure.** If the two firms could coordinate, they would both cut their price and reach the preferred outcome. In the real world, unlike in our parable, coordination is often difficult because the number of firms setting prices is large. *The moral of the story is that prices can be sticky simply because people expect them to be sticky, even though stickiness is in no one's interest.*[10]

CASE STUDY

Experimental Evidence on Coordination Games

What happens when economic actors, such as the firms in our parable, face a problem of coordination? Do they somehow manage to choose the preferred outcome, knowing that this outcome makes them both better off? Or do they fail to coordinate?

One way to answer this question is by experimentation. In two research studies, student volunteers were asked to play coordination games, such as the "game" in Figure 19-2. To maintain anonymity, the students played each other through computer terminals. To ensure earnest play, the students were rewarded with small amounts of money depending on how many points they won in the game.

Consider what strategy you would choose if you were playing the game in Figure 19-2. Remember that you don't know the strategy of the other player: you only know that the other player is facing the same decision you are. Would you cut your price or keep it high? Would your strategy change if the payoffs in the upper left corner were $100 instead of $30? Or if they were only $16?

The experimental evidence shows that economic actors do not always coordinate by choosing the preferred outcome. Whether coordination occurs

---

[10] For more on coordination failure, see Russell Cooper and Andrew John, "Coordinating Coordination Failures in Keynesian Models," *Quarterly Journal of Economics* 103 (1988): 441–463; and Laurence Ball and David Romer, "Sticky Prices as Coordination Failure," *American Economic Review* 81 (June 1991): 539–552.

depends on the specific payoff numbers and, therefore, varies from game to game. But, in some games, coordination failure is the most common outcome.[11]

The Staggering of Wages and Prices

Not everyone in the economy sets new wages and prices at the same time. Instead, the adjustment of wages and prices throughout the economy is staggered. Staggering slows the process of coordination and price adjustment. In particular, *staggering makes the overall level of wages and prices adjust gradually, even when individual wages and prices change frequently.*

Consider the following example. Suppose first that price setting is synchronized: every firm adjusts its price on the first day of every month. If the money supply and aggregate demand rise on May 10, output will be higher from May 10 to June 1 because prices are fixed during this interval. But on June 1 all firms will raise their prices in response to the higher demand, ending the boom.

Now suppose that price setting is staggered: half the firms set prices on the first of each month and half on the fifteenth. If the money supply rises on May 10, then half the firms can raise their prices on May 15. But these firms will probably not raise their prices very much. Because half the firms will not be changing their prices on the fifteenth, a price increase by any firm will raise that firm's *relative* price, causing it to lose customers. (By contrast, if all firms are synchronized, all firms can raise prices together, leaving relative prices unaffected.) If the May 15 price setters make little adjustment in their prices, then the other firms will make little adjustment when their turn comes on June 1, because they also want to avoid relative price changes. And so on. The price level rises slowly as the result of small price increases on the first and the fifteenth of each month. Hence, staggering makes the overall price level adjust sluggishly, because no firm wishes to be the first to post a substantial price increase.

Staggering also affects wage determination. Consider, for example, how a fall in the money supply works its way through the economy. A smaller money supply reduces aggregate demand, which in turn requires a proportionate fall in nominal wages to maintain full employment. Each worker might be willing to take a lower nominal wage if all other wages were to fall proportionately. But each worker is reluctant to be the first to take a pay cut, knowing that this means, at least temporarily, a fall in his or her relative wage. Since the setting of wages is staggered, the reluctance of each worker to reduce his or her wage first makes the overall level of wages slow to respond to changes in aggregate de-

[11] Russell Cooper, Douglas V. DeJong, Robert Forsythe, and Thomas W. Ross, "Selection Criteria in Coordination Games: Some Experimental Results," *American Economic Review* 80 (March 1990): 218–233; John B. Van Huyck, Raymond C. Battalio, and Richard O. Beil, "Tacit Coordination Games, Strategic Uncertainty, and Coordination Failure," *American Economic Review* 80 (March 1990): 234–248.

mand. In other words, the staggered setting of individual wages makes the overall level of wages sticky.[12]

CASE STUDY

If You Want to Know Why Firms Have Sticky Prices, Ask Them

How sticky are prices, and why are they sticky? As we have seen, these questions are at the heart of new Keynesian theories of short-run economic fluctuations (as well as of the traditional model of aggregate demand and aggregate supply). In an intriguing study, economist Alan Blinder attacked these questions directly by surveying firms about their price-adjustment decisions.

Blinder began by asking firm managers how often they change prices. The answers, summarized in Table 19-1, yielded two conclusions. First, sticky prices are quite common. The typical firm in the economy adjusts its prices once or twice a year. Second, there are large differences among firms in the frequency of price adjustment. About 10 percent of firms change prices more often than once a week, and about the same number change prices less often than once a year.

---

table 19-1

The Frequency of Price Adjustment

This table is based on answers to the question: How often do the prices of your most important products change in a typical year?

Frequency	Percentage of Firms
Less than once	10.2
Once	39.3
1.01 to 2	15.6
2.01 to 4	12.9
4.01 to 12	7.5
12.01 to 52	4.3
52.01 to 365	8.6
More than 365	1.6

Source: Table 4.1, Alan S. Blinder, "On Sticky Prices: Academic Theories Meet the Real World," in N.G. Mankiw, ed., *Monetary Policy* (Chicago: University of Chicago Press, 1994): 117–154.

---

[12] For more on the effects of staggering, see John Taylor, "Staggered Price Setting in a Macro Model," *American Economic Review* 69 (May 1979): 108–113; and Olivier J. Blanchard, "Price Asynchronization and Price Level Inertia," in R. Dornbusch and Mario Henrique Simonsen, eds., *Inflation, Debt, and Indexation* (Cambridge, MA: MIT Press, 1983), 3–24.

Blinder then asked the firm managers why they don't change prices more often. In particular, he explained to the managers 12 economic theories of sticky prices and asked them to judge how well each of these theories describe their firms. Table 19-2 summarizes the theories and ranks them by the percentage of managers who accepted the theory. Notice that each of the theories was endorsed by some of the managers, and each was rejected by a large number as

table 19-2

Theories of Price Stickiness

Theory and Brief Description	Percentage of Firms That Accepted Theory
Coordination failure: Firms hold back on price changes, waiting for others to go first	60.6
Cost-based pricing with lags: Price rises are delayed until costs rise	55.5
Delivery lags, service, etc.: Firms prefer to vary other product attributes, such as delivery lags, service, or product quality	54.8
Implicit contracts: Firms tacitly agree to stabilize prices, perhaps out of "fairness" to customers	50.4
Nominal contracts: Prices are fixed by explicit contracts	35.7
Costs of price adjustment: Firms incur costs of changing prices	30.0
Procyclical elasticity: Demand curves become less elastic as they shift in	29.7
Pricing points: Certain prices (like $9.99) have special psychological significance	24.0
Inventories: Firms vary inventory stocks instead of prices	20.9
Constant marginal cost: Marginal cost is flat and markups are constant	19.7
Hierarchical delays: Bureaucratic delays slow down decisions	13.6
Judging quality by price: Firms fear customers will mistake price cuts for reductions in quality	10.0

Source: Tables 4.3 and 4.4, Alan S. Blinder, "On Sticky Prices: Academic Theories Meet the Real World," in N. G. Mankiw, ed., *Monetary Policy* (Chicago: University of Chicago Press, 1994): 117–154.

well. One interpretation is that different theories apply to different firms, depending on industry characteristics, and that price stickiness is a macroeconomic phenomenon without a single microeconomic explanation.

Among the 12 theories, coordination failure tops the list. According to Blinder, this is an important finding, for it suggests that the theory of coordination failure explains price stickiness, which in turn explains why the economy experiences short-run fluctuations around its natural rate. He writes, "the most obvious policy implication of the model is that more coordinated wage and price setting—somehow achieved—could improve welfare. But if this proves difficult or impossible, the door is opened to activist monetary policy to cure recessions."[13]

19-3 | Conclusion

Recent developments in the theory of short-run economic fluctuations remind us that we do not understand economic fluctuations as well as we would like. Fundamental questions about the economy remain open to dispute. Is the stickiness of wages and prices a key to understanding economic fluctuations? Does monetary policy have real effects?

The way economists answer these questions affects how they view the role of economic policy. Economists who believe that wages and prices are sticky, such as those pursuing new Keynesian theories, often believe that monetary and fiscal policy should be used to try to stabilize the economy. Price stickiness is a type of market imperfection, and it leaves open the possibility that government policies can raise economic well-being for society as a whole.

By contrast, real business cycle theory suggests that the government's influence on the economy is limited and that even if the government could stabilize the economy, it should not try. According to this theory, the ups and downs of the business cycle are the natural and efficient response of the economy to changing technological possibilities. The standard real business cycle model does not include any type of market imperfection. In this model, the "invisible hand" of the marketplace guides the economy to an optimal allocation of resources.

To evaluate alternative views of the economy, research economists bring to bear a wide variety of evidence, as we have seen in this chapter's five case studies. They have used micro data to study intertemporal substitution, macro data to examine the cyclical behavior of technology, the minutes of Fed meetings to

---

[13] To read more about this study, see Alan S. Blinder, "On Sticky Prices: Academic Theories Meet the Real World," in *Monetary Policy,* N. G. Mankiw, ed. (Chicago: University of Chicago Press, 1994): 117–154; or Alan S. Blinder, Elie R.D. Canetti, David E. Lebow, and Jeremy E. Rudd, *Asking About Prices: A New Approach to Understanding Price Stickiness* (New York: Russell Sage Foundation, 1998).

test monetary neutrality, experiments to gauge the likelihood of coordination failure, and surveys to judge theories of price stickiness. Economists differ in which pieces of evidence they find most convincing, and so the theory of economic fluctuations remains a source of frequent and heated debate.

Although this chapter has divided recent research into two distinct camps, not all economists fall entirely into one camp or the other. Over time, more economists have been trying to incorporate the strengths of both approaches into their research. Real business cycle theory places a heavy emphasis on intertemporal optimization and forward-looking behavior, while new Keynesian theory stresses the importance of sticky prices and other market imperfections. Increasingly, theories at the research frontier meld many of these elements to advance our understanding of economic fluctuations. It is this kind of work that makes macroeconomics an exciting field of study.

Summary

1. The theory of real business cycles is an explanation of short-run economic fluctuations built on the assumptions of the classical model, including the classical dichotomy and the flexibility of wages and prices. According to this theory, economic fluctuations are the natural and efficient response of the economy to changing economic circumstances, especially changes in technology.

2. Advocates and critics of real business cycle theory disagree about whether employment fluctuations represent intertemporal substitution of labor, whether technology shocks cause most economic fluctuations, whether monetary policy affects real variables, and whether the short-run stickiness of wages and prices is important for understanding economic fluctuations.

3. New Keynesian research on short-run economic fluctuations builds on the traditional model of aggregate demand and aggregate supply and tries to provide a better explanation of why wages and prices are sticky in the short run. One new Keynesian theory suggests that even small costs of price adjustment can have large macroeconomic effects because of aggregate-demand externalities. Another theory suggests that recessions occur as a type of coordination failure. A third theory suggests that staggering in price adjustment makes the overall price level sluggish in response to changing economic conditions.

KEY CONCEPTS

Real business cycle theory	Solow residual	Menu costs
New Keynesian economics	Labor hoarding	Aggregate-demand externality
Intertemporal substitution of labor	New classical economics	Coordination failure

QUESTIONS FOR REVIEW

1. How does real business cycle theory explain fluctuations in employment?

2. What are the four central disagreements in the debate over real business cycle theory?

3. How does staggering of price adjustment by in-dividual firms affect the adjustment of the overall price level to a monetary contraction?

4. According to surveys, how often does the typical firm change its prices? How do firm managers explain the stickiness of their prices?

PROBLEMS AND APPLICATIONS

1. According to real business cycle theory, perma-nent and transitory shocks to technology should have very different effects on the economy. Use the parable of Robinson Crusoe to compare the effects of a transitory shock (good weather ex-pected to last only a few days) and a permanent shock (a beneficial change in weather patterns). Which shock would have a greater effect on Crusoe's work effort? On GDP? Is it possible that one of these shocks might reduce work ef-fort?

2. Suppose that prices are fully flexible and that the output of the economy fluctuates because of shocks to technology, as real business cycle the-ory claims.

   a. If the Federal Reserve holds the money sup-ply constant, what will happen to the price level as output fluctuates?

   b. If the Federal Reserve adjusts the money sup-ply to stabilize the price level, what will hap-pen to the money supply as output fluctuates?

   c. Many economists have observed that fluctua-tions in the money supply are positively cor-related with fluctuations in output. Is this evi-dence against real business cycle theory?

3. Coordination failure is an idea with many appli-cations. Here is one: Andy and Ben are running a business together. If both work hard, the busi-ness is a success, and they each earn $100 in profit. If one them fails to work hard, the busi-ness is less successful, and they each earn $70. If neither works hard, the business is even less suc-cessful, and they each earn $60 in profit. Work-ing hard takes $20 worth of effort.

   a. Set up this "game" as in Figure 19-2.

   b. What outcome would Andy and Ben prefer?

   c. What outcome would occur if each expected his partner to work hard?

   d. What outcome would occur if each expected his partner to be lazy?

   e. Is this a good description of the relationship among partners? Why or why not?

4. (This problem uses basic microeconomics.) The chapter discussed the price-adjustment decisions of firms with menu costs. This problem asks you to consider that issue more analytically in the simple case of a single firm.

   a. Draw a diagram describing a monopoly firm, including a downward-sloping demand curve and a cost curve. (For simplicity, assume that marginal cost is constant, so the cost curve is a horizontal line.) Show the profit-maximizing price and quantity. Show the areas that repre-sent profit and consumer surplus at this opti-mum.

   b. Now suppose the firm has previously an-nounced a price slightly above the optimum. Show this price and the quantity sold. Show the area representing the lost profit from the excessive price. Show the area representing the lost consumer surplus.

   c. The firm decides whether to cut its price by comparing the extra profit from a lower price to the menu cost. In making this decision, what externality is the firm ignoring? In what sense is the firm's price-adjustment decision inefficient?

What We Know, What We Don't

If all economists were laid end to end, they would not reach a conclusion.

— *George Bernard Shaw*

The theory of economics does not furnish a body of settled conclusions immediately applicable to policy. It is a method rather than a doctrine, an apparatus of the mind, which helps its possessor to draw correct conclusions.

—*John Maynard Keynes*

The first chapter of this book states that the purpose of macroeconomics is to understand economic events and to improve economic policy. Now that we have developed and used many of the most important models in the macroeconomist's toolbox, we can assess whether macroeconomists have achieved these goals.

Any fair assessment of macroeconomics today must admit that the science is incomplete. There are some principles that almost all macroeconomists accept and on which we can rely when trying to analyze events or formulate policies. Yet there are also many questions about the economy that remain open to debate. In this last chapter we briefly review the central lessons of macroeconomics, and we discuss the most pressing unresolved questions.

The Four Most Important Lessons of Macroeconomics

We begin with four lessons that have recurred throughout this book and that most economists today would endorse. Each lesson tells us how policy can influence a key economic variable—output, inflation, or unemployment— either in the long run or in the short run.

Lesson No. 1: In the long run, a country's capacity to produce goods and services determines the standard of living of its citizens.

Of all the measures of economic performance introduced in Chapter 2 and used throughout this book, the one that best measures economic well-being is

GDP. Real GDP measures the economy's total output of goods and services and, therefore, a country's ability to satisfy the needs and desires of its citizens. Perhaps the most important question in macroeconomics is what determines the level and the growth of GDP.

The models in Chapters 3, 4, and 5 identify the long-run determinants of GDP. In the long run, GDP depends on the factors of production—capital and labor—and on the technology for turning capital and labor into output. GDP grows when the factors of production increase or when the available technology improves.

This lesson has an obvious but important corollary: public policy can raise GDP in the long run only by improving the productive capability of the economy. There are many ways in which policymakers can attempt to do this. Policies that raise national saving—either through higher public saving or higher private saving—eventually lead to a larger capital stock. Policies that raise the efficiency of labor—such as those that improve education or increase technological progress—lead to a more productive use of capital and labor. All these policies raise the economy's output of goods and services and, thereby, the standard of living. It is less clear, however, which is the best way to raise the economy's productive capability.

Lesson No. 2: In the short run, aggregate demand influences the amount of goods and services that a country produces.

Although the economy's ability to *supply* goods and services is the sole determinant of GDP in the long run, in the short run GDP depends also on the aggregate *demand* for goods and services. Aggregate demand is of key importance because prices are sticky in the short run. The *IS–LM* model developed in Chapters 10 and 11 shows what causes changes in aggregate demand and, therefore, short-run fluctuations in GDP.

Because aggregate demand influences output in the short run, all the variables that affect aggregate demand can influence economic fluctuations. Monetary policy, fiscal policy, and shocks to the money and goods markets are often responsible for year-to-year changes in output and employment. Since aggregate demand is crucial to short-run fluctuations, policymakers monitor the economy closely. Before making any change in monetary or fiscal policy, they want to know whether the economy is booming or heading into a recession.

Lesson No. 3: In the long run, the rate of money growth determines the rate of inflation, but it does not affect the rate of unemployment.

In addition to GDP, inflation and unemployment are among the most closely watched measures of economic performance. Chapter 2 discussed how these two variables are measured, and subsequent chapters developed models to explain how they are determined.

The long-run analysis of Chapter 7 stresses that growth in the money supply is the ultimate determinant of inflation. That is, in the long run, a currency loses real value over time if and only if the central bank prints more and more of it. This lesson can explain the decade-to-decade variation in the inflation rate that we have observed in the United States, as well as the far more dramatic hyperinflations that various countries have experienced from time to time.

We have also seen many of the long-run effects of high money growth and high inflation. In Chapter 7 we saw that, according to the Fisher effect, high inflation raises the nominal interest rate (so that the real interest rate remains unaffected). In Chapter 8 we saw that high inflation leads to a depreciation of the currency in the market for foreign exchange.

The long-run determinants of unemployment are very different. According to the classical dichotomy—the irrelevance of nominal variables in the determination of real variables—growth in the money supply does not affect unemployment in the long run. As we saw in Chapter 6, the natural rate of unemployment is determined by the rates of job separation and job finding, which in turn are determined by the process of job search and by the rigidity of the real wage.

Thus, we concluded that persistent inflation and persistent unemployment are unrelated problems. To combat inflation in the long run, policymakers must reduce the growth in the money supply. To combat unemployment, they must alter the structure of labor markets. In the long run, there is no tradeoff between inflation and unemployment.

"And please let Alan Greenspan accept the things he cannot change, give him the courage to change the things he can and the wisdom to know the difference."

Lesson No. 4: In the short run, policymakers who control monetary and fiscal policy face a tradeoff between inflation and unemployment.

Although inflation and unemployment are not related in the long run, in the short run there is a tradeoff between these two variables, which is illustrated by the short-run Phillips curve. As we discussed in Chapter 13, policymakers can use monetary and fiscal policies to expand aggregate demand, which lowers unemployment and raises inflation. Or they can use these policies to contract aggregate demand, which raises unemployment and lowers inflation.

Policymakers face a fixed tradeoff between inflation and unemployment only in the short run. Over time, the short-run Phillips curve shifts for two reasons. First, supply shocks, such as changes in the price of oil, change the short-run tradeoff; an adverse supply shock offers policymakers the difficult choice between higher inflation or higher unemployment. Second, when people change their expectations of inflation, the short-run tradeoff between inflation and unemployment changes. The adjustment of expectations ensures that the tradeoff exists only in the short run. That is, only in the short run does unemployment deviate from its natural rate, and only in the short run does monetary policy have real effects. In the long run, the classical model of Chapters 3 through 8 describes the world.

The Four Most Important Unresolved Questions of Macroeconomics

So far, we have been discussing some of the broad lessons about which most economists would agree. We now turn to four questions about which there is continuing debate. Some of the disagreements concern the validity of alternative economic theories; others concern how economic theory should be applied to economic policy.

Question No. 1: How should policymakers try to raise the economy's natural rate of output?

The economy's natural rate of output depends on the amount of capital, the amount of labor, and the level of technology. Any policy designed to raise output in the long run must aim to increase the amount of capital, improve the use of labor, or enhance the available technology. There is, however, no simple and costless way to achieve these goals.

The Solow growth model of Chapters 4 and 5 shows that increasing the amount of capital requires raising the economy's rate of saving and investment. Therefore, many economists advocate policies to raise national saving. Yet the Solow model also shows that raising the capital stock requires a period of reduced consumption for current generations. Some argue that policymakers should not encourage current generations to make this sacrifice, because technological progress will ensure that future generations are better off than current generations. Moreover, even those who advocate increased saving and investment disagree about how to encourage additional saving and whether the investment should be in privately owned plants and equipment or in public infrastructure, such as roads and schools.

To improve the economy's use of its labor force, most policymakers would like to lower the natural rate of unemployment. Yet, as we discussed in Chapter 6, this is not an easy task. The natural rate of unemployment could likely be reduced by decreasing unemployment-insurance benefits (and thus increasing the search effort of the unemployed) or by decreasing the minimum wage (and thus bringing wages closer to equilibrium levels). Yet these policies would also hurt some of those members of society most in need and, therefore, do not command a consensus among economists.

Raising the rate of technological progress is, according to some economists, the most important objective for public policy. The Solow growth model shows that persistent growth in living standards ultimately requires continuing technological progress. This conclusion suggests that the worldwide slowdown in productivity growth that began in the early 1970s may be the worst economic development of the past half century. Despite much work on the new theories of endogenous growth, which highlight some of the societal decisions that determine technologicial progress, economists have not been successful at explaining the productivity slowdown, and policymakers have not been successful at finding ways to reverse it.

Question No. 2: Should policymakers try to stabilize the economy?

The model of aggregate supply and aggregate demand developed in Chapters 9 through 13 shows how various shocks to the economy cause economic fluctuations and how monetary and fiscal policy can influence these fluctuations. Some economists believe that policymakers should use this analysis in an attempt to stabilize the economy. They believe that monetary and fiscal policy should try to offset shocks in order to keep output and employment close to their natural rates.

Yet, as we discussed in Chapter 14, others are skeptical about our ability to stabilize the economy. These economists cite the long and variable lags inherent in economic policymaking, the poor record of economic forecasting, and our still-limited understanding of the economy. They conclude that the best policy is a passive one. In addition, many economists believe that policymakers are all too often opportunistic or follow time-inconsistent policies. They conclude that policymakers should not have discretion over monetary and fiscal policy but should be committed to following a fixed policy rule.

A related question is whether the benefits of economic stabilization—assuming stabilization could be achieved—would be large or small. Without any change in the natural rate of unemployment, stabilization policy can only reduce the magnitude of fluctuations around the natural rate. Thus, successful stabilization policy would eliminate booms as well as recessions. Some economists have suggested that the average gain from stabilization would be small.

Finally, not all economists endorse the model of economic fluctuations developed in Chapters 9 through 13, which assumes sticky prices and monetary non-neutrality. According to real business cycle theory, which we discussed in Chapter 19, economic fluctuations are the optimal response of the economy to changing technology. This theory suggests that policymakers should not stabilize the economy, even if this were possible.

Question No. 3: How costly is inflation, and how costly is reducing inflation?

Whenever prices are rising, policymakers confront the question of whether to pursue policies to reduce the rate of inflation. To make this decision, they must compare the cost of allowing inflation to continue to the cost of reducing it. Yet economists cannot offer accurate estimates of either of these two costs.

The cost of inflation is a topic on which economists and laymen often disagree. When inflation reached 10 percent per year in the late 1970s, opinion polls showed that the public viewed inflation as a major economic problem. Yet, as we discussed in Chapter 7, when economists try to identify the social costs of inflation, they can point only to shoeleather costs, menu costs, the costs of a nonindexed tax system, and so on. These costs become large when countries experience hyperinflation, but they seem relatively minor at the moderate rates of inflation experienced in most major economies. Some economists believe that the public confuses inflation with other economic problems that coincide with inflation. For example, growth in productivity and real wages slowed in the 1970s; some laymen might have viewed inflation as the cause of the slowdown in real wages. Yet it is also possible that economists are mistaken: perhaps inflation is in fact very costly, and we have yet to figure out why.

The cost of reducing inflation is a topic on which economists often disagree among themselves. As we discussed in Chapter 13, the standard view—as described by the short-run Phillips curve—is that reducing inflation requires a period of low output and high unemployment. According to this view, the cost of reducing inflation is measured by the sacrifice ratio, which is the number of percentage points of a year's GDP that must be forgone to reduce inflation by 1 percentage point.

Some economists think that the cost of reducing inflation can be much smaller than standard estimates of the sacrifice ratio indicate. According to the rational-expectations approach discussed in Chapter 13, if a disinflationary policy is announced in advance and is credible, people will adjust their expectations quickly, so the disinflation need not cause a recession. According to the real business cycle models discussed in Chapter 19, prices are flexible and money is neutral, so disinflationary monetary policy will not affect the economy's output of goods and services.

Other economists believe that the cost of reducing inflation is much larger than standard estimates of the sacrifice ratio indicate. The theories of hysteresis discussed in Chapter 13 suggest that a recession caused by disinflationary policy could raise the natural rate of unemployment. If so, then the cost of reducing inflation is not merely a temporary recession but a persistently higher level of unemployment.

Because the costs of inflation and disinflation remain open to debate, economists sometimes offer conflicting advice to policymakers. Perhaps with further research, we can reach a consensus on the benefits of low inflation and the best way to achieve that goal.

Question No. 4: How big a problem are government budget deficits?

In the 1980s and 1990s, large budget deficits were a primary topic of debate among policymakers in the United States and Europe. In the United States, the ratio of government debt to GDP doubled from 1980 to 1995—an event unprecedented in peacetime. Although the federal government's budget was under control by the late 1990s, the issue is likely to resurface as the large baby-boom generation reaches retirement age and starts drawing on government benefits for the elderly. As we discussed in Chapter 15, the effect of government budget deficits is a topic about which economists often disagree.

Most of the models in this book, and most economists, take the traditional view of government debt. According to this view, a budget deficit leads to lower national saving, lower investment, and a trade deficit. In the long run, it leads to a smaller steady-state capital stock and a larger foreign debt. Those who hold the traditional view conclude that budget deficits place a burden on future generations.

Yet not all economists agree with this assessment. Advocates of the Ricardian view of government debt are skeptical. They stress that a budget deficit merely represents a substitution of future taxes for current taxes. As long as consumers are forward-looking, as the theories of consumption presented in Chapter 16 assume, they will save today to meet their or their children's future tax liability. These economists believe that budget deficits have only a minor effect on the economy.

Still other economists believe that the budget deficit is an imperfect measure of fiscal policy. They agree that the government's choices regarding taxes and spending have great influence on the welfare of different generations. Yet, according to these economists, the budget deficit does not fully capture the generational impacts of fiscal decisions.

Conclusion

Economists and policymakers must deal with ambiguity. The current state of macroeconomics offers many insights, but it also leaves many questions open. The challenge for economists is to find answers to these questions and to expand our knowledge. The challenge for policymakers is to use the knowledge we now have to improve economic performance. Both challenges are formidable, but neither is insuperable.

Accelerator model: The model according to which investment depends on the change in output.

Accommodating policy: A policy that yields to the effect of a shock and thereby prevents the shock from being disruptive; for example, a policy that raises aggregate demand in response to an adverse supply shock, sustaining the effect of the shock on prices and keeping output at the natural rate.

Accounting profit: The amount of revenue remaining for the owners of a firm after all the factors of production except capital have been compensated. (Cf. economic profit, profit.)

Acyclical: Moving in no consistent direction over the business cycle. (Cf. countercyclical, procyclical.)

Adaptive expectations: An approach that assumes that people form their expectation of a variable based on recently observed values of the variable. (Cf. rational expectations.)

Adverse selection: An unfavorable sorting of individuals by their own choices; for example, in efficiency-wage theory, when a wage cut induces good workers to quit and bad workers to remain with the firm.

Aggregate: Total for the whole economy.

Aggregate demand curve: The negative relationship between the price level and the aggregate quantity of output demanded that arises from the interaction between the goods market and the money market.

Aggregate-demand externality: The macro-economic impact of one firm's price adjustment on the demand for all other firms' products.

Aggregate supply curve: The relationship between the price level and the aggregate quantity of output firms produce.

Animal spirits: Exogenous and perhaps self-fulfilling waves of optimism and pessimism about the state of the economy that, according to some economists, influence the level of investment.

Appreciation: A rise in the value of a currency relative to other currencies in the market for foreign exchange. (Cf. depreciation.)

Arbitrage: The act of buying an item in one market and selling it at a higher price in another market in order to profit from the price differential in the two markets.

Automatic stabilizer: A policy that reduces the amplitude of economic fluctuations without regular and deliberate changes in economic policy; for example, an income tax system that automatically reduces taxes when income falls.

Average propensity to consume (*APC*): The ratio of consumption to income (C/Y).

Balance sheet: An accounting statement that shows assets and liabilities.

Balanced budget: A budget in which receipts equal expenditures.

Balanced trade: A situation in which the value of imports equals the value of exports, so net exports equal zero.

Baumol–Tobin model: A model of money demand positing that people choose optimal money holdings by comparing the opportunity cost of the forgone interest from holding money and the benefit of making less frequent trips to the bank.

Bond: A document representing an interest-bearing debt of the issuer, usually a corporation or the government.

Borrowing constraint: A restriction on the amount a person can borrow from financial institutions, limiting that person's ability to spend his or her future income today; also called a liquidity constraint.

Budget constraint: The limit that income places on expenditure. (Cf. intertemporal budget constraint.)

Budget deficit: A shortfall of receipts from expenditure.

Budget surplus: An excess of receipts over expenditure.

Business cycle: Economy-wide fluctuations in output, incomes, and employment.

Business fixed investment: Equipment and structures that businesses buy for use in future production.

Capital: 1. The stock of equipment and structures used in production. 2. The funds to finance the accumulation of equipment and structures.

Capital budgeting: An accounting procedure that measures both assets and liabilities.

Central bank: The institution responsible for the conduct of monetary policy, such as the Federal Reserve in the United States.

Classical dichotomy: The theoretical separation of real and nominal variables in the classical model, which implies that nominal variables do not influence real variables. (Cf. neutrality of money.)

Classical model: A model of the economy derived from the ideas of the classical, or pre-Keynesian, economists; a model based on the assumptions that wages and prices adjust to clear markets and that monetary policy does not influence real variables. (Cf. Keynesian model.)

Closed economy: An economy that does not engage in international trade. (Cf. open economy.)

Cobb-Douglas production function: A production function of the form $F(K, L) = AK^\alpha L^{1-\alpha}$, where K is capital, L is labor, and A and α are parameters.

Commodity money: Money that is intrinsically useful and would be valued even if it did not serve as money. (Cf. fiat money, money.)

Competition: A situation in which there are many individuals or firms so that the actions of any one of them do not influence market prices.

Constant returns to scale: A property of a production function whereby a proportionate increase in all factors of production leads to an increase in output of the same proportion.

Consumer price index (CPI): A measure of the overall level of prices that shows the cost of a fixed basket of consumer goods relative to the cost of the same basket in a base year.

Consumption: Goods and services purchased by consumers.

Consumption function: A relationship showing the determinants of consumption; for example, a relationship between consumption and disposable income, $C = C(Y - T)$.

Contractionary policy: Policy that reduces aggregate demand, real income, and employment. (Cf. expansionary policy.)

Coordination failure: A situation in which decisionmakers reach an outcome that is inferior for all of them because of their inability to jointly choose strategies that would result in a preferred outcome.

Corporate income tax: The tax levied on the accounting profit of corporations.

Cost of capital: The amount forgone by holding a unit of capital for one period, including interest, depreciation, and the gain or loss from the change in the price of capital.

Cost-push inflation: Inflation resulting from shocks to aggregate supply. (Cf. demand-pull inflation.)

Countercyclical: Moving in the opposite direction from output, incomes, and employment over the business cycle; rising during recessions and falling during recoveries. (Cf. acyclical, procyclical.)

CPI: *See* consumer price index.

Crowding out: The reduction in investment that results when expansionary fiscal policy raises the interest rate.

Currency: The sum of outstanding paper money and coins.

Cyclical unemployment: The unemployment associated with short-run economic fluctuations; the deviation of the unemployment rate from the natural rate.

Cyclically adjusted budget deficit: The budget deficit adjusted for the influence of the business cycle on government spending and tax revenue; the budget deficit that would occur if the economy's production and employment were at their natural rates. Also called the full-employment budget deficit.

Debt-deflation: A theory according to which an unexpected fall in the price level redistributes real wealth from debtors to creditors and, therefore, reduces total spending in the economy.

Deflation: A decrease in the overall level of prices. (Cf. disinflation, inflation.)

Deflator: *See* GDP deflator.

Demand deposits: Assets that are held in banks and can be used on demand to make transactions, such as checking accounts.

Demand-pull inflation: Inflation resulting from shocks to aggregate demand. (Cf. cost-push inflation.)

Demand shocks: Exogenous events that shift the aggregate demand curve.

Depreciation: 1. The reduction in the capital stock that occurs over time because of aging and use. 2. A fall in the value of a currency relative to other currencies in the market for foreign exchange. (Cf. appreciation.)

Depression: A very severe recession.

Devaluation: An action by the central bank to decrease the value of a currency under a system of fixed exchange rates. (Cf. revaluation.)

Diminishing marginal product: A characteristic of a production function whereby the marginal product of a factor falls as the amount of the factor increases while all other factors are held constant.

Discount rate: The interest rate that the Fed charges when it makes loans to banks.

Discounting: The reduction in value of future expenditure and receipts, compared to current expenditure and receipts, resulting from the presence of a positive interest rate.

Discouraged workers: Individuals who have left the labor force because they believe that there is little hope of finding a job.

Disinflation: A reduction in the rate at which prices are rising. (Cf. deflation, inflation.)

Disposable income: Income remaining after the payment of taxes.

Dominated asset: An asset that offers an inferior return compared to another asset in all possible realizations of future uncertainty.

Double coincidence of wants: A situation in which two individuals each have precisely the good that the other wants.

Economic profit: The amount of revenue remaining for the owners of a firm after all the factors of production have been compensated. (Cf. accounting profit, profit.)

Efficiency of labor: A variable in the Solow growth model that measures the health, education, skills, and knowledge of the labor force.

Efficiency units of labor: A measure of the labor force that incorporates both the number of workers and the efficiency of each worker.

Efficiency-wage theories: Theories of real-wage rigidity and unemployment according to which firms raise labor productivity and profits by keeping real wages above the equilibrium level.

Elasticity: The percent change in a variable caused by a 1 percent change in another variable.

Endogenous growth theory: Models of economic growth that try to explain the rate of technological change.

Endogenous variable: A variable that is explained by a particular model; a variable whose value is determined by the model's solution. (Cf. exogenous variable.)

Equilibrium: A state of balance between opposing forces, such as the balance of supply and demand in a market.

Euler's theorem: The mathematical result economists use to show that economic profit must be zero if the production function has constant returns to scale and if factors are paid their marginal products.

***Ex ante* real interest rate:** The real interest rate anticipated when a loan is made; the nominal interest rate minus expected inflation. (Cf. *ex post* real interest rate.)

***Ex post* real interest rate:** The real interest rate actually realized; the nominal interest rate minus actual inflation. (Cf. *ex ante* real interest rate.)

Excess reserves: Reserves held by banks above the amount mandated by reserve requirements.

Exchange rate: The rate at which a country makes exchanges in world markets. (Cf. nominal exchange rate, real exchange rate.)

Exogenous variable: A variable that a particular model takes as given; a variable whose value is independent of the model's solution. (Cf. endogenous variable.)

Expansionary policy: Policy that raises aggregate demand, real income, and employment. (Cf. contractionary policy.)

Exports: Goods and services sold to other countries.

Factor of production: An input used to produce goods and services; for example, capital or labor.

Factor price: The amount paid for one unit of a factor of production.

Factor share: The proportion of total income being paid to a factor of production.

Federal Reserve (the Fed): The central bank of the United States.

Fiat money: Money that is not intrinsically useful and is valued only because it is used as money. (Cf. commodity money, money.)

Financial intermediation: The process by which resources are allocated from those individuals who wish to save some of their income for future consumption to those individuals and firms who wish to borrow to buy investment goods for future production.

Financing constraint: A limit on the quantity of funds a firm can raise—such as through borrowing—in order to buy capital.

Fiscal policy: The government's choice regarding levels of spending and taxation.

Fisher effect: The one-for-one influence of expected inflation on the nominal interest rate.

Fisher equation: The equation stating that the nominal interest rate is the sum of the real interest rate and expected inflation ($i = r + \pi^e$).

Fixed exchange rate: An exchange rate that is set by the central bank's willingness to buy and sell the domestic currency for foreign currencies at a predetermined price. (Cf. floating exchange rate.)

Flexible prices: Prices that adjust quickly to equilibrate supply and demand. (Cf. sticky prices.)

Floating exchange rate: An exchange rate that the central bank allows to change in response to changing economic conditions and economic policies. (Cf. fixed exchange rate.)

Flow: A variable measured as a quantity per unit of time. (Cf. stock.)

Fractional-reserve banking: A system in which banks keep only some of their deposits on reserve. (Cf. 100-percent-reserve banking.)

Frictional unemployment: The unemployment that results because it takes time for workers to search for the jobs that best suit their skills and tastes. (Cf. wait unemployment.)

Full-employment budget deficit: *See* cyclically adjusted budget deficit.

GDP: *See* gross domestic product.

GDP deflator: The ratio of nominal GDP to real GDP; a measure of the overall level of prices that shows the cost of the currently produced basket of goods relative to the cost of that basket in a base year.

General equilibrium: The simultaneous equilibrium of all the markets in the economy.

GNP: *See* gross national product.

Gold standard: A monetary system in which gold serves as money or in which all money is convertible into gold.

Golden rule: The saving rate in the Solow growth model that leads to the steady state in which consumption per worker (or consumption per efficiency unit of labor) is maximized.

Government purchases: Goods and services bought by the government. (Cf. transfer payments.)

Government-purchases multiplier: The change in aggregate income resulting from a one-dollar change in government purchases.

Gross domestic product (GDP): The total income earned domestically, including the income earned by foreign-owned factors of production; the total expenditure on domestically produced goods and services.

Gross national product (GNP): The total income of all residents of a nation, including the income from factors of production used abroad; the total expenditure on the nation's output of goods and services.

High-powered money: The sum of currency and bank reserves; also called the monetary base.

Hyperinflation: Extremely high inflation.

Hysteresis: The long-lasting influence of history, such as on the natural rate of unemployment.

Identification problem: The difficulty of isolating a particular relationship in data when two or more variables are related in more than one way.

Imperfect-information model: The model of aggregate supply emphasizing that individuals do not always know the overall price level because they cannot observe the prices of all goods and services in the economy.

Import quota: A legal limit on the amount of a good that can be imported.

Imports: Goods and services bought from other countries.

Imputed value: An estimate of the value of a good or service that is not sold in the marketplace and therefore does not have a market price.

Income effect: The change in consumption of a good resulting from a movement to a higher or lower indifference curve, holding the relative price constant. (Cf. substitution effect.)

Index of leading indicators: *See* leading indicators.

Indifference curves: A graphical representation of preferences that shows different combinations of goods producing the same level of satisfaction.

Inflation: An increase in the overall level of prices. (Cf. deflation, disinflation.)

Inflation tax: The revenue raised by the government through the creation of money; also called seigniorage.

Inside lag: The time between a shock hitting the economy and the policy action taken to respond to the shock. (Cf. outside lag.)

Insiders: Workers who are already employed and therefore have an influence on wage bargaining. (Cf. outsiders.)

Interest rate: The market price at which resources are transferred between the present and the future; the return to saving and the cost of borrowing.

Intermediation: *See* financial intermediation.

Intertemporal budget constraint: The budget constraint applying to expenditure and income in more than one period of time. (Cf. budget constraint.)

Intertemporal substitution of labor: The willingness of people to trade off working in one period for working in future periods.

Inventory investment: The change in the quantity of goods that firms hold in storage, including materials and supplies, work in process, and finished goods.

Investment: Goods purchased by individuals and firms to add to their stock of capital.

Investment tax credit: A provision of the corporate income tax that reduces a firm's tax when it buys new capital goods.

IS curve: The negative relationship between the interest rate and the level of income that arises in the market for goods and services. (Cf. *IS−LM* model, *LM* curve.)

IS−LM model: A model of aggregate demand that shows what determines aggregate income for a given price level by analyzing the interaction between the goods market and the money market. (Cf. *IS* curve, *LM* curve.)

Keynesian cross: A simple model of income determination, based on the ideas in Keynes's *General Theory,* which shows how changes in spending can have a multiplied effect on aggregate income.

Keynesian model: A model derived from the ideas of Keynes's *General Theory*; a model based on the assumptions that wages and prices do not adjust to clear markets and that aggregate demand determines the economy's output and employment. (Cf. classical model.)

Labor-augmenting technological progress: Advances in productive capability that raise the efficiency of labor.

Labor force: Those in the population who have a job or are looking for a job.

Labor-force participation rate: The percent of the adult population in the labor force.

Labor hoarding: The phenomenon of firms employing workers whom they do not need when the demand for their products is low, so that they will still have these workers when demand recovers.

Large open economy: An open economy that can influence its domestic interest rate; an economy that, by virtue of its size, can have a substantial impact on world markets and, in particular, on the world interest rate. (Cf. small open economy.)

Laspeyres price index: A measure of the level of prices based on a fixed basket of goods. (Cf. Paasche price index.)

Leading indicators: Economic variables that fluctuate in advance of the economy's output and thus signal the direction of economic fluctuations.

Life-cycle hypothesis: The theory of consumption that emphasizes the role of saving and borrowing as transferring resources from those times in life when income is high to those times in life when income is low, such as from working years to retirement.

Liquid: Readily convertible into the medium of exchange; easily used to make transactions.

Liquidity constraint: A restriction on the amount a person can borrow from a financial institution, which limits the person's ability to spend his future income today; also called a borrowing constraint.

Liquidity-preference theory: A simple model of the interest rate, based on the ideas in Keynes's *General Theory*, which says that the interest rate adjusts to equilibrate the supply and demand for real money balances.

LM curve: The positive relationship between the interest rate and the level of income (while holding the price level fixed) that arises in the market for real money balances. (Cf. *IS-LM* model, *IS* curve.)

Loanable funds: The flow of resources available to finance capital accumulation.

Lucas critique: The argument that traditional policy analysis does not adequately take into account the impact of policy changes on people's expectations.

M1, M2, M3: Various measures of the stock of money, where larger numbers signify a broader definition of money.

Macroeconometric model: A model that uses data and statistical techniques to describe the economy quantitatively, rather than just qualitatively.

Macroeconomics: The study of the economy as a whole. (Cf. microeconomics.)

Marginal product of capital (MPK): The amount of extra output produced when the capital input is increased by one unit.

Marginal product of labor (MPL): The amount of extra output produced when the labor input is increased by one unit.

Marginal propensity to consume (MPC): The increase in consumption resulting from a one-dollar increase in disposable income.

Marginal rate of substitution (MRS): The rate at which a consumer is willing to give up some of one good in exchange for more of another; the slope of the indifference curve.

Market-clearing model: A model that assumes that prices freely adjust to equilibrate supply and demand.

Medium of exchange: The item widely accepted in transactions for goods and services; one of the functions of money. (Cf. store of value, unit of account.)

Menu cost: The cost of changing a price.

Microeconomics: The study of individual markets and decisionmakers. (Cf. macroeconomics.)

Model: A simplified representation of reality, often using diagrams or equations, that shows how variables interact.

Monetarism: The doctrine according to which changes in the money supply are the primary cause of economic fluctuations, implying that a stable money supply would lead to a stable economy.

Monetary base: The sum of currency and bank reserves; also called high-powered money.

Monetary neutrality: *See* neutrality of money.

Monetary policy: The central bank's choice regarding the supply of money.

Monetary transmission mechanism: The process by which changes in the money supply influence the amount that households and firms wish to spend on goods and services.

Monetary union: A group of economies that have decided to share a common currency and thus a common monetary policy.

Money: The stock of assets used for transactions. (Cf. commodity money, fiat money.)

Money demand function: A function showing the determinants of the demand for real money balances; for example, $(M/P)^d = L(i, Y)$.

Money multiplier: The increase in the money supply resulting from a one-dollar increase in the monetary base.

Moral hazard: The possibility of dishonest behavior in situations in which behavior is imperfectly monitored; for example, in efficiency-wage theory, the possibility that low-wage workers may shirk their responsibilities and risk getting caught and fired.

Multiplier: *See* government-purchases multiplier, money multiplier, or tax multiplier.

Mundell-Fleming model: The *IS-LM* model for a small open economy.

Mundell-Tobin effect: The fall in the real interest rate that results when an increase in expected inflation raises the nominal interest rate, lowers real money balances and real wealth, and thereby reduces consumption and raises saving.

National income accounting: The accounting system that measures GDP and many other related statistics.

National income accounts identity: The equation showing that GDP is the sum of consumption, investment, government purchases, and net exports.

National saving: A nation's income minus consumption and government purchases; the sum of private and public saving.

Natural rate of unemployment: The steady-state rate of unemployment; the rate of unemployment toward which the economy gravitates in the long run.

Natural-rate hypothesis: The premise that fluctuations in aggregate demand influence output, employment, and unemployment only in the short run, and that in the long run these variables return to the levels implied by the classical model.

Near money: Assets that are almost as useful as money for engaging in transactions and, therefore, are close substitutes for money.

Neoclassical model of investment: The theory according to which investment depends on the deviation of the marginal product of capital from the cost of capital.

Net exports: Exports minus imports.

Net foreign investment: The net flow of funds being invested abroad; domestic saving minus domestic investment.

Net investment: The amount of investment after the replacement of depreciated capital; the change in the capital stock.

Neutrality of money: The property that a change in the money supply does not influence real variables. (Cf. classical dichotomy.)

New classical economics: The school of thought according to which economic fluctuations can be explained while maintaining the assumptions of the classical model. (Cf. new Keynesian economics.)

New Keynesian economics: The school of thought according to which economic fluctuations can be explained only by admitting a role for some microeconomic imperfection, such as sticky wages or prices. (Cf. new classical economics.)

Nominal: Measured in current dollars; not adjusted for inflation. (Cf. real.)

Nominal exchange rate: The rate at which one country's currency trades for another country's currency. (Cf. exchange rate, real exchange rate.)

Nominal interest rate: The return to saving and the cost of borrowing without adjustment for inflation. (Cf. real interest rate.)

Normal good: A good that a consumer demands in greater quantity when his or her income rises.

Okun's law: The negative relationship between unemployment and real GDP, according to which a decrease in unemployment of 1 percentage point is associated with additional growth in real GDP of approximately 2 percent.

100-percent-reserve banking: A system in which banks keep all deposits on reserve. (Cf. fractional-reserve banking.)

Open economy: An economy in which people can freely engage in international trade in goods and capital. (Cf. closed economy.)

Open-market operations: The purchase or sale of government bonds by the central bank for the purpose of increasing or decreasing the money supply.

Outside lag: The time between a policy action and its influence on the economy. (Cf. inside lag.)

Outsiders: Workers who are not employed and therefore have no influence on wage bargaining. (Cf. insiders.)

Paasche price index: A measure of the level of prices based on a changing basket of goods. (Cf. Laspeyres price index.)

Permanent income: Income that people expect to persist into the future; normal income. (Cf. transitory income.)

Permanent-income hypothesis: The theory of consumption according to which people choose consumption based on their permanent income, and use saving and borrowing to smooth consumption in response to transitory variations in income.

Phillips curve: A negative relationship between inflation and unemployment; in its modern form, a relationship among inflation, cyclical unemployment, expected inflation, and supply shocks, derived from the short-run aggregate supply curve.

Pigou effect: The increase in consumer spending that results when a fall in the price level raises real money balances and, thereby, consumers' wealth.

Political business cycle: The fluctuations in output and employment resulting from the manipulation of the economy for electoral gain.

Portfolio theories of money demand: Theories that explain how much money people choose to hold and that stress the role of money as a store of value. (Cf. transactions theories of money demand.)

Precautionary saving: The extra saving that results from uncertainty regarding, for example, longevity or future income.

Present value: The amount today that is equivalent to an amount to be received in the future, taking into account the interest that could be earned over the interval of time.

Private saving: Disposable income minus consumption.

Procyclical: Moving in the same direction as output, incomes, and employment over the business cycle; falling during recessions and rising during recoveries. (Cf. acyclical, countercyclical.)

Production function: The mathematical relationship showing how the quantities of the factors of production determine the quantity of goods and services produced; for example, $Y = F(K, L)$.

Production smoothing: The motive for holding inventories according to which a firm can reduce its costs by keeping the amount of output it produces steady and allowing its stock of inventories to respond to fluctuating sales.

Profit: The income of firm owners; firm revenue minus firm costs. (Cf. accounting profit, economic profit.)

Public saving: Government receipts minus government spending; the budget surplus.

Purchasing-power parity: The doctrine according to which goods must sell for the same price in every country, implying that the nominal exchange rate reflects differences in price levels.

_q_ theory of investment: The theory according to which expenditure on capital goods depends on the ratio of the market value of installed capital to its replacement cost.

Quantity equation: The identity stating that the product of the money supply and the velocity of money equals nominal expenditure ($MV = PY$); coupled with the assumption of stable velocity, an explanation of nominal expenditure called the quantity theory of money.

Quantity theory of money: The doctrine emphasizing that changes in the quantity of money lead to changes in nominal expenditure.

Quota: _See_ import quota.

Random walk: The path of a variable whose changes over time are unpredictable.

Rational expectations: An approach that assumes that people optimally use all available information—including information about current and prospective policies—to forecast the future. (Cf. adaptive expectations.)

Real: Measured in constant dollars; adjusted for inflation. (Cf. nominal.)

Real business cycle theory: The theory according to which economic fluctuations can be explained by real changes in the economy (such as changes in technology) and without any role for nominal variables (such as the money supply).

Real exchange rate: The rate at which one country's goods trade for another country's goods. (Cf. exchange rate, nominal exchange rate.)

Real interest rate: The return to saving and the cost of borrowing after adjustment for inflation. (Cf. nominal interest rate.)

Real money balances: The quantity of money expressed in terms of the quantity of goods and services it can buy; the quantity of money divided by the price level (M/P).

Recession: A sustained period of falling real income.

Rental price of capital: The amount paid to rent one unit of capital.

Reserve requirements: Regulations imposed on banks by the central bank that specify a minimum reserve–deposit ratio.

Reserves: The money that banks have received from depositors but have not used to make loans.

Residential investment: New housing bought by people to live in and by landlords to rent out.

Revaluation: An action undertaken by the central bank to raise the value of a currency under a system of fixed exchange rates. (Cf. devaluation.)

Ricardian equivalence: The theory according to which forward-looking consumers fully anticipate the future taxes implied by government debt, so that government borrowing today coupled with a tax increase in the future to repay the debt has the same effect on the economy as a tax increase today.

Sacrifice ratio: The number of percentage points of a year's real GDP that must be forgone to reduce inflation by 1 percentage point.

Saving: _See_ national saving, private saving, and public saving.

Seasonal adjustment: The removal of the regular fluctuations in an economic variable that occur as a function of the time of year.

Sectoral shift: A change in the composition of demand among industries or regions.

Seigniorage: The revenue raised by the government through the creation of money; also called the inflation tax.

Shock: An exogenous change in an economic relationship, such as the aggregate demand or aggregate supply curve.

Shoeleather cost: The cost of inflation from reducing real money balances, such as the inconvenience of needing to make more frequent trips to the bank.

Small open economy: An open economy that takes its interest rate as given by world financial markets; an economy that, by virtue of its size, has a negligible impact on world markets and, in particular, on the world interest rate. (Cf. large open economy.)

Solow growth model: A model showing how saving, population growth, and technological progress determine the level of and growth in the standard of living.

Solow residual: The growth in total factor productivity, measured as the percentage change in output minus the percentage change in inputs, where the inputs are weighted by their factor shares. (Cf. total factor productivity.)

Stabilization policy: Public policy aimed at reducing the severity of short-run economic fluctuations.

Stagflation: A situation of falling output and rising prices; combination of stagnation and inflation.

Steady state: A condition in which key variables are not changing.

Sticky prices: Prices that adjust sluggishly and, therefore, do not always equilibrate supply and demand. (Cf. flexible prices.)

Sticky-price model: The model of aggregate supply emphasizing the slow adjustment of the prices of goods and services.

Sticky-wage model: The model of aggregate supply emphasizing the slow adjustment of nominal wages.

Stock: 1. A variable measured as a quantity at a point in time. (Cf. flow.) 2. Shares of ownership in a corporation.

Stock market: A market in which shares of ownership in corporations are bought and sold.

Stock-out avoidance: The motive for holding inventories according to which firms keep extra goods on hand to prevent running out if sales are unexpectedly high.

Store of value: A way of transferring purchasing power from the present to the future; one of the functions of money. (Cf. medium of exchange, unit of account.)

Substitution effect: The change in consumption of a good resulting from a movement along an indifference curve because of a change in the relative price. (Cf. income effect.)

Supply shocks: Exogenous events that shift the aggregate supply curve.

Tariff: A tax on imported goods.

Tax multiplier: The change in aggregate income resulting from a one-dollar change in taxes.

Time inconsistency: The tendency of policymakers to announce policies in advance in order to influence the expectations of private decisionmakers, and then to follow different policies after those expectations have been formed and acted upon.

Tobin's q: The ratio of the market value of installed capital to its replacement cost.

Total factor productivity: A measure of the level of technology; the amount of output per unit of input, where different inputs are combined on the basis of their factor shares. (Cf. Solow residual.)

Trade balance: The receipts from exports minus the payments for imports.

Transactions theories of money demand: Theories that explain how much money people choose to hold and that stress the role of money as a medium of exchange. (Cf. portfolio theories of money demand.)

Transfer payments: Payments from the government to individuals that are not in exchange for goods and services, such as Social Security payments. (Cf. government purchases.)

Transitory income: Income that people do not expect to persist into the future; current income minus normal income. (Cf. permanent income.)

Underground economy: Economic transactions that are hidden in order to evade taxes or conceal illegal activity.

Unemployment insurance: A government program under which unemployed workers can collect benefits for a certain period of time after losing their jobs.

Unemployment rate: The percentage of those in the labor force who do not have jobs.

Unit of account: The measure in which prices and other accounting records are recorded; one of the functions of money. (Cf. medium of exchange, store of value.)

Value added: The value of a firm's output minus the value of the intermediate goods the firm purchased.

Velocity of money: The ratio of nominal expenditure to the money supply; the rate at which money changes hands.

Wage: The amount paid for one unit of labor.

Wage rigidity: The failure of wages to adjust to equilibrate labor supply and labor demand.

Wait unemployment: The unemployment resulting from wage rigidity and job rationing. (Cf. frictional unemployment.)

Work in process: Goods in inventory that are in the process of being completed.

Worker-misperception model: The model of aggregate supply emphasizing that workers sometimes perceive incorrectly the overall level of prices.

World interest rate: The interest rate prevailing in world financial markets.

U.S. Federal Government Budget Deficit (Adjusted for Inflation)

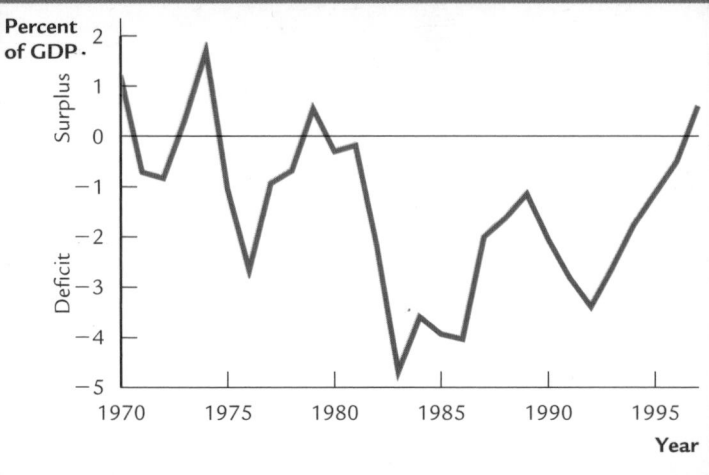

Money Growth (*M2*)

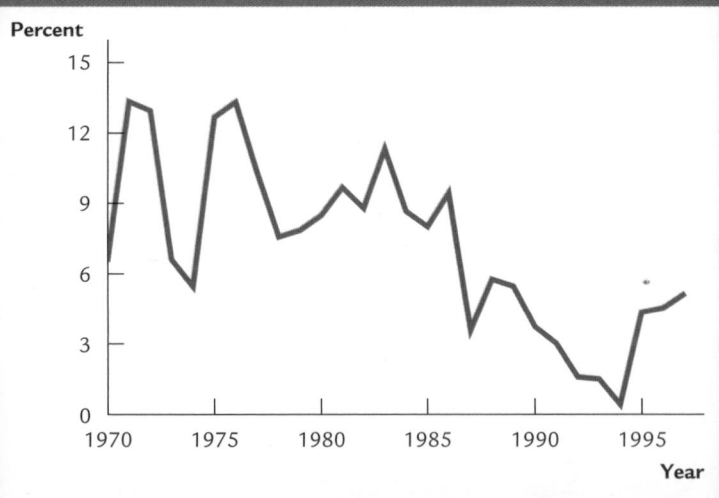